DATE DUE

GAYLORD
PRINTED IN U.S.A.

TOOL AND MANUFACTURING ENGINEERS HANDBOOK

VOLUME IX
MATERIAL AND PART HANDLING
IN MANUFACTURING

SOCIETY OF MANUFACTURING ENGINEERS
1998 Board of Directors

TOOL AND MANUFACTURING ENGINEERS HANDBOOK

FOURTH EDITION

VOLUME IX
MATERIAL AND PART HANDLING
IN MANUFACTURING

A reference book for manufacturing engineers, managers, and technicians

Philip E. Mitchell, CMfgT
Handbook Editor

Society of Manufacturing Engineers
One SME Drive
Dearborn, Michigan 48121

TMEH.

ISBN No. ISBN 0-87263-489-2 (v.9)

Library of Congress Catalog No. 82-60312

Society of Manufacturing Engineers (SME)

First edition published in 1949 by McGraw-Hill Book Co. in cooperation with SME under an earlier Society name, American Society of Tool Engineers (ASTE), and under the title of *Tool Engineers Handbook*. Second edition published in 1959 by McGraw-Hill Book Co. in cooperation with SME under earlier society name, American Society of Tool and Manufacturing Engineers (ASTME), and under title of *Tool Engineers Handbook*. Third edition published in 1976 by McGraw-Hill Book Co. in cooperation with SME under the title *Tool and Manufacturing Engineers Handbook*. Multivolume fourth edition published starting in 1983 by the Society of Manufacturing Engineers under the title of *Tool and Manufacturing Engineers Handbook (TMEH)*.

Printed in the United States of America.

The Library of Congress has cataloged the handbook as follows:

Tool and manufacturing engineers handbook: a reference book for manufacturing engineers, managers, and technicians/Thomas J. Drozda, Charles Wick, editors.—4th ed./revised—Dearborn, Mich.: Society of Manufacturing Engineers, c1983-<c1998>

v.<1-9>: ill.; 29 cm.
Vol. 2: Charles Wick, editor-in-chief, John T. Benedict, senior staff editor, Raymond F. Veilleux, associate editor; 3-4: Charles Wick, editor-in-chief, Raymond F. Veilleux, staff editor; 5: Raymond F. Veilleux, staff editor, Louis W. Petro, consulting editor; 6-7: Ramon Bakerjian, handbook editor, Philip E. Mitchell, staff editor; 8-9/Philip E. Mitchell, handbook editor.

v.1. Machining—v.2. Forming—v.3. Materials, finishing, and coating—v.4. Quality control and assembly—v.5. Manufacturing management—v.6. Design for manufacturability—v.7. Continuous improvement—v.8. Plastic part manufacturing—v.9. Material and part handling in manufacturing.

Includes bibliographies and indexes.
ISBN 0-87263-085-4 (v.1). —ISBN 0-87263-135-4 (v.2). —ISBN 0-87263-176-1 (v.3). —ISBN 0-87263-177-X (v.4). —ISBN 0-87263-306-3 (v.5). —ISBN 0-87263-402-7 (v.6). —ISBN 0-87263-420-5 (v.7). —ISBN 0-87263-456-6 (v.8). —ISBN 0-87263-489-2 (v.9).

1. Production engineering—Handbooks, manuals, etc. 2. Metal-work—Handbooks, manuals, etc. 3. Metal-cutting—Handbooks, manuals, etc. I. Drozda, Tom. II. Wick, Charles. III. Benedict, John T. IV. Veilleux, Raymond F. V. Bakerjian, Ramon. VI. Mitchell, Philip. VII. Society of Manufacturing Engineers.

TS176.T63 1983   670-dc19   82-60312
                                                        AACR 2 MARC
Library of Congress

PREFACE

The first edition, published as the *Tool Engineers Handbook* in 1949, established a useful and authoritative editorial format that was successfully expanded and improved on in the publication of highly-acclaimed subsequent editions. Further expansion of the Handbook is needed because of advances in manufacturing technology, increasing competitive pressure, and a significant diversification of information requirements for modern manufacturing.

Although greatly expanded and updated to reflect the latest in manufacturing technology, the coverage process in this edition is deeply rooted in the heritage of previous editions. Earlier volumes constituted a unique compilation of practical data detailing the specification and use of modern manufacturing equipment and processes. Other volumes in this Handbook series include: Volume I, *Machining*, published in 1983; Volume II, *Forming*, in 1984; Volume III, *Materials, Finishing and Coating*, in 1985; Volume IV, *Quality Control and Assembly*, in 1987; Volume V, *Manufacturing Management*, in 1989; Volume VI, *Design for Manufacturability*, in 1992; Volume VII, *Continuous Improvement*, in 1993; and Volume VIII, *Plastic Part Manufacturing*, in 1996.

The scope of this edition is multifaceted, offering a ready reference source of authoritative manufacturing information for daily use by engineers, managers, and technicians, yet providing significant coverage of the fundamentals of manufacturing processes, equipment, and tooling for study by the novice engineer or student. Uniquely, this blend of coverage has characterized the proven usefulness and reputation of SME Handbooks in previous editions and continues in this edition to provide the basis for acceptance across all segments of manufacturing.

In this, and other TMEH volumes, in-depth coverage of all subjects is presented in an easy-to-read format. Each chapter has an extensive *bibliography* compiled to provide further user resources. A comprehensive index cross-references all subjects, facilitating quick access to information. The liberal use of drawings, graphs, and tables also speeds information gathering and problem solving. Equations are included to show how different factors relate to each other and are used as a practical tool for quantifying portions of the manufacturing process.

The *contributors and reviewers* are listed at the beginning of each chapter. No written words of appreciation can sufficiently express the special thanks due to these professionals. Their work is deeply appreciated by the Society; but more importantly, their contributions will undoubtedly serve to advance the understanding of manufacturing throughout industry and will certainly help spur major productivity gains in the years ahead. Industry as a whole will be the beneficiary of their dedication. Much effort was made to acknowledge other material used in the handbook and is listed in the *reference* section of each chapter.

Philip E. Mitchell, CMfgT

Participants in the editorial development and production of this volume include:

EDITORIAL

John Coleman
Director of Publications

Karen Wilhelm
Publications Manager

Philip Mitchell
Handbook Editor

Larry Binstock
Senior Editor

Ellen Kehoe
Senior Editor

Fred Mason
Senior Editor

Donald Peterson
Senior Editor

Karen Augustin
Editor

Les Gould
Editor

Warren Sears
Editor

John Vacarri
Editor

George Watson
Editor

Rosemary Csizmadia
Production Team Leader

Frances Kania
Editorial Assistant

Dorothy Wylo
Editorial Assistant

Jennifer Courter
Copy Editor

TYPESETTING

The Northwest Group

GRAPHICS

Donna Hicks
Adcomp Services, Inc.

MARKETING

Phillip Roman
Manager

Denise Kaercher
Administrator

Special mention is made of the help and advice given by Les Gould, whose untimely death was a loss felt by all in the material handling industry.

SME

The Society of Manufacturing Engineers, headquartered in Dearborn, Michigan, USA, is an international professional society dedicated to serving its members and the international manufacturing community through the advancement of professionalism, knowledge, and learning. The specific goal of the Society is to advance scientific knowledge in the field of manufacturing and to apply its resources to research, writing, publishing, and disseminating information. "The purpose of SME is to serve the professional needs of the many types of practitioners that make up the manufacturing community. The collective goal of the membership is the sharing and advancement of knowledge in the field of manufacturing for the good of humanity."

The Society was founded in 1932 as the American Society of Tool Engineers (ASTE). From 1960 to 1969 it was known as the American Society of Tool and Manufacturing Engineers (ASTME), and in 1970, it became the Society of Manufacturing Engineers. The changes in name reflect the evolution of the manufacturing engineering profession, and the growth and increasing sophistication of a technical society that has gained an international reputation for being the most knowledgeable and progressive voice in the field.

Associations and Groups of SME—The Society provides complete technical services and membership benefits through a number of associations and groups. Each serves a special interest area. Members may join these associations and groups in addition to SME. They are:

Association for Electronics Manufacturing (EM/SME)
Association for Finishing Processes (AFP/SME)
Association for Forming & Fabricating Technologies of SME (AFFT/SME)
Composites Manufacturing Association (CMA/SME)
Computer and Automated Systems Association (CASA/SME)
Machine Vision Association (MVA/SME)
Machining Technology Association (MTA/SME)
North American Manufacturing Research Institute (NAMRI/SME)
Plastics Molders and Manufacturers Association (PMMA/SME)
Rapid Prototyping Association (RPA/SME)
Robotics International (RI/SME)

Members and Chapters—The Society and its associations have 70,000 members in 70 countries, and sponsor some 300 chapters, districts, and regions, as well as 240 student chapters worldwide.

Publications—The Society is involved in various publications activities encompassing handbooks, textbooks, videotapes, and magazines. Current periodicals include:

Forming & Fabricating
Integrated Design & Manufacturing
Manufacturing Engineering
Manufacturing Insights (a video magazine)
Molding Systems
SME Technical Digest
SME News
Journal of Manufacturing Systems

(cont)

Technical Quarterlies:
Composites in Manufacturing
Electronics Manufacturing
Machining Technology
Plastics
Rapid Prototyping
Robotics Today
The Finishing Line
Vision

Certification—This SME program formally recognizes manufacturing managers, engineers, and technologists based on experience and knowledge. The key certification requirement is successful completion of a two-part written examination covering (1) engineering fundamentals and (2) an area of manufacturing specialization.

Educational Programs—The Society sponsors a wide range of educational activities, including conferences, clinics, in-plant courses, expositions, publications, educational/training media, professional certification, and the SME Manufacturing Engineering Education Foundation.

Global Manufacturing Network (GMN)—SME's *Manufacturing Engineering, Forming & Fabricating, Integrated Design & Manufacturing*, and *Molding Systems* magazines publish their feature articles and others on the GMN web site (http://www.globalmfg.com). Magazine articles as well as technical papers, books, and videotapes can be looked up using a key word search. Many of the videotapes on the GMN web site have short video clips that can be viewed over the Internet. Also found are expositions, conferences, seminars, in-plant training opportunities, a jobs database, and a list of suppliers.

CONTENTS

VOLUME IX—MATERIAL AND PART HANDLING IN MANUFACTURING

Chapter 4—Storage and Inventory Planning

Chapter 5—Logistics

Chapter 6—Maintaining Material Handling Systems and Equipment

Chapter 7—Ergonomics and Manual Handling Systems

Chapter 8—Flexible Wheeled Handling Equipment

Chapter 9—Conveyors for Unit Load Handling

Chapter 10—Overhead Handling and Lifting Devices

Chapter 11—Storage Equipment

Chapter 12—Transport Packaging

Chapter 13—Automated Material Handling Equipment

Chapter 14—Worker Productivity and Ergonomic Assists

Chapter 15—Metalcutting

Chapter 16—Metal Forming

Chapter 19—Finishing, Painting, and Coating

Chapter 20—Moving and Handling Scrap and Waste

Appendix A—Industry Associations and Standards

SYMBOLS AND ABBREVIATIONS

The following is a list of symbols and abbreviations in general use throughout this volume. Supplementary and/or derived units, symbols, and abbreviations that are peculiar to specific subject matter are listed within chapters.

2D	two-dimensional
3D	three-dimensional

A-B

A	Amp (Ampere)
AAR	Association of American Railroads
ABC	Activity-based costing
ABM	Activity-based management
AC	Alternating current
ADC	Automated data capture
AEM	Automated electrified monorail
AGV	Automated guided vehicle
AGVS	Automated guided vehicle system
AHAM	Association of Home Appliance Manufacturers
AI	Automatic identification
AIAG	Automotive Industry Action Group
AISC	American Institute of Steel Construction
ANSI	American National Standards Institute
APS	Advanced planning and scheduling systems
APV	Attended program verification
ARA	After receipt of approval
AREA	American Railroad Engineering Association
AS/RS	Automated storage and retrieval systems
ASCE	American Society of Civil Engineers
ASCII	American National Standard Code for Information Interchange
ASN	Advance shipping notice
ASTM	American Society for Testing and Materials
BOM	Bill of material

C-D-E

CAD	Computer-aided design
CAT	Cross-aisle transfer
cc	Cubic centimeter
CCD	Charge-coupled device
CEMA	Conveyor Equipment Manufacturers Association
CFM	Cubic feet per minute
CIM	Computer-integrated manufacturing
CMAA	Crane Manufacturers Association of America
CMM	Coordinate measuring machine
CNC	Computer numerical control
CNG	Compressed natural gas
CO	Carbon monoxide
COE	Chain-on-edge
CP	Carrier present
CS/RS	Carousel storage and retrieval system

CTD	Cumulative trauma disorder
CV	Constant velocity
DC	Data collection
DC	Direct current
DIN	European equivalent of the American Society for Testing and Materials (ASTM)
DLC	Deep-lane shuttle car
DLT	Deep-lane transfer
DOT	Department of Transportation
EAN	European Article Numbering
ECN	Engineering change notice
EDI	Electronic data interchange
EDM	Electrical discharge machining
EFT	Electronic funds transfer
EIA	Electronics Industry Association
ELM	Enterprise logistics management
EOAT	End-of-arm tool
EOQ	Economic order quantity
EPA	Environmental Protection Agency
EPS	Expanded polystyrene
ERS	Evaluated receipt settlement
ESFR	Early-suppression-fast-response sprinkler
ETF	Electronic transfer feed
ETV	Electric track vehicle

F-G-H

FCC	Federal Communications Commission
FCS	Finite capacity scheduling
FDA	Food and Drug Administration
FEA	Finite element analysis
FHS	Flexible handling system
FIFO	First-in first-out
Fig.	Figure
FMRC	The Factory Mutual Research Corporation
FMS	Flexible manufacturing system
fpm	Feet per minute
ft	Feet
g	Gram
gal	Gallon
GMA	Grocery Manufacturers Association
GMP	Good manufacturing practice
gpm	Gallons per minute
GPS	Global positioning system
GUI	Graphical user interface
h	Hour
HD/DS	High-density dynamic-storage system
HIPO	Hierarchical input process output
hp	Horsepower

SYMBOLS AND ABBREVIATIONS

I-J-K

I/E	Inserter/Extractor
I/O	Input/Output
ICAM	Integrated computer-aided manufacturing
ICE	Internal combustion engine
ICM	Inverted chain monorail
ID	Inside diameter
ID	Identification
IMM	Injection molding machine
in.	Inch
in.^{2}	Square inch
in.^{3}	Cubic inch
IPF	Inverted power-and-free conveyor
IRR	Internal rate of return
ISO	International Organization for Standardization
ITA	Industrial Truck Association
J	Joule
JIT	Just-in-Time
kg	Kilogram
kPa	Kilopascal
KT	Kepner-Tregoe

L-M-N

L	Liter
lb	Pound
LCC	Life-cycle cost
LH	Left-hand
LIFO	Last-in last-out
LIM	Linear induction motor
LP	Liquid petroleum
LPG	LP-gas or liquid petroleum gas
LTL	Less than a truckload
m	Meter
m^3	Cubic meter
MES	Manufacturing execution system
MHIA	Material Handling Industry of America
MHS	Manual handling system
min	Minute
MIS	Management information system
MLD	Movable loading device
MMH	Manual material handling
MPS	Master production schedule
MRP	Material requirements planning
MRP	Manufacturing resource planning
MRPII	Manufacturing resource planning
MSD	Musculoskeletal disorder
MSDS	Material safety data sheet
MSHA	Mine Safety and Health Administration
MTBF	Mean time between failure
MTTR	Mean-time-to-repair
MUD	Movable unloading device
N	Newton
NC	Numerical control
NEMA	National Equipment Manufacturers Association
NFPA	National Fire Protection Association
NICAD	Nickel cadmium
NIOSH	National Institute for Occupational Safety and Health

NPV	Net present value
NWPCA	National Wooden Pallet and Container Association

O-P

OCM	Overhead chain monorail
OD	Outside diameter
ODETTE	Organization for Data Exchange by Teletransmission in Europe
OEM	Original equipment manufacturer
OHPF	Overhead power-and-free conveyor
OPC	Operations process chart
OSB	Oriented strand board
OSHA	Occupational Safety and Health Administration
OTC	Overhead trolley conveyor
P&F	Power-and-free
P/D	Pickup and delivery
PC	Personal computer
PCV	Positive crankcase ventilation valve
PDF	Portable data file
PDM	Product data management
PE	Polyethylene
PERT/CPM	Program evaluation review technique/critical path method
PFD	Process flow diagrams
PI	Profitability index
PLC	Programmable logic controller
PM	Preventive maintenance
PMT	Peak metal temperature
PO	Purchase order
PP	Polypropylene
PPH	Parts per hour
PS	Polystyrene
psi	Pounds per square inch
PVC	Polyvinyl chloride

Q-R-S

QC	Quality control
RF	Radio frequency
RFID	Radio-frequency identification
RFQ	Request for quotation
RGV	Rail-guided vehicle
RH	Right-hand
RMI	Rack Manufacturers Institute
ROI	Return-on-investment
rpm	Revolutions per minute
RRFQ	Response to request for quote
RSI	Repetitive strain injury
RULA	Rapid upper limb assessment
S/R	Storage and retrieval
S/RM	Storage and retrieval machine
SCAC	Standard carrier alpha code
SCARA	Selective compliance assembly robot arm
SEMCO	Statistical equipment maintenance control
sfpm	Surface feet per minute
SGV	Self-guided vehicle
SKU	Stock-keeping unit
SMED	Single-minute exchange of die

SYMBOLS AND ABBREVIATIONS

SPC	Statistical process control
SPD	Stationary pulling device
SPI	Society of the Plastics Industry
spm	Strokes per minute
SSPP	Static strength prediction program
STEP	Standard for the exchange of product data

T-U-V-W-X-Y-Z

TOC	Theory of constraints
TP	Travel permit
TPA	Trading partner agreement or handbook
TWA	Time-weighted average
UCC	Uniform Code Council
UHMW	Ultra-high molecular weight
UL	Underwriters Laboratories, Inc.
UN	United Nations
UOM	Unit of measure
UPC	Uniform plumbing code
U.P.C.	Universal product code
UPM	Use-point manager
U.S.	United States
USDA	United States Department of Agriculture
UV	Ultraviolet
V	Volts

VAN	Value-added network
VLM	Vertical lift module
VTL	Vertical turning lathe
VTL	Vertical transfer lift
WIP	Work-in-process
WMS	Warehouse management systems
www	World-wide-web
yd³	Cubic yard
yr	Year

SYMBOLS

•	Bullet
©	Copyright sign
°	Degree sign
μ	Greek mu. Also a prefix meaning *micro* (one-thousandth of)
$\geq$	Greater than or equal to
Σ	Greek sigma
Θ	Greek theta
$\leq$	Less than or equal to
$\approx$	Nearly equal to
%	Percent
$\pm$	Plus/minus
®	Registration mark
™	Trademark

CHAPTER 1

STRATEGY DETERMINATION AND PRODUCTION REQUIREMENTS

CHAPTER CONTENTS

INTRODUCTION

The well-managed company has carefully considered manufacturing strategies that define its core competencies and market its competitive advantages. The results are linked tactical processes supporting the strategies. One such tactic is *inventory management*. Decisions about whether or not to stock finished goods (and how much) and similar support decisions for component parts are critical to all material handling system designs. Material handling decisions made without understanding the overall strategy and the appropriate tactics may undermine the manufacturing strategy. The integration of material handling design with inventory tactics requires that the manufacturing engineer have a fundamental knowledge of inventory management, industrial engineering, and material handling engineering. This broader perspective will help the manufacturing engineer be more effective in optimizing the company's material handling activities.

BASIC MANUFACTURING CONCEPTS

Manufacturing technology has advanced in recent years and embraced new concepts aimed at boosting speed and efficiency while reducing cost. This section defines and discusses many of these concepts as they relate to planning and implementing a manufacturing strategy for meeting specific production requirements.

THE PRODUCTION ENVIRONMENT

There are four basic production environments to choose from: manufacture-to-stock, assemble-to-order, manufacture-to-order, and engineer-to-order. Choosing one of these environments is a funda-

mental strategic decision, but one that is heavily influenced by competitive pressures.

Manufacture-to-stock

Manufacture-to-stock, also known as *make-to-stock*, is "a production environment where products can be and usually are finished before receipt of a customer order. Customer orders are typically filled from existing stocks and production orders are used to replenish those stocks."[1] Examples of manufacture-to-stock products are consumer goods such as televisions, power hand tools, lunch boxes, and thousands of other off-the-shelf items. Since the manufacturer must quickly ship these products in response to customer orders, the products must be manufactured ahead of need and in quantities based on forecasted demand. In this environment, the accuracy of the forecast—in terms of quantity and timing—is more critical than in the other three production environments.

The consequences of forecast inaccuracies impact the entire organization. A forecast that exceeds actual demand wastes company money by creating excess inventory and may consume warehouse space needed for the storage of better-selling products. Forecasting below demand carries its own set of consequences. Trying to quickly manufacture more than what was forecasted usually results in chaotic and expensive expediting, putting strain on the entire supply chain. Of even greater consequence is the potential for lost sales. Customers (often retail stores) will order from the competition before allowing their own shelves to sit empty.

The relatively high volumes in many manufacture-to-stock environments and the stable nature of the routings and processes may allow a facility to adopt repetitive manufacturing. Dedicated machine tools and equipment, work cells, and synchronous flow, etc., all support a higher level of automation in material handling for manufactured components and assemblies. Purchased components, on the other hand, may still be delivered to the point of use via lower-level technology, unless consumption volumes are high enough to warrant flow replenishment.

Assemble-to-order

Assemble-to-order is "an environment where a product . . . can be assembled after receipt of a customer's order. The key components . . . used in the assembly or finishing process are planned, and possibly stocked, in anticipation of a customer order. Receipt of an order initiates assembly of the customized product. This strategy is useful where a large number of end products . . . can be assembled from common components."[2] Examples of assemble-to-order products are automobiles, office furniture, retail display units, and any product where color, fabric, or similar choices can be incorporated late in the manufacturing process. Like manufacture-to-stock environments, assemble-to-order environments plan production and

The Contributors of this chapter are: William M. Angell, President, W. M. Angell & Associates; *Walter Goddard,* President, Oliver Wight Companies; *John Layden,* President, Pritsker Corp.; *Randall Schaefer, CPIM,* APICS—The Educational Society for Resource Management (Grand Rapids Chapter) and Director of Systems Integration, Spartan Motors Inc.; *Debra L. Smith, CFPIM, CIRM,* APICS—The Educational Society for Resource Management (Grand Rapids Chapter) and Consultant in Manufacturing.
The Reviewers of this chapter are: James Cheng, Manufacturing Engineer, The Sine Companies; *Kermit Hobbs, Jr.,* Vice President of Manufacturing, Amadas Industries; *Richard K. Smith,* Faculty, Hope College and Material Coordinator, The Worden Company.

CHAPTER 1   STRATEGY DETERMINATION AND PRODUCTION REQUIREMENTS

inventory on the basis of a forecast. However, where the manufacture-to-stock environment forecasts the demand for completed end items, the assemble-to-order environment forecasts the demand for key components.

The consequences of forecasting below demand are similar to those in a manufacture-to-stock environment: expediting, potential for lost sales, and loss of customer good will. A forecast that exceeds actual demand may have less deleterious effects. Common components can be consumed by better-selling products and labor is not invested in final assemblies that are not sold.

Production volumes in an assemble-to-order environment could be similar to those in a manufacture-to-stock environment, and may therefore support a similar level of material handling automation for common manufactured components. Final assembly processes may range from manual to highly automated, and material handling support must be designed accordingly.

Since end products are not stocked, warehouse space is typically minimal and used for shipping preparation activities. Key components and subassemblies, however, are stocked, so the need for work-in-process storage is greater than in a manufacture-to-stock environment.

Manufacture-to-order

Manufacture-to-order, also known as *make-to-order*, is "a production environment where a product . . . can be made after receipt of a customer's order . . . ."[3] As a rule, this environment relies heavily on standard components and often on simple, custom variations of similar parts. Industrial punch presses, vehicle chassis, and standard conveyor systems are typically made-to-order.

Forecasts may be used to plan for predictable raw materials with long lead times and the capacity that will be needed. Detailed material planning and production are performed after receiving an order. This results in longer customer lead times than in manufacture-to-stock or assemble-to-order environments.

Volumes for finished goods are usually lower in a manufacture-to-order environment, although the volumes of certain components may be quite high. Therefore, stability in the component manufacturing process may support a relatively high level of material handling automation. Lower volume variations of these components and assemblies may or may not be as well served by this same level of automation. The degree to which the variations can be manufactured, using the same processes as the standard components, dictates the level of automation.

Engineer-to-order

An *engineer-to-order* environment is one with "products whose customer specifications require unique engineering design or significant customization. Each customer order results in a unique set of part numbers, bills of material, and routings."[4] Examples include products such as custom-designed capital equipment, stamping dies, plastic molds, and space shuttles.

Forecasts, if done at all, are used only to plan capacity and predict raw material usage. Product and process engineering are completed after receipt of a customer order, as are detailed planning and manufacturing. Some engineering may be completed prior to receiving the order for developing cost and delivery estimates, or to ensure form, fit, and function.

Engineer-to-order environments still rely heavily on traditional, functional groupings of machines. The low volumes and unique nature of these products almost always require general, nondedicated machine tools and equipment, and lower-technology material handling solutions. Facilities for engineer-to-order environments typically have a large reserve production capacity to accommodate widely-varying tasks and work load levels.

Environmental Combinations

While some companies maintain only one of the four production environments, it is more common for companies to combine the environments, either by strategic design or passive evolution. A company may exhibit manufacture-to-stock characteristics by stocking final products, such as mailboxes made of steel, while offering the same mailboxes in brass on a manufacture-to-order basis only. Such combinations affect not only the material flow, but also the number of points where material may be stored within the flow.

Companies may incorporate more than one environment for competitive reasons. The desire to be a single source supplier across its product line may drive a manufacture-to-stock company to round out its catalog by offering manufacture-to-order products as well. The desire to compete on speed of delivery may motivate a manufacture-to-order company to stock key components and subassemblies, offering higher-volume products on an assemble-to-order basis. An engineer-to-order company wishing to reduce cost can do so by standardizing its product. This is done by developing common components and key modules, and then building the remaining product around them. This adds manufacture-to-order features to an engineer-to-order company.

Job Shop and Flow Shop

Within the four basic production environments there are two different methods of organizing the facility: job shop and flow shop. Most facilities incorporate at least some features of each. The applicability of either job shop or flow shop varies within each of the four environments.

The *job shop* is "an organization in which similar equipment is organized by function. Each job follows a distinct routing through the shop."[5] This production organization is the traditional structure that manufacturing facilities have used since the beginning of the Industrial Revolution. Characteristically, all punch presses were physically grouped into one department, welders into another, drills into a third. Machines grouped in this fashion are not dedicated to specific products; they process numerous part numbers, in varying quantities and containers. Material may be routed through as many different paths as there are part numbers. Along these paths are stock and queue points, where material awaiting further processing must be stored. These features limit the choices for automated material handling and often point to lower technology methods.

A *flow shop* differs from a job shop in that it is "a form of manufacturing organization in which machines and operators handle a standard, usually uninterrupted, material flow . . . . The plant layout (arrangement of machines, benches, assembly lines, etc.) is designed to facilitate a product 'flow'. . . . Each product, though variable in material specifications, uses the same flow pattern through the shop."[6] While flow shop facilities have always existed, they typically supported mass-produced products with few variations. Recent trends toward synchronous manufacturing have brought flow principles to products previously manufactured by job shop methods (see Bibliography). The types of production machines in a flow shop may be identical to those in a job shop, but they are not grouped by function. Instead, the machines are aligned to support steady, contiguous processing and material movement. A flow shop typically has fewer stock points, and ideally, no queues. While pure assembly operations have used flow organization for years, recent emphasis has brought assembly line benefits to fabrication operations.

Manufacture-to-stock is an ideal environment for a flow organization. While a job shop grouping of machines may have some

CHAPTER 1 STRATEGY DETERMINATION AND PRODUCTION REQUIREMENTS

efficiencies for the production of individual components, the additional part handling and lead times in the job shop queues and stock points reduce these efficiencies. Most competitive companies in a manufacture-to-stock environment are moving toward flow shop organizations.

Assemble-to-order is an environment likely to exhibit a blend of job shop and flow shop organization. Flow shop organization may apply for standard, stocked components and subassemblies, as well as final assemblies where standard processes are used. However, where low-volume components require a range of processes, or where the various final assemblies require diverse processes, job shop organization may apply.

The extent that a flow shop organization applies to a manufacture-to-order environment is influenced by the extent of customized parts and processes. If the customized components share similar processes, flow shop organization has greater applicability; if processes are diverse, job shop organization may apply. The primary difference between an assemble-to-order and a manufacture-to-order facility may be its response to market-driven lead times, rather than degree of customization. When this is the case, the applicability of job shop or flow shop for manufacture-to-order is the same as described earlier for assemble-to-order.

Because engineer-to-order environments rely on functional groupings of machines, opportunities for true flow shop organization are limited. Many factories with little opportunity to use flow concepts have attempted to replicate a flow via flexible, portable material handling linkages (for example, motorized conveyors) to temporarily tie equipment together. Still, an engineer-to-order facility remains a bastion of traditional job shop organization.

LEAD TIMES

A well-managed company's production environment and organization are largely based upon responses to market-driven lead time. Aggressive companies strive to reduce lead time and turn it into a competitive advantage. In doing so, they may change the lead time standard within the marketplace. This generates internal changes for the aggressive company and triggers changes for its competitors and throughout the supply chain. The leader in systematic lead time reduction reaps the benefits, while competitors scramble to meet the new standard. Managed lead time reduction must affect the production environment, the production organization, or both, and will therefore impact material handling requirements.

Some elements of lead time are external to the company and there may be fewer opportunities to control and reduce them. Among the more common external lead times are those for procuring raw material and purchased components, inbound freight, outside processing, and outbound freight for delivery to the customer. The obvious methods of reducing these lead times include negotiating with existing suppliers and carriers, and making compliance with lead time standards a condition for new supplier selection. Another common method is to provide suppliers with a commitment that allows them to procure raw material in advance, on a low-risk basis. The supplier's raw material lead time is thereby decoupled from its fabrication and assembly lead time, resulting in a shorter external lead time for purchased components.

While reducing external lead time provides a competitive advantage by reducing total lead time to the customer, it has a limited impact on internal material handling. On the other hand, reducing internal lead time normally requires a re-evaluation of material handling systems.

These are the elements of internal lead time common to most manufacturing facilities:

- *Receiving and inspection lead time* is the "time built into the total lead time to accommodate necessary receiving and inspection requirements."[7] Material handling supports routine movement of material from unloading on the receiving dock through delivery to either storage or point of use. If an incoming inspection procedure is part of this process, temporary storage and additional moves to and from an inspection station may be required. Receiving and inspection lead times can be reduced or eliminated through supplier partnerships in which the supplier delivers certified, quality material directly to the customer's point of use. This method of receiving material has the most dramatic impact on material handling. Using self-certifying suppliers eliminates the material handling required for inspection of incoming materials.

- *Order preparation lead time* is "the time needed to analyze requirements . . . and to create the paperwork necessary to release a purchase order or a production order."[8] Many factories have eliminated shop order paper by distributing orders and schedules via computer. By eliminating the printing and distribution of shop paper, lead time for order preparation is reduced. Normally, a reduction in this lead time has little impact on material handling. However, if the shop paperwork is used to direct material handling activities, its elimination will require an alternative source of direction.

- *Setup lead time*, often called *setup time*, is "the time required for a specific machine, resource, work center, or line to convert from production of the last good piece of lot A to the first good piece of lot B."[9] This requires locating and moving tooling, fixtures, inspection equipment, production material and supplies, and containers to the work center. Small reductions in this lead time can be made by storing tooling, fixtures, etc., closer to the point of use, or by scheduling the movement while the work center is still processing the previous job. The largest portion of setup lead time consists of adjusting and tuning the process to yield good parts. Reductions in this portion of setup lead time can justify reductions in manufacturing lot sizes which, in turn, have a tremendous impact on material handling. For example, suppose a part has historically been manufactured in a lot size equal to a four-week supply, justified by an eight-hour setup lead time. If this lead time can be reduced to four hours, it follows that the lot size can be reduced significantly, perhaps to a two-week supply. While the benefits of doubling the inventory turns are substantial in both cost and storage, the material handling activities related to this setup also double. Assuming a part's annual requirement remains the same, halving the lot size doubles the number of setups. There are also downstream effects on move time.

- *Run time* is the "time required to process a piece or lot at a specific operation."[10] This is the time parts are worked on and its impact on material handling is straightforward. If a machine completes 100 pieces per hour, the quantity and frequency of material moves to and from the machine are obviously less than if the machine completes 100 pieces per minute. If run time can be significantly reduced, more time is available to process other parts, increasing the frequency of setups and associated material handling.

- *Queue time* is the largest component—as much as 90%—of internal lead time. It is "the amount of time a job waits at a work center before setup or work is performed on it."[11] The amount of chaos in a factory is proportionate to its queue length. Long queue times require more storage area for work-in-process, more searching for and retrieval of the next job, more handling damage, and more rescheduling and expediting that

CHAPTER 1   STRATEGY DETERMINATION AND PRODUCTION REQUIREMENTS

confuses factory priorities. Queue times can be reduced by adding capacity to increase throughput or by improving setup lead and run times. Queue times can be managed by releasing work to the factory no earlier than necessary, or by more drastic measures, such as establishing queue goals for each work center and continuing production at each center until its queue is reduced to the goal level. If additional capacity is unavailable, and reductions in setup lead and run times do not provide adequate throughput, pushing the work center (including material handling support) until it reaches its daily queue goals may be a harsh, but necessary remedy. Because queue lead times represent up to 90% of internal lead time, controlling queues is vital to ensure that factory due dates are met. When viewed from this perspective, enforcing daily queue goals appears less harsh. It is a quick and reasonably inexpensive stop-gap measure until additional capacity is procured or the process is re-engineered toward Just-in-Time (JIT) or synchronous manufacturing.

- *Move time* is "the time that a job spends in transit from one operation to another in the plant."[12] Factors that dictate the frequency of moves include lot size, part and container size, the available space to store parts at the work center after processing, and the urgency of downstream demand for parts. Successful setup reductions and corresponding decreases in lot sizes will generate more frequent handling activity and increase move time, unless material handling capacity is made available for the greater frequency of moves. Factors that dictate the length of move lead time are the distance to be covered, the method and technology of material handling, and the amount of time it takes for material handling to recognize the need to move material and respond. The distance factor can be reduced when a facility evolves from job shop to flow shop organization. At a minimum, machines are moved closer together and connected with either automated material handling or a simple hand-off on a piece-by-piece basis. Alternatively, production machinery can be mobile so that temporary "cells" can be set up quickly, enabling multiple operations to be performed with minimal handling. The recognition and response portion of this lead time can be thought of as post-operation queue time because it is time spent waiting in line. In this case, it is waiting to be moved, rather than waiting to be processed. This delay is responsible for the majority of move time within a facility. Factories often fail to manage this wait time. Where moves are people-controlled (for example, moves by fork lift or handcart), lead time can be managed effectively by establishing realistic, time-related performance expectations. For example, if material handlers are given two days to move material from one machine to another, the total planned lead time for a part must include two days for each operation on the routing. If, on the other hand, material handlers are given two hours, the impact on total planned lead time is minimal. Enforcing a simple rule, such as requiring that all material processed during a shift (or half shift, etc.) is moved by the end of the same shift, is all the control most job shop environments need to manage the wait portion of move time. As with the distance factor, transition from job shop to flow shop organization will reduce or eliminate the wait.

Lead times are a major factor in material handling system design and methods. A managed reduction of lead times often generates changes that can increase material handling requirements. Manufacturing Engineering plays an important part of managing these changes to decrease material handling as lead times are reduced, and to propose handling systems that provide further lead time reduction.

INVENTORY MANAGEMENT

Inventory management is the process of planning and controlling the quantity and timely availability of material. This includes raw material and purchased parts, manufactured components, subassemblies and assemblies, and finished goods. While inventory is managed on a part-by-part basis, it is classified and measured in the aggregate by total value, number of days' supply on hand, inventory turnover, total throughput, or some variation of these measurements. These aggregate measures have little effect on material handling. However, the way parts are managed individually has an impact on material handling that eclipses even the impact of lead time.

Planning the timing and quantity of parts that are acquired, either by purchase or manufacture, is manipulated by the use of order policies. *Order policies* "refer to any rules put in place to systematically increase order quantities above the exact amount required for whatever time increment is being used or to modify the due dates of orders."[13] In a Just-in-Time (JIT) philosophy, the best order policy is one-for-one; manufacturing produces exactly what is needed, just when it is needed. This yields negligible inventory levels and forces a focus on high quality and customer service. Outside of JIT manufacturing, order policies can provide controls to regulate inventory levels, reflecting factory realities. The more common order policies involve lot sizing, a fixed period order factor, an order minimum, order multiples, safety stock, and scrap factors. These order policies can manage individual inventory items as a major part of an integrated inventory management system.

Order Policies

Order policies are the result of any of several techniques that determine the order quantity for a manufactured or purchased part. These techniques are mathematical formulas that attempt to strike a balance between ordering/setup costs, and the carrying costs of inventory. Common lot sizing formulas are one-for-one, economic order quantity, and any round number agreed to by involved parties. Inventory management literature is rife with complex and sophisticated variations that may have application in specific environments.

The lot sizing impact on material handling revolves around frequency and leftovers. A larger lot size will typically satisfy current, as well as some future, demands resulting in less frequent orders. Material handling will require fewer deliveries of raw material or components, but will have more processed parts left over to move and store. On the other hand, a smaller lot size will result in more frequent orders and more frequent deliveries, but fewer processed parts left over to move and store. Lot sizing of one-for-one, often called "as required," will result in the most deliveries of material and movement of processed parts, but will leave none left to store beyond immediate requirements.

Fixed period order factor. Fixed period order factor is a lot sizing technique with unique characteristics. While other lot sizing techniques yield a fixed quantity satisfying the requirements for varying periods of time, the fixed period order factor yields a varying quantity, which satisfies requirements for a fixed period of time. For example, a fixed period order factor of 15 days will result in adding together each day's requirement for the next 15 days and planning an order for the total quantity.

For manufactured parts, the fixed period order factor dictates how many times per year (or month) a given setup will be performed, and how many times the part will be manufactured. Where capacity is limited by lengthy setups, a fixed period order factor controls the frequency of those setups. For purchased material, this order policy will dictate how many orders are received per year (or month). This is a particularly valuable tool when material is purchased from afar and inbound freight costs approach the value of the material.

CHAPTER 1   STRATEGY DETERMINATION AND PRODUCTION REQUIREMENTS

For material handling, a fixed period order factor generates a reasonably predictable number of deliveries to and from a work center or receiving dock. It also dictates the length of time parts are stored in advance of need. It will not, however, predict the quantity of parts delivered, moved, or stored.

Order minimum. Order minimum is the most common order policy for purchased parts, and is similar to lot sizing for manufactured parts. While lot sizing may yield either fixed or variable quantities without restriction, an order minimum dictates an order quantity always equal to, or greater than, the predetermined minimum. This technique accommodates price breaks by codifying the break point. When the amount purchased must be rounded up to the minimum, the quantity received is likely to exceed short-term requirements, and the excess must be stored.

Order multiples. Order multiples serve to round up quantities calculated by other order policies. For purchased parts, an order multiple is a fixed quantity that usually represents a standard package amount. With an order multiple of 50, a requirement of 49 pieces will generate an order for 50 pieces; a requirement of 51 pieces will generate an order for 100. The degree to which order multiples generate order quantities in excess of current requirements is the degree to which this excess must be stored.

For manufactured parts, the order multiple typically accommodates specific process characteristics, such as the number of cavities in a plastic mold or the number of parts formed with each stroke of a punch press. However, the primary benefit of these order multiples is in facilitating the administration of standardized containers. Standard containers simplify material handling and optimize limited storage space. Order multiples and standard containers are appropriate for high-volume, frequently-used parts. However, most factories have many parts subject to infrequent use or shelf life restrictions, which are poorly-suited for management by order multiples.

Safety stock. Safety stock is inventory held in excess of anticipated demand. It is most appropriate for finished goods in a manufacture-to-stock environment, and protects the customer from stockouts caused by forecast errors. It also protects the factory from the chaos of reacting to stockouts. Like finished goods, service and repair parts may be an appropriate application for safety stocks because their demand is also subject to forecast error. Occasionally, fluctuations in the supply chain justify the use of safety stocks for raw material or components.

Safety stocks are usually small quantities that have a negligible impact on material handling. However, there is a long-term impact on storage because safety stocks are intended to be maintained indefinitely and must be rotated properly.

Scrap factors. Scrap factors anticipate scrap by increasing the planned quantity requirements. For a process where the scrap rate can be reasonably predicted, a percentage factor can be applied to either a part's master record or the bill-of-material record. This ensures that a sufficient number of parts are started in the process to yield a sufficient number of good ones. For example, if 1,000 lb (454 kg) of steel is required, a scrap factor of 5% will result in ordering 1,050 lb (476 kg). The extra 50 lb (23 kg) will be routinely received, moved, and stored with the required 1,000 lb (454 kg). Thus, scrap factors have a negligible impact on material handling prior to processing the material. On the other hand, if a given manufacturing run results in a scrap rate of less than the anticipated 5%, then either the remaining raw material or the excess processed parts must be stored until future requirements consume them.

Reducing Inventory

The paradigm "less inventory is always better" often leads to thoughtless reductions in inventory, for which a company pays a high price. Reductions, made without specific improvements and

regard to factory realities, can produce unexpected and unwanted results such as:

- Reduced capacity—smaller lot sizes result in more setups; more setups result in less available run time.
- Reduced customer service—elimination of safety stocks may result in more stockouts.
- Reduced schedule attainment—elimination of scrap factors may result in shortages of manufactured parts.
- Increased costs, such as:
  - No longer qualifying for purchased-part price breaks because of reduced order minimums.
  - Increased indirect labor because of more setups.
  - Increased expediting and overtime costs because of more stockouts and shortages.

The difference between a thoughtless reduction in inventory and a well-planned reduction lies in recognizing and balancing the trade-offs. The most risk-free approach to reducing inventory is a systematic process of continuous improvement. The first step is to align the various order policies with current factory reality. For example, ensure that scrap factors reflect recent experience and lot sizes amortize current setup costs (rather than past, preliminary estimates). Even as the first step is under way, begin the process by improving on the realities in the factory. This requires teamwork and focus throughout the organization.

Lot sizes are major builders of inventory. They are tolerated because they amortize the costs of lengthy setups in critical work centers. Continuous improvement goals target setup times in those work centers and drive systematic reductions. As a result, lot sizes should be reduced to reflect these new setup realities. Done properly, this process will result in less inventory, without increasing overall setup time and reducing available capacity. Smaller lot sizes will lower work-in-process inventory (and its storage requirements), but will increase material handling frequency. Balancing these two elements is a fundamental material handling concern in reducing lot sizes.

Order minimums on purchased material also build inventory, assuring low piece prices by reflecting price breaks. Continuous improvement goals should target supplier negotiations to yield low piece prices for smaller order quantities. This will reduce inventory levels for purchased material with little, if any, increase in piece costs. When reductions in incoming material quantities are synchronized with manufacturing lot size reductions, both raw material and work-in-process inventory levels, and their corresponding storage requirements, go down. The frequency of material handling, however, will increase with more deliveries of smaller quantities. These principles also apply to order multiples.

A perfect sales forecast would eliminate the need for carrying safety stocks of finished goods. However, forecasts are inherently inaccurate and safety stocks buffer the factory and customer from their effects. A continuous improvement goal would challenge the organization to develop more measurably accurate forecasts, justifying a lowering of safety stocks. A more aggressive approach would be to shorten manufacturing cycle time through JIT and synchronous manufacturing principles. This improved ability to respond quickly to changes in customer demand would justify a further reduction—or elimination—of safety stocks. A complete elimination of safety stocks would cancel the need to store and rotate them.

The only way to justify reducing scrap factors is to succeed in reducing scrap. A continuous improvement goal should identify and eradicate the many causes of scrap. A focus on scrap reduction targets preventive maintenance, tooling maintenance and repair, process control, employee training, design for manufacturability, and material handling. The principles embodied in JIT and synchronous manufacturing heighten awareness and reliance on quality and sup-

CHAPTER 1   STRATEGY DETERMINATION AND PRODUCTION REQUIREMENTS

port major reductions in scrap factors. Decreasing scrap factors will lower lot sizes, and therefore, reduce the need to move and store work-in-process and raw material inventory. A side benefit to material handling is a reduction in the amount of scrap that must be removed for disposal.

Planned inventory reductions via a systematic attack on the causes of inventory, can result not only in lower inventory levels, but also in other improvements of potentially greater impact. No one function determines inventory levels or their reduction; it is a team effort requiring various talents. Material handling can be both the recipient and driver of improvements.

PUSH AND PULL MANUFACTURING

Push systems and pull systems are two broad categories of manufacturing planning and execution systems. At the heart of the planning portion of either system lies several common features. Traditional push systems are typically supported by manufacturing resource planning (MRPII), which encompasses a full range of both planning and execution functions. These include the production plan, master schedule, rough cut capacity analysis, material requirements planning (MRP), detailed capacity requirements planning, production scheduling and control, and feedback. Pull systems may use the same MRPII features for planning (production plan, master schedule, rough cut capacity analysis, and material requirements planning for raw material and purchased components only), but have no formal equivalent to perform detailed capacity requirements planning. Furthermore, in pull systems, the execution activities of production scheduling and control are decoupled from the MRP activities and replaced by replenishment methodologies that tend to be more visual and signal-based. For additional discussion of MRP and MRPII, see "Manufacturing Resource Planning" of this chapter.

It is primarily in the execution portion that push and pull systems diverge. Material requirements planning not only plans, but is also the execution driver for a typical push system. MRP analyzes the master schedule and available inventory, and yields a list of net requirements. Order policies and lead times are then applied to provide a delivery schedule for purchased material and due dates for manufactured parts, both supporting the master schedule timing. MRP will plan material availability throughout the purchase and manufacture lead time horizon, and generate a push schedule. Feedback from executing the schedule is then used for replanning.

While the execution portion of a push system is tied to its planning portion (via order launch start dates derived from a comparatively static master schedule), a pull system decouples execution from planning. A pull system draws material through the manufacturing process when signaled by the consumption of material at downstream operations, or the need for replenishment of buffer stocks. Common signals include kanban cards, light boards, buzzers, and visual triggers, such as empty and full containers or empty and full designated spaces. In some cases, material handling is the carrier of the signal, and where material handling must respond to a pull signal, an immediate response is required. Because pull schedules represent current production, they typically do not provide the lead time to procure raw material, or the reaction time to adjust future capacity. Consequently, pull systems generally use the same planning features as push systems to plan purchased material and perform rough-cut capacity analysis.

Just-in-Time

The extension of pull execution is Just-in-Time manufacturing. JIT is a total philosophy for operating a manufacturing enterprise. It attacks waste throughout the entire process—from order entry and engineering, to production and invoicing—and demands continuous

improvement. JIT is so dissimilar from traditional manufacturing practices that it requires a company-wide focus to develop the necessary culture and cannot be successfully implemented by any one person or department. Within the production arena, some of the major challenges that JIT must address are reducing setup times, reducing lot sizes (the goal is a lot size of one unit), reducing cumulative lead times, and reducing scrap and rework. Re-engineering the manufacturing process toward synchronous manufacturing will drive improvements in these four areas and allow for less complicated bills of material. Simpler bills of material make production reporting and inventory management easier, and reduces overall inventory.

JIT may rely on pull signals to authorize material movement and production. In addition to responding to these signals, there are other material handling implications in a JIT factory. Work cells may require only a simple one-piece-at-a-time hand-off between workstations. Alternatively, the hand-off may be automated. In either case, the material continues to flow instead of sitting in queues awaiting processing. As queues are reduced, work-in-process storage becomes unnecessary. As manufacturing lot sizes approach one, no excess finished goods are produced, freeing up storage space and the need to manage this inventory. Since fewer parts are handled at a given time, material handling equipment may be simplified or downscaled. On the other hand, the frequency of material moves increases dramatically.

A logical evolution for JIT would extend these execution principles into the planning portion. This extension is dependent upon short lead times for purchased material, and either a stable demand or sufficient capacity to either handle spikes in demand or changes in product mix. MRP strengths can be managed to introduce JIT principles into the material planning process. Fundamental to MRP are order policies and lead times. Ideally, these reflect current factory realities. For example, lot sizes reflect current setup times, scrap factors reflect recent scrap history, and purchased material lead time reflects current experience. A strength of an MRP system is its ability to accommodate factory realities, enabling the planning process to proceed regardless of the order policy size or lead time length. In contrast, JIT will not tolerate long lead times and large lot sizes. Therefore, JIT activities attack factory realities by driving order policies and lead times toward zero. Early in this evolution, MRP can reflect these improvements, but will still produce schedules based on due dates.

As these improvements are carried through to purchased material, and as supplier delivery and quality become reliable, the need for advance material planning is minimized, allowing date-driven push schedules to be replaced by pull signals. Under these circumstances, however, a master schedule should continue to be managed to plan long-range capacity requirements and provide the basis for financial projections.

The incorporation of JIT principles throughout the supply chain brings with it the same quantity, speed, and frequency response mandates as internal JIT activities, as well as the potential for suppliers to deliver to the points of use within the factory. This creates a dynamic material handling and communication environment with further opportunities for improvement.

Constraints Management

Constraints management is a methodology for identifying bottlenecks. It focuses planning and execution functions on them, minimizing their impact by maximizing their output, until they are no longer bottlenecks. A *bottleneck* is a ". . . resource whose capacity is less than the demand placed upon it."[14] Constraints management, which may incorporate features of both push and pull systems, keeps material flowing to the bottleneck from upstream operations and

CHAPTER 1 STRATEGY DETERMINATION AND PRODUCTION REQUIREMENTS

schedules downstream operations on the basis of the managed output of the bottleneck. This may involve buffer stocks ahead of the bottleneck to assure continuous material availability, and perhaps even safety stocks of raw material backing up the buffers. A bottleneck must never run out of material to process and must be kept running. Typically, relief operators cover breaks and lunches, and maintenance and material handling personnel may even be dedicated to support bottleneck operations.

MRP bases production schedules on due dates, and pull/JIT determines production schedules on downstream consumption of material. However, constraints management schedules production through a bottleneck, simply because it is a bottleneck. Failure to obtain sufficient production through a bottleneck will cause downstream shortages.

When a work center ceases to be a bottleneck, either through a decrease in demand or an increase in capacity, constraints management identifies the next bottleneck and aggressively attacks its limitations. Since buffer and safety stocks may be established to support bottlenecks and the bottlenecks continually shift, the size and placement of material storage requirements fluctuate. This need to continually refocus on material handling support of successive bottlenecks, each with potentially unique material storage and movement requirements, presents a challenge to a factory's material handling flexibility.

Push and pull systems differ in their scheduling and communication methodologies. They require different material handling and storage responses. Therefore, plans to change or improve the manufacturing process or change from one methodology to another must include input from material handling designers.

RESOURCE PLANNING AND SCHEDULING CONCEPTS

Manufacturing companies gain a competitive advantage whenever they satisfy customers by producing products reliably, swiftly, and economically. In turn, this requires highly effective planning and scheduling processes to synchronize the availability of resources: material, labor, equipment, tooling, engineering specifications, space, and money. Misaligning any one resource creates a serious problem. While the other expensive resources wait, costly expediting chases the shortages. Hot lists and red tags are the signs of poor planning and scheduling. Late deliveries and extra costs are the painful penalties.

The challenge is not planning, however, it is having the capability to replan. As soon as plans are laid out, changes such as inaccurate forecasts, customers changing their orders, engineers revising bills of material, absent operators, equipment breaking down, broken tooling, late deliveries from suppliers, rejected material, emergency orders arriving, and management altering policies begin to take place. The goals of resource planning and scheduling are to maintain plans that correctly reflect these changing needs while, at the same time, ensuring that the plans are attainable.

Two events have occurred that make replanning practical. First is the advent of hardware and software, with their ability to store vast amounts of data and analyze it quickly. Second is the body of knowledge that has now matured into a tool kit of proven approaches. The combination provides companies with the capability to generate high-quality plans. No longer are there any legitimate excuses for poor planning and control.

SERVING THE CUSTOMER

"Don't put the cart in front of the horse" is the same as saying "Don't put tactics ahead of strategies." Before selecting the right tools, every manufacturing company must decide on a key strategy. The right combination of tools can then be assembled to make the strategy happen. Figure 1-1 illustrates the choices. The major events, from initial design to final delivery, are represented along the horizontal axis. Each step takes time and adds costs, reflected in the vertical axis that indicates from zero expenditure of labor and material to 100% of costs. The greater the investment, the swifter the delivery to the customer. Conversely, the fewer events completed before the order arrives, the longer the customer waits to receive the product. The question is, how many of the events must be completed prior to a customer order arriving?

Understanding the relationship between delivery time and manufacturing lead time contributes to the answer. Delivery time reflects the gap between receipt of a customer order and delivery of the product, whereas manufacturing time represents how long it takes to design, purchase, manufacture, and deliver the product. Whenever the manufacturing time is less than the desired delivery time, there is no need to acquire materials before customer orders arrive. However, if delivery time is shorter than the manufacturing time, most or all of the steps must be accomplished before the orders arrive. Leading-edge companies gain their advantages by applying speed not only to reduce delivery time, but to also slash manufacturing lead times.

How are customer needs best met? This is largely determined by two factors. First, in most industries, there is a common standard for delivery time. For example, food products are expected to be available on the grocery shelves for immediate availability to consumers. In contrast, it is suitable for a complex, nonstandard machine to take several weeks for delivery. The second factor deals with competitors. Speed of deliveries along with price, quality, and product performance are competitive weapons. To beat competitors, manufacturing companies must offer a significant differential in at least one of these four categories or similarities in all of them.

Most companies develop many strategies for servicing customers. Some products may be stocked in distribution centers, while others are located centrally. Some components can be built early, but the salable product is finished after receipt of orders. Perhaps raw materials can be stocked, but no manufacturing is started until orders arrive. For special products, steps are not started without a confirmed customer order. As conditions change within the company and marketplace, revised strategies must be initiated.

By portraying the choices and predicting consequences, the Planning department becomes a major contributor to resolving these important issues. It is the executives, however, who need to make the final decision. The Planning department is then able to administer the techniques to carry out management's strategies.

THE PLANNER'S TOOL KIT

This section describes proven tools and explains how these approaches can be applied successfully by skilled users for:

- Aggregate planning.
- Master scheduling.
- Material planning.
- Capacity planning.
- Plant scheduling.
- Supplier scheduling.

Aggregate Planning

The purpose of aggregate planning is to provide an overall framework for reconciling the demands of the marketplace with the capa-

CHAPTER 1   STRATEGY DETERMINATION AND PRODUCTION REQUIREMENTS

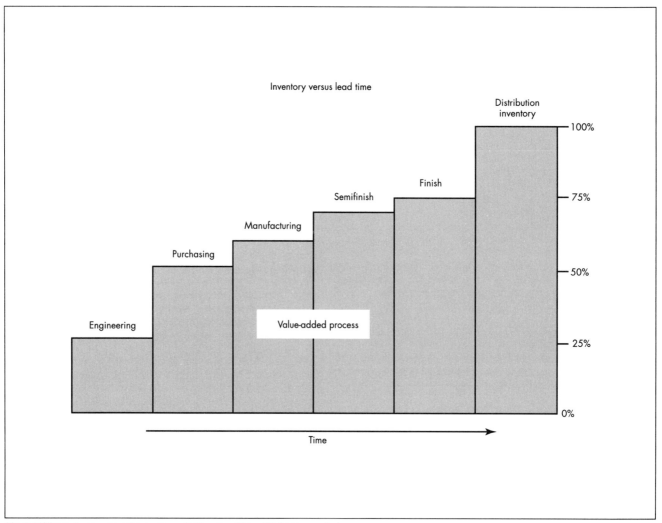

Fig. 1-1 Where do you meet the customer? *(Courtesy Oliver Wight Companies)*

bilities of the manufacturing place. The senior management team is responsible for producing two aggregate plans, the business plan and the sales and operations plan. Together, these plans provide both the direction and limitations within which all of the detailed processes operate.

All manufacturing companies have a business plan projecting at least a year into the future. In monetary terms, it projects what is expected to happen, specifying gross revenues, profits, and cash flows. From the approved business plan, budgets are developed for the individual departments. Generally, the business plan remains fixed for the fiscal year as it is used as a benchmark for judging performance.

The sales and operations plan has many important differences from the business plan. The planning horizon normally extends beyond the fiscal year to provide guidance for activities requiring long lead times, such as acquisition of capital equipment, negotiations with suppliers, and finding new channels of distribution. Furthermore, it is a rolling plan—as one month goes by, a new month is added. It must be flexible if it is to respond to shifts in the marketplace or changes in the company's capabilities. Broad categories or "families" of products are reviewed in the planning process. Generally, six to twelve families would be sufficient for an individual com-

pany. Whereas the business plan is expressed in monetary units, the sales and operations plan uses operating units of measure such as pieces, pounds, tons, and feet.

A stripped-down version of a sales and operations planning output report is shown in Fig. 1-2. On the left side of the report are three time periods (generally months) comparing actual to expected performance. The right side displays future projections. Looking at the figure from top to bottom, you see three blocks of information: at the top is the sales plan, the middle is the production plan, and the bottom represents either finished goods inventories for make-to-stock products or backlogs (all orders booked, not yet shipped) for make-to-order products.

On a monthly basis, the general manager and staff review performance against plans for the prior months, focusing on appropriate changes for future plans. Tough questions have to be asked and answered:

- Is there a need for change?
- How soon should the change occur?
- What are the consequences of not changing?
- What are the costs of changing?
- What can be done to improve the projection accuracy?
- What will improve the reliability of commitments?

CHAPTER 1 STRATEGY DETERMINATION AND PRODUCTION REQUIREMENTS

The resolution of these questions results in approved sales and supply plans. The senior sales and marketing person is accountable for implementing the sales plan and the senior manufacturing/operations person is responsible for the execution of the supply plan, with support from Engineering and Purchasing.

The sales plan is broken down into salable configurations that become projections of demand for the master schedulers. The master schedulers also take into account existing inventories, plus available capacity to create their plans. The sum of what they schedule, when added up by time period and by family, must reconcile with the aggregate supply plans. In essence, each supply plan becomes a budget for the master schedulers to spend.

Likewise, the business and sales and operations plans must reconcile. Converted to monetary units, the sales and operations plan should equal what is in the business plan. Allowing these two plans to vary is a guaranteed way to create costly confusion. Whenever there are two sets of numbers in place, somebody will be following one while his or her teammates follow the other.

Master Scheduling

As the name implies, this is the master of all of the subsequent schedules issued to the factory, suppliers, and Engineering. For make-to-stock products, it would generally be expressed in end-item configurations, called *stock-keeping units (SKUs)*. If the company meets the customer below the end-item level, however, other choices are usually more practical. For example, when options are offered to customers, the master schedulers will frequently schedule these options. When the key issue is capacity availability, the master schedule would be expressed in capacity terms. In these two situations, a finishing schedule would be created after the customer orders arrive to reflect salable products.

Figure 1-3 shows an output report for a master schedule item. The bottom row represents the current plan as previously created by the master scheduler. To ensure that accountability can be assigned to the master scheduler, the computer should not be allowed to automatically change the existing plan. It is important that judgment by a skilled scheduler be used to separate significant changes from trivial ones. Insignificant changes may cause a lot of extra work, as minor revisions permeate the rest of the planning system. Where the changes are deemed critical, good judgment is also necessary to separate what is practical from what is impossible to execute.

Above the "master planning schedule" row in Figure 1-3 is information summarizing marketplace needs, as well as projected inventory levels. Software systems not only calculate these data, but analyze the projections to create action messages. These messages are valu-

Make-to-stock

Sales		–3	–2	–1
Sales plan		120	120	120
Actual				
Difference				
Cumulative difference				

Family: 1500

Current	+1	+2	+3	+4
120	125	125	125	125

Production

Production plan		125	125	125
Actual				
Difference				
Cumulative difference				

125	125	125	125	125

Inventory

Planned		108	113	118
Actual	103			
Difference				

123	123	123	123	123

Fig. 1-2 Sales and operations planning work sheet. *(Courtesy Oliver Wight Companies)*

CHAPTER 1   STRATEGY DETERMINATION AND PRODUCTION REQUIREMENTS

able input to the schedulers, calling their attention to various situations, such as the need to reschedule quantities earlier or later, add more to their plan, cancel unnecessary quantities, or react to a past-due situation.

For example, note that the master schedule quantity in week three is not needed until week four. The due date is earlier than the need date. If the master scheduler feels that this is unimportant or too late to change, then no action is initiated. On the other hand, to maintain the correct priorities at the lower levels and to free up capacity so that other master schedule items can be moved into week three, it may be very desirable to reschedule.

The key to maintaining correct priorities is the comparison between the scheduled due date for existing orders and the need date. The computer calculates the need date by comparing what is available in inventory, plus any existing schedules, against total demand. Stated in other terms, it is testing to see if the supply plan equals the demand plan, period by period. Whenever the plans are misaligned, an action message is generated. In this example, the message would recommend rescheduling from week three to week four.

Another important aspect of master scheduling is promising when new customer orders can be delivered. The row called "available to promise" represents the uncommitted portion of the master schedule. It is calculated by subtracting existing commitments (customer orders already promised) from the total supply (available inventory plus scheduled quantities). What remains provides a quick and reliable means for responding to questions about when incoming customer orders can be shipped.

	Past due	1	2	3	4	5	6	7	8
Forecast						3	5	5	5
Actual demand		10			10	2			
Projected available balance		0	0	10	0	5	0	5	0
Available-to-promise						8		10	
Master planning schedule (MPS)		10		10		10		10	

Fig. 1-3 Output report for master schedule item "A." *(Courtesy Oliver Wight Companies)*

Material Planning

The purpose of material planning is to answer these questions:

- What do we need?
- How much?
- When?

There are two approaches for determining these answers. One is quantity-based and the techniques used are re-order points and the two-bin system. The other is time-based and uses material requirements planning (MRP).

Re-order points. Re-order points are determined by calculating the average demand during the replenishment lead time, plus safety stock. The resulting figure is compared against available daily inventory, which is the sum of stock on hand plus existing schedules. Whenever the re-order point is equal to or greater than the available inventory, a message to replenish is generated. Safety stock is used as protection against two types of uncertainties: forecast inaccuracy (representing uncertainty of demand) and unreliable completion of schedules (representing uncertainty of supply). Users should always put greater emphasis on correcting the causes of these uncertainties, rather than accepting the extra costs of safety stocks.

There are two main disadvantages to the re-order point approach. Because there is no way to compare due dates to need dates, it cannot maintain correct priorities for shop and purchase orders. Secondly, it presumes that future usage will resemble that of the past, which may or may not be true.

Two-bin system. Although the two-bin system and re-order points operate similarly, the two-bin system does not require daily inventory transactions to be recorded. Rather, it separates inventory into two locations, and whenever one becomes empty, it triggers a re-order for more material. The second bin must contain adequate inventory to satisfy the average demand during the replenishment lead time, plus safety stock.

Material requirements planning. MRP operates differently. Some of the data are the same, such as average lead time, desired replenishment quantity, safety stock, on-hand balance, and existing schedules. However, two additional inputs distinguish MRP: the use of the master production schedule and structured bills of material. A structured bill of material links all components in a parent/component manner as illustrated in Fig. 1-4. It operates like a road map, directing the master schedule to each of the components needed to manufacture it. The requirements on these components are called *dependent demands,* since they are directly related to the needs of the parents. In contrast, re-order points use *independent demands*, meaning that they are forecasted as if requirements were occurring randomly. Whenever you can replace forecasting with dependent calculations, the resulting planning activity is far superior.

Figure 1-5 shows material planning for part B, a component of product A. The gross requirements come from the master plan for product A, as shown in Fig. 1-3. Part B has enough inventory to service all of these needs until week six. At this point, all of the inventory is depleted, which will cause MRP to recommend a replenishment quantity three weeks earlier, based on the lead time to replenish part B. This recommended order is called a *planned order*, because it has not yet been converted to a scheduled order. Planned orders serve many purposes: they explode the bill of material to become the requirements at the next lower level (planned orders at the parent part number automatically become demands for all components of the parent). When a planned order appears in the current period, an action message is generated reminding the scheduler to convert it to a scheduled receipt. Finally, planned orders feed other processes, such as financial and capacity planning.

CHAPTER 1 STRATEGY DETERMINATION AND PRODUCTION REQUIREMENTS

Capacity Planning

The purpose of capacity planning is to determine how much labor and equipment, by time period and work center, will be required to carry out the master plan. A *work center* is defined as a group of operators with similar skills, or equipment with similar capabilities. Whenever the projections indicate that existing capacity does not match what is necessary to satisfy requirements, the planners must determine what can be economically done to correct the situation or change the master plan.

Capacity planning can use an infinite or finite approach. The infinite approach projects the impact of requirements on all of the selected work centers, without regarding whether or not these work centers are capable of satisfying the requirements. The objective is to see what is required and then attempt to make it happen. If there

is a problem that cannot be resolved, the planners present the options to the master scheduler to work out an alternative plan.

The finite planning approach has a computer schedule jobs into each work center, by time period, up to a predetermined level of capacity. If more capacity is needed, the computer adjusts schedules forward or backward into other time periods. In this manner, it attempts to balance out the overloads and underloads. But, if the end result cannot support the master plan, action similar to that for the infinite approach must be initiated to cope with the situation.

There are advocates for each approach. Where there is a paced assembly line or a one-piece product being manufactured, such as a casting, the finite approach is likely to be preferred. Where there are many components being manufactured and assembled into salable products, the infinite planning approach is generally favored. To be

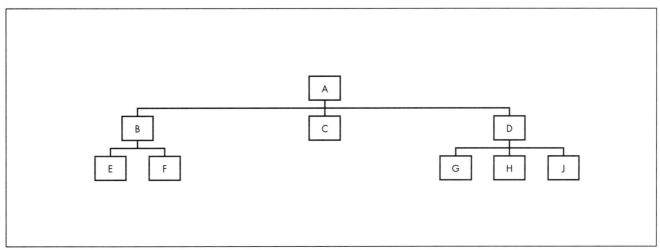

Fig. 1-4 Bill of material structure. *(Courtesy Oliver Wight Companies)*

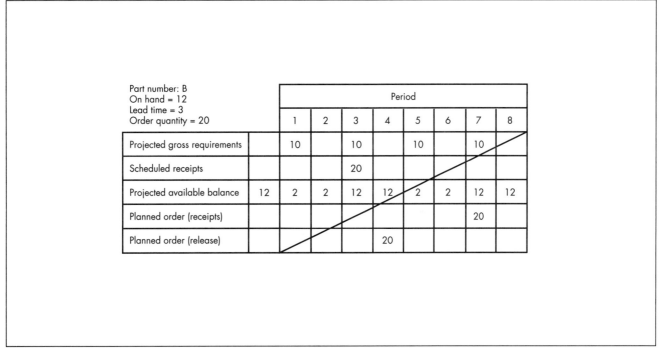

Fig. 1-5 Material planning for part "B." *(Courtesy Oliver Wight Companies)*

CHAPTER 1 STRATEGY DETERMINATION AND PRODUCTION REQUIREMENTS

valid, the master plan must have both material and capacity when required. If one or both cannot be available when needed, the master schedule quickly degenerates into a useless wish list.

Rough-cut capacity planning is a simpler means of predicting capacity. All companies have a small number of bottlenecks or key constraints. A quick way to test whether a proposed plan is realistic or not is to focus initially on these limited resources. The assumption is that if the bottlenecks look acceptable, odds are good that the other work centers will not present a problem.

Plant Scheduling

The purpose of plant scheduling is to communicate correct, up-to-date priorities to the factory. Jobs in the factory are competing for scarce resources: labor and equipment. To assign work to operators effectively, operator skills, machine capabilities, and priorities must be assessed.

In a flow shop, where the product follows a predetermined path, the job of communicating priorities to the factory is straightforward. Typically, the first operation is scheduled in a sequence of jobs that represents the needs of the marketplace, as well as the economics of manufacturing. All subsequent operations simply follow the same sequence, avoiding the need for additional communications concerning priorities.

Managing a job shop is more difficult when the traffic pattern through the various work centers varies from job to job. If the total time to complete all of the operations is very short (a day or two), flow shop procedures can be followed. Often, however, lead times are longer and priorities are likely to change before jobs are completed. What was initially urgent may not be needed as quickly because of changes in the master plan, while other jobs are needed much earlier for the same reason. In these situations, all work centers need to be advised of the latest priorities.

Priorities are frequently calculated by operational due dates. This requires routing and scheduling rules. The routing identifies the operations required to make each manufactured part number and estimates the time needed to make one unit plus set up equipment. Scheduling rules contain estimates of time to move work from one operation to the next, plus the queue time (average waiting time) for each of the work centers that the job will pass through. By considering the due date of each scheduled job from MRP as well as the routing and scheduling rules, milestones can be calculated as to when each operation should be completed to finish the job on time.

Backward and forward scheduling. There are two choices for calculating milestones. *Backward scheduling* starts from the due date of each job and establishes milestones from the last operation to the first step. *Forward scheduling* begins by finding when the first operation can be started and then establishes milestones for all subsequent operations.

Where multiple components are needed to make products, companies generally prefer backward scheduling so that all components can be synchronized to arrive at the required time. Products that do not require assembly, such as castings, are candidates for forward scheduling. Determine what operations have been completed and where the jobs are located before communicating priority changes to the factory.

Push versus pull. Kanban is another approach that works in either a flow shop or job shop and has gained worldwide acceptance throughout many industries. Simplicity is one of its strengths because it requires few, if any, transactions. A second advantage is that it fixes a maximum limitation on the size of queues.

With the conventional push system approach, queues of jobs wait their turn ahead of the operator. The sizes of queues vary depending on work arriving and the volume completed. As soon as the operation is finished, the job moves to the next operation; that is, it is "pushed" to where it needs to go. With kanban, the queues are located after the operator (representing work completed), but not yet moved. The next operation focuses on the "customer," and until the customer needs more work, nothing is moved. When the customer signals that work is needed, it is *pulled* from its supplier. Whenever the total queue reaches its predetermined maximum, the operator is no longer authorized to continue producing at this work center. Instead, he or she would look for other productive activities, such as working at a different work center, practicing setups, working on preventive maintenance, joining a problem-solving group, or doing housekeeping.

How does kanban determine what job to work on next? If there is a limited variety of part numbers, the answer is to simply replace what has been taken. If a customer pulls part K from the supplier, the supplier replenishes part K. Whenever the variety of part numbers is significant, however, this approach works poorly. The supplier's queue must have at least one of every possible part that the customer may request. To avoid high queues, companies have combined the attributes of kanban with those of MRP. Since MRP is a forward-looking planning system, it knows what jobs are needed next. By issuing a schedule to both the customers and suppliers, the queues can still be small because the supplier will always be anticipating and working on what the customer needs next.

Supplier Scheduling

While it is important that the Planning department communicates with the inside shop (the factory), it is just as important that good communications are established with the outside shops (the suppliers). Purchase orders were the main vehicle for doing this. Presently, negotiations with suppliers are separated from the day-to-day communications with them. Purchase orders confirm the results of the negotiations and supplier schedules authorize deliveries. This process provides the supplier long-term visibility of the customer's needs (in this case, the manufacturer).

Negotiations cover important aspects, such as determining which suppliers are approved, establishing price based on long-term requirements, and defining lead times and order quantities. In essence, the terms and conditions of the relationship are detailed. Supplier schedulers then plan the release of work so that material arrives in time to service the inside shops. Figure 1-6 shows a report listing all of the active part numbers currently being purchased from one supplier. Note the asterisk next to some of the quantities. This denotes those schedules that will not be changed automatically. Rather, if there is a need for change in this near-term zone, the customer will call to determine if the supplier can accommodate it.

These guidelines, called *time fences* (shown in Figure 1-6), are very important to both the customer and supplier. The supplier wants a fair opportunity to deliver on time and to do so economically. If the short-term requirements were to change daily, faster than suppliers can react, they would not be able to perform efficiently. From the customers' point-of-view, reliability as well as swiftness is desired. But, there is no sense in demanding immediate changes that will be either impossible to receive or delivered at an unacceptable premium. Time fences define the relationship in a manner that is fair to both parties.

Beyond the area containing firm plans (denoted by the asterisks in Fig. 1-6), the quantities represent the customer's best estimate of future requirements. These would be planned orders if an MRP system is in place. Each time MRP analyzes the need for materials, planned orders are automatically changed because new conditions are found. From a supplier's viewpoint, the future visibility is extremely helpful. These data become the input for capacity and material planning. Instead of the supplier forecasting these future needs,

CHAPTER 1 STRATEGY DETERMINATION AND PRODUCTION REQUIREMENTS

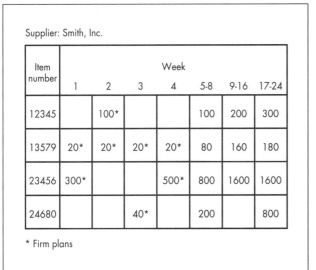

Supplier: Smith, Inc.

Item number	Week						
	1	2	3	4	5-8	9-16	17-24
12345		100*			100	200	300
13579	20*	20*	20*	20*	80	160	180
23456	300*			500*	800	1600	1600
24680			40*		200		800

* Firm plans

Fig. 1-6 Supplier schedule. *(Courtesy Oliver Wight Companies)*

the customer is providing dependent demands. Although planned orders may change, they still represent a better projection than the supplier's forecasts.

Working as a team benefits both the customer and supplier. Sharing valid information becomes the bond linking good partnerships. With it, the supplier can manage business in a better manner, resulting in greater reliability, less cost, higher quality, and increased swiftness.

MANUFACTURING RESOURCE PLANNING

It is mandatory for all manufacturing companies to do aggregate planning, master scheduling, material planning, capacity planning, shop scheduling, and supplier scheduling. These activities are necessary to acquire raw materials, convert them into salable products, and ship them to customers. One approach to integrate these activities is shown in Fig. 1-7. This operating system is called Manufacturing Resource Planning (MRPII). It remains the generally-accepted approach for planning and scheduling all of the resources that manufacturing companies need.

A key feature of MRPII is that, given accurate data, it plans in matched sets of resources. Only when labor, material, equipment, tooling, specifications, space, and money are available at the right place and time can a company quickly and economically convert raw materials to products and deliver them in a competitive manner. Missing any resource stops the flow. Until the missing resource is provided, having all of the others waiting adds unnecessary costs.

Supply chain management extends the linkage from the company upward to the customers' customers and downward to the suppliers' suppliers. This chain should connect the ultimate consumer and the first producer. Requirements flow down the chain to streamline the flow of products up the chain. Better customer information helps the suppliers improve their operations. The extension of this in both directions constitutes a major competitive advantage.

Before companies can build effective partnerships with customers and suppliers, they must demonstrate the capability of controlling their operations. Well-managed customers know the consequences of a weak link in the chain. They want partners that can convert better information into significant benefits for them. In the same manner, a company without control cannot possibly provide valid plans to its suppliers, even if it announces its intentions of being a good partner.

The arrows in the MRPII schematic in Fig. 1-7 point in both directions. Unfortunately, some companies use it only in the top-down direction, communicating plans from the front office down to the factory floor. Unavoidable problems will cause some schedules to be unattainable. If the users cannot possibly execute the plans, they must come up with the best possible alternative and advise other users of the situation. Without an equally strong upward flow of information, valid plans cannot be maintained.

For example, if a supplier cannot deliver on time, Purchasing must swing into "damage control":

- Can the supplier deliver a partial shipment on time?
- Should overtime and premium transportation be authorized?
- Is there an alternative supplier who can help?, etc.

If no practical alternative can be found, then the factory schedulers must react:

- Is there any safety stock that can be used?
- Can lead times be compressed?
- Are there any interchangeable parts that could be used?, etc.

Only when all practical alternatives have been exhausted should the master scheduler be notified that the plans cannot be carried out.

For feedback to be effective, there are two principles that must become standard operating procedures: "Silence is approval" and "The last choice to solve a problem is to change the master plan." Saying nothing means that the job can be done. But speaking up does not mean that the plan will be automatically changed. Rather, all options and their consequences first must be explored. The attitude must be to correct the situation somehow, and only as a last resort change the master plan.

PROCESS RE-ENGINEERING

Process re-engineering derives from a strategic, competitive motivation. If a re-engineering effort cannot be linked to improvements in quality, delivery, speed to market, or cost and price control, then the purpose and benefit of the effort should be examined.

A material handling system is seldom re-engineered for its own sake. Rather, it is a tactical initiative resulting from plans to re-engineer products or processes (including inventory processes) to support a company's competitive strategies. Material handling redesigns may support new processes for existing products, processes for new products, inventory management improvements, or similar tactical activities.

A re-engineering effort for existing products may have only a minimal impact on the material handling design if the same basic material handling and storage requirements remain unchanged. In such cases, a change of storage location or container size may be all that is required. In contrast, re-engineering a process may result in major changes, such as the re-organization of equipment into a work cell or the combining of drilling operations onto a computer numerical control (CNC) machine. Large-scale process changes, which simplify the process, are likely to simplify the supporting material handling requirements. The manufacturing engineer, as part of the re-engineering team, can ensure that simplicity, cost, and efficiency are considered in the design.

A material handling design to support a new product may provide the opportunity to exercise creative license in a new environment. The responsible manufacturing engineer will focus on simplicity, efficiency, cost, throughput, and capacity as appropriate to the production environment. However, for new products it is more common to require some or many of the same processes as existing products. In these instances, the material handling design must not only support the new product, but continue to support existing

CHAPTER 1   STRATEGY DETERMINATION AND PRODUCTION REQUIREMENTS

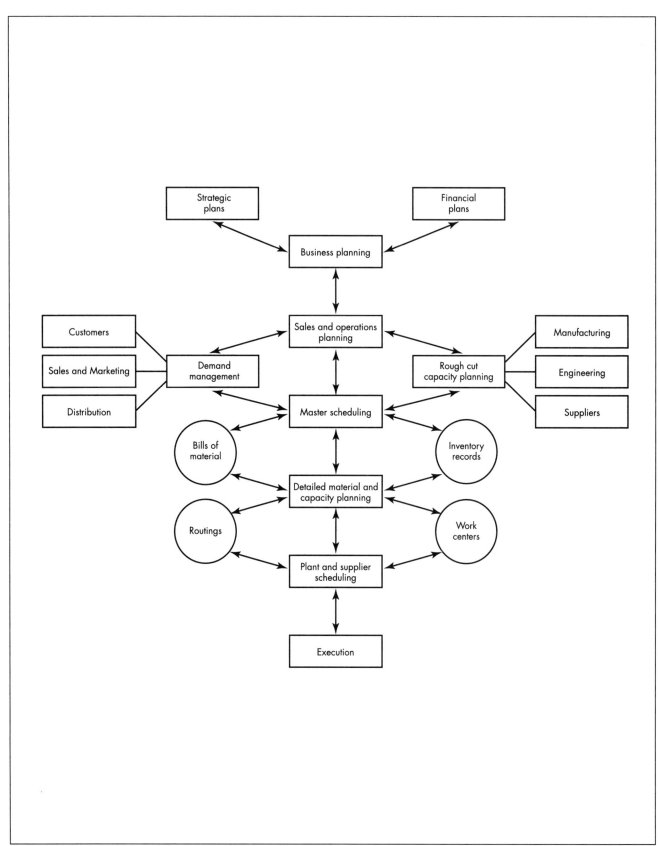

Fig. 1-7 Manufacturing Resource Planning (MRPII). *(Courtesy Oliver Wight Companies)*

CHAPTER 1   STRATEGY DETERMINATION AND PRODUCTION REQUIREMENTS

products. This will require a re-evaluation of the nature and capacity of the existing system, and provide opportunities for improvements.

Re-engineering inventory processes may be required as part of a JIT initiative or a general inventory reduction mandate. Regardless of the reason, this kind of re-engineering always addresses order policies and lead times.

Process re-engineering is a form of continuous improvement. However, it is a total rethinking of a tactical process. In either case, the manufacturing engineer must effectively integrate material handling design into the larger re-engineering effort.

PROCESS PLANNING AND FLOW ANALYSIS

If a company's current manufacturing operations are not meeting expectations, it is time to look at making some changes. However, determining what to change, what to change to, and how to change is not easy. There are many ways to reach manufacturing goals. Each change carries a cost and a benefit. Selecting steps that incrementally improve the operation have a far greater probability of success than making a giant leap of faith.

To answer the first two questions—what to change and what to change to—involves a systematic process of assessing the manufacturing operations. Determining how to change is a management problem that is often considered too lightly. After the targets of opportunity, the desired new processes, and the philosophy of change have been identified, the project becomes an implementation problem. At every step in the analysis process it is necessary to continuously check assumptions and progress. Good documentation is critical to success.

Dividing the process into phases with interim goals will keep it in control. Specific documentation goals during the process will ensure constructive participation and provide a benchmark for progress measurement. Frequent and thorough communication assures that the direction is understood and acted upon.

The major phases of a project are:

• Phase I—Planning.
• Phase II—Design.
• Phase III—Implementation.

While the primary interest in this chapter is planning, it is important to understand where it fits in the overall scheme. This section describes the components of each phase. In later chapters, the design and implementation phases are expanded.

PHASE I—PLANNING

In the planning phase, the initial objective is to identify study team members and project roles, responsibilities, and schedules. Team members must bring a diverse set of skills and, most importantly, open minds. By carefully describing the role of each member, one can ensure that individual strengths can compensate for weaknesses in other areas. Setting initial goals and schedules will help every member focus on the results that help build a successful project. Another key part is a thorough understanding of the current environment. They need to learn what leading edge companies have used for effective solutions. Otherwise, team members are likely to be trapped into automating what is in place today rather than evaluating innovative alternatives. No large plan should proceed very far

prior to a thorough evaluation of costs and payback time. There also should be an organization structure for managing the project. The following steps provide a method to capture, format, and analyze the data used to develop a master plan.

1. Provide primary information in the initial investigation. Operating personnel provide the primary information. This means that the vision of the operation must be learned from the Plant Manager and key people. Documenting the key parameters of the operation provides the reference base for the steps that follow. The major parameters include goals, objectives, operating policies, and measurements. Initial descriptions of physical facilities and resources are also part of the documentation.

2. Develop an operational assessment. This establishes the project's starting point, based on a detailed written and graphical description of the current operation. To arrive at this description, it is necessary to interview a broad range of personnel and collect data about products, processes, resources, customers, and suppliers. The assessment document organizes this information and accurately describes the operating environment. This is the "as-is" description. An analysis of the findings in the description will identify opportunities and problems. These are listed in tabular format by area. Where possible, the listing will include the cost of problems and opportunities in manufacturing units or any easily understood form.

3. Define a vision and requirements statement. The critical "as-is" information should be defined in both qualitative and quantitative terms. From this, a list of functional needs or requirements is developed with descriptions categorized by functional area. The key problems, those with the greatest impact on the operation, become the basis for the project vision. This statement identifies the opportunities and problems that will be addressed. The statement limits the scope to a finite set of tasks and goals.

4. Advance a conceptual design. The conceptual design develops from the vision statement. Using available technology, processes, and procedures, a minimum of three alternatives are specified for each task defined in the vision statement. These are documented in text, tables, and diagrams and may be explored with focus groups and simulation to validate cost and impact. The goal is to determine the real cost of each solution and assess the value of the improvement to the operation. In preparing alternatives, consider the starting point of the equipment and resources. Taking a manufacturing process that is 20 or 30 years old to fully automated cells may be dramatic because the people will probably not adapt quickly enough to make the project successful. Alternatively, consider full automation as the long-range goal and establish the steps necessary to get there.

5. Select a master plan. After evaluating all alternatives, develop a detailed model of the "to-be" operation with appropriate documentation. This will be a detailed description of the tasks and operation in its final configuration. The costs and benefits of each task are part of the description.

6. Phase-in the focus plan and perform cost/benefit analysis. This plan compares the "as-is" and "to-be" states. It develops a sequence of steps that moves the organization, equipment, systems, and facilities from their current state to the desired one. These are sequenced and timed so that operational requirements are met with minimum disruption and expense. Identify "quick hitters" (miniprojects that provide immediate return with minimal investments), which will build participation and confidence in the project. The final cost/benefit analysis is completed according to the project scope defined in the master plan.

CHAPTER 1   STRATEGY DETERMINATION AND PRODUCTION REQUIREMENTS

PHASE II—DESIGN

As in Phase I, the separation of activity into discrete steps ensures a smooth flow of information. This phase is a seamless transition of the planning phase. In this phase, the conceptual design solidifies while the following steps are done:

1. Develop a functional description of the solution components and their interfaces that describes what will solve the problems documented in the master plan. It will describe the operating conditions, processes, functions of management and the production people, and interfaces with equipment, other systems, and people. The document may contain initial test plans and acceptance criteria for each major component. For complex processes or operations, the design should be validated through computer simulation or other tools. As a validity test, provide sample sections of the functional descriptions to potential vendors for comment.

2. Define pre-bid requirements. In this step, put the functional description of each solution component in pre-bid format. This includes the documented acceptance criteria, rules for make/buy decisions, and purchase requirements for bids.

3. Initiate the general design. This step covers the integration of tactical control and material movement. While some parts of the functional description may require new systems and equipment, it is also important to identify operating policies and procedures affected by the change. Changes in internal policies and procedures must fit with the overall project plan. For example, an ISO 9000-certified facility will require documentation changes that are part of the overall program. Identify and prepare summary documentation for all affected policies and procedures.

4. Review vendor recommendations. The selection of possible vendors begins during development of the functional description. Depending on the scope of the project, this may involve a variety of vendors with specific skills or equipment or system suppliers capable of providing a complete solution. As soon as potential vendors receive the draft requirements, they will begin to contest the bid specifications. This process often provides valuable suggestions. Review each suggestion for validity and application. If appropriate, revise the functional requirements; however, do not include proprietary information. An evaluation of the financial and business stability of potential vendors is necessary to ensure selection of a compatible, responsible partner. On the basis of the proposals and an initial evaluation/selection, schedule vendor presentations and/or site visits. The vendors may choose to submit proposals for a complete, consistent solution or provide components for review by the project team. Solutions will be the result of a cooperative effort involving all members of the project team.

5. Integrate and make requirements. For those requirements that cannot be satisfied with standard products and services of a single vendor or vendors, it may be necessary to develop requirements for an integration activity. This activity may be satisfied either internally or from another vendor. The specifications will describe the integrated product/service. This description may include the manufacture and integration of the affected components. Determining the approach to the acquisition of the components and services is part of the vendor response evaluation.

6. Develop the final general design—the culmination of the preceding efforts. This step documents the design, including the implementation sequencing and strategy. These documents identify costs, timing, and risk management. The final cost matrix and activity schedule for the implementation effort complete this phase.

PHASE III—IMPLEMENTATION

The implementation phase requires developing the plan, defining the purchase requirements, completing the plan, creating education and training plans, implementing the plan, and finally, reviewing it for final acceptance. This phase is the implementation of the whole solution—the project. This includes the integration of the human and machine interfaces with the future operating environment.

1. Develop the plan. This step documents the specific implementation plan. It may require verification of the simulation model and data. Coordination of subsystem designs and completion of the integration activity are the most important activities. Detailed test plans and acceptance criteria are developed for use at final acceptance and inclusion in the purchase orders.

2. Define the purchase requirements. The specific requirements are negotiated and purchase orders are issued to the selected vendors. These combine the refined functional descriptions, purchasing terms and conditions, and acceptance test criteria with the project schedule.

3. Complete the plan. This step completes the operating policies and procedures, addresses the nonstandard/custom integration requirements, and finalizes the design of the applications software and machine controls. Individual vendors will produce detailed designs which describe how they will meet functional description requirements. The detailed design will define the system architecture, all hardware and software, system equipment and human interfaces, and other equipment. Software designs are sufficient to program, while hardware designs permit procurement of all physical equipment.

4. Create education and training plans. The plans, documentation, and training materials will bring all resources to a performance level necessary to operate and maintain the system and equipment. The selection and scheduling of resource training become part of the overall schedule. In addition, all policy and procedure changes begin during this activity. The documentation, training, and scheduling activities fit into the project plan.

5. Implement the plan. Implementation originates with the installation of the first changes to the facility. These should be changes to policies and procedures that will positively impact the operation and begin preparing people for future changes. By the time the first physical changes occur, the work force should be ready and willing to accept new ways of operating. For equipment and systems, testing follows a natural progression. It starts with unit testing of both off-the-shelf and nonstandard components. This progresses to ever larger subsystem tests of the machines, machine controls, communications, and applications software. This brings the project on-line in a phased, controlled manner and assures that infantile failures and design flaws are identified, isolated, and corrected early in the process. Unit and subsystem testing check the performance of each part against the acceptance test criteria. When performance is acceptable at the subsystem level, the integration testing begins. This is a comprehensive set of tests administered under operating conditions. At the beginning, the tests will include only normal operations. A separate set of tests should address design error handling. When all functions operate according to design, the full integration testing will push the system to the design limit.

6. Evaluate the plan for final acceptance. The project team will conduct the final acceptance tests using plant personnel. Dur-

CHAPTER 1   STRATEGY DETERMINATION AND PRODUCTION REQUIREMENTS

ing an agreed-upon period, the system operates normally with the regular staff. It is important to have a problem logging procedure for this activity. This will give the vendors critical information necessary to correct the problems. When the system passes all acceptance criteria, the vendors receive a written acceptance. This normally starts the warranty period.

DEFINE MATERIAL AND INFORMATION FLOW

There are many tools available to help with layouts, information flow, and material flow selections. However, until one understands and documents the existing flow of material and information between processes, it is difficult if not impossible to identify problems. For new projects, it is equally important to define how material and information will flow between processes to make certain the facility will meet all requirements. These projects have an advantage since changing flows only requires the movement of blocks on a drawing.

There are many techniques for documenting material flows:

- Operations process charts.
- From-to charts.
- Generic flow charts.
- Flow charts for information flow.
- Gane-Sarson charts (see Bibliography for more information).
- Hierarchical input, process output (HIPO) diagrams are a design tool set that uses function blocks to describe all processes and data. Since there is no context or directional indication of flow, the user must clearly understand the total description for the tool set to be useful.
- Demarco-Yourdon diagrams are structured tool sets for making software analysis follow more closely to the engineering design processes. The tool sets use data flows to link processes. As a hierarchical structure, the diagram begins with general process descriptions linked by global data flows. Each process goes through successive decompositions, with data flows becoming increasingly more detailed. The structure revolves around processes using inputs from one or more sources to produce a result. The result then flows to another process or processes or data store. There are no unterminated processes in the final analysis. While Demarco-Yourdon diagrams are an effective tool for software development, they do not link directly to physical or material flows (see Bibliography).

WHAT TO CHANGE

The three phases of a project provide a backbone structure for changing the manufacturing environment. The many ways to plan work, schedule resources, organize operations, run equipment, and otherwise meet customer demands, illustrate the complexity of the process. To have a chance of improving an operation, a systematic method for examining and measuring current operations is needed. Defining the as-is condition is the most overlooked step. Too often, people will use intuition to determine what is wrong with a process or operation. Sometimes these feelings are 100% correct, but tangible proof is necessary to facilitate change.

Assessment of the "as-is" condition has two objectives: to determine what real problems exist and to provide enough data to convince others. It must provide an unbiased appraisal of present conditions. An accurate report of current operations will be the foundation of all improvement activities. This evaluation process must be done without preconceived solutions.

Determining the real needs of the facility is a complex activity. It requires an objective assessment of data on orders, inventory levels, planning, scheduling, and resource usage, etc. Corporate goals defined by a mission statement are important in the overall program. The goals will establish the conditions for evaluating performance.

ANALYSIS: AS-IS CONDITIONS

The first step in the analysis is the description of the current or "as-is" conditions. These include descriptions of existing processes and material and information flows. A combination of written and graphic descriptions will help everyone understand the analysis process. The traditional approach is for a manufacturing person to develop a material or process flow chart. At the same time, a data processing person would explain the information flow. This approach does not include critical linking information necessary to perform the process or make the moves.

A more effective way is to systematically break down the existing operation into discrete processes. An existing operation may be a new facility where the operation exists only on paper. After breaking down the operation into a series of independent processes, one can connect them to describe the complete operation. The connecting links are the material and information flows.

Manufacturing operations may include dozens of independent processes. Often they relate in different ways, depending on products. An added complication is that the information for a process can change its functions. This is one of the reasons why it is called complex. Unless these operations are separated, it will be difficult to understand them. Further complicating the operation will be cross flows of material to satisfy the specific process needs of a product.

Models can help explain a process and should involve as many people as possible. By starting at a high level and expanding the views of each independent process, the contributions and description accuracy are maximized. At the same time, the model must remain simple and direct so that the user is not burdened by details. A simple model will not attempt to capture all of the intricate details of the manufacturing operation.

The as-is description of an *ICAM* (integrated computer-aided manufacturing) *def*inition process is also known as the *zero* level, hence the name IDEF0. The IDEF0 function model captures the decisions, actions, and activities of an organization or system. It comes from a well-established graphical language known as "structured analysis and design technique." It is both a procedure and a language that describes the operation. Taking a hierarchical approach permits getting to the level of detail necessary. The modified approach described here combines both physical and information flows.

Figure 1-8 shows a process box with basic information and physical flows. The process is an activity or function modifying inputs to produce the outputs. It uses resources to transform, while controls limit or constrain the process. The structure becomes the language, but to be effective, a process or set of procedures are needed to use it.

The process of identifying the elements of the IDEF0 model is important to ultimate success. Our objective is to understand the entire operation so that decisions are made in the context of the whole. To accomplish this, begin with a statement of purpose for the effort. While this is easy to say, it may be extremely difficult to achieve. The statement should define the scope of the problem, but should not limit the boundaries—maintaining some flexibility for options.

A cement plant can illustrate these concepts (see Figs. 1-9 and 1-10). The purpose of the effort was to improve quality and reduce the cost per ton of material through improved maintenance. The goal of the effort was simple, limited by restricted capital funds. Figure 1-9 identifies the major processes with the material and information flows. These initial diagrams were expanded to show the cost of resources and the progressive cost per ton of material.

The expanded diagram identified significant maintenance costs in several specific operations. Within the scope of the original goal,

CHAPTER 1   STRATEGY DETERMINATION AND PRODUCTION REQUIREMENTS

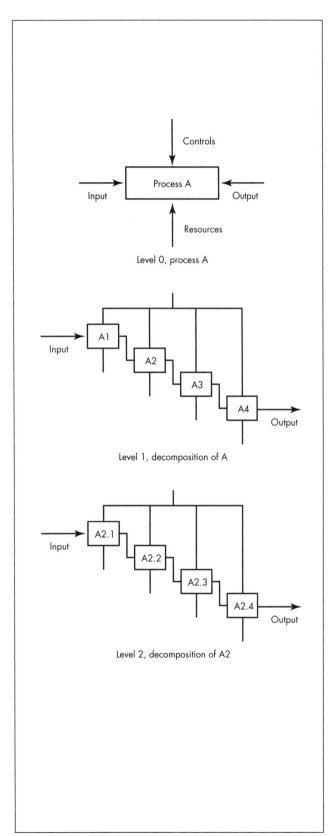

Fig. 1-8 IDEF0 hierarchical modeling system. *(Courtesy W. M. Angell and Associates)*

maintenance training programs with spare part recommendations and new manuals were started. The company decided to install a new power distribution system with a probable payback of less than six months. The payback was actually several months sooner.

In the broadest sense, the analysis process begins with the goal of the facility, which may be to satisfy customers with the right product at the right time. A more restrictive goal may be to reduce the processing time for a specific product. Regardless, the analysis begins by building a general model and then progressively expanding or improving the level of detail in the area under study.

DEFINE THE PROCESSES

In addition to defining material and information flows, define the processes. These are the functions that change or transform information and material. Typically, there will be a combination of information and material arriving at a process and leaving it for the next process. The information will describe the actions required to transform the material and what to do with the resulting material.

The purpose of any analysis approach is to enhance communication. Charts and diagrams can simplify the often complex languages of manufacturing and information processing. By developing independent descriptions of each process, information can be learned from those who are the active participants. The process of building a graphical model allows even the most inarticulate individuals to participate in the analysis.

The U.S. Air Force commissioned the development of a set of tools to help explain the role of computers in manufacturing. These help with the definition and understanding of integrated computer-aided manufacturing (ICAM). While the tools address a specific environment, they apply to a wide range of applications. These tools provide a graphical representation of the basic elements of all processes. An adaptation of the ICAM definition process allows us to effectively blend material and information flow. This combines information and material flow on the same diagram.

A description of a process includes data on the type of transformation, the rate, raw materials in, finished materials out, and waste. In addition, it includes a description of the resources required and the controls or limitations unique to the process. For a simple milling machine operation, the description includes the physical capacity of the machine, type and rate of cutting, and the functions performed by an operator. For some operations, it is enough to define the mill in terms of a description of the transformation only, for example, "6-in. (152-mm) bar stock cut to door bracket number 1245 at a maximum rate of six per hour." Measurements of waste may come from an output weight or percent yield.

To perform the required operations in this example, the mill operator requires a set of instructions. These describe the setup, operating conditions, expected results, quality measurements, and destination of the finished materials and waste. The instructions may also define the type of information sent with the materials. There may be a set of generic instructions for the process to minimize the instructions with each item.

A complex process, such as that in a cell, is capable of performing a wide variety of operations. It depends on both generic and item-specific instructions. Cells become more difficult to define at lower levels of the hierarchy. It is rarely necessary to get to that level of detail because the problems are of a more global nature.

Usually, a functional breakdown provides sufficient detail. However, sometimes imagination is required to break operations into good subsets. For example, facilities using cells are more demanding. In this case, a logical breakdown into cells A, B, C, etc., may be sufficient. The goal is to provide a coherent description of raw material

CHAPTER 1   STRATEGY DETERMINATION AND PRODUCTION REQUIREMENTS

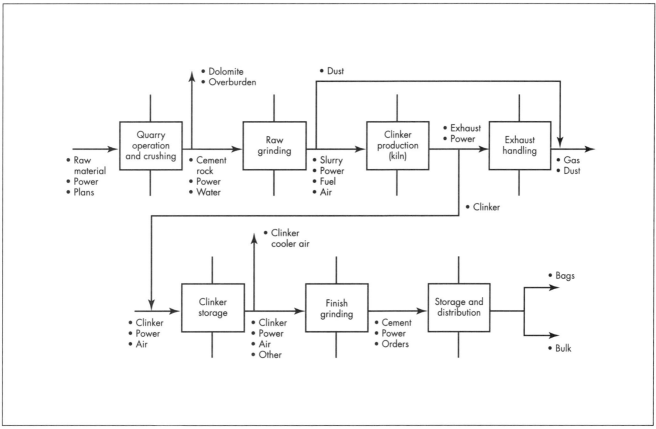

Fig. 1-9 Cement plant example showing overall process. *(Courtesy W. M. Angell and Associates)*

flow into the processes, the transformations, and finished items coming out. The most effective approach is to start with the total facility and then break up the processes as necessary to get a good understanding of the total operation.

Equalizing Material Flow

In all processes, remember that what goes in must come out. It is surprising how often people forget that simple rule. In a manufacturing operation, the physical flow is usually clear. Raw materials flow in and finished goods and waste leave the process. Finding the data that support the information flow may be a more difficult task, especially in the case of waste. However, applying that simple rule starts the process of identifying the elements of the IDEF0 model.

By following the material flow, each step is identified in which a transformation takes place. Those transformations are the processes in the first level of the IDEF0 model. The next lower level is a better place to identify work-in-process (WIP) and raw material storage.

Determining What is Done with Material

Now, with the processes and basic material flows identified, it is important to learn how and why the transformations took place. In most operations, a set of instructions comes with the material. Instructions may also be defined at the process and are started when material and other instructions arrive. The instructions may include such things as quantity requirements, machine setup, steps, and quantity. In addition, the instructions will state where the material goes next.

Quality and Quantity

It is not enough to have material flowing out of an operation. To learn from the process, determine what actually happened. The standard measurements of quantity, quality, time, material used, scrap, etc., describe the conditions. Some of this information will be used in subsequent steps. More complete information will help determine how to effectively use the operation in the future.

Process Capacity

The plant capacity is no greater than the capacity of the slowest operation. This means the capacity of each process is important in the overall analysis. It is reasonable to consider capacity in terms of the input and output at the second level. However, until one reaches the third level, defining the detail capacity may result in too much information. Rolling the process capacities up to the second level cross checks the plant capacity. The expression of process capacity must use consistent units. While machine capacity is one factor, the description must include details of setup and breakdown to complete the picture.

The process definition must include times for setting up, waiting, and processing. The processing time for each product at each process will often require an estimate. Since different products may have different processing times, use an average and minimum/maximum for the first rough pass. As the model becomes more refined, processing times may be made product-specific. It is important to understand why the time is product-dependent. Setup and queue times are also part of the process definition. If a process setup time is sufficiently complex to require a breakdown of the process, it is reasonable to include a function for queue time. Each of these steps

CHAPTER 1   STRATEGY DETERMINATION AND PRODUCTION REQUIREMENTS

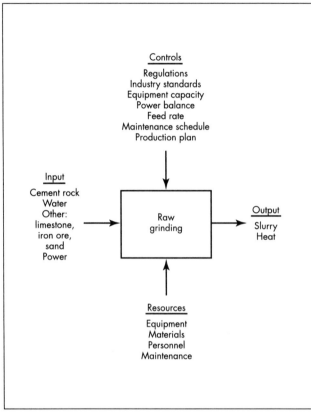

Fig. 1-10 Cement plant example with raw grinding step expanded. *(Courtesy W. M. Angell and Associates)*

improves the understanding of the operation. No assumptions are permitted unless they are included in the diagram and process descriptions.

Resources

The definition of resources supporting a process usually covers machines and equipment. In addition, it should include less tangible resources such as operators, supervisors, and planners. Support organizations such as maintenance, inventory control, and process design also can be important resources. Computer and control systems are resources when they plan, schedule, track, and run machines.

Process Controls

Why is it necessary to define the controls on a process? In classical control theory, a process is an open loop if the output is totally independent of the input. Applying this concept to a manufacturing plant, the output might be shoes with an input of a steel plate. There are natural limitations, such as wood products requiring raw wood materials, and physical limits, such as the size of a machine bed, maximum rate of travel, and type of cut. A wide variety of administrative controls, such as quality or environmental limits on the amount of material discharged up a smoke stack, will limit the production rate. In addition to these, there are the controls required to achieve operational stability.

A simple feedback system on a milling machine may control the feed rate as a function of the energy consumed by the drive motor. This is an example of using the output (motor power) to alter operation of a machine (feed rate). In modern control theory, we sample the output to predict changes. If sample measurements on an item

show a gradual drift, corrections to the machine program can keep production within quality limits.

It is important to identify all types of controls. Some are direct or planned, such as a schedule, machine capacity, and resource assignment. Others are indirect, such as environmental and supply controls. Unintentional controls include operator behavior, unnecessary and unproductive procedures, and machine wear.

Transportation and Storage

Each process is an independent operation. Looking at each process independently allows identification of constraining activities. Additionally, consider transportation between processes as a separate function, even if it is part of the total system. Transportation is always a support activity, although in some facilities it works its way into a primary function status. Storage is also a separate set of processes. It may be a simple buffer, work-in-process, a general warehouse, or unintended buffer. The location of the storage system should not affect its position in the logical flow.

Continuous Improvement

Planning and scheduling systems have been correctly described as "amoral." They do not judge accuracy of inventory, structuring of bills of material, length of lead times, size of order quantities, etc. Instead, systems simply accept all data, process it, and provide users with the resulting information. Continuous improvement, on the other hand, challenges everything. No matter how good the performance is today, it can be done better tomorrow. There is no end to improving quality, customer service, productivity, inventory turns, and product performance.

Anything that does not add value to the product is considered wasteful. By constantly identifying and attacking wasteful activities, not just in the factory, but throughout the whole company, major improvements occur.

All of the functions reviewed in this section are affected by continuous improvement efforts. Examples include:

Setups and changeovers. Rather than accept setups that require time and generate costs, users are applying single-minute exchange of die (SMED) principles (see Bibliography) to reduce setup time dramatically.

Queues. The bulk of inventories are waiting for operators, waiting to be moved, waiting to be issued, and waiting to be sold. By correcting the causes for queues, inventories can be significantly reduced which, in turn, slashes lead times.

Bills of material. Instead of thinking that several levels of processing are required, companies are flattening them. If you can drive purchased material through the manufacturing operations into a salable product, then only two levels exist—the top (the raw material) and the bottom (the finished product). Eliminating levels eliminates transactions and inventories, both wasteful.

Stockrooms. The conventional approach is to put purchased materials into stockrooms as they are received and return components to stockrooms after being manufactured. The activities of receiving, issuing, and moving are wasteful. An alternative is point-of-use storage, which stores the material as close to where it will be consumed as possible.

Plant layout. Many companies group similar skills and machines with similar capabilities into work centers. An alternative is to create cells, where differing skills and machines are tightly clustered. The objective is to have materials enter the cell and come out the other end as quickly and completely as possible.

Quality. By correcting the causes of bad quality at their sources, many improvements occur. For approved suppliers, customers no longer need to verify quality. In a similar manner, operators are taking the responsibility for monitoring and ensuring high quality, rather

CHAPTER 1   STRATEGY DETERMINATION AND PRODUCTION REQUIREMENTS

than having other groups check the results. As quality improves, scrap factors in the planning system decrease.

Safety stock. Users are rejecting the ideas that uncertainty of demand and uncertainty of supply are permanent problems; continuous improvement corrects the causes. It views safety stock as an expensive waste of money.

Mix model scheduling. A quest for economy of scale has led many companies to batch scheduling, which favors large batch sizes. The best strategy is to produce only what the customers want, when they want it, without incurring extra costs.

By aggressively applying the principles and techniques of continuous improvement, companies are dramatically improving the information flow from order entry through invoicing, and the material flow from acquisition to delivery. The combination of tight controls and constant improvements enables manufacturing companies to respond to changes in their marketplaces faster, more reliably, more economically, and with better quality.

PROBLEM DEFINITION

One of the major benefits of going through a detailed analysis of the as-is condition is the understanding that everyone gains. Documenting the entire manufacturing operation transforms intangible intuitions into objective, quantitative descriptions. Even if the project scope addresses only one part of the operation, it is beneficial to do a high-level analysis of the entire facility. This validates the input and output of the target operations.

The IDEF0 model puts everyone at the same level of understanding. It is easy to see the flows of information and material. While there may be additional discussion about specific processes, resources, controls, or flows, the general description of the facility should be reasonably accurate.

The process of identifying problems begins with a listing of problems, the probable causes, and the measurable effects. It is a working list because there will be several iterations before true problems are identified. The key to this process is determining the measurable effect on the operation. How can a major problem, with no measurable effect on productivity, cost of production, or loss of quality exist? By quantifying problems, we make most of the intuitive issues disappear. It is possible that the definition of a problem may require collecting and evaluating additional data.

Missed delivery schedules, poor quality, excessive costs, high rework, lost orders, etc., are indications of problems. To determine the cause requires research and reliance on the data collected to build the model. An examination of a few types of problems follows to provide a clearer perspective.

CONSTRAINTS

Missed delivery schedules are the most common problem. If the theoretical plant capacity based on the expected throughput of each machine or cell is used, there usually will be problems. The difficulty is that material rarely flows linearly through a plant. Some operations take longer than others and the mix of products may affect the efficiency of any given process. The process descriptions in the model will describe the effect of changing from one product to another. Examine each process, constraining the operation to determine if the constraints are operational or procedural. Operational limits typically depend on resources such as equipment, labor, handling, and maintenance. Procedural constraints include setup or operating procedures, schedule, and operator job knowledge.

During the development of the model, there were several visits to the production operation. Did the model identify those areas with an accumulation of material either in front of an operation or following it? Was there an accumulation of work-in-process in any area? These are clues to problems. If one process is slower than the others, expect to find an accumulation of WIP at the input. If this is happening, additional study of the process is necessary. In a description of the theory of constraints (TOC), processes are identified which constrain an operation.

The opposite of a constraint is excess capacity. Processes with excess capacity can put a strain on slower operations. It may not be cost-effective to run these processes continuously, even at a reduced rate. Identifying these processes may become important when alternative solutions are considered. These processes do not need any particular attention, at least in the beginning of the analysis.[15]

PHYSICAL MATERIAL FLOW

The nature of physical material handling problems depend on the item size and material quantity. For example, electronic components and assemblies require different types of handling than rolls of steel in a rolling mill. The first level analysis should determine whether the handling techniques are consistent with the material. It is instructive to examine who is doing the moving and why. Are the move distances and quantities moved consistent with the process requirements? This involves the location of processes, lot size, and available movement paths.

The model describes each operation in terms of processing time. To this description, it is necessary to add the features required to move materials. Avoid the impulse to describe the moves in terms of the current equipment or systems. The transport functions are the important concepts.

Do the processes include input and output buffers? If so, determine why they exist and how long material waits. Are the buffers driven by the operators or the operation? Some operators become very uncomfortable when they do not see a day's work before them. The critical time in any process is the percentage of value-added time compared to the total time an item is in the process. This may lead to a study of ways to eliminate or minimize buffers. As noted earlier, the load size is important for efficient processing. Unfortunately, the optimum load size for one operation may be different from that of another, so compromise is necessary.

Material flow should follow the path of least resistance. Using the model and a layout of the facility, identify real paths for material. If the flows cross or run counter to the primary flow, this may be the source of some of the difficulties. Materials with poorly-defined flows often get lost or delayed. The organization of cells may require counterflows. If this is the case, make certain the facility has sufficient space to efficiently handle the flow.

INFORMATION FLOW

Information flows in a manufacturing facility may range from the most modern and efficient to the most archaic. The as-is model and descriptions include a complete description of information required at each process. They also include the information coming from the process. There is a trade-off on providing information to a process. If the time-honored job sheet is used for production information, then the operator needs detailed "how-to" information at the process. If there are difficulties with operator performance, carefully evaluate all information going to the process.

If there are difficulties tracking work, look at the information flowing from all processes. Is it timely, accurate, and sufficient? If operators perform quality checks at the processes, are there sufficient data to analyze the effect of progressive quality degradation?

CHAPTER 1   STRATEGY DETERMINATION AND PRODUCTION REQUIREMENTS

This can occur when parts pass through progressive stages of fabrication or assembly.

Part of the information flow includes the planning and scheduling activities. Process conflicts are an indication that scheduling is not loading equipment or workstations correctly. Is Planning using the correct business model? As more companies move toward supplier inventory, forecasting and agile scheduling become critical. Does the information model support this activity?

QUALITY

The model and description of the facility will address a variety of quality-related issues. The quality measurements at each process may determine if an item meets specifications, but does this mean it will meet customer requirements? What happens to the quality data after the measurements are complete? How and when an organization responds to quality issues have significant effects on cost and customer satisfaction. Product returns may indicate customer dissatisfaction. The reasons must be carefully analyzed.

The most effective use of quality data is at each process. Check to see if operators perform frequent quality checks and correct the process accordingly. If not, bad products might be made until Quality Control personnel make independent checks and give the operator feedback.

Some clues that indicate quality problems are cost overruns, product rework, and customer returns. Is there a special process set up to handle rework? This may be unnecessary if there is a way to design quality into the product or correct problems at the source. Constant cost overruns may indicate inefficient operations. An analysis of the model can show where costs occur. Incremental increases above expected levels will clearly identify problems. The analysis may show there are difficulties with the design, equipment setup, equipment operation, materials, tools, or operator skill. Customer returns are a difficult subject because there are so many reasons for them. If they are the result of defects, the source of the quality problem must be clearly identified. Do reworked returns receive the same quality checks that new products receive?

RESOURCE LIMITATIONS

The availability of trained personnel will significantly impact the efficiency of any operation. The analysis must address this. Frequent schedule changes may indicate problems with having the right resources available at the right time. Assigning more people to a problem gives the appearance of correcting it, but is really only a quick fix.

Machine capacity and capability may also prevent the facility from meeting plant objectives. An examination of equipment must be in context of the overall goal of the facility. Equipment with excess capacity may be either an opportunity or a problem. The equipment may be able to perform additional tasks, but it may create scheduling problems.

HANDLING AND STORAGE

The handling and storage systems typically receive the most attention in the analysis. Most people feel that the solution to their manufacturing problems is more storage, faster material delivery, or more automation. While the analysis may result in one or more of these changes, it is not a given. The flow of material to and from the individual processes will determine the location and type of problems. If model, description, and physical facility indicate substantial WIP material buildup around several processes, the challenge is to learn why. For example, aging or curing steps in a process may suggest the need for a formal storage area.

The handling and storage of raw materials are functions of scheduling and supplier delivery capability. The goal is to have enough raw material on hand to make the current schedule. Excess inventory may indicate poor planning or forecasting. It may also indicate a mismatch between production scheduling and planning. The analysis process remains the same. Do not hesitate to ask questions. Challenge legacy procedures and independently calculate actual raw material demand based on current production. Ask if there are better ways to have suppliers keep your production requirements filled.

Work-in-process inventory is the production manager's back-up resource. This represents work that will keep production running if the normal schedule is completed. It also may indicate part shortages, which are planning and scheduling problems. The ideal is to approach zero WIP inventory, but in practice, it may not be possible. The model will drive consideration of the real need for WIP. Resolution may require the involvement of process people if there are curing or aging needs.

Another area often overlooked is the tool crib. Idle machines may be the result of a tool shortage. For companies that have a large tool inventory, there is also the problem of tracking tools. Tools that are not sharp run slower and produce more scrap and off-specification material. The model will again provide the vehicle for identifying problems and opportunities in this area.

References

1. Cox III, James F., Blackstone, Jr., John H., and Spencer, Michael S., (eds). *APICS Dictionary*, 8th Ed. Falls Church, VA: American Production and Inventory Control Society, 1995.
2. Ibid.
3. Ibid.
4. Ibid.
5. Ibid.
6. Ibid.
7. Schaefer, Randall. *Inventory Management Seminar*, APICS University Series. Grand Rapids, MI: APICS Grand Rapids Chapter, 1996.
8. Ibid.
9. Cox III, James F., Blackstone, Jr., John H., and Spencer, Michael S., (eds). *APICS Dictionary*, 8th Ed. Falls Church, VA: American Production and Inventory Control Society, 1995.
10. Ibid.
11. Ibid.
12. Ibid.
13. Schaefer, Randall. *Inventory Management Seminar*, APICS University Series. Grand Rapids, MI: APICS Grand Rapids Chapter, 1996.
14. Goldratt, Eliyahu M., and Cox, Jeff. *The Goal*. Croton-on-Hudson, NY: North River Press, 1984.
15. Ibid.

Bibliography

Davis, Alan M. *Software Requirements—Analysis and Specification*. Englewood Cliffs, NJ: Prentice Hall, 1990.
Demarco, Tom. *Structured Analysis and System Specification*. New York: Yourdon Inc., September 1981.
Forrester, Jay W. *Industrial Dynamics*. Portland, OR: Productivity Press, 1961.
Gane, C., and Sarson, T. *Structured Systems Analysis: Tools and Techniques*. New York: Improved System Technologies, 1977.
Goddard, W., and Ling, R. *Orchestrating Success: Improve Control of the Business with Sales and Operations Planning*. New York: John Wiley and Sons, Inc., 1988.
Groover, Mikell P. *Automation, Production Systems, and Computer Integrated Manufacturing*. Englewood Cliffs, NJ: Prentice Hall, 1987.
Layden, John E. "Sign of the Times." *Manufacturing Systems Magazine* June 1997.

CHAPTER 1 STRATEGY DETERMINATION AND PRODUCTION REQUIREMENTS

Noreen, Eric, Smith, Debra, and Mackey, James T. *The Theory of Constraints and Its Implications for Management Accounting*. Croton-on-Hudson, NY: North River Press, 1995.

Shingo, Shigeo (translator Dillon, Andrew P.). *A Revolution in Manufacturing: The SMED System*. Portland, OR: Productivity Press, 1985.

Srinkanth, M., and Cavallaro, H. *Synchronous Manufacturing: Principles for World-Class Excellence*. Cape Coral, FL: Spectrum Publishing, 1990.

Turbide, David A. *MRP+: Adaptation, Enhancement, and Application of MRPII*. New York: Industrial Press, 1993.

Vail, Peter S. *Computer Integrated Manufacturing*. Boston: PWS-Kent, 1988.

Yourdon, Edward, and Constantine, Larry L. *Structured Design—Fundamentals of a Discipline of Computer and Systems Design*. New York: Yourdon, Inc., 1978.

Yourdon, Inc. *Yourdon Systems Method: Model-Driven Systems Development*. Englewood Cliffs, NJ: PTR Prentice Hall, 1993.

CHAPTER 2
MATERIAL HANDLING ANALYSIS

CHAPTER CONTENTS

PRINCIPLES AND ECONOMICS OF MATERIAL HANDLING

This section presents an overview and discusses:

- Labor utilization.
- Inventory turnover.
- Facility utilization.
- Equipment utilization.
- Material cost.
- Synergistic effect of integration.
- System service life and flexibility.

OVERVIEW

A company invests in material handling automation to improve the economic performance of the organization. This can be accomplished by reducing the value of labor or the average assets employed per unit of output. Most likely, improvements will be generated in both areas.

The economic benefits may be direct or indirect. Direct economic benefits come from the reduction or elimination of nonvalue-added functions such as material handling labor. Indirect economic benefits are those that accrue to the company when resources made available through automation are redeployed in a value-added function. When a strategic goal such as shorter customer lead times is achieved, in part through use of automated material handling, the economic benefit could be considered either direct or indirect. The system could provide an indirect economic benefit as an essential program component to gain a competitive advantage. The system also could be seen as providing a direct economic benefit by avoiding an investment in the additional material handlers needed to achieve the shorter lead time without automation.

It is generally understood that automated material handling equipment reduces the labor required to move material and reduces the floor area occupied by inventory. Less well understood is the fact that controls integrated with the company's planning system, material handling equipment, and workstations generate major savings in inventory and indirect and direct labor. A controlled automated material handling system can be much more than simply a collection of equipment that stores and delivers material and has a control system. The system can store, retrieve, and deliver information that is accurate and timely in the same way that it handles material. It can integrate islands of automation and bridge the gap between the company's official control system and actual activity on the shop floor. This control and integration allows delivery of everything required to perform an operation—material, supplies, tooling, and instructions—to the right place at the right time. An automated material handling system, when combined with an effective planning system, can allow material to flow smoothly from receipt to shipment with minimum interruption. A significant amount of nonvalue-added slack can be taken out of the processes affected by the system.

The interruption in material flow, both planned and unplanned, is a principal cause of excessive operating cost and investment in a conventional factory. Time is money. This applies to material and facility time as well as to direct and indirect labor time. Material stored or in queue is an idle asset. The floor space consumed by this inventory is an idle asset as well. Movement of material is an operation and generates cost in the same manner as a process operation. It not only requires the time of labor and equipment for execution; material movement must be planned, scheduled, supervised, and reported. Material must first be located. Then it must be removed, transported, and stored. Transactions must be processed for the moves. The material in stores must be periodically checked and counted.

If material cannot be located or delivery is late, any number of operational problems can result. Production equipment and labor may be idled. A customer delivery may be late. An expedited delivery from a supplier may be required, causing an expediting surcharge and extra freight cost. The job in process may have to be stopped and the material put aside or returned to stores. The job may have to be split, requiring an additional setup. Nonconforming material may be used or nonscheduled operations started to minimize direct labor delays. The former generates quality problems and the latter generates excess inventory. To compensate for incorrect inventory and delivery delays, safety stocks are built up in storerooms and excessive lead times are established in the planning system. Excessive lead times result in queue inventory that consumes a large portion of the available floor area of a plant. To better understand the effect of material handling on factory economics, consider the odyssey of a unit of raw material in a conventional lot-oriented plant, shown in Fig. 2-1. Of the 54 steps:

- 27 steps are waiting.
- 11 steps are transportation.
- Eight steps are storage and retrieval.
- Eight steps are productive operations.

Clearly, material at rest is a cost magnet. This, along with the number of material moves and lack of real-time knowledge of material quantity and location, is a significant driver of nonvalue-added cost in a manufacturing plant. Automated material handling can cause dramatic improvements in these areas by achieving tight, coordinated control over material and eliminating nonvalue-added activities.

As production planning systems are improved, production capacity is brought more into balance and equipment setup times are reduced, Just-in-Time material delivery becomes more feasible. Internal lead times can be shortened and the amount of material held in storerooms can be reduced. Re-arrangement of equipment

The Contributors of this chapter are: William M. Angell, President, W. M. Angell & Associates; *Edward J. Phillips,* President, Sims Consulting Group, Inc.; *W. Allen Sullivan, CPA,* Chief Financial Officer, Spirax-Sarco, Inc.; *Marc Young,* Consultant, CIMulation, Inc.
The Reviewers of this chapter are: James Cheng, Manufacturing Engineering Manager, The Sine Companies, Inc.; *Fred Larson,* Estimating Manager, Daifuku U.S.A., Inc.; *Tesfay Meressi,* Assistant Professor, University of Massachusetts.

CHAPTER 2   MATERIAL HANDLING ANALYSIS

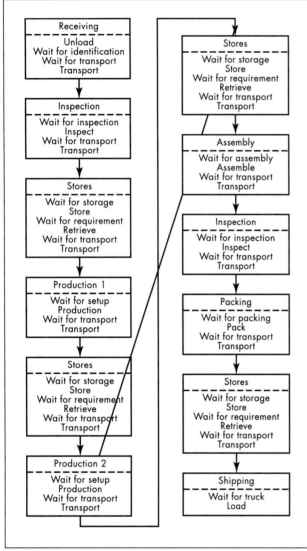

Fig. 2-1 Conventional material flow. *(Courtesy W. A. Sullivan, CPA)*

into cells simplifies and shortens transportation paths. Each of these improvements serves to reduce inventory and floor space utilized by that inventory. When production is synchronized, movement of material in and out of stores is not needed. Transportation labor, equipment, and space can be reduced significantly.

However, despite these improvements, the need for material handling persists. With high-end item variety, it is normally not feasible to totally synchronize material flow from suppliers, through the various production steps, and out to the customer. Material must still be held in queue at points between suppliers and production, between production steps, and between production and the customer. As product variety increases and lot sizes become smaller, the number of material movements can actually increase. With lower inventories, a stockout impacts more operations. Quantity and location accuracy become more critical.

Any point where material is held waiting for further processing or shipment is and always has been an opportunity for material handling automation. Likewise, any point where material is entered into a process or transferred between operations is also a material handling automation opportunity. The difference lies in the magnitude

of labor, space, and inventory savings opportunities. Generally, these savings opportunities are smaller under Just-in-Time manufacturing. What has increased is the cost of material flow disruption and, therefore, the economic benefit of avoiding disruption. These factors have combined to shift the focus of material handling in synchronized manufacturing to smaller, simpler systems that emphasize fast response, tight control, operator safety, and ease of reconfiguration. Opportunities to provide economic benefit remain, but the automation investment size and focus must be consistent with the magnitude of the benefit opportunity.

LABOR UTILIZATION

A variety of target functions of labor can be reduced or eliminated by material handling systems.

Direct Labor
- Waiting time (for instructions, material, tooling, material removal).
- Loading and unloading material and tooling.
- Setups due to expedited runs and short runs caused by stockouts.
- Lost time due to lifting injuries and fork lift accidents.

Indirect Labor
Material handling.
- Waiting for instructions.
- Obtaining pick and store information.
- Locating material.
- Identifying items.
- Storing and retrieving material.
- Loading and unloading equipment.
- Delivering material.
- Lost time due to lifting injuries and fork lift accidents.

Inventory counting.
- Selecting cycle count.
- Counting material.
- Reconciling cycle count.
- Recording transactions.
- Correcting transactions.
- Performing stock checks.
- Taking annual physical inventory.

Inventory control.
- Expediting.
- Scheduling.
- De-expediting.

Supervision
- Arranging transportation.
- Determining routing.

Purchasing
- Expediting delivery.

Ultimately, labor savings are realized through the elimination of a salary which otherwise would have been paid. The clearest evidence that labor savings have been achieved is the elimination of a position that currently exists. Anything less tangible is open to question. To return the actual dollars spent on the system, actual dollars must be removed from the payroll. Where material handling automation actually performs tasks that have been done by one or more people, it is not difficult to realize the automation savings. However, since material handling automation focuses on the improvement of processes, savings can be spread across multiple departments. Only part of the work of several different people may be eliminated. Actually realizing savings in such a situation presents a difficult chal-

CHAPTER 2   MATERIAL HANDLING ANALYSIS

lenge for management. Management's difficulty in achieving claimed system benefits translates into a credibility problem for the project sponsor. This credibility problem can be particularly acute if the savings opportunity exists in a department different from that of the project sponsor.

When work eliminated is performed by measured direct labor, management normally will accept that partial job savings will be ultimately realized as payroll reductions. This treatment implies that direct labor constitutes a common pool of labor. A savings of a few hours from one person is generally assumed to be realized in one of the following ways:

- As a reduction of overtime.
- Through combination with other improvement projects and the ultimate elimination of a full position.
- Through attrition.
- Through avoidance of a position otherwise needed to handle volume growth.

When eliminated work is performed by unmeasured indirect labor, management treatment can change drastically. Without measurement standards, savings of less than a full person can be lost to the company. It is a common belief in management, often grounded in painful experience, that without measurements "work expands to meet the time available." As a result, management will frequently not allow partial-person indirect labor savings to be claimed in an automation project justification. This is particularly frustrating for the automation engineer who has developed a project that clearly eliminates indirect labor functions. If the savings value is not recognized, the project may not pass the required "hurdle" rate of return and will be rejected. If this happens to multiple projects, the opportunity to affect real cost reduction through job combination is lost. Since no one project can be justified on its own merits, none are implemented. This is a logic trap that repeats itself.

The economic reality of partial-person savings can be very similar for both direct and indirect labor. A direct labor force is frequently static over extended periods of time. Realizing a partial person savings may have to wait for the person affected to be trained on a different piece of equipment to achieve overtime reduction or wait for a retirement or resignation to achieve an attrition reduction.

A good supervisor of indirect labor will understand the workload and capacity of the department. If the supervisor acknowledges the value of the work reduction from the automation project, that supervisor should be prepared to make productive use of the time made available. This use may be on a temporary project until the results of another improvement project are achieved and two positions can be combined. Alternatively, the time made available can be redeployed to a value-added function that saves money or has the potential for increasing revenues. A company utilizing activity-based management (ABM) is in an excellent position to identify and value partial-person indirect labor savings. By highlighting excess or short indirect capacity, ABM facilitates job combination and elimination or resource redeployment.

Without ABM or some other means to identify indirect job combination opportunities, the supervisor of the department realizing the savings may have to identify alternative value-added uses of the resources and obtain management's approval. By counting redeployment as a savings credited to the automation project, management is, in effect, approving the funding of the alternative use of the time. Incorporating redeployment of resources to other value-added uses into the project justification can present additional difficulty. The "other value-added use" becomes the economic benefit of the reduction in indirect labor time. However, the other value-added use may be part of a separate project that has additional investment and a separate justification. It may be possible to combine the projects under one proposal. Often the more practical approach is to value indirect labor savings at cost in the automation proposal and to reference the redeployment of the resource to the other project.

INVENTORY TURNOVER

To understand the relationship between automated material handling systems and inventory reduction, it is important to go back to the basics. Inventory exists because it was ordered before it was needed. Ideally, a manufactured or purchased item would be received just at the time it was needed for either further production or shipment. Production is in balance when the value of inputs per day exactly equals the value of outputs. When input exceeds output, inventory will grow. When input is below output, inventory will decline. If lead times are reduced by changing due dates and start dates to bring them closer to the date and time the item is required, a temporary reduction in input will result. This, in turn, will cause the inventory to decline.

In most operations, material spends between 75 and 90% of its time in storage or on the floor waiting for inspection, transportation, production, assembly, or shipment. In automating a material handling system, the objective should be to minimize these wait times and, instead, flow material from receiving to production, and then on to assembly, packing, and shipping with a minimum of delay.

Automated material handling systems can help reduce the time of material ownership by providing accurate and timely information showing material availability with quantity and exact location, and matching this information with material requirements. This capability, combined with fast, accurate, and coordinated material movement, allows inventory to be reduced through shortened lead times, reduced safety stocks, and fewer items ordered in error. Slack, both planned and unplanned, can be taken out of the system. Along with reduced inventory, accuracy results in improved customer service. The statement "time is money" applies to material as well as labor. By improving material throughput, we reduce the period of time the material is owned and, therefore, the investment in inventory. Because the goal is to have material flow uninterrupted from receipt directly through each production step, it follows that whatever causes material to stop, other than the production process, is a potential savings target.

Flow interruption that can be addressed by automated material handling includes the following.

Work-in-Process
- Wait for transportation.
- Wait for process.
- Wait for storage.
- Wait for missing component.
- Load/unload time.
- Setup time waiting for tooling receipt or removal.

Stock Inventory
- Planned buffer stock: to compensate for stockout due to inaccurate stock status and to accommodate irregular production lead times.
- Storage time.
- Retrieval time.

FACILITY UTILIZATION

Traditionally, floor area savings have played a major role in justifying material handling automation projects. Such savings continue to be important where a company is expanding operations. However, where operations are stable or contracting, companies often find themselves with a significant amount of floor space that they cannot readily sell or lease. Each company's need for floor space

CHAPTER 2   MATERIAL HANDLING ANALYSIS

must be given careful consideration in a project justification. Target functions that can be reduced or eliminated are chiefly material storage areas, material queue areas, and transportation paths.

Automated material handling reduces floor space utilized for storage by stacking material vertically. Some automated storage and retrieval systems (AS/RSs) are over 100 ft (30 m) tall. They have been installed in basements and specially excavated pits. With an AS/RS, transportation space required for storage and retrieval is reduced. With miniload AS/RS, space between tiers is reduced. The quantity of material in queue is reduced through tighter control, thereby requiring less floor space. Material in queue can be stacked in vertical carousels and small miniloads. Transportation paths can be reduced to the width required for conveyor or automated guided vehicle system (AGVS).

EQUIPMENT UTILIZATION

Material handling systems can reduce the need for costly production equipment by reducing downtime. Like labor, production equipment is idle when material, tooling, or information is not available at the machine at the right time. Also, failure to remove loads on time can delay start of the next operation. Such downtime can significantly reduce available capacity hours. Reduction of the downtime through material handling automation can provide economic return to the company through the benefits of reduced overtime premiums, reduced production lead times (reduced inventory, reduced floor space, improved customer service), or the avoidance of the cost of a new machine.

Automated material handling systems replace conventional material handling equipment. The conventional equipment replacement cost is avoided and is a direct offset to the investment in automation. Similarly, avoided cost of conventional equipment maintenance, repair, and fuel and power is a recurring savings.

When automated material handling equipment is teamed with a real-time material handling control system, the equipment is utilized more efficiently. As a result, lower investment in the automated equipment should be required.

MATERIAL COST

An automated material handling system can decrease material cost by reducing:

- Premiums for expedited delivery.
- Material handling damage.
- Pilferage.
- Obsolescence.

Improved inventory accuracy reduces the frequency of stockouts (inventory depletion). When a stockout occurs, material may have to be obtained from a supplier through expedited delivery. Suppliers frequently charge premium prices in such situations and volume discounts are typically lost. In addition, freight cost for a small, rush order is substantially higher than normal. As a result, automating material handling can lower material purchase cost and freight.

Material held within the confines of an automated material handling system is protected from damage. Positioning is more precise, resulting in less damage while the material is being transported. This reduces scrap and rework cost.

Material access is controlled more tightly in an automated storage system. Computer controls can further restrict access to authorized personnel and lower the cost of material lost through pilferage.

Inaccurate inventory quantities cause material to be ordered when it is not needed. When the items ordered in error are specials or slow moving, they may have to be written off. Material handling automation improves the accuracy of stock status and reduces obsolescence loss.

SYNERGISTIC EFFECT OF INTEGRATION

The effect of integrating information and material flow on total facility performance must be given careful consideration in assessing the impact of automation. By integrating information and material flow, dramatic improvements in material throughput can be achieved. If the area being automated is a bottleneck, the improved throughput should result in shorter internal lead times and lower material handling cost. The shorter internal lead times should cascade through the plant and yield lower work-in-process and stock inventories and improved customer service. As the project becomes more extensive and more bottlenecks are relieved, the positive impact of the program increases. This is positive synergy. The benefit of the whole automation program is greater than the arithmetic sum of the benefits of the individual projects. Unit cost can be significantly reduced and a substantial improvement in asset turnover realized.

Negative synergy can also occur. This phenomenon is sometimes referred to as *suboptimization*. Here, individual process components are optimized, but downstream or upstream capacity constraints are not relieved. As a result, material backs up at later operations or the automated facility is frequently idle. The end result is that many of the performance improvements generated by the automated operation do not flow through as an improvement to total company capacity or financial performance. In fact, total company financial performance may decline because depreciation charges, maintenance, and utility cost from the automation project can outweigh whatever direct, tangible economic benefits are realized.

Even more serious negative results can occur when automation creates a bottleneck. Material handling automation has a unique ability to constrict a facility and reduce total throughput. With conventional material handling, practical material movement capacity is limited only by the number of transportation paths and picking faces that can be accessed simultaneously. To achieve the maximum economic benefits of automation, material movement between multiple operations is often routed across the system, thus limiting production capacity of the operations served to the capacity of the material handling system. This also creates a single point of failure for all operations served. The capacity of the automated system is not simply the capacity of the slowest component or the sum total of the capacities of multiple pieces of equipment. Instead, system throughput needs to be measured with a mathematical simulation that gives proper recognition to blocking factors, computer response time, equipment downtime, and demand surges. Even when a single piece of equipment is used, capacity must consider the speed of the equipment, the capacity of the operator, and delays induced by computer controls. Developing a realistic assessment of a system that includes multiple automated components can be a complex but critically important task.

To have the project justification stand in total or in part on economic benefits that have traditionally been considered "soft," there must be reasonable assurance that these savings can be realized. Soft savings include indirect labor, inventory, and frequently even floor area. The best way to ensure that these benefits will in fact provide a return on the company's investment is to design the system within the context of a facility-wide automation plan. With such a plan, actions that need to be taken to realize targeted savings opportunities are identified, planned, and scheduled.

SYSTEM SERVICE LIFE AND FLEXIBILITY

What size and type of product will be produced in the facility in five years? In 10 years? What quantities of those products will be required? Providing answers to questions like these is key to determining the system's design life. Frequently, the service life of automated material handling equipment exceeds the economic life of the system. If the system is designed in such a way that changes in product size, weight, and volume cannot be easily handled, or the system cannot be expanded, the system service life can be quite short. As the scope of the system becomes broader, the risk increases.

To control this risk, possible changes in product and volumes handled by the system need to be assessed. The system design should provide for these changes through the stated design year. When prediction of future demand is difficult, equipment should be selected that can be readily reconfigured across the likely load range. When facility rearrangement is probable, equipment that can be easily moved is desirable. Tradeoffs between material handling cost savings, investment, and flexibility often need to be evaluated. The solution offering the greatest cost savings under the current volume and product mix may prove to constrain throughput or may not be able to handle product physical parameters under a future product mix. This very crucial consideration can be evaluated by performing sensitivity analyses on different design alternatives. The economic impact of variations in service life can be determined by eliminating the projected benefits at the end of different service lives. Alternatively, the cost of reconfiguring the proposed system can be estimated. This cost is entered into the justification calculation as a required supplemental investment at various points in the project life.

POTENTIAL BENEFITS OF MATERIAL HANDLING SOLUTIONS

The economic benefits of the principle material handling products such as automated storage and retrieval systems, automated transportation, and controls are described in this section.

AUTOMATED STORAGE AND RETRIEVAL SYSTEM (AS/RS)

This category of material handling equipment includes miniload and unit load stacker cranes and carousels with automated extractor and inserter mechanisms. This equipment retrieves material faster and with fewer workers than conventional storage. Also, worker safety is dramatically improved when the load is presented to the operator in a way that minimizes reaching and bending. Product damage and pilferage are reduced because the material is held within the protective confines of the system until it is required for production or shipment. These features generate savings in these areas:

- Labor—storage and retrieval, lost time due to accidents.
- Inventory—storage and retrieval, waiting for storage.
- Insurance—medical claims.
- Material—reduced scrap and rework, reduced shrinkage.

Physical limitations of the system and fewer operators result in greater location and quantity accuracy by reducing unauthorized issues and motivating greater emphasis on accuracy. Potential savings areas include:

- Labor—locating material; expediting; waiting for material, supplies, and tooling; setup (short runs made to compensate for depleted items).
- Inventory—planned buffer stock to compensate for variations in on-hand balance accuracy, work held waiting for delayed or missing component, stock ordered in error.

High-density storage can be achieved when the complete tote is presented so that the operator can reach down and have unobstructed access to its full envelope. This is equivalent to fully suspended drawer storage. This advantage is generally not available with conventional

carousels equipped with shelves. In addition, totes are stacked with a minimum of space between tiers, resulting in effective use of available "air rights." These two features combine to cause dramatic reductions in the use of floor area. Further, only minimum heat, air conditioning, and lighting are required in the storage areas. Thus, potential savings can be found in reduced floor area for material storage and lower utility costs.

AUTOMATED TRANSPORTATION

A floor conveyor allows rapid automatic delivery of material directly to designated areas. Transportation paths are reduced to the width required by the conveyor. Accidents and damage to material and equipment are reduced. Potential savings areas include:

- Labor—moving material; waiting for materials, supplies, tooling; loading and unloading; locating material; arranging transportation; expediting; lost time due to accidents.
- Inventory—waiting for transportation, transportation time.
- Floor area—material queue areas and transportation paths.
- Scrap and rework—material damaged in transit.
- Insurance—medical claims from material handling accidents.
- Equipment—fork lift purchase, lease, or depreciation, and fork lift maintenance.

Overhead conveyors and monorails provide the same benefits as floor conveyors. In addition, they further reduce accidents and their attendant costs by keeping moving machinery and material away from personnel. One drawback is lower accessibility which makes maintenance more difficult. A major additional benefit is the release of floor area for other purposes.

Automated guided vehicles offer the same benefits as floor-level conveyors. In addition, they can share transportation paths with people. Much of their incremental benefits results from their flexibility. If a lot is rejected at any point, it may be diverted for rework with a minimum of delay to subsequent lots. Rescheduled material can be moved ahead with little disruption to other lots. Further, routing can be changed to facilitate new or changed processes quickly and at relatively low cost. Additional savings occur in labor (less line changeover) and inventory (less waiting for processing).

CONTROLS

Controls can perform a wide range of activities, from recording activities that have already happened to directing activities. Such systems can automatically record material activity, which is the most critical and difficult information to gather on a timely and accurate basis. Data collection and correction often consume a significant portion of the time for direct labor personnel, first-line supervisors, storekeepers, production planners and expediters, certain accounting personnel, and data entry personnel. However, it is the control accuracy and timeliness features of the system that allow for the greatest reductions in indirect labor time, excess lead time, and safety stocks.

For information to have significant impact on operations, it must be correct and timely. The control system must exactly mirror the physical status of inventory items in real-time. All of the following must be correct: part number, quantity, location, and supplemental data such as lot control and quarantine codes. There are several reasons why inventory data are often inaccurate. The most common reason is unrecorded transactions. Other reasons are duplicate transactions, keypunch errors, poorly written transactions, putting the wrong data on the input form, delayed data entry, and erroneous cycle count adjustments.

Material control systems improve data accuracy by posting transactions automatically, concurrent with movement of the material. Data fields keyed by individuals are reduced or eliminated. Also, when timely, accurate data are available to the person responsible

CHAPTER 2   MATERIAL HANDLING ANALYSIS

for data input, that person is motivated to keep it accurate. Accuracy is data quality. As operations come increasingly under computer control, the criticality of data accuracy becomes more apparent and attention to data quality increases.

Labor savings that can result from data accuracy and timeliness include reduced time for:

- Locating material—arrival at or departure from a location recorded automatically by scanner and specific locations marked with a bar code. Scanning the lot number and location number can generate a locator record or confirmation of a computer-directed action.
- Waiting for material—accurate real-time tracking of material location allows immediate visibility and rapid expediting.
- Waiting for instructions—by identifying a material lot number and machine number, instructions can be immediately displayed or printed at the workstation.
- Checking and correcting information—initial data entry accuracy is dramatically increased with bar code scanning and on-line editing.
- Expediting orders—component material can be located in seconds and routed to the next operation.
- Maintaining parallel records—with an integrated system, the amount of time spent maintaining redundant records and feeding the official system is dramatically reduced. Meanwhile, the control system works far better because it utilizes much more accurate data.
- Data entry—data entry is either performed automatically or key strokes are reduced to a minimum.

Control, achieved through accurate and timely information showing material availability with exact quantity and location, allows reduction of inventory through shortened lead times, reduced safety stocks, and fewer items ordered in error. Along with reduced inventory, the accuracy results in improved customer service. Further, reduced floor stock results in less floor area being required.

AS/RS Controls

Adding a real-time inventory control system to an automatic storage and retrieval system (AS/RS) can provide such features as updating inventory location records, directing the AS/RS to an appropriate pick or store location, controlling access to parts, allocating specific locations to orders, posting transactions automatically to business computers, and automatic receipt of pick and count requests from the business computer. Greater location accuracy results in a significantly higher level of accuracy-related savings.

Order allocation. This feature allows parts in a specific location to be assigned to a scheduled order and locks out attempts to use those parts unless the allocation is released by a supervisor. Material can then be physically moved to production after the work has been scheduled with low risk of part shortages. Similarly, material scheduled for shipment can be held in stores until it is physically required. This not only reduces floor area and search time, but allows items to be de-expedited and reprioritized quickly and efficiently and reduces cannibalization of lots. Potential savings include:

- Labor—setup (short runs to compensate for shortage items); expediting; waiting for material, supplies, tooling; assembling complete shipments; de-expediting.
- Inventory—material in queue waiting for processing, material in queue waiting for shipment, de-expediting time.
- Floor area—material queue area.
- Receivables—less retention for incomplete shipments.

Host interface feature. This generates savings in transaction processing and correcting at a range of levels, depending on the degree of interface and data collection automation. Potential labor savings includes that for maintaining parallel records, data entry, checking and correcting data, and scheduling picking activity.

Cycle count feature. This allows cycle counting to be handled in off-peak hours. The inherent data accuracy reduces count reconciliation time. Counting with a full pan presented to an experienced operator in a well-lighted area reduces count time and increases count accuracy. Potential labor savings includes that for counting material and count reconciliation.

Quarantine feature. This allows items to be stored under strong location control in the AS/RS before inspection is performed. Items can then be scheduled for inspection on a priority basis, resulting in fewer stockouts and less inspection time. Lead times for inspection processing can be reduced as well. Potential savings are:

- Labor—locating material (inspection area); waiting for material, supplies, tooling; setup (short runs to compensate for shortage items); expediting (inspection area).
- Inventory—material in queue waiting for inspection.
- Floor area—material queue area, inspection area.

Kitting feature. This can save time preparing pick lists and reduce system peak time activity by putting all of the kit parts in the same bin during off-peak periods. Also, by issuing only the exact quantity required to the shop floor, quality and on-hand accuracy are improved and queue inventory is reduced. Potential savings are:

- Labor—scheduling.
- Inventory—waiting for processing.
- Scrap and rework—material damaged in process.
- Equipment—AS/RS equipment lease, purchase, or depreciation; maintenance and utilities.

Automated Transportation System Controls

The primary function of transportation control systems is to ensure the delivery of the right load to the right place. Depending on their level of sophistication, these systems may record availability and location of workstations, loads in transit, and transportation equipment. Physical movement of the lot may be initiated manually or automatically. Routing files may be downloaded automatically from a host computer. Shortage material may be moved ahead quickly, and de-expedited lots may be routed to stores with a minimum of coordination and communication. With an automated guided vehicle system (AGVS), less automated equipment is required because dispatching is better controlled. Potential savings include:

- Labor—scheduling; maintaining parallel records; locating material; identifying items; checking and correcting data; data entry; arranging transportation; expediting; waiting for material, supplies, tools; waiting for instructions; setup (short runs to compensate for missing items).
- Inventory—planned buffer stock to compensate for variations in production completion time, work held for delayed components, waiting for transportation, waiting for processing.
- Floor area—material queue area.
- Receivables—less retention for incomplete shipments.
- Equipment—automatic transportation equipment lease, purchase, or depreciation; maintenance and utilities.

REALIZING BENEFIT POTENTIAL

Ensuring that the material handling system is an economic benefit to the company and "pays back" can be a time-consuming and challenging task. Such systems are not "plug and play." They

CHAPTER 2   MATERIAL HANDLING ANALYSIS

typically interface to the company's production, logistics, and information systems. The material handling system must be designed to meet the unique requirements of all three. Further, to make the most effective use of the material handling system's capabilities, some or all of the systems to which the material handling system interfaces must be altered as well. In other words, to realize a material handling system's potential, the way the company does business must be changed, at least to some degree. There are six major tasks that must be completed to make sure the system pays:

1. Determine the company's objectives for the system. Translate these objectives into physical and economic requirements that are consistent with the company's long-term marketing and manufacturing strategy.
2. Prepare a system design that will meet these requirements with a high degree of certainty.
3. Prepare a project justification that is supported by commitments to the targeted savings by the responsible managers.
4. Sell the project to top management.
5. Manage a carefully planned procurement and implementation that is monitored to ensure that key system objectives are not compromised in favor of short-sighted purchase cost savings.
6. Track the savings targets after implementation to ensure that committed actions are implemented.

A common approach is to first identify a solution and then the savings that will result from that solution. A more effective approach is to first determine cost reduction goals and then design a program tailored to achieving them. This ensures that the program will be an economic benefit to the firm. If a solution is selected first, the particular economics of that solution may not fit the company's situation. This can result in considerable time and effort devoted to the design of a system that cannot meet economic justification requirements and must be abandoned. Even worse, management momentum may force implementation of an inappropriate system that does not benefit the company.

The following sections are based on the premise that the starting point for functional and physical design of a system is to define the economic goals. Essentially, this is a design-to-cost approach. However, the reality is that many material handling projects start with the perception that one or more specific material handling solutions might benefit the company. The information that is developed by the techniques described in these sections can be utilized regardless of which comes first—the economic need definition or the selected solution.

DETERMINE OBJECTIVES FOR THE SYSTEM

How do we set the objectives for the system? By comparison with competitors? By comparison with other industries? Either can provide a valid starting point. Benchmarking is useful in provoking challenges to traditional assumptions and providing insight as to what results might be achievable. However, neither is appropriate for system justification and tracking. Differences in the target environment—product, customer, vendor, facility, labor force, management philosophy—make it extremely difficult to draw valid conclusions as to the impact of the system. Realistic goals need to be established on an absolute, not a relative, basis. The starting point is the preparation of a detailed analysis of the unique cost profile of the target facility. Goals can then be established in terms of actual resource savings potential.

DEFINE AND QUANTIFY CURRENT LEVELS OF RESOURCE FUNCTIONS

Resources targeted for improvement include material, labor, equipment, and floor space. Functions of these resources that are

targeted for improvement are often referred to as *nonvalue-added*. A description of savings opportunities provided by material handling automation is provided in "Overview," at the beginning of this chapter. It is helpful to define and quantify both value-added and nonvalue-added functions of the resources. This will reduce the possibility of overstating the savings opportunity. The resource savings potential is best handled at a detail level when it is expressed in terms of worker-hours, days of throughput, and floor area. These units of measure are much easier to relate to the functions of the material handling systems than costs. Also, the potential distortion of different inflation assumptions can be isolated and controlled. Finally, the savings potential is associated with defined physical areas of the facility to better identify the beneficial impact of a particular automation project.

Because an automated material handling system generates significant savings in cost areas that are traditionally not measured, the conventional accounting system is not of much help in defining the potential economic impact of the project. A cost profile must be developed by analysis of processes across organizational boundaries.

Several target labor functions can exist within one job description. Finding the functions can start with either observing activities in the shop, warehouse, or office, or reviewing a detailed organization chart, or both. Isolating specific positions usually requires both review of position descriptions and discussions with supervisory personnel. Once isolated, the savings potential can be estimated by time study, sample period time reporting, or supervisory estimates. Table 2-1 shows a sample labor functional analysis.

Methods for identifying the reasons why inventory exists are even less refined than those for isolating functions of indirect labor. Significant reductions in inventory can be of major benefit to the economic well-being of a firm. However, since a variety of solutions address the different causal factors that create inventory, it is important that the inventory values associated with these causal factors be identified. These values can be identified by:

- Analyzing transaction history of on-hand balances by date received and issued for high-dollar-value items.
- Analyzing decision rules (that is, safety stock levels, lead times, re-order points) in the planning system.
- Analyzing a sample of production and purchase releases and then tracing through to shipment of those items.

The next step is to break the inventory down by function and physical area. This is made easier if the inventory is approached in terms of days of product ownership. Inventory days on hand can be calculated by Eq. 1:

$$DOH = AIB \div ADI \tag{1}$$

where:

DOH = days on hand
(the number of working days that stock is available)
AIB = average inventory balance (value on hand)
ADI = average daily inventory (usage)
(amount of stock used $\div$ total number of days in this period [month, quarter, year])

for example:

AIB = \$10,000
ADI = \$500
DOH = $AIB \div ADI$
DOH = \$10,000 $\div$ \$500
= 20 days on hand

CHAPTER 2   MATERIAL HANDLING ANALYSIS

TABLE 2-1
Labor Functional Analysis

Labor Category	Labor Function	Department						Total Incurred (h)
		Production 1		Production 2		Assembly		
		%	Hours	%	Hours	%	Hours	
Direct Labor								
Setup								
	Retrieve tooling	5	262	7	482	16	359	1,103
	Deliver tooling	10	523	12	827	11	248	1,598
	Lower old fixture	1	52	2	138	1	23	213
	Remove prior fixture	25	1,308	23	1,585	5	113	3,006
	Lift/position new fixture	5	262	7	482	3	68	812
	Install new fixture	39	2,039	30	2,068	44	989	5,096
	Deliver prior fixture	10	523	12	827	11	248	1,598
	Store prior fixture	5	262	7	482	9	203	947
	Total	100%	5,231	100%	6,891	100%	2,251	14,373
Run								
	Load material	18	3,331	27	3,812	22	2,226	9,369
	Tend machine/process	71	13,141	55	7,766	65	6,578	27,485
	Unload product	11	2,036	18	2,542	13	1,315	5,893
	Total	100%	18,508	100%	14,120	100%	10,119	42,747
Wait								
	Instructions	22	1,235	17	1,021	18	1,279	3,535
	Material	32	1,796	35	2,103	44	3,125	7,024
	Tooling	26	1,460	30	1,802	22	1,563	4,825
	Equipment repair	14	786	11	661	7	497	1,944
	Product removal	6	337	7	421	9	639	1,397
	Total	100%	5,614	100%	6,008	100%	7,103	18,725
Maintenance			1,822		1,579		2,114	5,515
Other			2,156		2,235		1,944	6,335
Indirect Labor								
Material handling								
	Wait for instructions	7	415	9	587	6	413	1,415
	Obtain information	4	237	5	326	7	482	1,045
	Locate material	6	356	7	456	11	757	1,569
	Identify items	7	415	2	130	12	825	1,370
	Pick/store material	19	1,126	22	1,433	17	1,169	3,728
	Load/unload equipment	14	830	12	782	9	619	2,231
	Deliver material	23	1,362	27	1,760	18	1,238	4,360
	Record transactions	11	652	13	847	16	1,101	2,600
	Other	9	533	3	196	4	275	1,004
	Total	100%	5,926	100%	6,517	100%	6,879	19,322
Supervision								
	Obtain material	8	312	9	370	16	443	1,125
	Obtain tooling	9	351	13	534	5	139	1,024
	Scheduling	21	818	18	740	17	471	2,029
	Expediting	25	974	20	823	26	720	2,517
	Training	18	702	22	904	15	416	2,022
	Other	19	741	18	740	21	582	2,063
	Total	100%	3,898	100%	4,111	100%	2,771	10,780
Total Payroll Time			43,155		41,461		33,181	117,797
Lost Time								
Personal		30	1,331	32	1,244	40	1,183	3,758
Lifting injuries		27	1,199	33	1,283	39	1,153	3,635
Material handling accidents		22	977	14	544	11	325	1,846
Other accidents		21	932	21	816	10	296	2,044
Total		100%	4,439	100%	3,887	100%	2,957	11,283

Note: The inventory balance and issues valuations must use consistent cost element valuation methods, that is, with or without labor and/or overhead.

This data should be readily available from the controller's office or from the inventory control department. A breakdown by physical area and function within a defined physical area helps pinpoint savings potential. The analyses should be prepared for all physical areas of the facility. They can then be posted to a master work sheet to summarize the facility-wide savings potential by target function.

Identifying floor area savings potential is relatively straightforward. Storage areas, material queue areas, transportation paths, and production equipment can be identified on a scale drawing of the facility. The floor area utilized by each function can then be calculated with reference to the drawing scale.

ESTIMATE FUTURE LEVELS OF RESOURCE FUNCTIONS

A projected cost profile for the technology currently installed is developed by estimating the growth in the value of the target functions over the system service life. Management may consider the system as a key enabling technology to help achieve an objective other than cost reduction and/or volume growth. In this situation, target functions should be estimated at a level necessary to achieve this objective without utilizing material handling automation.

Care should be taken to ensure that the savings opportunities have been developed around a consistent set of assumptions for target volume and product mix.

Deciding the number of years to estimate is always difficult. The further out the projection is taken, the less likely the estimates will hold true. However, basing economic evaluations on the current cost profile can be more dangerous than projecting future requirements. Use of the current cost profile implicitly assumes that such costs will prevail throughout the period on which the justification is based. Such a static assumption can result in an undersized system or a justification based on production that is to be discontinued. Management typically has a planning horizon with which it is reasonably comfortable. Five years is common. Also, management usually has explicitly or implicitly established a minimum desired service life assumption for significant capital investments. This is often the depreciable life used for financial accounting purposes. When the desired service life extends significantly beyond the product volume forecast, sensitivity analysis can be employed to evaluate a range of possible outcomes. Management can then assess the risk of not achieving the desired payback.

VALUE ECONOMIC REQUIREMENTS

Ideally, the new system would reduce to zero all nonvalue-added functions addressed by the technology. Realistically, some of the target functions can be eliminated, reduced, or not be affected at all for a variety of reasons. However, the starting point for selecting and prioritizing material handling automation solutions should assume that these functions will be totally eliminated. The savings opportunities should be converted to dollars and summarized by target function and physical area. Conversion of the savings targets to dollars can follow the procedures described as follows.

Inflation

Inflation is an economic reality, but it can distort and confuse project justification calculations. To ensure that all investment projects are evaluated consistently, each company's guidelines on the subject should be followed. However, clearer identification of the basic economics of a project are achieved when the analyses are pre-pared consistently in constant dollars. The constant-dollar base year needs to be clearly stated.

Labor Hour Savings Valuation

Labor hours saved should be priced at the average hourly wage rate plus fringe benefits. Valuing labor savings with standard cost overhead rates should be avoided. Direct labor reduction projects may have little impact on many overhead functions. Only overhead functions specifically affected by the project directly or indirectly should be valued. However, an allowance for supervision should be added using a normal span of control relationship.

Inventory Savings Valuation

Days of ownership saved are multiplied by the value of average daily issues of material and input of production labor (including fringe benefits) into the target area. As with labor savings, general overhead should be excluded from the valuation of savings. Inventory is an asset, much like the investment in the material handling system. As an asset, inventory is treated as a one-time savings, to be offset directly against the value of the system investment. In other words, the cost of the system to be compared to net recurring savings is the net of the system cost less reduction in inventory and other one-time savings. Inventory carrying cost should not be used in project justification calculations. Carrying cost is a concept that is somewhat useful in determining purchase and production lot sizes. Its use in project justifications distorts the calculations and usually undervalues projects with significant inventory savings potential.

Floor Area Savings Valuation

Floor area consumed by target functions is easily measured. The area should be valued by using one of the following methods that best fits the company's situation:

- Cost of new construction (one-time purchase value) plus utilities and maintenance (recurring savings).
- Cost of renting facilities plus transportation cost, if needed, and utilities, maintenance, and security.
- Market value of floor area vacated plus maintenance (and utilities if the area can be isolated).

PREPARE FOR MEETING ECONOMIC REQUIREMENTS

The starting point for the design should be a summary of potential savings by function and physical area developed as outlined previously in "Determine Objectives for the System." The greatest savings opportunity should normally be given the highest priority for investigation.

Sizing the Investment that can be Supported

The payback formula can be worked backward to "design-to-cost" and determine the investment that could be supported by potential savings (see Eq. 2, 3, and 4). This approach also can be used to equate recurring savings with one-time savings such as inventory reduction.

$$\text{Recurring savings equivalent} = \frac{\text{inventory savings}}{\text{payback period}} \qquad (2)$$

For example: if the recurring savings potential is $500/year, the inventory savings potential is $1,000, and the required payback period is four years (equivalent to a 25% pretax cash return on investment), then

CHAPTER 2   MATERIAL HANDLING ANALYSIS

$$\text{Recurring savings equivalent} = \frac{\$1,000}{4} = \$250$$

Total equivalent recurring savings = recurring savings   (3)
potential/year + recurring savings equivalent

Total equivalent recurring savings = \$500 + \$250 = \$750

Supportable investment = total equivalent recurring   (4)
savings × required payback period

Supportable investment = \$750 × 4 = \$3,000

Note: this assumes that the selected solution totally eliminates the target function and there are no significant recurring costs from the project.

Relating Solutions to Resource Functions

By identifying and valuing savings targets by functional area, the process of relating the benefits of specific system solutions to savings goals is easier. The possibility of overstating total program savings potential is reduced. To understand the system benefits in functional terms, the capabilities of the systems under consideration must first be understood. Potential savings areas for a number of material handling system solutions were listed previously in "Potential Benefits of Material Handling Solutions." Deeper understanding of system features and benefits can be developed by:

- Attending industry seminars and trade shows.
- Studying trade magazines and books.
- Visiting installations.
- Visiting vendor facilities.
- Retaining experienced consultants to evaluate alternatives.

Develop the Savings Potential for Each Resource

The savings potential can now be developed for each resource area. Table 2-2 shows the development of labor savings potential. This technique is applicable to all resource areas. The procedure is:

1. List the target resource functions addressed by material handling automation.
2. Determine the values of these resource functions (see Table 2-1).
3. Identify the resource functions that can be totally eliminated by material handling automation.
4. Assess the percentage reduction for the resource functions partially eliminated. Apply this percentage to the total potential for the savings area to obtain the partial savings.
5. Total the potential savings.

Assessment of the savings impact from each solution (Table 2-3) requires a simulation or "walk-through" of the method of operation expected to be followed after the solution is implemented. This simulation is best evaluated and understood if it is reduced to writing through a flow chart and narrative description of the operation. Sensitivity analysis is particularly valuable here because the final selection of the potential savings value for a solution will normally be, in large part, judgmental. However, the range of error has been restricted by first determining the total savings potential.

PREPARE A THOROUGH PROJECT JUSTIFICATION

A key to realizing the economic benefits of a material handling system is the preparation of a detailed project justification that pinpoints and quantifies the targeted savings. The justification is, in effect, the heart of a detailed project plan. It quantifies the functional specifications for the system in dollar terms.

The Return on Investment (ROI) Formula and Material Handling Systems

The net savings and investment should be summarized by resource as shown in Table 2-4 and calculated in Eq. 5 and 6.

Net recurring savings = labor and fringe benefits +   (5)
facility rental and other costs − project operating costs

Net investment = initial project cost − inventory   (6)
reduction − value of equipment avoided

A wide variety of calculations are used by companies to evaluate the economic benefit of proposed projects. These calculations range in sophistication from the simple payback period to internal rate of return and discounted cash flow. Each has its own unique advantages. A full discussion of these techniques is beyond the scope of this handbook. However, the data development approaches that have been described will meet the needs of most economic justification calculation methods. The relative advantages of the various techniques are less of an issue than the quality of the basic economic assumptions. Too often, a focus on the mechanics of a particular sophisticated evaluation technique will blind management to errors or omissions in valuing the essential economic considerations.

A key to preparing the calculations properly is the classification of costs and benefits between one-time and recurring. One-time costs and benefits are combined to determine the net investment that is to be recovered. These include both capital and expense project costs such as system purchase price, special programming, and operator training. Likewise, recurring benefits and costs are combined to determine the net value of the investment's return. Recurring costs include software and hardware maintenance contracts and additional power costs.

The basic return on investment (ROI) calculation is:

$$\text{ROI} = \frac{\text{net annual recurring savings}}{\text{net investment}} \qquad (7)$$

The result is expressed as a percentage.

Payback period is simply the reciprocal of the basic ROI calculation as shown in Eq. 8.

$$\frac{\text{Payback}}{\text{period}} = \frac{\text{net investment}}{\text{net annual recurring savings}} \qquad (8)$$

The result is expressed in years. See Table 2-5 for a sample payback calculation.

Incremental Volume

When an automation project relieves a key facility bottleneck, incremental sales may be realized. Incremental sales can have a very favorable effect on profits. When using this benefit in an economic justification, care must be taken to ensure that all costs and investments (for example, accounts receivable and inventory) associated with the additional sales are deducted to compute a net benefit. Usually, some form of conventional material handling solution could relieve the bottleneck, but in a less efficient manner. In this situation, the benefit of relieving the bottleneck should be determined as an avoidance of the costs necessary to accomplish the objective through the lower-cost solution.

Cost Avoidance

Automated material handling often returns significant economic benefits through cost avoidance. In other words, by utilizing the system, another cost, which otherwise would have been incurred, need not be spent. The cost avoidance technique is frequently used to value floor area and production equipment cost savings. The avoided

CHAPTER 2   MATERIAL HANDLING ANALYSIS

TABLE 2-2
Total Material Handling Automation Labor Savings Potential

Labor Category	Labor Function	Production 1 Savings %	Production 1 Hours	Production 2 Savings %	Production 2 Hours	Assembly Savings %	Assembly Hours	Total Potential Savings (h)
Direct Labor								
Setup								
	Retrieve tooling	100	262	100	482	100	359	1,103
	Deliver tooling	100	523	100	827	100	248	1,598
	Lower old fixture	75	39	75	104	75	17	160
	Remove prior fixture	0	0	0	0	0	0	0
	Lift/position new fixture	75	197	75	362	75	51	610
	Install new fixture	0	0	0	0	0	0	0
	Deliver prior fixture	100	523	100	827	100	248	1,598
	Store prior fixture	100	262	100	482	100	203	947
	Total		1,806		3,084		1,126	6,016
Run								
	Load material	25	833	50	1,906	30	668	3,407
	Tend machine/process	0	0	0	0	0	0	0
	Unload product	25	509	50	1,271	30	395	2,175
	Total		1,342		3,177		1,063	5,582
Wait								
	Instructions	50	618	30	306	25	320	1,244
	Material	80	1,437	60	1,262	80	2,500	5,199
	Tooling	70	1,022	55	991	75	1,172	3,185
	Equipment repair	0	0	0	0	0	0	0
	Product removal	65	219	50	211	70	447	877
	Total		3,296		2,770		4,439	10,505
Maintenance		0	0	0	0	0	0	0
Other		0	0	0	0	0	0	0
Indirect Labor								
Material handling								
	Wait for instructions	90	374	80	470	100	413	1,257
	Obtain information	100	237	100	326	100	482	1,045
	Locate material	100	356	90	410	100	757	1,523
	Identify items	75	311	95	124	80	660	1,095
	Pick/store material	100	1,126	100	1,433	100	1,169	3,728
	Load/unload equipment	100	830	80	626	65	402	1,858
	Deliver material	100	1,362	100	1,760	100	1,238	4,360
	Record transactions	80	522	85	720	90	991	2,233
	Other	50	267	50	98	50	138	503
	Total		5,385		5,967		6,250	17,602
Supervision								
	Obtain material	75	234	80	296	85	377	907
	Obtain tooling	75	263	75	401	60	83	747
	Scheduling	25	205	50	370	50	236	811
	Expediting	40	390	60	494	50	360	1,244
	Training	0	0	0	0	0	0	0
	Other	0	0	0	0	0	0	0
	Total		1,092		1,561		1,056	3,709
Total Payroll Time			12,921		16,559		13,934	43,414
Lost Time								
Personal		0	0	0	0	0	0	0
Lifting injuries		70	839	80	1,026	95	1,095	2,960
Material handling accidents		85	830	85	462	80	260	1,552
Other accidents		0	0	0	0	0	0	0
Total			1,669		1,488		1,355	4,512

CHAPTER 2   MATERIAL HANDLING ANALYSIS

TABLE 2-3
Material Handling Automation Solution Savings

Labor Category	Labor Function	Savings Potential	Production 2 Department						Total Program Savings (h)
			Controlled AS/RS		Controlled AGVS		Systems Integration		
			%	Hours	%	Hours	%	Hours	
Direct Labor									
Setup									
	Retrieve tooling	482	80	386	0	0	20	96	482
	Deliver tooling	827	0	0	90	744	10	83	827
	Lower old fixture	104	0	0	0	0	0	0	0
	Remove prior fixture	0	0	0	0	0	0	0	0
	Lift/position new fixture	362	0	0	0	0	0	0	0
	Install new fixture	0	0	0	0	0	0	0	0
	Deliver prior fixture	827	0	0	90	744	10	83	827
	Store prior fixture	482	80	386	0	0	20	96	482
	Total	3,084		772		1,488		358	2,618
Run									
	Load material	1,906	0	0	0	0	0	0	0
	Tend machine/process	0	0	0	0	0	0	0	0
	Unload product	1,271	0	0	0	0	0	0	0
	Total	3,177		0		0		0	0
Wait									
	Instructions	306	0	0	0	0	100	306	306
	Material	1,262	35	442	30	378	35	442	1,262
	Tooling	991	45	446	30	297	25	248	991
	Equipment repair	0	0	0	0	0	0	0	0
	Product removal	211	0	0	70	148	30	63	211
	Total	2,770		888		823		1,059	2,770
Maintenance		0	0	0	0	0	0	0	0
Other		0	0	0	0	0	0	0	0
Indirect Labor									
Material handling									
	Wait for instructions	470	25	118	25	118	50	234	470
	Obtain information	326	22	72	18	59	60	195	326
	Locate material	410	73	299	0	0	27	111	410
	Identify items	124	100	124	0	0	0	0	124
	Pick/store material	1,433	100	1,433	0	0	0	0	1,433
	Load/unload equipment	626	0	0	100	626	0	0	626
	Deliver material	1,760	0	0	100	1,760	0	0	1,760
	Record transactions	720	40	288	20	144	40	288	720
	Other	98	0	0	0	0	0	0	0
	Total	5,967		2,334		2,707		828	5,869
Supervision									
	Obtain material	296	42	124	35	104	23	68	296
	Obtain tooling	401	39	157	34	136	27	108	401
	Scheduling	370	28	104	22	81	50	185	370
	Expediting	494	59	291	18	89	23	114	494
	Training	0	0	0	0	0	0	0	0
	Other	0	0	0	0	0	0	0	0
	Total	1,561		676		410		475	1,561
Total Payroll Time		16,559		4,670		5,428		2,720	12,818
Lost Time									
Personal		0	0	0	0	0	0	0	0
Lifting injuries		1,026	64	657	20	205	0	0	862
Material handling accidents		462	32	148	53	245	0	0	393
Other accidents		0	0	0	0	0	0	0	0
Total		1,488		805		450		0	1,255

CHAPTER 2   MATERIAL HANDLING ANALYSIS

TABLE 2-4
Material Handling Automation Solution Savings Valuation

| Labor Category | Wage and Benefit Hourly Rate | Production 2 Department | | | | | | | |
| | | Controlled AS/RS | | Controlled AGVS | | Systems Integration | | Total Savings | |
		Hours	$	Hours	$	Hours	$	Hours	$
Direct Labor									
Setup	$23	772	17,756	1,488	34,224	358	8,234	2,618	60,214
Run	$21	0	0	0	0	0	0	0	0
Wait	$22	888	19,536	823	18,106	1,059	23,298	2,770	60,940
Total		1,660	37,292	2,311	52,330	1,417	31,532	5,388	121,154
Indirect Labor									
Material handling	$19	2,334	44,346	2,707	51,433	828	15,732	5,869	111,511
Supervision	$28	676	18,928	410	11,480	475	13,300	1,561	43,708
Total		3,010	63,274	3,117	62,913	1,303	29,032	7,430	155,219
Total Payroll Time		4,670	100,566	5,428	115,243	2,720	60,564	12,818	276,373
Lost Time*	$9	805	7,245	450	4,050	0	0	1,255	11,295
Total Labor Savings			$107,811		$119,293		$60,564		$287,668

*Valued at overtime premium plus FICA. Impact on insurance costs is valued separately.

TABLE 2-5
Payback Calculation

| | | Production 2 Department | | | |
		Controlled AS/RS	Controlled AGVS	Systems Integration	Total Program
Recurring Savings (Net)					
Savings ($)	Labor	107,811	119,293	60,564	287,668
	Workers compensation	15,750	18,900	0	34,650
	Facility rental avoided	12,105	3,890	0	15,995
	Material cost	11,890	17,250	9,970	39,110
	Total	$147,556	$159,333	$70,534	$377,423
Costs ($)	Maintenance (net)	30,600	38,900	18,000	87,500
	Utilities (net)	3,250	4,900	1,280	9,430
	Total	$33,850	$43,800	$19,280	$96,930
	Net recurring savings	$113,706	$115,533	$51,254	$280,493
Investment (Net)					
Costs ($)	System cost	520,000	455,000	95,000	1,070,000
	Personnel training	11,000	9,000	10,500	30,500
	Facility rearrangement	48,000	27,500	0	75,500
	Installation/integration	26,500	17,000	9,800	53,300
	Total	$605,500	$508,500	$115,300	$1,229,300
Savings ($)	Inventory reduction	42,510	26,780	18,700	87,990
	Equipment avoided	15,900	12,100	11,000	39,000
	Total	$58,410	$38,880	$29,700	$126,990
	Net investment	$547,090	$469,620	$85,600	$1,102,310
Payback Period		4.81 years	4.06 years	1.67 years	3.93 years
Return on Investment (Before income taxes, depreciation, and interest)		20.8%	24.6%	59.9%	25.4%

CHAPTER 2   MATERIAL HANDLING ANALYSIS

costs are directly offset against the system cost to compute a net investment. To claim these savings, there needs to be compelling evidence that the cost avoided would have in fact been spent.

This technique is particularly useful when the material handling system is proposed to help achieve a corporate objective other than cost reduction. Such objectives include increased volume, improved customer service, and improved quality. In such situations, the investment and operating costs to achieve the defined objective are determined in two ways: first by assuming that conventional material handling is employed and then by assuming material handling automation is used. The difference in investment and operating cost between the two scenarios is computed and becomes the justification for the automation. This approach assumes that the project to achieve the specified objective with conventional material handling would have been approved (for example, it would have stood on its own merits).

Care needs to be taken in determining the base (nonautomated) scenario. A realistic, consistent set of assumptions needs to be utilized. The current method of operating should be extrapolated out to the planned higher level of performance. As information on the current method of operating becomes available, the economics should be easy to calculate. However, sometimes it is just not practical to extrapolate the base scenario. This can occur when the current equipment is obsolete and no longer available. It can also occur when achievement of the noncost objective using the base scenario leads to an unrealistic assumption (for example, requiring a new facility). If a practical solution exists that requires a lower investment than the proposed solution, this next best alternative should be substituted as the base scenario. The computation would then proceed as previously outlined. Investment and operating cost necessary to achieve the noncost objective with the alternative solution are computed. The net reduction in operating cost under the proposed solution is compared to the net increase in investment to determine if the proposed solution is justified.

Program versus Project Justification

Piecemeal implementation of a broad-scope project presents a mechanical problem in submitting individual economic justifications for the pieces. The whole program typically will generate savings in excess of the savings of the total for the components. There are several ways around this problem. In each case, the entire program should be justified under a master appropriation request. Then individual components can be handled by any of the following:

- Not requiring separate justifications.
- Limiting the justification process to a comparison with a lower-cost alternative.
- Accepting a lower justification value.

Unless a new facility is planned, most companies are not able to install totally new material handling and storage systems at one time. Instead, they install piecemeal. This can be effective if the piecemeal implementation is part of a top-down plan. If the piecemeal implementation is an integral part of a total plan to improve material and information flow in the facility, the total savings can be greater than the sum of the savings from each component part. However, if each piece is implemented without thought to the total flow, the whole may well be less than the sum of the parts.

SELL THE PROJECT TO TOP MANAGEMENT

To get management support: obtain firm costs, document the project savings, provide a realistic implementation schedule, and plan the effective use of outside consultants.

Obtain Firm Costs

A final assessment of solution cost and benefits should be performed before preparing and submitting a project funding request. This will require closer involvement with potential vendors. Most vendors are willing to provide a rough budgetary estimate of cost before a project is funded. However, when development of specifications for quotation is started, it is important to narrow the field of probable vendors, since they will begin to expend an increasing and often very costly effort assisting in the development of the project.

Document Savings

By specifically identifying current and projected spending levels and describing how the project will achieve the savings, the task of selling the project to management and tracking the savings is made much easier. Because much of the justification for an automated material handling system is derived from savings in areas that are not measured, management needs clear and credible documentation of the savings source. This includes specific commitments from the managers who are required to achieve the planned savings.

Provide a Realistic Implementation Schedule

The implementation schedule needs to realistically assess the time each project phase will take. The schedule should be prepared on an ARA (after receipt of approval) basis. Savings normally cannot start until the system is fully operational.

Use of Outside Consultants

During development of the program plan, engineering firms or vendors are often brought in to perform a paid study to assess and refine the solutions and estimate their costs and benefits. Such studies are very valuable because they ensure that adequate, professional, and objective attention is given to assessing the viability and accuracy of the program. This is particularly important in a phased program where some projects will not be implemented for several years. Vendors are frequently unwilling to devote significant design effort to such projects without compensation because of the high level of uncertainty as to whether they will be selected to implement the projects.

MANAGE CAREFULLY PLANNED PROCUREMENT AND IMPLEMENTATION

These phases must be carefully monitored to ensure that key system objectives are not compromised in favor of short-sighted purchase-cost savings. It is easy to lose sight of the key features of the system that are needed to realize the savings targets. It is also easy to adversely affect throughput by purchasing components that are substandard. Once again, the preparation of a detailed economic justification that stipulates how the savings will be realized is of major benefit. The project proposal becomes the functional baseline.

Vendor selection should be based on demonstrated technical and management capability plus financial strength. Implementing an automation program requires a close and comfortable partnership between customer and vendor. There are too many variables in an automation project for a distant relationship to be effective.

Thorough planning and tight control throughout procurement and installation are key to implementing an effective material handling system. PERT/CPM (program evaluation review technique/critical path method) is particularly valuable in identifying early start opportunities and critical path items.

TRACK THE SAVINGS TARGETS AFTER IMPLEMENTATION

Tracking is essential to ensure that committed actions are implemented. Commitments to savings that were made during the project

CHAPTER 2 MATERIAL HANDLING ANALYSIS

design phase can easily be forgotten after implementation. Spending budgets need to be adjusted to reflect the targeted savings once the system is operational. The implementation needs to be audited to ensure that all of the benefits that were anticipated are realized.

SUMMARY

Automated material handling systems can provide very substantial economic benefits to manufacturers. But they also can damage the manufacturer's economic performance. Following the techniques outlined previously can substantially increase the probability of a successful implementation. These efforts can place considerable demands on the project leader and take more time than management might desire, but the result of this effort can be a program of significant and long-term benefit to the firm—and the avoidance of the cost of disruption.

ANALYSIS TOOLS AND METHODS

Computer-based analysis tools, computer-based simulation, work simplification, analyzing load size, and analyzing plant layout are various methods and tools used to identify material handling problems and develop solutions.

COMPUTER-BASED ANALYSIS TOOLS

This section addresses some of the uses for operations analysis tools in manufacturing environments. Supported by improvements in computer power available at low prices, and the vast array of software tools available on personal computer (PC) platforms, PC-based systems are becoming the tool of choice for most analysis applications. Among these PC-based systems are discrete event simulators, computer-aided design (CAD) system add-ons, spreadsheet and spreadsheet-based tools, and flow-chart-based tools. Issues surrounding the use of these systems will be discussed, and various software tools will be presented.

Manufacturing and material handling analysis tools are composed of a wide mixture of odds and ends developed over the years. Spreadsheet software is the main workhorse because of its flexibility and basic calculator-type functionality, but now other tools that have been used only in specialized cases can be integrated with spreadsheets and each other to develop a more complete picture of a material flow strategy.

Initially, computer tools for material handling and manufacturing engineers consisted mainly of spreadsheets and special program languages for simulation. With the advent of easy-to-use development tools, user-friendly computer interfaces, and PC-based CAD tools, engineers can now find a program to do just about any type of analysis they want to do. The major question is not whether a tool is available, but whether the tool available can be used cost-effectively. In analysis software, as in many other types of software, there is a balance that must be reached between the price paid to use the software and the benefits (or in this case, amount of reduced risks) gained from using the software. If the expense cannot be justified against the risk reduction, then the tool is not a good one for the application. Expenses include initial costs of the software, training on how to use it, and engineering time. It also should be noted that initial work with a new tool may not be 100% correct, and that some backward steps may need to be taken.

The goal of any analysis is to reduce the risk of making the wrong decision, and to increase the likelihood of making the right decision. If a back-of-the-envelope calculation is enough to isolate the right decision, then no further analysis is needed. In many cases, a spreadsheet analysis is sufficient to isolate a decision. This is especially true for making a decision about discrete choices. Spreadsheets are typically not the tool for making design decisions, however. Graphical tools that allow scaled layouts are necessary in most cases for determining how a material handling system will fit the process it is designed to serve. Simple systems may not even require a CAD program to determine the best design. Experienced designers know, however, that the first design put on paper is rarely the best, and is very rarely the last. So in most cases it will pay to use a CAD tool for design.

Another issue that must be addressed in deciding which tool to use is whether the tool will be used once or many times. A planning tool that is used once to decide about where a facility should be located has a much different usage pattern than a tool used for monthly schedule analysis. Although most of the analysis needs for material handling are of an infrequent nature, there are certain types of analyses that are done often enough to warrant a more expensive or more sophisticated tool. An example might be an equipment capacity analysis that is done once or twice a year.

Finally, as software programs become able to communicate with each other easily, more and more users and developers are finding reasons to integrate different programs. This is certainly true of analysis software. Many CAD programs can generate standard graphic files that can be imported into other tools. Other capabilities in CAD programs have improved over the years so that three-dimensional views can be generated, or certain attributes about objects in the drawing can be retrieved easily.

A CAD program should be able to import and export DXF or IGES files even if it is not the software of choice. This is important for facility layouts which can be worked on within one application and then imported into another application via DXF exporting and conversion. Other files generated from spreadsheet programs can be used as inputs to other programs. Most manufacturing resource planning (MRP) systems have the ability to export and import files to at least one type of spreadsheet standard format, which allows actual schedules and routings to be analyzed.

Simulation software improvements have made it easier to use and to import or export data. This is becoming especially important when the simulation models are used repeatedly with new data as the process conditions change. Models can be fed with data that reflect current work-in-process inventory (for example, to help planners decide how best to allocate resources in the next time period, whether that be the next day, the next week, or the next year). The main reason why manufacturing engineers would want to consider integration is that a manufacturing strategy represents a multifaceted picture of requirements for supporting the business strategy. To understand the entire picture, different types of analyses are done. These analyses need similar data and the output from one might be the input from another. For instance, forecast data on what products need to be produced, and when, might be needed in a simulation model, a material flow analysis, a cost analysis, and a capacity analysis. By integrating these analyses, redundant inputting of data can be avoided, along with the difficult task of making sure a scenario is consistent from one model to the next.

Flow-charting Tools

Flow-charting is a practice that is just as old and as widely employed as using spreadsheets. It is used to describe software or control logic, the functions of a machine, the steps in a procedure, or the flow of cash through an accounting system. In manufacturing, chemical engineers and control systems engineers use it extensively to describe the workings and control of a process plant, and quality

CHAPTER 2   MATERIAL HANDLING ANALYSIS

engineers use it to describe inspection procedures. Systems engineers use it to describe the flow of data in a network. Manufacturing engineers need it to describe the flow of products through the manufacturing system. A process flow chart shows the manufacturing process. Flow charts are standardized in the continuous processing industries as process flow diagrams (PFDs) that lead to the development of piping and instrumentation drawings.

Where the industry is not as automated, flow charts help to communicate the flow rules, volume splits to one route or another, and other information that helps describe material flow. The example in Fig. 2-2 shows many different types of information in a single flow chart. The different box shapes indicate whether the product or assembled item is coming from outside the process, through a processing step, through a material handling device, or waiting in a queue. Numbers on the chart indicate volumes, splitting and combining rules, and sometimes processing or travel time. This type of flow chart is useful for communicating the process to other groups inside or outside the company and for determining how new or existing products are affected by routing paths.

As in many situations, this flow chart was developed for a well-established manufacturer whose process had never been flow-charted until the company needed to look at improving the process. The chart helped the company's managers understand the process and started them on a path of determining the best way to improve the process. (Another occasion when a company would want to flow-chart its process is when it has a new product or when it is planning a major renovation or capacity increase for an existing product line.) Charting the process flow helps a project team understand what the existing process is and why certain steps are necessary (or not).

There are highly flexible and very inexpensive tools available to make flow charts. These tools are designed to allow designers and engineers to build flow charts using predesigned templates for shapes, and even systems. Some of these help guide the user by formatting the work space, but in so doing, they reduce the ability to customize the chart. It will usually take some experimentation to find the tool that one likes, and that fits the purpose while still allowing the freedom needed. These differences in functionality versus flexibility are significant, but these tools are low in cost, so the user can afford to have a false start without serious consequences.

An emerging category of flow-charting software is one where flow chart information is exported or imported to another form to be used for other purposes. An example is software that can convert process flow information between a chart and understandable text. It was designed to help drawing-averse people build flow charts simply by typing in text. Other versions extended this capability by tying the chart into a series of spreadsheets, which allow a semiautomatic analysis of the process.

Figure 2-3 shows part of a process that was built with this type of software program. The process in this case is one for routing jobs through a machining company, where various drawings and numerical control (NC) code programs needed to be developed, depending on the type of job. The flow chart is quite complicated because of the many options that a job can have, but it also looks more complicated than it really is. In normal practice, the decision points shown in this chart may simply be replaced with two different lines emanating from the last process step. Figure 2-2 is an example of this type of flow chart.

After the flow chart in Fig. 2-3 was established, data were gathered to determine how many jobs had the various options described and how long each option took. These data were then reduced to get statistical process time averages and volume splits. In the flow analysis software, a tool that links a spreadsheet to the flow chart, the data were then entered as shown in Table 2-6. This table shows the cost of each step, given a fixed cost per hour for people, and the average process times. The analysis software then systematically calculates total cost and time for each potential path or variation through the shop as shown in Table 2-7. The first three columns show the entire range of costs, process times, and probability of occurrence for each type of job. This is useful for pricing different job types, scheduling resources, or for planning. The next two columns are a further refinement, and give a weighted average for both cost and time, which can be inputs to contribution margin calculations. This will be covered further in the "Cost Analysis Tools" section of this chapter.

Layout Analysis Tools

Layout, or material flow, analysis is a wide subject—more than one book has been written on layout analysis by itself. Layout analysis is done whenever a new facility is being considered, when a process is being revamped, or when the material flow needs to be scrutinized to reduce work-in-process (WIP) or movement costs. Most of these books do not talk about using the computer for layout analysis, but there is a wide body of knowledge about how to design a floor plan and how to place equipment for a given product mix. This discussion is limited to the use of computers, or more correctly phrased, decision support systems, in layout analysis. The user will need to gage how best to use these systems to support and refine layout decisions.

The first step in this type of analysis is to develop flow charts for all of the products being produced in a single facility. Where there is a single product or family of products, this is tedious, but where there are hundreds of products, it is not feasible. In this case, products should be grouped into families, using routings as the basis for the family. Typically, MRP systems will have routings already entered, and most of these systems can export the routings to a comma delimited file, or directly to a spreadsheet. Once it is in the spreadsheet, the routing information can be used to sort the products into families. Most companies have only five or six families—not more than 10—even if they have hundreds of products.

Once these flow charts, or major routing families, have been developed, there are a number of different branches that can be taken depending on what type of information is needed and what the product routing data look like. The simplest analysis that could be done would be to develop a material flow matrix, using the spreadsheet. This is simply a chart showing frequency versus routing family type, or frequency versus machine or process step. Figure 2-4 shows an example of a material flow matrix, where routings from the flow chart example are listed in descending order across the horizontal axis and frequency is shown on the vertical axis. This helps to visualize the importance of one type of routing, or family, versus another, and directs the analyst to concentrate improvement efforts or layout analysis on the more frequent routing.

Another use of this data would be for developing a from-to chart. This chart is helpful in deciding which material flow route is most heavily used and can help in a layout design. Using a spreadsheet to list all the routings, or families of routings, the analyst must sort for all the flows from one process step to all the other potential next steps, and add up the frequencies across all families, to produce a chart showing frequency versus routing path. In case it is desired to use this data for determining which path to automate, the analyst should not combine routes that go back against the flow of another route. Material flow automation equipment, such as conveyors and overhead rails, does not lend itself well to flow in two directions. In doing a layout analysis, however, one would want to combine the forward and backward movement of parts because the total amount of material flow should determine how close one work center should be to another.

CHAPTER 2   MATERIAL HANDLING ANALYSIS

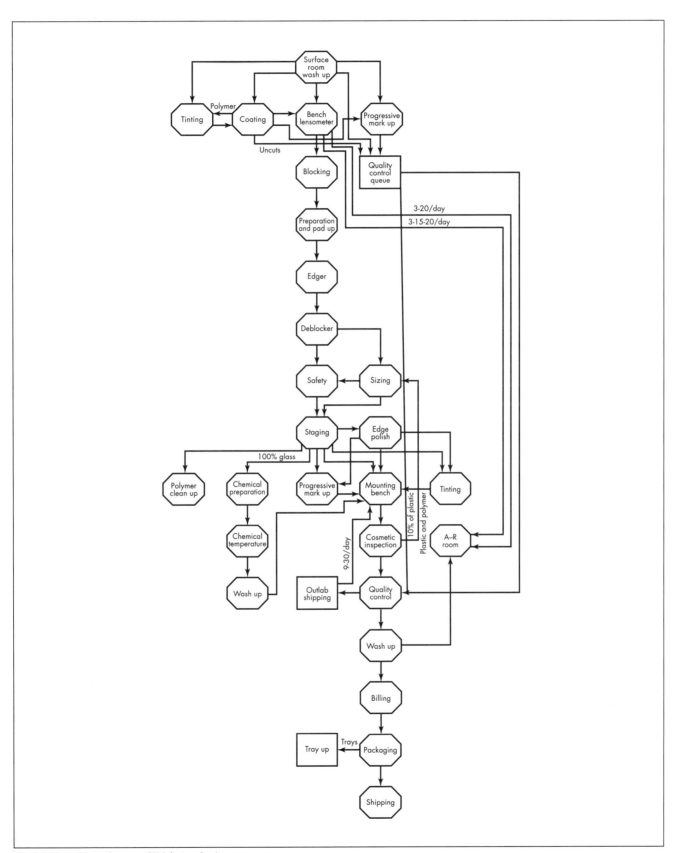

Fig. 2-2 Flow chart. *(Courtesy CIMulation, Inc.)*

CHAPTER 2   MATERIAL HANDLING ANALYSIS

In material flow analysis programs, routings can be entered in for each part type manually, or automatically if there is a large number of parts. The idea is to look at the intensity of material flow between work centers. This intensity can actually be shown graphically on top of a potential layout design (Fig. 2-5). By linking distances to the material flow data, the total distance traveled can be calculated and used to score a certain layout against another.

Now that we have some of the basic concepts mastered, we can go through a layout development. The main tool needed for this is CAD software. Templates or blocks should be made up for each machine or work center, including storage or working areas needed for the machine. A total area required for each processing area can then be calculated by totaling all machine areas for that process step.

A layout planning program uses the area sizes needed, the "AEIOUX" relationships, and form factors to help design a layout. The "AEIOUX" relationships simply categorize the importance of how close one work center should be to another. "AEIOUX" represents:

"A"   Absolutely important that they are close.
"E"   Extremely important that they are close.
"I"   Important that they are close.
"O"   Ordinary importance of being close.
"U"   Unimportant that they are close.
"X"   Important that they are apart.

Listing relationships in this way helps to quantify data that are qualitative. For example, they can express the undesirability of placing a paint booth near a welding booth, in number form. A relationship chart like that shown in Fig. 2-6 is drawn after the user has entered the pertinent relationship information. The different categories are then assigned numbers, starting with 100 for "A" relationships, down to −250 for "X" relationships. For instance, there might be a supervisor who looks over two different processing areas, and

that might be a reason to assign an "A" to the relationship between those two areas. In the paint booth/welding booth example, an "X" would be assigned to keep them as far apart as possible. The numbers are then used to score a layout. The numbers have no significance except in relation to each other.

The program takes these relationships and steps the user through putting process areas on a plan, starting with the "A" relationships and continuing down as far as the user has categories listed in the relationship chart. The objective is to place those areas that should be close to each other first, so as to minimize distances traveled. Once this is done, the tool allows the user to move the areas around to see if there is a better layout, and then scores the layout so the user can compare it to other designs. It is thus a decision support tool, grading the alternatives, but not trying to optimize the layout.

Cost Analysis Tools

There are many different ways to do cost analysis for material handling, and most of them involve the use of spreadsheet software. There are a few tools, however, that can be used for cost analysis and simulation. Before we discuss these, though, we need to discuss what the cost analysis objectives should be. In most cases, we would like to look at the lowest overall production or capital costs. But in some situations, we may want to study how one layout compares with another, or how one material handling design compares with another, particularly when one design is capital-intensive and the other is resource-intensive.

If we take as our goal finding the lowest total costs (capital and production combined), given a number of different scenarios, we can start to build a cost model using spreadsheet software. The first step is to determine the cost categories that will be used to roll up the final numbers. Let us assume that we are looking at a new family of products in a new facility. The final numbers that might be of

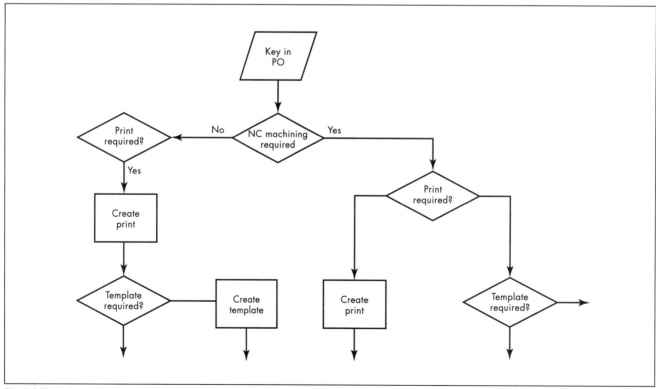

Fig. 2-3 Flow chart. *(Courtesy CLEAR Software, Inc.)*

CHAPTER 2   MATERIAL HANDLING ANALYSIS

TABLE 2-6
Process Times and Costs

Engineering Process Steps	Cost ($)	Time	Rate per h ($)
Key in purchase order	19.00	0.483	40.00
NC for machine required?			
Create print?			
Create print	31.00	0.616	50.00
Template required?			
Make milling machine template	21.00	0.416	50.00
Torch cutter required?			
Make NC code for torch cutter	13.00	0.266	50.00
Scrub print	77.00	1.533	50.00
Scrub print required?			
Scrub print	77.00	1.533	50.00
Template required?			
Make milling machine template	21.00	0.416	50.00
Torch cutter required?			
Make NC code for torch cutter	13.00	0.266	50.00
Scrub print required?			
Scrub print	77.00	1.533	50.00
Make NC code for machine	101.00	2.010	50.00
Print required?			
Create print	31.00	0.616	50.00
Template required?			
Make template for milling machine	21.00	0.416	50.00
Torch cutter required?			
Make NC code for torch cutter	13.00	0.266	50.00
Template required?			
Make template for milling machine	21.00	0.416	50.00
Torch cutter required?			
Make NC code for torch cutter	13.00	0.266	50.00
Shop process	23.00	0.466	50.00

NC = Numerical control

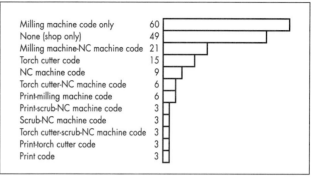

Fig. 2-4 Material flow bar chart.

interest would probably include total capital required, total product cost (per product), total direct and indirect workers required, and possibly contribution margin for each product in the family.

To reach these final numbers, we could develop a chart of cost categories similar to that shown in Fig. 2-7. The categories are designed to capture any potential cost associated with the production of the products, including direct and indirect costs. Direct costs are those that can be attributed directly to a particular product, while indirect costs need to be allocated across all the different products made in the facility. We use the ratio of product direct costs to total direct costs as a method to allocate indirect costs. Under the capital cost categories, there is direct capital and indirect capital, allocated in the same way as the other costs. Material handling is almost always put in the indirect capital area.

Capital is not rolled up like other costs because it is a one-time cost, instead of a cost per piece or per period. It must therefore be allocated over time by using the company's cost of money and standards for machine and facility life. Table 2-8 shows one way in which totals for all these categories might be shown for all products made in the course of a year. In our spreadsheet, this is where the indirect cost allocation is calculated.

TABLE 2-7
Analysis Results for Numerical Control (NC) Machines and Torch Cutters

Path	Cost ($)	Time (min)	Probability	Weighted Average Cost ($)	Weighted Average Time (min)
Print-NCG-scrub-machine	271.00	5.524	1.50	4.07	0.08
Print-torch cutter-scrub-machine	264.00	5.374	1.50	3.96	0.08
Print-scrub-machine	251.00	5.108	1.50	3.76	0.08
Scrub-machine	220.00	4.492	1.50	3.30	0.07
NCG-machine	164.00	3.375	10.50	17.21	0.35
Torch cutter-scrub-machine	233.00	4.758	1.50	3.50	0.07
Torch cutter-machine	156.00	3.225	3.00	4.69	0.10
Machine	143.00	2.959	4.50	6.44	0.13
Print-NCG	94.00	1.981	3.00	2.83	0.06
Print-torch cutter	87.00	1.831	1.50	1.30	0.03
Print	73.00	1.565	1.50	1.10	0.02
NCG	63.00	1.365	35.00	22.20	0.48
Torch cutter	56.00	1.215	7.50	4.19	0.09
None (shop only)	43.00	0.949	24.50	10.44	0.23
Total				$88.99	1.87

NCG = Milling machine code

CHAPTER 2   MATERIAL HANDLING ANALYSIS

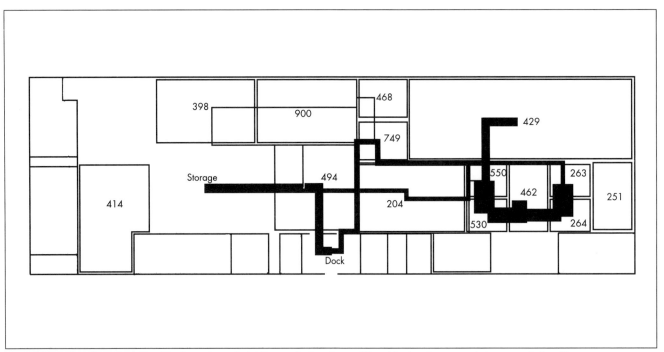

Fig. 2-5 Example of layout relationship drawn by material flow analysis software. The wider bands represent stronger relationships.
(Courtesy CIMulation, Inc.)

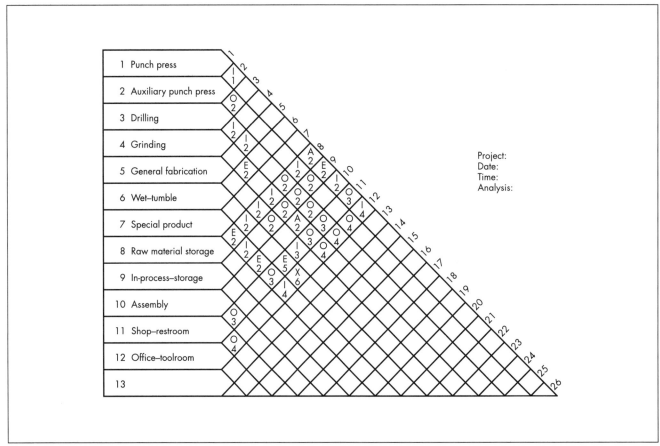

Fig. 2-6 Relationship chart drawn by layout planning software. *(Courtesy CIM Technologies)*

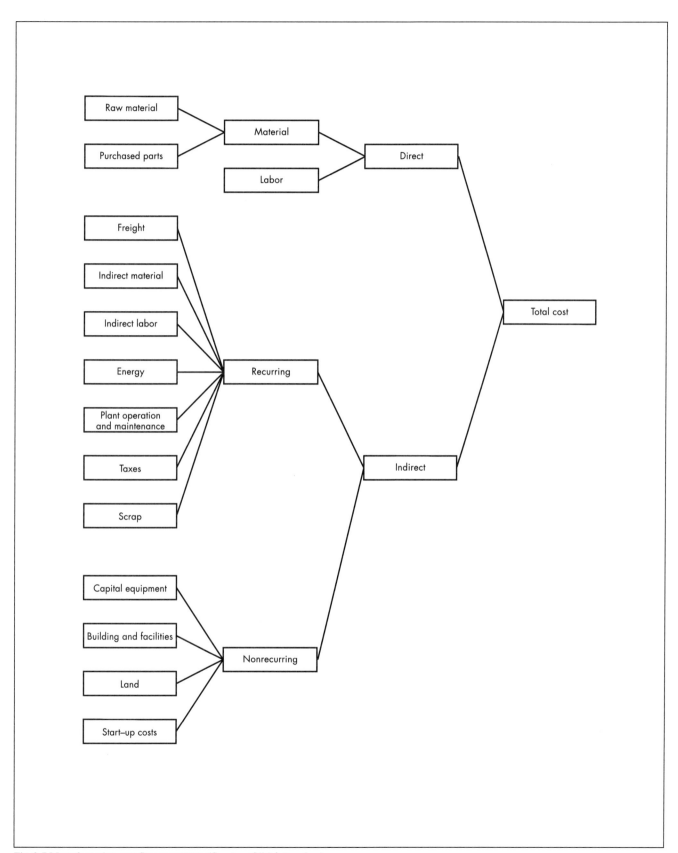

Fig. 2-7 Manufacturing cost flow summary. *(Courtesy CIMulation, Inc.)*

CHAPTER 2   MATERIAL HANDLING ANALYSIS

Once the spreadsheet model is set up to account for all the costs on a per-year basis, we can move to deciding what variables we want to study in our example. These can be anything in the cost model, but for now let us assume that the degree of material handling automation is one of the variables. We might first look at a baseline model where all material handling is done by indirect laborers. An estimate of how many people this involves must be made and that number added to the cost model. One way to estimate this is to use a material flow analysis software tool, with fork lifts as the method for moving material. This would give the number of fork lift operators needed, given a certain operator efficiency (usually less than 50% because of fork lifts traveling while empty).

Another way to do this is to use discrete event simulation software. Data from simulations are more detailed and helpful in determining how production throughputs are affected by different levels of automation. Simulation can be integrated loosely into the cost model by running the simulation model with a certain number of fork lifts or conveyor segments, and then re-entering that number and the results of the simulation back into the cost model. Each scenario would then have a simulation and a cost model run. These should both be saved as separate scenario names, so that they can be compared with other scenarios.

Further integration, like that shown in Fig. 2-8, would tie the layout developed with layout analysis tools and production data coming from a business system, and machines and material handling data coming from simulation, all ending up in the cost model. Much of the data needed in one tool are needed in the others, and integrating the tools like this eliminates some of the need to ensure that data in one part of the scenario are consistent with the data in others. To do this, however, the user needs to pick tools that are as open as possible, or in other words, conform to standards for data transfer and importing and exporting.

COMPUTER-BASED SIMULATION

Discrete event simulation, as opposed to continuous simulation, is the modeling of systems whose variables change as a result of a discrete event, instead of being defined by differential equations. The discrete event may be a unit of time, an arrival of a transporter, or the start of a shift. Monte Carlo methods are used to generate the random numbers needed to drive a distribution of possibilities. All of these events are used in modern simulation tools to define a manufacturing system. Simulation software has evolved from text-based operating systems to graphical user interface (GUI) systems, which do not require the mastering of a computer language. These simulators include easy-to-use model-building tools, output viewers to look at the statistics generated during the simulation, and graphical animation that allows easy understanding of what is being modeled. The advances in computing power for PCs and the simulators have brought simulation out of the mainframe and into the hands of anyone who can use a GUI program. This has created growth in the number of people using simulation, which has fueled faster development in the tools and the ways they are used.

Animation is probably the single biggest advance in simulation tools. Early simulators built for early GUI operating systems used text-based graphics, which were a big step up from looking at a sheet full of numbers. Now exact layouts or even photographic-quality animations can be used to show realistic models. This is important for communicating the model to others not familiar with the process, and for combining material handling design with floor layouts and product arrangement. The simple turning of a product to align it with a machine may be an important component of how a material handling design works, and a simulator must be able to handle that to be useful to a material handling designer. This is also

why it is important for the simulator to be able to import graphics from a CAD system. A shop floor background drawn to scale in CAD can then be used to study layouts, and in the simulator to drive the distances between locations, which will determine how long it takes a transporter to travel from one location to another. Good simulators will then output statistics on transporter travel, both full and empty, so that a detailed analysis on the utilization of transporters can be made.

Simulation is used when the system under consideration is too complicated for spreadsheet analysis, or is not well understood, or a system's performance is to be tested to optimize logistic requirements. It is also useful for providing plant performance data to justify and minimize capital expenditures. Material handling designers, however, will be most interested in seeing how a particular design performs against other alternatives. Simulation models help to define the appropriate level of increased automation with manual operations, and the data generated could lead to new concepts in the design. A baseline model is established, and as improvements are identified, they are compared against the baseline to see how it would affect important production parameters. This means that the model could be used on a more regular basis, not just for initial design. Engineers have even gone as far as to integrate production data with simulation tools to use existing inventories and production requirements in models for testing or making schedules. System integrators use the graphical abilities to help sell and prove new designs.

Outputs from simulation also have been integrated with spreadsheets, custom viewing, and data analysis tools, allowing an engineer to reduce the voluminous data output from simulation into just the data of interest. This helps when cost and layout analysis need to be integrated with simulation output. For example, simulation output data, such as utilization of personnel and product mix throughput, can be used to support cost models, as discussed previously in "Computer-based Analysis Tools."

Simulating Conveyors and Monorail Systems

The primary reason for using simulation in the design and analysis of conveyor systems is to determine how the conveyor affects the rest of the system. With simple conveyor systems, such as a paint line monorail, it is fairly simple to determine what loads the system will handle, given a speed and product size. When some of the variables start to change, however, the effects of these changes are not easily determined. What is the effect, for instance, of a surge of product on an accumulating conveyor? Will throughput be the same when all product flows through the conveyor at the average speed instead of in batches? These dynamics are not easily modeled in spreadsheets, but are only the starting point for simulators. Simulator tools go much further by analyzing the effect of downtime or the difference between using only one offloading person instead of two.

In using simulators for conveyor-based systems, the first step is to develop a layout of the system. There are simulators that allow layout of a conveyor system within the simulator, but it is almost always better to do this in a CAD tool, and then to import the layout into the simulator. Details for onloading and offloading, transitions between different sections, and widths of support structures versus actual conveying widths make a difference in an actual layout and should not be ignored. The ability to import CAD graphics is therefore an important consideration in selecting a simulation tool.

The next step is to determine how the conveyor system will be segmented, and how product is loaded on and off each segment. Segments can be separated by transition point, accumulation, or machine locations. The ability of the particular simulator to model accumulation and transitions will determine the next step. Some have these capabilities built in, while others require effort on the part of the user to account for them.

CHAPTER 2   MATERIAL HANDLING ANALYSIS

TABLE 2-8
Total Manufacturing Costs at 140,000 Units/Year

	8 in. Disk ($)	6.5 in. Disk ($)	4 in. Disk ($)	Total ($)
Direct materials	7,496,684	6,241,414	3,386,467	17,124,565
Direct labor	519,444	519,444	611,111	1,649,999
Indirect labor	1,263,988	1,263,988	822,380	3,350,356
Indirect materials	778,685	778,685	506,631	2,064,001
Utilities	373,497	373,497	243,006	990,000
Property taxes	343,123	343,123	223,244	909,490
Plant operation and maintenance	311,247	311,247	202,505	824,999
Scrap	319,382	319,382	207,798	846,562
Start-up costs	60,570	60,570	39,408	160,548
Depreciation and amortization	1,622,603	1,622,603	1,055,704	4,300,910
Total	$13,089,223	$11,833,953	$7,298,254	$32,221,430
Cost per unit	$93.49	$84.53	$52.13	$230.15

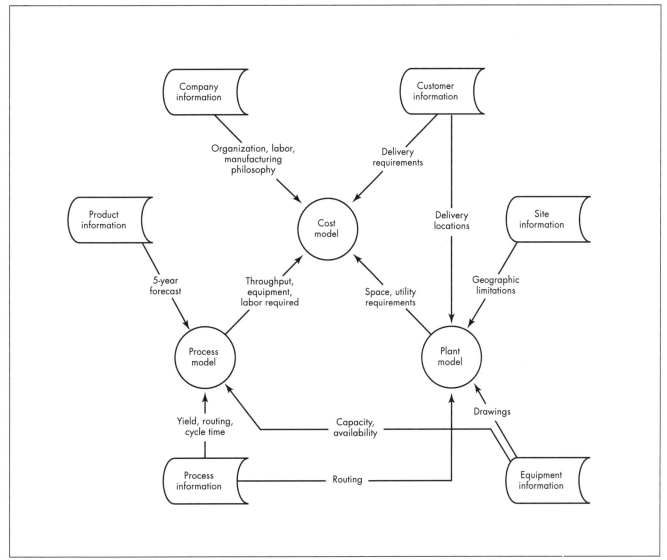

Fig. 2-8 Manufacturing strategy analysis. *(Courtesy CIMulation, Inc.)*

CHAPTER 2   MATERIAL HANDLING ANALYSIS

Figure 2-9 shows the layout of a conveyor system as drawn in CAD software. Product flows from left to right through a production line and gets loaded on the conveyor at the middle of the drawing. Product then flows to a transition, where larger product turns and accumulates on a short section of roller conveyor before being offloaded manually, and smaller product flows around the loop to accumulate before being offloaded at the same spot. Figure 2-10 shows how conveyor sections in the simulator were overlaid on top of the layout. Because we are interested in the conveyor design only, we modeled the production line as an accumulating conveyor that feeds the onload spot. The onload spot is where two people load a short transfer conveyor with product. The transition point was modeled as a simple location that feeds large product in one direction and small product in the other. Accumulating conveyors were then used to model both the large and small product conveyor sections.

The goal of this analysis was to see what length of conveyor is needed to handle production of either the large or small product, given the shift schedules of the people loading and unloading product. This particular model took only four hours to build, since most of the work of developing the layout was already done in the CAD system. The results that were determined by the analysis were simply how many of each size are accumulated in each section before the product is offloaded, or in terms of the simulator, the maximum contents of those locations.

Simulating Other Material Handling Systems

Other types of material handling systems, such as automated guided vehicles (AGVs), fork trucks, and overhead cranes, are not as complicated as conveyor systems. They can be modeled simply as a resource that carries product from one location to another. Some simulators require that the product be joined to the carrier, since they allow only one entity to move between locations. This will work in most cases, except where other product needs to be joined as a subassembly, or where it is necessary to keep track of pallets or totes as well as product. Such simulators should be avoided if possible.

Figure 2-11 shows an AGV system that carries product between machines, a wash station, and a coordinate measuring machine (CMM) station before going to a load and unload station. The goal of this simulation was to determine how the utilization of the AGVs affects the throughput and utilization of the machines they feed. This would then determine how many AGVs should be used and whether they should feed a single zone or the entire system. The results of the simulation were reduced to a set of utilization and throughput numbers as shown in Fig. 2-12. Pulling only those numbers out of the simulation output helped in analyzing the data because all of the pertinent numbers were in one place. It also helped in presenting results to the end users.

Where there are three-dimensional (3D) issues that must be analyzed, as in the case of a warehouse conveying system that has over and under transfer conveyors, it is sometimes useful to use simulators that can easily develop 3D models. A complicated AS/RS can be modeled in 2D simulators by using the distribution functions to model the time it takes to place and pick from shelves. The details of how the unit retrieves from the shelves are lost, but not everyone is interested in those details.

Comparing Alternative Systems

In analyzing systems with simulation tools, it is necessary to have a goal for how the model will be built and a plan for how the results will be used. An example of a goal is the ability to use the model to study how throughput is affected when certain variables are changed. Another example is the ability to minimize cost or other variables by changing the number of operators or cranes, or chang-

ing to an alternative material handling system while keeping throughput constant. Having a goal helps to determine the time frame to be used, the level of detail needed in the model, whether existing inventories need to be included, and other details. Not having a goal makes it difficult for anyone to determine if the model works, and the model will be less useful than it could be.

The plan for how to use the model is a somewhat broader concept, for even if a goal is defined, it is still necessary to determine where the modeling effort fits into an improvement or initial design effort. In most cases, modeling should be done on the front side of any improvement effort, but in others, designers use modeling to check and optimize a pre-existing design. Figure 2-13 shows a strategy that might be used for manufacturing process improvements. In this strategy, as in most, the first step is to find out how well the process is performing now. Without simulation, this might be done by gathering data from the process to quantify throughputs, resources used, and other outputs given certain inputs. When simulation is used the input parameters feed the model, and then the model is so that the outputs match the actual adjusted outputs.

After the model is validated, it can be used to perform a matrix of what-if analyses that will help to identify possible options for improvements. This can be either planned or unplanned, because sometimes, when the results of a model are seen, unexpected results lead to a change that was not previously considered. This is why simulation provides such a high return on investment. In these cases, there might not be a design in mind, and a set of alternative options will have to be compared. These options can be simulated even if the design does not exist. For example, if there is a suspicion that reducing the travel time between workstations would increase operator utilization, the time can be reduced in the model without knowing if it is feasible. If it is shown that the change made is significant, further work can be done to find out if the option will work. If the change is not significant, there is no point in pursuing the option any further. This is another way that simulation can save the company money.

Certain simulators make comparison easier by providing tools for setting up scenarios, interacting with the model during the course of a simulation, or even looking at multiple scenarios at the same time. Having the ability to change parameters easily within the same scenario is important for users who do not want to or cannot interact directly with the data in the model. Some simulators set up macros for variables just for that purpose, and then allow the user to run multiple replications to get statistically good data that are analyzed with other data in the same scenario. This is important when the major alternatives have variables within them that need to be evaluated for sensitivity to change. Figure 2-14 shows several different conveying layouts that can be run at the same time. The simulator permits other submodels to be imported into the model being worked on, which allows the review of multiple models during the same simulation run. This is helpful when there are fine-detailed differences between alternatives that need to be viewed while the models are running.

WORK SIMPLIFICATION

Work simplification and cost reduction should be two of the prime objectives of any material handling analysis. In a competitive environment, it is an absolute must for organizations to simplify and improve their operations. Competition forces all in industry to get better at what they do; otherwise they will not survive. Since the very beginning of the industrial revolution, work simplification and methods improvement efforts have been the main focus of manufacturing and industrial engineers. No successful company today has prospered without the benefit of directed efforts at work simplification.

CHAPTER 2   MATERIAL HANDLING ANALYSIS

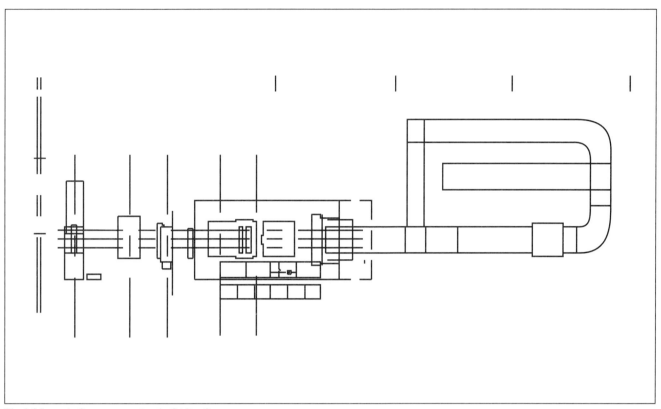

Fig. 2-9 Layout of conveyor system in CAD software.

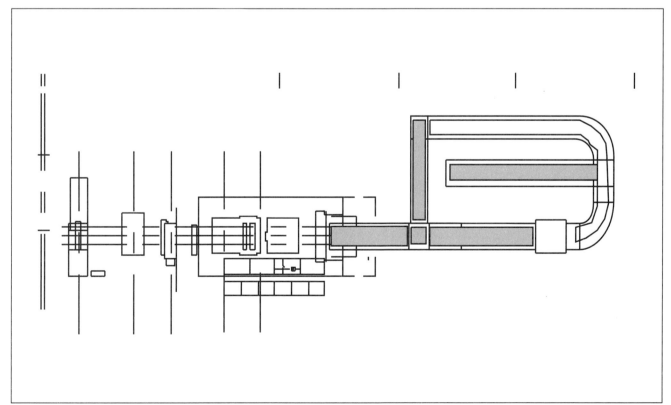

Fig. 2-10 Conveyor sections overlaid on the layout.

CHAPTER 2 MATERIAL HANDLING ANALYSIS

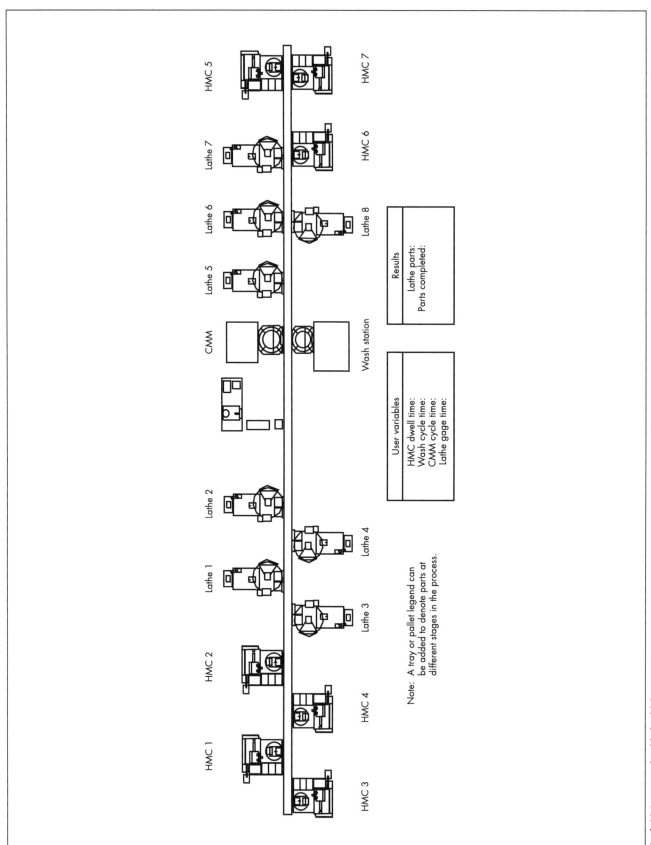

Fig. 2-11 Automated guided vehicle system.

CHAPTER 2   MATERIAL HANDLING ANALYSIS

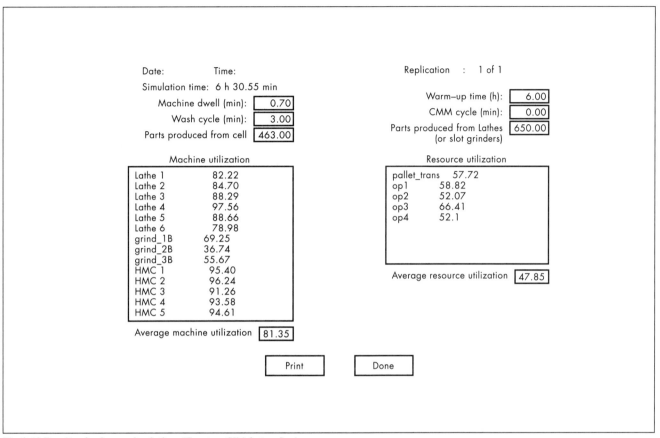

Fig. 2-12 Results of software simulation. *(Courtesy CIMulation, Inc.)*

Persons engaged in manufacturing should always strive to reduce the amount of human physical labor and exertion required to move and transport materials. This makes sense from the point of view of human compassion, as well as from purely economic, ergonomic and injury-prevention points of view. Before determining or finalizing the material handling systems and layouts that we will employ in our plant, it is wise to review the existing manufacturing operations and simplify them wherever possible. In other words, the planner should not jump into developing layouts before trying to improve the current or proposed operations. There are several old clichés that every layout planner and materials handling engineer should try to remember and live by. One of them is the KISS principle: "Keep It Sane and Simple." Another is the wise old adage that "the best material handling system is no material handling system at all." That adage stems from the fact that material handling, in itself, adds no value to the part or product we are handling, but it does add cost. The basic questions to be asked for all activities and materials movements are:

- What operation are we doing and what materials are we moving? Can we combine an operation with another one and eliminate the movement of material? For example, can an operator at the first production operation replace the need for a separate, stand-alone, incoming inspection function? Can a machine operator perform value-added assembly work during a cycle in lieu of just having an idle wait period?
- Why are we performing the operation and why are we moving materials at all? Can we eliminate the operation or the handling altogether? Can we simplify it? For example, can we in-

tegrate all inspection operations into the production operations? Can we use returnable containers to eliminate the dunnage materials and labor involved in unnecessary packaging or unpacking at the shipping and receiving areas?
- Where do we need to move the material to? Can we shorten the distance? Can we move several items at a time to reduce the number of trips? Are there straight-running aisles? If not, why not? Can we have point-of-use delivery and storage?
- When and how often are we performing the operation and when do we need to move the material? Can the schedule be changed to reduce the number of handlings without affecting customer service or "starving" the next operation?
- How are we performing the operation or moving the material? Can we redesign the handling container to help ourselves? How many nonvalue-added pickups and setdowns are we making?
- Count them and reduce them! Do we have "deadheading"—empty return trips by materials handling equipment? If so, can we correct the situation? What is the actual time utilization of our mobile equipment?
- Who is performing the operation or moving the material? Are there two-person lifting jobs? Is skilled labor used for moving materials? Is direct or indirect labor used for moving materials? Can the secondary operation or materials movement be done within a machine cycle? Is productivity lost because of the time it takes to move materials? Will the vendor bring materials directly to the point of usage?

It makes little sense to duplicate current problems without attempting improvements first. Frequently, time constraints will not

CHAPTER 2 MATERIAL HANDLING ANALYSIS

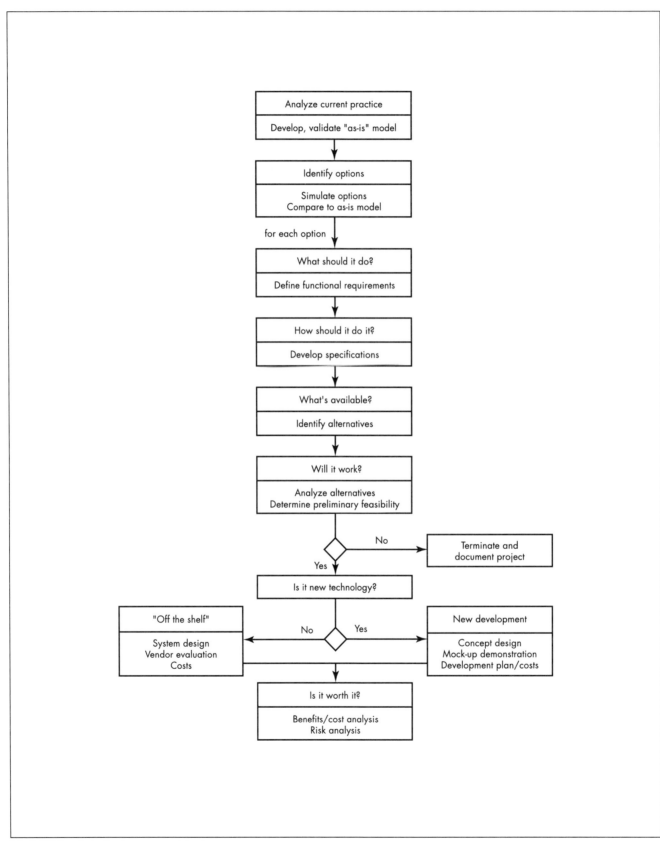

Fig. 2-13 Manufacturing improvement strategy.

CHAPTER 2 MATERIAL HANDLING ANALYSIS

allow a full, detailed work simplification analysis, but that is no excuse for not trying. The development of a new layout offers a golden opportunity for improvements in materials handling. In most situations that opportunity may not present itself again for a very long time.

Work simplification is an important prerequisite to any proposed plant rearrangement or revised layout. In addition to the previous questions, the four key tasks involved in work simplification are easy to remember. They can be summed up in the acronym SECS:

Study
Eliminate
Combine
Simplify

Plantwide Material Handling Simplification

During the 1500s, people simplified their materials handling methods by implementing equipment-based tools. They simplified their work by using crude wheelbarrows, jib cranes, bucket elevators, and waterwheels. Most of these improvements were made to simplify the brute-force carrying methods of the day and to improve safety. In the mid-1800s, bridge cranes, conveyors, and hoists were implemented. Arguably the most significant improvement, from an equipment point of view, was the advent of the first powered industrial truck in 1906. The real explosion and expansion of powered material handling transport equipment occurred in the 1920s and 1930s, when a variety of powered lift trucks for the factory came into widespread use. Even though the newer side loaders, 4D trucks, turret trucks, and stand-up reach trucks are common, the basic concept of the 1920s and 1930s—the sit-down fork lift truck—is still in wide use today.

However, work simplification and methods improvements do not always involve equipment choices. Overall plant (macro) layout and detailed work center (micro) layout also play a large role in work simplification and reductions in labor content. In many situations, the cost savings potential for work simplification at the micro level far outweighs the cost savings potential at the macro level. We will cover the questions to be asked at a micro level after covering the macro issues.

At the macro level, one of the first questions we should ask is: have we considered the 20 principles or guidelines of material handling as developed by The College Industrial Committee on Material Handling Education and published by The Material Handling Institute? You may have to modify these principles for a Just-in-Time or cellular manufacturing approach, but they still offer some worthwhile guidelines. The fourth principle is the simplification

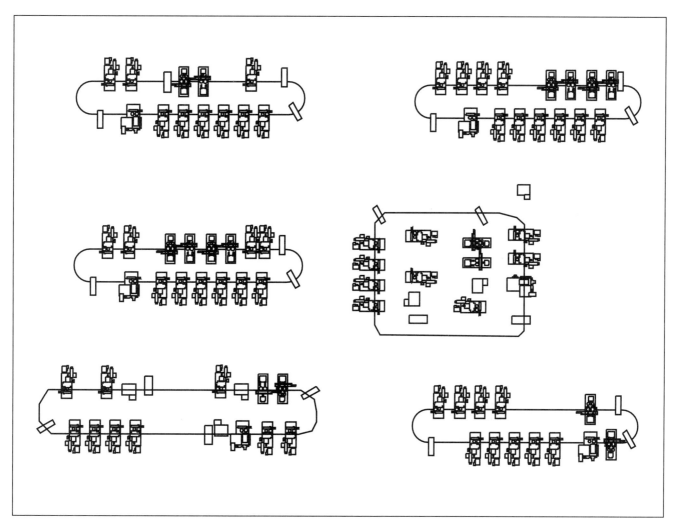

Fig. 2-14 Multiple layouts in the same model drawn by discrete event simulation software. *(Courtesy CIMulation, Inc.)*

CHAPTER 2   MATERIAL HANDLING ANALYSIS

principle: "Simplify handling by reducing, eliminating, or combining unnecessary movements and/or equipment." This principle prompts the following questions regarding macro material flow and handling within a plant:

- Can we increase the size of the handling container or batch size to reduce the number of material handling trips? (Of course, we do not want to violate a small-batch philosophy that offers other benefits.)
- Can we move the output area of a workstation closer to the input area of this or a different workstation? Doing so may allow a material handling person to bring materials to a workstation and take materials away on the return trip.
- Have we developed an optimum plant layout that minimizes material handling costs and distance traveled? Can we eliminate long and/or awkward handling operations?
- Can we justify a better handling device? For example, fifty 40-lb (18-kg) bags on a pallet may be more efficiently moved with a fork lift truck making one trip than by one person carrying one bag on each of 50 trips. Similarly, long lengths of pipe or other materials may be more efficiently moved with a side-loading truck, turret truck, or overhead crane than with a common fork lift truck that has to safely maneuver the material along a relatively narrow aisleway.
- Can we move several different bill-of-material items at one time? Can we schedule a series of material drop-offs and returns, allowing for a multipallet transporter or "mule train" type of delivery system?
- Can we reduce or eliminate *deadheading*? That is, can we reduce the number of people and equipment movements in which no load is carried on return trips?
- If a material handler must move materials out of the way to get to the unit needed, can we use selective storage racks or flow-through racks? These types of racks will facilitate getting parts off the factory floor and help provide better material control and reduced material handling effort.
- If we have long distances to travel with materials, can we use powered conveyors or automated guided vehicles for material transport? This will reduce the amount of labor associated with moving materials.
- In an assembly area, can the product be placed on movable dollies, trays, or carts that can simply be pushed to the next operation, instead of calling for a mobile piece of material handling equipment?
- Can a simple pallet jack be used to move materials short distances instead of a fork lift truck, crane, or other device?
- Conversely, have we considered automating or mechanizing the handling operation? Can a miniload type of automated storage and retrieval system be justified?
- Can the complexity of different part configurations be overcome by using a common handling container for most parts?
- Can we make use of gravity in getting materials to and from an operation or between upper and lower floor levels?
- Do we have enough of a fork-truck fleet spread all over the factory to justify centralization of resources into a radio-dispatched pool?
- Can we eliminate paperwork and paperwork transport and at the same time speed up material handling notification by using computerized methods, e-mail, or facsimile machines?
- Can outside suppliers store and handle materials and deliver these materials to the point of use on the factory floor?
- Can we change the packaging on our incoming materials to eliminate the handling of trash? Can the vendor supply a stackable and nestable returnable container that also serves as our internal storage and handling container?
- Can we combine work centers or cells to provide common material pickup and setdown points?
- Have we considered a visual or electronic material handling "need" communication system within the factory? For example, simple light bulb notification points, internal electronic data interchange (EDI), bar coding, kanban cards, etc.?
- Have we charted and questioned every handling operation? Is it needed at all? Can it be combined with another operation or completely eliminated? Have we considered combining or moving some of our manufacturing operations to eliminate the need for material handling between the operations?
- Can we standardize the types of handling and transport equipment and containers being used? It is easier and less costly to service and maintain common pieces of equipment.
- Can we combine inspection, storage, and material transport in the same vehicle or operation?
- Are all of our transport aisles straight, without any turns? Every time a vehicle makes a turn there is a cost involved. The vehicle must apply its brakes, decelerate, turn, and then accelerate back to normal speed. There are also safety hazards associated with turning, particularly if there are blind spots. In addition to the continuing incremental high operating costs, vehicles in plants with aisle turns have higher vehicle maintenance costs.
- Can we eliminate any need for "slave" pallets? Similarly, we should eliminate any transfer of parts from one container to another simply because different containers are used for material handling.

Using the Operations Process Chart as a Work Simplification Tool

The operations process chart is probably one of the most useful tools for the manufacturing and industrial engineer. At the macro level, these charts are frequently called *consolidated operations process charts* (see Fig. 2-15). These types of charts show the overall process flow within the plant or about the site. They show the movement of materials from department to department or work center to work center. Usually, only the major flows of materials are shown. One should not forget to add process flows for rework or return loops as well as scrap and trash. Another important consideration is the flow of empty containers back to their starting points. All of these important facets are not in the mainstream of our thoughts and are frequently overlooked. Consolidated operations process charts are very useful for developing quantified flow diagrams. They are a tremendous help in developing optimum plant layouts (at the macro level) as well as optimum material handling plans.

Micro operations process charts (OPCs) for manufacturing a particular product or part also can be extremely useful in work simplification. However, the engineer or planner should refrain from taking a chart like the one in Fig. 2-16 as a given, without first questioning the process. By questioning, it is meant that the principles of work simplification should be applied. The basic questions outlined in the last section should be addressed. It may be a mistake (or lost opportunity) to take the OPC at face value and to arrange a material handling system between the detailed work centers in the same sequential relationship as depicted on the existing OPC.

For example, the numbers noted beside the bubbles shown in Figs. 2-17 and 2-18 indicate the standard times allowed for those operations. Whether we use predetermined, engineered time standards for new operations or actual measured time from stopwatch studies is not important. If the objective is to design an efficient

CHAPTER 2   MATERIAL HANDLING ANALYSIS

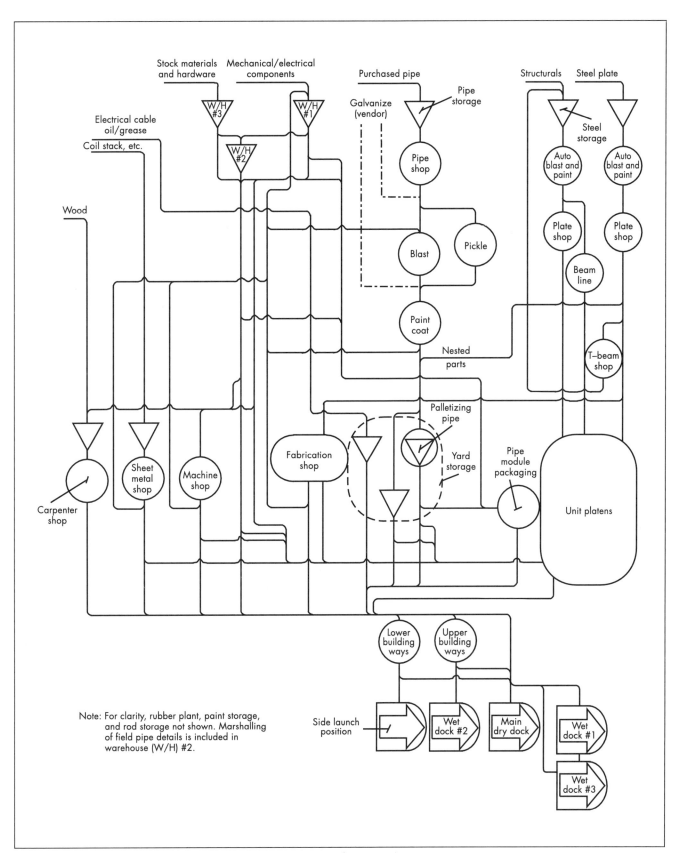

Fig. 2-15 Consolidated operations process chart. *(Courtesy U.S. Maritime Administration)*

CHAPTER 2   MATERIAL HANDLING ANALYSIS

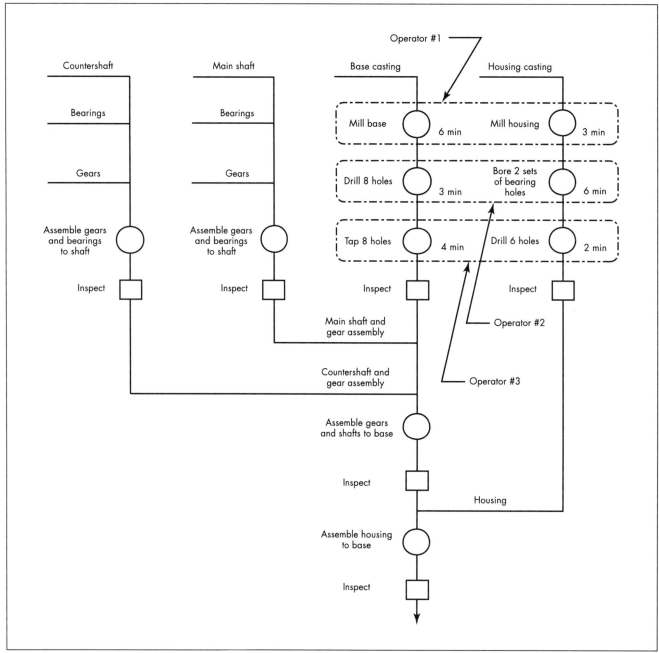

Fig. 2-16 Example operations process chart. *(Courtesy The Sims Consulting Group, Inc.)*

operation, it is important that the standard times be known and that they be accurate. If we take Fig. 2-17 at face value and develop a layout, we might simply combine the six operations shown into three pairs of operations to get a nine-minute cycle time. The third set of combined operations would have three minutes of slack or idle time, but the first two sets of combined operations would have zero idle time. The total production and total capacity of the operation would be capped at 160 pieces per day. The calculations at the bottom of Fig. 2-18 show the results of the combination using three operators on each of three work shifts. But is that the best we can do?

If we instead change the proposed layout and combine the operations to achieve a six-minute cycle, we can potentially achieve much

better productivity. In fact, with only a minor change in the layout, we can totally eliminate the third shift portion of this operation. We can achieve the same overall current production, with fewer people overall, on two shifts. With this seemingly minor change, we can also increase total capacity by 50% to 240 pieces per day. How can we physically achieve that magnitude of change without speeding up the work pace and alienating the employees? Figure 2-18 shows the new combined operations. The operations are now performed with four people on each of two shifts (eight people compared to nine previously). The savings results are tabulated in Fig. 2-19.

Keep in mind that we did not change the detailed operations themselves. The standard hours or minutes of work content remained the

CHAPTER 2   MATERIAL HANDLING ANALYSIS

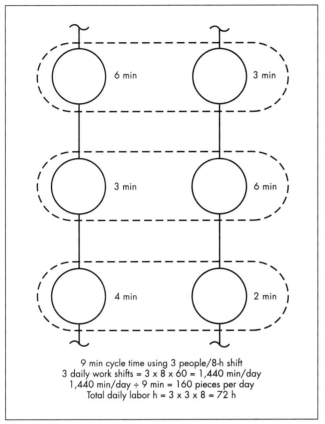

9 min cycle time using 3 people/8-h shift
3 daily work shifts = 3 x 8 x 60 = 1,440 min/day
1,440 min/day ÷ 9 min = 160 pieces per day
Total daily labor h = 3 x 3 x 8 = 72 h

Fig. 2-17 Micro operations process chart—nine-minute cycle.
(Courtesy Edward J. Phillips)

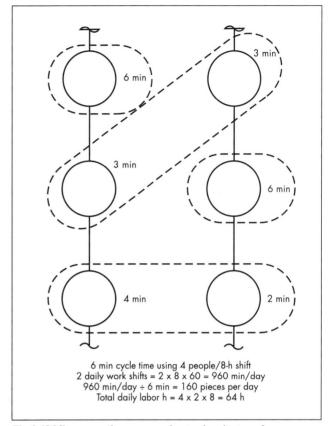

6 min cycle time using 4 people/8-h shift
2 daily work shifts = 2 x 8 x 60 = 960 min/day
960 min/day ÷ 6 min = 160 pieces per day
Total daily labor h = 4 x 2 x 8 = 64 h

Fig. 2-18 Micro operations process chart—six-minute cycle.
(Courtesy Edward J. Phillips)

For the same production output:

- Labor reduction $= \dfrac{72 - 64}{72} \times 100 = 11\%$

- Cycle time $= \dfrac{9 - 6}{9} \times 100 = 33\%$

- Headcount, fringes, payroll taxes $= \dfrac{9 - 8}{9} \times 100 = 11\%$

- Reduced support services associated with a third shift

Fig. 2-19 Tabulation of savings with six-minute cycle.
(Courtesy Edward J. Phillips)

same. All we changed were the individual operator responsibilities within the cell, the material handling sequence/flow, and the layout to facilitate the new combinations.

One of the most famous sages of quality, W. E. Deming, has been credited with transforming Japanese industry through the implementation of his 14 points or principles of quality. One of Deming's 14 principles was his call for the elimination of time standards. As can be noted from the previous example, that principle may apply very well in some cases, but it does not apply everywhere. This is demonstrably true when you are trying to analyze and improve a particular manufacturing situation. To be successful, you need a baseline measurement from which to gage progress or change.

To summarize, the operations process chart is an invaluable tool for the user to simplify operations and reduce costs. It does this by helping the visualization process for rearranging layouts and material handling operations.

Value-added versus Nonvalue-added Operations

It would be very enlightening if we could physically stay with, follow, and time a typical part as it spends its life sitting and moving through a typical factory. If we could look at a traditional job shop operation using a process-dominated layout, we would have operations such as shown in Figure 2-20. The reader will note that in the dozen or so steps shown, only one adds actual value to the part. We graphically depict the time used for these operations in Figure 2-21.

The time to perform the step "perform operation" is not totally value-added time. Figure 2-21 shows how much time can be classified as nonvalue-added in that step. Determining the small part of

CHAPTER 2   MATERIAL HANDLING ANALYSIS

1. Receive raw material   ____ _____

2. Move to incoming inspection   ____ _____

3. Move to storage/staging   ____ _____

4. Place in storage   ____ _____

5. Remove from storage   ____ _____

6. Move to first operation stack   ____ _____

7. Pick up part   ____ _____

8. Perform operation   ____ _____

9. Place in outgoing stack   ____ _____

10. Move to WIP storage   ____ _____

11. Repeat steps 4 through 10   ____ _____

12. And so on . . .   ____ _____

Fig. 2-20 Tracing a typical part's life through the factory.
(Courtesy Edward J. Phillips)

time that makes up the step "perform operation" shows that only a small portion of that time is actually adding value to the part. In traditional large batch-oriented, process-department types of layouts, the great majority of time is wasted in queues, material handling, and storage. A well-designed manufacturing cell, with small batch sizes, would reduce wasted time, wasted material handling, and keep bloated inventory storage to a minimum.

One of the keys to developing work simplification in material handling is to eliminate the unnecessary nonvalue-added handling and storage operations. A build-to-order, demand-pull manufacturing cell goes a long way to accomplishing this goal. Theoretically, the cellular factory builds only what has been ordered by the customer and has a reduced need for bloated inventories of raw and work-in-process inventories. We need to simplify our handling methods and move from (a) to (b) as shown in Fig. 2-22.

Methods Improvements—What to Look For

While analyzing material handling within micro work centers doing repetitive work, one of the objectives should be to find an optimum cycle time with minimum work-in-process inventories. It should be noted that the optimum cycle time for maximizing productivity is not always the minimum cycle time. In some instances, higher productivity and a better labor balance is achieved by increasing cycle time. The required capacity, allowable investment, and space available will also be factors affecting the selection of the optimum cycle time. Each case is different and few generalizations can be made.

In all situations, whether the work is repetitive or nonrepetitive, human factors and ergonomics are very important considerations.

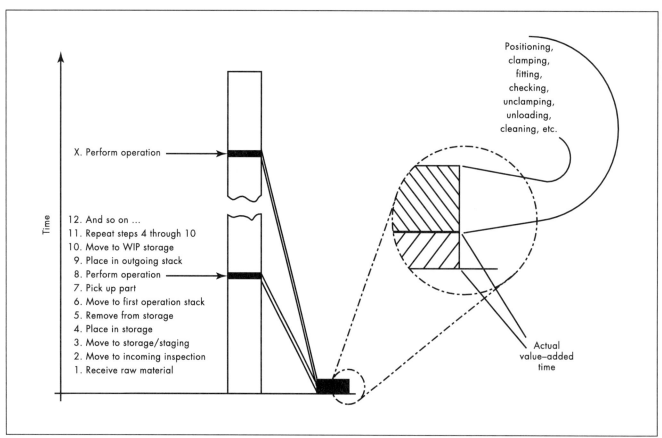

Fig. 2-21 Time to perform operations on part. *(Courtesy Edward J. Phillips)*

CHAPTER 2   MATERIAL HANDLING ANALYSIS

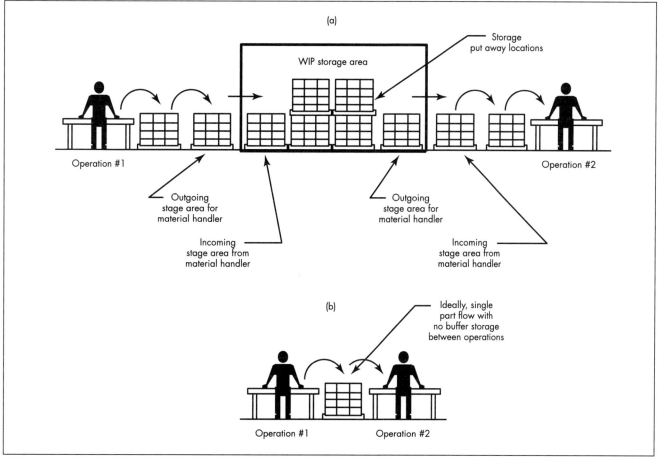

Fig. 2-22 Material handling—complicated (a) and simple (b). *(Courtesy Edward J. Phillips)*

When we are trying to improve work methods within any work center, we should look for the following lost time or wasted motions:

- Adjusting.
- Bending over.
- Carrying or transporting.
- Checking.
- Choosing.
- Cycling to the wrong rhythm.
- Disassembling.
- Gaging.
- Idle chatter.
- Idleness.
- Measuring.
- Orienting.
- Prepositioning.
- Positioning.
- Pulling.
- Pushing.
- Reaching.
- Resting.
- Searching.
- Stooping.
- Turning around.
- Unnecessary paces.
- Waiting.
- Walking.

The occurrence of any of these items or events indicates the use of either poor methods or a poor layout, or both. These events should be noted and eliminated wherever possible. All of these wasted time/ motion events can be corrected with innovativeness, procedural changes, equipment, tooling, or a combination of all of these.

ANALYZING LOAD SIZE

The process of defining load size requires an understanding of large versus small load sizes and the effect of unit load size on the manufacturing cycle time.

Large versus Small Unit Loads

Deciding how big or small the load includes consideration of how load sizes were done in the past, batch sizes, the effects of unit load and container configurations, developing a "common denominator" container configuration, and dual-use manufacturing and shipping containers.

A history of change. As noted earlier, the Material Handling Institute and the U.S.-based, College-Industry Committee on Material Handling Education developed 20 principles, published more than a quarter of a century ago as "The Principles of Material Handling." The 20 original principles were basically fundamental rules. They were derived from the commonsense practices followed by many progressive companies and consultants of that era. The 20 principles were expanded later with the addition of a few more. Most of the original principles are still true today, with the possible exception of one of them: the unit size principle.

CHAPTER 2   MATERIAL HANDLING ANALYSIS

What was not recognized by the educators and consultants of that era was the deleterious effect the observance of this principle had on the overall internal costs incurred by the enterprise. This large load principle was pounded into the heads of young manufacturing and industrial engineers for years and, unfortunately, is still being espoused by some educators. The potentially harmful downstream effects of using large batches and handling loads of discrete items is still not recognized today by many manufacturers.

Batch size considerations. Why can large loads lead a manufacturer into trouble? Let us just think for a moment about the physical effect on work-in-process inventories. As an example, suppose we are making a subassembly that is 2 ft³ (0.057 m³) in size and we have 10 separate manufacturing operations to complete each subassembly. Also, suppose we are working with right-hand and left-hand components; that is, a complete product consists of two mirror-image subassemblies. We can plan either one manufacturing cell with, say, a batch size of two subassemblies (1 ft³ [0.028 m³] in volume) or a traditional, departmentalized manufacturing arrangement with 10 departments and a batch size of 256 subassemblies (128 product pair units). We select a 256-subassembly batch because we are following the large load principle and can move the entire batch in one fork truck movement (carrying two 64-ft² [6-m²] pallets at a time). We have not discussed how we are physically going to move each of the two-piece batches, but let us assume that the large load principle clearly has much lower material handling transport costs associated with it. Let us now ask some general questions about the two different manufacturing and handling systems.

- Which system do you suppose will carry a higher inventory and need the most floor space to house the inventory?
- Which system is more likely to have the highest inventory carrying costs?
- If a defective assembly is found at your shipping dock, which system is liable to result in the highest inspection labor, scrap, and rework costs?
- Which system is more likely to need a pallet rack installation to store materials?
- Which system will probably need a more sophisticated material control hardware/software system?
- Which system would be easier to schedule and expedite?
- Would the small batch process require a fork lift truck?
- What are the depreciation or lease costs for the fork lift truck?
- What are the annual costs of maintaining the fork lift truck and training its operators?
- What does the operator of the fork lift truck do when he or she is not moving materials?
- Which system would probably incur the most product damage costs in handling operations?
- How many lead persons will you need with each system?

These questions are admittedly biased toward favoring small unit loads. That bias recognized, the reader will probably agree that, unless we were consuming an inordinate amount of internal resources in moving the individual small batches, the large load principle would not be the best choice. Clearly, this condition changes when the products reach the shipping dock. At the shipping dock, the large load principle usually (but not always, depending on the wishes of our customer) comes back into play. Notwithstanding a Just-in-Time delivery schedule, either you or your customer may want to accumulate large loads or batch mixed loads at the shipping point to gain the advantage of lower freight costs.

Every manufacturing plant will have its own special situations where the typical rules do not apply or they are overridden by other, more important, factors. The important point to remember is that larger unit load sizes usually lower material handling transport costs but have a tendency to increase costs in other areas.

The effects of unit load and container configuration. The lot sizes used in a manufacturing cycle are frequently determined by factors that are beyond one's immediate control. Typical examples of controlling processes are batch chemical processes or batch heat-treating processes that have a predetermined mass quantity input.

Let us look at the pros and cons of using small handling containers in a cell or assembly line type of operation.

Pros:
- Less total line length required.
- Containers may be moved without mechanical assistance.
- Fewer returns of unused parts to the stockroom and provides increased control.
- Allows more staging area for mixed model lines.
- Faster part changeovers.
- Supports Just-in-Time/kanban environment.

Cons:
- Requires higher amount of replenishment labor.
- May require purchase, storage, and maintenance of many tote-size containers.
- Small containers may reduce amount of line expansion flexibility for new products.

Analyze each situation separately because it is difficult to make generalizations. On balance, small container sizes and small batch sizes generally offer more benefits than large batch sizes, at least within work centers. The opposite is true for transporting materials between work centers. However, large container sizes invariably have a tendency to increase raw and work-in-process inventories.

Universal container configuration. When considering any kind of material handling plan within a complex manufacturing operation, one may easily become overwhelmed by the myriad of detail requirements for handling a multitude of parts or products. This problem usually arises when we are trying to develop a plantwide material handling mechanization scheme. Frequently, it helps to try to categorize or classify the various parts to be handled into manageable groupings. It is usually wise to concentrate on a common container design. The design should be focused on a container configuration that is compatible with mechanized transport. A container is normally configured to hold as many varied parts as possible and is called a *common denominator handling unit*. Typical considerations or questions to be asked include:

- Is it possible to develop a single, standardized container or tote box configuration for most parts, products, and components?
- Can we design the container for conveyor transport or have it include a mechanical interface for automated lifting?
- If not for all items, can we develop a universal container to handle the great majority (perhaps 80%) of the items?
- Is it possible to balance the production rates and product cube movements between individual work centers so that the handling or transport system can become the in-process production bank?
- If we are using a traditional approach, our container will tend to be biased toward a large size (which may be correct in some situations). If we are considering a JIT approach, we should consider the use of the smallest size acceptable configuration.
- We should also investigate how we can best handle, knock down, or nest containers, so we can utilize cube space for both loaded and unloaded containers.

Dual manufacturing and shipping containers—a special case. Before leaving the subject of containers, we should add one note of warning or caution about the design of returnable type containers that are shipped to customers. Sometimes containers or movable cart/containers can be designed too well. There have been many instances where stackable carts and containers were so well designed that customers hoarded them and used them for their own storage system. In other words, the "returnable" containers were not all returned. The customers used the containers in their own plant instead of installing pallet racks or other storage devices.

One company in particular was producing a very competitive, commodity-type building product approximately 12–16 ft (3.7–4.9 m) in length. As an aid to handling the product within their plant, and to simplify the loading of truck shipments, they developed a very well designed wheeled cart that was movable by hand or lift truck, and was stackable as well. Instead of the previous time-consuming process of manually hand loading individual long cartons of product on trucks, they could now use a fork lift truck with a boom attachment to load the carts of bulk (uncartoned) product directly onto shipping trucks. The manufacturer also saved money by eliminating unnecessary cartoning materials. Likewise, at the customer's site, the carts could be quickly offloaded from the delivery truck, saving a significant amount of labor and handling of dunnage (trash).

The customers were supposed to remove the product, knock down the carts for compact nesting, and then return them. However, the customers liked the stackable carts so much they did not remove the product immediately, but instead used the stackable carts for their own storage of parts at the beginning of their fabrication processes. They would only pull a cart out of service when it was nearly empty and another full one was available to replace the empty one. When the manufacturer complained about the hoarding of carts, the customers essentially dictated that unless they were allowed to keep them, they would purchase their product needs from another supplier. The stackable, wheeled carts cost more than $900 each to fabricate and the manufacturer was stuck with a perpetual cart inventory at suppliers, valued at more than $1 million. To add insult to injury, subsequent field visits disclosed that some of the customers were even storing product from several of the manufacturer's competitors in the carts. Again, one must be careful to avoid traps such as the one cited when implementing a returnable container policy. At the very least, a strongly worded pricing or lease arrangement with the customers for holding returnable containers should be instituted before implementing such a program.

Effect of Unit Load Size on Manufacturing Cycle Time

The size of the handling unit or batch can have a large impact on shop cycle time and speed of delivery. Most companies using a pull type of scheduling system will try to design their operations with the smallest size batch or unit load possible. Companies operating with a push type of scheduling system will opt to use large batches (that are consistent with their inventory goals). Of course, in some operations, the existing equipment or process capabilities may determine the optimum batch size. See "The Effects of Unit Load and Container Configuration" of this chapter. When considering small batch sizes, the reader needs to determine whether there is a direct, dependent link between all operations. For example, it does little good to convert or plan an operation as single piece flow if the parts must be manually queued at large batch processing points such as heat treating, electroplating, or batch washing.

The important considerations are:

- The customer's order characteristics, for example, delivery lead time, quantities, shipping package size and configuration, expected variances in ordering patterns.
- The sequential routings required in the shop.
- The cycle time of equipment used in the build process.
- The capacity of each piece of processing equipment used in the build process.
- The bottleneck operations in the manufacturing processes.
- The size and configuration of raw material packages and work-in-process containers.
- The material handling equipment to be used for transporting equipment between work centers and throughout the plant.
- The staging space allowed, which is usually measured as a function of time. (For example, one hour of work-in-process [WIP] storage allowed before a workstation. The amount of material is converted to a floor space requirement.)
- Inventory objectives, including inventory turn goals.

If we are promising 24-hour delivery of custom orders (with no WIP or finished parts inventory), the batch sizes of our processes and our material handling container transfers must be small enough to meet this objective. For example, if only one of the operations in a multistep process takes, say, five minutes and we have a batch size of 500 parts, it will take much more than 24 hours just to get a total batch through that one operation, let alone the other operations that may be required. This will be the case if all material transfers are in a batch mode (as opposed to a continuous transfer mode). Most quick-response, Just-in-Time order systems will be designed for the smallest possible unit load for handling.

Changes in work-in-process inventories can have a significant impact on a company's operations and financial performance. In most cases, if a company can reduce its inventories, it can free up investment capital and reduce the financing and handling costs associated with the inventory. In addition to the operational costs required to house and handle inventory, there is also an opportunity cost that is lost. The money tied up in inventory cannot be used for capital investment. If the money could be freed up, it would allow the company to invest in capital improvements. Before one can get a capital project approved, a payback hurdle rate that the project must surpass has to be calculated. This is the percentage return on investment (ROI) below which the company will not approve the project. Most companies require an ROI of 25% or more before they will invest in a capital improvement project. That payback hurdle rate forms a large portion of the real cost of carrying inventories. This forces the company to take money from someplace else at the imputed penalty cost of the ROI rate.

Most progressive companies will add the handling and storage costs to this ROI figure to develop their total inventory carrying costs. Without a detailed analysis, the total cost of carrying inventories should be approximated at 30–35% (25% opportunity cost added to an estimated 5–10% storage and handling cost). A generally accepted figure to use for most companies is one-third or 33%. That is, the annual cost of carrying inventory is approximately 33% of the inventory's cost.

Let us look at an example of the assembly of a high-tech medical product with an in-plant average cost of $500. Figure 2-23 shows a "before" layout of the assembly operation. If we assume each incoming and outgoing container is (on average) half full, we will have a total inventory of 114 units. If we multiply that by the cost, the inventory value for this particular proposed layout is $500 × 114 units = $57,000.

If we change the layout to the one shown in Fig. 2-24 (and thereby increase the cycle time), we will get an inventory reduction of 68

CHAPTER 2   MATERIAL HANDLING ANALYSIS

units. The new layout will give us an inventory value of $34,000. We will therefore have freed up $23,000, which can be used for a one-time capital investment elsewhere in the company. (Obviously the cost of making the change also must be considered.) We have also reduced our ongoing inventory carrying costs. If we use the 33% figure previously discussed, we will incur an imputed ongoing annual savings of $0.33 \times (\$57,000 - \$34,000) = \$7,590$.

The changed layout and cycle time also allow a tremendous increase in efficiency and productivity. The goal here was to eventually move to single piece flow. With 10% overtime, the new layout with four people will produce the same amount of units as the "before" layout with 10 people. Overall efficiency and productivity are improved dramatically with the new layout. This is principally a result of the elimination of hand pulls and pushes, unnecessary paces, and other nonvalue-added activities, and the implementation of mutual assistance between operators. This is required to balance the work effort.

One must keep in mind, however, that reducing the inbound and outbound container size as shown in the example will have an increasing effect on indirect material handling costs. Even though we will save some of these costs by putting the input location close to the output location, as shown in the "after" figure, we will need to double the number of trips to and from the area. These increased costs also must be taken into account in calculating the effects of smaller unit loads.

In a manufacturing environment with constantly changing set-ups and model variations, the unit container size used can be very important. Figure 2-25 shows the potential effect of container size or handling increment on lot cycle times for various lot quantities. In all cases, we assume there is a transfer to the next operation only when the handling container is full.

ANALYZING PLANT LAYOUT

Physical changes to the process will require modifications of plant layout. There are several systems available to facilitate that process and many good texts that address facility planning. The objective is to develop a continuous flow of material with limited cross-overs and backflow. There are no fixed rules, only compromises.

Since the primary objective is to consider alternatives, then block layouts are effective tools. These will help the person visualize major flows and the general organization. Block diagrams begin with a description of each function and a table showing the importance of relationships between functions. The analysis proceeds with a system determination of moves (direct, channel, or central), the transportation units, and methods for movement. Since the flows of materials are not consistent and will range in size and unit configuration, there will be a number of alternatives to consider. The chapter bibliography has a list of resources that describe these techniques in greater detail.

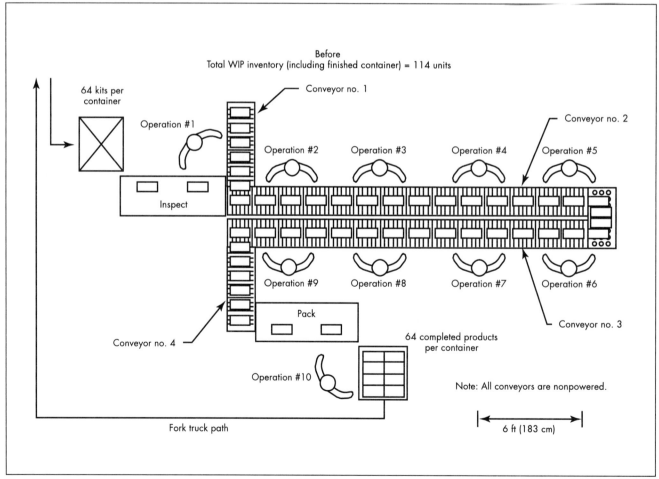

Fig. 2-23 "Before" layout of assembly operation. *(Courtesy Edward J. Phillips)*

CHAPTER 2   MATERIAL HANDLING ANALYSIS

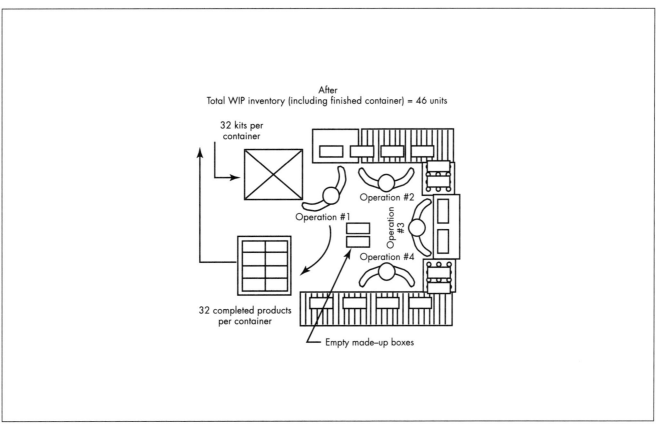

Fig. 2-24 "After" layout of assembly operation. *(Courtesy Edward J. Phillips)*

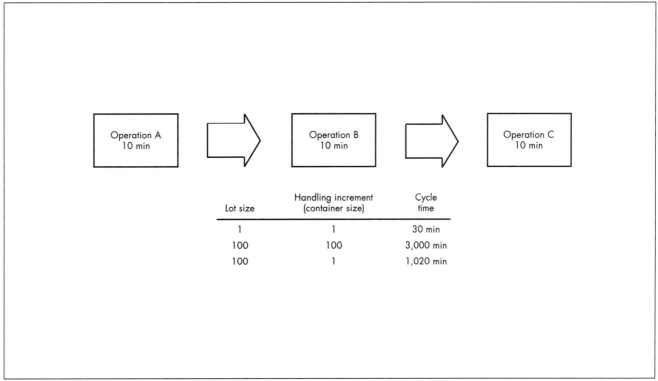

Fig. 2-25 Cycle time to get first lot output.

CHAPTER 2   MATERIAL HANDLING ANALYSIS

REQUIREMENTS DEFINITION

We constantly search for solutions to our problems. Many times, we find solutions and then begin to find specific problems that fit. These solutions come from our personal experience with a particular individual or supplier on a different problem. By extension, we will accept solutions from a known source even before taking the time to discover the real nature of the problems. A simple analogy is placing a piece of adhesive bandage on a broken arm. It may cover up the wound but does not correct the problem.

Some people consider the appearance of a solution to be more important than the problem. How often have we been in the position of defending a solution independent of the problem it addressed? As computer systems came of age, many companies bought computers because everyone else did it. The question was not "will a computer solve the problem?" but "what kind of computer should we buy?" The solution to the latter question was usually easy.

A correct diagnosis is the key to the development of a solution or set of solutions, regardless of the nature of a problem. To find the true source of the problem, we need to collect and analyze data systematically. Data come from a wide variety of sources and in a variety of forms. The analysis will consider and weigh the value of each input. Often during the analysis, key data are missing or in an unusable form. This requires going back and getting the missing data in a usable form or making strategic assumptions.

A strategic assumption allows us to bridge the gap between the known and the unknown. It begins with a statement of the missing information and then lists the assumptions. Often, once everyone knows the nature of the deficiency, someone in the organization will be able to provide the missing parts. If not, the reviewers will validate the assumptions and the analysis can proceed.

Data collection and analysis will determine how well the problems get solved. To arrive at a logical end point, one needs to follow a systematic process. This section presents a method for collecting, analyzing, and presenting data. Figures 2-26 through 2-31 show several typical questionnaires for each level of the organization.

Since we deal with both subjective and objective data, it is critical to isolate one from the other. Both are necessary and important, so it would be foolish to throw away data just because they are opinions. Data presented as objective may simply be a formal way of presenting subjective information. Personal computers make it easy to make neat, convincing reports that appear to document reality. Even the most sophisticated companies generate reports by the ton which have little real meaning and value.

For example, an inventory report should report what is physically on the shelves, but how much of it is real and useful? Often, the real relationship is not seen between production, sales, and inventory. Items will sit on the shelf, products will get returned, items damaged or disappear, but none of this will be reconciled until a physical count is taken. How management views the inventory will often determine how and what gets reported.

Another area requiring special consideration is the accounting of all material flowing into and from workstations or cells. The laws of energy and material conservation still hold. That simply means that energy produces either heat or work, and material in equals material out.

Reporting systems may not track material and energy flows to the individual work centers. A flow model will permit tracking material throughout the operation. This model will consider what goes into each process and what comes out. The forms of the input and output will be significantly different, but in all cases, input will equal output. Identification of these flows is important to the clarification of the overall process.

KEY CONSIDERATIONS

Although the process is the fundamental concern, beyond the process are needs in such areas as safety, security, regulations, work rules, and environmental considerations. Keeping these in mind during the requirements definition will help achieve success in the manufacturing process. A review of the key considerations will permit focusing our efforts on the important information and material flows later in the process.

The manufacturing process is the major consideration. The ultimate goal is to create and run the process as efficiently as possible. Effectively dealing with the flow of information and material can reduce the total cost of production. Processes achieve success by correctly using information to monitor and control each activity during operation, not after. The definition of that process is the primary objective.

The IDEF process model (Fig. 2-32) is a hierarchical method of defining the manufacturing process that allows complete description in as much detail as necessary (IDEF was developed under the Air Force Program for Integrated Computer-Aided Manufacturing [ICAM]. The acronym IDEF comes from "ICAM definition." IDEF produces a model structure to represent the function of a manufacturing system). There are five elements in the model: the process or function, inputs, outputs, resources, and controls. As we expand each process, we gain additional detail in terms of all elements.

Processes can be described as operations or functions that transform. Thinking about processes in terms of transforming shape, configuration, size, or state will allow sorting those operations that add value from the rest. For example, a milling machine operation transforms a piece of material into a defined shape. According to the IDEF process model, the process inputs are the raw material, the program to drive the machine, a work order, and energy. Resources are the operator, machine, tools, fixtures, cooling fluid, maintenance, and transportation. Controls are the physical machine control limitations, machine capacity, and work rules. The outputs are the finished parts, scrap, and data about product quantity and quality.

Safety

Safety concerns require us to ensure that operations do not expose operators to hazardous conditions. We usually think about the danger of physical harm that often results from boring, monotonous operations. Protecting operators from exposure to hazards is one part of ensuring safety in such operations. However, effectively using operator intelligence is far more important to safety than physical guards. An engaged operator will pay attention to the details important to safe operation of the equipment.

Associated with safety is the issue of ergonomics. Repetitive operator activities require careful consideration, and data collection may therefore include a review of specific physical activities. It is not usually necessary to examine all physical activities. However, activities requiring lifting, twisting, and frequent precise positioning should receive specific attention. There are many sources of information about good ergonomic practices. A general review of one or more of these before beginning data collection is sufficient to develop an awareness (see Chapter 7).

Security

What is security and how does it apply? Protection of company assets is one part of the security issue. This may involve controlling access and tracking tools and equipment. Security also applies to information and material flow. Knowing who is operating specific

ORDER PICKING QUESTIONNAIRE

Company: _____Date:_____
Name: _____Title:_____
Address: _____
_____
City: _____State:_____Zip:_____
Phone: (_____)_____Ext:_____Fax:_____
Products:_____

If you have multiple zones or areas for different product lines, complete the following information for each area.

Area:_____

Labor Information	Normal	Peak
Number of shifts per day:	_____	_____
Hours per shift:	_____	_____
Days per week:	_____	_____
Number of persons per shift		
Picking:	_____	_____
Checking:	_____	_____
Packing:	_____	_____
Replenishing:	_____	_____
Consolidating (or general order preparation):	_____	_____

Order Information	Case Pick		Unit Pick	
	Average	Peak	Average	Peak
Number of lines per day:	_____	_____	_____	_____
Number of units (pieces) per day:	_____	_____	_____	_____
Number of orders per day:	_____	_____	_____	_____
Number of cases shipped per day:	_____	_____	_____	_____

SKU Usage	Case	Unit
Total number of stock-keeping units (SKUs):	_____	_____
Number of SKUs for broken case picking:	_____	_____
Number of SKUs for automated picking (est.):	_____	_____
Number of SKUs filling 80% of orders:	_____	_____
SKUs in high velocity forward pick area:	_____	_____

Productivity	Case Pick		Unit Pick	
	Average	Peak	Average	Peak
Current activity rates (lines per person/h)				
Pick:	_____	_____	_____	_____
Check:	_____	_____	_____	_____
Pack:	_____	_____	_____	_____
Replenishment:	_____	_____	_____	_____
Percent lines in error (at checker):	_____	_____	_____	_____
Percent orders with error (at checker):	_____	_____	_____	_____
Percent of orders shipped with errors:	_____	_____	_____	_____

Operating Cost

Straight time wage rate: $_____per h
Fringe benefits factor (percentage):   _____%
Shift premium: $_____per h
Overtime premium: $_____per h
Typical percentage overtime used: _____%
Material cost per order: $_____
Other direct cost per order: $_____
   Describe:_____
Other indirect cost per order: $_____
   Describe:_____
Cost to correct one shipped error: $_____

Fig. 2-26 Order picking questionnaire. *(Courtesy W. M. Angell & Associates)*

CHAPTER 2   MATERIAL HANDLING ANALYSIS

Facility

Picking area: _____ ft²
    Equipment: _____

Checking area: _____ ft²
    Equipment: _____

Packing area: _____ ft²
    Equipment: _____

Shipping area: _____ ft²
    Equipment: _____

Reserve storage: _____ ft²
    Equipment: _____

Plans for expansion or consolidation
    Describe:_____
    _____
    _____
    _____
    _____
    _____

Provide a sketch of the facility with dimensions.

General

Planned growth in number of SKUs:	_____% per year	
Planned growth in orders:	_____% per year	
Current order turnaround:	_____hours	
Are SKUs bar-coded?	[ ] YES	[ ] NO
Code:	_____	
Are cases bar-coded?	[ ] YES	[ ] NO
Code:	_____	
Are multi-packs identified by separate SKU numbers?	[ ] YES	[ ] NO
Are shipping containers bar-coded?	[ ] YES	[ ] NO
Code:	_____	
Do your shipping labels conform to any standard?	[ ] YES	[ ] NO
Identify standard:	_____	
Are you using electronic data interchange (EDI)?	[ ] YES	[ ] NO
Number of EDI customers:	_____	
Number of EDI suppliers:	_____	
Does your operation require that items are:		
Packed in an orderly manner?	[ ] YES	[ ] NO
Randomly packed with packing material added?	[ ] YES	[ ] NO
Individually labeled during the picking process?	[ ] YES	[ ] NO
Identified and controlled by lot or serial number?	[ ] YES	[ ] NO

What is the make and model number of your host computer?
_____

Other

Describe your current picking operation (for example, pick and pack, batch pick, zone pick, etc.):
_____
_____
_____

Describe your requirements for sequencing, sorting, and grouping of products or orders:
_____
_____

Product data (history file): provide an average month's data for products to be handled. Include: product (SKU) number, product description, quantity used, storage location(s), cost per item, unit and size of issue unit (product code or length, width, height).

Order data (order file): provide four to 10 individual days of orders that reflect normal usage. Each day will include: order number, product numbers, quantity of each product, and shipping container size. If orders are cyclical, provide weekly or monthly summaries depending on the cycle. It may be necessary to look at complete raw data for a period if the order swings are substantial.

Fig. 2-26 (cont.) Order picking questionnaire.

CHAPTER 2   MATERIAL HANDLING ANALYSIS

REQUIREMENTS DEFINITION QUESTIONNAIRE

Material Handling Study
Task 1 Initial Investigation

Objective: Build a solid information base about people, processes, and plans.
Project: Improve material flow within the facility.

Major subtasks:

1. Task: define goals and information needs—discussion about tasks.

2. Task: top level discussions to establish parameters and expectations—individual interview questionnaire.

3. Task: organization—general questions, organization current and future.

4. Task: define the processes, material, and information flow—general questions, IDEF model development.

5. Task: product definitions—current and future.

6. Task: complete initial investigation.

Fig. 2-27 Requirements definition questionnaire, Task 1—initial investigation. *(Courtesy W. M. Angell & Associates)*

pieces of equipment not only helps with security, it also permits tracking problems associated with specific people. This permits correction of the problem through training.

Rules and Regulations

Many industries must follow extensive regulations imposed by local, state, and federal agencies like the U.S. Environmental Protection Agency (EPA) and the Occupational Safety and Health Administration (OSHA). These affect processes, waste processing and disposal, emissions, and a wide variety of supporting activities. Understanding how the regulations apply to the specific situation is the critical issue. This is a factor in the design of new processes or rework of existing processes.

Shops often have specific work rules regulating who can do what. This becomes a factor if the facility problems require a redesign. The layout, work cells, and work flows may require discussions and renegotiations before they can change. It is important to know this before starting with the requirements definition.

For most operations, a tabulation of environmental requirements is usually all that is necessary. The environment becomes a factor when product stability, accuracy, and susceptibility are important. Special humidity or temperature requirements of equipment and processes become part of the general requirements.

DATA COLLECTION

Data collection is the cornerstone of the requirements definition. It begins with a plan and scope of effort. The scope describes the range of the project and puts boundaries on the effort. It also describes the objectives of the program. A good plan includes the tasks to be accomplished and a schedule. The plan will also outline the probable sources of data. These sources are existing documentation, new reports generated from the existing data, and, most important, the people who are part of the existing process. Using the IDEF model as the skeleton will improve the process and provide a way to measure progress.

Existing reports usually describe the operation as management wishes it to be seen. Determining whether they properly reflect what is happening may require some detective work. The most important

reports are those which detail production labor, raw material receipts, finished goods shipments, and inventory. These are the foundation of the financial reports, so they are usually fairly accurate. In addition, the production planning reports provide insight into the sales and marketing goals. Use this information to fill in the inputs and outputs of each process and identify the resources.

Detailed scheduling plans and reports give us a way to cross-check the actual output of each process. Since scheduling usually requires a knowledge of the processes, the scheduling people provide a degree of insight into the process not otherwise available. Their data checks the processes described in the IDEF diagram. The observation of processes is a cross-check of the scheduling process.

An analysis of the shipment reports gives us valuable information about the products. From these reports, we can determine the total number of active products. The analysis should cover orders at least for a full year, on a monthly basis. Additional year-end summaries for the previous three years may give some historical perspective. This will also permit estimating the number of additions and deletions that normally occur during a year.

Getting the order data in a magnetic format will make manipulation fairly easy. The data can then be loaded into a personal computer (PC) with a database. The database allows us to perform sorts and sums according to different criteria. The goal is to develop a profile of product usage which will go into the model. Often the formats of the data are not compatible, so some simple translations are necessary. Very large ASCII-delimited files can be imported into a database one block at a time (ASCII is the American National Standard Code for Information Interchange).

The order reports will produce an order and product distribution by reporting period. Usually, monthly reports are sufficient. However, in some industries, demand changes dramatically during a month, so weekly and sometimes daily reports are necessary to examine the monthly detail. The product distribution will show the demand by reporting period for each product. People often automatically assume the 80:20 rule; that is, 20% of the product produces 80% of the orders. Unless there is a positive check, making this assumption can be risky. In addition, knowing the monthly or weekly flow provides valuable data about resource requirements.

CHAPTER 2   MATERIAL HANDLING ANALYSIS

REQUIREMENTS DEFINITION QUESTIONNAIRE

Individual Interview Questionnaire #1
(Management)

1. What is your position and role in the project?
    *   Job description:_____
    *   Organization:_____
    *   How does your department/organization support the facility?_____

2. What are your goals for the project?
    *   Short term—facility/your department:_____
    *   Medium term—facility/your deparment: _____
    *   Long term—facility/your department:_____

3. What are the business objectives of the facility?
    *   Short term:_____
    *   Medium term: _____
    *   Long term:_____

4. What changes will occur at the facility?
    a) How will your operation change?_____
    b) What changes do you see in other areas?_____
    c) Will the business change as the result of facility changes?_____

5. What are the major obstacles to change in the facility?_____

6. What are your major concerns in the following areas?
    a) Incoming materials/receiving:_____
    b) Inspection:_____
    c) Raw material
       *   Handling (operations and mechanisms):_____
       *   Transportation (type, units transported, routing):_____
       *   Control (what type, how, mechanisms):_____
    d) Work-in-process (WIP)
       *   Handling (operations and mechanisms):_____
       *   Transportation (type, units transported, routing):_____
       *   Control (what type, how, mechanisms):_____
    e) Finished goods
       *   Handling (operations and mechanisms):_____
       *   Transportation (type, units transported, routing):_____
       *   Control (what type, how, mechanisms):_____
    f) Storage (supplies, raw material, WIP, finished goods):_____
    g) Shipping:_____
    h) Quality control:_____
    i) Maintenance:_____
    j) Information services:_____
    k) Production planning and control:_____

Fig. 2-28 Requirements definition questionnaire for management. *(Courtesy W. M. Angell & Associates)*

REQUIREMENTS DEFINITION QUESTIONNAIRE

Individual Interview Questionnaire #2
(Supervisors and Workers)

1. What is your position and role in the project?
   - Job description:_____
   - Organization:_____
   - How does your department/organization support the facility?_____

2. What are your goals for the project?
   - Short term—facility/your department:_____
   - Medium term—facility/your department:_____
   - Long term—facility/your department:_____

3. What is your specific area of responsibility?_____

4. How can your operation change to become more efficient?_____

5. What opportunities for change do you see in other areas?_____

6. What are the major obstacles to changes in your operation?_____

7. What are your major concerns?
   - Handling:_____
   - Transportation:_____
   - Storage:_____
   - Control:_____

Specifically cover each of the following areas.
   - Incoming materials/receiving:_____
   - Inspection:_____
   - Raw material (roll stock):_____
   - Work-in-process (WIP) (rolls):_____
   - Finished goods (rolls, sheets):_____
   - Storage (supplies, raw material, WIP, finished goods):_____
   - Shipping (products, waste, recycle):_____
   - Quality control:_____
   - Maintenance:_____
   - Information services:_____
   - Production planning and control:_____
   - Product engineering:_____

Fig. 2-29 Requirements definition questionnaire for supervisors and workers. *(Courtesy W. M. Angell & Associates)*

CHAPTER 2   MATERIAL HANDLING ANALYSIS

REQUIREMENTS DEFINITION QUESTIONNAIRE
General Questions—Products
(Product Manager, Purchasing)

1. Raw material
   a) Types and sizes (current, projected):_____
   b) Annual volume by types:_____

2. WIP—combination matrix
   a) Run size by product (minimum, maximum, average):_____
   b) Start-up time by products:_____
   c) Special conditions by product:_____

3. Product matrix
   a) Sizes:_____
   b) Volume by size:_____
   c) Product growth forecast:_____

4. Packaging requirements by product
   a) Unit packaging:_____
   b) Shipping units (pallet, unit):_____
   c) Destinations by product:_____
   d) Carrier (truck load, < truck load, parcels, other): _____

5. Planning by product
   a) Planning schedule:_____
   b) Product production cycle:_____
   c) Product lag time (maximum and minimum time from production order to shipment):_____

Fig. 2-30 Requirements definition questionnaire for products. *(Courtesy W. M. Angell & Associates)*

REQUIREMENTS DEFINITION QUESTIONNAIRE
General Questions—System Flows
Using the definitions in the figure for the IDEF model, for each major process:

1. Define the major processes. Begin with the following.
   a) Receiving:_____
   b) Raw material storage:_____
   c) Process 1:_____
   d) Process 2:_____
   e) Process 3:_____
   f) Process 4:_____
   g) Packaging:_____
   h) Finished goods storage:_____
   i) Shipping:_____

2. What are the inputs to each process (description and rate)?
   a) Material:_____
   b) Information:_____

3. What are the outputs of each process (description and rate)?
   a) Material:_____
   b) Information:_____

4. What resources are necessary to perform the process?
   a) Equipment—maximum capacity, normal rates:_____
   b) People:_____
   c) Facility:_____

5. What are the controls?
   a) General facility:_____
   b) Process-specific:_____

6. Organization structure
   a) Current:_____
   b) Future:_____

Fig. 2-31 Requirements definition questionnaire for system flows. *(Courtesy W. M. Angell & Associates)*

CHAPTER 2   MATERIAL HANDLING ANALYSIS

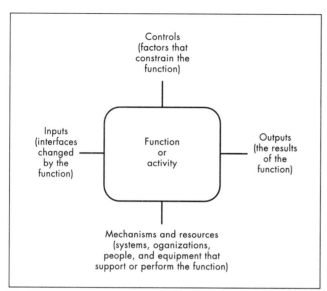

Fig. 2-32 The IDEF model. *(Courtesy W. M. Angell & Associates)*

An inventory report is usually available. This will almost always show the on-hand inventory by location. More sophisticated facilities will have an inventory usage history. This is generally a monthly report. It will show aging inventory, and when compared with the annual usage report, it will show excess inventory. We are looking for practical ways to minimize inventory and make inventory management more efficient.

Product mix is critical to the setup and operation of a manufacturing facility. Each product has a set of operations process charts, usually available from the scheduling people. From the product and order distribution reports, we can examine alternative ways to produce similar products consistent with the product demand.

Families of product have similar characteristics, at least from a manufacturing viewpoint. Demand is not usually such that a production run will consist entirely of members of the same family and as a result, have reduced setup and changeover time. However, it is important to identify patterns that can improve setup time and raw material usage.

Depending on the products and the facility, different products will take different routes through production. The proper blend or mix of products depends on machine capability, setup time, and material availability. To make reasonable decisions, it is necessary to consider each product separately. The data collection should develop information which will permit creation of a process matrix.

Consideration of the flow into and out of each manufacturing process is another way of looking at capacity. While machine capacities are usually quite specific, they typically underestimate flow time. The complete flow includes steps leading to and from the machine. A comparison of actual flow and theoretical capacity provides yet another benchmark for evaluation.

Another part of the flow is information. To start an operation, information to a process tells the operator what, when, and how. During the operation, additional data may change the conditions or modify the process. Data collection provides the tools to measure the output quantity and quality. The form of the information flow is important and is part of the data collected.

Identifying the data flows is not always easy. The first step is to determine what data are necessary for each operation. What is the form, for example, written work orders or electronic transfer to the local controller? The next step is to learn what information is avail-

able during the operation. What measurements are manually or automatically performed? How are they used to control the operation?

Moving material and information from one operation to another requires planning and coordination. Quantifying that data and putting it into a usable form is the challenge for the data collection activity. At each step in an operation, decisions must be made about where to go next. The availability of information to make those decisions is critical. The data collection effort should be looking for the nature of the real problem.

Data collection must also include information on the actual load configurations. This may mean going to the floor and actually measuring loads coming out of each operation. Measuring and selecting loads is discussed in this chapter in "Analyzing Load Size."

A matrix of machine and equipment capacities will help describe the operation. This information is usually available from the equipment manufacturer. In many facilities, work cell development activities have done a good job of quantifying the capacity.

FLOW ANALYSIS

The flow analysis will make use of the data collected. There are several ways to show material flows. The complexity of the process has a major impact on the method. An overly simple flow chart may fail to properly identify problems. At the other extreme, a highly complex flow model may require so much time that it loses its value.

There are several PC software programs available to make the charting or modeling task easier. Since flows tend to change often, it is convenient to simply update the computer image. If the charting or modeling technique is simple enough, a set of hand-drawn charts may satisfy the needs of the project.

Examples of flow models are classical flow diagrams, from–to charts, and the IDEF model. All have certain strengths, but the choice really depends on the preference of those describing the process. The objective is to develop a model that describes the complete operation. It must be in sufficient detail to show the problems and not so complex that it obscures the deficiencies.

Information flows are usually more difficult to measure and analyze. For this function, we may adopt the same charting methods often used by software people. Several processes include common flow charts. These are effective for the specific purpose but are difficult to blend with material flows.

Many manufacturing operations have simple direct-line operations. In these situations, products go through the same steps. Minor changes at each workstation easily handle product changes. This is the exception; because most manufacturing operations produce a wide variety of products with complex and overlapping paths. The flow in these situations is best understood on a machine basis.

For most operations, an analysis tool combining material and information flows provides the best information. A modified IDEF model performs this function well. As a hierarchical model, processes can expand to the level of detail necessary. The modification is to show material flows below the input and output arrows and the information above the arrows. The data collected can be tabulated with the IDEF model.

Determining what is flowing often depends on the unit of measure. While the easiest way to measure is usually on a unit basis, the net flow often requires consideration of the load configuration. Discussion of the load size is important because it emphasizes the importance of batch or load size. Using an equivalent unit load analysis also helps simplify the process.

The from–to chart is especially useful for complex operations. This will describe how material physically moves through the manufacturing facility. It underscores the importance of properly measuring the actual throughput of each step in the operation.

CHAPTER 2   MATERIAL HANDLING ANALYSIS

The IDEF diagram allows us to quantify flows into and from individual processes. In addition, the process allows us to match information flowing into and from the operation. The combination of information and material flow gives us critical data about how the process is being controlled.

DATA ANALYSIS

Data analysis is the keystone of the requirements definition process. Proper data are necessary to evaluate any operation. Getting the right data from a manufacturing operation is often difficult. The main objective of data collection is to determine corporate and facility goals and relate them to what is actually happening. Different people in the organization will provide information about different aspects of the operation.

Understanding that each individual has a unique contribution to the organization allows us to target specific groups to get specific types of information. The top levels will develop the business objectives, internal problems, and long-range plans. They are also important to establishing the scope of the effort.

Other levels of the organization provide specific knowledge about how the facility is operating. General management will describe the operation in terms presented by the reporting system. They will use the corporate goals and reported results to develop a description of the operation. Their understanding of how the workers achieve the results is sometimes limited. The objectives of this group may be significantly different from those of the people doing the actual work.

Supervisors and workers focus on getting prescribed tasks done. Their description will focus on specific tasks required to do the work. Because there are often unrelated goals of supporting groups, it is not unusual to find activities that actually fight each other when they should complement each other.

In some companies, there are often two organizations: one represented by the top levels of management and the formal organization chart, and the other, an informal organization that actually gets the job done. When these two organizations diverge, the informal organization gets product out the door. The formal organization spends most of the time trying to figure out what is going on by using formal reporting.

Reports describe the status of the organization in terms defined by the corporation and top management. They do not address how the results were achieved. It is for this reason that we must understand the organization and how everyone functions. This allows us to read and understand the formal reports.

The normal reporting system does not provide information relating directly to the true material flow. For this reason, it is usually necessary to combine information from several reports.

Since we start the data analysis with at least the first two levels of the IDEF diagram filled in, we have a benchmark. The diagram provides an opportunity to interview individuals at different levels in the organization. Using a specific set of questions tailored to the project, we define the products, corporate and individual goals, processes, and material and information flows.

During this definition process, we will learn about the planning and reporting structure. Specific reports and reporting systems will give us a detailed understanding of what is going on in the organization. They will allow completion of the detail elements in the IDEF diagram and associate throughput quantities with each process.

Just as important, however, is what the reports do not tell us. Such things as waste, scrap, rework, and excess inventory usually do not appear on any formal reports. If they do, the numbers generally reflect what management expects rather than actual numbers. However, by considering total raw material input and total finished goods shipped to customers, we can calculate scrap and waste. Other reports, often informal, will provide labor hours for rework. If there is a specific group doing rework, it is usually possible to follow additional material flows into the process.

DOCUMENT UNDERSTANDING

One of the most critical activities in the requirements definition process is preparing the documentation. While there are many ways to establish requirements, all have a common thread: they rely on documentation. By documenting what we learn as we progress through analysis, we are in a position to analyze the results objectively instead of subjectively, as we do when we guess about the results of an analysis before thoroughly reviewing the situation.

The outline in Fig. 2-33 is an example of a document structure. The outline includes the major categories that require consideration in the analysis. While some will seem inappropriate to the task at hand, experience shows addressing all categories produces the best results. It leaves little to abstract, subjective consideration. Following the outline also ensures that the critical information is in a form that everyone can understand.

The documentation and analysis process is an iterative one. That means the document lives for the duration of the analysis. An effective approach is to assign an individual the coordination responsibility, including collecting data and responding to questions. To do this, the individual must follow a highly structured set of activities. If a person with the skills and objectivity necessary is available for this assignment, that person must be given complete access to all data and people in the organization.

Often, the best internal person is already overloaded. Paying for the services of an outsider with the appropriate skills may be preferable to reassigning or adding to the responsibilities of an internal person and the effects such action would have on the organization. An outsider will also bring additional perspective. Furthermore, the person will relieve the organization of the tasks of organizing and producing documents, analyzing the data, and suggesting alternatives. An outside, objective observer is also able to avoid many of the political problems. Presenting information that challenges the status quo without offending is often difficult for an insider.

The process begins with the development of a simple two- or three-level model of the operation. With the model used as a reference, additional data build until the "as-is" operation is complete. The model usually does not threaten people, and it helps bring them into a discussion of what they contribute to the organization. The type of information individuals offer depends on their job and often their history with the organization.

In the following paragraphs, we will discuss the major headings of the outline. The information required for each topic will depend on the project. However, "Business/management objectives" and "Organization" are important for all projects. "Operating environment" usually establishes the physical conditions. The remaining topics are the most project-dependent.

"Business/management objectives" begins with the organization's mission statement. Specific goals should exist for the business unit involved with the project. If no mission statement is available, it will be necessary for top management to establish one. The business goals will also describe the relationship of the organization with its customers and suppliers.

Although many organizations lack a basic mission statement, by starting to answer questions about such a statement, the members of the organization can begin to consider the reason for their existence. By the time the requirements definition is complete, it should include this key statement of purpose. It will permit a valid consideration of alternative solutions to specific problems discovered during the process.

CHAPTER 2   MATERIAL HANDLING ANALYSIS

1. Business/management objectives
   a. Statement of company policy
   b. Business goals
   c. Unique goals/objectives for departments or divisions
   d. Customers
   e. Suppliers

2. Organization
   a. Structure
   b. Purpose
   c. Who, what
   d. Review process—who, what

3. User and management functions
   a. Who, what, when for each function
   b. Description of operating functions (not organization)
   c. Management—typical
      • Accounting
      • Marketing
      • Business development
      • Planning
      • Management information systems (MIS)
      • Quality
      • Engineering
      • Purchasing
   d. Operating—typical
      • Production control
      • Quality control
      • Receiving
      • Inventory
      • Warehouse (raw, work-in-process)
      • Line, cell, and functional departments (all)
      • Warehouse (finished work)
      • Shipping
      • Traffic

4. Operating environment
   a. Geographic
   b. Physical facilities
      • Office
      • Production
      • Storage
      • Shipping/receiving
   c. Computer systems
      • MIS enterprise
      • Production control
      • Inventory control
      • Shop floor control
      • Networks
   d. People
      • Formal organization
      • Informal organization
      • Key personnel

5. Major input and output
   a. Material flow
      • Receiving
      • Storage
      • Processing (each step)
      • Storage
      • Shipping
   b. Information flow
      • Planning
      • Purchasing
      • Receiving
      • Processing (each step)
      • Inventory
      • Shipping
      • Labor
      • Equipment use

6. Major processing activities
   a. Each major process
   b. Process descriptions—how, when
   c. Resources—who, what
   d. Measurements
   e. Controls

7. Interface requirements
   a. Customer
   b. Supplier
   c. Internal

Fig. 2-33 Outline of requirements definition document. *(Courtesy W. M. Angell & Associates)*

While the mission statement is the backbone for achieving goals, the strategic plans are the tools. Developing strategic plans is another major purpose of this section of the document. The strategic plans will address each area under consideration with a specific set of tasks designed to support the overall goals of the organization. These plans will address the relationship with customers and suppliers in terms of the expected results. They will also address specific goals and plans of each department or division of the company.

"Organization" documents the formal structure of the company. A well-run company will establish a structure for accomplishing the goals. Each part of the structure will be briefly described as to its purpose, the resources available, and the processes required to accomplish its purpose. For many small companies, this section will be only a few paragraphs. However, larger companies require more detail. It is important to document what actually exists even if it means identifying duplication of effort.

"User and management functions" is clearly the most complex part of the documentation task. It lists some organizational and operational functions but is not intended to be comprehensive. User functions are those that produce the products and services. Management functions are the supervisory activities. By documenting these functions separately, activities are identified which are at cross-purposes. For each function we will develop descriptions of the function, the resources, and the relationships with other functions.

The degree of detail in this section depends on the scope of the project. If the organization is undergoing a total review, then descriptions of each operating activity are necessary. At the other extreme, consideration of a single cell or group of activities will require discussion of only the involved functions. For limited projects, it is valuable to address activities which act as customers and suppliers to the activity under review. This applies even if the activity is an external supplier or customer.

CHAPTER 2   MATERIAL HANDLING ANALYSIS

"Operating environment" is often considered too obvious to warrant much effort. The geographical and physical aspects of the facility, including the computer systems, are usually easy to identify and document. Nevertheless, it is important to properly document them so that everyone understands. If there are special temperature or environmental requirements for the process, this is the place to describe them.

Computer systems are becoming more common and complex. If the project goal includes modernizing all or parts of the computer systems, it is critical to establish the current baseline. A statement in the "Business/management objectives" section will describe the goals and expected results of the upgrade.

In regard to the "People" subsection, all organizations have some type of formal organization; this is described in number two of the outline. However, many companies also have an informal organization which solves problems and delivers the products and services. It is not unusual to find one or two individuals who "make things happen." Problems occur when this informal organization becomes pervasive or operates without the full understanding of management.

Documenting the informal organization requires care. We neither want to blow the whistle nor arbitrarily cause the informal function to go away. It needs to be understood so that the needs it satisfies can be effectively addressed. This is one area most effectively handled by an outsider. The internal team can develop solutions once the problems are understood.

"Major input and output" describes both material and information flows. The flow of material and information in an organization closely parallels that in the human body—as long as all major inputs and outputs are in balance, the system operates well. Too often projects consider only material flow because it is thought that is where the problems lie. In reality, information and material flows must closely coordinate for an effective operation.

Building the IDEF model is an easy way to develop an understanding of both material and information flows. We build the model by examining the requirements of each process in terms of information needs and the materials it transforms. The output of a process will be the transformed material and scrap with information about the results. The information out may also include data about quality and resource usage.

The description of the major processing activities in number six supports the input and output descriptions. By describing the processes in terms of transformations of materials or information, we may find multiple combined activities. This is typical of a manufacturing cell. By starting with a simple description of the basic process, we can later break it down into components as necessary. If there is no need to expand a combined process because it is operating efficiently, we remain at the basic level.

The process descriptions should include a discussion of measurements and controls. Controls with proper measurements can regulate rate, quality, and function. The documentation will describe existing operations. For processes that handle many different products, it is important to show how the controls and setup change from one product to another.

"Interface requirements" is last in the documentation of the existing operation. The most easily understood interface requirements are the basic interactions with the suppliers and customers. However, these are becoming more complex because of the arrival of electronic data interchange (EDI). Even preparing to implement EDI will require careful documentation of existing interactions.

The internal interface requirements address the need to link financial systems with the various manufacturing systems. Interactions between inventory and manufacturing systems are typical. The document will describe how production transfers to inventory either as finished goods or work-in-process. Interactions between sales, shipping, and inventory systems are also important.

OPPORTUNITIES AND PROBLEMS

After completing the documentation of the existing conditions, we are in a position to list opportunities and problems. This listing does not attempt to classify or rank problems. The list will simply describe the nature of each problem and opportunity within the range of the original project. If real problems outside the original scope appear, the document will still identify them but they should not be part of the project evaluation. Before starting the evaluation, we will divide the problems by type or function.

Material handling opportunities and problems are usually the easiest to identify. When material accumulates in front of a workstation, there is some type of problem. Likewise, a workstation stopped because there is no material indicates a problem with an earlier process. The goal is to find the process or processes constraining the operation. There may be different constraints for different products.

Information flow problems may appear during the material flow analysis. An operator may wait for a machine control program to be downloaded or a work order or quality control standards to arrive. We identify the information flow problems just as we did the material flows, again listing the problems and providing a brief description of the nature of the problem or opportunity.

After identifying the main constraint, we look for reasons. Listing all possible causes will permit isolation and eventually identification of the primary cause of the constraint. The process will include an evaluation of such things as operator handling, machine processing, physical manipulation, machine setup, and availability of setup and processing information. If we find the constraint is the result of a material or information shortage, we must move to where that material or information originates.

Process problems are more difficult to identify. That is why we list problems and identify possible causes without trying to solve the problems. A process problem will show up in the quality or rate of data collected. For example, a quality problem may manifest itself as a high rejection or rework rate; additional steps may be necessary to complete the process.

The last step in the listing of problems and opportunities is putting them in a priority order. If a problem appears which is outside the described scope, it must be put aside and considered separately. This is necessary to preserve the integrity of the definition process. However, the problem may be serious enough to warrant a change in scope so that it can be considered with the other problems and opportunities. The priority of the problems and opportunities establishes the order of consideration. It also may be possible to combine or link problems. By asking a series of why and what-if questions, we often effectively expand our understanding of the operation and the true nature of the problems. There may be more links between problems than appear after the initial listing.

Collecting the data and writing the basic requirements definition may involve only a few people; however, the analysis is a team effort. The analysis process is as important as the result. It requires the best efforts of all to analyze the problems and focus on those that are most important. The process also will focus attention on the facility activities from an entirely new direction. The key result of this problem analysis and review is a prioritized list of problems.

ALTERNATIVE SOLUTIONS

The selection of alternative solutions is the next step in the process. It should start with no more than three problems from the list. The process will be to examine different ways to solve each of the

CHAPTER 2   MATERIAL HANDLING ANALYSIS

problems. Solutions should range from extremely simple to the most exotic conceivable. A simple solution may only change procedures, modify a material route, change or eliminate paperwork, change the work unit, or change schedule sequences. Complex solutions may add or change material handling equipment with the addition of a new manufacturing execution system (MES).

A range of solutions will incrementally build from the simple to the most complex. The range of solutions will stretch the conceptual envelope and provide a range of costs. The cost range permits evaluation of the return on investment. Starting simple has an advantage because the first successful projects set the tone for all future projects. This is particularly important if this is the first major change.

As solutions begin to take form, we collect data on the cost and impact on the organization. The cost model will include the system cost and the costs of equipment, installation, training and documentation, annual maintenance, and lost production (during start-up). On the positive side, we will consider the lower unit cost resulting from such benefits as lower labor, reduced raw material, and reduced scrap. In addition, there are intangible benefits from improved throughput, customer service, and market penetration. It is important to be realistic.

The financial people will have their measurements for projects. They will also provide guidance on the cost relief available for various alternatives. The intangible benefits are often difficult to quantify in enough detail to permit use in the economic analysis. If the financial people use unit cost for profit consideration, they will accept a lower overhead per unit. Improved response time reduces inventory levels and the corresponding carrying cost.

The effect of a major change in the equipment and systems is substantial. A major change in the facility management system is the most pervasive. It will affect every part of the organization, and it may take a very long time to recover costs and productivity. The cost of adding shop floor control, manufacturing execution systems, or even an enterprise execution system will be much greater than the direct cost of hardware and software. If that is a solution, everyone must fully understand the impact and life cycle cost involved.

Material handling systems address a specific set of material flow needs. Whether the need is to transfer material automatically between work cells or to and from storage, consideration of the advantages of all available mechanisms depends on many factors. Load size, units per load, handling characteristics, and time between load and unload points all play an important role. The cost of these systems has an extremely wide range. Knowing exactly the flows and load characteristics will permit selection of effective alternatives.

The data collected and written in the requirements definition document is referred to for selection and evaluation of all systems and equipment. As each problem is addressed, the requirements are checked to make certain the problem is properly understood and the solution is compatible with the environment.

Throughout the evaluation process, the emphasis must continue to be on the three levels of solutions for each problem. An effective mechanism is to challenge the team to develop the simplest solution and then work on a global solution. The simple solutions will draw out cost-and-benefit issues while the global solution will force longer range thinking. With the global solutions, it is important to continuously review the cost and benefit of each feature.

Once the simple and global solutions are in some written form, it is time to look at compromise issues. These will drive a solution or set of solutions toward the practical. During this step, we will continue to examine the costs and benefits. Since we know the upper and lower limits, these solutions tend to be very rational. The costs are usually in line with reasonable returns and the probability of success is good.

In examining alternatives, listing the problems will direct us to the most critical needs. Problems can and will range from fairly simple scheduling or tracking issues to fundamental product problems. The scheduling and tracking problems may begin with poor material flow, but are more likely the result of poor information flow. Major process constraints are often the result of a poor manufacturing design. Market-driven operations may suffer because of long setup times, lengthy design-to-production times, or a difficult product changeover.

Process Re-engineering

Process re-engineering becomes an issue when products or product components go through a series of complex operations. The material and information flow diagrams will often reveal many limited value-added steps. Time spent waiting for something to happen is a clear sign of a problem. Multiple operations requiring manual handling are also an indication of structural problems. Frequent bottlenecks at one particular station may indicate a workstation capacity problem.

When these problems are present, it is important to step back and examine the process. This examination will involve a development of a clear statement of the product objectives. Product objectives include market requirements, cost goals, and process requirements. Market and cost requirements are usually closely related. It is important to have a clear definition of the market size and percent penetration. It makes a big difference if your market potential is 100 units at $1,000 each or 100,000 units at $1.

Redesigning the process or product to save a few cents per unit has little value if we are producing only 100 units. Process re-engineering is not just taking cost out of the product. It involves focusing on market goals as well as positioning the operation to achieve the desired penetration. If this requires reducing the cost of the product, we can focus attention on the product.

Process re-engineering begins by asking what is necessary to produce the product or component. It will also include a review of the item itself for manufacturability. Building the complete process without preconceived ideas may result in a significantly different operation. Then the problem becomes one of developing a migration from the current operation.

Rapid Response and Flexible Manufacturing

Rapid response manufacturing is a way to react to changes in market demand for a variety of products. The development of work centers focuses on the ability to easily change configuration. Product runs should be limited to a smaller number of units and use systems and equipment which can easily change. Computers can control the tooling, setup, and routing to accommodate products requiring a wide variety of operations.

Flexible manufacturing consists of a group of processing stations, interconnected by an automated material handling and storage system and controlled by an integrated computer system. We can look at ways to solve our problems by applying these concepts. However, it is not just a matter of grouping processing stations. The concepts will not work unless material flows precisely as defined by Just-in-Time material movement. With JIT, we ensure delivery of material and tools to the work centers precisely when they are needed. There is no buffering before or after a work center.

Material and Data Flows

A critical process in the analysis is matching the material and data flows to the degree of automation. How much automation is always a serious question because it is not cheap and it affects workers. Material flows are usually the primary subject of any analysis.

CHAPTER 2   MATERIAL HANDLING ANALYSIS

This is because it is easy to see the flow of material. The automation of other processes is also part of this analysis. New machine centers, work cells, and computer-controlled equipment will provide significant improvements in productivity.

Data flows are often overlooked. Automating the flow of information may produce significant gains at a very low cost. Work orders, inventory tracking, and operation reporting offer major opportunities for improvement. The first alternative is to make certain all data passed to and from a workstation are necessary. Ask what data are needed to run the workstation and what data support following operations. Eliminate everything else.

Once the definition of the necessary data in and out is complete, look at how that information moves. If the amount of data is sufficiently small, paper may continue to work well. However, if there are any data links, such as employee number and time, to machine operations or product measurements, it may be cost-effective to develop an automated data collection system. Simple data collection systems can be relatively inexpensive—a single PC and a package program, for example. Interactive systems and those collecting data from many sources will require customization of standard software packages. Networks of PCs and PC-like devices will provide all the data necessary for an effective operation.

Results of Solution Evaluation

The requirements definition will provide the information needed to specify the solutions. This will eventually lead to the development of a production and inventory control system.

The keys to a winning manufacturing production and inventory control system are:

- A production and inventory control system that is part of the winning manufacturing processes.
- A production and inventory control system that is straightforward and transparent.
- A production and inventory control system that is MRP II-based.

While MRP II concepts may not necessarily be the ones that are used, they nevertheless will focus efforts on those features and functions that are truly necessary. Limiting the scope of the alternatives will also limit the cost of the solutions.

PROJECT MANAGEMENT

Successful project management includes consideration of planning and analysis, design and development, procurement, implementation, and timely support and modification.

OVERVIEW

Purchasing a material handling system that will accomplish both the short- and long-term goals of the company is in itself a project. This project must encompass the review of all potential system benefits, development of a functional system design, preparation of an acceptable justification, vendor selection, issuing the contract, and implementing the system. This section discusses the steps required to help ensure project success. These steps provide a road map for project design and implementation.

An automated material handling system frequently changes the way a company operates. Scheduling, executing, and reporting material movement are performed automatically. Traditionally, such activities were conducted at a low organizational level with little understanding at a managerial level of procedures, resources required, and strategy alternatives. With the decision to consider automating these activities, management is now asked to make a sizable invest-

ment in something that had previously been considered a detail. Numerous decisions must be made, starting with the product to be handled, projected activity rates, and load sizes and weights. These decisions impact a wide range of separate organizational functions. Decisions must be made by marketing, materials management, production, personnel, facilities engineering, manufacturing engineering, and data processing. As the questions are posed to each of these areas, the lack of in-depth understanding of the logistics of the organization can become highly and embarrassingly visible. Obtaining consensus and commitment in such an environment is extremely difficult. The result all too often is a system that does not adequately meet the company's needs.

Thorough planning is the key to designing and implementing an effective material handling system. However, in planning the system, it must be recognized that the system has a closed-loop life cycle (Fig. 2-34). There is no perfect material handling system. An automated material handling system serves as the arteries and nerves of an operation. As the organization changes, the system must change and adapt with it. A key objective of the system design should be achieving sufficient flexibility to maximize the time between modification and full redesign. Flexibility reduces the risk of obsolescence and increases the system's useful life. This flexibility normally comes at the price of increased initial cost, or lower operating cost savings. However, flexibility by design can yield lower cost over the system's full life cycle (Fig. 2-35). This tradeoff is one of the many decisions that must be made within the context of the organization's strategic objectives.

The program life cycle consists of planning and analysis, design and development, procurement, implementation, and support and modification.

PLANNING AND ANALYSIS

This phase should be a logical outgrowth of the organization's strategic plan. Direction should be provided from the strategic plan on such matters as projected volume by product line, cost reduction goals, and level of capital investment. Also, specific investment projects and their goals should be identified. Here, the fruits of intense internal lobbying for projects by engineering, production, and materials groups are realized through approval to conduct a feasibility study for an automated material handling system project.

Once the decision is made to conduct an automated material handling feasibility study, a project leader needs to be assigned. The project leader provides a single point of focus for both communication and decision making. He or she may be assigned full- or part-time and may be supported by internal engineering personnel or, as frequently happens, an outside engineering firm. The study will include a technology assessment and a cost/benefit/risk analysis. The study should result in a preliminary concept, an automation master plan, and a preliminary economic justification. The results of the feasibility study are submitted to management and, if approved, the projects are included in the organization's capital plan with a defined priority and expenditure period. The planning and analysis steps include:

- Environmental analysis.
- General requirements determination.
- Commission feasibility study.
- Project management assignment.
- Technology assessment.
- Cost/benefit/risk analysis.
- Preliminary concept definition.
- Master plan.
- Economic analysis and justification (preliminary).
- Program approval (capital plan level).

CHAPTER 2   MATERIAL HANDLING ANALYSIS

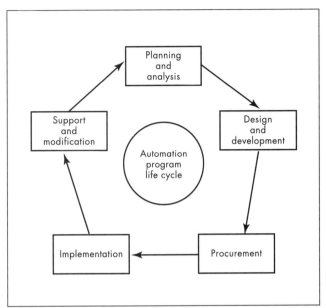

Fig. 2-34 Automation program life cycle. *(Courtesy W. A. Sullivan, CPA)*

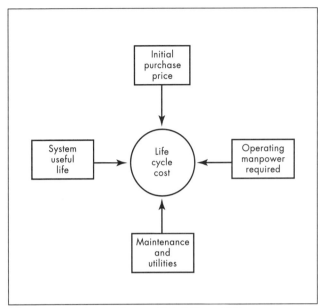

Fig. 2-35 Life cycle cost. *(Courtesy W. A. Sullivan, CPA)*

DESIGN AND DEVELOPMENT

The capital plan level approval is followed by the design/development phase. The first step is the assignment of a project leader and team. The project leader may be the same person who led the feasibility study. However, the project team must be broadened to include representatives of all functional areas affected (Fig. 2-36). Depending on project scope, representation is needed for: marketing, personnel, manufacturing, engineering, production control, purchasing, material management, plant engineering, operations, finance, and insurance.

The design study may be conducted by an in-house engineering staff if such a capability exists. Frequently, however, an independent engineering firm or material handling system vendor will be retained to perform the study. This phase consists of:

- Design study commissioning.
- Project management assignment.
- Detailed definition of environment and goals.
- Structured analysis of requirements.
- Analysis and evaluation of alternative solutions.
- Preliminary design.
- Plant layout.
- Interface planning and definition.
- Component and system capacity analysis.
- System description of operation.
- System operating resource definition.
- Implementation planning.
- Configuration control planning.
- Acceptance test planning.
- Vendor evaluation and definition of criteria.
- Economic analysis and justification (formal).
- Project approval.

At this stage, the user group must establish a detailed definition of the system's goals and scope. Goals and scope include cost reduction areas and values, impact on quality, design year, material volumes handled, physical areas served, human resource impact, level of control, and control integration. This definition is a key input to the study process and cannot be delegated to an outside consultant.

A structured analysis of requirements is performed to define the environment. This definition includes:

- Design level physical input and output frequency (average, peak, and peak duration).
- Load configuration and weight.
- Input and output points.
- Physical interfaces.
- Control system interfaces.
- Desired staffing level and functions.

The requirements analysis is followed by an evaluation of alternative solutions and generation of a conceptual design and plant layout. The effectiveness of the design is evaluated by simulation and is fine-tuned by using optimization strategies. The conceptual design is finalized and descriptions of operations—in both primary and degraded (partial failure) mode—are prepared. A reliability plan also should be prepared. The operating resource requirements—workers, utilities, and maintenance—are then evaluated. Ergonomics and safety features must be considered. Also, at this point, it is important that flexibility (the ability to change the system) be evaluated and life cycle cost be defined.

The result of the effort expended to this point should be a solid design concept that satisfies the organization's intangible goals as well as its tangible goals.

The design/development phase is finished with implementation planning, configuration control planning, acceptance test planning, establishment of vendor evaluation criteria, and preparation of a detailed economic justification. The results of the initial economic evaluation may require reassessment of system scope and design. When an acceptable justification is completed, the result of this effort—if properly done and if the company's goals have not changed—should be formal project approval.

PROCUREMENT

Formal project approval starts the procurement phase. The project manager is assigned and the project team—usually the same team that handled the design/development phase—is formed. The procurement phase includes these steps:

CHAPTER 2   MATERIAL HANDLING ANALYSIS

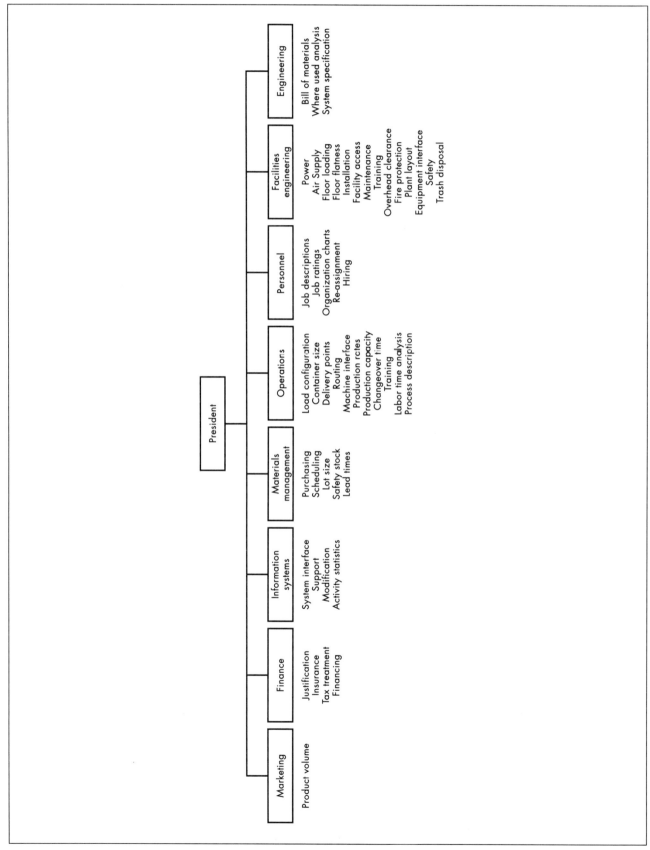

Fig. 2-36 Organizational areas of impact. *(Courtesy W. A. Sullivan, CPA)*

CHAPTER 2   MATERIAL HANDLING ANALYSIS

- Project manager assignment.
- Vendor scope definition.
- Vendor qualification.
- Prebid conference.
- Request for Quotation (RFQ) preparation.
- Definition of selection criteria.
- RFQ issuance.
- Response to vendor questions.
- Proposal receipt.
- Proposal evaluation.
- Oral presentation.
- Vendor selection.
- Final funding approval.
- Contract negotiation.

Vendor scope is defined by identifying the vendor qualifications that are required. Are separate vendors going to provide the AGVS, conveyor, AS/RS, production equipment, and building? If so, who will have responsibility to integrate the components into a working system? The industry is then surveyed to determine which vendors have the capability to successfully meet the defined scope. Literature is obtained, references checked, and sites visited.

Preparation of a proposal typically requires considerable effort on the part of the vendor. Similarly, proposal evaluation can be a difficult, time-consuming, and often confusing task for the proposal team. To obtain the best quality proposal and limit the time and effort required of the proposal team, the number of qualified vendors should normally be reduced to three at this stage. Selection of qualified vendors should be based on such factors as relevant technical experience, project management capability, system reliability, availability of service, workmanship quality, system ergonomics, system safety, financial strength and, very important, the prospects for developing a comfortable vendor-customer working relationship. The design and installation of an automated material handling system requires close teamwork between customer, vendor, and consultant. Strict reliance on an arms-length contractual approach usually extends the project implementation period and limits the ability to deal with unforeseen circumstances effectively.

Equal access to the project team should be allowed for the qualified vendors prior to preparation of the RFQ. This allows the vendors time to understand the company's goals and to discuss alternative solutions openly. This review process is often started with a prebid conference where the prospective bidders are presented with system goals, functional requirements, design concept, budget, and evaluation criteria. Bidders should be told whether best and final prices will be requested or entertained, and they are informed about arrangements for project team contacts. A visit to the installation site by the vendors is also desirable. Actual discussions between the project team and the individual vendors follow. Meetings with all vendors together are seldom productive, since each vendor wishes to protect its unique approach. This review elicits vendor suggestions that may be incorporated in the RFQ.

The RFQ should specify, as a minimum, system function and performance requirements, system concept, physical and environmental limitations, special requirements, terms and conditions, system due date, and acceptability of alternatives. It also indicates the bid due date, address to which it should be delivered, and whether a line-by-line response is required. If future expandability and/or integration is desired, vendors should be asked to explain how this can be accomplished with their proposed systems.

Preparation of an RFQ at this point should be fairly straightforward if all of the preceding steps have been taken. Very detailed RFQs are excessively demanding on the project team, delay the project, and are frequently counterproductive. They limit the vendor's creativity, can generate excessive cost where the vendor must modify a standard component to meet a noncritical specification, and can eliminate qualified vendors. More general, functional specifications allow the selection process to focus on technical capability and whether the proposed system satisfies the objectives. Relatively minor design changes—either for subsequent specification changes or for dissatisfaction with certain items in the vendor's proposal—can be negotiated once a cost and technical baseline is established. Accordingly, there is nothing to be gained by delaying the RFQ issuance until all specification refinements are incorporated. There is no "perfect" specification. It will change up through final design sign-off for a variety of reasons.

At the time the RFQ is prepared, the team should define its vendor selection criteria. This is done through the creation of a matrix that lists the selection criteria and assigns a numeric weighting factor to each. A numeric scoring method is also defined.

The RFQ is mailed to the short list of preferred vendors. Vendors will respond with questions and, possibly, requests for a visit to the site and access to the project team. These visits can be time-consuming and can be minimized if contact with the project teams is allowed before the RFQ is issued. The project team leader controls responses to vendor questions to ensure consistency. Where the questions result in modifications to or significant clarification of the RFQ, this information should be provided to all vendors in writing. Similarly, if an extension of the due date is granted to one vendor, it should be granted to all vendors.

When the proposals are received, they are logged in and reviewed for conformance with the specifications. The proposals are evaluated and ranked on the basis of the previously determined evaluation criteria. Differences in offering scope are identified and valued. If the prices significantly exceed budget, the specification may have to be scaled back and the vendors asked to amend their prices accordingly. Major revisions may require obtaining increased budget or issuing a revised RFQ.

A set of written questions is prepared and sent to each vendor. Oral presentations are scheduled. At these presentations, each vendor conducts a design and implementation plan walk-through and responds to prepared and impromptu customer questions.

The project team reviews the result of the numeric scoring and subjective factors. With this review, the team should be in a position to select the preferred vendor. Final appropriation funding is obtained and all vendors are notified of the selection. Typically, the selected vendor is asked to meet with the project manager and any open issues are reviewed. A letter of intent is negotiated and signed by both parties or a purchase order number is issued to the vendor. In either case, the customer takes responsibility for costs incurred on their behalf by the vendor until a formal contract or purchase order is issued and accepted. Negotiations of initial changes in deliverables and changes to terms and conditions follow, resulting in a signed contract or an accepted purchase order.

IMPLEMENTATION

The implementation phase includes these steps:

- Project management assignment.
- Design review and approval.
- Establishing configuration control.
- Detail design.
- Equipment production.
- Controls programming.
- Site preparation.
- Installation.
- Documentation.
- Operational training.

CHAPTER 2 MATERIAL HANDLING ANALYSIS

- Safety training.
- Acceptance testing.
- System acceptance.

The implementation phase begins during the contract negotiation period with the preliminary design effort, the appointment of the customer project manager, and establishment of the project team. Contract amendment approval procedures are also defined at this stage, and design review meetings are scheduled. Milestone approval procedures are established and long-lead-time procurement items are placed on order.

Next, the schedule is refined and the preliminary design is reviewed and approved. Design changes are priced by the vendor, and then negotiated and approved. It is essential that all significant design changes be identified and approved at this stage. Changes at later stages of the project can have major adverse cost and schedule impact. An acceptance test plan and final acceptance test criteria are negotiated and committed to writing.

A detailed project plan is prepared and time-phased. The plan should include identification of the critical path, scheduling alternatives, and early start opportunities. As a minimum, a Gantt chart should be prepared and updated regularly by the project manager. More complex projects can benefit from PERT/CPM analysis. A detailed, time-phased spending budget is also prepared. A reserve for contingencies needs to be established and controlled by the project manager. Depending on how firm the specifications are, the value of this reserve should range from 10–15% of the total project value. Each purchase order, change order, and work order needs to be recorded at the time it is issued. Waiting for accounting reports that show only invoices paid is not adequate to control the cost of the project. Each commitment of funds must be recorded and the cumulative value compared to the budget. Significant variances need to be identified and corrective action taken where possible. Sometimes savings can be achieved in one phase of the project that compensate for excessive costs in another phase. Managing project cost in this way can be particularly dangerous, however. Apparent savings gained by reducing or eliminating certain features can adversely affect system performance and compromise planned operational savings. This can cause the system to fail to achieve the planned economic goals. Establishment and control of a management reserve and carefully evaluating the cost and benefits of changes is a far more effective way of controlling project cost.

Completion of the preliminary design review starts the detailed design phase. This is followed by equipment production and controls programming and then site preparation and installation. System components are tested individually, then integrated, and the full system is tested.

Normally, training is begun during the testing phase. The training should consist of a system operational overview for management and all others affected by the system, plus classroom and on-the-job training of system operators and maintenance personnel. Both operation and maintenance training must include safety instruction. Training should be scheduled early so that key customer personnel can be made available for this critical phase. It is helpful if customer personnel charged with system maintenance visit the vendor facility during equipment production and programming of controls. This allows them to gain familiarity with the theory of operation for both equipment and controls. Maintenance personnel should also participate in the installation for the same reason.

Presentation and review of documentation should accompany training. Also, the initial spare-part stock should be ordered at this time. This stock should include both warranty and nonwarranty items, whether or not the vendor provides a parts and labor warranty. Most failures can be repaired by customer personnel, and the repair will be made more quickly if customer maintenance personnel install the replacement part. The vendor will then replenish the customer's stock. The implementation phase ends with successful completion of acceptance testing and formal system acceptance.

SUPPORT AND MODIFICATION

The system is now placed in service and the operation, support, and modification phase is started. This phase consists of these steps:

- Performance monitoring and analysis.
- Preventive maintenance.
- Component repair.
- Retraining.
- Equipment modification and upgrade.
- Software enhancement.
- Control retrofit and upgrade.
- Cost-effective procurement.

System operations should be monitored closely, particularly during the first several months, to ensure that expected performance is realized. System failures should be logged, summarized at least monthly, and analyzed. Recurring failures may necessitate a change in the customer operation or maintenance procedures, or require an equipment adjustment or modification. Some vendors will perform this failure tracking and analysis. Performance tracking and analysis is a key factor in achieving high system reliability.

Preventive maintenance (PM) is critical to a successful reliability program. PM must be scheduled and the equipment made available in accordance with the schedule. Maintenance procedures must also be monitored. When new operators or maintenance personnel are assigned, they should go through training equivalent to that provided with system delivery. If this is not done, system reliability and safety can degrade over time. Some vendors offer retraining as a service or videotapes of operator and maintenance training.

As the needs of the organization change, there will be requests to modify the system software and such features as load size, routing, and quantity of vehicles. Also, equipment improvements may become available that will improve system performance or reliability. The recognition of the need for such modifications and the ability to affect them can be critical to extending the system's useful life. Most vendors are willing to perform system modifications or equipment retrofits. Depending on their capability, in-house maintenance personnel or independent contractors may be able to modify the system as well. If this activity will result in equipment being out of service for an extended period of time, careful planning must go into the modification/retrofit program to ensure continuation of operations at an acceptable level while the equipment is not available. Careful planning and design is also required to ensure that the modifications/retrofit are completed on time.

When the system can no longer be modified or equipment upgraded sufficiently to meet the organization's changing needs, planning for a new system should begin.

SUMMARY

In reviewing the steps in a material handling system's life cycle, we have covered a large number of activities. With regard to the planning and procurement phases, the duration of these activities will vary with the complexity of the system, experience and commitment of internal resources, and the degree of participation of independent consultants. However, a range of three to six months per phase is normal. Implementation should run from six to 18 months, depending on the amount of software and the availability of the target site.

It should now be readily apparent that anticipating each of these activities and planning for them will have a major positive impact on the smoothness and speed of implementation, the system's effectiveness, and its life cycle cost.

Reference

1. Adapted from an original publication of the Material Handling Institute, Charlotte, North Carolina and reprinted here with permission. The text was a presentation on project management which appeared in the Proceedings of AGUS '86.

Bibliography

Considerations When Planning and Implementing Integrated Material Handling Systems. Charlotte, NC: Integrated Systems and Controls, A Product Section of the Material Handling Institute, 1992.

Gane, C. and Sarson, T. *Structured Systems Analysis: Tools and Techniques.* New York: Improved System Technologies, 1977.

Groover, Mikell, P. *Flexible Manufacturing.* Englewood Cliffs, NJ: Prentice-Hall, 1987.

Kannewurp, Adolph, and Ward, Richard. *Guidelines for Developing Effective Contracts for Integrated Material Handling Systems.* Charlotte, NC: Integrated Systems and Controls, A Product Section of the Material Handling Institute, 1990.

Muther, Richard, et al. *Systematic Layout Planning (SLP), Systematic Handling Analysis (SHA), Systematic Planning of Industrial Facilities.* Marietta, GA: Richard Muther & Associates, 1994.

Muther, Richard, et al. *The Basics of Material Handling: A Foundation for Better Planning and Results.* Material Handling Show and Forum, April 1996.

NCIC: Non-traditional Capital Investment Criteria. Charlotte, NC: Integrated Systems and Controls, A Product Section of the Material Handling Institute, 1993.

Phillips, E. J. *Manufacturing Plant Layout.* Dearborn, MI: Society of Manufacturing Engineers, 1997.

Phillips, E. J. *Two-Day Training Workshops on Designing Manufacturing Cells.* Dayton, OH: Wright State University, 1997.

Phillips, E. J. *Two-Day Training Workshops on Manufacturing Plant Layout.* Dearborn, MI: Society of Manufacturing Engineers, 1997.

Rao, Ashok, et al. *Total Quality Management: A Cross Functional Perspective.* New York: John Wiley & Sons, 1996.

Sims, E. Ralph, Jr. *Precision Manufacturing Costing.* New York: Marcel Dekker, 1995.

Smith, Richard T. *Manufacturing Myopia: Failure in Systems Realization.* SME Blue Book Series. Dearborn, MI: Society of Manufacturing Engineers, 1993.

Suzaki, Kiyoshi. *The New Manufacturing Challenge: Techniques for Continuous Improvement.* New York: Free Press, 1987.

Tompkins, James A. *Winning Manufacturing.* Norcross, GA: Industrial Engineering and Management Press, 1989.

Tompkins, James A., and White, John A. *Facility Planning.* New York: John Wiley & Sons, 1984.

Vail, Peter S. *Computer Integrated Manufacturing.* Boston, MA: PWS-Kent, 1988.

Virtual Manufacturing: Simulating Reality, videotape. Dearborn, MI: Society of Manufacturing Engineers, 1995.

Yourdon, E., and Constantine, L. L. *Structured Design: Fundamentals of a Discipline of Computer Program and Systems Design,* 2nd Ed. Englewood Cliffs, NJ: Prentice-Hall, 1979.

Yourdon, Inc. *Yourdon Systems Method: Model-Driven Systems Development.* Englewood Cliffs, NJ: Yourdon Press, 1993.

CHAPTER 3

PRODUCT IDENTIFICATION AND TRACKING

CHAPTER CONTENTS

INTRODUCTION

As raw materials and parts are issued to the manufacturing operation and processed into finished products, it is important to be able to identify items at any point in the production sequence, to track the product or any of its components through the manufacturing processes, and to track any activity that expends resources or advances the manufacture of product. Historically, product identification and tracking have been manual processes. Even as computer-based inventory control and manufacturing planning systems became commonplace, the functions of recording within manufacturing were usually paper-based. The manually collected data were then forwarded for data entry into the corporate computer system.

These manual data recording and collection systems are notoriously subject to error. Each time the data are recorded or re-recorded, there is the opportunity for error through misrecording, transposition, omission, or double entry. Even the initial recording process is subject to such errors. When the original paperwork is gathered, there is also a chance for recorded data to be lost. The information is then keyed into a computer, introducing another opportunity for human error in the keying process. Moreover, considerable time can pass between the state described by the data and the state that exists when the data are accessed.

Automated data capture (ADC), also called *automatic identification* (AI), is a general term for a number of technologies that provide the ability to attach information about a physical object to that object in such a way that the data can be communicated to a computer application without human keying or written documentation. Three methods of ADC are discussed in this chapter: linear bar codes, two-dimensional (2D) codes, and radio-frequency identification (RFID) tagging.

The ability to track parts and material, whether manually or automatically, is essential not only for material handling, but for quality tracking and control. "Where appropriate, the supplier shall establish and maintain procedures for identifying the product from applicable drawings, specifications, or other documents, during all stages of production, delivery, and installation."[1]

When a project for material and parts traceability is undertaken, one of the first decisions is whether to do it manually or automatically. While there are some instances where manual data collection is the most cost-effective solution, automated data capture technologies generally provide the most accurate, effective, and efficient methods for identifying and tracking parts and material.

IDENTIFICATION OF LEDGERED STOCK-KEEPING UNITS

In principle, there is no difference between rules for manual identification methods and those for automated methods. In practice, however, computerized systems are more rigorous and less forgiving of error than manual systems. Organizations that have converted from manual to computerized systems generally fret about rigor and inflexibility, but in the end usually find that the benefits of a computerized system outweigh minor inconveniences.

There are many manufacturers for whom automatic part identification is too complicated and expensive. These are generally small companies with limited production runs. The following sections offer guidelines for manual identification methods. Readers should bear in mind that, although the details may differ, these principles are just as applicable to automated systems.

UNIQUE SKU

The fundamental rule is that, only if two parts have the same form, fit, and function (the three Fs) is it permissible to give them the same stock-keeping unit (SKU) number—the unique number assigned to a part in paper identification systems. This means that only trivial differences are tolerable, such as a slight difference in the appearance of a finish in parts supplied by two different manufacturers. The corollary rule, of course, is that every stock part and material must have a unique SKU number. These rules force us to recognize that any difference demands a unique SKU number. This uniqueness is the means of controlling important matters such as shelf life and use of the correct alloy.

Products such as drugs and parachute webbing have shelf lives. Parachute webbing, after a certain number of months, may no longer be used for personnel parachutes, but only for freight-drop service. When those months have passed, the webbing must acquire a different SKU number and be stored separately.

In another example, certain steam turbines may use either cast-steel or cast-iron steam chests, depending on pressure. It is vital that two separate SKU numbers be applied. Similarly, separate numbers

---

The Contributors of this chapter are: Frank Gue, PE, Consultant, Industrial Education Services; *Robert C. Keeton, CMfgT,* Manufacturing Engineer, Borg-Warner Automotive; *Marilyn S. Sherry,* Program Manager, Automotive Industry Action Group; *David Studebaker,* President, Studebaker Technology, Inc.

The Reviewers of this chapter are: James Cheng, Manufacturing Engineer, The Sine Companies, Inc.; *John Layden,* President, Pritsker Corporation; *Hal Mather,* Consultant.

CHAPTER 3   PRODUCT IDENTIFICATION AND TRACKING

are essential for mild steel versus high-strength steel, that look alike and may cause confusion that can lead to disaster.

ENGINEERING AND PURCHASING RESPONSIBILITIES

Engineering departments must buy into the identification scheme the company has decided to adopt. Traditional manual systems often find bills of materials calling for parts to be made of vaguely described material such as "mild steel" or "oiled silk." These callouts must be replaced by a unique, unambiguous identification of the desired part or material, although the descriptive wording is also valuable and may remain on the line item contents. Descriptive wording should use military stores vocabulary practice, for example "BOLT, HEX, STEEL, 1 IN 8 THD." It is then simple to sort all the BOLT, HEX, STEEL SKUs into one list for cost reduction and similar activities.

Purchasing departments must deal with inconsistent numbering systems. No two firms are likely to have the same, or even similar SKU identification systems. Thus, purchase requisitions will arrive in Purchasing with nonindustry-standard SKU numbers, particularly for raw materials such as paints or steel. The firm must find its way around this as best it can. A few of the ways are:

- Design the firm's SKU identification system so that it can accept industry-standard designations.
- If the firm has enough clout, get suppliers to agree to meet the firm's specifications as expressed in the identification system.
- Between the Engineering and Purchasing departments, develop a cross-reference so that Purchasing can convert the numbering system before ordering.
- Use a combination of these methods.

NUMBERING SYSTEMS

There are two types of numbering systems: *significant*, where the characters have meaning, and *nonsignificant*, where the characters are arbitrary.

An advantage of a nonsignificant system is that there are virtually limitless combinations of numbers that can be developed from a few digits, especially if alphabetic characters are allowed. For example, a four-digit numeric system could accommodate $9 \times 10 \times 10 \times 10 \times 10$ or 90,000 SKUs (not permitting zero as a first digit)—more than enough for most companies.

An advantage of a significant numbering scheme is that it becomes a useful and meaningful language for shop people. In one company, for example, material number 10110A1 is universally recognized as flat, hot-rolled, low-carbon steel of a certain chemistry. One disadvantage of this system is that the code requires seven characters (plus three more for a size code). Another disadvantage is that significant systems, unless cleverly designed, run a serious risk of running out of digits, since usually only one or two digits span a fairly wide variety of shapes, chemistries, or other attributes. For example, if one digit in the seven-digit code is reserved for shape, the firm had better be sure that it will never have more than 36 different shapes—flat, round, hexagonal, square, etc.—or it will have to compromise the code (the number 36 arises from the number of available characters: 10 numbers and 26 letters).

Despite disadvantages, sooner or later significant systems seem to be preferred. They carry so much useful information that they cannot be ignored. For example, it is practical to use the drawing and item number as part of the SKU number because of several system integration advantages thus derived.

SIZES OF STOCK MATERIALS

Raw materials such as steel, wood, and printed circuit board are subject to the same form-fit-function rules as parts, but the rules must

be applied in a different way. One way is to apply the SKU number to the recognized industrial size (for example, $0.5 \times 96 \times 120$-in. [$1.3 \times 243.8 \times 304.8$-cm] hot-rolled steel), and to retain that SKU number after a sheet has been partly used. The rationale is that the important uniqueness (chemistry and thickness) has been retained, and that any part later cut from the same sheet has to fit within the *offcut* (remainder), so the SKU uniqueness rule has been respected and maintained.

Such raw materials can be further identified by adding a size code of two or three digits to the unique SKU number. This unfortunately adds to the length of the SKU number, but the added digits also can be significant; in plate steel and similar materials, for example, the size code in some cases can simply be the thickness in decimal inches.

Accounting for offcuts of stock materials can be an expected difficulty. For example, firms risk distorting costs by charging for a full sheet regardless of the amount actually used, and then charging nothing for a job that uses the offcut. To a certain extent, accounting requirements conflict with efficient material utilization and common sense. However, the typical 30% manufacturing waste expected when nonnesting parts must be cut cannot be ignored, and the SKU number system that the company chooses has to play a part in solving this shop-floor level problem in some sensible way.

UNITS OF MEASURE

For stock parts, the unit of measure is usually the *piece*, abbreviated *pc*. But for stock raw materials, the situation is more complex, and there are three kinds of unit of measure to be considered: purchase, ledger, and usage. Again, sheet steel provides a good example. The purchase unit of measure is the pound or kilogram. But the ledger unit for stock sheets and usage on engineering drawings is square feet or square centimeters. Accordingly, considerable effort must be expended to assign up to three units of measure along with an SKU number and conversion information.

In either manual or computer systems, a person or program must convert among these three units to cost the product, order material, pay bills, etc. As a firm moves from a manual to a computer system, this becomes a very demanding process (for example, the firm that thought it had ordered one 45-gal [20-kg] drum of lube oil but received 45 drums instead because the units of measure [drums versus gallons] were confused).

NONLEDGERED PARTS

Typically, firms identify SKUs for stocked items quite rigorously, but not as stringently for bought-to-order, work-in-process items. It pays to assign an SKU number to work-in-process materials even though the firm may not intend ever to stock them. This is because these objects are stocked for some period before they are used. If we fail to open a temporary ledger account for them, we risk loss of control over expensive assets. Many firms order and re-order expensive materials while high-value offcuts remain unaccounted for in stores or on the shop floor (for example, materials such as partial bobbins of copper wire and drums of special lubricants or adhesives). The solution is to assign an SKU number with a zero re-order quantity, track usage, provide a bin location, etc., for a work-in-process material that is likely to be subjected to this kind of mishandling.

TRACING AND TRACKING

Tracing and tracking of stock is required for parts which, if they fail, can be dangerous or catastrophic to the public (for example, failure of a turbine blade in a natural gas pipeline pump) or to specific personnel or operations (for example, failure in an avionics module in a fighter aircraft). A firm may also use it to follow its

CHAPTER 3   PRODUCT IDENTIFICATION AND TRACKING

quality in field service by recording the condition of parts during routine, nonbreakdown maintenance.

For example, SKU number 12345-23 is traceable to stock order number 23, which in turn, is traceable to purchase order number 7654 for castings from supplier XYZ, heat number 9384. Further, SKU number 12345-23 was used on finished products having serial numbers 11 to 99. The quality control records developed during the manufacturing process are on file with the archived records for these serial numbers.

Thus, the tracking system must identify the part from its source and manufacturing history, and from its destination. That is, the products, by serial number, of which each part is a component.

Dependable tracing and tracking systems are complex and expensive, requiring nontypical system integration. Firms using them do so because they must (for example, a Department of Defense requirement) or because the payoff is very high (for example, avoiding large warranty or recall costs). The integration requirement must be met by a company-wide agreement on the coding system to be used, since the Engineering, Purchasing, Manufacturing, and Quality Assurance departments must adhere to it at all stages.

Most of the higher-performance manufacturing software packages include tracing and tracking modules that minimize cost and risk of error by extensive use of bar coding and other relatively failure-proof recording methods. Firms using manual systems must reconcile themselves to the cost of a great deal of manual record keeping. Training of personnel, both at start-up and on a routine refresher basis, is essential.

A quality- and records-conscious arm of the organization, such as Quality Assurance, should administer the tracing and tracking subsystem. This department should run periodic simulations to ensure that some hypothetical problem can be traced to its source and that any of its quality records can be easily accessed.

CONTROLLING CHANGES BY PART IDENTIFICATION

Engineering changes demand tight control if costs are to be met and product quality maintained. Such changes are controlled through the release or subnumber of the engineering drawing.

Falling back on the unique identification and the form-fit-function rules given previously, we can see that engineering change notices (ECNs) can be of two kinds: those that do or do not change the three Fs of the part. The former are generally responses to an important engineering change that must be rigorously complied with, as by observing phase-out dates and quantities, surplus reworking, etc. The latter are generally responses to cost reduction activities, such as reducing the amount of nonworking metal in a casting. Since the three Fs do not change, it is merely necessary to feed the new stock in as soon as possible to capture the savings. In either case, the situation is controlled by an extension of the engineering drawing item number that renders the new issue unique, even though the drawing item number has not changed.

The engineering release number is an integral part of the unique identity of the component and must be treated with the same respect and attention as the rest of the identification. For instance, it is never permissible to omit the engineering release number from any manufacturing documentation.

AUTOMATED DATA CAPTURE (ADC)

Regardless of the technology used, implementing an ADC-based product identification and tracking system is a major project, on a level of complexity equivalent to implementing computer numerical control (CNC) or computer-aided design (CAD). When planning for product identification and tracking, more than in-plant logistics support must be considered. Product traceability is a broad, cross-functional, and even cross-company, application. It starts with the assignment of product identification, usually by the design engineer, carries through production, where lot number or even individual serial number traceability may be involved, and continues through warehousing and shipment on to the end user. Suppliers may be involved in the process when identification of raw materials and components is required. A project for product identification and tracking should not be undertaken as a single-department activity, but should involve a cross-functional team representing all those involved.

In addition to the cross-functional aspects of an ADC product identification project, there are many technical and standard-based details to be understood and attended to. Before beginning an ADC project, the team should become familiar with any standards that might apply to the use of ADC in their company and industry. Many industry associations have standards for product identification and the application of ADC for identification. Among them are:

- The Automotive Industry Action Group (AIAG) in the United States and the Organization for Data Exchange by Teletransmission in Europe (ODETTE).
- The Electronics Industry Association (EIA).
- The Association of Home Appliance Manufacturers (AHAM).
- The Health Industry Business Communications Council.
- The Uniform Code Council (UCC) sets standards in the United States and the European Article Numbering (EAN) associations affect standards for European countries.

Beyond industry standards, there are national and international standards that affect the ways in which ADC technologies should be used. In the United States, some of the standards for bar code use are published by the American National Standards Institute (ANSI). Additional standards are constantly developing at all levels—industrial, national, and international. At least three committees under the International Organization for Standardization (ISO) are currently developing standards for various areas affecting ADC. The appropriate industry organization should always be consulted for standards that might affect a specific application.

CONSIDERATIONS FOR ADC

After the cross-functional team has educated its members about the standards that apply, it should investigate ADC technologies. The team should map out the entire product life cycle, beginning from when the product identification is attached to the part until it is no longer needed by anyone in the chain of suppliers and users. This process map can be used to evaluate a number of questions that will help in choosing the appropriate ADC technology for the application. Some of the important questions to be considered are:

- What data need to be collected? Is the information numeric only or does it include text? Is it identification- (ID-) only or does it include descriptive information? If the data consist of just basic ID, such as an employee number, a job or work order number, a product ID, or a material code, then any of the media are candidates. If the data consist of more than 15 or 20 characters, then the simple "picket fence" bar codes are probably too limited. The more data that must be handled with each read, the more important the speed of processing will be.
- What volume of data needs to be collected? If the volume of data is small, then the costs per unit of data will be much less significant and the speed of each read will be less important with small volumes.

CHAPTER 3   PRODUCT IDENTIFICATION AND TRACKING

- Define the environmental factors to which the target item will be exposed.

  - Temperature ranges.
  - Humidity, moisture, or ice.
  - Corrosives.
  - Weather.
  - Dirt or grease.
  - Airborne particles (metal fragments or abrasive dust).
  - Radiation of various types, including visible light, infrared, ultraviolet, radio frequency, and electromagnetic.

- What are the environments where the data will be read? (The same factors apply as in the previous item, except here we are concerned not only about the medium carrying the data, but also with the reading device.)
- Over what period of time must the data be accessible (hours, days, weeks, months, or years)? Will they be read once or twice or many times? Some media are very fragile and either do not have a long life, or cannot be read and reread many times. At the other extreme, some media are practically indestructible.
- Do you need to be able to change the contents of the data, or are the data static? If the data need to be updated at any time, then only those media that support changes in their data contents would be appropriate (magnetic stripe, active or passive radio frequency [RF] tags, touch buttons—all media where the data are stored electronically, not through printing).
- Will the data be read when the item is moving or still? Reading the data from a moving item generally requires a higher-cost solution in terms of the medium, the reader, or both.
- What is the value of the data and what is the cost of incorrect or missing data? If the information represented by the data has great value or the cost of correcting data or replacing missing data is high, then one would certainly be justified in selecting a higher-cost solution if it sufficiently reduces this risk.
- What methods of affixing the identifier medium to the objects are feasible? If the object has peculiar characteristics that make either affixing the medium or reading it difficult, it may quickly narrow the choices of feasible options. For example, if the item is embedded within something at the time the medium is to be read, then a bar code medium would be ruled out.
- What are the costs of the alternatives? Evaluate the total solution cost and benefit in a normal engineering fashion. Cost items that must be taken into account include:

- The medium (for example, bar-coded labels, RF tags).
- Recording of the data onto the medium (for example, printing bar codes, recording onto RF tags), including the cost of the process and equipment required to do the recording.
- The reliability and durability of the medium relative to requirements, and the cost of replacing lost or damaged labels or tags.
- Reading the medium, including the cost of the process and equipment necessary to read the information.
- Support equipment, software, maintenance services, engineering services, etc., required to make all of this work.

With this information in mind, it is possible to evaluate the available ADC technologies and choose the one that will work best. The following sections discuss the three technologies in common use. Table 3-1 provides a concise comparison of the technologies.

LINEAR BAR CODES

"Linear bar code" is another term for what we have been calling just plain "bar code" for over 30 years. Today, the technology is commonplace in many industries. In manufacturing, it has become virtually indispensable.

Linear bar codes come in over 50 varieties, called *symbologies*. Three of the most popular are universal product code (U.P.C.), Code 39, and Code 128 (see Fig. 3-1). The most familiar symbology for anyone who shops in a large retail outlet, is the *U.P.C.* symbology (related to the international symbology, European article number [EAN]) used to identify stock for retail sale. This symbology incorporates a predefined, numeric only, part numbering scheme. It allocates five numeric digits to a manufacturer's ID code assigned by the Uniform Code Council, and five numeric digits to the part identification assigned by the manufacturer. No other data may be encoded using U.P.C. This code is required by most grocery and many retail industry customers for point-of-sale identification. Although there are some smaller variations, the U.P.C. symbol with its human-readable interpretation generally takes a space about 1.5-in. wide × 1-in. high (38 × 25 mm).

The most widely used linear bar code in the industrial supply chain is the *Code 39* symbology. Unlike U.P.C., Code 39 has no required data content. The symbology can encode numeric digits, uppercase alphabet, and a limited set of special characters, such as the decimal point. Code 39 is widely used in the aerospace, appliance, automotive, defense, and electronics industries, among others. Most

TABLE 3-1
Comparison of Part Identification Technologies

Technology	Advantages	Disadvantages	Major Manufacturing Applications
Linear bar code	Well understood, simple, low-cost, many options for labeling and readers, many suppliers	Limited storage capacity, maximum read distance proportional to code size	General tracking of bulk and unit parts, materials, employees, and jobs
2D code	Large storage capacity in small area, extremely reliable reads	More costly readers, limited number of suppliers, limited read distance	Tracking of bulk and unit items needing an on-board database, parts having limited area for code
Radio frequency identification	Remote reading, easy updating, larger storage capacity, many items can be read simultaneously	Expensive tags and readers, single-vendor systems (very little standardization)	Tracking of parts that cannot be physically accessed, parts needing an on-board database

CHAPTER 3   PRODUCT IDENTIFICATION AND TRACKING

Fig. 3-1 Representative linear bar codes. (*Courtesy Zebra Technologies Corporation*)

of these industries require or recommend the use of field identifiers, as defined in ANSI MH10.8.2, within the encoded data stream. For example, a lot number would be preceded by the data identifier "1T." So if the lot number was 123X45, then the data in the Code 39 symbol would be "1T123X45." Since the data in a Code 39 symbol vary in length, so does the size of the symbol. In the proportions most commonly used for part marking, a common reference for the size of a Code 39 symbol is 0.25-0.5-in. (6-13-mm) high, and roughly 0.16-in. (4-mm) wide per character, plus about 0.75 in. (19 mm) for required overhead.

A third linear code, rising in popularity, is *Code 128*. This symbology can encode all of the 128 characters in the American standard code for information interchange (ASCII) character set. It is not as widely used for part tracking as U.P.C. or Code 39, in part because it is a newer code, developed after many industries had already set their bar code standards. Because Code 128 incorporates a data condensation algorithm, it can generally fit more data into a smaller width than Code 39. Depending on the data stream, a Code 128 symbol will be 10 to 50% narrower than a Code 39 symbol, although it will usually be the same height. Data fields encoded in Code 39 symbols have a practical size limitation somewhere between 19 and 26 characters per symbol. Even the denser Code 128 will only carry 25-50 characters in a symbol. If the goal is to tie a container or a part into a database record on a computer, this number of characters is sufficient.

Code 39 linear bar codes have been the standard for the U.S. Department of Defense and the automotive, electronics, aerospace, and other manufacturing industries for over 10 years. U.P.C. symbology has been growing in use worldwide for almost 20 years. Of the three technologies (linear bar code, two-dimensional code, and radio-frequency identification), linear bar code is by far the best understood, as well as the easiest and least expensive to implement.

The reader should be aware that even though linear bar code technology has been in widespread use for over 15 years, it still is an advanced, optical-based technology with many critical details. If you are not familiar with terms such as "X dimension," "quiet zone," "wide-to-narrow ratio," "aperture," and "verification" as they apply

to linear bar codes, you need to attend a training course before you plan your implementation.

Linear bar codes offer the lowest initial cost and very high reliability. Today, there are a multitude of suppliers who provide hardware and software to print and read these symbols, and thousands of people who are experienced in using them. That cannot be said for either of the other technologies.

Symbology Variety and General Requirements

Why are there so many different symbologies? The reason is that engineers from different equipment manufacturers and industries developed their own symbologies, each emphasizing what its creators thought were the most important factors. Linear bar code symbology designs are a combination of tradeoffs between different desirable properties. Some of the desirable properties include:

- A self-checking code structure.
- A large character set: both numeric and alphabetic.
- A small "footprint."
- A simple structure.
- Easy printing.
- Easy decoding by a scanner.
- A constant character width, so different data consisting of the same number of characters yield a constant bar code size.

The familiar *linear picket fence bar code* consists of a series of alternating rectangular printed bars and white spaces. Depending on the design of a particular code, the information may be encoded by the width of the bars and spaces, or by their grouping into modules defining the individual characters. In either case, the basic concept is to use the bars and white space to define a binary code that carries data. In addition to the portions of a code that actually carry the data, other sections include *silent space* (white space before and after the code to let the scanner know where the code actually is), or *start and stop codes* (which serve the same purpose as the silent space). There are also *embedded check codes* that use algorithms to allow the scanner to check for errors in its interpretation of a code it has just read.

Some codes are numeric only, but highly standardized. Some support the full numeric and alphabetic character set, making them more useful for a wide range of coded information. Other codes are designed to print well with less expensive printers (such as dot matrix printers) or to fit into a smaller space (for use on smaller objects). There are also codes that have stronger checking ability built into them to maximize reading accuracy.

When deciding whether to use bar coding in your application, one of the key choices is which bar code symbology to use. The experts who sell bar code printing equipment and bar code scanners are good resources for assistance with this choice.

The following examples of bar code symbologies illustrate some of the tradeoffs involved. U.P.C. symbology was designed to be easy to print on a variety of products and surfaces, with a variety of printing technologies. U.P.C. codes are assigned to companies in the United States by the Uniform Code Council (UCC). There is a registration fee based on the sales size of the firm. Once a firm has received its identifying code (the first portion of the U.P.C. code), it is responsible for assigning its own product identifiers (the second portion of the U.P.C. code) and communicating its complete product identity codes to its trading partners. The UCC controls use of the manufacturer's ID code anywhere outside the company. The code is numeric only and is designed for predefined or repetitive IDs (that is, the same ID is specified for all items of the same class).

Code 39 or 3 of 9 (three wide elements [bars or spaces] in a group of nine) is probably the most widely used bar code symbol-

CHAPTER 3 PRODUCT IDENTIFICATION AND TRACKING

ogy. It is used in many types of manufacturing and is considered the standard code for applications in the electronics and automotive industries. Code 39 is also used in many military applications for product identification. It was the first symbology to use the full character set of numerals and the letters from A through Z.

Code 128 was developed to provide a more compact code with strong error checking ability built in. This code encompasses the full 128-character ASCII set within its basic structure.

Another very familiar bar code symbology is the Postnet code used by the United States Postal Service for mail sorting. Design requirements for Postnet included the ability to print and read codes at very high speed on nonuniformly-sized items. Postnet codes are a combination of uniform-width, full-height and half-height bars, separated by uniform-width white space, with the data followed by a check digit.

With Code 25 or 2 of 5 (two wide elements [bars or spaces] in a group of five), the information is encoded via the width of the printed bars with the white space serving only to separate the bars. Code 25 is used for warehouse inventory, baggage handling, airline cargo, and ticket coding. Because this symbology resulted in long slender codes that made scanning labels with lasers in a warehouse environment difficult, a design modification known as Interleaved 2 of 5 was developed, in which both the bars and spaces carry information, thus providing a more compact code.

Implementing Linear Bar Coding

After deciding to use linear bar coding for product identification and data collection, it is necessary to analyze a number of issues to determine what type of code to use, how to apply the code to the items, how to read the codes, etc. The first task is to define the purpose of the product identification use. If the identification use is limited to tracking items within the manufacturing operation, there is much more flexibility and fewer requirements to satisfy than if the labeling is to be used by customers or consumers of the product. Usually, when product identification uses are outside the organization, the options are limited as to code symbology, type and size of label, and even what data are encoded. We assume here that product identification applies only to the manufacturing organization. An analysis of a bar code implementation includes considerations of:

- Physical characteristics.
- Information needed.
- The labeling environment.
- The postlabeling environment.
- Required life expectancy of the label.
- Reading conditions.
- Costs.

Physical characteristics. What are the characteristics of the item to be identified? If the item is very small, the bar code must either be small or attached to a tag, container, or accompanying paperwork. Some examples include electronic parts such as resistors or integrated circuit chips, fasteners such as screws or rivets, electrical contacts used in switches, gemstones, and some dentist's tools.

Many products will not allow the attachment of a foreign object such as a bar-coded label. Examples are items whose surface is too irregular (for example, a threaded shaft) or whose surface must not be contaminated (for example, a steel bearing). This constraint would also apply to many products intended for consumption, such as food and many pharmaceutical products. A whole branch of technology has developed around transporting the bar codes for such products. The most common approach is simply to code a container, then make sure that the material is kept in the same container throughout processing. Obviously, if the product identification must continue to

points beyond the manufacturer's control of the handling, then the identification must somehow be permanently affixed to the product. For such products, it is now possible to use embossed or etched bar codes. For example, some tire manufacturers have successfully included a code in their tire molds. A manufacturer of ink jet printers uses laser etching to imprint a coded serial number onto some parts. These are two-dimensional codes, however, and generally require special equipment or techniques to be read reliably.

Many lower-cost or high-volume products do not require individual identification as they move through the plant, so the products are accompanied with bar-coded identification attached to a container, tag, or paperwork. This approach is generally easy to implement and less expensive than placing an ID on each item. It also works well with items whose principal need for identification is as a member of a lot, and whose specific identity does not need to extend beyond the manufacturing process.

Information needed. What information about the item needs to be available and in what context? In general, the least expensive approach is for the item identity to act as an index for the data. It also fully describes the item. Sometimes this is called the "license plate" approach: the bar code itself does not contain any meaningful data, but simply acts as a pointer to data stored elsewhere.

When the product identification medium must contain a lot of information, the processes of creating, maintaining, and reading that identification are likely to be increasingly expensive. Remember that if any updating of the identification data is required, then a bar code is not suitable. With the development of 2D symbologies, it is now feasible to print codes that contain a fair amount of data. Such codes might be appropriate to provide machine-readable information about the contents of the shipment and product handling, or shipping instructions printed on the container or shrink-wrapped pallet.

In cases where the code should be confidential, or its visibility would be considered obtrusive or ugly, there are now invisible inks that can be printed on other printing if necessary. The invisible ink can be read in infrared light. So it is possible, in some cases, to print identification codes on a product without anyone other than the intended recipient even being aware a code is present.

Labeling environment. What is the environment in which the bar code will be applied? Is the bar code used in the middle of a high-speed, automated production process (one extreme) or is the product individually handled during a work center-to-work center movement (the other extreme)? Is the product clean and dry when the bar code is attached, has it been bathed in oil during a machining operation, or has it just exited a furnace? Each of these environments are challenges for the application of bar-coded information.

The factors that affect the application of a bar-coded label are the speed and motion direction of the target part, its temperature, its surface cleanliness, and atmospheric contaminants. Because of the wide range of situations that can arise, there is an equally wide range of solutions that have been developed. A wide variety of machinery is available to apply labels. In addition, many different adhesives have been developed to address different circumstances both at the time of application and thereafter.

In some cases where the product has to be labeled in the middle of a high-speed automated operation, ink jet printers print bar codes on the product. This kind of printing requires the right combination of product surface and scanning equipment so that the code can be read reliably later.

Postlabeling environment. What is the environment in which the item will exist after it has been labeled? Will the environment be particularly hot, cold, wet, caustic, or acidic? Will the item be exposed to a wide range of temperatures? (A label adhesive that stands up to one temperature extreme may wilt in the opposite extreme.)

CHAPTER 3   PRODUCT IDENTIFICATION AND TRACKING

Will the label be exposed to bright light for an extended period? (Bright light has a destructive effect on labels printed on thermal paper.) Exposure to high humidity for an extended amount of time could cause labels to wrinkle (becoming unreadable) or fall off.

Will the item be stacked where the label may be covered up when it needs to be read? Will abrasion from one source or another damage, detach, or destroy the bar code? In such instances, the label may need to be on a tag rather than attached directly to the surface of the part.

Required life expectancy. How long should a label last and how often will the label need to be read? The longer that it must be readable, the more durable the label must be and the more permanently it must be affixed. This issue is very closely related to the preceding issue (the storage environment) and the following one (the environment in which the bar code must be read). Wear by abrasion or other means must be addressed to make sure the item identification lasts as long as it is required.

Reading conditions. What are the conditions under which the bar code will be read? Depending on the intended use of the product identification and the planned travels of the item, a wide variety of environmental and operating conditions may need to be considered. Outdoor reading may require an ability to read wet labels. In another instance, reading the vehicle identification numbers located just inside the windshield of cars requires equipment designed to compensate for the reflections and refractivity of curved glass. Reading products stored 20-ft (6-m) high on a warehouse rack requires large, simple codes and long-distance scanners. Reading codes on a moving assembly line requires that the codes be easy to locate (by the scanners) and correctly read the first time every time. For items where codes may be obscured by dust or grease, we may want to consider using codes that are designed to be read at some wavelength other than that of visible light (such as infrared).

Costs. What costs are involved and how do these compare to the benefits? What are the costs of applying the labels or bar codes on the object? Perhaps more important, what are the costs of a missing or unreadable bar code? And what are the costs of relabeling items?

The initial cost of applying bar codes is usually much smaller than the subsequent cost of problems. Therefore, it usually pays to spend a little more to do the job right at the outset. When the bar code on an item is unreadable or missing at the time it is supposed to be read, we could be faced with an item that has completely lost its identity, or whose identity may be quite difficult to recover. This might not be terribly important where the purpose of identity is just to provide a production count, but if the item is a serial-numbered object such as a critical aircraft component, for example, then that loss of identity may be sufficient to render the item unusable. In such a case, the cost of a lost bar code may amount to the cost of the item itself. The cost of relabeling such an item is not just the cost of creating and applying a new label. That is likely to be small. The significant cost is the effort required to determine the item's identity with sufficient certainty. In other instances, the cost of a bar code not being readable may be a slowdown or stoppage of an automated process.

One advantage to most bar codes is that a misread is unlikely. Because the bar code contains check characters that allow the scanner to validate the integrity of the code as it is read, one gets either a good read or no read.

TWO-DIMENSIONAL SYMBOLOGIES

The codes discussed so far have been designed as *license plate codes*: codes that serve to identify the item and direct a lookup into a computer database for information about the item, but by themselves do not contain any item details.

There have been a number of attempts over the years to develop a bar code symbology that can contain information about the labeled item, such as listing the contents of a package on the outside of the package. Because codes that contain information (rather than simply acting as identifiers) are inherently more complex, both the printing and scanning of these codes require more sophisticated printers and scanners. The successful development of such codes had to await advancement in the related areas. The symbologies that have been developed to contain information are called *2D codes* because the symbology uses two dimensions to represent data.

Two-dimensional symbologies first appeared in the late 1980s, but very little equipment was available to read or print them until the mid 1990s. There are over two dozen different 2D symbologies available, each with its strengths and weaknesses. The developers of 2D codes prefer that they not be called "bar" codes, because they are not made up of bars and spaces, but rather of black and white cells, looking somewhat like a crossword puzzle. The arrangement of cells can hold much more data than the old linear codes. Many symbologies such as Code 39, I-205, Codabar, Code 128, Code 93, Code 49, and Code 16K, etc., are generally considered public domain for the end user and have ANSI standards. Symbologies such as PDF417, Code One, Maxicode, and Datamatrix are generally considered public domain for the end user but do not have an ANSI standard yet. Others, such as Vericode®, are proprietary and exclusive to certain manufacturers. In all cases, it is wise for the user to determine the restrictions (if any) for the symbology before deciding to use it.

Types of 2D Codes

There are basically two different types of 2D symbologies: *stacked* (or multirow) *codes* and *matrix codes* (see Fig. 3-2). Stacked codes such as PDF417, in the simplest description, are like one long bar code broken into sections and stacked one section upon another. Portable data file (PDF) indicates the intended use of this new symbology. Matrix codes, such as Datamatrix, encode the data in arrangement of regular polygon-shaped cells where the distance of adjacent elements is uniform. Bits of data are scattered through the area according to an algorithm unique to each type of matrix code.

PDF417 was the first widely-used 2D symbology. It can be read with special laser scanner technology that is not very different from that used to scan linear bar codes. This makes PDF417 the least expensive alternative in terms of scanning equipment. PDF417 is used most often for applications involving container labels and paperwork, rather than marking of parts. While it can encode large amounts of data, the standard form of PDF417 does not scale down well for small part marking. In the proportions most commonly used for part marking, a square PDF417 symbol 1.3 in. (33 mm) on a side would be required to hold between 25 and 90 characters.

The Datamatrix 2D code is slightly newer than PDF417, and requires more advanced (and generally more expensive) technology for scanning. Laser-based scanners are not commercially available for matrix codes like Datamatrix, and so a camera-like, charge-coupled device (CCD) technology must be used. Datamatrix has been chosen by the aerospace, automotive, electronics, and semiconductor industries in the United States as the preferred 2D symbology for part marking and labeling. In the proportions most commonly used for part marking, a Datamatrix symbol can hold up to 89 characters of data in a square slightly over 0.33 in. (8.4 mm) on a side. Datamatrix scales down extremely well, and, when very fine marking is used, it is possible to get 62 characters of data into a square symbol only 0.13 in. (3.3 mm) on a side.

Some other 2D codes in use include Maxicode for high-speed sortation applications, Code 49, Code 16K, and Code One. We should

CHAPTER 3   PRODUCT IDENTIFICATION AND TRACKING

PDF417

Datamatrix

Fig. 3-2 Representative two-dimensional codes. (*Courtesy Zebra Technologies Corporation*)

note that while read errors in linear bar codes are typically only about one in one million characters read, tests with PDF417 and Datamatrix gave results of zero errors in over 35 million symbols scanned. So, not only are these new symbologies more powerful, but they are more reliable.

Advantages and Limitations of 2D Codes

The 2D codes offer the advantage of a much smaller size for similar amounts of data than is possible with linear bar codes. For example, a part number, vendor ID, and part serial number can be placed in a space less than 0.08 in. (2.0 mm) on a side. The same information could take more than three symbols using more than 2 × 6 in. (51 × 152 mm) with Code 39. A 2D code allows marking small parts or packages that cannot be marked with linear bar codes.

For those who need the information, but do not have instant access to a computer database all the time, 2D symbologies offer much greater data capacity than linear bar codes. How much data? In a demonstration, the Gettysburg Address has been encoded into a 2D symbol 2 × 3 in. (51 × 76 mm). Of course, a relatively expensive scanner with a large data screen built into it is needed to retrieve the data from the 2D code. But at least it can be retrieved.

The 2D symbologies are more complex than linear bar codes, both in the optics required to read them and in the computer power needed to encode and decode them. None of the readers that are in common use today for scanning linear bar codes can read the leading 2D symbologies. The scanners for 2D require better optics and bigger processor chips, so they are higher in cost. The technology is an emerging one, still unproven on any large scale. There are only a few companies offering equipment to read the codes at this time.

The 2D technology is very attractive to those who cannot—or do not want—to live with the restrictions of linear bar codes. It is important that a prospective user understand the application requirements and cost justification before applying 2D symbologies. It may be better to keep linear bar codes and use 2D only where linear bar codes cannot work. Reviewing the process requirements will help the user make that determination.

The 2D symbologies offer many advantages over linear bar codes: error correction capabilities, greater data capacity, and increased area efficiency. These advantages allow many new applications, such as individual part marking, encoding quality information, encoding material safety data sheets (MSDS), and package sorting.

Area efficiency. Two-dimensional symbologies offer improved area efficiency over linear bar codes. *Area efficiency* is defined as the ratio of the amount of information (in bits) to the area of the symbol. There are two methods for determining the area efficiency, depending on how the area of the symbol is defined:

- Measure the area in "square modules"—the individual squares, circles, or hexagons that compose the symbol. For example, a symbol that is 20 modules wide and 20 modules high has an area of 400 square modules. This method is ideal for comparing the marking or printing time of various symbologies, assuming that, for a given printing method, it takes the same amount of time to mark each module. Printing time must be considered in selecting a symbology to ensure that adequate capacity is available.
- Measure the area in terms of surface area (for example, square inches or square millimeters). Many symbologies may be eliminated from consideration simply because they cannot fit the data in the area available.

A high area efficiency can be exploited in the following ways:

- A smaller symbol can be printed for a given amount of data and square-module size. This permits less area to be allocated for bar coding.
- A symbol equal in size and data quantity can be printed using larger square modules than a symbol of low area efficiency (that is, at a larger scale). When it comes to bar codes, bigger is better; larger size will help make the symbol more robust to environmental factors that could destroy it.
- The symbol can contain more data for a given size and square-module dimension (that is, more data in the same area). As noted previously, printing more data is becoming highly desirable, and if it takes additional area, it comes at an additional cost. If more data can be squeezed into the same area, the added costs are restricted to the time of marking.

Scanning technologies. The type of bar code used dictates the type of scanner (reader) required. There are four general types of readers: wands, lasers, raster lasers, and area scanners using charged coupled devices (CCDs). The traditional linear bar code can be scanned using any of these technologies. Code 49 and Code 16K (2D stacked symbols) cannot be scanned effectively by a wand. PDF417 requires the use of a raster laser or CCD. All of the 2D matrix symbols require a CCD to image them. However, there is research being done to adapt the other technologies listed. Because of these limitations, the type of scanner selected may dictate the symbology used. Wands range in price from $100-$500. Lasers are $300-$1,200, and raster lasers are $1,000-$5,000, and a CCD equipped with a decoder will cost $3,000-$7,500. Despite the fact that 2D CCDs are the most expensive, they are still the most robust for handling any code. Linear CCDs cost from $300-$700.

2D Symbology Selection Criteria

When selecting a 2D symbology, the selection criteria used by the AIAG is provided as a recommendation:

- The proposed symbology must be in the public domain.
- A public symbology specification must be on file with a recognized regulatory group (for example, ANSI, EIA, etc.).

CHAPTER 3   PRODUCT IDENTIFICATION AND TRACKING

- The proposed symbology must be free of litigation.
- The symbology should be supported by multiple sources of readers and printers.
- There should be evidence of symbol efficiency, readability, and error correction capability.
- The symbology should be independently tested.
- The data capacity for a single symbol and the concatenation of symbols should be proven.

Symbology Structure

Each symbology has its own unique features and limitations. The subsequent sections compare the structures of various symbologies and their weaknesses.[2]

Data elements. Data elements are the individual squares, circles, or hexagons that are arrayed to make a 2D symbol. Most of the symbologies use square elements, with the exception of Maxicode. Maxicode has hexagon-shaped data elements, which provide the best packaging density. However, because of scanner resolution limitations, the hexagon-shaped elements need to be larger than the squares. Thus, the space efficiency is the same for either shape.

Although Datamatrix usually has square elements, it can be made with any of the shapes listed. The choice of shape depends on the symbology and the printing method selected. Datamatrix can be printed by laser etch, ink jet, dot peen, thermal transfer, and other methods. If dot peening is used, the data elements will be circles.

Finder patterns. For a scanner to locate, identify, and orient the symbology, a finder pattern is required. Datamatrix has a solid perimeter on two adjacent sides and an alternating pattern on the other two sides. PDF417 has start and stop characters repeated vertically on each side of the symbol, resembling a linear bar code. Maxicode utilizes a bull's-eye pattern located in the center of the symbol. Code One has a center pattern of alternating bars and spaces.

Centrally located finder patterns that have a repeating black and white pattern are ideal for high-speed scanning using a fast linear search algorithm. Since PDF417 does not have a repeating pattern, a slower linear search algorithm is required. Datamatrix has a more complex finder pattern than the other three symbologies previously described, requiring an even slower two-dimensional search algorithm. Fortunately, Datamatrix readers exist that are capable of performing 20 reads per second, so this is not usually a serious issue.

Shapes and sizes. Datamatrix and PDF417 are variable density symbologies. In fact, Datamatrix can be produced in 48 different sizes and PDF417 can be any size ranging from four to 928 symbol characters. Maxicode comes in only one size. Code One has eight sizes available and an additional six sizes for ink jet printing.

Since CCD cameras virtually have a square field of view, it is desirable to print square matrix symbologies. Most printers available print Datamatrix in a square format. Code One and Maxicode are nearly square. PDF417 has a variable ratio of width to height, making it rectangular. This configuration is more efficient than a square version because there are fewer start and stop patterns (that is, overhead).

Quiet zones. All of the symbologies, except Code One, require a quiet zone around the perimeter of the symbol. The *quiet zone* is an area that must be void of printing. Generally, the larger the quiet zone, the faster the symbol can be located by the scanner. Datamatrix requires a quiet zone of 10% of the perimeter's length and width on all sides. PDF417 requires a quiet zone equal to two square modules on all sides. Maxicode requires 0.25 in. (6.4 mm) of quiet zone on all sides.

Error correction and detection. All of the matrix symbologies and PDF417 use Reed-Solomon error correction. Reed-Solomon codes can correct large errors, such as those introduced by a corner torn from the symbology. Datamatrix can also use convolution codes for error correction in place of Reed-Solomon. Convolution codes can correct randomly scattered errors more efficiently than the Reed-Solomon method.

Maxicode and Code One arrange the information into compact shapes to take full advantage of Reed-Solomon error correction and detection. In fact, the error correction characters find and correct discrepant characters. This requires two correction characters per error. Because of their construction, the level of error correction is fixed (that is, only one level) for both of these symbologies.

PDF417 is the only stacked symbology known to have error correction capabilities. By using character parity, it is able to find most errors. Thus, only one error correction character is required to correct each error.

Unlike Code One and Maxicode, PDF417 and Datamatrix have multiple levels of error correction. This is desirable for applications with poor print quality, severe environmental factors, or extreme scanning requirements. Additional characters are required in PDF417 and Datamatrix for error detection.

Despite the fact that 2D symbologies possess error correction capabilities, they are unable to correct any errors in the data fields that specify the error correction level. This is an advantage for symbologies with a fixed level of error correction, since they do not have these fields.

Determining When to Use 2D Symbologies

Many justifications for the use of 2D symbologies have been stated, such as the need for part serialization and automated data collection. However, using 2D symbologies is not necessary to perform either task. Generally, if a linear bar code can do the job, then use it. Linear bar codes are a proven technology and the total implementation cost will be less than that of 2D symbologies.

Radio-frequency identification (RFID) tags can also perform these functions. However, if a part is manually handled, the use of RFID tags is not practical. Two-dimensional symbologies are ideal for applications that meet one or more of the following conditions:[3]

- Size of product prohibits encoding data in a linear bar code.
- Environment would easily damage a linear bar code.
- Labels are not permitted and material prohibits printing a linear bar code directly on the product.

RADIO-FREQUENCY DATA COMMUNICATIONS

Radio-frequency (RF) data communications is the technology by which portable or remote wireless data collection devices communicate in real-time back to a host computer system or network. Use of RF devices is relatively expensive because of the cost of the radios and transponder. There are three ways that RF data communications can be used as part of a data collection system:

- Integrating a commercial mobile data network carrier into the data collection system is the method used the least. This is generally appropriate only if the data collection devices are traveling over a wide area (such as across town). Not only is there the added expense of higher-priced equipment, but there are communications subscription and use fees as well.
- A common use of RF in data collection is as a wireless communication replacement for the cable in a network or host-terminal connection. This use of RF is appropriate when the data collection (DC) device must be mobile or when the environment precludes a cable connection between the DC device and computer system. An RF/DC system is also often implemented when real-time access to the data is needed for either on-line validation or database updates gathered with portable devices.

CHAPTER 3   PRODUCT IDENTIFICATION AND TRACKING

• In a *radio-frequency identification (RFID) system*, both the device and the scanner use a radio to communicate. The RFID device, called a *tag*, may be passive (it can be read via a radio inquiry) or it may be active (it contains a battery and broadcasts information over a short distance). RF devices can be simple identification devices (that is, of the "license plate," ID-only type), they can contain some static data (for example, an inventory of the contents of a pallet or container), or they can contain data and be updatable (that is, identification of a part and the history of the last operation performed on it). RF devices are infrequently used, mostly because of their expense and the added cost of the data collection equipment required.

Radio-frequency Data Transmittal

Until recently, all RF/DC systems used narrow band data communications. A system had a single assigned frequency that had to be licensed by the Federal Communications Commission (FCC). A relatively small range of frequencies was available for assignment, and if another system was already installed close by, it might preclude the installation of a new system. The transmitters in such a system have a range of several thousand feet, and systems located too closely together can interfere with one another. The frequency range used for these systems is also susceptible to interference with and by other radio communication devices used by government and public service agencies.

However, many new systems now use spread-spectrum RF technology that uses a controlled process of transmitting over more than one frequency at relatively low power. Spread-spectrum systems have no licensing requirement, are less susceptible to interference, and transmit data at higher speed. Because they use lower power, spread-spectrum systems that cover more distance or service terminals outdoors may require RF repeaters.

For any RF system, communications tests should be run by qualified engineers before a final design is adopted. These tests are needed to assure that the devices can communicate in all the configurations and situations where they will be used when finally in production. Testing needs to be done at the times of day and week when the planned system will be used. The testing should be done by—or at least approved by—the firm from whom the RF equipment will be purchased. Ask your vendor to guarantee the successful operation of your RF/DC system on the basis that you follow their recommendations. This site survey process is probably the most critical step in designing a successful RF/DC system.

Radio-frequency Data Collection

RFID is the RF technology that most closely resembles linear bar coding and 2D symbologies, yet it is an entirely different automatic data capture technology. The bits of data in an RFID tag cannot be seen. There are three components to an RFID system: a transponder (or tag) where the data are stored, an antenna for communicating with the tag, and an interface or reader that allows communication with the outside world. Like 2D codes, RFID tags can potentially hold a lot of data.

As noted, the tags can be active (read-write capable) or passive (read-only). Read-only tags have simple static data embedded into them that cannot be changed, just like a bar code after it has been printed. Read-write tags allow the data on the tag to be updated, something that cannot be done with a linear or 2D code. RFID memory sizes are available in capacities from one bit to a virtually unlimited upper limit (although most have 256,000 bytes as an upper limit). Another characteristic is "passive" versus "active," which refers to the way in which the tag obtains the power it needs to provide the information back to the antenna (simple reflection versus self-contained battery power). As with linear bar codes and 2D symbologies, there are many technical details that need to be understood before an RFID installation can be successful.

Advantages and Limitations of RFID

Beyond its ability to hold large amounts of data and access the data randomly, the great advantage of RFID is the considerable distance at which a tag can be read. A 2D symbol may hold as much data as an RFID tag, but it is still necessary to get close enough to see or even touch the 2D symbol to retrieve the information. RFID tags, in contrast, can be read at distances up to several yards (meters) away. They also can be scanned in the dark, something that is impossible for the optical-technology linear bar codes and 2D symbols.

RFID is the premier technology in harsh environments and where optical scanning is not possible. Read-write tags allow data updates easily, are reusable, have fewer process steps, and often have lower total system operating costs (although not initial costs) to accomplish the same task as linear bar codes or 2D symbologies. This is especially true if updating of data is involved.

Some potential uses for RFID technology include:

• Hazardous material identification.
• Personnel badges.
• Vehicle identification for tolls and customs clearance.
• Shipment identification for customs clearance.
• Manufacturing process control.
• Conveyor control.
• Tool and die identification, set up, and maintenance records.

However, RFID is very expensive to install compared to bar code or 2D. The use is still not widespread, and unlike the buyer of bar code and 2D technology, the RFID buyer is usually locked into a single vendor for all parts of the system. The current major concern with RFID is the lack of a workable open protocol standard in the public domain, either for the three technology pieces (tag, antenna, and reader) or for the format of the data encoded in the tag. Without open standards, a user is tied to a sole source for all RFID components, and the source's system is not compatible with other systems.

The history of other technologies shows that open technology standards lead to wider acceptance, lower prices, and greater availability. Committees at ANSI and the ISO are working to develop open protocol standards for RFID, but it may be some time before they are established. Once an open protocol is established, providers of tags, antennas, and readers will be able to focus on providing the products necessary to allow greater use of this emerging technology.

Until open protocol standards force a more competitive market, RFID is by far the most expensive of the three technologies from a total system cost. The buyer will most likely be locked into a single-vendor solution, which probably will not work if the information to be tracked needs to be available external to the user. A prospective buyer should carefully review the process requirements and cost justification to determine the best use for this technology.

INTEGRATING SENSORS AND CONTROL

Integration of sensors and control into a product identification system requires more attention than the basic data collection design requires. This is because automatic controls under the operation of sensors are generally intended to perform actions without human intervention.

CHAPTER 3   PRODUCT IDENTIFICATION AND TRACKING

SORTATION

The most common use of sensors and automatic control in a production identification system is for automatic sortation. All of the major carriers of mail and packages use coded labels, read these labels with stationary scanners, and then sort the material according to the address information coded on the label.

Of course, an automatic sortation system must handle the items without damaging them. But beyond that, the key design criteria in the context of product identification are labeling, encoding, scanning, decision-making, and control. In an automatic sortation system, the scanner must be able to find the bar codes and read them reliably at high speed. This means that the codes must be printed on a secure label or printed directly on the items. The bar code must always be visible to the scanner. Therefore, the orientation of the device must be controlled so that the code always faces the scanner, or more than one copy of the code must be placed on the item, or the item must be scanned from all sides. The scanners must be able to read and decode the bar codes at whatever speed the items are moving down the sortation line.

The decision-making and control functions for sortation are relatively simple at the design and logic level. The key element is to synchronize the action triggered by the control function with the event that is to be controlled. This means triggering the sortation device at just the right time to properly route each item to the correct destination. The routing mechanism is more of a mechanical engineering subsystem than part of the product identification system. All the data collection and control system must do is determine which route is appropriate for each item and transmit a command to send it there (see Fig. 3-3).

AUTOMATIC STORAGE AND RETRIEVAL SYSTEMS

An automatic storage and retrieval system (AS/RS) includes a set of racks that stores and retrieves items by a computer-controlled mechanism that operates on horizontal and vertical tracks extending throughout the racks. When an item enters the system, its bar code is read to identify the product. The system then puts the item away and remembers what is stored where. It is important that the bar codes be positioned so that they can be reliably found by the scanner. When an item is retrieved, the bar code is read again to assure that the correct item has been picked.

Obviously, a sensor-based material control system can be guided by product identifiers other than bar codes. An AS/RS unit, for example, might be much easier to implement if the products are identified by RFID tags rather than bar-coded labels. This is because RF tags are essentially omnidirectional; they can be read regardless of the product's orientation.

AUTOMATED GUIDED VEHICLES

An *automated guided vehicle* (AGV) is a free-standing, cart-like vehicle whose travel path is controlled by signals, usually sent through wires embedded in a factory or warehouse floor. When used in a material movement application, AGVs are often a variation of the sortation or material routing function. An AGV can be loaded with material and then automatically routed to the appropriate location by sensors reading the labels or other identifiers on the vehicle, or on the contents of the vehicle.

In this application, as in the others, the product identifiers must be easily and reliably read. It is often difficult to predict or control

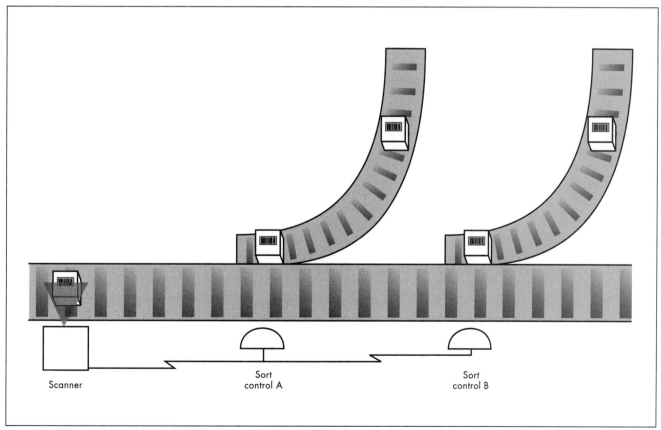

Fig. 3-3 Automatic sortation system. (*Courtesy Studebaker Technology, Inc.*)

Scanner   Sort control A   Sort control B

CHAPTER 3   PRODUCT IDENTIFICATION AND TRACKING

the exact orientation of the product at the point its identification will be read. So the engineering of the process requires ingenuity and the design must be thoroughly tested before it is implemented.

DATA STORAGE AND POSTPROCESSING

After the data have been collected and transmitted back to a host, they should be processed first for validation and, once validated, used for control, management information, and record keeping. It is best if validation is done in real-time as the data is collected, so that any flaws in the data can be identified while there is still the opportunity to correct them. If validation does not occur until some time after the conclusion of the event being tracked, then correction of any errors will be much more difficult, perhaps impossible.

When the validated data have passed to the host, they can be used for a variety of purposes. Some of the more typical uses are:

- Tracking raw materials into the production cycle.
- Tracking work-in-process as it completes each production step and moves to the next step in production.
- Tracking the quantity of work-in-process that is queued at each step and the length of time that it has been queued (one goal of production engineering is to economically minimize both quantity and time).
- Tracking work-in-process as it is shipped to and received from secondary vendors for outside operations (for example, plating or heat treating).
- Tracking finished production into inventory ready to ship.
- Tracking finished goods as they are shipped and recording order fulfillment.

In addition to the status and inventory information that is accumulated in this process, the data are used for various aspects of corporate accounting. Depending on exactly what is gathered, the data could support costing, billing, payroll, production standards calculations, and inventory control, as well as other functions such as quality control, vendor analysis, and electronic data interchange (EDI). Most corporate record keeping depends in one way or another on data collected from the production operations, and automation of that collection process can maximize the timeliness and accuracy of the data while minimizing the cost of the collection process.

PARTIALLY AUTOMATED SYSTEMS

No matter how automated a product identification and tracking operation is, it still needs manual systems to complement and support the automated systems. When all product identification and tracking was done manually, items were labeled with handwritten or preprinted labels or tags. Identification was a matter of reading the text description; tracking was a matter of recording the location of the item and then communicating that information when it was needed. Today, we automate the appropriate portions of this process to reduce costs and increase the accuracy of the data being tracked.

But automation usually occurs in stages, and some functions remain based on manual systems until the next stage of automation is justified. For example, when the use of bar code labels is first implemented, the label application process is often manual. This means that a set of procedures (that is, a system) is needed to assure that the correct bar code label is applied to the right item. The labels must be applied so that they do not fall off and oriented so that they can be easily read. In other words, all the constraints discussed in previous sections of this chapter must be addressed in the manual systems as well. The manual systems must be well-integrated with the automated systems, and each must complement the other.

For example, when shipments of consumer electronic goods are being moved to the dock in preparation for shipping, it may be necessary to manually collect product serial number information as the pallets are made up. Special labeling may also need to be manually created at the same time, identifying pallet contents. On the other end of the material flow, it is quite normal to have a manual system controlling the identification of material at receiving. Material that arrives from vendors is often not identified in a manner consistent with the customer's internal standards. So the material must be unloaded, sorted, verified, and labeled before it can be put under the control of the automated tracking system. Any received material that cannot be verified or does not pass the initial inspection remains under control of the manual system pending return to the vendor. The manual system smoothly feeds the automated system.

Often, manual systems surround the automated systems, defining their boundaries for operation. For example, when a material identification system is set up to automatically print and apply labels to items passing on a production line, the feeding of product ID codes and the definition of the beginning number in a serial number sequence are set manually and verified by manual oversight. In another example, where reusable containers have permanent bar code labels, a manual procedure associated with cleaning the containers also includes scanning the code to reset the recorded container condition back to "empty." If the scanning step in this manual procedure is missed, then the container is not identified as available for reuse.

When a manual system is implemented or modified, a primary concern is establishing clear goals for it. Another important concern is ease of use. The manual system must be well-integrated with other manual and automated systems, and to ensure accuracy, it must provide checks and balances and include a verification step.

DATA COLLECTION POINTS

The basic rules for identifying the proper point at which to collect data are relatively simple. As far as these rules are concerned, it really does not matter whether the data collection is automated or manual. Data should be collected at the following points:

- Where control is needed. Whenever a control action is taken, it should be done with the best information possible. This means that there should be a data collection point immediately prior to any point where an automated control action will occur. Conversely, it is reasonable to say that we should not execute an action on an item unless we have just collected data about the item and have knowledge of its present status. The same principle applies to any point where a manual control action will take place. A sensor reading, as discussed in the section "Integrating Sensors and Control," is a form of data collection if the reading is retained and stored.
- Where a count is needed. If any action could have affected the items since the last data collection point, then another data collection point is appropriate. Counts can be done by manual quantity entry, automatic counting as part of a machine or conveying

CHAPTER 3   PRODUCT IDENTIFICATION AND TRACKING

operation, or weighing, among other ways. If we know the current counts for items, we can commit to their delivery to customers or their use in subsequent manufacturing operations.

- Where security is needed. Whenever it is important to provide security for the items, it is appropriate to have a data collection point to confirm that items have (or have not) reached that location. If the data collected include time and date (and most automated data collection systems do), there will be a clear audit trail of the items. This can be helpful for audit, safety, or insurance purposes.
- When material must be located. Data collection can provide the location of the items being tracked. This can be done either explicitly, by collecting location (bin, bay, building, work center, etc.) as part of the data, or implicitly, based on the location of the data collection device. When the current location of items is known, it obviously is much easier to obtain the items when they are needed or to determine their status in terms of progress through a series of manufacturing operations. Collection of location, along with date and time, provides a movement history for the items being tracked.
- When material moves from one sphere of control to another. This is obviously a special case of the need to locate material just discussed. But in this case, it is necessary not only to know where the material is, but to define who is currently responsible for it. This issue is particularly important for materials such as hazardous items (for example, chemicals, explosives, weapons, and radioactive material), medical materials (for example, medicines, narcotics, surgical instruments, and prosthetic implants), and especially valuable items (for example, museum art, jewels, and precious metals in volume).
- Wherever specific information about the item being tracked is needed. For example, when a heat of metal is tracked through processing, at some point it is necessary to know the temperature of the metal. At that point, data must be collected. If a product is processed through a liquid bath and its weight is needed before and after the bath, then data must be collected at both points. If production is being controlled by statistical process control (SPC) or a similar sampling technique, then it is necessary to measure and collect data at particular control points in the production processes.

Good information about products, production processes, and the movement and flow of materials through operations can be had only through timely, accurate data collection.

PRODUCT DATA MANAGEMENT

Product data management (PDM) is the combination of the acts of storing, organizing, retrieving, communicating, consolidating, synthesizing, or in any other way productively manipulating data that define and describe products. Most of the time, PDM has been used on engineering data about products. Such data include drawings (perhaps from a computer-aided design [CAD]), bills of material, manufacturing specifications, material specifications, etc. PDM originally centered around the process of management and control of changes in product design and specifications.

PDM in its fullest form will impact all of the product-related areas of the company, including Product Engineering, Sales, Process Engineering, Document Management, Marketing, Management Information Systems, Planning, and Production Control. The goal is to provide all areas of the firm access to all the available information about products (see Fig. 3-4).

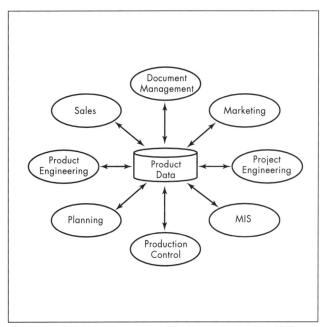

Fig. 3-4 Product Data Management (PDM) permits sharing of information throughout the firm. (*Courtesy Studebaker Technology, Inc.*)

Each area of the business is responsible for maintaining the product data that it controls. Marketing should maintain product sales forecasts and Sales should maintain sales history data. Product Engineering should maintain bills of material and manufacturing specifications. Document Management should maintain drawings and manufacturing procedure documentation. Process Engineering should maintain production process information and Planning should maintain production plans. Management Information Systems (MIS) should provide the tools for the storage, integration, and data retrieval maintained by the other departments. Production Control should have data about the status of production activity.

In most businesses, these different types of information are not well-integrated. As a result, even if the business has separate systems for each of the different types of data, it is not realizing the maximum possible benefits from its own data and does not really have a full-fledged PDM system. Each of the business's systems typically stores its segment of the product data in a separate database, and may use different database software or at least different sets of rules for defining the data indices, primary file structure, and methods of display. It is often difficult or impossible to correlate Marketing's forecasts with Production Control's production status or with Engineering's bills of material. It is likely to be just as difficult to correlate the cost data maintained by Accounting with the product design data maintained by Engineering. But each of these correlations, if feasible, would give a clearer picture of the possible, planned, and actual impacts of each product on the business.

In the specific realm of product identification and tracking, we are most interested in ensuring the accurate capture, storage, retrieval, and intelligent interpretation of data regarding the movement, location, and activities affecting our products. The first goal is to make sure this information is reliable and useful in itself (that is, without regard to the overall corporate need to address the larger picture inherent in PDM). But as soon as we have achieved our primary goal, we should raise our sights to the goal of sharing our data and ensuring that it integrates with other product-related data within our company. By following this step-by-step approach of achieving lesser

CHAPTER 3   PRODUCT IDENTIFICATION AND TRACKING

goals, then moving on to higher goals, we will increase our likelihood of success and decrease the probability of failure. But it is important, even as we make the first step, to keep the long-term goals of integration with other corporate data firmly in mind, so that we do not make early design choices that preclude the long-term goal. The long-term goal is to make the corporate database more useful and powerful through identification and eventual prediction of relationships and interdependencies in various activities.

References

1. International Organization for Standardization (ISO). ISO 9001, Clause 4.8. Geneva, Switzerland: ISO, 1987.
2. Williams, Ted. *Two-Dimensional Symbologies*. Dedham, MA: Laserlight Systems, Inc., 1994.
3. Barkan, Christina, Proddy, Dennis, and Earle, Timothy. "Exploring the Benefits and Future of 2D Symbology." Presentation at ID Expo Conference. San Jose, CA: Advanstar Communications, November 1995.

Bibliography

"ADC Takes its Place as a Productivity Tool." *Modern Materials Handling—ScanTech News*, November 1996.

AIAG-B-1. *Bar Code Symbology Standard*. Southfield, MI: Automotive Industry Action Group (AIAG), 1984.

AIAG-B-3. *Shipping/Parts Identification Label Standard*. Southfield, MI: AIAG, 1985.

AIAG-B-4. *Individual Parts Identification Label Standard*. Southfield, MI: AIAG, 1984.

Allais, D. C. *Bar Code Symbology*. Everett, WA: INTERMEC, 1985.

American National Standards Institute (ANSI) MH10.8M American National Standard for Materials Handling. *Bar Code Symbols on Unit Loads and Transport Packages*. New York: ANSI, 1983.

Automatic ID News. Cleveland, OH: Advanstar Communications.

Global AIM Network Yearbook and Buyer's Guide 1997. Halifax, United Kingdom: AIM International, Auto ID Services, 1997.

Harmon, C. K. *Lines of Communication*. Peterborough, NH: Helmers Publishing, 1994.

ID Systems. Peterborough, NH: Helmers Publishing.

Integrated Design & Manufacturing. Dearborn, MI: Society of Manufacturing Engineers.

Longe, K. M., and Brenner, L. B. *Bar Code Technology in Health Care*. Cleveland, OH: Advanstar Marketing Services, 1993.

Managing Automation. Atlanta, GA: Thomas Publishing Company.

Manufacturing Engineering. Dearborn, MI: Society of Manufacturing Engineers.

Manufacturing Systems. Radnor, PA: Chilton Publications.

Palmer, R. C. *The Bar Code Book*. Peterborough, NH: Helmers Publishing, 1995.

Plossl, K. R. *Engineering for the Control of Manufacturing*. Englewood Cliffs, NJ: Prentice-Hall, 1987.

"Shop Floor Data Collection Eliminates Tracking Errors." *Modern Materials Handling—ScanTech News*, October 1996.

Studebaker, D.A. "I'm Late, I'm Late." *APICS—The Performance Advantage*, August 1996.

Studebaker, D.A. "The Right Place at the Right Time." *APICS—The Performance Advantage*, May 1995.

Studebaker, D.A. "What's Happening Boss?" *Assembly*, October 1995.

Technical Review. Halifax, United Kingdom: AIM International, Auto ID Services, 1996.

Wang, Y. P. and Bravman, R. *PDF417, A Two-Dimensional Bar Code System*. Dayton, OH: Uniform Code Council, 1989.

CHAPTER 4

STORAGE AND INVENTORY PLANNING

CHAPTER CONTENTS

INTRODUCTION

This chapter begins by describing key storage planning phases. Then, it defines the material storage environment, storage plan goals and criteria by business organization, business computer systems storage criteria, and product storage and flow characteristics. Finally, it shows how to calculate storage equipment quantity and floor area, discusses centralized versus decentralized strategies, and inventory storage method alternatives.

While material handling and computer system solutions seem to have all the glory, their success and sophistication depend heavily on the storage strategy selected. Storage and inventory planning is very important.

The phrase *storage strategy* in this chapter refers to alternatives having a unique combination of storage methods and their capacities. Storage methods can range from floor spots to conventional racks to automated dispenser systems. The storage method capacity is a function of the products or inventory stored in them.

Storage method planning greatly affects overall material storage efficiency and flow performance. Balancing storage methods with acceptable return on investment (ROI) requires serious engineering analysis. The selection will affect employees and the business for a long time.

There are too many situations where reputable storage equipment and material handling vendors were technically correct in their recommendations but the implementation failed. In severe situations, companies have closed facilities or initiated lawsuits. The storage and material handling market is complex and the requirements for equipment compatibility, service support, and reliability are all major factors in an integrated system. Successful storage implementation requires a good plan.

Storage planning is divided into two major steps. The first step is defining the business need (in terms of cost, schedule, and performance) and selecting the best storage strategy. The second step is developing detailed technical specifications and implementing the equipment. Information needed for the second step is obtained internally (from existing facility layouts, procedures, computer systems) and externally (from reference books, government agencies, insurance companies, equipment vendors, and engineering consult-

ing services). This chapter focuses on the first major step of planning for storage. It emphasizes the development of the inventory storage strategy and inventory profiles. It also provides a storage planning baseline that can be enhanced to meet many projects.

KEY STORAGE PLANNING PHASES

The planning and implementation of the best storage strategy is accomplished by selecting effective people, exercising good project management, and accessing knowledgeable storage engineering resources. It begins with selecting a storage project team and ends after executing two important storage planning phases. Tables 4-1 through 4-4 show a storage plan schedule. The "100" series of design tasks are described in Table 4-1 as Phase I and the "200" series of strategic tasks are described in Table 4-2 as Phase II. The "300" and "400" series of tasks illustrate the detail design and implementation tasks as shown in Tables 4-3 and 4-4 (but are not described in this chapter).

SELECT A STORAGE PROJECT TEAM

A "champion" of the storage plan must be selected who can organize the needed people and provide leadership for the plan.

The project team size and required skill sets are a function of the project's magnitude. If management is reluctant to create a team (usually due to other priorities), make them aware of the importance of the following indirect benefits:

- Employees of differing backgrounds work together.
- Improved organizational networking and cooperation.
- Cross-training permits employees to acquire new skills and knowledge.
- Solutions biased in one perspective are avoided.
- Failures caused by employee lack of commitment are avoided.
- Employees participate in major decisions.

Select highly effective team members and run high quality meetings. Look for these desirable characteristics in each person:

- Clear thinker.
- Emotionally stable.
- Seeks responsibility.
- Dependable.
- Interacts well with others.
- Excellent in his or her field.
- Strategic thinker.
- Willing to help others succeed.

PHASE I: DEFINE GENERAL STORAGE DESIGN REQUIREMENTS

This phase includes bringing the storage team together, collecting information, and defining the evaluation criteria and rules.

First, define (in business terms) the impact of what "no change" in storage means to the organization—this helps define the importance and scope of the storage plan. Second, recruit key representa-

The Contributor of this chapter is: Jim McNamara, CPIM, Senior Consultant, The Sims Consulting Group.
The Reviewers of this chapter are: E. Ralph Sims, Jr., PE, CMfgE, Professor Emeritus—Industrial Engineering, Ohio University; Bruce Steffens, Material Handling Engineering Project Manager, Arlington Rack and Packaging Company.

CHAPTER 4 STORAGE AND INVENTORY PLANNING

TABLE 4-1
Design Tasks for Storage Plan

Task ID	Task Description	Days	Prior Task	Operator Representative	Engineer Representative	Completion Date
100	General design requirements					
105	Direct/indirect material analysis	_____		_____	_____	__/__
110	Operations and process analysis	_____		_____	_____	__/__
115	Order release analysis	_____		_____	_____	__/__
120	Information flow analysis	_____		_____	_____	__/__
125	Trends and technologies	_____		_____	_____	__/__
130	Material storage profile	_____	105	_____	_____	__/__
135	Material handling profile	_____	110	_____	_____	__/__
140	Purchasing activity profile	_____	115	_____	_____	__/__
145	Storage information requirements	_____	120	_____	_____	__/__
150	Organize collected information	_____	125–145	_____	_____	__/__
155	Analyze collected information	_____	150	_____	_____	__/__
160	Develop storage models	_____	155	_____	_____	__/__
165	Approve general design requirements	_____	160	_____	_____	__/__

TABLE 4-2
Strategic Tasks for Storage Plan

Task ID	Task Description	Days	Prior Task	Operator Representative	Engineer Representative	Completion Date
200	Define/evaluate/select storage strategy					
205	Design rules/constraints	_____	165	_____	_____	__/__
210	Material handling equipment requirements	_____	165	_____	_____	__/__
215	Computer interaction requirements	_____	165	_____	_____	__/__
220	Manual procedure requirements	_____	165	_____	_____	__/__
225	General equipment specifications	_____	165	_____	_____	__/__
230	Review vendor information	_____	225	_____	_____	__/__
235	Detail storage requirements	_____	205–230	_____	_____	__/__
240	Develop storage alternatives	_____	235	_____	_____	__/__
245	Compare storage alternatives	_____	240	_____	_____	__/__
250	Select best alternative	_____	245	_____	_____	__/__

TABLE 4-3
Detail Design Tasks for Storage Plan

Task ID	Task Description	Days	Prior Task	Operator Representative	Engineer Representative	Completion Date
300	Detail storage method design and procurement					
305	Develop administration procedures	_____	250	_____	_____	__/__
310	Inventory location analysis	_____	250	_____	_____	__/__
315	Computer system interfaces	_____	250	_____	_____	__/__
320	Define support activity	_____	250	_____	_____	__/__
325	Create bid evaluation guide	_____	250	_____	_____	__/__
330	Detail performance bid specifications	_____	250, 325	_____	_____	__/__
335	Issue requirements for quote (RFQ)/receive bids	_____	330	_____	_____	__/__
340	Review/select vendors	_____	325	_____	_____	__/__
345	Approve and order equipment	_____	340	_____	_____	__/__

tives of the business units responsible for the operational success of the project. Third, recruit departments responsible for the technical success of the storage equipment. For example:

1. The Management Information Systems (MIS) department must assure maximum compatibility with existing and future computer functions (bar coding, picking automation, warehouse management systems, etc.). Key inventory control features on the computer system must be supported by any new storage plan and allow the exchange of data between programs.

2. Engineering must assure storage plan compatibility with material handling and building requirements (both current and future). They may influence vendor and equipment selection—especially from an ongoing maintenance perspective.

CHAPTER 4   STORAGE AND INVENTORY PLANNING

TABLE 4-4
Implementation Tasks for Storage Plan

Task ID	Task Description	Days	Prior Task	Operator Representative	Engineer Representative	Completion Date
400	Storage strategy implementation					
405	Monitor equipment and building progress	_____	345	_____	_____	__/__
410	Support start-up effort	_____	345	_____	_____	__/__
415	Finalize administration procedures	_____	345	_____	_____	__/__
420	Administer procedure training	_____	415	_____	_____	__/__
425	Supervise receipt and installation	_____	345	_____	_____	__/__
430	Perform acceptance tests	_____	425	_____	_____	__/__
435	Operation training	_____	430	_____	_____	__/__
440	Maintenance training	_____	430	_____	_____	__/__
445	Complete all documentation	_____	405–440	_____	_____	__/__
450	Measure tangible expectations	_____	425	_____	_____	__/__
455	Obtain project sign-off	_____	450	_____	_____	__/__
460	Identify future enhancements	_____	455	_____	_____	__/__

After organizing the project team, develop the storage evaluation criteria. A suggested methodology is described in more detail later (see *Defining the Material Storage Environment* in this chapter). At the end of Phase I, expect the storage "vision" to be clear. If contradictory expectations exist, then keep working on it until everyone has the same understanding.

PHASE II: DEFINE/EVALUATE/SELECT STORAGE STRATEGY

This phase requires acquiring up-to-date knowledge about storage method capabilities and their implementation impact. The alternatives are a function of performance specifications, the vendors selected, and preliminary bids (providing budgetary costs, suggested vendor models, estimated delivery times, and implementation).

Understanding the implementation requirements is critical. Each vendor or storage strategy will have specific site preparation needs, business procedures, acceptance testing methods, employee training, and perhaps computer interfaces. Reduce the impact on existing operations during implementation by creating contingency procedures (if implementation is not completed on time). Some projects call for state-of-the-art storage equipment but the implementation risks are not studied thoroughly—leading to overruns in costs and operational interruptions.

The storage performance specifications depend heavily on the evaluation criteria developed in Phase I. Phase II requires active participation from experienced engineering resources residing internally (Industrial or Plant Engineering) or outside (engineering consulting firms and selected vendors).

As a rule, provide three storage plan strategies that are significantly different. For example, the project team may choose from:

1. Lowest technical risk, capital cost, lead times, performance, and implementation impact.
2. Medium technical risk, cost, lead times, performance, and implementation impact.
3. Highest technical risk (state-of-the-art), cost, lead times, performance, and implementation impact.

Select the best storage strategy by having the project team evaluate the alternatives presented by Engineering (who have already done a technical evaluation). This is accomplished by using the evaluation criteria and rules agreed upon by all parties during the first phase.

At this point, consensus has been achieved regarding the best storage strategy and organizational buy-in is complete. Everyone involved knows the benefits and risks associated with their respective areas of the selected strategy. A common vision has been achieved.

The last responsibility of the storage plan team is to review and approve the schedule (usually developed by Engineering and the project leader). After the schedule is approved, planning is complete and all effort is focused on implementing the plan (Tables 4-3 and 4-4).

After the schedule is approved, the Operations, MIS, and Engineering departments must work closely together to make it happen.

DEFINING THE MATERIAL STORAGE ENVIRONMENT

This section describes the methodology for defining the evaluation criteria of the storage strategies and includes the following:

• Survey organization to develop goals.
• Identify storage plan rules that must be satisfied.
• Define tangible goals and evaluation criteria.
• Define intangible goals and evaluation criteria.
• Kepner-Tregoe (KT) methodology.

SURVEY ORGANIZATION TO DEVELOP GOALS

The storage plan must solicit important business and technical objectives and constraints from all affected departments. Define the success criteria early in the project to avoid misunderstandings later.

Obtain the proper level of involvement. In some cases, the department manager may only monitor team decisions (to ensure alignment with company direction). In other cases, management should actively participate to ensure a good project solution. Try to understand the perspectives of other personnel and departments:

• Owner, Chief Operations Officer, Chief Financial Officer, or Plant Manager.
• Financial Management.
• Manufacturing/Quality Control/Quality Assurance.
• Materials and Transportation.
• Production Control and Scheduling.
• Human Resources and Safety Engineering.
• Industrial and Plant Engineering.
• Computer Systems Management.

IDENTIFY STORAGE PLAN RULES THAT "MUST" BE SATISFIED

While conducting the interviewing process, identify what criteria must be met for a storage strategy alternative to be viable. "Must"

CHAPTER 4   STORAGE AND INVENTORY PLANNING

requirements are usually technical, but also can be business expectations. Examples of "must" criteria include:

- Government rules and building codes.
- Plant engineering and safety engineering standards and constraints.
- Key operations procedures, computer systems, or material handling method constraints.
- Critical business and computer systems goals, policies, and constraints.
- Critical operations, material handling and storage procedures, shop floor policies, and constraints.

All other criteria that are not "musts" are considered "wants." "Wants" are rated on a scale of one to nine where "nine" means high importance and a "one" means low importance.

DEFINE TANGIBLE GOALS AND EVALUATION CRITERIA

While collecting the "must" and "want" criteria, determine how they can be measured objectively. The adage "that which is measured gets done" is often true. It is important to determine how the storage plan success will be measured after implementation. The more objective and measurable a business criterion is, the better. Quantify as many of the broad business goals as possible. For example, change the intangible goal "improve stock availability" to a tangible "98+% stock availability."

Tangible criteria provide uniform, objective comparisons between storage plan alternatives. Whenever possible, implement the tangible goals as business performance expectations of management.

DEFINE INTANGIBLE GOALS AND EVALUATION CRITERIA

Intangible criteria are equally important but are not measurable. They are sensitive to organizational skills, experience, knowledge, and a level of acceptance.

Some intangible criteria can greatly affect the success of the project. Perceptions regarding the vendor's ability to deliver on time or the durability of a storage method may not be quantifiable. Prejudice and uncertainty can be reduced by visiting other installation sites. However, there is no guarantee that the same vendor with the same equipment will have the same success in this project. Only those members with pertinent experience, skills, or authority should evaluate intangible criteria.

KEPNER-TREGOE™ (KT) METHODOLOGY

KT methodology is easy for the team to learn but requires effort to implement effectively. Its major advantage is that it clearly separates "must" from "want" criteria during the storage evaluations.[1]

Viable storage alternatives are required to satisfy all "must" criteria. The best alternative will have the highest score of "want" criteria.

The key to implementing the KT method is wisely deciding what are "musts" and weighting the "wants." If one criterion has a weight factor of four while another has a weight factor of eight, that implies one criterion is twice as important.

Two examples of KT work sheets are illustrated in Tables 4-5 and 4-6. Table 4-5 shows how an individual would rate several alternatives and determine what is best. Table 4-6 illustrates how to integrate the perspectives from several team members and arrive at a unanimous decision.

The Kepner-Tregoe Work Sheet

A complete explanation of this methodology is outside the scope of this chapter. However, a brief summary is provided because of its importance to the storage planning process.

The first step is to obtain evaluation criteria from each team member. Categorize each criterion as tangible or intangible and as either a "must" or a "want." Have each team member weight each "want" design criterion from one to nine.

Each team member should receive a copy of all the other individual team member work sheets to broaden his or her awareness. These work sheets provide valuable performance information to guide Engineering through the maze of possible storage methods.

If necessary, assign a relative weight to each team member. For example, financial considerations may have significant weight in a large storage capacity addition; MIS concerns may have high weight in automated storage applications; and sales concerns may have high

TABLE 4-5
Kepner-Tregoe™ Storage Evaluation Work Sheet

Project name: _____

Organization: _____
Member: _____

Weight Factor	First Alternative Member Rating	First Alternative Calculated Score	Second Alternative Member Rating	Second Alternative Calculated* Score	Third Alternative Member Rating	Third Alternative Calculated* Score	Criteria Description
							Tangibles:
M(ust)	Yes		No	XXX	Yes		Less than xx ft height
9	9	81.0	9	81.0	8	72.0	Less than 6 months to install
7	7	49.0	6	42.0	4	28.0	$$$ per storage location
		65.0		XXX		50.0	Tangible score
							Intangibles:
M(ust)	Yes		Yes		No	XXX	Consistent with strategy
7	6	42.0	8	56.0	7	49.0	Security features
4	7	28.0	6	24.0	9	36.0	Implementation ease
		35.0		40.0		XXX	Intangible score
		50.0		XXX†		XXX†	Overall rating

* Criteria weight factor × member rating = calculated score
† Alternative rejected because "must" criteria not satisfied

NOTE: If "must" criteria are not met then the evaluation score for the alternative is equal to zero.

CHAPTER 4   STORAGE AND INVENTORY PLANNING

TABLE 4-6
Kepner-Tregoe™ Storage Team Evaluation Work Sheet

Date: _____

Member Weight	First Alternative		Second Alternative		Third Alternative		Organization and Team Member
	Member Rating	Calculated* Score	Member Rating	Calculated* Score	Member Rating	Calculated* Score	
							Tangibles:
50%	7.0	3.5	XXX	0.0	7.0	3.5	Manufacturing/JPM[†]
20%	5.0	1.0	5.0	1.0	5.0	1.0	Quality control/EJP[†]
30%	7.0	2.1	7.0	2.1	7.0	2.1	Engineering/RPK[†]
		6.6		3.1		6.6	Tangible score
							Intangibles:
50%	4.5	2.3	4.5	2.3	XXX	0.0	Manufacturing/JPM[†]
30%	5.0	1.5	5.0	1.5	7.0	2.1	Quality control/EJP[†]
20%	7.0	1.4	7.0	1.4	10.0	2.0	Engineering/RPK[†]
		5.2		5.2		4.1	Intangible score
		5.9		4.1		5.4	Overall rating

* Member/organization weight × member rating = calculated score
† Initials of team member

weight when considering geographical storage locations. It simply depends on the scope of the storage plan.

STORAGE PLAN GOALS AND CRITERIA BY BUSINESS ORGANIZATION

One requirement of a good storage design is to identify who determines its success and how it will be measured. It is imperative for support organizations (staff functions, MIS, Engineering) to always realize that they are serving a business need, and that storage and inventory planning also supports these needs.

EVALUATION CRITERIA

Solicit evaluation criteria from a wide variety of personnel in other departments such as:

- General Manager and Financial.
- Manufacturing or Quality Control.
- Supervision.
- Materials and Transportation Management.
- WIP Inventory Management.
- Production Control and Shop Scheduling.
- Engineering.

During interviews, discuss the following criteria. Convert as many as possible to tangible criteria.

General Manager and Financial Perspectives
- Improve competitive advantage.
- Improve net profit and cash flow.
- Improve return on investment.
- Improve business ability to change the amount of resources according to current needs.
- Improve business practices/discipline.
- Improve management span of control.
- Improve performance/productivity.

- Improve accuracy and timeliness of information.
- Criteria should be consistent with business strategy.

Manufacturing or Quality Control Perspectives
- Improve flexibility.
- Improve throughput (via WIP buffers).
- Reduce human judgment requirements.
- Improve handling of items.
- Improve automation.
- Improve reliability.
- Improve staging of materials near point-of-use.
- Reduce material handling travel times and distance.
- Reduce indirect labor requirements.
- Improve open floor space.
- Improve worker control of material flow in area.
- Reduce large stock rooms/cluttered areas.
- Reduce flow to remote storerooms or warehouses.
- Avoid unnecessary inventory damage, mix, and aging.
- Reduce material flow and request turnaround time.

Supervision Perspectives
- Improve general appearance and image.
- Improve control by using an inventory zoning methodology.
- Improve working conditions and employee satisfaction by avoiding daily performance variations and inefficient double handling.
- Maximize material flow or movement effectiveness by avoiding lengthy unnecessary travel and maximizing labor utilization (for example, able to pick from both sides of aisle on one pass).
- Improve safety and housekeeping by providing ample storage capacity to avoid double handling.
- Reduce unproductive walking.
- Improve job satisfaction.
- Reduce manual paperwork.
- Improve use of real-time information.
- Improve productive potential of people.
- Improve working conditions.
- Improve employee discipline.
- Reduce fatigue, injuries, and error via ergonomics.
- Reduce dependency on labor market.

CHAPTER 4   STORAGE AND INVENTORY PLANNING

Materials and Transportation Management Perspectives
- Maximize inventory accessibility.
- Assign major inventory to individual work zones/flow.
- Group items as a function of weight, shape, and special storage environment requirements (for example, hazardous material).
- Maximize storage effectiveness and versatility by categorizing item flow rates and periodically reassigning its slot space (explained in more detail later).
- Avoid use of overflow, off-site, or contingency storage.
- Reduce redundant storage.
- Reduce lot sizes and move quantities.
- Reduce containers to hold fixed, smaller quantities.
- Improve effectiveness of indirect activity.
- Improve space utilization.
- Improve inventory turns.
- Improve tracking of materials.
- Reduce customer returns and damaged items.
- Reduce physical inventory and cycle count effort.
- Reduce identification errors and material shrinkage.
- Ergonomic considerations and standards compliance.

Work-in-process (WIP) Inventory Management Perspectives
- Reduce WIP movement frequency.
- Reduce WIP inventory levels.
- Reduce move quantities and WIP clutter.
- Reduce rework and wasted material handling.
- Improve velocity of material through the factory.
- Reduce inventory stagnation and investment in WIP.

Production Control and Shop Scheduling Perspectives
Improve ability to:
- Make-to-order.
- Manufacture smaller lots.
- Manage peak demands.
- Meet tighter schedules.
- Respond to unplanned events.

Engineering Perspectives
- Reduce waste (time and space).
- Improve business ability to change the amount of resources according to current needs.
- Reduce organization barriers.
- Provide flexible, fast-change storage.
- Maintain consistency with long-range plans.
- Develop ability to easily expand and contract.
- Avoid material handling constraints.
- Have minimal disruption and rearrangement.
- Define needed mobility of storage method.
- Develop standardization and interchangeability of parts.
- Have physical flexibility to store a wide range of items.
- Maximize material handling method effectiveness.
- Optimize maintenance/toolroom/stockroom locations.
- Reduce travel time for tools and replacement parts.
- Maximize storage effectiveness and space utilization without incurring excessive capital costs or throughput degradation.
- Guard against natural events such as earthquakes, hurricanes, and extreme temperatures, and provide a secure environment to prevent pilferage, fire, sabotage, and accidents.
- Improve preventive maintenance on automated storage to minimize unscheduled downtime.

BUSINESS COMPUTER SYSTEMS CRITERIA FOR STORAGE FUNCTIONS

The following section discusses large business systems such as manufacturing resource planning (MRP II) and warehouse management systems (WMS). It does not include a discussion of custom equipment automation systems or computer interfaces (for example, downloading pick requirements to horizontal carousels).

An often overlooked source of storage planning criteria is available from internal MIS analysts supporting in-house computer systems. Also, outside computer software services (engineering and package vendors) can provide a wide spectrum of strategies. If your storage area does not seem to need computer system support, then validate why it does not. It most cases, it should.

If the storage area has computer systems support, determine which functions of the system are used and which are not. Determine why some functions are not used and decide whether they may be useful. This storage project may provide the opportunity to enhance inventory control.

If the storage plan is for a new facility, determine what computer system will manage the inventory in the storage area. If a specific software package has been selected (for example, WMS or MRP II), have someone on the team who is very familiar with its features and operation. However, if a specific vendor package has not been selected, the selection process should still proceed or be concurrent with the storage plan.

Automation vendors often have software business partners or in-house software resources experienced with their equipment. This generally reduces implementation risks and creates turnkey storage opportunities.

COMPUTER SOFTWARE CAPABILITIES
Significant productivity is achieved by maximizing the compatibility of the storage equipment with the computer systems. The following are typical capabilities expected in optimal software packages.

General Inventory Storage Functions
- Material transaction tracking by location.
- User-defined inventory zones.
- User-defined material transaction and status codes.
- "Freeze" inventory by location.
- Verification codes per location (to improve storage flow accuracy).
- Output print/read bar code labels for turnaround documents.
- Multiwarehouse inventory reporting/summaries.
- Distinguish between different grades of same item per storage location (for example, new versus used).

Receiving Capabilities
- User defined inventory put-away location rules.
- Warn of early purchase deliveries and vendor over-shipments (may require temporary storage to return).
- Identify incoming quality control procedures per item received (may require temporary storage area).
- Browse expected storage put-away requirements for the day.
- Cross-dock support for hot items.
- Identify country of origin or owner of inventory (may affect inventory zone).
- Assign lot and serial numbers.
- Receive at multiple locations.

CHAPTER 4   STORAGE AND INVENTORY PLANNING

Bulk (Reserve) and Forward (Loose) Inventory Capabilities
- Inventory replenishments of forward (loose) pick storage areas by location.
- Replenishment pick lists are available.
- Supports bin locations containing backflush items in shop areas. *Backflush* is the deduction from inventory records of the component parts used in an assembly or subassembly; for example, very low-cost screws or nuts. These are manually scheduled for replenishment because the on-hand inventory is only estimated.
- Supports put-away and pick quantities across multiple locations (that is, pallets plus cases plus loose pick).
- Multibin control within each storage location (for example, small parts).
- Provides put-away and pick lists in a variety of ways.
- Ability to complete one order and one line at a time.
- Sequential inventory zones (partial order pick and then pass it on to the next zone until completed).
- Parallel inventory zones (partial order pick and match with other partial picks until the order is complete).
- Makes batches of picks for several orders and segregates them.
- Wave picks several orders, segregates them by wave, then consolidates several waves to complete order.
- Pick inventory hot sheet (that is, unscheduled pick).

Shipping Capabilities
- Shipping dock floor spot location management.
- Browse open shipments by item and storage/dock location.

Temporary Storage—WIP Material Capabilities
- Staging of kits in advance of manufacturing.
- Work center queues.
- Obsolescence management.
- Incomplete or inactive work orders.
- Orders awaiting quality control disposition.
- WIP inventory accountability to physical work order.
- WIP inspection status reporting.
- Backflush of low-cost item work order usage.

INVENTORY STORAGE AND FLOW CHARACTERISTICS

So far, this chapter has taken a top-down perspective to storage planning. This next section shows the importance of balancing it with a bottom-up perspective that focuses on the storage item and how it flows through the storage area(s). This balancing effort is more tedious but just as critical as setting the high-level goals and objectives.

Inventory, as described in this chapter, refers to stock or items for support of production (raw material and work-in-progress), supporting activities (maintenance and operating supplies), and customer service (finished goods and spare parts). It does not include the broader perspective of resale equipment and facilities. To have good inventory management, the user must define the following:

- Inventory put-away unit of measure.
- Storage capacity by type.
- Special storage environment needs.
- Special inventory vendor and owner needs.
- Special material transportation needs.

- Inventory pick frequency.
- Inventory handling.

INVENTORY PUT-AWAY UNIT OF MEASURE (UOM)
First, it is necessary to categorize the items that determine the types of storage locations required. For example, electrical supply warehouses store long TV attenna cartons differently than resistors. These items are sorted and assigned to storage location and put-away unit-of-measure (UOM) categories.

Ideally, a put-away UOM for a bulk storage method (for example, pallet) should have the same number of pick units (for example, 40 cases) for each inventory. This allows a computer system to easily schedule combinations of pallet and case picks. Similarly, the put-away UOM for a forward pick area method (for example, case) should have the same number of loose units in each (per product).

For example, a bulk put-away UOM for an item may be a full pallet that requires 60 ft^3 and weighs 1,000 lb. In the loose pick area, the replenishment put-away UOM may be a carton that requires 1.5 ft^3 and weighs 25 lb. (All of the examples in this chapter are calculated using U.S. customary units but it would have been just as easy to substitute SI units.)

The volume and footprint (length and width) of the put-away UOM determines storage location type, size, and maximum units per location. A bulk location may have one or more pallets while a forward location may have one or more cases.

STORAGE CAPACITY BY TYPE
Next, determine the storage volume of the item(s). For example, bulk storage may have to be sensitive to wide seasonal variations while the loose storage areas could be limited (that is, their replenishment frequency varies during the year).

In bulk areas, the number of locations is a function of the location assignment methodology (fixed or random). Similarly, the number of locations for loose pick areas may be fixed (to minimize pick travel) or variable (to minimize pick shortages).

An easy example of the impact on storage is a large textbook order for one title by a school. An order for 1,234 books of one title may require several picks from several locations:

- Full pallets picked from bulk locations.
- Full cases picked from partial pallet bulk locations.
- Loose books from forward pick locations.

SPECIAL STORAGE ENVIRONMENT NEEDS
Group items are those that require special storage and handling together. Examples of this include items that require special security, temperature control, fire or explosion containment (fluids, gases), and unusual shapes.

SPECIAL INVENTORY VENDOR AND OWNER NEEDS
Material movement efficiency can be greatly improved, in some cases, by locating large receipts in one area instead of distributing the items throughout a facility—especially in case of overseas receipts. Also, in shared warehouse or fulfillment situations, it may be desirable to consolidate all material owned by a customer into one area.

SPECIAL MATERIAL TRANSPORTATION NEEDS
In certain situations, material handling costs can be greatly decreased by using the same transportation and storage container for all materials. For example, reusable containers, slip sheets, special pallets, or custom carriers can be optimized for transportation. The storage locations also can be designed for them.

CHAPTER 4   STORAGE AND INVENTORY PLANNING

Other situations occur with unusual inventory shapes and weights. Heavy dies, steel plates, and coils may require custom gantry cranes.

INVENTORY PICK FREQUENCY

How frequently an item is picked can affect its physical location. This is not to be confused with the shipping dollar or units (volume) of the item. For example, two items could have the same shipping dollar volume but one had only one order (for example, pallet pick) while the other had 40 orders (case picks). The picking frequency and effort between the two are significantly different enough to affect the location assignment.

It is important *not* to zone inventory by material volume or value. Instead, create a separate ABC report showing inventory activity as the number of visits to pick from a storage location.

INVENTORY HANDLING

The inventory storage must be compatible with the handling method used to store and retrieve the item. It could be embarrassing to install bulk storage locations too high or have aisles too narrow for certain trucks. Conversely, excessively wide aisles can hurt manual order picking productivity. A variety of automated distribution equipment is available. Typical examples include automated storage and retrieval systems (AS/RS), carousels, case and item dispensers, and robotic cells.

Other examples of special handling considerations include overhead cranes to move awkward items such as steel plates and coils. In this instance, make sure the storage is accessible and minimizes operation interference among multiple cranes.

CALCULATE STORAGE EQUIPMENT QUANTITY AND FLOOR AREA

There are software packages available that can simplify this process by handling large volumes of item characteristic data (for example, size, weight, etc.), so multiple storage strategies can be more easily developed and compared. The methodology has been around a long time and is described in more detail in other reference books. The following is a condensed procedure for determining storage equipment and floor area requirements. For each storage method/ inventory put-away UOM combination that must be stored, follow these steps and determine:

1. All the stock keeping unit (SKU) volumes that have similar put-away UOM.
2. The peak volume for each put-away group.
3. The appropriate size of the storage location to handle the put-away UOM group.
4. The number of locations required per storage method module (width, height, and depth). Then calculate the maximum net payload capacity per equipment module.
5. The floor area required per storage equipment module.
6. How many storage modules are required, adjusted by a safety factor for empty locations needed to handle day-to-day storage variance.
7. The total floor area that the storage modules require.

The following describes these steps in greater detail:

1. Identify all the stock keeping unit (SKU) volumes that have similar put-away UOM. Using their put-away height as a guide, normalize their payload to one footprint (that is, depth and width).

$$A_p = D_p \times W_p \qquad (1)$$

where:

A_p = Put-away payload footprint (ft²)
D_p = Put-away payload depth (ft)
W_p = Put-away payload width (ft)

For example, a group of items (group A) all use the same pallet size (42 × 42 in.) at the receiving dock for transport and put-away. The calculated footprint area is 12.25 ft².

$$A_p = 3.5 \times 3.5 \text{ ft}$$
$$A_p = 12.25 \text{ ft}^2 \text{ put-away payload footprint}$$

2. Estimate the peak storage volume for each put-away group. Calculate what space all the material would occupy if thrown into one large pile (with no racks) during the peak annual inventory time. Carefully consider the impact of seasonal fluctuations (SKU storage volumes may be low at some times while high at others). The volume for each SKU can be estimated in a variety of ways. The most common method is to determine the SKU value or SKU units per standard storage volume. Then, using inventory control reports, extrapolate the required volume per SKU to get the specific storage method. If SKUs are assigned permanent locations, then simply use the available volume of the locations and do not bother calculating inventory volume.

$$V_{SKU} = Q_{SKU} \times R_{SKU} \qquad (2)$$
$$V_p = \text{The sum of all } V_{SKU} \text{ in put-away group}$$

where:

V_{SKU} = SKU storage volume during peak period
Q_{SKU} = Quantity or dollar value during the peak period
R_{SKU} = Ratio of storage volume per quantity or dollar value
V_p = Put-away group storage volume (ft³)

For example, put-away group A has two SKUs. The peak storage time is in April. The first SKU occupies 2 ft³ per item while the second SKU occupies 4 ft³ per item. The projected storage in April for the first SKU is 2,000 items and 1,000 items for the second SKU. This means 4,000 ft³ is required for each SKU. The total put-away for group A is 8,000 ft³.

$$V_{SKU1} = 2,000 \times 2 \text{ ft}^3 = 4,000 \text{ ft}^3 \text{ required for SKU}_1$$
$$V_{SKU2} = 1,000 \times 4 \text{ ft}^3 = 4,000 \text{ ft}^3 \text{ required for SKU}_2$$
$$V_p = V_{SKU1} + V_{SKU2}$$
$$V_p = 4,000 + 4,000 \text{ ft}^3 = 8,000 \text{ ft}^3 \text{ for group } A$$

3. Determine the appropriate size of the storage location to handle the put-away UOM group.

$$V_p = A_p \times H_p \qquad (3)$$
$$V_l = D_l \times W_l \times H_l$$
$$\%_u = V_p \div V_l$$

where:

V_p = Put-away payload volume (ft³)
A_p = Put-away payload footprint (ft²)
H_p = Put-away payload height (ft)
V_l = Physical location volume
D_l = Physical location depth
W_l = Physical location width
H_l = Physical location height
$\%_u$ = Payload utilization percentage for volume space

For example, the SKUs in put-away group A have a typical height (before put-away) of 39 in. The payload volume is cal-

CHAPTER 4   STORAGE AND INVENTORY PLANNING

culated to be 40 ft³. To accommodate this volume and normal variance, the storage method will use locations that are $4 \times 4 \times 4$ ft for this put-away group (that is, 64 ft³ required per location). Put-away group A payload occupies about 63% of the location space. This is used for comparison of storage efficiencies among location sizing alternatives.

$$V_p = A_p \times H_p$$
$$V_p = 12.25 \text{ ft}^2 \times 3.25 \text{ ft} = 40 \text{ ft}^3 \text{ payload}$$
$$V_l = D_l \times W_l \times H_l$$
$$V_l = 4 \times 4 \times 4 \text{ ft} = 64 \text{ ft}^3 \text{ location}$$
$$\%_u = V_p \div V_l$$
$$\%_u = 40 \div 64 \text{ ft}^3 = 63\% \text{ location utilization}$$

4. Determine the number of locations per storage method module (width, height, and depth). Then calculate the maximum net payload capacity per equipment module.

$$N_{ml} = N_h \times N_w \times N_d \qquad (4)$$
$$V_{mp} = N_{ml} \times V_p$$

where:

N_{ml} = Total number of put-away locations per module
N_h = Number of levels or shelves high
N_w = Number of locations wide
N_d = Number of locations deep
V_{mp} = Storage module payload capacity (ft³)
V_p = Put-away payload volume per put-away location

For example, a storage module (at time of installation) is five locations high, two locations wide, and one location deep. The 10 locations can each hold 40 ft³ of group A. The total storage capacity of the module is 400 ft³ for group A.

$$N_{ml} = N_h \times N_w \times N_d$$
$$N_{ml} = 5 \times 2 \times 1 = 10 \text{ locations per module}$$
$$V_{mp} = N_{ml} \times V_p$$
$$V_{mp} = 10 \times 40 \text{ ft}^3 = 400 \text{ ft}^3 \text{ of group } A \text{ per module}$$

5. Determine the floor area required per storage equipment module. This requires adding the storage module footprint (that is, width × depth) to floor area losses for aisles, columns, sprinkler systems, etc.

$$A_l = D_l \times W_l \times N_w \times N_d \qquad (5)$$
$$A_m = A_l + (\%_a \times A_l)$$

where:

A_l = Storage module location footprint area
D_l = Put-away location depth (ft)
W_l = Put-away location width (ft)
N_w = Number of locations wide per module
N_d = Number of locations deep per module
A_m = Total storage module footprint required (including aisles and maintenance access)
$\%_a$ = Each storage layout configuration has its own aisle or storage space ratio

For example, our module is two locations wide and each has an area dimension of 4×4 ft. The calculated 32 ft² of storage location area needs aisles to get to it. The ratio of aisle space to storage location space is 56% for the planned layout configuration. As a result, each storage module needs to allow

18 ft² for aisles and maintenance. Therefore, total floor area required per module is 50 ft².

$$A_l = D_l \times W_l \times N_w \times N_d$$
$$A_l = 4 \times 4 \times 2 \times 1 \text{ ft} = 32 \text{ ft}^2 \text{ per module (without aisles, etc.)}$$
$$\%_a = \text{Design estimate of 56\% for support (unique to aisle and storage configuration)}$$
$$A_m = A_l + (\%_a \times A_l)$$
$$A_m = 32 \text{ ft}^2 + (56\% \times 32 \text{ ft}^2) = 50 \text{ ft}^2 \text{ per module (with aisles)}$$

6. Determine how many storage modules are required and adjust by a safety factor for empty locations needed to handle day-to-day storage variance.

$$N_m = (V_m \div V_{mp})(1 + \%_s) \qquad (6)$$

where:

N_m = Total number of storage modules
V_m = Put-away group storage volume (ft³)
V_{mp} = Payload volume capacity per module
$\%_s$ = Empty location safety factor

For example, the total payload volume requirement for group A is 8,000 ft³. The payload capacity of the inventory storage module is 400 ft³. Considering previous inventory fluctuation experience, we use an empty location safety factor of 10%. The number of storage modules for group A inventory is 22.

$$N_m = V_p \div V_{mp}(1 + \%_s)$$
$$N_m = (8000 \div 400 \text{ ft}^3)(1 + 0.1) = 22 \text{ storage modules}$$

7. Determine the floor area that the storage modules require.

$$A_s = N_m \times A_m \qquad (7)$$

where:

A_s = Total floor area for group A storage
N_m = Total number of storage modules
A_m = Total footprint required per storage module (including aisles and maintenance access)

For example, 22 storage modules were needed for group A. It was previously determined that 50 ft² were needed per module (for example, storage + aisles + maintenance). Therefore, 1,100 ft² of floor space must be allocated for the modules to store group A.

$$A_s = N_m \times A_m$$
$$A_s = 22 \text{ modules} \times 50 \text{ ft}^2 = 1,100 \text{ ft}^2 \text{ total}$$

The procedure, by calculating the number of storage modules required, allows calculation for budgetary estimates for both the equipment investment and the floor area they occupy. The steps described earlier must be repeated for each put-away group (that is, storage × put-away UOM combination). The floor area information is required later for preliminary facility layouts of the storage areas. It is useful to compare the storage method efficiencies both in terms of location utilization and floor area utilization. Location utilization affects storage equipment procurement cost (number of modules) while area utilization affects facility (floor space) and material handling costs (travel).

CHAPTER 4   STORAGE AND INVENTORY PLANNING

CENTRALIZATION VERSUS DECENTRALIZATION STRATEGIES

This topic is one of several that receive special storage planning attention. The primary purpose of decentralization is improved inventory storage service. It can range from providing several storage areas under one roof to using buildings located in several countries. This service includes minimizing transportation time delays and all related costs (for example, transportation, on-site inventory, downtime, etc.).

If the inventory is zoned or categorized by a set of rules, it can be decentralized (for example, ownership, storage environment, activity, and volume).

Examples of decentralization include:

- Construction equipment manufacturers provide replacement parts the same or next day to improve sales. The customers are very sensitive to equipment breakdowns and are accustomed to getting replacement parts the same or next day.
- An automotive part supplier, with same-day turnaround contracts for inventory, requests the use of third party or dedicated facilities close to its major Just-in-Time (JIT) customers.
- Large manufacturing or assembly companies who distribute their inventory storage areas within one building to minimize production interruptions and costs caused by waiting for either direct or indirect materials.
- Direct shipping from multiple supplier(s) to the customer instead of from one warehouse. Some vendors provide special packing services (for example, labels) that make it appear as though the item was shipped from the distributor who was originally contacted.
- Local fulfillment services located in major metropolitan areas can hold vendor or customer owned items until contacted to deliver or allow pick-up the same day. Typically, they also provide kitting, packing, and relabeling services.

From a storage planning perspective, the following inventory service strategies are some of the many examples:

- Locate specific finished goods next to the source manufacturing plants or the primary customers (for example, automotive).
- Place all inventory requiring special handling and storage at one location or see that all locations have the same special handling storage capabilities.
- Dedicate an entire storage area to one vendor and customer or share a storage facility, operated by a third party, with other vendors and customers.

The decentralization possibilities are endless unless the storage plan evaluation criteria are defined. The evaluation criteria listed before were only general considerations. Storage evaluation criteria unique to decentralizing are more specific and have three major perspectives: financial, service and transportation, and operations.

FINANCIAL

The financial evaluation of decentralization should be done carefully to identify both obvious and hidden costs and savings.

For example, decentralization can fragment customer orders among several locations and increase the total transportation costs per order. The following are considerations where key assumptions should be developed and evaluated.

Geographical Storage Location

Consider the impact of:

- Foreign trade zones and laws.
- Local property tax laws.
- Transportation costs.
- Land and building investment.
- No location change.
- Reliability of transportation services.

Inventory Storage (Within Each Site)

Consider its effect on:

- Labor (both hourly and supervisory).
- Inventory carrying costs.
- Capital investment in storage and handling equipment.
- Operational efficiency and performance.
- Back-orders and market share.
- Inventory storage changes.
- Reliability of transportation services.

SERVICE AND TRANSPORTATION

The service and transportation evaluation must carefully identify both obvious and hidden service attributes and risks. Sometimes decentralization is required to meet service agreements. However, it may cause significant, undesirable performance among locations.

Using the previous example, decentralization can fragment customer orders among several locations and cause customer frustration (that is, when several deliveries are made for the same order). The following considerations will help form key assumptions.

Ranking Inventory Service Performance by Customer and Vendor

Some manufacturing companies protect the customer service performance of their replacement part warehouses by physically locating them away from their manufacturing plants. They are willing to incur the additional double-handling to thwart the tendency of manufacturing to borrow parts to meet production schedules. The borrowing increases the frequency of stock shortages that, in turn, adversely affect customer service.

Express Transportation Considerations

- Departure time of express services at closest airports, both domestic and international.
- Truck departure cut-off time of air shipments (for example, transportation and waiting for other trucks to unload at airport).

Surface Transportation Considerations

- Types of transportation available (for example, barge, rail).
- Surface transportation competition and its ability to minimize double-handling between source and destination.
- Proximity to primary customers (for example, to reduce transit costs and transit time).
- Arrival and departure time of major transportation services.
- Transportation service dependability (for example, being at the dock doors of local or customer site on time).

JIT Customer Considerations

- Availability of land to provide storage sites adjacent to primary supplier(s) or customer(s).
- Third party storage facilities available that handle the shipping needs of one or more clients and are closer to key clients.
- Security and trace capability at remote sites.

CHAPTER 4   STORAGE AND INVENTORY PLANNING

OPERATIONS

Lastly, the operations evaluation must carefully identify both obvious and hidden warehouse productivity attributes and risks. Decentralization allows the facility to be more aware of the needs of the vendors and customers in its territory.

Using the same example as before, decentralization can decrease SKU throughput and storage capacity because the facilities are smaller and less able to handle wide operational variances. The following considerations are where key assumptions are developed and evaluated.

Industry Trends and Benchmarks
- Inventory turns and accuracy.
- Inventory value and area ratios.
- Inventory flow and labor hours.
- Third-party warehousing and logistics.

World Class-*A* MRP II Operation
- 95+% Inventory record accuracy.
- 95+% Manufacturing schedule performance.
- 95+% Supplier delivery performance.
- 95+% Customer service delivery to promise.

FDA Guidelines
- Identification and tracking.
- Handling, storage, and distribution.
- Packaging and labeling control.

ISO 9001 Standards
- Control of customer supplied inventory.
- Inventory identification and tracking.
- Nonconforming inventory control.
- Handling, storage, packaging, preservation, and delivery.

JIT Guidelines
- Satisfy customer demand.
- Perform with perfect quality.
- Accomplish zero unnecessary lead times.
- Eliminate waste.
- Maximize flexibility.

Special Storage and Handling Requirements
- Fire safety—rubber and certain chemicals.
- Health safety—acid-base/carcinogens.
- Refrigeration—food.
- Security—high value items, dangerous inventories.
- Fluids—compressed gas, liquids, powder, pellets.

Warehouse Productivity
- Items and lines picked per hour per inventory storage method.
- Warehouse productivity by material handling method.
- Employee incentive programs.
- Employee turnover.
- Put-away timeliness and housekeeping.
- Picking error rates.
- Efficient cycle counts and physical inventories.
- Inventory (item) characteristics affecting storage and flow.
- Orders shipped versus the time period after receipt of order.

INVENTORY STORAGE METHOD ALTERNATIVES

As mentioned in the beginning of this chapter, a storage strategy consists of effectively combining several storage methods. This section discusses planning considerations for a wide variety of different storage methods. The purpose of this discussion is to make sure all viable storage methods have been considered.

All of the effort previously invested in defining the inventory storage evaluation criteria (that is, Phase I) is heavily used at this point. Each type of storage method is evaluated individually against the evaluation criteria (using the Kepner-Tregoe methodology). This evaluation helps determine which items (and how many) are stored in each storage method.

CONVENTIONAL STORAGE METHODS

It is important to identify all the ways each item in the storage population will be picked for replenishment or shipping to determine the best "put-away UOM." To maximize picking performance, the put-away UOM is limited to two levels of picking.

The first pick level allows picking the entire put-away UOM while the second level allows a subunit to be efficiently picked. Limiting to two levels improves physical or cycle count efficiency. For example, bulk storage could allow pallet and case picks only, while forward storage or the WIP area may allow multi-item packets and loose pick only.

In summary, one item can require several storage methods to maximize picking performance. The quantity of each storage method (and the number of locations within each) depends on how the inventory is distributed throughout the facility. Ease of the physical and cycle count is considered when determining the amount and how the inventory is stored.

If possible, avoid mixing different items within a physical location. The combination of one-item locations along with random put-away location assignment offers dramatic increases in inventory accuracy. This is possible because locations can be "picked empty" more frequently which, when verified, is equivalent to a cycle count of zero.

BULK (RESERVE) INVENTORY STORAGE METHODS

Bulk storage normally handles the two top levels of either large put-away or pick items for a particular site—such as pallets and cases stacked on the pallets. It is also used for loose (less than a case) items that are not conveyable or that require very wide pick faces (large items or items that cannot be placed in conveyable totes or cartons).

Some distributors pick only the top level (for example, pallets) to maximize storage and automated handling efficiency. They depend on off-site, third parties to distribute the contents of each pallet to small order customers.

In situations where a two-level pick occurs (for example, pallet and case picking), one location is selected for case picking at a time (until it is empty) before using a new pallet for more cases.

Additional bulk storage situations include inventory returns, put-away, kitting, repackaging, quality release, etc. From a bulk storage planning perspective, each of the following conventional storage methods must be examined for its viability:

CHAPTER 4 STORAGE AND INVENTORY PLANNING

• Static shelving and racks.
• Two-deep rack.
• Drive-in or drive-through rack.
• Cantilever rack.
• Floor stacking and pallet stacking frame.
• Portable racking.

FORWARD (LOOSE) INVENTORY STORAGE METHODS

Forward storage normally handles the bottom two levels—such as cartons and loose items per carton. For example, in a warehouse, forward storage methods normally contain items that can be placed in conveyable totes or cartons.

The storage capacity of the forward locations is a function of the replenishment algorithms used. Some companies minimize replenishment requests while others minimize forward pick aisle lengths. Storage capacity of forward pick locations must also take into account the effort needed to perform cycle or physical inventory counts.

Typical examples of forward (loose) inventory storage methods include:

• Carton or pallet gravity flow racks.
• Modular cabinets or drawers.
• Rotating or stationary bins.
• Movable shelf storage (for example, space savers).

AUTOMATED STORAGE METHODS

The justification for automated storage equipment varies widely—usually it requires confidence that the investment is used for a long time and significantly improves item flow performance. The challenge is to break these broad concepts down into tangible and intangible evaluation criteria.

Improved item flow performance is not limited to material flow. Other benefits of automation include:

• Quality control (controlled storage environment).
• Security (difficult to access item manually).
• Inventory accuracy and tracking (for example, 99+%).
• Labor utilization (avoid travel losses).
• Material handling uniformity (put-away, picking).
• Company image and market share.
• Floor area utilization.
• Material accuracy.
• Operation consistency.
• Synergy with other automation.
• Meet or exceed industry benchmarks or trends.

While it is easy to become enthusiastic about an automated solution, an important engineering responsibility is to look at the potential risks with that same amount of energy. Try to anticipate the perspectives or concerns of people most uncomfortable with an automated storage method. Their concerns will include:

• Realizing the expected return on the investment.
• Mean-time-between-failures (MTTF).
• Mean-time-to-repair (MTTR).
• Likelihood of significantly different inventory introductions.
• Obsolescence of current items.
• Additional ongoing maintenance costs.
• Frequency of machine control changes.
• Downtime during equipment modifications.
• Quality of custom, state-of-the-art engineering.
• Implementation management (budget and schedule).
• Likelihood of major facility changes.
• May require additional investment in special totes, pallets.
• Constant change of equipment software controls.
• Possible low utilization of expensive equipment.

Automation requires high quality, active commitment from both the vendor and the customer to succeed. Strong project management and engineering skill is required to adapt effectively to unforeseen situations caused by custom, one-of-a-kind designs. Typically, there is higher anxiety and frustration during the implementation but the reward of well-designed automation is usually worth all the debugging effort. In short, automation requires a great investment in organizational capital, time, and patience.

The investment required for a stand-alone automation operation is significantly less than one that requires integration (that is, with computer systems and other automation). It is very important to plan the overall automation integration and design the equipment with the needed capabilities. Implement each storage automation individually and get it running smoothly in stand-alone mode first. Then continue with implementing the interfaces. The justification for this approach is the required need for back-up administrative procedures when the automated interfaces fail for any reason. It also ensures modular design.

All automated storage methods emphasize higher storage efficiency but have material flow limitations. If wide variances in material flow exist, make sure the capacity requirements satisfy 90+% of the expected demand (that is, accept the reality that the equipment will be idle frequently).

Maximum automated storage flow is seldom improved by adding additional labor. Do not expect to be able to have people easily access the storage locations when the equipment does not work—it is usually not designed that way. The operational reliability of all these units depends greatly on (1) the initial design, (2) effective preventive maintenance, and (3) periodic major rework.

Automated Storage and Retrieval Systems (AS/RS)

This equipment usually requires payloads and items stored in totes, skids, or pallets compatible with the AS/RS and surrounding temporary storage (for example, conveyors, automated guided vehicles [AGVs], etc.). Random pick or put-away has a wide range of applications (including delivery directly to workstations). In situations where a large volume of SKUs is stored (for example, in beverage companies), high-density storage is possible by sequentially queuing the material and releasing it on a first-in first-out (FIFO) basis.

Carousels

This alternative moves material and totes to the employee instead of the employee moving material. These units are normally considered for randomly picking small items that are able to fit in one or more compartments per carousel shelf. Two to four of these units can be grouped together into pods run by one employee. The pod allows one carousel to be stocked or picked while the others are rotating to the next needed position. In addition, several pods can be strung together as inventory zones for order pick-and-pass routing strategies. Common types of carousels include horizontal, vertical, rotary rack, and twin bin.

Vertical Storage Modules

These units are similar to AS/RS because they transport payloads one at a time between the storage location and the pick-up/delivery station. The major difference is that they only travel one axis (that is, up and down) while an AS/RS travels two axes (that is, down the aisle and up/down). They can have pick-up and delivery stations on several different floors. The key benefit of these units is their modularity, storage security, and minimal floor area requirement.

As discussed before, the other advantage of automated storage is the synergy with other automation equipment—namely mechanical interfaces and real-time computer systems. For example, some com-

CHAPTER 4 STORAGE AND INVENTORY PLANNING

panies and vendors can orchestrate their automated storage equipment with automated material handling via supervisory computer control. A work center can request material that is retrieved immediately by an AS/RS, queued on a conveyor, picked up by an AGV, and delivered to the employee.

It is an ongoing trend to reduce the turnaround time from when the material is requested to the final delivery. The use of computers for coordinating the activity of dissimilar material storage areas continues to grow in importance. Serial communication between business systems and material storage equipment is evolving from periodic batch downloads and uploads to subsecond, on-line response. The thirst for faster and minute-by-minute responsiveness has given rise to manufacturing execution systems (MES), pick-to-light flow racks, and intelligent storage, dispensing, and handling equipment.

In summary, developing sound business evaluation criteria of possible storage methods is especially important when it comes to automation. The previously developed evaluation criteria help maintain the business commitment needed for success.

TEMPORARY STORAGE METHODS

This section briefly discusses the relationship of temporary storage to permanent storage. It can be applied to a recirculation conveyor accumulating picked orders before releasing them to the shipping area or to WIP storage areas (for example, portable bins or racks). It also can be applied to FIFO accumulation conveyors that transport material directly from one point to another.

Temporary Storage Queue Sizing and Modeling

The use of modeling software and techniques for determining temporary storage queue size is increasing. Normally, the queue capacity is a function of inventory flow rates (that is, units per hour) and the number of buffer hours required (both usually depend on experience). Spreadsheets are used for simple sizing (for example, inventory storage volume per flow ratio × projected inventory flow). They can also perform statistical simulation to estimate the flow distribution through a work area for a variety of products, machines, and lot sizes.

In recent years, sophisticated modeling software has become easier to use and requires less training or specialization to get useful results. However, considerable modeling skill, operations research knowledge, and practical experience are required for effectively using it.

Acceptance of modeling depends a lot on management's understanding of how it was designed and if the results are close to past experience. For example, it may be difficult for production management to accept a 10% inventory shortage probability when they are expected to meet customer ship dates 100% of the time.

Temporary Storage Queue Applications

Currently, the trend is to minimize temporary storage capacity to minimize WIP. The methods can be separated between discrete storage (for example, carts, bins) and continuous storage (for example, conveyors). Temporary storage applications are used:

- For reducing material handling labor and travel caused by excessive service request frequency and reducing assembly and process downtime caused by waiting for available, needed parts.
- As inter-workstation queues for "agile" production among work centers to avoid production schedules from becoming "fragile."
- When workstation load and unload queues are needed to avoid unnecessary employee travel to access parts for his or her assembly area or operation.
- As pick-up and delivery (P&D) queues in warehouse operations to efficiently move material.

- As hold and suspense queues to absorb surges in quality assurance and quality control activity.
- As returns queues for inspection to determine the disposition of items previously shipped.

Temporary Storage Queue Methods

Kanban is one example of a production methodology that relies on limited temporary storage queues (limited number of carts between work centers). Some often-used temporary queue methods include the following alternatives:

- Conveyors (monorail, power-and-free, roller, belt, etc.).
- Load and unload assist devices (tilt stands, rotation assistance).
- Gondolas and bins.
- Material carts and automated guided vehicles (AGVs).
- Dispensers (also vibratory bowl feeders.)

In summary, temporary storage queue capacity is a function of the production rules and inventory storage profile for the organization. Again, the evaluation criteria (developed in Phase I) are critical to storage planning success. Typical situations include:

- If a shop has excessive capacity, the queue may be designed around WIP control rules (for example, hours of float allowed between consecutive work areas).
- If a shop has insufficient capacity or is producing a wide variety of inventory with a few work centers, the queue may be designed around maximizing work center efficiency.
- Temporary queues may be required to optimize both conventional and automated storage area activities.

INVENTORY DATING SYSTEMS (STORAGE LIFE)

A major consideration regarding storage planning is inventory storage life. The most frequent use of inventory dating is first-in first-out (FIFO)/last-in last-out (LIFO) inventory flow.

Inventory dating is very common in the foods, pharmaceuticals, and chemical industries, although other uses exist. For example, engineering change control is required to discontinue the use of an older item that is replaced by a newer item in other industries.

The storage planning requirement's definition for inventory dating is obtained from the existing or planned business computer systems. MIS and/or inventory management usually provides a good definition of how dated inventories are controlled. Again, this dimension must be defined as a tangible evaluation criterion and may require compatibility with computer data collection technologies (for example, bar code).

Typical date- or time-dependent storage criteria may include support for:

- FIFO/LIFO material flow policies.
- Serial or lot number control.
- Reporting aging, obsolete, or slow moving inventory.
- Cycle counting or physical inventory capabilities.
- On-line (time and employee) transaction history.
- Average or last costs for items.
- ABC analysis for cycle counting.
- Cycle-count work sheets and post-quantity adjustments.
- Shelf-life limits on items (for example, adhesives).

STORAGE PLANNING SUMMARY

Most storage equipment technical problems can eventually be solved. One of the greatest storage planning responsibilities is to get

CHAPTER 4   STORAGE AND INVENTORY PLANNING

an objective view of the business by working effectively with its business leaders. Storage planning requires effective communication skills as the foundation of its success.

The major storage planning steps can be applied to other business tasks. This chapter emphasized the following steps:

1. Get business leaders involved in the beginning of the project.
2. Practice a proven storage planning methodology.
3. Develop high quality evaluation criteria.
4. Identify high quality storage strategy alternatives.
5. Develop an implementation plan.
6. Maintain project management and commitment.

Reference

1. Kepner, C. H., and Tregoe, B., B. *The Rational Manager: A Systematic Approach to Problem Solving and Decision Making.* New York: McGraw-Hill, 1965.

Bibliography

APICS Council. *CPIM Dictionary.* Falls Church, VA: APICS Inc., 1992.

APICS Council. *CPIM Inventory Management Reprints.* Falls Church, VA: APICS Inc., 1994.

APICS Council. *CPIM Just-In-Time Reprints.* Falls Church, VA: APICS Inc., 1994.

APICS Council. *CPIM Systems and Technologies Reprints.* Falls Church, VA: APICS Inc., 1993.

APICS Council. *CPIM Material and Capacity Requirements Planning Reprints.* Falls Church, VA: APICS Inc., 1994.

Hodson, William K. *Maynard's Industrial Engineering Handbook*, 4th Edition. New York: McGraw-Hill, 1992.

McNamara, James P. *Layout Design Evaluation Methodology*, AUTOFACT '95 Conference Publication. Dearborn, MI: Society of Manufacturing Engineers, November, 1995.

Mulcahy, David H. *Warehouse and Distribution Operations Handbook.* New York: McGraw-Hill, 1994.

NAVSUP Publication 529, Warehouse Modernization and Layout Planning Guide. Ohio: The Sims Consulting Group, Inc., 1985.

Sims, E. Ralph. *Planning and Managing Industrial Logistics Systems.* New York: Elsevier Science, 1991.

Tompkins, James A., and Harmelink, Dale. *Distribution Management Handbook.* New York: McGraw-Hill, 1993.

Tompkins, James A., and Smith, J.D. *The Warehouse Management Handbook.* New York: McGraw-Hill, 1988.

CHAPTER 5
LOGISTICS

CHAPTER CONTENTS

INTRODUCTION

Logistics was traditionally defined as the art and science of obtaining, producing, and distributing material and product in the proper place and in the proper quantities.[1] Today, *enterprise logistics management* (ELM) can be viewed as a global concept, encompassing "the entire materials management and production scheduling spectrum throughout the entire value-added pipeline from final customer/consumer all the way back to the supplier of the rawest material."[2] Planning and execution transactions take place in seconds. It may be days or weeks out of the planning cycle and focuses production on customers. Since time is money, inventory reduction frees up working capital for other purposes. Customers as well as suppliers see time as money (inventory, transportation, and processing) which places pressure on the functional areas to reduce logistics processing time. Logistics is a process, not a function, dealing with time.

Traditional logistics functions such as purchasing, scheduling, inventory management, and shipping can rely heavily on paper documents and account for more product lead time than the actual manufacturing process. Paper methods make changes difficult to track and implement, resulting in the right parts not being available at the right time. More time is needed to re-order the proper materials and many companies respond by carrying additional inventory.

In recent years, logistics processes have seen many changes. Customers have demanded shorter lead times, reduced costs, and improved quality. To meet these demands, many traditional documents and methods were automated and streamlined. Still, many companies use traditional paper processes. This chapter provides an overview of traditional methods and future trends in logistics. Topics covered are:

- Ordering and receiving processes.
- Shipping to meet customer expectations.
- EDI service providers.
- Inventory management.

Understanding the logistics functions and methods will help manufacturing professionals determine the most cost-effective solutions for delivery, cost, and quality.

ORDERING AND RECEIVING PROCESSES

Ordering is the first component of product lead time, therefore, accuracy and timeliness are critical to the prompt and exact delivery of products. The ordering process includes planning what to order and generating purchase orders for the supplier. A supplier receives an order from a customer, processes the order, and translates it into material and manufacturing requirements. These requirements are passed on to the supplier's supplier and down the supply chain. There also may be a supply chain within the company, as parts move from process to process. The goal for the supplier, whether inside or outside the company, is fulfilling the customer's order on time, within budget, and at the level of quality expected.

DETERMINING WHAT, WHEN, AND HOW MUCH TO ORDER

When a customer order is received, the supplier must first determine what component material is needed to produce the item(s). Three of the most commonly used methods to determine component requirements are re-order point, computerized material planning systems, and pull systems.

Re-order Point

Perhaps the oldest method for determining material requirements is re-order point. With this method, the planner tracks the usage of an item and bases future purchases on how much was used in the past.

$$\text{Re-order point} = (\text{usage} \times \text{lead time}) + \text{safety stock} \qquad (1)$$

where:

Usage	= number of pieces used in a typical week
Lead time	= number of weeks to receive the material from a supplier
Safety stock	= number of pieces held in inventory to protect against unplanned usage

Re-order point was developed before the widespread availability of computers and is simple enough to be managed with manual records. Whenever an item is taken from inventory, its balance is adjusted. When the item's balance hits the re-order point, a purchase order (PO) or a release is issued to the supplier. Re-order point can work well for items with very predictable, regular usage. Shortcomings of the method are:

- It is not based on current customer orders.
- It uses no future information, only history.
- It responds slowly to changes in demand. If an item's demand rises quickly, the manufacturer will have an inventory shortage; if the demand falls, excess and obsolete inventory result.

The Contributors of this chapter are: Ronald Dalton, *Original Equipment Project Manager, Libbey-Owens-Ford Co.;* **Monica Fox,** *Field Engineer, Michigan Manufacturing Technology Center.*
The Reviewers of this chapter are: Hal Mather, *President, Hal Mather, Inc.;* **Elena J. Mondini,** *Senior Operations Analyst, Frigidaire Company, Home Comfort Products Division.*

CHAPTER 5 LOGISTICS

Re-order point is still used on a regular basis by most manufacturers, however, its use is limited primarily to nonproduction items due to its reliance on past information. In today's fast changing environment, it is not responsive enough to provide the level of delivery performance, measured by the number of customer orders delivered on time in the correct quantity.

Computerized Material Planning Systems

Manufacturing resource planning (MRPII) is the integration of management planning, scheduling, forecasting, capacity planning, and buying to achieve the defined objectives of a manufacturing operation; it is not a computer program, but an operating philosophy (see Fig. 5-1).

Rather than relying on historical usage information, these systems provide a direct link between purchase orders for components and customer orders. As customer orders are received, they are entered into the computer with a quantity and due date. The computer stores a *bill of material* which details the components necessary to produce the item. The system develops planned purchase orders for all required components and when approved, the planned purchase orders are released and printed from the computer system. The purchase orders are stored in the computer to support progress tracking.

The link between supplier and customer orders greatly reduces the chance of obsolete inventory and inventory shortages. Other advantages of MRPII systems include:

- Engineering changes and due date changes are automatically integrated into the plan.
- One production plan is used by all functional areas for planning and scheduling.
- The computer can handle large amounts of products.

- The computer makes it possible to generate summary management reports.
- The system can be used to forecast future requirements if product lead time is greater than customer lead time.

There are, however, a few disadvantages to using this system. These include:

- The system is more expensive to operate.
- Extensive data input is required.
- The system is very complex.
- The system is sensitive to errors.
- The operator must have extensive education to operate it.

While MRPII systems do offer several advantages, users will find manual ways to get the information they need to successfully meet customer requirements if they feel the computer is providing them with erroneous information. The day-to-day priority changes at the shop floor level are not always handled well with an MRPII system. Users are investigating the use of Manufacturing Execution Systems (MES) (some include Theory of Constraints Models[3]) that may help with handling day-to-day priorities.

Pull Systems

Pull systems schedule production by using customer orders as a goal rather than forecasts, and the basis is visual. The speed of response affects the customer's ability to make changes. Speed is what separates push from pull systems. A formal planned approach that includes accurate customer orders, purchasing plans, and manufacturing schedules is essential to operating a successful pull strategy.

One approach to a pull strategy that is popular and very successful with repetitive manufacturers is known as *kanban*, or visually-

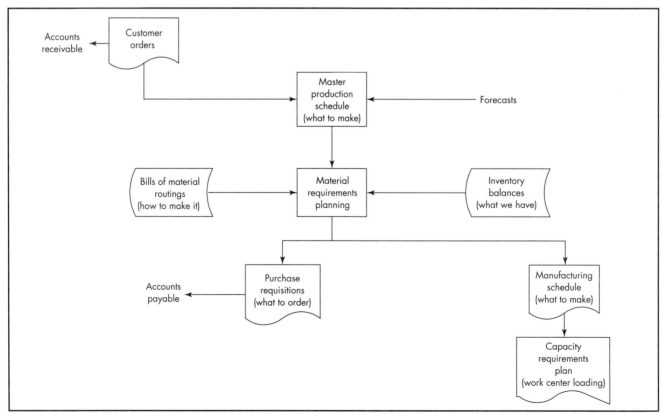

Fig. 5-1 Manufacturing resource planning (MRPII).

controlled production. Kanban is not easy to implement because there are many variants; it works best when product standardization is high and bill of material (BOM) accuracy is very important. The kanban system is used to order more parts when inventory has been depleted to a predetermined limit. The visual cues—a card, bin, or yellow line on the production floor—indicate the number of parts needed to be produced or the number of parts that can accumulate between production steps.[4]

Kanban also can be used to order components from suppliers. The kanban card can be transmitted in several ways:

- Cards are pulled at the supplier location as product is shipped.
- Cards are returned to the supplier when the customer picks up the next shipment.
- Cards are electronically sent or faxed to the supplier as the parts are used in the customer's facility.
- Empty containers are returned to the supplier as the kanban signal.

A successful kanban system relies on discipline and carefully implemented visual controls. The system requires:

- Standard container quantities.
- Short lead times.
- Zero-defect manufacturing.
- Well-trained operators.
- Direct communication between supplier and customer.

Kanban uses the one-less-at-a-time approach. Many companies remove kanbans (cards) from the system one at a time to gradually expose manufacturing problems that are hidden by excess inventory. Benefits of a successfully implemented pull system include:

- Reduced inventory and obsolete inventory.
- Reduced lead times.
- Reduced space requirements.
- A simple, visual means of scheduling and tracking production which is linked directly to customer requirements.

PLACING TRADITIONAL ORDERS

The process for manually placing orders includes:

- A request for quote.
- A purchase order.
- Repetitive purchasing.

The *request for quote* (RFQ) is the next step in the ordering process after requirements have been established for new parts. Traditionally, the RFQ is a paper document which specifies the quantity, delivery, and sometimes the target price of the desired material. It is often accompanied by a print which includes material and dimensional specifications. A manufacturer receiving an RFQ will often send one to its suppliers to obtain material pricing for sub-components. Each supplier in the supply chain develops preliminary manufacturing process information which is used to generate manufacturing costs and pricing. When completed, the final price quotations are returned to the customer. This process is not needed for repetitive purchasing.

The RFQ process can take several days or weeks depending on the complexity of the product and the length of the external supply chain. As the number of suppliers increase, more RFQs need to be completed.

In addition to time, another potential drawback of the paper RFQ process is the print or drawing specifications that are sent with it. Any drawing changes made during the RFQ process are difficult to track through the supply chain. Again, the longer the chain, the more chances for error.

The RFQ process ends when a *purchase order* (PO) is generated for the selected supplier. The PO is a document formalizing a purchase transaction between a customer and a supplier. Unlike the RFQ, the PO is an agreement to actually purchase the quoted parts or supplies. It is an agreement that defines:

- Quantity.
- Description and specifications.
- Price.
- Delivery date and method.
- Payment terms.

In the traditional ordering process, the PO, like the RFQ, is a paper document that usually has multiple copies so that all parties have a permanent record of the agreement. Typically a purchase order can have four or more copies that are distributed to:

- Purchasing (original).
- Receiving (to match with the packing slip for verifying part number, quantity, and delivery dates).
- Accounts payable (to match with invoice and packing slip).
- Supplier.
- Purchase originator.

Computer systems, such as an MRPII system, eliminate much of the manual effort to generate a PO and track it internally. Purchase order information is on-line where all employees can access it. However, the supplier still does not have a direct link to the customer. Time is required for the supplier to get the paper copy and enter it as a customer order. Any changes to the PO follow the same process. For many of today's manufacturers, the traditional ordering process is not timely enough.

Each functional area keeps a copy of the PO until the transaction is complete. If changes are necessary before the PO is complete, care must be taken to notify all departments that received a copy of the original PO to prevent error.

Customers often issue blanket purchase orders for frequently purchased components. Blanket POs specify contract terms and price, while regular releases indicate quantities and due dates for the material. Blanket POs save the time it takes to set up a new PO each time an item is purchased and often the releases can be issued by someone outside of Purchasing such as a material planner. As with the PO, the release may have several copies and is usually distributed to:

- Material control (original).
- Receiving (to match with the packing slip for verifying part number, quantity, and due date).
- Supplier.

Although blanket POs can reduce some paperwork, development and distribution of releases are still manual processes. Accuracy and timeliness can be an issue, especially for manufacturers with short lead times and unstable schedules.

RECEIVING

Receiving material from suppliers involves both physical movement and processing of the material as well as processing paperwork. The process ensures that the material is suitable for the intended use and that the supplier is paid for the material according to the purchase order contract. In this section, we review the traditional process and the current and future trends in processing material receipts.

Traditional Receiving Process

Similar to the traditional ordering process, the receiving process relies on many paper documents. The process starts with the receipt of material which is accompanied by a packing slip that details what

CHAPTER 5 LOGISTICS

is in the shipment. The packing slip usually contains information such as:

- Packing slip number and ship date.
- The item or part number.
- The customer purchase order number.
- Quantity shipped.
- Price (optional).

The packing slip is compared to both the physical material and the purchase order for accuracy and any discrepancies are noted on the packing slip so the supplier can be notified. Some companies also produce a *receiver,* a document verifying the receipt of the material and the information on the packing slip. Copies of the receiver are distributed to the Accounts Payable department, material planners, and the purchaser. The receiver and/or the corresponding packing slip and PO are filed together until the arrival of the supplier invoice. If necessary, the material is inspected for compliance to dimensional specifications before it is either stored in inventory or sent to the production floor.

The supplier invoice is typically sent to the Accounts Payable department. When it arrives, the invoice is matched to the correct packing slip and PO. This matching process is known as a three-way match (purchasing-supplier-receiving) and can be very time-consuming. A person must physically find the matching documents and check for errors in item numbers, pricing (discrepancies between the PO and the invoice), quantities, and ship dates. Once verified, Accounts Payable personnel issue a check to cover the invoice.

The manual three-way process can lead to many errors. Part numbers can be copied incorrectly when generating a receiver or the prices shown on a supplier invoice may differ from the PO price. MRPII systems which include accounting capabilities streamline the receiving process by eliminating many manual files. For example, when parts arrive, the receipt is entered into the system which automatically matches it to the purchase order. Similarly, entry of the supplier invoice will automatically link it to the PO receipt. Any inconsistencies in part numbers, pricing, or quantities are found by the computer.

Current Trends in Receiving

Bar code receiving is a cost-effective method for reducing errors and eliminating nonvalue-added work. Just as items in a grocery store have bar code labels, so do all of the components used by a manufacturer. AIAG (Automotive Industry Action Group) and ANSI (American National Standards Institute) standards for printing bar code labels provide a standard among suppliers and customers. Bar code shipping labels can be printed by the supplier or purchased from a third-party vendor. Printing technologies have greatly improved the reliability and speed of printing bar code labels on demand. Customers use bar code readers to scan supplier labels and enter the information into inventory tracking, purchasing, and quality control systems. Suppliers and customers can also use these standardized bar code labels to track material flow internally.

To implement bar code receiving a company must have:

- A computerized inventory system linked to a bar code station.
- A bar code station consisting of a computer with software to read bar codes.
- A bar code reading device such as a wand or laser scanner.
- A bar code printer or supplier of pre-printed labels.

Many MRPII systems are available with integrated bar code capability. Integrated bar coding speeds implementation and increases benefits of data collection. Plant environment is also a consideration in setting up bar coding since laser scanners are more durable and reliable than wand readers in dusty, oily manufacturing environments. However, they are also more costly. Radio frequency data links make the process of getting data into inventory control systems faster and easier. As with other technologies, user training is essential to the success of the system.

The benefits of a successfully implemented bar code system are:

- Fewer input errors.
- On-line confirmation of purchase order information such as quantity and due date.
- Immediate, on-line update of inventory, purchase orders, and accounts payable.
- A computerized record of all receiving transactions.

Eliminating the physical review of material is another method for streamlining the receiving process. Certification of suppliers reduces or eliminates the need to inspect incoming material. Suppliers become certified by passing customer audits of their manufacturing reliability and quality systems. Once certified, customers rely on the supplier to send in material which meets specifications so that incoming inspections are unnecessary. See Chapter 3 of this handbook for more information on bar coding.

Future Trends in Receiving

Future trends in receiving involve the changes introduced by electronic data interchange (EDI). These trends in the receiving area revolve around paperless payment, automated inventory updating, and shared data.

Paperless payment. Paperless payment is an extension of the electronic invoicing and payment via electronic funds transfer (EFT). The trend is to pay based upon the received shipment information. No invoice is generated by the supplier. The customer pays according to the shipping documentation accompanying the shipment after reconciliation with the appropriate order and pricing information. This process is called *evaluated receipt settlement* (ERS). ERS drives the movement to efficiency by eliminating the need to transmit an electronic invoice. Instead, the customer can pay based upon the shipping document (in the case of EDI, an ASC X.12 856, commonly called the advance shipping notice [ASN]). This transaction set specifies items shipped from the supplier location. The ASN is not transmitted to the customer until the shipment has physically left the supplier's shipping dock. The ASN contains all of the pertinent shipment data including the standard carrier alpha code (SCAC) defining the transportation agent, packing slip and bill of lading numbers, ship-to information, and information describing the physical makeup of the shipment. The customer uses the ASN to match information from the purchase order and the receiving process to ensure that the shipment is correct.

Automated inventory update. This involves the use of electronic shipping information. When a shipment is received, the received data are compared to the quantities called out on the ASN transaction set. If there is agreement, the in-stock inventory is updated electronically without keying in the received quantity data. To maximize efficiency, the receiving process should utilize bar code labels and scanning on the receiving dock as previously described.

The concept of shared data in the receiving area is an extension of that previously described in the Order Processing section. By sharing data between shipping, receiving, and inventory systems, the problem of resolving cumulative quantities can be addressed. Reconciliation of cumulative quantities in customer and supplier databases is a constant problem for many trading partners. By sharing data in their systems it is possible to determine where the discrepancy lies in a much more timely manner. If it is a matter of an in-transit shipment, this would be resolved by looking at the last shipment received in the customer's data and the last shipment in the supplier's data. Linking the applications would move cumulative quantity resolution to the level where exception processing could be partly automated. This is the ultimate goal for this innovation.

ELECTRONIC DATA INTERCHANGE FOR ORDERING

The introduction of electronic data interchange (EDI) into the ordering process does not change what activities take place but greatly impacts how business data flow. To understand this difference let us take a brief look at some basic EDI concepts and principles.

The name *electronic data interchange* somewhat defines this technology. EDI involves moving business data, such as orders and forecasts, electronically. However, the same could be said for faxing this information. The major difference is that EDI technology moves data between computers in a machine-ready format. Originally, there was not much difference between fax and EDI. EDI was defined as moving forms electronically, which was often referred to as "rip and read" EDI. After refinement of this definition, EDI was defined as the movement of business data electronically from computer-to-computer. The difference here was that the receiving EDI software would send an electronic acknowledgment that the data had been received and were at least syntactically correct. This is commonly called *two-way EDI*. Companies exchanging EDI documents in either of these ways are referred to as *trading partners*. Both of these definitions or models have several weaknesses. Let us use the ordering process to demonstrate the shortcomings of these definitions.

Traditionally, the company wishing to place the order would take the information from the order generation process and manually input the data into their EDI transmission software. The data would be transmitted to the receiving firm's EDI software. The receiving firm would then print the order, review it, and input the data into their order processing system. The delays in processing data and the potential for errors are obvious. Paper copies of the data must be moved from one desk to another. The potential for being lost or delayed in someone's in-basket is often realized. Repetitive manual data input raises the possibility of errors. This entire process is time- and labor-intensive.

To eliminate the majority of these problems, *EDI* is now defined as the movement of business data between customer and supplier application systems. Thus in the scenario described earlier, the customer's order generation process would be integrated with his or her outgoing EDI software, thereby eliminating the need for manual intervention. On the supplier's end, the receiving EDI software would automatically transfer the data to the order entry system for auditing and processing.

While not completely eliminating the potential, this integration reduces the chances for delay and errors in the process. This is why the definition of EDI today is the application-to-application transfer of business data between trading partners. To accomplish this involves computers, software, and communications of some type.

Hardware and Software Requirements

No matter what type of computer hardware used in your business, whether it is a large mainframe, a mid-range machine, or a personal computer, the odds are that there is an EDI system available for use. The main considerations when using the computer for EDI are to make sure there is enough disk space to store the additional data and that a modem, or some type of networking device, can be added for communications. The simplest and mostly widely used communication method is standard telephone lines. Depending on the volume of EDI data, it may be possible to share the line with other applications or even a voice line. However, many firms use a reserved line for EDI communications to remove any possible conflicts, therefore eliminating a potential operational bottleneck.

The next item required is EDI software, commonly referred to as *translation software*. The translation term is used because this software translates business data into the required format, as agreed upon between the customer and supplier, and then places it in an electronic envelope for transmission. When using EDI, the business data are referred to as the transaction set. For instance, a purchase order is called an ANSI ASC X.12 850 transaction set. This formal terminology points out that formats for transaction sets have approved standards. In the previous example, "ANSI ASC" stands for the American National Standards Institute Accredited Standards Committee. This group defines standards so that companies utilizing this technology will have a common basis for establishing EDI. The "X.12" refers to the standards as they are used in North America. The international standard, governed under the auspices of the United Nations (UN), is called the EDIFACT standard.

Many industry sector groups, such as the Automotive Industry Action Group (AIAG), publish subsets of these standards for use with particular trading partnerships in that sector. It should be noted that while the precise format of transaction sets is agreed upon by the trading partners, the guidelines as determined by standards groups should be followed as closely as possible. This simplifies processing, especially when a firm has multiple trading partners. When selecting an EDI translation software vendor, make sure that the product provided can be implemented for both X.12 and EDIFACT transaction sets according to the ANSI, ASC, and UN standards.

The next item required is the communication network to physically transmit the EDI data to the receiver. While a few companies provide a direct connection for suppliers to their internal EDI system, most firms utilize value-added networks (VANs) to provide the communication capability. A VAN provides more than just a physical connection for the two firms exchanging EDI data. It also provides an electronic mailbox for each firm exchanging EDI data. When a firm sends an EDI transaction set to a VAN, it includes the identification of the company to receive the data. The VAN takes the transaction and moves it to the electronic mailbox of the receiving firm. When the receiving firm checks its mailbox for transactions, the data are transmitted to the receiver's EDI computer. The VAN provides tracking information including size, information type, date, time, and number of transaction sets transmitted. In addition, a VAN will maintain the transaction set for a specified amount of time after delivery in case retransmission is required. VANs also maintain connections to other value-added networks.

EDI to Reduce Order Cycle Time

Re-examine Fig. 5-1 showing the MRPII process and information flow and see how EDI would impact it.

Quoting. The two EDI transaction sets used in the quote process are the request for quote (RFQ) and the response to request for quote (RRFQ). The customer will send the RFQ to the trading partner asking for a quote. The RFQ contains not only what product is required but also delivery requirements. After estimating the price and ensuring that the schedule can be met, the trading partner sends the RRFQ back to the customer.

The quoting process may involve several iterations if requirement changes are made or agreements are renegotiated. In either case retransmission of a new RFQ may not be necessary but a new response to RFQ should always be sent to the customer. Every received EDI transaction set receipt should be acknowledged. This practice should be maintained until the trading partners are certain

CHAPTER 5   LOGISTICS

that the communications are being completed successfully as a routine matter.

Order acknowledgment. Once a quote has been accepted, the customer will send the purchase order to the supplier. This contains all the necessary data to fulfill the delivery. Similarly, the EDI transaction set has quantity requirements on a line item basis, ship-to and bill-to information, contact names, and other appropriate information. As with other EDI transaction sets, a functional acknowledgment should be sent upon receipt. But in the case of a purchase order, a purchase order acknowledgment is generated and sent to the customer. The purpose is to confirm the details of the purchase order to ensure that there are no misunderstandings.

If the customer wishes to change the purchase order, a purchase order change transaction set is generated. In response, to verify the change, the supplier generates and transmits a purchase order change acknowledgment.

Materials Management with EDI

The MRPII diagram in Fig. 5-1 uses forecast data as one of its inputs. In the world of EDI, this information is provided via the planning schedule with release capability. This transaction set provides information in weekly lots for required deliveries. The transaction set is transmitted weekly from the customer to the supplier. In addition to the required parts for delivery, the schedule contains additional weeks of part quantities for authorizing material purchases plus monthly planning quantities for an additional period of time. A typical form will provide four weeks of manufacturing authorization, four weeks of raw material authorization, and six to nine months of planning information. After the transaction set is audited, the forecast information should be input into the MRPII system for future runs.

EDI Implementation Considerations

Implementing EDI is not technically difficult. It is a well-defined, mature technology. However, it is necessary to plan carefully. As in most projects, it is best to pilot the implementation in a controlled manner before moving into full production. Selecting your first trading partner for a pilot is an important consideration. This may be a client who has requested the use of EDI and consequently will be the first EDI trading partner. One of the best ways to implement EDI is to work with a customer or supplier who is experienced in EDI and willing to help with the implementation.

Other important considerations are to make your staff aware of the reasons for using EDI and to make sure they are well-trained in whatever skills they will need for the new technology.

The most important task when implementing EDI is to align your business practices to properly leverage the new technology. Using old manual processing practices with EDI will decrease the potential for improvement and can cause a loss of efficiency and productivity while increasing costs. Planning the new business processes that will be enabled by EDI implementation will require more effort than the technical installation. But business process modification is where the largest improvements in productivity and cost savings will be made.

EDI is not just for large corporations. Small and medium-sized companies can realize sizable gains in productivity and reduce cost by modifying their business practices to take advantage of EDI technology. The main benefits of implementing EDI are the efficiencies gained in moving business data electronically and the associated internal productivity gains. Examples include:

Lower data entry costs. By streamlining business practices and eliminating the redundancy of entering data at each process step, costly manual entry is greatly reduced. Information is made available to all who need it in a much faster time frame.

More accurate records. The elimination of multiple data entry steps reduces the chance for error. Entering the data once, electronically, at the beginning of processing and then reusing it throughout the various internal activities greatly increases the accuracy of processing steps.

More accurate decisions possible. Having more accurate data available in a shorter time period permits more accurate decision making. Planning schedules can be released faster to production scheduling. Shipping can be planned to take advantage of multiple shipments or lower rates. Suppliers can be notified faster concerning material needs.

Reduced inventories. By reducing information processing time and having more accurate information, inventory levels can be reduced. With the improved information, just-in-case inventories are no longer needed. One small firm that implemented EDI was able to reduce batch sizes and resulting inventory levels by one-third, resulting in reduced costs.

Reduced order time. A direct by-product of introducing EDI is the acceleration of the order-to-production-to-invoicing-to-payment cycle. This can provide a better cash flow within the organization.

Greater customer satisfaction. All of these benefits lead to the most important benefit in today's customer-oriented business world—a more satisfied customer. Customers are looking for firms that can provide more accurate orders, delivered faster, at a competitive price. EDI can assist in establishing this higher level of customer service.

Current EDI Trends

EDI has been used by many trading partners since the late 1970s. During that time, it has evolved from a basically one-on-one trading partner network. Today, EDI is a robust environment of networked trading partners exchanging transaction sets across traditional political and geophysical boundaries. In general, the trends cover the following areas.

Shared data. Many customers now permit suppliers to inquire into their databases to monitor stock levels and thereby determine when shipments should be made. The supplier does not have to wait to be notified by the customer as to when stock is needed.

Integrated applications between customer and suppliers. This concept takes data sharing one step further. The application systems are integrated and no intermediate EDI software is required to generate the transfer of business data. Systems are directly linked and provide data updates as needed for the appropriate transaction.

Electronic invoicing. This is becoming a common extension of traditional EDI transaction processing. An electronic invoice is generated at the time of shipment and transmitted to the customer. This eliminates the need for printing and mailing of a paper invoice.

Potential Benefits of New EDI Applications

The current trends discussed have all of the benefits previously stated for EDI. They offer the promise of extending these benefits even further. Sharing data and applications can further accelerate the order process cycle. In addition, this holds the promise of resolving the cumulative quantity issue. Quite often firms disagree on the number of items shipped and received. By working with the customer's database, the resolution of this problem will be easier.

Electronic invoicing speeds the payment cycle in much the same way that the order process is improved with EDI. Mail delays are eliminated and on-time payments are improved. However, it should be noted that if a customer has a 30-day accounts payable cycle, EDI will not shorten that period. Most firms still pay on the same cycle after EDI, but the payment is not delayed by inaccuracies or delays in delivery of the invoice.

Future EDI Trends

Companies successfully using EDI in the ordering process have seen many benefits, especially a shorter order cycle. Future trends in order processing will continue to work on shortening the order cycle but will also strive to make EDI easier and more accessible to manufacturers. Two areas where advances are likely are in use of the Internet and integration of engineering and material systems.

A new trend entering the EDI environment is the Internet and its associated on-line capability, the world-wide web (WWW). Many companies have looked to the Internet as a way to reduce their VAN charges (or in the case of some small firms, eliminate them completely). Many EDI software providers are releasing Internet-based products. While the use of the Internet is having an impact on today's business environment, there are still reasons to be cautious about complete dependency upon it for delivering business data. There is no one entity in charge of the Internet. If data are lost or delayed, it can be very difficult to determine what went wrong or who is responsible. There are efforts under way to resolve these issues and remove these obstacles to using the Internet for time-sensitive transmissions.

Another reason often cited for avoiding the use of the Internet for business use is the lack of security. While security is a problem, there are methods to resolve this issue. Encryption packages are available for encoding data so that the transmission is secure. Use of these packages will increase processing costs for Internet transactions and must be considered when calculating the cost savings of Internet use as compared to a VAN.

A few firms are using web-based forms to allow input of purchase order data and shipping information from very low-volume suppliers who do not have EDI capability.

Engineering blueprints and drawings play a key role in the planning and ordering process. The ability to electronically transfer drawings between companies improves the accuracy of the information and the timeliness with which changes can be implemented. For example, in the quoting process, electronic copies of the drawing and process documents are used by suppliers in place of the current hard copy sent with the RFQ. Electronic exchange of engineering data between customers and suppliers improves overall communication and provides opportunities for concurrent engineering which significantly reduces new product lead time.

Most companies would also benefit from linking internal engineering and material control systems. Computer-aided design (CAD) and MRPII systems both contain product data but since they are not linked, both must be maintained. For example, CAD systems usually contain a parts list or bill of material to detail the components required to make a product. The MRPII system uses the bill of material to generate component requirements for production but since the systems are not linked, the bill of material must be manually loaded into the MRPII system.

In addition to CAD systems, many companies have purchased product data management (PDM) systems to manage several engineering documents including the bills of material, engineering change notifications, process sheets, and inspection sheets. These documents come from several sources such as the CAD system, word processors, and PC databases. PDM systems not only record the engineering data, they also provide control of the approval process, ensuring that all engineering changes are properly approved and that everyone is working with the correct version. Often, Engineering maintains the original documents in the CAD or PDM systems, and sends paper copies to material personnel to enter into the MRPII system.

Many professionals have recognized the redundancy of the PDM and MRPII systems and are working on ways to integrate the systems to improve information sharing. Then, as engineering changes are recorded in the PDM system, they can automatically update the bill of material or the routing in the MRPII system. Integration of the two systems is an important step in streamlining the planning and ordering process to reduce product lead time and improve data accuracy.

SHIPPING TO MEET CUSTOMER EXPECTATIONS

As with quality, order fulfillment or delivery performance is now a key component of competitiveness. Customers set delivery dates to maintain a continuous flow of material to support manufacturing operations. Customer expectations for delivery are typically 98-100% on-time and in the correct quantity. Many suppliers feel the push for Just-in-Time (JIT) shipments has caused increased inventory levels and therefore, increased costs. If approached in a different way, however, JIT not only satisfies short delivery times, it can reduce inventory and manufacturing costs. Meeting delivery performance expectations requires not only efficient shipping methods, but more importantly, manufacturing that is flexible and responsive to customer needs.

LEAN MANUFACTURING AND JIT

Lean manufacturing, or Just-in-Time manufacturing, is an approach to achieving excellence in a manufacturing company based on the continuing elimination of waste. Waste applies to all aspects of manufacturing, not just inventory. Elements of lean manufacturing and JIT which are critical to reducing manufacturing lead time are:

- Lengthy changeovers are eliminated.
- Manufacturing processes are moved closer together, such as in manufacturing cells.
- Pull signals are used to authorize production.
- Routine preventive maintenance.
- Certify suppliers to provide defect-free components.
- Manufacturing processes that can produce quality products.
- A philosophy of continuous improvement.
- Just-in-Time shipments to customers performed without increasing inventory levels, but only if the entire manufacturing organization is educated and organized to carry out the philosophy of providing only what is needed, in the quantity needed, at the quality required, and the time desired.

SHIPPING

Until recently, transportation got little attention and was usually left to the discretion of the shipping or traffic department to choose the lowest cost method. With the implementation of JIT and the emphasis on eliminating the wastes associated with inventory, timeliness and reliability have become important considerations along with cost. Customers want smaller quantities and more frequent deliveries but without significantly increased transportation costs. Transportation methods available fall into two categories: using a dedicated service or putting your shipment into an existing system.

Dedicated service is provided by either a contracted trucking or air charter service or by a company's own fleet. Dedicated trucks are typically used for truckload hauls and standardized routes where a truck services the same companies on a daily or weekly basis. Depending on volumes, the truck may pick up a load of parts at one

CHAPTER 5   LOGISTICS

supplier or share the truck among suppliers on a "milk run" in which one truck picks up components at several suppliers on a daily basis before delivering them to the customer. Milk runs have worked particularly well for companies using JIT manufacturing and kanban. Dedicated ground transportation is generally priced by the mile and offers the shortest delivery times for regular ground service. Expedited truck service is also available for a higher price. Dedicated air charters are the fastest method for expediting shipments but usually have substantially higher prices than either expedited ground service or nondedicated air freight.

Nondedicated services usually involve consolidation or pooling of "less than truckload," or LTL, shipments from several unrelated sources. Several companies send small shipments to a central consolidation point where the material is unloaded, sorted, and reloaded by destination. Depending on the circumstances, the consolidation and eventual shipment may take anywhere from one to four days. Typically, the material is handled two to three times as opposed to once for the dedicated shipment, therefore, the possibility of damage is greater. LTL services are priced by the pound and are less expensive for shipping small quantities. Delivery times are less predictable, even though cut-off times for pickups are less flexible than dedicated services. Pooled air freight services use consolidation methods similar to LTL shipments but are more reliable in their delivery schedules and less expensive than air charter.

The best transportation method depends on a company's objectives for customer service and cost. Dedicated services are often faster and more reliable, but carry an increased cost. Nondedicated services have improved greatly in recent years due to computer software which facilitates efficient routings and tracks individual shipments. If shipments are carefully scheduled, nondedicated services can also reduce inventory and help customers achieve their delivery objectives.

Contrary to what some suppliers believe, customer emphasis on on-time delivery does not mean they expect suppliers to increase the number of expedited shipments. Expedited shipments mean increased costs for suppliers and ultimately, increased costs to the customer. Again, the emphasis should be on a JIT manufacturing philosophy which produces the product on time rather than resorting to extraordinary transportation methods. The trend toward global sourcing and global markets will make international logistics increasingly important.

SUPPLIER RESPONSIBILITIES

Increased competition among suppliers has led to increased customer demands in many areas, including logistics. Customers are constantly striving to find suppliers who will give them better quality and smaller, more frequent deliveries at a lower cost. Many customers have developed programs and measures for their suppliers to implement to ensure that they keep up with the demand for improvements.

Suppliers are pressured to continuously improve and reduce costs. Areas where customers have demanded supplier responsibility are:

- New technology implementation and use.
- Internal processes audited and improved.
- Quality and material system certifications.
- Product pricing.
- Subsuppliers are given similar technology and process improvements.
- Demands of multiple programs should be met.

New Technology

Historically, technology has been a way for companies to increase productivity and reduce costs. For instance, automated machine con-

trols, and load and unload devices have allowed manufacturing companies to reduce the need for direct labor. In the same way, computers have reduced the need for clerical staff. Knowing the potential for cost reductions, quality improvements, and delivery improvements, customers often require their suppliers to invest in new technologies so they too can benefit. Examples of customer demands for technology include:

- Logistics, where EDI is used for quoting, ordering, and receiving material and advanced shipping notification.
- Engineering, where computers and EDI are used to exchange drawings and dimensional specifications and notify suppliers of engineering changes.
- Quality, where computerized tools are required including coordinate measuring machines (CMMs), automated in-line gaging, and statistical process control programs.
- Accounting, where EDI for invoicing and payments, and activity-based costing are being used.

These are just a few examples of technologies that suppliers must either implement or risk losing customers to other suppliers that have successfully made the changes.

Auditing and Improving Internal Processes

In addition to technology, companies can also reduce costs and improve productivity by having stable, controlled processes. These include both the manufacturing processes, and any business processes used to control engineering, inventory, quality, shipping and receiving, and accounting. Customers often perform audits to ensure that suppliers have well-documented procedures and can provide proof that they are being followed. For instance, the process for implementing engineering changes is critical for determining that customers get products at the correct engineering level at the correct time. Customers will audit suppliers' methods for receiving, recording, communicating, and implementing engineering changes. Typically, a customer will audit several of his or her suppliers' processes before granting certification.

During audits, customers also verify that suppliers have programs for their own internal audits and continually improve their processes. What is considered a good process today, may be obsolete in five years, so suppliers must strive to update and improve.

Quality and Material System Certifications

In recent years, quality and quality management have become the central focus of most companies. Initially, most customers developed their own quality standards and audited suppliers for compliance to them. This forced many suppliers to adopt two or more different and sometimes redundant customer-specific quality systems, each requiring maintenance and support. In addition, each customer's on-site audit might last one to three days and require several additional days for preparation, resulting in considerable downtime and lost productivity.

Recently, different industries have moved to adopt the ISO 9000 quality standards. ISO 9000, and QS 9000 for the automotive industry, are globally recognized standards that ensure that certified companies comply with basic quality principles and techniques. Companies receive third-party audits and registration to prove they are compliant to the ISO 9000 quality standard. These standards have allowed both customers and suppliers to streamline their quality efforts by implementing and maintaining a single quality management system.

Implementing ISO 9000 requires companies to document, assess, and improve processes and procedures that are already in place. In doing so, a company is able to define and track performance of exactly what takes place within the company, including business practices, operational procedures, and manufacturing process steps. The ISO 9000 and QS 9000 quality systems include:

- Documentation of processes and procedures.
- Written policies.
- Work instructions for each task.
- Auditing of processes.
- Tracking results.
- Process improvement.

The 20 elements of ISO 9000 focus primarily on quality-related processes such as inspection, handling nonconforming product, and process control, although some cover processes such as design control and purchasing.

In addition to ISO 9000 and QS 9000, Ford Automotive Operations has developed a standard for materials management systems referred to as MS 9000. MS 9000 is designed to complement QS 9000 by addressing materials management system requirements not covered in the broader scope of an organization's quality system. Suppliers to Ford need to certify that their material systems are compliant with elements of this standard which include:

- Contract review.
- Scheduling.
- Purchasing.
- Product identification and traceability.
- Shipping.
- Inventory management.
- Handling, storage, packaging, and delivery.

ISO 9000, QS 9000, and MS 9000 are designed to reduce the effort required to audit suppliers while ensuring they are compliant with globally accepted standards. Many more customers and industries are expected to adopt these standards and demand that their suppliers do the same.

Pricing

Although product quality and JIT delivery have received great attention, customers have been unwilling to pay a higher price to meet these objectives. In fact, many customers have imposed automatic yearly price reductions over the course of a long-term contract. As previously discussed, customers expect suppliers to reduce overall cost by implementing a Just-in-Time philosophy which includes EDI, ISO 9000, and lean manufacturing as well as the implementation of new technology. Customers often cite shared cost savings as the reason for demanding suppliers to implement certain programs or technologies.

Many customers have also demanded access to internal cost information as they begin to develop long-term partnerships with their suppliers. This cost information may be used by the customer in several ways to:

- Provide insight into the supplier's actual costs so that the customer can assist with ways to reduce them. Again, the customer would expect to share in any savings he or she is able to help the supplier achieve.
- Assure that the supplier is receiving a price adequate to ensure its long-term survival. Some suppliers price themselves out of business by lowering prices without reducing internal costs.
- Make accurate comparisons between suppliers as to which manufacturing methods provide the best quality for the best price. A low cost could mean that essential quality requirements are not being met.

Many of the technologies that are being used for sharing engineering and logistics information also can be used to share cost information. Electronic interchange of cost and pricing information can be achieved by linking accounting and quoting systems. Some suppliers have provided their customers with electronic quoting templates that allow customers to produce their own quotes for components. This is especially true with standardized products such as tooling, spare parts, and expense items such as nuts and bolts. This type of sharing again reduces lead time to receive quotes and also reduces the personnel costs in developing them.

Activity-based costing (ABC) is another method customers are beginning to use to ensure they are receiving accurate quotes from suppliers (see Fig. 5-2). Activity-based costing is founded on the premise that costs not directly attributable to a product, such as support personnel cost, are incurred because of a company's activities. These activities exist because they support either other activities or ultimately, the company's products and services. With activity-based costing, the cost system first attributes costs to activities and then flows the costs into products and services based on their consumption of the activities.[5]

Suppliers and customers can use activity-based costing to accurately determine the true costs of ordering, scheduling, and shipping products. Other costing methods tend to mix these costs in with other manufacturing overhead costs. For instance, one company that manufactured and distributed plumbing connectors wanted to better understand its manufacturing costs. To the company's surprise, an ABC model illustrated that approximately one-half of its cost was in product distribution activities such as inputting customer orders,

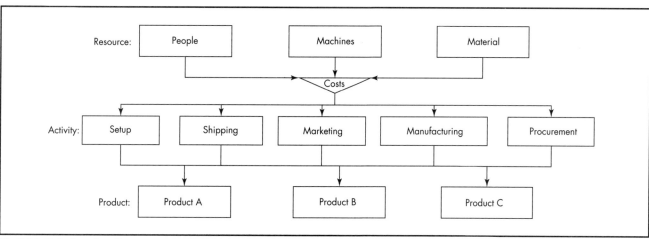

Fig. 5-2 Activity-based costing.

CHAPTER 5   LOGISTICS

picking orders, and shipping orders. As a result of the ABC model, companies are targeting many distribution activities as priorities for improvement as well as assigning extra charges to customers with complex packaging specifications.

Knowing the true costs for managing the supply chain allows companies to better evaluate the implementation of cost-effective EDI technologies. ABC can be used in the same way to evaluate many other activities in a manufacturing organization.

Assist Subsuppliers with Process and Technology Improvement

Many customers are expecting their first-tier suppliers to assist second- and third-tier suppliers in the supply chain with implementing technology and process improvements. Customers know that they will indirectly benefit from such changes. Subsuppliers, however, often have very limited resources for making such improvements and must rely heavily on the first-tier suppliers for knowledge. They sometimes share systems that require hardware and software and may form partnerships to negotiate better contracts with trucking companies, outside processors, or other service organizations.

Meeting the Demands of Multiple Programs

Many suppliers have tried to address each new customer demand as a new program which requires its own implementation plan and resources. This has led to the development of a complex system of procedures, programs, and support which is very costly and defeats the customer's desire for improved quality and delivery at reduced cost. Suppliers can achieve greater benefits by looking for links between each customer-imposed initiative to determine how resources can be used to satisfy multiple requirements at once. For example, an MRPII system can be used to satisfy many elements of ISO 9000, and provide the hardware and software necessary for electronic data interchange. Similarly, an activity-based costing initiative may provide valuable information about areas to focus improvement efforts to satisfy the QS 9000 requirement for continuous improvement programs. Customer initiatives are more likely to receive support from many functional areas of an organization if they are linked together. The result is lower implementation cost as well as a greater chance for success.

TRADING PARTNERSHIPS

Trading partnerships are established when two companies agree to do business with each other using EDI for the exchange of business data. The scope of these agreements can vary greatly. All such partnerships must have a trading partner agreement (TPA) or handbook. It must contain what transaction sets will be used including their exact format and content, the communications setup, formal business processes, transaction set exchange timing requirements, staff contact names, and problem resolution procedures. This document can include other aspects of doing business such as, how pricing will be handled for long-term contracts; how technical data, specifications and drawings are to be exchanged; and to what level the customer will be responsible for EDI training and process improvement with his or her suppliers. It can even include how data and applications will be shared.

Long-term Contracts

One major aspect of long-term contracts that EDI can support is pricing. While prices are sometimes guaranteed on such contracts, there is often the need for price updates, especially on multiyear contracts. By having an agreed upon schedule for pricing updates, the new price data can be sent to the customer for inclusion into budgeting and product cost calculations. This can be done by a purchase order change generated by the supplier or by providing a new quote. Catalog pricing also can be updated via EDI.

Other aspects of long-term contracts such as quantity commitments, engineering changes, and even part discontinuation can be addressed by EDI. Transaction set data exist to cover all of these scenarios.

Concurrent Engineering

EDI can be used to address many issues within concurrent engineering. Transaction sets exist for sending specifications, drawings, and even environmental compliance data. This set allows for inclusion of most pertinent data and drawing files. In addition, many other transaction sets include fields for engineering change levels and data necessary for establishing materials properties and characteristics.

A true joint design effort can be supported by EDI. In one mode of operation, a customer can send new drawings as part of a quote process to provide the supplier with updated information to ensure an accurate quote. Another mode of operation would be for the customer to send a partial design with a request to the supplier to complete the design on a particular part or subassembly. Upon completion, the supplier would send the finished drawing to the customer for approval.

EDI can even be used to support the standard for the exchange of product data (STEP) technology. STEP files can be included in a transaction set. This merger of EDI and STEP technologies is a possible way of resolving issues of data transfer in the concurrent engineering environment.

Customer Supplied Training and Assistance

Several large companies provide direct training and assistance to their EDI suppliers. This can take the form of a very extensive trading partner handbook, telephone support via an EDI help-desk, and by providing transaction set templates for some common EDI translation software. These firms supply various vendors with their transaction set definitions so that they can maintain libraries of the templates for potential trading partners. Another service often offered is to establish discount rates with the customer's preferred VAN to encourage usage by trading partners. This service helps the customer control his or her own VAN costs by minimizing cross-connect fees to other VANS.

In a few cases, large trading partners have even negotiated discount prices on EDI translation software. This encourages supplier trading partners to use a package with defined transaction set templates and known performance characteristics. Once again, this is a way for large firms to minimize their costs for adding and supporting new EDI trading partners.

EDI SERVICE PROVIDERS

There are several types of vendors who will provide assistance in implementing EDI systems. EDI software vendors, value-added network companies, and independent consulting firms are the three most common. The major difference is in the perspective they bring when providing services.

Most EDI software vendors are very good at the technical implementation of the translation packages and usually can provide adequate assistance in integrating EDI with manufacturing software applications. As would be expected, VAN vendors are proficient at providing communication services. There are even some vendors that provide both types of products and services.

Independent EDI consultants have differentiated themselves by offering vendor selection services and business process reengineering services for internalizing EDI into daily business activities. Until recently, what has traditionally been missing from these vendors is supply chain management services.

Supply chain management is best defined as utilizing EDI to maximize efficient business processes with both your customers and suppliers. It involves assisting your suppliers as well as your customers to become EDI capable. Supply chain management means that your firm takes the lead at not only implementing EDI transactions with all of your trading partners, but also assisting them in the proper integration of EDI into their internal systems. Selecting a service provider to assist your company in this endeavor requires careful screening.

Make sure the vendor selected for this activity is providing systems and services that meet your true requirements. Many vendors who provide software and network services will sell supply chain management services based on their products alone. Look for a vendor who will work with a broad array of software packages and network services. Finding such a vendor will usually guarantee that you have found a service provider who will work with your best interests in mind.

INVENTORY MANAGEMENT

An inventory management strategy strives to minimize inventory investment and handling costs while supporting other objectives of the company such as:

- Customer service.
- Manufacturing production.
- Transportation costs.
- Space utilization.

Inventory, including raw materials and work-in-process to finished goods, provides for fluctuations in customer orders, inefficiencies in manufacturing such as long setup times, poor quality or machine breakdowns, and for minimizing transportation costs associated with extra inventory. While inventory is necessary for these reasons, it also is detrimental to the company because it:

- Reduces capital available for improvements and equipment.
- Takes up valuable floor space.
- Requires additional resources, such as material handlers and inventory clerks.
- Increases the opportunity for product mix-up.

Lot sizing techniques such as economic order quantity (EOQ), part-period balancing, and period order quantity are being used less frequently. Companies have recognized that these methods increase on-hand inventory to cover for inefficiencies in the ordering and manufacturing processes. For example, ordering costs, which are components of the EOQ calculation, are much lower when newer techniques, such as MRPII and EDI are used. Traditional inventory methods also fail to include the costs of wastes associated with excess inventory such as extra material handling, time required to identify and search for items, and the possibility of damage, scrap, and obsolete inventory.

No single method or formula can be used to calculate inventory levels and order policies and quantities. Accurate information is key to making good decisions about inventory. There must be a drive for lower levels of inventory through continuous improvement. Required information includes:

- Customer expectations for lead time and delivery.
- Information about manufacturing processes such as setup times and equipment sharing.
- Transportation methods.
- Current inventory balances.
- Relative costs of inventory, transportation, and setups.
- Usage frequency.

MRPII systems are excellent tools for maintaining this information. They provide integrated information about customer delivery dates, component requirements, product routings, shipment routings, and part usage. The information is used in conjunction with inventory balances to project what components are needed, at what time, and in what quantity. Suggestions are made regarding what items to purchase and manufacture while also tracking obsolete items. The objective is to only have those items available which are needed to satisfy the customer orders listed in the system. A continuous improvement goal should be the drive for the lowest level of inventory that can be maintained without impairing operations.

Kanban, as described earlier, is a method of controlling inventory and visually controlling production. Other methods of inventory management are:

- "ABC" analysis.
- Centralized versus decentralized inventory.
- Consigned inventory.

Many MRPII systems also provide an ABC analysis of inventory. ABC analysis uses the "80-20 rule" to focus attention on controlling quantities of expensive and high volume items. "A" items are the top 80% of dollar volume items, "B" items are the next 15%, and the "C" items are the lowest 5%. Higher inventory levels of the low-value items have little effect on total inventory investment and at the same time minimize the attention needed to manage these items. This strategy is very successful in lowering overall inventory investment while still maintaining customer service.

Centralized safety stock for low-volume items can also reduce inventory while maximizing customer service. *Safety stock* is inventory that is carried over and above customer requirements to protect against fluctuations in customer orders and disruptions in manufacturing. When an item is used in several locations, a central stock can be used to cover the requirements. While this strategy minimizes inventory investment, it can increase transportation cost. Again, all factors must be reviewed in making the final decision on where and how much inventory to keep on hand.

A decentralized inventory philosophy also has advantages and disadvantages. Decentralized inventory can be more effectively managed since it is stored closer to the point of use and is controlled by the individuals responsible for using it to build product and satisfy customer requirements. With a decentralized philosophy, the users of inventory take more ownership for maintaining accurate records and meeting target inventory levels.

Consigned inventory is another way to reduce inventory investment while maintaining production and customer service levels. Customers keep supplier components on hand at the customer's location but do not pay for the parts until they are used. While some companies may view this as a way to reduce cost, often the supplier will pass along the cost of keeping the inventory in the price of its products. Therefore, unless other, more fundamental changes are made to the manufacturing or logistics processes, the costs of carrying inventory have only been shifted, not reduced.

CHAPTER 5   LOGISTICS

CONCLUSION

As with all other aspects of manufacturing, the trend for logistics is to decrease costs and improve service. Many new methods have been developed and are being designed to assist in making these changes. The overall philosophy is to improve accuracy and timeliness of communication and data exchange with EDI, and to use JIT to reduce inventory and maintain customer service. Together, these practices will minimize product lead time by reducing the ordering and shipping cycles, inventory investment, and manufacturing costs.

References

1. *APICS Dictionary,* Seventh Edition. 1992.
2. Goldratt, Eliyahu M., and Cox, Jeff. *The Goal: Excellence in Manufacturing.* New York: North River Press, 1984.
3. Gunn, Thomas G. *In the Age of the Real-time Enterprise—Managing for Winning Business Performance with Enterprise Logistics Management.* Essex Junction, VT: Omneo, an imprint of Oliver Wight Publications, Inc., 1994.
4. *Materials Resource Planning Technology Application Guide,* Edition 2. Network for Excellence in Manufacturing, 1995.
5. *Activity-Based Costing: Know Your Costs and Make a Profit.* Network for Excellence in Manufacturing, 1996.

Bibliography

Ackley, S. "Bar Code Technology in the New Millennium." *The Performance Advantage.* Falls Church, VA: APICS, July 1996.
Activity-Based Costing Technology Application Guide. Network for Excellence in Manufacturing, 1996.
Childs, J. "Transportation and Logistics." *The Performance Advantage.* Falls Church, VA: APICS, April 1996.
Electronic Data Interchange Project Planner. Southfield, MI: Automotive Industry Action Group, 1994.
Frey, S. *Warehouse Operations: A Handbook.* Beaverton, OR: M/A Press (Dilithium Press), 1983.
Gopal, C., and Cypress, H. *Integrated Distribution Management: Competing on Customer Service, Time, and Cost.* Homewood, IL: Business One Irwin, 1993.
Hoekstra, CPIM, Sjoerd, and Romme, Jac. *Integral Logistic Structures: Developing Customer-oriented Goods Flow.* New York: Industrial Press, 1992.
Kimberly, P. *Electronic Data Interchange.* New York: McGraw-Hill, Inc., 1991.
Lambert, D. M., and Stock, J. R. *Strategic Logistics Management.* Homewood, IL: Irwin, 1993.
Materials Requirements Planning Technology Application Guide. Network for Excellence in Manufacturing, 1995.
Metzgen, F. *Killing the Paper Dragon.* Portsmouth, NH: Heinemann Newness, 1990.
Muglia, V. *Enterprise Information Exchange: A Roadmap for Electronic Data Interchange for the Manufacturing Company.* Dearborn, MI: Society of Manufacturing Engineers, 1993.
Nicoll, A. D. *Creating an Effective JIT Customer/Supplier Partnership.* CPIM Just-in-Time Reprints. Falls Church, VA: APICS, Inc., 1991.
Quality Management Systems for Manufacturing Technology Application Guide. Network for Excellence in Manufacturing, 1996.

CHAPTER 6

MAINTAINING MATERIAL HANDLING SYSTEMS AND EQUIPMENT

CHAPTER CONTENTS

INTRODUCTION

Maintenance excellence can be described as a progressive and continuous improvement journey toward an organization's vision of success. Organizational commitment to the process of continuous maintenance and reliability improvement is the key to achieving maintenance excellence, which leads to organizational success.[1]

The maintenance function does have an end product: plant capacity. Maintenance program improvements that increase the time equipment is used are directly reflected in increased production and sales revenue. Proposed improvements to a maintenance program should be sold to management with reference to these profits. The value of the type of maintenance performed can be expressed as:

$$V_P = \frac{Q_P \times S_P}{C \times T} \tag{1}$$

where:
V_P = value perceived
Q_P = quality perceived
S_P = service perceived
C = cost
T = time

The value of maintenance and reliability to the enterprise is directly proportional to the quality of its work and its level of service.

The above-the-line values add to the company's performance. Meanwhile, decreases in below-the-line items of cost and time boost value. An important element in this formula is the subscript P, which stands for perception.[2] How these attributes of a maintenance function are perceived are a direct indication of the value to the organization. Maintenance does not cost—it pays.

MAINTENANCE PROGRAM OBJECTIVES

The major benefits or objectives of a good maintenance program include:

- Reduced production downtime with related savings and customer benefits due to fewer breakdowns.
- Reduced overtime pay for emergency and breakdown repairs.
- Fewer large-scale emergency and repetitive repairs, hence reduced peak demand for maintenance manpower and facilities.
- Lower repair costs for simple repairs made before breakdowns, because less manpower, and fewer skills and parts are usually needed for planned maintenance than for breakdowns.
- Fewer product rejects and less spoilage because of properly adjusted operating equipment.
- Postponement or elimination of cash outlays for replacement.
- Less standby equipment is needed, thus reducing capital investment.
- Decline of maintenance cost—labor and materials—on asset items in the program.
- Good record keeping to identify items with high maintenance costs, leading to investigation and correction of causes such as poor maintenance practices, misapplication, operator abuse, and obsolescence.
- Shift from inefficient reactive maintenance to less costly, scheduled maintenance and better work control.
- Better spare parts control, leading to a minimum inventory.
- Better industrial relations because production workers do not suffer involuntary layoffs or loss of an incentive bonus due to breakdowns.
- Greater safety for workers, leading to lower compensation and insurance costs.
- Improved cost control from data obtained during operation of the preventive, predictive, or proactive maintenance programs.
- Increased employee morale due to a feeling of operator ownership and an awareness of management interest in the condition of handling equipment.
- Lower unit cost of manufacture as a result of the savings in the cost of operations.

MAINTENANCE TYPES

The most common types of equipment maintenance are:

- Reactive.
- Preventive.
- Predictive.
- Proactive.
- Lubrication.

Reactive Maintenance

The unplanned repairs made during equipment failure are the most undesirable and, in the long range, the most costly type of maintenance. Half of industrial maintenance activity is *reactive*, resulting in significant costs due to unplanned downtime and damaged machinery.[3]

Preventive Maintenance

The goal of interval-based *preventive maintenance* is to provide control of planned maintenance activities rather than allowing machine breakdowns and unanticipated expenses.

Studies have shown that the successful implementation of preventive maintenance can provide a 30% decrease in maintenance costs

The Contributor of this chapter is: Dale P. Brautigam, PE, Vice President, Manufacturing and Engineering, LubeCon Systems, Inc.
The Reviewers of this chapter are: Robert King, Supervisor, Technical Publications, Conveyor Standard Products, Rapistan Demag Corporation; **Bruce Kothe,** Plant Engineer, Giddings and Lewis, Assembly Automation.

CHAPTER 6   MAINTAINING MATERIAL HANDLING SYSTEMS AND EQUIPMENT

relative to the expenses associated with reactive maintenance. The drawback is that a large amount of unnecessary maintenance is performed to ensure that no machine is allowed to fail while in service.[4]

Predictive Maintenance

Predictive maintenance, where breakdowns are anticipated and eliminated, is accomplished by applying technologies such as vibration analysis, lubricant analysis, and thermography to measure the condition of machinery, determine what problems are present, and decide when corrective action should be performed.

There are several benefits derived from predictive maintenance. Among these are:

- Repairs and maintenance can be planned and carried out without interrupting production. A 2-10% increase in production availability can be obtained by implementing a predictive maintenance program.
- Maintenance needs can be anticipated and planned effectively. As a result of performing predictive maintenance, plant emergency work orders (the result of reactive maintenance) can be reduced to less than five percent of total work orders, and overtime to three percent or less of total maintenance man-hours.[5]
- Product quality is improved. Quality is often adversely affected by mechanically-degraded equipment. Because it is frequently measured as a final process step, substantial off-quality product can be created before a machinery problem is detected. Predictive technologies, such as statistical equipment maintenance control (SEMCO), vibration analysis, and lubricant analysis can measure the mechanical condition of machinery so that corrections can be made before quality is compromised by equipment malfunction.[6]
- Safety is enhanced due to maintenance activities being anticipated, planned, and completed in a nonemergency environment, resulting in reduced exposure to hazardous conditions.
- Substantial energy savings are realized due to the elimination of high-energy vibration sources, such as misalignment and imbalance. The proper use of lubricants can also reduce machine power consumption by 10-15%.

A properly-implemented predictive maintenance program will usually result in savings in the first two years that are 10-50 times greater than the total program costs, and improve future planning.

Proactive Maintenance

Proactive maintenance can be described by the old saying, "An ounce of prevention is worth a pound of cure." The goal of *proactive maintenance* is to apply advanced investigative and corrective technology to extend machinery life. In its ideal form, proactive maintenance aims to eliminate reactive maintenance on a manufacturing component forever.

One benefit of proactive maintenance is that respective problems in equipment design that shorten component life are identified and eliminated. Verification from vendors that new and rebuilt equipment are free of defects should be required. This guarantee should include standards for the performance acceptability of vendor products or services, and be closely monitored to assure that these standards are met.

It is important that equipment installation be performed to precise standards. This leads to extended equipment life, and identifies and eliminates operating factors that can shorten service life.

Proactive maintenance consists of several technologies which, when combined, can lead to consistent life extension of equipment. Implementation of a maintenance program requires a balanced integration of preventive, predictive, and proactive maintenance strategies. These improvement strategies are not independent and draw upon each other's strengths to achieve reliable plant capacity.[7]

Lubrication

A good lubrication program is an integral part of an effective preventive, predictive, and proactive maintenance program. Many equipment failures can be attributed to improper lubrication practices.

A well-planned and properly-implemented lubrication program will more than pay for itself in reduced downtime, lower maintenance costs in both parts and labor, and reduced energy costs.[8]

The activities to achieve and carry out an effective lubrication program are:

1. Conduct a plant lubrication survey.
2. Establish lubrication schedules and improve selection and application of lubricants.
3. Implement a lubricant analysis program.
4. Develop fluids management and quality assurance procedures.
5. Perform the activities required to implement the lubrication management program.

Consider the use of specialty lubricants such as synthetics and thin-film/dry-film boundary lubricants as a proactive measure to reduce wear and increase equipment life. These lubricants can be automatically applied to areas of wear on material handling equipment not previously lubricated, such as the pins and links on chain conveyors, rollers, side bars on all sizes of roller chain, open gears, as well as slides and guides. The thin-film and dry-film boundary lubricants work especially well in abrasive environments.

Automated lubrication has significant technical advantages when compared to manual lubrication. Data from bearing manufacturers have shown lubrication-related distress is responsible for at least 50%, and perhaps as much as 70%, of all bearing failures worldwide. Thoroughly well-engineered automatic lubrication systems applying either oil or grease will ensure that:

- The time lapse between relubrication events is optimized.
- Accurately predetermined, metered amounts of lubricant enter the bearing "on time" and displace contaminants.
- The integrity of bearing seals is safeguarded.
- Supervisory instrumentation and associated means of monitoring are available at the point of lubrication for critical bearings.[9]

EQUIPMENT CONDITION AND PERFORMANCE ANALYSIS

This section discusses:

- Determining what equipment should be inspected.
- Inspection criteria.
- Inspection frequency.
- Inspection schedule.

This phase of the maintenance activity is one of the most important, since it requires rather extensive investigation and forms the basis for developing a number of major policies.

DETERMINING WHAT EQUIPMENT SHOULD BE INSPECTED

To decide what should be inspected, ask the following questions:

- How critical is the piece of equipment? Will failure cause a major shutdown of the entire production line?
- Is the safety of employees or plant involved?

CHAPTER 6   MAINTAINING MATERIAL HANDLING SYSTEMS AND EQUIPMENT

• Is standby equipment available in case of failure?
• Does the cost of maintenance exceed downtime expense and cost of repair or replacement?
• Does the normal life of the equipment, without preventive, predictive, or proactive maintenance, exceed manufacturing needs (is obsolescence expected before failure)?

Obviously, the type of equipment and management's policy on equipment performance will influence the answers to these questions. In many cases, the decision on what to inspect may be guided by knowing whether a failure in upkeep or adjustment of the equipment will harm either production or the employee, or will waste plant assets.

INSPECTION CRITERIA

To determine what items or factors should be inspected, the most useful source of information may be the service manual for the equipment under study. A complete file of service manuals on all handling equipment should be kept in a central location. Other sources of helpful information are the maintenance personnel and the sales/service representatives of the equipment suppliers. After the items to be inspected have been identified, it is advisable to record them in the form of checklists, which may be of two types:

• General—applicable to several types of equipment.
• Specific—applicable to only a certain piece of equipment.

INSPECTION FREQUENCY

The first step in determining the frequency of inspection is to make an engineering analysis of the equipment in question from the following points of view:

• Age, condition, and value.
• Severity of service.
• Safety requirements.
• Hours of operation.
• Susceptibility to wear.
• Susceptibility to damage.
• Susceptibility to getting out of adjustment.
• Service record.
• Past maintenance work orders.
• Conduct interviews with maintenance personnel and operating supervision.

After making this analysis, the determination of inspection frequency may be established as follows:

1. Implement a computerized maintenance management system.
2. Select initial inspection cycles based on experience and the recommendation of the manufacturer.
3. Keep records of the maintenance requirements on the equipment and adjust frequency as appropriate.
4. Set up a filing system.
5. Review frequency of inspection to suit changes in operation; that is, increase the frequency as the equipment becomes older, as usage is increased, or as other conditions warrant.

To ensure the continued validity of the inspection cycle, it is advisable to check new equipment more frequently. It is also worthwhile to require that inspectors indicate on the checklist whether the frequency cycle should be increased or shortened.

INSPECTION SCHEDULE

Under normal circumstances, setting up an inspection schedule involves determining calendar dates that will meet the frequency requirements most efficiently. Most plants will find that maintenance inspection and service functions fall into the following three groups:

• Routine upkeep. Work is done at regular short intervals (adjusting, lubricating, cleaning) while equipment is operating or idle.
• Periodic inspections. This covers work done at prescribed intervals on equipment that is either running or shut down—as may be observed by visual inspections, tear-down inspections, overhauls, scheduled replacement of parts, etc.
• Contingent work. This includes work done at indefinite intervals when equipment is shut down for other purposes.[10]

MAINTENANCE SUGGESTIONS

This section focuses on maintenance suggestions for flexible wheeled handling equipment, conveyors, overhead handling and lift devices, storage equipment, transport packaging, and automated material handling systems.

FLEXIBLE WHEELED HANDLING EQUIPMENT

Flexible wheeled handling equipment includes nonpowered floor equipment and industrial trucks.

Nonpowered Floor Equipment

Nonpowered floor equipment consists of devices that are constructed with a platform or rack mounted on wheels and casters that are propelled manually or attached to a power medium such as a tractor, tow chain, or cable.

Caster and wheels.
1. Conduct standard tests with spring-balance readings on standard floor areas, rail sections, etc., for tractive effort, swiveling effort, and deflection effort. Make these tests monthly on all hand-moved, floor-supported wheeled equipment, testing under load and empty.
2. Test wheel resiliency by definite measure at least once per month, replacing springs or tires as needed.
3. Lubricate at least once per month.
4. Check lubricant retainers at least once per month.
5. Check track grooves, flanges, and treads for worn spots.
6. Check tires for creep, looseness, and oil deposits (sign of tires rolling over oily floors). Remove sharp or hard embedded objects from rubber. Check metal treads for true crown and damage.
7. Check wheeled device for corner-to-corner teetering due to uneven wear of wheels. Rematch wheels or restore correct diameters.
8. Check the supporting members where the casters or wheels are fastened for stiffness, alignment, and firmness.
9. Check tightness of swivel and bearing bolts, and all load-bearing parts for breaks and deformations.

Trailers.
1. Check all tires at least once per month for signs of misaligned wheels, running rubber through oil pools, and other abuse. Remove all embedded steel chips and other hard objects from solid-rubber tires once per day.
2. Check all wheels at least once per month. If wear is uneven because of such factors as one pair of wheels steering and the other not, or one end of the trailer is more heavily loaded than the other, interchange the wheels at least once every two months.
3. Check chassis frame at least once per month for deformed, damaged, sprung, or loose members.

CHAPTER 6   MAINTAINING MATERIAL HANDLING SYSTEMS AND EQUIPMENT

4. Check stacking angles of devices for deformation, breakage, or sharp edges due to wear or mishandling while loading and unloading.
5. Lubricate at least once per month, using a chart or checklist to make sure no fittings are missed.
6. Check all bearings, at least once per month, for signs of shock-load damage, erosion, and wear.
7. Check all steering members, including casters, fifth wheels, true tracking or true radius, or turns on four-wheel steerers, at least once per month.
8. Check alignment of all members at least once per month, including alignment of nonsteering wheels with true centerline of chassis, alignment of loading and unloading devices with chassis, and alignment of load braces with true directions of loads.
9. Check all load-handling members such as lift truck mechanisms, hydraulic mechanisms, scales hopper mechanisms, and in-transit mixers at least once per month.
10. Once per month tow the empty trailer at high speed over a rough surface, and listen for noises indicating loose parts.

Hand push trucks.
1. Lubricate at least once per month, all wheels, steering mechanism, hopper gates, and other moving parts, except those having sealed-in lubrication.
2. Inspect the mechanical condition of all wheels at least once per month, and the treads of rubber-tired wheels at least once per week, removing all steel chips and other hard objects from the rubber.
3. At least once per month, inspect all wooden parts for splintering, and tighten loose bolts and rivets.
4. Check all hand grips for smoothness and friction at least once per month.
5. Check all noses and other lifting surfaces for bending, abrasion, hinge freedom, and tightness at least once per month.
6. Check all grabs, clamps, holding chains, and bands at least once per month, and replace any that are stretched, deformed, or unsafe.
7. Check all stake sockets, stakes, lifting lugs, shelves, brackets, and other auxiliary devices at least once per month.
8. At least once per month, check all brakes and other devices intended to hold the truck while loading, unloading, or going down grades.
9. Check rubber parts, springs, and cushioning members at least once per month.
10. Paint according to chart or checklist designations at least once per year. Keep pigment paints off wooden parts where it might conceal splits and other dangerous places. Keep paint off rubber parts. Do not paint hand grips.

Industrial Trucks

Industrial trucks provide flexible handling of materials along variable flow paths. One of the most familiar types is the fork lift truck, which uses a pair of forks riding on a vertical mast to engage, lift, lower, and move loads. Lift trucks may be manually propelled or powered by electric motors, gasoline, liquid petroleum (LP) gas, or diesel-fueled engines.

Gasoline trucks. Maintenance steps for gasoline trucks are based on the following:

• Weekly or 40-60 operating hours under normal conditions.
• Monthly or 300-600 operating hours under normal conditions.
• Quarterly to annually or 1,000-5,000 operating hours under normal conditions.

Weekly or 40-60 operating hours, normal conditions.
1. Check fan and accessory belt tension.
2. Check oil pressure.
3. Service battery and battery connections.
4. Check oil starter motor and generator.
5. Check brake pedal travel.
6. Check brake master cylinder and all hydraulic lines.
7. Check hoist and tilt cylinders for leaks and wear.
8. Check hydraulic oil level and system for leaks.
9. Protect cooling system if temperature require.
10. Check radiator and hoses for leaks.
11. Steam-clean machine.
12. Lubricate completely, not overlooking the following:

   • Adjust and lubricate lift chains.
   • Lubricate inner slides and upright supports.
   • Lubricate piston-head sprockets.
   • Lubricate tilt cylinder pins and lift brackets.
   • Check drive axle lubricant.
   • Check steering gear oil.
   • Lubricate steering axle.

13. Check tires, remove foreign objects, and inflate pneumatic type properly.
14. Operate hydraulic equipment. Drive and check the truck while it is in motion.

Monthly or 300-600 operating hours, normal conditions. This generally includes all items on the weekly list, plus the following.
1. Change engine oil and oil-filter cartridge.
2. Clean ore replace crankcase breather. Check outlet pipe.
3. Clean fuel bowl and strainer.
4. Check engine timing.
5. Check and adjust carburetor, idle speed, governor, and degasser to proper operating settings.
6. Check and adjust clutch free play.
7. Clean air cleaner.
8. Check main generator voltage.
9. Check and clean spark plugs and distributor points.
10. Check generator brushes and commutator.
11. Clean hydraulic breather cap.
12. Grease water pump.
13. Blow out radiator core.
14. Clean gas filler cap screen and sump filler cap.
15. Clean axle air vent.
16. Check universal joints for wear.
17. Check springs, U-bolts, clips, and shackle bolts.
18. Check steering mechanism, alignment, and turning radius for wear.
19. Check wheel bearings for wear.
20. Engine tune-up, including:

   • Check compression of each cylinder.
   • Adjust tappets.
   • Adjust governor.
   • Clean fuel pump screen.
   • Replace fan belts if necessary.
   • Check fan, water pump, and generator bearings.
   • Check cylinder head, manifold, and oil pan bolts.

21. Inspect universal joint.
22. Tighten drive axle bolts.
23. Inspect and equalize lift chains.
24. Check upright wear.
25. Check lift bracket rollers.
26. Check drift with capacity load.

CHAPTER 6   MAINTAINING MATERIAL HANDLING SYSTEMS AND EQUIPMENT

27. Inspect gland packing.
28. Check oil level in transmission and fluid drive.
29. Check brake lining, drums, and wheel cylinders.
30. Repack and adjust wheel bearings.
31. Tighten hub flange bolts.
32. Check hydraulic pump, control valve, and lines.
33. Check muffler for breaks.
34. Drain, flush, and refill radiator.
35. Tighten all bolts, nuts, and screws.

Quarterly to annually or 1,000-5,000 operating hours, normal conditions. This generally includes items on the weekly and monthly lists, plus the following.

1. Complete engine overhaul.
2. Disassemble, inspect, and replace worn parts of:

   • Transmission.
   • Differential.
   • Hoist cylinder (repack).
   • Tilt cylinders (repack).

3. Disassemble channels, inspect rollers, wear strips, etc.
4. Check carriage for distortion, chain anchors, and rollers.
5. Disassemble trailing assembly, inspect king pins, steer knuckle pins and bushings, and replace worn parts.
6. Disassemble hydraulic brake system, check wheel cylinder, brake lines, fittings, lining, master cylinder, and drums.
7. Disassemble steering gear and check for worn parts.
8. Drain, flush, and refill hydraulic tank.
9. Remove, wash, inspect, and lubricate lift chains.
10. Check trueness of forks.
11. Wash and paint truck as needed.

Figure 6-1 is a checklist for gasoline truck maintenance arranged according to duty cycles (day, week, month, etc.) and systems (brakes, axle, etc.).

Electric trucks. Maintenance for electric industrial trucks should include the following steps.

Weekly to monthly maintenance activities.

1. Controller.

   • Check for freedom of movement and burned control tips—replace if necessary.
   • Check and tighten loose terminals.
   • Lubricate.

2. Contactors.

   • Check for burned contacts—replace if necessary.
   • Check for freedom of movement and sufficient overtravel of plunger.
   • Check and tighten loose terminals.
   • Check for gap and spring tension.

3. Resistors.

   • Check for burned coils—replace if necessary.
   • Clean by blowing out with dry compressed air.
   • Check and tighten loose terminals.
   • Check coil insulators for cracks and burns (replace if necessary).

4. Switches.

   • Check for loose terminals and worn contacts.

5. Motors.

   • Inspect commutator for burning and pitting (clean if necessary).

	For Average Duty Cycles		
	Day	Week	Month
Brakes			
Operation and "feel"	●		
Leakage in lines or master cylinder		●	
Shoes, linings, connections			●
Hand brake and brake lock	●		
Safety seat break	●		
Drive axle and differential			
Axle ends (without wheels)			●
Unusual noise	●		
Oil level		●	
Clutch and transmission			
Clutch pedal operation and "feel"	●		
Unusual noise	●		
Oil level	●		
Cooling system			
Water or antifreeze level	●		
Leakage in lines, fittings, etc.		●	
Water pump mountings and operation			●
Fan operation, belt tension		●	
Electrical system			
Batteries: water level, specific gravity	●		
Batteries: terminals, cables		●	
Gage operation and accuracy	●		
Generator operation	●		
Starting-motor operation			●
Generator and motor brushes			●
Controller: dirt, points		●	
Wires and terminals		●	
Engine			
Crankcase lubrication level	●		
Oil filter		●	
Cylinder head: gaskets, leaks			●
Manifold damage or leaks			●
Muffler mounting and condition			●
Cleanliness		●	
Operation and "feel"	●		
Operation and temperature	●		
Fuel system			
Air cleaner mounting, cleanliness		●	
Fuel pump operation		●	
Fuel supply	●		
Fuel filler cap screen		●	
Other filters (as on diesels)		●	
Hydraulic system			
Tilt and life operation, oil level	●		
Pump, valves, tank		●	
Tank filler cap		●	
Lift chain: adjustment, wear		●	
Brackets and slides: wear, leaks			●
Steering			
Tie rods, pins, spindles, etc.			●
Steering operation and "feel"	●		
Miscellaneous			
Fire extinguishers			●
Tires and wheels	●		
Fasteners and connections		●	
Linkages		●	
Cleanliness		●	

Fig. 6-1 Gasoline industrial truck checklist.

CHAPTER 6   MAINTAINING MATERIAL HANDLING SYSTEMS AND EQUIPMENT

- Check for worn brushes—replace if necessary.
- Check brush holders for free clearance and spring tension.
- Check for excessive foreign material, carbon dust, etc.
- Check motor insulation and terminal studs.
- Clean motor with compressed air.
- Examine motor coupling for proper lubrication.

6. General wiring.

- Check battery cables and connections.
- Inspect wiring for chafing, worn insulation, and burning.
- Check and tighten loose terminals.

Annual maintenance activities.
1. Remove motor, dismantle, and clean all parts.
2. Check terminals, insulation, and bushings.
3. Inspect brush holders for tightness, proper radial position, angle, and spacing.
4. Check brushes for bearing and length.
5. Check armature for shorts and grounds.
6. Check insulation for fraying and charring.
7. Check commutator for discoloration, high or low bars, and looseness—true up if required.
8. Check wire banding for tightness—reband if necessary.
9. Inspect shaft for straightness and examine bearings.
10. Inspect for dynamic balance—check all field coils and connections.
11. Test for insulation shorts, grounds, and open circuits.
12. Clean and inspect motor couplings.
13. Repack motor with proper lubricant—reseal if required.

CONVEYORS

This section discusses the following types of conveyors:

- Roller conveyors.
- Belt conveyors.
- Portable conveyors.
- Chain conveyors.
- Drag, flight, screw, apron, and general conveyors.

Roller Conveyors

Roller conveyors consist of a series of rollers supported in a frame over which objects are advanced manually, by gravity, or by power.[11]

1. Once per month test the gravity or efficiency of all fixed systems by sending a standard test unit down the rolls. Check its speed of travel with a stopwatch and observe its distance of travel, watching its behavior on turns, etc.
2. Lubricate all rolls intended to be lubricated at least once per month. Inspect all that are not to be lubricated to make sure of the absence of lubricant, or to remove lubricant and correct any damage done by it.
3. Spin all rolls once every two months, watching for signs of binding, and listening for undue looseness at the bearings.
4. Operate all live rolls, live guides, tilt sections, and other velocity-imparting mechanisms under test conditions at least once per month.
5. Check and service the power-transmission members of live rolls and guides at least once per month, or in accordance with the power transmission schedule.
6. Trip all automatic devices (such as switches, selectors, and counters), check the automatic control of live rolls, guides and tilters, and test alarms and safety blocks monthly.
7. Operate all hand-control mechanisms, such as spur switches, switch locks, turntables, and load-positioning brakes monthly, paying special attention to those seldom used.

8. Examine all extra heavy sections on which loads are dropped, production operations are performed, etc., once per month. Check for types of damage likely to be caused by operating conditions.
9. Check all portable roller conveyor sections when the permanent systems are examined.
10. At least once per year, examine the sections where the load on one end of the rollers is heavier than on the other, or where the traffic is heavier than on other sections. Turn rollers end-to-end to equalize bearing wear. Also interchange rollers or whole sections between light traffic areas and heavy traffic areas.

Belt Conveyors

A *belt conveyor* is an endless fabric, rubber, plastic, leather, or metal belt operating over suitable drive and tail pulleys and belt idlers, or a slide bed for handling bulk materials, packages, or objects placed directly upon the belt.[12]

1. Make a list of the damage hazards incident to every installation. Schedule the maintenance examinations so that special attention is paid to the probable damages from each hazard, with the frequency of examination indicated by the seriousness of the hazards.
2. Make some of the examinations just before starting up, after the belt has been idle for a day or overnight. Belts can be subject to slow elastic shrinking after the elongating tensions of their day's work—examination may show that the belt needs to be slackened when resting.
3. Repair all cuts immediately.
4. Vulcanize patches on worn surfaces of rubber conveyor belts, or repair with metal splices or belt manufacturer's repair products.
5. Watch the fastener. Replace or repair at the slightest sign of cracking or breaking of fasteners or tearing of fabric.
6. Inspect the places where cleats or other devices are fastened to belts.
7. Inspect the under or drive side of the belt for signs of slipping, lubricant spilled from idlers, dirt or conveyed materials being carried between belt and pulleys, and frozen or sticking idlers.
8. Clean belt regularly if subject to greasy, solvent-bearing, chemical-damaging, or other damaging materials—or if cleanliness is needed for plant operation. When cleaning, soak the dirt loose first, wash it away gently with a mild soap, and use steam hoses or strong caustics only as the last resort.
9. Check the amount of power needed for moving the belt when loaded. If this demand goes up, make sure that it is not due to sticking idlers, pulleys out of line, abraded slide or guide boards, overtightening at take-up, or some other belt-damaging factor.
10. Inspect the belt surroundings for oil drippage from machinery located above the belt, weather leaks in housing, solvent fumes from processes flowing over the belt, sunlight getting at the rubber belt, and other hazards.

Portable Conveyors

Portable conveyors are any type of transportable conveyor having supports that provide mobility.[13]

1. Arrange to have each type of portable conveyor checked and serviced with permanent types: portable roller with permanent roller conveyor, portable belt with permanent belt conveyor, and so on.

CHAPTER 6   MAINTAINING MATERIAL HANDLING SYSTEMS AND EQUIPMENT

2. Test limit switches of portable elevators daily.
3. Check and service all motors and electrical parts by the plant electrical maintenance schedule, giving special consideration for equipment used outdoors.
4. Lubricate at least once every two weeks.
5. Check and service belts, buckets, and cleats monthly as part of the plant belt conveyor maintenance schedule. Keep belt edges sealed.
6. Operate all safety catches, position locks, interlocks, and other safety devices under test conditions monthly.
7. Check all brakes, especially load brakes monthly.
8. Check the mechanical conditions of all bearings, gears, and similar operating parts at least once per month.
9. Check and service all chains, ropes, slings, and similar parts as per the plant maintenance schedules for such parts.
10. Check the weather protection, dust- and fire-hazard protections, and the life of all parts.

Chain Conveyors

A *chain conveyor* is any type of conveyor that has one or more chains acting as the conveying element.[14]

1. Clean, check, and service the drive motor once per month.
2. Immediately after the motor checkup, take a power reading with an ammeter with the conveyor uniformly loaded.
3. Check, service, and operate all remote controls, especially the emergency stops, once per month.
4. Trip all automatic controls, warning signals, and overload protections at least once per month.
5. Check the lubricant level in the motor reducer or the gear reduction, and lubricate the system, making sure no fittings are missed, once per month or as per the plant lubrication schedule.
6. Check all sprockets, bearings, load-carrying devices, chains, take-ups, and similar parts for alignment and position at least once per month.
7. Operate all governors, timers, and speed-governing devices throughout their complete ranges at least once per month, timing their performance with a stopwatch.
8. Check the operations of blowers, baffles, shields, and other devices intended to keep chemical fumes, abrasive dusts, and other damaging elements away from the chain and other structural alignment features, at least once per month.
9. Check the plumbness, tightness, and firmness of supports, the truth of sprocket axes with the intended plane of travel of the chain, and other structural alignment features at least once every six months, and more often if possibilities of misalignment are high.
10. At monthly inspection periods, operate the system under no load at various speeds and listen for indications of dragging rollers, chain rubbing due to misalignment, neglected bearings, and looseness of any part.
11. Check automatic lubricators for operation and accuracy and fill reservoirs as required monthly, or more frequently if environmental conditions dictate.

Drag, Flight, Screw, Apron, and General Conveyors

A *drag conveyor* is a type of conveyor having one or more endless chains which drag bulk materials through a trough.[15]

A *flight conveyor* is comprised of one or more endless propelling media, such as a chain, to which flights are attached, having a trough through which material is pushed by the flights.[16]

A *screw conveyor* is a conveyor with a screw revolving in a suitably-shaped stationary trough or casing fitted with hangers through ends or other auxiliary accessories.[17]

An *apron conveyor* is a conveyor that has a series of apron pans forming the moving bed, connected to a roller chain system with internal or external rollers or wheels.[18]

1. Lubricate at least once per month, making sure that pressure grease intended to force dirt away from bearing entrances performs its full function, and that bearings not intended to be lubricated are not lubricated. Remove any excess grease which might become a dirt-gathering hazard or contaminate the materials being handled.
2. Check all bearings at least once per month by observing the operations of the parts which they carry, listening for evidence of dirt or grit penetration and examining for looseness.
3. Examine all parts which are intended to be reversed for even-wear distribution at least once per month, and reverse well in advance of the time when wear becomes serious.
4. Check all units for alignment with each other and for plumbness, levelness, and alignment of parts monthly.
5. Trip all automatic controls and other automatic mechanisms such as switches, overload protections, antireverses, and counters, at least once per month, paying special attention to the ones that seldom need to function in actual service.
6. Operate all hand-controlled apparatus, such as tensioners, plows, gates, chute position loaders, and unloaders, at least once per month, operating over full range as well as normal service range.
7. Check and service the motors in accordance with the electrical maintenance schedule at least once per month, operating all remote controls and interlocks under test conditions and correcting any defects.
8. Immediately after establishing correct conditions of motors, use an ammeter to make a power-consumption check of each motor under test conditions, or under a positively known load of materials being handled. Any serious increase of power demand from month to month indicates serious incipient trouble.
9. Once per month check the conditions and functionings of all product control devices, such as built-in stirrers and mixers, heating and cooling coils and their product contact areas, or thermal-transfer surfaces, and all dust controls, fire-hazard controls, static eliminators, etc.
10. Once per month, or at other practical intervals, operate the entire system unloaded and at high operating speed. Listen for indications of loose or worn parts—tighten, repair, and restore as needed.
11. Check automatic lubrication system for operation and accuracy, and fill reservoir as required monthly, or more frequently if environmental conditions dictate.
12. Once per month inspect wheels or rollers for flat spots that indicate nonturning components and possibly bad bearings.

OVERHEAD HANDLING AND LIFT DEVICES

This section discusses maintenance suggestions for the following types of overhead handling and lift devices:

- Chain blocks.
- Hand hoists.
- Power hoists.
- Wall and floor cranes.
- Power cranes.
- Grabs, slings, and holding devices.
- Mobile cranes.

CHAPTER 6   MAINTAINING MATERIAL HANDLING SYSTEMS AND EQUIPMENT

Chain Blocks

A *chain block* is a hoisting device that consists of a hook, lifting chain, and a drum or container for storing unused chain and gearing to provide a mechanical advantage to the operator.

1. When not in use, store in a hanging position, affording easy visual inspection and safe storage.
2. Clean and inspect at regular intervals.
3. Check pitch by measuring 20 links at least once per month. Maximum permissible stretch: lift chains, 5-10%, dependent on service; 1% on pocket wheel chains; consult manufacturers' specifications.
4. Check for gouging, wear, marking, and deforming once per month. Return chain worn 10% of an area at any point to manufacturer for repair.
5. If the link juncture points are badly worn, correct the operating conditions, if possible.
6. Iron and low-carbon chain should be checked for work hardening. Iron should be periodically annealed and steel less frequently normalized.
7. Heat-treated steel and alloy chain should not be annealed or normalized, except by a chain manufacturer.
8. When chain runs on load sheaves, as in chain hoists, examine the sheaves to determine if the chain links become worn or stretched.
9. Lubricate chain once per month, and especially at the link juncture points, using molydisulfide lubricants, which are waterproof and will stay in place. Lubricate chains used in foundries or similar places, where an extremely gritty or dusty atmosphere prevails, with thin-film and dry-film boundary lubricants.
10. Measure the load hooks, especially if used for hooking over the chain. Slightly deformed hooks can be straightened, but if they are badly bent they should be replaced.

Hand Hoists

Hand-powered hoists usually consist of a chain or cable hoist that is mounted on a manually-propelled trolley.

1. Lubricate all parts intended to be lubricated at least monthly, and more often if in extremely dusty, hot, or wet places. Pay special attention to chain pockets.
2. Guard against lubricating the wrong parts. Some types of lever hoists are not to be lubricated at all, and some differential types will not sustain load if given too much oil.
3. After lubricating, check load brakes to full capacity.
4. After lubricating, operate all parts rapidly under full load and no load; listen carefully for noises which may indicate worn gears, sheaves, sprockets, bearings, or looseness of any parts.
5. When lubricating, clean the outside of the case thoroughly and look for signs of oil leakage indicating faulty bearings or shields, or spillage indicating that too much lubricant has been used.
6. Lubricate roller chains monthly with thin-film and dry-film lubricant, even though no other parts of the devices on which they operate are to be lubricated.
7. Inspect load hook monthly. If any sign of spreading, suspect damage to hoist parts due to overloading or other abuse.
8. Measure load chain at least annually. If the length of any 20 consecutive links exceeds proper length by as much as three percent, replace the chain.
9. Inspect chain monthly for signs of such abuse as hooking load hook over chain instead of using slings. If one or two links are damaged, have new ones welded in by the hoist manufacturer.
10. Inspect, lubricate, and maintain all overhead parts, such as trolleys and wheels, monthly.

Power Hoists

Power hoists consist of a chain or cable that is wound on a drum, powered by either compressed air or electricity.

1. Check the load chain monthly for signs of abuse. If stretched as much as 3%, replace.
2. Check the load hook and its fastening to the chain monthly. Look for signs of loads having been applied to their point instead of their middle.
3. Check the load brake monthly for any irregularity of operation or any drifting at full load.
4. Lubricate with utmost care, monthly or at appropriate intervals. An electric hoist has electrical and mechanical elements assembled in the smallest possible space; extra care must be taken to keep lubricants out of the electrical insulation.
5. Check and service motors and electrical or air parts monthly.
6. Trip limit switches at least once per day.
7. Check breathing holes on oil cases at least monthly.
8. Check casing and all air-circulating passages for cleanliness at least monthly, and more often if working in dirty or oil-laden atmospheres; blow out or clean out, if necessary.
9. Check wheels for signs of wear, track for levelness and true joints, and all positioning apparatus for accuracy monthly.
10. Operate hoist under no load monthly, trying every speed and every function including traveling, reversing by limit switch, taking curves, hoisting, and lowering. Listen for any noises indicating loose or worn parts. Check and tighten any loose bolts, screws, and parts.

Wall and Floor Cranes

A *wall and floor crane* is comprised of a runway secured to the wall and a rail mounted on the floor. The bridge that carries the lifting hoist is supported by wheels on the wall runway, and a mast on the opposite end of the bridge contains wheels that run on the floor rail. This is usually called a *gantry crane*.

1. Check all rails for parallelism once per month, including one wall and one floor rail support, two wall or column rail supports, and portable rail supports.
2. Lubricate and clean once per month, especially any electrical mechanism or other heat-dissipating surfaces.
3. Service casters and wheels according to their maintenance schedule and requirements.
4. Inspect all bearings once per month, including mast top thrusts, radials, and trolley wheels.
5. Check all top and other braces for true alignment once per month. Alignment should be such that brace and beam will swing together without any loosening or binding at any point throughout the complete arc of swing.
6. Operate and inspect once per month all outriggers, removable-beam end columns, and other devices that are used only for occasional extra heavy loads.
7. Inspect and service all hooks, grabs, slings, ropes, chains, and hoists according to the maintenance schedules that apply to them.
8. Check and service all electrical parts and mechanisms in accordance with the electrical maintenance schedule.
9. Check and service all batching, pouring, weighing, and other devices attached to the crane once per month, or in accordance with their maintenance schedules.

CHAPTER 6   MAINTAINING MATERIAL HANDLING SYSTEMS AND EQUIPMENT

Power Cranes

A *power crane* is comprised of an electrically-powered runway, and a bridge and hoist system that can move a load in a straight or variable path, from one point to any other point in a prescribed operating area.

1. Put every crane on the plant lubrication schedule.
2. Inspect and adjust all brakes regularly and at the first sign of trouble. Investigate at once if an AC brake increases its normal humming sound. Check the gap of the magnet; if too great, the coils will burn.
3. Check the operation of the limit switch.
4. Keep all dirt, grease, and foreign matter away from them.
5. Put motors, brushes, contacts, etc., on the electrical maintenance schedule.
6. Replace cables if kinked or badly worn.
7. Check wheels by circumference; remachine if the difference in any driver part is 0.125 in. (3.2 mm) or more.
8. Inspect all hoisting gear. Check hooks for spreading and marring, and check load hook nut for backing off.
9. Inspect rails, spread joints, deformed rails, gage, and parallelism for alignment, especially at the points where the crane picks up, discharges, or positions heavy loads.
10. Inspect all bolts, nuts, gaskets, and other parts for tightness.

Grabs, Slings, and Holding Devices

1. List all parts and members by the types of failures to be expected of their materials (heat treatments, etc.). Inspect each by the type of damage to which it is liable.
2. Know which part of a grab or sling will first betray signs of overload, abuse, or ordinary wear; check weekly.
3. Check chain rings for stretch, marring, and deformation at least once per month.
4. Check books, shackles, and bars for stretch, deformation, correct positions of nuts and fastenings, crosshead wear, and marring, at least once per month.
5. Check chains for marring, stretch, and deformation at least once per month as per chain maintenance schedule; check wire and other ropes as per their maintenance schedules.
6. Lubricate all parts including chains and wire ropes at least once per month, more often if working under hot or abrasive conditions.
7. Inspect all bearings, such as the pivots of tongs and the ways of the traveling members of grabs monthly.
8. Operate and inspect all brakes at least once per week, especially the ones that use friction to control the extent to which a grab squeezes a load.
9. Inspect all mechanical parts for looseness, deformation, marring, wear, and adjustment at least once per month.

Mobile Cranes

A *mobile crane* is comprised of a diesel- or gasoline-powered vehicle mounted on wheels with a lifting mechanism that operates through a boom system.

Daily or eight operating hours.

1. Inspect machine thoroughly, checking operation of all controls, levers, etc. Examine it for signs of damage or tampering, or leakage of water, fuel, or oil.
2. Check cables and clamps for fraying, looseness, or need of lubrication.
3. Inspect machine and engine for loose or broken bolts, cracks, worn parts, etc.
4. Check tires for proper inflation under current operating conditions, equal pressure in all tires, remove stones or embedded objects, and repair cuts or damage.
5. Check fuel supply; be sure no foreign substances get into the system while filling.
6. Drain air reservoirs daily to ensure clean-air supply and prevent freezing in cold weather.
7. Check radiator level for antifreeze protection.
8. Check oil level in compressor if self-lubricated.
9. If conditions require it, for tacks, lubricate center-pin bushings, traction shaft, track roller and drive sprocket bushings, drive chains, etc.
10. Check levels of crankcase oil, oil in engine chain case, and hydraulic reservoirs.
11. Lubricate sleeve bearings.
12. Check lubrication of open gears, as well as crowd, retract, and propel chains.
13. Lubricate dipper handle.
14. Service air filters or fuel filters if operating conditions require it.
15. Inspect all clutches daily for grease and slippage.
16. Inspect reserve supplies of oil and lubricants, check on emergency equipment, tools, and spare parts.

Weekly or 40-100 operating hours.

1. Service oil filter.
2. Grease water pump.
3. Service air compressor.
4. Lubricate steering gear, propeller shaft, brake shafts, boom-hoist shafts, roller shafts, center post, emergency brake, starter, generator, distributor, and front spring leaves.
5. Lubricate antifriction bearings—horizontal and vertical, shafts, clutches, power take-offs, sheaves, etc.
6. Check lubrication of machinery deck gear case, engineer gear-reduction unit, hoist and boom-hoist gear cases, truck gear case, etc.
7. Check oil level of transmission and differential.
8. Check crawler link pins.
9. Check cables and cable drums, boom angles, and connections (do not lubricate dragline or pull shovel drag cables).
10. Oil conical rollers, turntable gear, and control linkage.
11. Check clutch cones, lining and adjustment, and brake bands.
12. Check turntable roller path.
13. For engine maintenance in general, follow the manufacturer's recommendations.
14. Inspect motors, check and clean controller contacts, etc.

Monthly or 200-250 operating hours.

1. Change and clean oil filter.
2. Check and adjust brakes or test air-brake system.
3. Service compressor, drain, and refill oil.
4. Inspect sheaves.
5. Check racks and pinions on dipper stick.
6. Check and lubricate slew rack and pinion, center post, and slew roller paths.
7. Check operation and lubricate limit switches and safe load indicators.
8. Service wheel bearings and clutch release bearing.
9. For engine maintenance in general, follow the manufacturer's recommendations.

STORAGE EQUIPMENT

The most common types of storage equipment to be maintained are baskets, boxes, bins, chutes, hoppers, and silos.

CHAPTER 6   MAINTAINING MATERIAL HANDLING SYSTEMS AND EQUIPMENT

Baskets, Boxes, Bins

1. When empty, weigh all baskets and boxes subject to high temperatures, acid or other corrosive baths, or abrasive wear at least once per month. Weight is the best index for determining the degree of overall wear and is necessary for scale control of materials in process.
2. Once per month examine areas subject to greatest friction, abrasion, shovel damage, etc.
3. Check all stacking and lifting battens, angles, lugs, and flanges for strength, alignment, and mechanical condition at least once per month.
4. Check all hand grips and other parts which may come into contact with personnel at least once per month or as the safety program may direct.
5. Check all contours intended to facilitate unloading and loading, such as rounded corners and flared tops or mouths, for correct mechanical condition at least once per month.
6. Check the cleanliness of baskets, boxes, and bins which handle parts or materials intended for fine finishing, high accuracy operations, heat treating, placing, etc., at intervals ranging from several times per day to once per day, depending upon the service performed.
7. Operate all hinges, cover locks, and other moving parts under test condition at least once per month.
8. Check and maintain all casters, wheels, and similar parts as per the maintenance schedules applying to them.

Chutes, Hoppers, and Silos

1. Once per year or as necessity dictates, clean thoroughly, remove all rust and other corrosion, and repaint all surfaces not subject to heavy abrasion.
2. Inspect all parts subject to abrasion. Look for holes where rivets have fallen out and similar places where abrasion starts easily and progresses rapidly.
3. Inspect all brick, tile, and concrete linings. Replace or repair as needed.
4. Remove all wear plates, remove all rust and repaint the surfaces which the plates shield, and reverse the plates or replace with new ones if badly worn.
5. Check alignments, plumbness, and levelness; either restore the plumbness or make provisions for the wear.
6. Remove foreign materials from boots, screens, pockets, and other devices intended to catch them.
7. Inspect and service all bearings, gears, and other moving parts on gates, dumps, and like equipment.
8. Operate heating or cooling equipment under test conditions. Fix any defects in parts, instruments, or insulation.
9. Operate all fire control, dust control, sprinklers, blowers, alarms, and other safety equipment under test conditions at least once per month.
10. Inspect carefully for loose bolts, rivets, broken chains, and other parts.
11. Operate magnetic separators under test conditions.
12. Check conditions of all ladders and other equipment used by maintenance personnel.

TRANSPORT PACKAGING

Transport packaging includes the maintenance of pallets, skids, scales, pneumatic- and hydraulic-cylinder devices, and fiber rope.

Pallets

1. When a deck board is broken or split to a point where the holding power of its fastenings is impaired, replace it.
2. Never attempt to renail a badly split deck board.
3. If nail fastenings protrude above deck boards, they should be carefully hammered back before the pallet is damaged.
4. If a bolt and nut fastening works loose, tighten it at once.

Skids

1. Check for levelness and for corner teetering; correct any unevenness that will throw strains on the skid frame, the trucks that carry the skid, or the stack or tier where the skid may be the bottom member. Check at intervals varying from one week to one year, depending on the type of work that the skid performs. Check with maximum load for underclearance, sagging supports and deck boards, and other hindrances to proper operation of lift truck.
2. Check and maintain all wheels according to the maintenance schedule.
3. Check the mechanical condition of all stake pockets, batten strips, crane-lift lugs, tiering fittings, bracings, and legs.
4. Check the tightness of all lag screws, bolts, rivets, and spikes; be sure that none have loosened to protrude and mar the materials being handled, or become safety hazards.
5. Check skid tops for smoothness, flatness, cleanliness, depths of corrugations, or other devices intended to hold or position the loads.
6. Check all wooden parts for splintering, splitting, warping, and similar weakening damage; check bolts for looseness due to warpage of lumber.
7. Paint at least once per year. Do not paint wooden parts with pigment paints that will conceal damage.

Scales

1. Examine for signs of abuse, such as splintered platforms and dented surfaces.
2. Check for accuracy; the higher the importance, the more frequent the check.
3. Check platforms for levelness. The load can be unevenly distributed and the wear is faster.
4. Check for misuse or neglect of lubrication. An oil can, used in the wrong places, can make a scale deceptive.
5. Thoroughly examine the wheels of every scale that travels on the floor, overhead rails, etc.
6. Check all electrical parts or connections of scales; make sure they are as sensitive and accurate as intended. Carefully check electrical remote control devices.
7. Check the alignment, operation, and condition of all damping devices, such as dashpots.
8. Clean all concealed parts that are not shielded from dust.
9. Inspect all pits for debris, condensation, oil seepage, and other hazards.
10. Inspect for tightness all seals and enclosures that are supposed to be dust, oil, moisture, or otherwise tight.

Pneumatic- and Hydraulic-Cylinder Devices

1. Once per month load each device to full capacity and hold it, watching for creep and changes in pressure. Listen for indications of leakage.
2. Clean outsides of cylinders and other heat-dissipating surfaces at least once per month.
3. Check the temperature of the incoming air or hydraulic fluid at least once per month if the device is connected to a circulating system also used by other devices.
4. Check and clean filters and strainers on circulating systems at least once per month.

CHAPTER 6   MAINTAINING MATERIAL HANDLING SYSTEMS AND EQUIPMENT

5. Remove condensate from air cylinders and entrapped air or gases from hydraulic systems monthly or as needed.
6. Check, adjust, or replace packings once per month or at first sign of leakage.
7. Renew, refill, or clean and replace hydraulic fluid once per month or at the first sign of inadequacy.
8. Check, adjust, repair, or replace all pneumatic and hydraulic connections once per month or at the first sign of trouble.
9. Make hydrostatic overload tests immediately after any extensive repairs or upon suspicion of weak parts that might fail at critical moments. This should be performed annually under normal conditions or at intervals as required by local or national safety codes for pressure devices.
10. Check, trip, and operate all automatic controls; check and service all hooks, chains, bearings, and electrical parts as per the plant maintenance schedules applying to them.

Fiber Rope

1. Periodically reverse the rope, end for end. Give all sections equal wear.
2. Examine for signs of chafing and correct the causes.

3. If chafing is unavoidable at ends or other sections that do not pass over sheaves, use windings or other protections.
4. Where parts are seriously worn or chafed, cut out the damaged sections and connect good ends with long splices.
5. Examine all new splices after short periods of service. A good splice can have 90% the strength of the original rope, a poor one only 2%.
6. Untie and retie all knots periodically.
7. Examine for evidence of exposure to oil penetration, chemical damage, overheating, and weather.

AUTOMATED MATERIAL HANDLING SYSTEMS

Automated systems are used for storage and retrieval, as well as other handling operations.[19] Both unit load and parts storage can be partially or fully automated if warranted by the application. Figure 6-2 shows the recommended maintenance and intervals.

Unit load high-rise storage rack systems range from 30-100 ft (9-30 m) in height. Systems at the shorter end of the scale may be served in aisles by high-rise lift or turret trucks, or by stacker cranes.

Automated storage and retrieval machines (AS/RS) are usually computer-controlled.[20]

CHAPTER 6   MAINTAINING MATERIAL HANDLING SYSTEMS AND EQUIPMENT

Inspection/Check	Maintenance Interval*						
	D	W	M	Q	SA	A	Other
General							
1. Visually check the storage and retrieval machine for any abnormal indications or conditions.	●						
2. Before placing the storage and retrieval machine into operation, visually check the storage aisle for personnel, improperly stored loads, and obstruction.	●						
3. Perform an operational test of the storage hardware and secure using required mounting retrieval machine.	●						
4. Clean all optics and associated reflectors or targets used on the storage and retrieval machine using suitable cleaning agents and clean, lint-free rags. Verify proper adjustment.			●				
5. Verify that all hardware is in place and tightly secured using required mounting hardware.					●		
6. Check for broken or cracked welds.					●		
End of aisle panel assembly							
1. Verify emergency-stop push button functions.	●						
2. Check indicator lamps and replace bulbs if burned out.	●						
3. Verify operation of all switches and controls.	●						
4. Check safety interlocks.		●					
5. Check to ensure all electrical connections are tight.				●			
6. Check to ensure printed circuit board assemblies are securely mounted using recommended mounting hardware.					●		
7. Verify that all hardware is in place and tightly secured.					●		
8. Clean inside of electrical cabinet using a vacuum cleaner and soft bristle brush.						●	
9. Clean contractor contacts using suitable contractor cleaning solvent.						●	
Floor truck assembly							
1. Perform a visual inspection of floor truck assembly. Note: refer to floor truck tracking test procedure and floor truck guide roller adjustment procedure sections in the equipment manual for specific maintenance procedures.	●						
2. Inspect the guide rollers.	●						
3. Check for any oil leaks.	●						
4. Clean optics and associated reflectors and targets. Verify proper adjustment.			●				
5. Lubricate drive wheel bearings.				●			
6. Lubricate idler wheel bearings.				●			
7. Check lubricant level in gearboxes.				●			
8. Visually check operation of all moving parts. Listen for sounds indicating improper operation.				●			

* D = Daily   Q = Quarterly
  W = Weekly   SA = Semi-annually
  M = Monthly   A = Annually

Fig. 6-2 Recommended maintenance and intervals for automated material handling equipment (also known as automated storage and retrieval system [AS/RS]).[20]

CHAPTER 6   MAINTAINING MATERIAL HANDLING SYSTEMS AND EQUIPMENT

Inspection/Check	Maintenance Interval*						
	D	W	M	Q	SA	A	Other
9. Inspect drive and idler wheels for excessive wear such as flat spots or worn flanges. Remove excessive oil and grease using a suitable solvent and clean, lint-free rags.					●		
10. Inspect guide rollers to ensure proper adjustment. Visually ensure guide rollers are not worn.					●		
11. Verify that rail sweeps and required mounting hardware are in place. Mounting hardware should be tight.					●		
12. Inspect floor truck splice plates to ensure all hardware is in place and tightly secured with no missing bolts.					●		
13. Inspect weldments for cracks.					●		
14. Verify that all hardware is in place and tightly secured using required mounting hardware.					●		
15. Perform floor truck tracking test procedure to ensure floor truck is centered on floor rail.						●	
Floor rail 1. Perform a visual inspection of floor rail. Floor rail should be free of grease, oil, and obstacles. There should be no excessive rail flake or flat spots.	●						
2. Verify that all hardware is in place and tightly secured using required mounting hardware.					●		
Head traverse assembly 1. Visually check the head traverse assembly for any abnormal indications or conditions.	●						
2. Check wire rope and wire rope terminations for any irregularities. Note: refer to wire rope inspection and mast assembly plumbing procedure in the equipment manual for specific maintenance procedures.	●						
3. Observe power rails during storage and retrieval machine operation. Check for excessive sparking and noise.	●						
4. Inspect wire rope in accordance with the wire rope inspection section in the equipment manual.			●				
5. Lubricate wire rope sheaves.				●			
6. Check wire rope sheaves for abnormal wear.				●			
7. Visually check operation of all moving parts. Listen for sounds indicating improper operation.				●			
8. Verify that guide roller blocks are fastened securely in place using required mounting hardware.				●			
9. Visually check guide rollers for excessive wear.				●			
10. Inspect yoke assembly. Assembly should be reasonably level.				●			
11. Verify that all hardware is in place and tightly secured using required mounting hardware.					●		
Horizontal drive assembly 1. Inspect the horizontal drive assembly.	●						
2. Inspect the motor casing and its vents.	●						
3. Visually check for oil leaks.	●						

Fig. 6-2 (cont.) Recommended maintenance and intervals for automated material handling equipment.[20]

CHAPTER 6   MAINTAINING MATERIAL HANDLING SYSTEMS AND EQUIPMENT

Inspection/Check	Maintenance Interval*						
	D	W	M	Q	SA	A	Other
4. Perform a visual and operational test of the drive. Note: refer to manufacturer documents for additional information.	●						
5. Check brushes for excessive wear and arcing.			●				
6. Clean commutator using a vacuum cleaner to remove carbon dust. Use a clean, lint-free rag to wipe commutator.			●				
7. Adjust brakes on horizontal drive motor.			●				
8. Clean exterior motor casing and vents to provide adequate airflow to the motor.			●				
9. Check to ensure all electrical connections are tight.			●				
10. Check lubricant level in gearboxes. Verify vent plug is in place, clean, and tight.			●				
11. Verify required hardware is in place and properly secured.					●		
12. Every four years or 10,000 hours, whichever comes first, drain and flush gearboxes. Fill gearboxes with new lubricant.							●
Lift carriage assembly 1. Visually check the lifting carriage assembly for any abnormal indications or conditions.	●						
2. Check wire rope and wire rope terminations for any irregularities.	●						
3. Clean all optics and associated reflectors or targets used on the storage and retrieval machine using suitable cleaning agents and clean, lint-free rags. Verify proper adjustment.			●				
4. Inspect wire rope in accordance with the wire rope inspection section in the equipment manual.			●				
5. Verify that catching device is free of grease and oil, with exception of linkages.			●				
6. Visually check operation of all moving parts. Listen for sounds indicating improper operation.				●			
7. Check wire rope sheaves for abnormal wear.				●			
8. Lubricate wire rope sheaves.				●			
9. Verify that guide roller blocks are fastened securely in place using required mounting hardware.				●			
10. Visually check guide rollers for excessive wear and adjustment.				●			
11. Lubricate guide roller bearings.				●			
12. Ensure the fork assembly is level.				●			
13. Verify that lifting carriage is square in storage aisle.				●			
14. Lubricate catching device linkages.					●		
15. Check adjustment of catching device.					●		
16. Check for broken or cracked welds.					●		
17. Verify that all hardware is in place and tightly secured using required mounting hardware.					●		
18. Check operation of catching device by performing a catch.						●	

Fig. 6-2 (cont.) Recommended maintenance and intervals for automated material handling equipment.[20]

CHAPTER 6   MAINTAINING MATERIAL HANDLING SYSTEMS AND EQUIPMENT

Inspection/Check	Maintenance Interval*						
	D	W	M	Q	SA	A	Other
Maintenance control panel assembly							
1. Verify emergency-stop push button functions.	●					✓	
2. Check indicator lamps and replace bulbs if burned out.	●						
3. Verify operation of flashing warning light and horn.	●						
4. Verify operation of all switches and controls.	●						
5. Check safety interlocks.		●					
6. Verify proper operation of SEMI (semi-automatic) mode from maintenance platform.		●					
7. Check to ensure all electrical connections are tight.					●		
8. Check to ensure printed circuit board assemblies are securely mounted using recommended mounting hardware and adjustment.					●		
9. Verify that all hardware is in place and tightly secured.					●		
10. Clean inside of electrical cabinet using a vacuum cleaner and soft bristle brush.						●	
11. Clean contractor contacts using suitable contractor cleaning solvent.						●	
Maintenance platform assembly							
1. Visually check maintenance platform assembly for any abnormal indications or conditions.	●						
2. Check wire rope and wire rope terminations for any abnormal indications or conditions.	●						
3. Inspect wire rope.			●				
4. Check wire rope sheaves for abnormal wear.				●			
5. Lubricate wire rope sheaves and guide roller bearings.				●			
6. Check for broken or cracked welds.					●		
7. Verify that all hardware is in place and tightly secured using required mounting hardware.					●		
Mast assembly							
1. Visually check mast assembly for any abnormal indications or conditions.	●						
2. Check wire rope and wire rope terminations for any irregularities.	●						
3. Inspect wire rope.			●				
4. Clean all optics and associated reflectors or targets used on the mast assembly using suitable cleaning agents and clean, lint-free rags. Verify proper adjustment.			●				
5. Check wire rope sheaves for abnormal wear.				●			
6. Lubricate wire rope sheaves.				●			
7. Raise lifting carriage assembly just short of upper mast limit switch. Trip limit switch by hand and verify that main line contractor drops out (storage and retrieval machine must be reset). Limit switch should be adjusted to activate before any part of lifting carriage assembly comes into contact with any obstruction. Repeat this procedure to test lower limit switch.					●		

Fig. 6-2 (cont.) Recommended maintenance and intervals for automated material handling equipment.[20]

CHAPTER 6   MAINTAINING MATERIAL HANDLING SYSTEMS AND EQUIPMENT

Inspection/Check	Maintenance Interval*						
	D	W	M	Q	SA	A	Other
8. Verify that magnetic limit switches are tightly secured within unistrut. Magnet switches should be centered on magnets.					●		
9. Raise lifting carriage assembly to upper and lower limits of travel. Verify that magnetic limit switches slow and stop vertical travel prior to tripping mechanical limit switches.					●		
10. Inspect mast splice plates to ensure all hardware is in place and tightly secured with no missing bolts.					●		
11. Check for broken or cracked welds.					●		
12. Verify that all hardware is in place and tightly secured using required mounting hardware.					●		
13. Check mast assembly to ensure that it is plumb.						●	
Mast ladder (if equipped)							
1. Inspect mast ladder for damage.		●					
2. Verify safety harness is available for use when mast ladder is used. Inspect harness for wear and replace when damaged beyond repair.		●					
3. Verify that all hardware is in place and tightly secured using required mounting hardware.					●		
Operator cab							
1. Verify emergency-stop push button functions.	●						
2. Verify safety interlocks, drop main line contractors out on horizontal, vertical, and fork dive assemblies when any operator's cab door is opened.	●						
3. Check indicator lamps and replace bulbs if burned out.	●						
4. Verify operation of flashing warning light and horn.	●						
5. Verify operation of all switches and controls.	●						
6. Verify proper operation of MAN (manual) mode from operator's cab assembly.		●					
7. Verify proper operation of SEMI (semi-automatic) mode from operator's cab assembly.		●					
8. Check to ensure all electrical connections are tight.					●		
9. Verify that all hardware is in place and tightly secured.					●		
Optical devices							
1. Verify that all optical devices and associated reflectors or targets used on the storage and retrieval machine are properly aligned, present, and functioning.	●						
2. Clean all optics and associated reflectors or targets used on the storage and retrieval machine using suitable cleaning agents and clean, lint-free rags.			●				
3. Verify that all hardware is in place and tightly secured.						●	
Safety devices							
1. Verify the proper operation of all safety devices (especially emergency stops) and heed all safety precautions.	●						

Fig. 6-2 (cont.) Recommended maintenance and intervals for automated material handling equipment.[20]

CHAPTER 6   MAINTAINING MATERIAL HANDLING SYSTEMS AND EQUIPMENT

Inspection/Check	Maintenance Interval*						
	D	W	M	Q	SA	A	Other
2. Visually check the speed governor for any abnormal indications or conditions. Clean as required. Verify speed governor is free of lubricants that may cause a failure or slippage of the speed governor cable or catching device.	●						
3. Verify lead seal is in place on speed governor. Do not use storage and retrieval machine if seal is broken. When seal is broken, replace speed governor.	●						
4. Check speed governor cable terminations for any irregularities. Trim (with sidecutters) any frayed wires.	●						
5. Inspect speed governor wire rope cable.			●				
6. Verify that catching device is free of grease and oil with exception of linkages. Verify that vertical guide rail is free of grease and oil.			●				
7. Check speed governor wire-rope cable sheaves for abnormal wear.				●			
8. Lubricate catching device linkages.					●		
9. Check adjustment of catching device.					●		
10. Verify that all hardware is in place and tightly secured using required mounting hardware.					●		
11. Check operation of catching device by performing a catch.						●	
Shuttle fork assembly 1. Perform a visual inspection of the assembly. Note: refer to operating instructions for the DS telescoping fork mechanism in the vendor section of the equipment manual for additional information.	●						
2. Verify operation of the assembly and drive.	●						
3. Check for any oil leaks.	●						
4. Clean optics and associated reflectors or targets. Ensure optics are properly adjusted.			●				
5. Place a roll box on the fork assembly so that it is approximately 0.375 in. (9.5 mm) off center. Verify that load overhang optics can detect a load overhang. Optics should be tightly held in place by mounting hardware.			●				
6. Place a roll box on the fork assembly and verify that the load detect optics detect the load. Optics should be tightly held in place by mounting hardware.				●			
7. Ensure load guides are in place, in good condition, and properly secured.				●			
8. Check fork displacement. Ensure forks fully extend to both the right and left. Forks should return to center within ±0.125 in. (±3.2 mm).				●			
9. Verify safety rails are in place and securely fastened.				●			
10. Check tension of leaf chain.				●			
11. Check tension of drive chain.				●			
12. Visually check operation of all moving parts. Listen for sounds indicating improper operation.				●			

Fig. 6-2 (cont.) Recommended maintenance and intervals for automated material handling equipment.[20]

CHAPTER 6 MAINTAINING MATERIAL HANDLING SYSTEMS AND EQUIPMENT

Inspection/Check	Maintenance Interval*						
	D	W	M	Q	SA	A	Other
13. Lubricate leaf chain.				●			
14. Lubricate drive chain.				●			
15. Lubricate running surfaces of telescoping unit and base member.				●			
16. Lubricate engaging pin and splined shaft.				●			
17. Verify that all hardware is in place and tightly secured using required mounting hardware.					●		
Shuttle fork drive assembly 1. Perform a visual and operation test of the drive. Refer to fork mechanism section in the vendor section of the equipment manual for additional information.	●						
2. Visually check for oil leaks.			●				
3. Clean exterior motor casings and vents to provide adequate airflow to the motors.			●				
4. Check to ensure all electrical connections are tight.			●				
5. Adjust brakes on both main and microspeed motors.			●				
6. Adjust clutch on main motor.			●				
7. Check lubricant level in gearboxes.				●			
8. Verify required hardware is in place and properly secured using required mounting hardware.					●		
9. Every four years or 10,000 hours, whichever comes first, drain and flush gearboxes. Fill gearboxes with new lubricant.							●
Storage machine aisle 1. Perform a visual inspection of storage machine aisle. Ensure aisle is free of personnel, obstructions, and material overhangs. Note: refer to drawings for component identifications and functions.	●						
2. Verify access gates (or doors) are in place, closed, and locked.	●						
3. Pull emergency stop pull cord and verify main line contractors are reset only after pull cord has been reset.	●						
4. Perform a visual inspection of floor rail. Floor rail should be free of grease and oil.	●						
5. Visually check the storage and retrieval machine for any abnormal indications or conditions.	●						
6. Clean all optics and associated reflectors or targets used in the storage and retrieval machine aisle using suitable cleaning agents and clean, lint-free rags. Verify proper adjustment.			●				
7. Check hydraulic fluid level in hydraulic bumpers. Add as required. Check for leaks.				●			
8. Verify that magnetic limit switches are tightly secured within unistrut. Magnet switches should be centered on magnets.					●		

Fig. 6-2 (cont.) Recommended maintenance and intervals for automated material handling equipment.[20]

CHAPTER 6 MAINTAINING MATERIAL HANDLING SYSTEMS AND EQUIPMENT

Inspection/Check	Maintenance Interval*						
	D	W	M	Q	SA	A	Other
9. Move storage and retrieval machine to each horizontal limit of travel. Verify that magnetic limit switches slow and stop horizontal travel prior to contact with hydraulic bumpers at each end of aisle.					●		
10. Verify that all hardware is in place and tightly secured using required mounting hardware.					●		
Upper guide rail 1. Visually check upper guide rail assembly for any abnormal indications or conditions. Note: refer to mast assembly plumbing procedure section in the equipment manual for specific maintenance procedures.	●						
2. Visually check operation of all moving parts. Listen for sounds indicating improper operation.				●			
3. Verify that guide roller blocks are fastened securely in place using required mounting hardware.				●			
4. Visually check guide rollers for excessive wear.				●			
5. Verify that all hardware is in place and tightly secured using required mounting hardware.					●		
Vertical drive assembly 1. Visually check vertical drive assembly for any abnormal indications or conditions.	●						
2. Check wire rope and wire rope terminations for any irregularities.	●						
3. Visually check for oil leaks.	●						
4. Perform an operational test of the drive.	●						
5. Inspect wire rope in accordance with the maintenance inspection log.			●				
6. Check brushes for excessive wear and arcing.			●				
7. Clean commutator using a vacuum cleaner to remove carbon dust. Use a clean, lint-free rag to wipe commutator.			●				
8. Adjust brakes.			●				
9. Clean exterior motor casing and vents to provide adequate airflow to the motor.			●				
10. Check to ensure all electrical connections are tight.			●				
11. Check lubricant level in gearbox. Verify that vent plug is in place, clean, and tight.				●			
12. Lubricate cable drums.				●			
13. Check cable drums for abnormal wear. Check all wire rope terminations at cable drum. Ensure terminations are properly made and tightly secured using required hardware.				●			
14. Lubricate wire rope cables.				●			
15. Visually check operation of all moving parts. Listen for sounds indicating improper operations.				●			
16. Verify that all hardware is in place and tightly secured using required mounting hardware.					●		

Fig. 6-2 (cont.) Recommended maintenance and intervals for automated material handling equipment.[20]

CHAPTER 6   MAINTAINING MATERIAL HANDLING SYSTEMS AND EQUIPMENT

Inspection/Check	Maintenance Interval*						
	D	W	M	Q	SA	A	Other
17. Every four years or 10,000 hours, whichever comes first, drain and flush gearbox. Fill gearbox with new lubricant.							●
Vertical guide rail 1. Visually check the vertical guide rails for any abnormal indication or conditions. Note: refer to machine catching device and lift carriage assembly guide roller adjustment procedure section in the equipment manual for specific maintenance procedures.	●						
2. Verify that catching device and vertical guide rails are free of grease and oil with exception of catching device linkages.			●				
3. Dampen a clean, lint-free rag with light oil and wipe vertical guide rail as required to prevent rust. Dry vertical guide rail using a dry, clean, lint-free rag.				●			
4. Check for broken or cracked welds. Remove any burrs, rail flake, or rust using emery cloth or a fine file.					●		
5. Check adjustment of catching device.					●		
6. Check operation of catching device by performing a catch.						●	

Fig. 6-2 (cont.) Recommended maintenance and intervals for automated material handling equipment.[20]

References

1. Burgess, Jack. "Maintenance Management of Material Handling Systems Installations." A one-day workshop by Tomkins Associates. Chicago, IL: Material Handling Institute, Inc., February 1997.
2. Baldwin, Robert C. "Calculating the Value of Maintenance." *Maintenance Technology*, September 1996: 7.
3. Blanche, K.M., and Landgraff, R.M. "North American Benchmarks." *Maintenance Technology*, November 1991: 28-32.
4. Witt, Ray H. "World-Class Maintenance Doesn't Cost—It Pays." *Modern Castings*, July 1992: 32-33.
5. Ibid.
6. Brautigam, Dale P., PE, and Norman, R.M. "Cut Costs with Predictive Maintenance." *Modern Castings*, April 1992.
7. Witt, Ray H. "World-Class Maintenance Doesn't Cost—It Pays." *Modern Castings*, July 1992: 32-33.
8. Brautigam, Dale P., PE. "Planning and Implementing a Good Lubrication Program." *Maintenance Engineering Handbook*. New York: McGraw-Hill, Inc., 1995: 9.1-9.9.
9. Block, Heinz P., PE. "Automatic Lubrication as a Modern Maintenance Strategy." *Maintenance Technology*, January 1997.
10. Witt, Ray H. "World-Class Maintenance Doesn't Cost—It Pays." *Modern Castings*, July 1992: 32-33.
11. Kulwiec, Raymond A. *Basics of Material Handling*. Chicago, IL: The Material Handling Institute, Inc., 1981.
12. Ibid.
13. Ibid.
14. Ibid.
15. Ibid.
16. The Conveyor Terms and Definitions Committee of the CEMA Engineering Conference. "Conveyor Terms and Definitions." CEMA No. 102-1994. Manassas, VA: Conveyor Equipment Manufacturers Association, 1994.
17. Kulwiec, Raymond A. *Basics of Material Handling*. Chicago, IL: The Material Handling Institute, Inc., 1981.
18. Apple, James M. "Materials Handling System Maintenance." *Facilities and Plant Engineering Handbook*. New York: McGraw-Hill, Inc., 1973: 60, 63, 65, 89-104.
19. The Conveyor Terms and Definitions Committee of the CEMA Engineering Conference. "Conveyor Terms and Definitions." CEMA No. 102-1994. Manassas, VA: Conveyor Equipment Manufacturers Association, 1994.
20. King, Robert. *Preventive Maintenance Manual*. Grand Rapids, MI: Rapistan DeMag, AS/RS Equipment, March 1996.

CHAPTER 7
ERGONOMICS AND MANUAL MATERIAL HANDLING

CHAPTER CONTENTS

INTRODUCTION

The transportation of materials from loading docks to assembly lines, from packages to assembly, and from one operation to another is common to most manufacturing facilities. Material and part handling operations can be either wholly or partially performed by a human worker. *Manual material handling* (MMH) is the physical act of lifting, lowering, carrying, holding, pushing, or pulling objects, or moving material from one location to another for manufacturing or assembly. The basic approaches for dealing with manual material handling issues are:

- Select the worker with proper capabilities for the job.
- Modify the environment to suit the healthy or injured worker.

Historical data have linked MMH to a large percentage of work-related lost time injuries. In fact, one source estimated that 70% of lower back injury claims were linked to material handling.[1] According to an Occupational Safety and Health Administration (OSHA) press release, 65% of repetitive strain injuries (RSIs) reported involved the back and 32% affected the upper extremities. Insurers awarded an estimated 2.73 million workers compensation claims for RSIs, costing employers more than $20 billion. Indirect costs to employers are estimated to be five times that amount.[2]

Overexertion while maneuvering objects was the most frequently cited of all disabling events or exposures and occurred in one-sixth to one-third of the cases in every industry division.[3]

Overexertion injuries resulting from manual material handling are a global problem, in all industrial countries. For example, in the United Kingdom, back-related problems account for more than 25% of all accidents.[4] In New Zealand, 24% of all overexertion injuries are the result of handling materials manually.[5]

DETERMINING PHYSICAL LIMITS

The need to contain the cost and severity of injuries resulting from handling materials manually has forced many countries to im-

pose an upper limit on the amount of weight that an individual can handle safely in the workplace. While federal, local health and safety agencies, and private research organizations in some countries have provided such weight limits and guidelines for designing manual handling jobs, to develop an effective MMH policy, other factors must be evaluated.

Because MMH is recognized as a significant cause of work-related lost time injuries, the scientific community has developed a number of risk assessment tools for evaluating manual material handling tasks. These are often referred to as analytical indicators and are driven by variables known as work parameters.

Work parameters include variables that pertain to the following job attributes:

- The frequency, precision, cycle time, and duration of the task.
- The workstation components (containers, dunnage, fixtures, tools, layouts, material flow, and movement patterns).
- Characteristics of parts and materials (size, weight, orientation, subassemblies, and part mix).
- Environmental conditions (temperature, humidity, air movement, and air quality).

These parameters can help identify those factors that may contribute to an increase in the physical demands and stresses of a manual material handling task.

Analytical indicators belong to three main risk assessment methods: psychophysical, biomechanical, and physiological. Some analytical indicators incorporate more than one of these methods, and will be referred to in this chapter as multidisciplinary risk assessment methods.

PSYCHOPHYSICAL ASSESSMENT METHODS

The psychophysical method for evaluating manual tasks is one in which subjects or workers determine the relationship between work factors and the perception of physical stress, exertion, fatigue, and discomfort on the body.[6]

MMH guidelines or tables exist for evaluating lifting, lowering, pushing, pulling, and carrying procedures.[7] The tables for each of these activities were derived from psychophysical experiments, in which a number of independent variables were used and participants were asked under what conditions they felt they could manually handle various ranges of weights. The parameters that varied were the vertical travel distance of the load, vertical height of the load from the ground, and the duration and frequency of the task. For carrying, pushing, and pulling tasks, the distance carried was also an independent variable. The load limits in the tables are based on percentiles—the percent of the industrial population that reported they could perform the task under the defined conditions. Separate tables exist for male and female populations.

The Contributors of this chapter are: Don Chaffin, PhD, Director, Center for Ergonomics, University of Michigan; **D. Glenn Jimmerson,** Automation Systems Specialist, Assembly Manufacturing Technology Development, Ford Motor Company; **Bradley Joseph, MPH, PhD, CPE,** Corporate Ergonomics, Industrial Hygiene and Occupational Health and Safety, Ford Motor Company; **Anil Mital, PhD, PE, CPE,** Professor, University of Cincinnati; **Catherine Sowden,** Ergonomist, Sandalwood Enterprises, Inc.

The Reviewers of this chapter are: Robert Andreas, President, Ergonomics Engineering, Inc.; **D. Glenn Jimmerson,** Automation Systems Specialist, Assembly Manufacturing Technology Development, Ford Motor Company; **Bradley Joseph, MPH, PhD, CPE,** Corporate Ergonomist, Industrial Hygiene and Occupational Health and Safety, Ford Motor Company; **Catherine Sowden,** Ergonomist, Sandalwood Enterprises, Inc.

CHAPTER 7   ERGONOMICS AND MANUAL MATERIAL HANDLING

Several additional books contain reference tables for weight and force limits for lifting, carrying, pushing, and pulling tasks under a variety of circumstances. These tables are easy to use and valuable for identifying hazards in typical MMH tasks. However, the user is constrained by the variables considered in each table (see Bibliography).

BIOMECHANICAL ASSESSMENT METHODS

Biomechanics can be defined as the application of physical laws and engineering concepts to an understanding of how the human body acts and reacts to motion and external forces.[8] Many biomechanical models have been developed to estimate the internal strength requirements resulting from external loading. These models typically predict static strength requirements at various joints (elbow, shoulder, lower back), as well as lower back compression values.

There are a number of models that have been developed to estimate the strength requirements of a task. For example, 2D and 3D static strength prediction programs (2D SSPP, 3D SSPP) are based on moment of force calculations using the body as a linked segment model.[9] The basic premise is that when an external load is applied to a person (from a weight in the hands, or push and pull force), the body must internally generate an equal and opposite force to maintain control of the load. The linked segment approach will calculate the "reaction moments" at various joints (elbow, shoulder, lower back, hips, etc.) required to stabilize the load in the person's hands. Depending on the complexity of the human model used in the tools, muscle and ligament contributions to the reaction force can be considered. Both of these models estimate compression forces in the back as a comparison to the National Institute for Occupational Safety and Health (NIOSH) tolerance limit for most workers.[10] These models are very useful in determining the strength requirements of a task. However, they are currently limited to static efforts and cannot evaluate the effects of repetitive activities. Potential physical effects are determined by a risk assessment of musculoskeletal disorders (MSDs) caused by doing the task.

PHYSIOLOGICAL ASSESSMENT METHODS

Physiology is a science that studies the processes and functions of an organism, in this case, the human body.[11] The use of physiological principles in the field of ergonomics determines the effort required by the cardiovascular system during work. Key ergonomic factors are repetition, forcefulness, and posture. Generally, physiological evaluations determine the metabolic requirements of the human during work, also defined as *energy expenditure*.

There are both direct and indirect methods for measuring energy expenditure. Direct methods, such as oxygen consumption measurement, are best utilized in a lab setting. There are a number of indirect methods for estimating the energy requirements of a given task. Research efforts from scientists have been able to correlate direct measurements from the lab to activities performed in the workplace.[12,][13] Typical activities that can be evaluated by these tools are lifting, walking, carrying, and gross motor activities.

In the field, these models ask the participant to break down the complete operation into classes of activities such as walk, carry, or heavy arm work, as well as record the duration of each of these activities. In turn, a metabolic cost for each activity is assigned and summed over the entire operation. NIOSH refers to an acceptable caloric expenditure for a person at work. The NIOSH values depend on the vertical lift location and the duration of the lifting task. The limits range from 2.2 kilocalories/min within a two- to eight-hour duration and a vertical lift greater than 30 in. (76 cm), to 4.7 kilocalories/min with less than one hour duration when the vertical lift is ≤ 30 in. (76 cm).[14]

Metabolic requirements of an operation can be affected by ambient temperatures and humidity. Heat load (a combination of air temperature, air velocity, radiant heat, and relative humidity) influences a person's physiological and psychological behavior. At the very least, heat stress causes discomfort leading to reduced work rate, increased irritability, reduced alertness, a feeling of fatigue, and increased accident rates. MMH activities performed in a hot and humid climate tend to elevate heart rates and increase body temperatures, decreasing MMH capacity. Adequate rest and replenishment of body fluids are essential when work is performed in a hot climate. Cooling jackets also may be used to keep the body's core temperature from rising.

MULTIDISCIPLINARY RISK ASSESSMENT METHODS

There are several methods used to evaluate multiple risks in MMH jobs. For example, a 1981 NIOSH equation was used to calculate weight limits for lifting, based on a number of work parameters and past research on manual material handling from the fields of biomechanics, physiology, epidemiology, and psychophysics. Rather than identifying individual factors, this method considered many simultaneously. The work parameters used in the equation were:

- Horizontal distance away from the body that the object is held.
- Object vertical height from the floor at the origin of the lift.
- The vertical travel distance of the load.
- Lifting frequency.
- Duration of the lifting task.[15]

NIOSH Work Practices Guide and Revised NIOSH Equation

In response to further developments in manual material handling research, NIOSH released a revised equation in 1993. The variables previously required were revised and new ones were added to allow for asymmetrical postures, as well as the coupling between the object and the person's hands[16].

NIOSH equation use is limited to the following conditions:

- Only two-handed lifts are applicable. Lifts performed while seated or kneeling are not considered.
- It is assumed that manual handling activities other than lifting are minimal and do not require significant energy expenditure.
- The equation does not account for unpredicted conditions, such as unexpectedly heavy loads, slips, or falls.
- The environment is assumed to be controlled, with no extreme temperatures or humidity.
- The object or load being lifted is assumed to be stable.

Rapid Upper Limb Assessment

The rapid upper limb assessment (RULA) tool is a relatively coarse evaluation method that considers posture, static efforts, repetition, and force. A number from one to seven is calculated, ranking the operation based on the exposure to risk factors associated with upper limb disorders.[17]

REDUCING MMH RISKS

Many worker-, work-, and environment-related factors are considered risk factors in performing MMH activities. They must be controlled or modified in some systematic manner to reduce the risk of MMH injury. For a detailed discussion and research concerning

CHAPTER 7   ERGONOMICS AND MANUAL MATERIAL HANDLING

possible risk factors, the reader is referred to other reference books (see Bibliography).

Engineers cannot always design an operation that allows the worker to meet all of the recommended lifting practices, and operators do not always have control over the conditions in which they must perform an MMH task. As a result, there have been many strategies adopted by employers to abate the risks associated with manual material handling. These strategies may be classed into two groups, administrative and engineering controls.

ADMINISTRATIVE CONTROL OF RISK FACTORS

Administrative controls are those strategies implemented by management to control the exposure time and work organization to reduce risk factors for workers. Typical administrative controls are job rotation, employee placement, rest breaks, personal protective equipment, and training.

Training

Many health and safety programs provide employees with back education programs to reduce the number of work-related back injuries. These programs are designed to make people who perform MMH tasks aware of factors that can increase their risk for injury. More importantly, they aim to familiarize employees with the workplace factors that they can control to reduce the physical effort required to perform such tasks.

Training can be in a classroom setting, on the job, or in a controlled setting. The purpose of training could be to educate employees in the hazards of manual material handling or to enhance their physical capabilities, thereby reducing the risk of injury.

Classroom training. Classroom instruction on the hazards of MMH activities should be an integral part of a training program. At the very least, workers should learn about the risk factors, and do's and don'ts that will mitigate the negative impact of these factors. Often, worker behavior and attitude can make a huge difference in controlling injury hazards.

Physical training. Physical training is a suggested method to enhance a worker's physical capabilities. The argument has been that since the overall effects of physical training are positive and lead to greater muscular strength, MMH capacity, cardiovascular capability, and endurance time, workers will be better protected against injury hazards.[18,19] There is, however, scant evidence concluding that enhanced working capacity from physical training also leads to a reduction in back disorders and improvements in productivity.[20] Only a handful of investigations have reported a reduction in lower back pain following physical training.[21,22,23] In fact, research results suggest that physically fit individuals are just as likely to hurt themselves as those who are not physically fit. Further, the enhanced capabilities from physical training are diluted over time unless the job continues to physically tax workers to at least 50% of the levels they were subjected to during training. Physical training, however, may improve a person's outlook and, therefore, should be encouraged.

Training for safe handling methods. The concept of safe lifting methods is frequently mentioned in safety literature. These methods include rules such as "maintain a straight back when lifting" and "lift with your legs, not your back." These rules, however, must be applied with care, as they do not fit every situation. For instance, these rules cannot be applied for lifting bulky objects. It should be clearly understood that rules for safe handling of materials do not cover every situation and, if applied blindly, can do more damage than good.

Perhaps the best rule is to remember that each situation is different and there is no single correct way to handle materials manually.

Task Duration

The duration of task performance must be considered when designing an MMH job. In general, as the task duration increases, the metabolic energy expenditure level of the operator also increases, due to the cumulative effects of fatigue. Furthermore, the metabolic energy expenditure level that can be maintained decreases with the task duration. Conversely, if the task duration decreases, the load weight and workload can increase. However, the increase in weight must be within the biomechanical tolerance limits of the musculoskeletal system.

Work Organization

Work organization includes workplace geometry, fixed postures, rest pauses, and job rotation. Constant re-orientation of a load, postural instability, and slower and more cautious movements are some of the outcomes of inappropriate workplace geometry. Loading, unloading, and maintenance are some of the routine activities that may be performed in inadequate spaces.

Posture and Handling Techniques

A *load* is characterized by its shape, size, and weight. The weight of the load is perhaps the most important load characteristic in situations where the load will be handled manually. The weight of the load usually determines how strenuous a job is.

It is generally agreed that the load should be as small as possible. Larger loads not only make the handling awkward, but they lead to higher physiological costs and greater spinal stresses. If a load cannot fit between the knees, it is probably too large for manual material handling. When possible, the load dimension in the *sagittal plane* (plane dividing the body into left and right) should be as small as possible to minimize stress on the back muscles. Muscular strength also decreases as the distance in the sagittal plane increases. The load dimension between the hands (in the frontal plane) is less critical, but nevertheless should be minimized. The height of the load is the least critical of the three dimensions. Practical considerations such as measuring and describing physical variations (anthropometry) and the ability to clearly view obstructions in the worker's path should determine this dimension.

In general:

- Loads should be stable, rigid, uniform, and compact.
- The heavier end of the load should be held by the preferred hand or arm and, when possible, close to the body.

Handles or couplings provide load and postural stability during material handling. A good coupling between the individual and the floor is also essential if the load is to be carried, pushed, or pulled.

In general:

- Loads should have handles or handholds.
- Shoes should provide adequate friction to prevent slipping.

Frequency of handling is often one of the most critical, but least controllable, factors that influence an individual's capability to perform MMH activities. Control of frequency is essential if the goal is to reduce fatigue and overall job strain. In general, the MMH capacity increases as the frequency of handling decreases. Increasing load tends to reduce frequency. For example, when moving a pallet of roofing material with a fork lift is compared to moving each bundle of shingles. Repetition is also interrelated with forcefulness and posture. Furthermore, a reduction in frequency of handling leads to an increase in endurance time. MMH activities that require frequent handling should either be redesigned to reduce the frequency, or

CHAPTER 7 ERGONOMICS AND MANUAL MATERIAL HANDLING

mechanical equipment should be used to aid the handling. This is especially true when frequent handling is combined with awkward postures and heavy loads.

ENGINEERING CONTROL OF RISK FACTORS

Engineering controls are those changes to the process or product implemented to reduce the exposure to risk. Examples are workstation design changes such as work heights, platforms, tooling, and automation.

Manual handling systems (MHS) are devices designed to reduce the physical effort required to handle material manually. MHS fall into the following categories.

- *Positioners* are devices used to orient and locate an object for processing, for example, lift or tilt tables and conveyors (see Fig. 7-1).
- *Manipulators* are devices designed to partially or fully support and manipulate an object (tools, parts, or materials). Examples of manipulators are hoists and articulated arms (see Fig. 7-2). The manual handling systems described in this chapter are those used on-line and require some physical interaction with a human operator. Refer to Chapter 14 of this handbook for more information on these devices.

Although for many tasks MHS have proven to be effective for reducing the strain related to MMH, there also have been some unexpected outcomes resulting from their installation in manufacturing facilities:

- MHS (especially manipulators) are often not employed due to the greater time required to use the systems, compared to performing the task manually.
- MHS have been found, in some cases, to require more energy to operate than if the task was performed manually.
- Operators of MHS complain of the devices being too awkward and cumbersome. Many modifications and reiterations are often required to get the system functioning at an acceptable level for the operation to be completed productively and comfortably for the operator.
- Due to the high inertial element of MHS operation, peak back stresses exceeding acceptable limits have been noted.

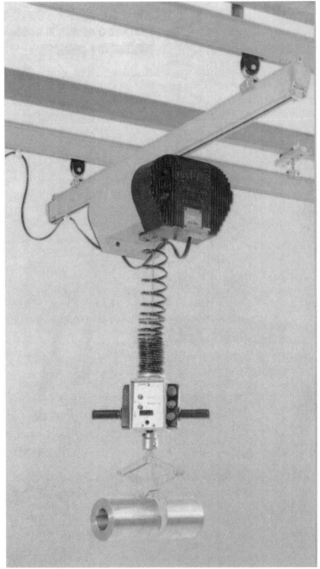

Fig. 7-2 Manipulator—overhead suspended hoist.

Fig. 7-1 Positioner—lift and tilt table.

- Awkward postures are often observed while an operator is using an MHS, due to the size of the system and the clearance required. This has resulted in new health complaints such as shoulder strain, despite eliminating the causes for low back strain.

Each of these outcomes results in increased cost, either from lost time injuries or inefficient and inflated capital fund expenditures. Unfortunately, not trying to alleviate the physical requirements of the MMH task compromises employee health and well-being and quality, and increases workers' compensation claims and absenteeism.

These outcomes should not lead an employer to conclude that the use of MHS as an ergonomic solution is not prudent. Rather, this indicates that there are areas related to the selection, design, and installation of MHS that need to be carefully considered.

To optimize the application of MHS, a strategy for the selection and design of manual handling systems is shown in Fig. 7-3. This strategy includes guidelines for the selection, design, and installation of an MHS.

CHAPTER 7   ERGONOMICS AND MANUAL MATERIAL HANDLING

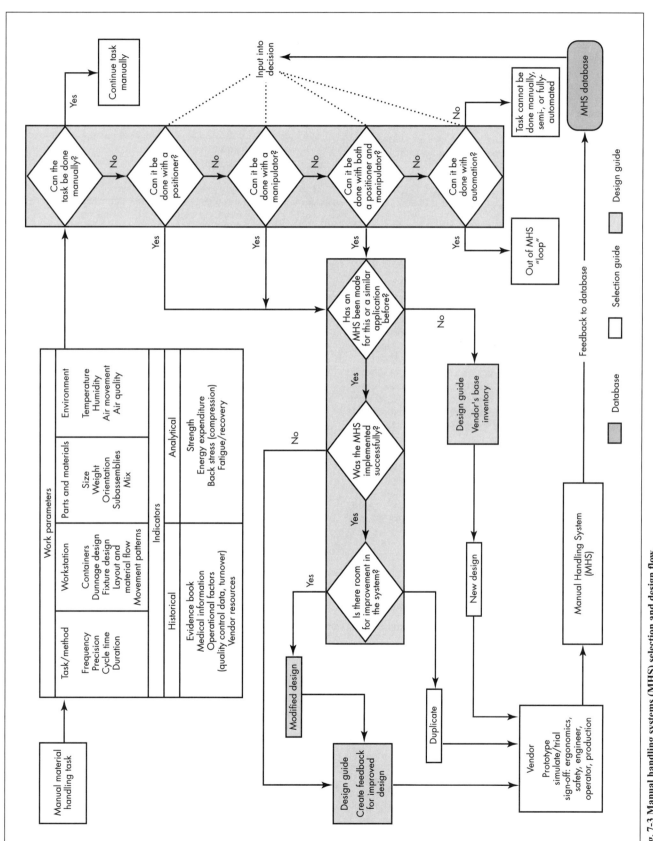

Fig. 7-3 Manual handling systems (MHS) selection and design flow.

CHAPTER 7   ERGONOMICS AND MANUAL MATERIAL HANDLING

SOLVING MMH ERGONOMIC ISSUES

Many manufacturing facilities have implemented automation, not only as an ergonomic solution, but to optimize productivity. As an alternative to full automation, manual handling devices and systems have been increasingly used, since the human interaction with the system supports more flexibility and complexity in the task. The selection and design of material handling systems are engineering solutions to high-risk MMH tasks.

WORK PARAMETERS AND INDICATORS

There are many factors to consider when evaluating the need for an MHS, as well as the appropriate selection, design, and installation of an MHS. These factors can be divided into two groups: work parameters and indicators.

Work parameters include the frequency, precision, cycle time, and duration of the task; workstation components (containers, dunnage, fixtures, tools, layouts, material flow, and movement patterns), characteristics of parts and materials (size, weight, orientation, subassemblies, and part mix), and environmental conditions (temperature, humidity, air movement, and air quality). Evaluation of these parameters can help identify factors that may contribute to an increase in the physical demands and stresses of an MMH task.

Indicators are divided into two subgroups. The first of these is *historical data* such as medical records, quality performance, productivity, and supplier experience. The second is *analytical data* derived from ergonomic evaluation tools for strength, fatigue, recovery, energy expenditure, and measurement data. These data can identify the problem areas of a specific task and can sometimes be used to predict problems with related or similar operations.

The combination of any or all of the work parameters and indicators is used in the decision-making process to determine whether an MHS will be appropriate for use at an operation. With this information and MHS criteria (cost, materials, safety features, speed, etc.), a data-driven decision can be made. These parameters not only contribute to the decision-making process from an ergonomics perspective, but also from a manufacturing business perspective.

SELECTION GUIDE

After data are available to support the decision-making process, a selection guide can be used to help answer these questions:

- Can the task be safely done manually, or is a manual handling system necessary?
- If a manual handling system is necessary, which one is most appropriate?

To answer the first question, the work parameters are collected to provide input to the analytical tools (indicators). An estimate of risk for injury is then derived and historical data are evaluated to determine past performance (injury records, medical visits, etc.). From these elements an estimate of risk can be made, along with a decision as to whether an MHS is necessary.

The second question is more difficult to answer. All workstation parameters need to be considered. This means that many manufacturing specialists at the facility need to be involved: engineering, material handling, health and safety, ergonomics, and most importantly, the affected operator. To adequately address the ergonomics of the workstation design, an understanding of the physical and cognitive interaction between the operator and the MHS must also exist.

When this relationship is defined, choose the MHS type. A positioner is generally the simplest and least expensive option since, in many cases, the part or object may precipitate a hazardous lift due simply to an inability to access it. A lift/tilt or rotate table may solve the ergonomic problem quickly and cheaply. However, it may be impossible to achieve the optimal location and orientation due to work parameters. The object may be too heavy or cumbersome, or the travel distance with the load may be too great, making a manipulator the better aid. In some situations, the operation may require a combination of both a positioner and manipulator to optimize the manual handling of the object.

If neither of these semi-automated devices can alleviate the physical demands of the job, automation may be an appropriate solution. If so, the decision process for the most appropriate automation system is beyond the scope of this chapter. See Chapter 13 for automated material handling solutions. If, in the rare case, neither semi-automation nor full automation will work, then the operation cannot be driven as planned, and the engineer will have to go back to the drawing board.

DATABASE

To support this proposed strategy long-term, a database must be maintained with references to previous, current, and state-of-the-art applications of MHS. This can be a very valuable resource when determining whether a material handling system is necessary, and if so, which one is most appropriate.

MHS logged in the database are categorized according to criteria considered critical in the successful selection, design, and installation of a safe and productive MHS. Some of the possible criteria that may be standard for the description of MHS entries include:

- Force required at the hands and directions of force.
- Number of hands required to operate the MHS.
- Time and speed of the MHS.
- Height of hands for operation.
- Floor surface characteristics and requirements.
- Part manipulation requirements.
- Part packaging constraints.

Not only are physical characteristics of the MHS entered, but part and object details are provided, as well as feedback from each facility that has, or is using the MHS. This feedback identifies what made the MHS installation successful, as well as what improvements need to be or were made.

The database is intended to be accessible at a variety of sites. A database in the form of a binder or written list can serve the same purpose, depending on the number of users and their proximity to the resource. A computerized database also enables large manufacturing corporations to share best practices across facilities worldwide. It can also include photographs and even video clips to illustrate an MHS application.

REDUCING MUSCULOSKELETAL INJURY HAZARD

Workers engaged in physical work are subjected to both internal and external forces. The result is a strain on the worker's musculoskeletal and physiological systems. The overall goal of ergonomics is to help develop an efficient workplace and sufficiently reduce the stress imposed upon the body to minimize musculoskeletal and physiological strain.

Currently, no specifications exist regarding the design of MHS that adequately address potential ergonomic issues. There have, however, been some preliminary studies investigating the impact of MHS design on the human user.[24,25,26,27]

CHAPTER 7   ERGONOMICS AND MANUAL MATERIAL HANDLING

From this and additional research, a design guide for manipulators might advise to:[28]

- Decrease hand forces.
- Decrease the need for accuracy.
- Decrease the horizontal travel distance with a load.
- Decrease the weight of the MHS.
- Decrease the vertical travel distance with a load.
- Avoid torso rotation.
- Keep efforts at waist level.
- Use careful brake design to prevent stressful acceleration and deceleration of the load.

An ideal design guide will provide specifications for suppliers of MHS and serve as a general outline of critical information listed in the database. The guide will not only provide the buyer with a consistent, systematic approach for specifying MHS, but will also assist the suppliers in providing a product that better satisfies customer requirements.

SUPPLIER BUILD AND PROTOTYPE BUY-OFF

At the point where all information has been gathered regarding the current needs of a facility for an MHS, the requirements are given to the supplier or manufacturer to initiate the design and production of the MHS.

Critical to the successful integration of the MHS into a facility is the early and continuous involvement of operators in the development of the MHS at the supplier. This includes design reviews, prototype and working model reviews, and final buy-off at the supplier site. Those who should be involved in some or all of these reviews are the engineer, safety representatives, ergonomics representatives, the affected operators, skilled trades, appropriate union representatives (if a unionized facility), production managers, and any other local representatives deemed necessary. Finally, for complex manipulators, operator training before full production helps ensure operator acceptance and a smooth integration and launch.

THE NEED FOR MORE RESEARCH

The tools used to evaluate manual material handling tasks enable the user to identify risk with a reasonable level of confidence that hazardous situations will be identified. This may not be true when one is trying to assess the risk associated with the use of MHS, especially manipulators. The current evaluation tools make assumptions regarding the MMH task, such as:

- There is no acceleration or deceleration of the load.
- The line of action of the load is in the direction of gravity.
- The lift is performed with two hands, there is no twisting of the torso during the lift (the left and right sides of the body are mirror images of each other), and that the load is stable throughout the lift.

These assumptions are violated with material handling systems, since acceleration and deceleration of the load is common and the direction of force is generally in the lateral plane, rather than the direction of gravity, and the left and right sides of the body are rarely doing the same thing.

The absence of an evaluation tool for these circumstances can be partially attributed to the lack of information relating these types of activities to the physical capabilities of a human operator. There is a significant gap in the research regarding the long-term effect of repetitive, dynamic, push-and-pull efforts on the human body.

Further, the success rate for a first time installation of an MHS is affected by time standards, which do not relate specifically to the use of an MHS. There does seem to be a consensus, however, that using a manipulator for an otherwise manual job takes more time.

These relationships are being investigated and the research results will contribute to the use of MHS in the following ways.

- Goals of the research are:
  - To identify the ability of existing risk assessment methods to determine whether a particular material handling task can be done safely manually.
  - To improve current ergonomic evaluation tools so they can be used to evaluate the risk of an MHS operation, and to investigate different MHSs and their relationships to the human user, so the proper MHS can be chosen for an operation.
- A design guide and database: research should provide insight into what parameters of the workstation, the MHS, and the human operator are important to the successful application of an MHS. These parameters will become criteria for both the design guide given to suppliers and for the description of the MHS in the database.
- Time prediction: engineers will be better able to estimate the time required for the use of an MHS and gain insight as to what types of MHS will affect the time required to use them.

MANUAL HANDLING SYSTEMS MODEL APPLICATION

A particular manual handling systems model can take on either a proactive or reactive approach to design.

Proactive Design

Ergonomic evaluation tools enable identification of those manual material handling jobs that pose an increased risk for injury to the operator, and can be applied to one or many jobs to identify those areas where MHS may be needed. The risk assessment also can be used to prioritize jobs that need change.

For example, in automotive manufacturing, this strategy is especially beneficial during the design of new production lines. Early identification of potential ergonomic problems enables engineers in a facility to design operations for the human operators. At the early stages of job design, an engineer can abate the risk of injury or better facilitate the implementation of MHS by affecting workstation layout, tooling design, and process allocation.

Reactive Design

Prioritization also can be reactive, with the addition of historical information to further prioritize operations requiring improvements from an ergonomics perspective.

This strategy can also help identify jobs that are good candidates for MHS, as well as which MHS is the most appropriate. Reactive analysis allows engineers at a facility to draw on experiences (both success and failures) at other facilities.

SAFETY ASPECTS OF MMH

Federal, state, and local safety regulations should always be followed. Several common-sense rules can help ensure material handling safety.

- Educate employees in safe procedures.
- Allow enough room to maneuver in the workplace and provide enough space for materials, shelves, and tables.
- Minimize static work components; or use mechanical aids.

CHAPTER 7   ERGONOMICS AND MANUAL MATERIAL HANDLING

- Provide adequate rest allowances to overcome fatigue.
- Consider pinch point locations.
- Properly use lockouts.

Manual material handling also involves a number of other hazards. Routine safety analysis should be carried out to eliminate or minimize these hazards. Managers, supervisors, and employees should be trained to identify and report:

- Surfaces likely to abrade, puncture, or cut.
- Surfaces likely to be exposed to gusts of wind (for example, sheets of glass or boarding).
- Surface features likely to catch on clothing.
- Lack of adequate handles or gripping surfaces.
- Liability to swing (when a long load is held centrally, for example, a ladder).
- Obstruction of vision (for example, when climbing stairs, steps, or going down a slope).
- Contents of the container (toxins, acid).
- Disabling glare that might cause collision.
- Slippery floors.
- High temperatures, open flames.
- Atmospheric pollutants (for example, dust, smoke, fumes).
- Unstable platforms.
- High noise level and vibration (may reduce vigilance, affect grip strength).

Protective equipment includes shoes, gloves, vests, trousers, goggles, respirators, aprons, overalls, and masks. Personal protective equipment should not increase the force requirements of the task, as for example, might stiff or bulky gloves. Each of these devices serves a specific need. Shoes, for example, provide proper coupling between the individual and the floor. Similarly, goggles protect the eyes from disabling glare, and masks and respirators protect the individual from inhaling toxic fumes, smoke, and dust. Proper protective equipment should be selected to suit the hazard.

In general:

- Protective clothing should permit free movement. Gloves should fit and allow maintenance of dexterity, and shoes should be of a nonslip type, comfortable, and waterproof.
- Protective clothing should be easily removable and, if possible, allow for personal cooling to protect from body metabolic heat build-up.

References

1. CTD News Online, excerpts from May 1995 issue, http://www-zeus.desy.de/~mark1/ctd/ctd.html.
2. OSHA press release. "Preventing Repetitive Strain Injuries." Washington: U.S. Department of Labor, December 1996.
3. Bernard, T.E. *Metabolic Heat Assessment* (prepared for the Motor Vehicle Manufacturers Association). Tampa, FL: College of Public Health, University of South Florida, 1991.
4. Health and Safety Commission. *Handling Loads at Work—Proposals for Regulations and Guidance.* London: Health and Safety Executive, 1991.
5. Accident Rehabilitation & Compensation Insurance Corporation, 1994.
6. Occupational Ergonomics.
7. Snook, S.H., and Cirello, V.M. "The Design of Manual Handling Tasks: Revised Tables of Maximum Acceptable Weights and Forces." *Ergonomics* 1991, 34 (9): 1,197-1,213.
8. UAW/Ford Ergonomics Process. Ann Arbor, MI: The Regents of the University of Michigan, 1988, 1991; The UAW-Ford National Joint Committee on Health and Safety, 1991.
9. Chaffin, D.B., and Andersson, G.B. *Occupational Biomechanics,* 2nd Edition. New York: John Wiley and Sons, Inc., 1991.
10. Waters, T.R., Putz-Anderson, V., and Garg, A. *Applications Manual for the Revised NIOSH Lifting Equation* (Publication # PB94-

176930). Cincinnati, OH: U.S. Department of Health and Human Services, January, 1994.
11. UAW/ Ford Ergonomics Process. Ann Arbor, MI: The Regents of the University of Michigan, 1988, 1991; The UAW-Ford National Joint Committee on Health and Safety, 1991.
12. Bernard, T.E. *Metabolic Heat Assessment* (prepared for the Motor Vehicle Manufacturers Association). Tampa, FL: College of Public Health, University of South Florida, 1991.
13. Garg, A., Chaffin, D.B., and Herrin, G. "Prediction of Metabolic Rates for Manual Materials Handling Jobs." *American Industrial Hygiene Association Journal* 1978, 39 (8): 661-674.
14. National Institute for Occupational Safety and Health (NIOSH). *Work Practices Guide for Manual Lifting.* NIOSH Technical Report No. 81-122. Cincinnati, OH: U.S. Department of Health and Human Services, NIOSH, 1981.
15. Garg, A., Chaffin, D.B., and Herrin, G. "Prediction of Metabolic Rates for Manual Materials Handling Jobs." *American Industrial Hygiene Association Journal* 1978, 39 (8): 661-674.
16. Waters, T.R., Putz-Anderson, V., Garg, A., and Fine, L.J. "Revised NIOSH Equation for the Design and Evaluation of Manual Lifting Tasks." *Ergonomics* 1993, 36 (7): 749-776.
17. McAttamney, L., and Corbett, E.N. "RULA: A Survey Method for the Investigation of Work-related Upper Limb Disorders." *Applied Ergonomics* 1993, 24 (2): 91-99.
18. Ayoub, M.M., and Mital, A. *Manual Materials Handling.* London: Taylor and Francis, Ltd., 1989.
19. Sharp, M., and Legg, S. "Effects of Psychophysical Lifting Training on Maximum Repetitive Lifting Capacity." *American Industrial Hygiene Association Journal* 1988, 49: 639-644.
20. Snook, S.H., Campnelli, R.A., and Hart, J.W. "A Study of Three Preventive Approaches to Low Back Injury." *Journal of Occupational Medicine* 1978, 20: 478-481.
21. Dehlin, O., Berg, S., Hedenrud, B., Anderson, G., and Grimby, G. "Muscle Training, Psychological Perception of Work and Low Back Symptoms in Nursing Aides." *Scandinavian Journal of Rehabilitation Medicine* 1978, 10: 201-209.
22. Karvonen, M.J., Jarvinen, T., and Nummi, J. "Follow-up Study on the Back Problems of Nurses." *Instructional Occupational Health* 1977, 14: 8.
23. Meyers, J., Riordan, R., Mattmiller, B., Belcher, O., Levenson, B.S., and White, A.W. "Low-back Injury Prevention at Southern Pacific Railroad—5 Year Experience with a Back School Model." Paper Presented at the International Society for the Study of the Lumbar Spine Annual Meeting, May 16-20. Paris: International Society for the Study of the Lumbar Spine, 1981.
24. Resnick, M.L. *Biomechanics, Kinematics, Psychophysics and Motor Control in the Application of Material Handling Devices (MHDs).* PhD Dissertation. Ann Arbor, MI: University of Michigan, 1993.
25. Woldstad, J.C., and Chaffin, D.B. "Dynamic Push and Pull Forces While Using a Manual Materials Handling Assist Device." *IIE Transactions.* Norcross, GA: Institute of Industrial Engineers, 1997.
26. Chaffin, D.B. *Lecture Notes.* Ann Arbor, MI: University of Michigan, 1996.
27. Chaffin, D.B., Herring, G.D., Keyserling, W.M., and Garg, A. "A Method for Evaluating the Biomechanical Stresses Resulting from Manual Materials Handling Jobs." *American Industrial Hygiene Association Journal* 1977, 38: 662-675.
28. Chaffin, D.B. *Lecture Notes.* Ann Arbor, MI: University of Michigan, 1996.

Bibliography

Bhattacharya, A., and McGlothin, J.D. *Occupational Ergonomics Theory and Applications.* New York: Marcel Dekker, 1996.

Hughes, R.E., Chaffin, D.B., Lavender, S.A., and Andersson, G.B.J. "Evaluation of Muscle Force Prediction Models of the Lumbar Trunk Using Surface Electromyography." *Journal of Orthopaedic Research* 1994, 12.

Lee, K.S., Chaffin, D.B., and Parks, C. "A Study of Slip Potential During Cart Pushing and Pulling." *IIE Transactions.* Norcross, GA: Institute of Industrial Engineers, 1992.

Mital, A., Nicholson, A.S., and Ayoub, M.M. *A Guide to Manual Materials Handling,* Second Edition. London: Taylor & Francis, Ltd., 1997.

National Institute for Occupational Safety and Health (NIOSH) Back Belt Working Group. *Conclusions and Recommendations on the Use of Back Belts to Prevent Work-related Back Injuries.* Washington: NIOSH, 1994.

CHAPTER 7   ERGONOMICS AND MANUAL MATERIAL HANDLING

Nussbaum, M., and Chaffin, D.B. "Development and Evaluation of a Scalable and Deformable Geometric Model of the Human Torso." *Clinical Biomechanics* 1996, 11 (1).

Resnick, M. "Kinematics, Kinetics, and Psychophysical Perceptions in Symmetric and Twisting, Pushing, and Pulling Tasks." *Human Factors* 1996, 38.

Rodgers, S.H. "A Functional Job Analysis Technique." *Occupational Medicine: State of the Art Reviews* 1992, 7 (4).

Rodgers, S.H. "Job Evaluation in Worker Fitness Determination." *Occupational Medicine: State of the Art Reviews,* April-June 1988, 3 (2).

Rodgers, S.H. "Recovery Time Needs for Repetitive Work." *Seminars in Occupational Medicine* March 1987, 2 (1).

Salvendy, G., and Karwowski, W. *Ergonomics in Manufacturing: Raising Productivity Through Workplace Improvement.* Dearborn, MI: Society of Manufacturing Engineers, 1998.

Snook, S.H. "The Design of Manual Handling Tasks." *Ergonomics,* 21.

U.S. Department of Labor. "Characteristics of Injuries and Illnesses Resulting in Absences from Work-1994." Washington: U.S. Department of Labor, 1996.

CHAPTER 8

FLEXIBLE WHEELED HANDLING EQUIPMENT

CHAPTER CONTENTS

THE INDUSTRIAL FORK LIFT TRUCK

In 1933, the industrial lift truck came into use in American industry. It featured the basic mechanical scheme fundamental to the machines in current use: a gasoline-powered, internal combustion engine (ICE) or battery; a mast with forks located on the front of the truck; hydraulic lifting and tilting of the mast; under-the-load, front-wheel drive; rear-wheel steering; and equal speeds in forward and reverse.

Prior to the development of this machine, the stacking of goods and materials was achieved largely through the use of human effort. As a result, materials were stored at floor level (unstacked) and much square footage was required for inventories of raw material, work-in-process, and finished goods.

With the coming of the fork lift truck, American industry experienced a revolution in the practice of material handling. Factories now had a powerful, compact machine that could turn in tight circles, shuttle loads back and forth, and stack them. The new truck was an innovation that increased efficiency, reduced costs, freed workers for more productive tasks, and gave new meaning to the concept of space utilization. It revised factory architecture since the stacking of goods meant less floor area was required.

IMPACT ON INDUSTRY

In more than a half century since its invention, the lift truck has become an essential link in the distribution chain. It has never become obsolete. Over time it has evolved into the most ubiquitous, state of-the-art, mobile material handling machine, and it is found in every factory, warehouse, and cargo-handling facility worldwide.

Two principal advances took place over the years: the gradual improvements in counterbalanced lift truck technology, which have allowed the machine to handle increasingly heavy loads and to raise them to greater heights; and the development of dozens of different kinds of machines, each designed to carry out a specialized material handling assignment. As new material handling needs arose, new types of trucks were developed. Moreover, industrial truck manufacturers reaped the benefits of more sophisticated and stronger materials and fuels, and continued to advance overall technology, improving travel and lifting speeds, ease of operation and maintenance, safety, operator comfort, environmental impact, and machine durability.

There is no doubt that the blossoming of the families of industrial trucks played a significant role in the continually improving efficiency and productivity of manufacturing and storage facilities. For example, factories and warehouses were once low-level structures. But as the ability of the counterbalanced lift truck to reach greater heights increased, buildings were erected with higher roofs to accommodate higher stacks of goods and materials. With the development of the narrow-aisle truck, inventories can now be stored at heights in excess of 50 ft (15 m). Modern plants, warehouses, and distribution centers are designed to take advantage of these material handling strategies. Buildings are now taller and they require less land.

Too often, factory managers do not really appreciate the impact that the industrial truck can have on productivity and profitability, and frequently, they fail to see the need to properly merge industrial truck operations into the manufacturing process. Fixed material handling equipment, such as conveyor systems or automated storage and retrieval system (AS/RS) schemes, are given a great deal of thought, primarily because they are fixed, and it is costly to change what has been permanently installed. Because industrial trucks are mobile machines that can go anywhere at any time, their need to be integrated into the manufacturing operation is often overlooked.

Of the many types of mobile lift trucks in use today, by far the most popular are sit-down, counterbalanced lift trucks powered by either an ICE or a battery (see Figs. 8-1 and 8-2). Their function is to lift, transport over short distances, and stack materials. Since they are self-propelled and manned by human operators, they are the most versatile of all material handling machines. Their fundamental role in the manufacturing scheme is to assure the uninterrupted flow of raw materials, semifinished and finished products, and to assure that these products are sent on their way to the marketplace in a timely fashion. Indeed, depending on the industry, material handling may account for 30-75%, or more, of the cost of making a product.[1]

The intelligent utilization of lift trucks and lift truck fleets is essential to a successful manufacturing strategy. Many pitfalls await an unwary plant manager, such as:

- Trucks improperly selected for a given material handling task.
- Improperly trained operators.
- Trucks with poor ergonomics, which may leave drivers fatigued and inefficient.
- The operation of trucks beyond their useful economical lives.

The Contributors of this chapter are: Gene F. Schwind, Executive Editor, "Material Handling Engineering"; *John Prentice,* Director, National Service, Nissan Fork Lift Corporation, N. America.
The Reviewers of this chapter are: Gene F. Schwind, Executive Editor, "Material Handling Engineering"; *Ned Ramm,* Manager, Government & Export Sales, Drexel Industries.

CHAPTER 8   FLEXIBLE WHEELED HANDLING EQUIPMENT

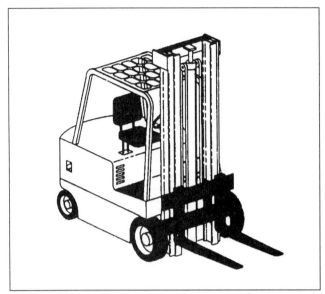

Fig. 8-1 Sit-down, ICE, cushion tire, counterbalanced fork lift truck. *(Courtesy Industrial Truck Association)*

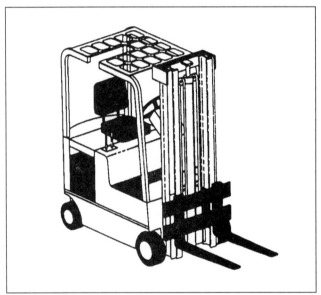

Fig. 8-2 Sit-down, electric, cushion tire, counterbalanced fork lift truck. *(Courtesy Industrial Truck Association)*

• Trucks improperly maintained.
• An unhealthy environment in the plant from truck emissions.
• The lack of careful plans to integrate the safe interaction between trucks and pedestrians.

Clearly, something as simple as a lift truck down for unscheduled repair, or any unfulfilled task, such as unreplenished inventories or tardy Just-in-Time (JIT) deliveries, can cause a slowdown or a stoppage in the manufacturing flow. These kinds of problems eventually find their way into the net earnings figure of a company.

As a result of the massive personnel downsizing American industry has experienced in recent years, many companies have lost key individuals who have taken with them crucial skills and knowledge. As a result, the selection and management of industrial trucks

and truck fleets have often fallen into the hands of individuals insufficiently experienced in the subject or who do not have enough time to devote to this important consideration.

Because material handling plays such an important and influential role in industry, it is essential for the manufacturing engineer to understand the fundamental aspects of the use and management of industrial trucks: selection and fleet standardization, operation and replacement, maintenance, and operator training.

CLASSES OF INDUSTRIAL TRUCKS

The Industrial Truck Association (ITA), an organization created to advance the technical, safety, and product performance standards of the industrial truck industry, has organized the industry's products into seven classes of the most widely-used industrial trucks (see Table 8-1). Other types of industrial trucks, not included in the ITA's classification, are:

• Specialty lift trucks which can handle almost any shape of load and perform any designated function.
• *Automated guided vehicles* (AGV) perform material handling tasks without benefit of a human operator. These machines usually carry unit loads and are guided to their destinations by a wire embedded in the plant floor or a strip painted on the floor.
• *Self-guided vehicles* (SGV), also unmanned machines, carry out the same tasks as the AGV, but navigate through a plant via a laser guidance system. No wire embedment is required.

Refer to Chapter 13 of this handbook for more information on AGVs and SGVs.

TABLE 8-1
Classes and Types of Trucks

Class	Type of Truck
Class I	Electric motor rider
	Counterbalanced, stand-up
	Counterbalanced, three-wheel, sit-down
	Counterbalanced, cushion tire, sit-down
	Counterbalanced, pneumatic tire, sit-down
Class II	Electric motor narrow-aisle
	High-lift straddle
	Order picker
	Reach-type outrigger
	Sideloader (platform)
	Sideloader (high-lift pallet)
	Turret truck
	Low-lift platform
	Low-lift pallet
Class III	Electric motor hand truck
	Low-lift platform
	Low-lift walkie pallet
	Tractor (draw-bar pull under 999 lb [453 kg])
	Low-lift walkie/center control
	Reach-type outrigger
	High-lift straddle
	Single-face pallet
	High-lift platform
	High-lift counterbalanced
	Low-lift walkie/rider pallet
Class IV	Internal combustion engine/cushion tire
Class V	Internal combustion engine/pneumatic tire
Class VI	Electric and internal combustion engine tractors
Class VII	Rough terrain fork lift truck

CHAPTER 8 FLEXIBLE WHEELED HANDLING EQUIPMENT

COUNTERBALANCED LIFT TRUCKS

The counterbalanced lift truck is functionally a lever, and provides reliable lift and transport of loads. These trucks are commonly fitted with forks of various lengths and styles designed to lift, carry, and stack a wide range of loads. For special applications, such as handling unitized and nonunitized paper rolls, steel coils, logs, cargo containers, etc., special carriage attachments replace the forks.

The fulcrum of this "lever" is located at the center of the front axle. Ideally, the load on the forks is positioned so that its center of gravity is located at a point 24 in. (61 cm) from the front of the fork face. All weight behind the fulcrum point, including the battery or cast iron counterweight, counterbalances the load and provides a safety margin.

TYPICAL APPLICATIONS

The typical material handling tasks for counterbalanced trucks include: unloading trucks, trailers, and rail cars; moving incoming raw materials to storage; moving raw materials from storage to manufacturing; moving work-in-process from one workstation to another; moving finished goods from manufacturing to storage; and moving finished goods from storage to shipping. Stacking and unstacking, of course, are also major truck functions. Moreover, the truck handles peripheral assignments, such as removing scrap and waste, functioning as a maintenance aid, and hauling miscellaneous loads.

To appreciate how successfully it has evolved to carry out its material handling assignment, one should consider the following: a typical engine-powered, 5,000-lb (2,268-kg) capacity lift truck has an overall length (aft of the truck to the front of the fork face) of about 88 in. (224 cm), while its width is approximately 41 in. (104 cm). Yet this machine, occupying only about 25 ft² (2 m²) of floor space, can lift a 5,000-lb (2,268-kg) load to a height of about 14 ft (4 m).

Counterbalanced lift trucks are manufactured for load capacities from 2,500-100,000 lb (1,134-45,360 kg). The latter are used as container handlers. In factory and warehouse applications, the most widely-used trucks are those in the 4,000-lb (1,814-kg), 5,000-lb (2,268-kg), and 6,000-lb (2,722-kg) load capacity ranges.

The lift truck's principal operating components are the mast and carriage assembly (plus forks), the power train and prime power source, steering and braking systems, the hydraulic system, and the welded frame and structure.

TIRES

The selection of tires for counterbalanced lift trucks is based mainly on the weight of the loads the truck will carry, and the surface over which the truck will travel. There are two types of tires commonly used.

- *Cushion tires* are composed of natural or synthetic rubber permanently mounted on a steel wheel. They are used on trucks with load capacities of from 2,500-15,000 lb (1,134-6,804 kg) and are designed for indoor use over even surfaces, such as smooth concrete, where load-cushioning is not a major requirement.
- *Pneumatic tires* are very heavy-walled tires inflated to high pressures to a point where they behave like solid cushion tires. They are used primarily on counterbalanced trucks up to 100,000-lb (45,360-kg) or more. Their larger diameter makes them suited to outdoor use over smooth but semi-improved surfaces. *Solid pneumatics* look like pneumatics, but are filled with cushion rubber.

MAST TYPES AND OPERATIONS

The most significant constituent on the lift truck is the mast, the major components of which include:

- A stationary outer upright.
- One to three movable, inner sections (depending on mast type).
- A system of cylinders and lifting chains.
- A carriage and two matched forks.
- A load backrest on the carriage.
- A cylinder to tilt the mast and load.
- Various optional devices such as a fork carriage side shifter, or attachments such as a clamp, rotator, etc.

A lift truck can be equipped with one of four different types of masts, with various collapsed and extended heights. The standard mast, a two-stage mechanism, is composed of an outer, stationary upright assembly, and an inner upright assembly and carriage that raises the load. It can reach a maximum height of about 10 ft (3 m).

The *full-free mast* is another two-stage design that also raises loads to about 10 ft (3 m). This type of mast differs from the standard mast because it has primary and secondary lift modes.

The *full-free triple mast* will reach about 15 ft (4.6 m) with its load, and has three nesting uprights (stationary, intermediate, and inner) plus a carriage. Like the full-free mast lift truck, it has primary and secondary lift modes.

The *quad mast*, reaching about 20 ft (6 m) with its load, has four nesting uprights (one stationary, two intermediates, and one inner) plus a carriage. Like the full-free and full-free triple, this low-volume option mast has primary and secondary lift modes. Primary lift raises the carriage up the inner upright. Secondary lift unnests the movable uprights and elevates them simultaneously. These lift modes are sequenced by pressure ratios.

All four masts have a feature called *free lift*, defined as the distance the forks and carriage can travel before the top of any moving member (carriage or inner upright) exceeds the height of the stationary upright, thus increasing the operating height of the truck. In the case of the standard mast, free-lift distance is usually 4 in. (10 cm). Full-free, full-free triple, and quad masts have free-lift distances of about 56 in. (142 cm).

In material handling operations, this valuable feature allows lift trucks to haul and stack loads while inside confined areas, such as railroad cars and trucks, without limiting their ability to move under low-door overheads.

HYDRAULIC SYSTEM AND OPERATION

The basic hydraulic process which powers lift truck masts and peripheral mechanisms is similar on all lift trucks. It is modified, however, to accommodate larger load capacity trucks, or to handle different mast types and special optional load-handling devices.

In addition to its prime function of raising and lowering the mast, the hydraulic system also actuates other truck or mast functions:

- Mast tilting, where the truck operator tilts the mast forward or backward, is a feature that facilitates load retrieval, handling, and placement. When tilted backward, the mast keeps the load from falling off the forks during travel. Tilting the mast forward eases the movement of the forks in and out of the pallet fork pockets.
- An optional load-side shifter shifts the load laterally to either the right or left. This helps the truck operator insert the forks into the pallet fork pockets without moving the truck. It also increases the accuracy with which pallet loads can be positioned.
- Other load-handling options such as clamps (for grasping either cylindrical- or oblong-shaped loads) and rotators which

CHAPTER 8   FLEXIBLE WHEELED HANDLING EQUIPMENT

can grasp and rotate a load 360°, will also call for additional cylinders to be added to the hydraulic system.
- Vehicle power steering is accomplished through a double-acting hydraulic cylinder mounted above the steering axle beam utilizing oil from a priority valve.

REACH TRUCKS

Reach trucks are narrow aisle trucks designed to operate within 6-ft (1.8-m) wide aisles. They are able to enter these aisles to store and retrieve unit loads, while standard sit-down, counterbalanced trucks require 12-14 ft (3.7-4.3 m) aisles.

Reach trucks come in a number of styles that are differentiated only by the way the forks move forward to engage a load.

The most common reach truck style used in the U.S. is the *pantograph*, or *scissors-type reach* (see Fig. 8-3), also called a *narrow-aisle reach* truck. Between the vertical load backrest of the fork carriage and the lift truck mast is a scissors-type mechanism that connects the load backrest and fork carriage to the mast carriage mount. Hydraulic cylinders inside the scissors assembly extend the fork carriage forward over the truck's outriggers. This reach mechanism is often used at floor level. There, the forks are extended out ahead of the outriggers and into the pallet openings. The load is lifted and then retracted over the outriggers.

In the aisle, the truck is elevated to the height of the empty opening. The truck turns into the rack with the load, and the truck's outriggers enter the rack beneath the floor-level, rack load support beams. Off a single aisle, the racks may be two or three loads deep.

One load deep, the operator sets the load down on the rack beams. If the rack is two deep, the fork carriage and load are extended, and the load is positioned in the rear opening. The reach mechanism may have a tilt feature that tips the load in position so it is free of the rack and against the backrest for safer extraction.

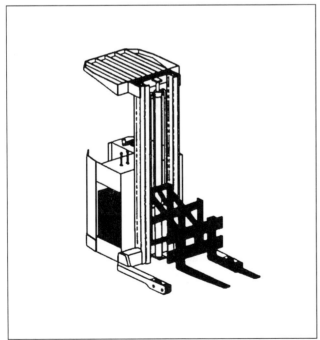

Fig. 8-3 Narrow-aisle reach truck. *(Courtesy Industrial Truck Association)*

A variation of this truck may have a *double pantograph* reach. This means that the truck can drive into a rack bay and reach two deep in a single rack to deposit or retrieve a load.

Some European-style reach trucks, called *rolling mast reach trucks*, are also sold in the U.S. These trucks have very heavy outriggers with channels in them. The mast and fork carriage assembly is mounted on rollers, and the whole mast travels forward and back in the outrigger channels. When the truck is to reach forward, the mast, carriage, and forks move forward to engage and pick up the load.

ATTACHMENTS TO STANDARD LIFT TRUCKS

Reach fork attachments can be added to standard lift trucks to give them reach capability. One such *scissors-reach* style attachment works the same as those that are part of a standard reach truck. With a *telescoping fork* attachment, hydraulic cylinders bored into each fork move individual fork covers forward or back in retrieving the load. The change in load center with either of these attachments will necessarily reduce the capacity of the lift truck.

Attachments should not be added to lift trucks without prior approval of the lift truck manufacturer. When attachments are added to standard lift trucks, a modified truck data plate must be issued and installed on the lift truck.

SPECIAL LIFT TRUCKS

Fork trucks handle standard loads, but in manufacturing there are many loads that are not standard. Special trucks handle these nonstandard jobs, and have been modified to do so since the first lift trucks were brought into manufacturing plants.

Die handlers are an example. *Die-handling walkie trucks* can maneuver in and out between presses with dies of any size and weight. These may be fitted with roller beds and truck-powered push/pull plates. The die set is drawn aboard from the die storage rack, moved to the press, and elevated and aligned with the press bed. On-board truck hydraulics then push the die set off the truck bed and position it on the press bed. Die handling trucks in the 50,000-lb (22,680-kg) capacity range are not unusual.

Similar special trucks may be used for moving jigs and fixtures in and out of machine tools.

Explosion-proof (EX) trucks (rated by Underwriters Laboratories or Factory Mutual Insurance) may be required for use in areas where a fire or explosion could be caused by a spark of any kind.

The truck body and forks of EX-rated trucks are covered with brass plates so that no sparks will be produced from objects striking the truck. Special tires conduct static electricity away and plastics are used for wear points. The truck operating controls and many components are enclosed in bolted National Electrical Manufacturers Association (NEMA)-type enclosures so that no spark or fire from the components can escape into the surrounding atmosphere. Such trucks might be used in chemical or munitions manufacturing.

Ram trucks equipped with a single, large-diameter ram extending from the carriage pick up and transport metal coils from storage to punch press lines. Many costly, high-finish coils are completely wrapped in steel and protective coverings, and the truck's ram permits removing the wrap without changing the shape or damaging the inside diameter of the coil. Such coils may weigh 50 tons (45,360 kg).

Almost all lift truck manufacturers will make some special modifications to the trucks they build. Highly specialized trucks are made by custom lift truck manufacturers.

CHAPTER 8 FLEXIBLE WHEELED HANDLING EQUIPMENT

SIDELOADERS IN MANUFACTURING

Many manufacturing operations require the handling of long or awkward loads (such as lumber, bars, tubes, and structural or other bulky shapes) between the shipping docks and the point of use or process. These loads may be handled by overhead equipment using slings and chains.

Another method of handling them, in usual plant floor aisles, is with a sideloader. In all cases, the loads handled will be limited to those that can be counterbalanced by the weight of the vehicle when the forks are extended or positioned off to the side.

Sideloaders fall into three categories:

- The first type of sideloader has a large, open center bay in which the mast and fork carriage travel perpendicular to the travel direction of the truck. On this type of sideloader, the forks extend off to the side, pick up a long load, retract over the truck bed, and set the load down on the bed. The load may extend over either or both ends of the vehicle. The fork carriage itself may be constructed so that there are forks in the center of the pickup bay, and one each at either end of the vehicle. This arrangement offers greater support for very long and flexible loads, such as bundles of thin tubing. This type of sideloader may steer from the front or rear, or even have four-wheel steering. Power options include gasoline, LP-gas, battery, or diesel power, depending on vehicle size, use, and plant conditions. Diesel and gasoline models are often used in primary metals manufacturing.
- A second type of sideloader can pick up a load by driving the forks under it and then, turning all four wheels so that the truck can maneuver, traveling in any chosen direction. This type of machine is a combination of a straddle truck and a counterbalanced lift truck. Sideloading capability comes from four steerable single or tandem wheels where one or more may be powered. The truck can drive under a long load or insert the forks under it, lift it and retract it, and deposit it on straddle-type legs. The wheels on the ends of these straddle legs, as well as those under the body of the lift truck, are turned hydraulically to face any travel direction. Long loads can be handled to travel parallel to the travel path or crosswise to it. These battery-powered trucks are highly maneuverable for handling both cube and long loads in and around machine tools, although sizable aisles are required.
- The third type of sideloader, often referred to as a *front/sideloader*, is a forward-facing vehicle that looks like a conventional fork lift truck; and indeed, it can function as either a conventional fork lift truck or a sideloader (see Fig. 8-4). Its mast can be swung 90° to point the forks sideways and extend them out past the side of the truck. This enables long loads to be balanced on the forks and carried parallel to the direction of travel. Further, the fork carriage traverses across the face of the lift truck. This type of truck can, for example, drive up alongside a pallet load, insert its forks into the load by traversing the mast and carriage, lift the load, and draw it back into the truck envelope area for transport.

SPECIAL FEATURES

There are two useful features associated with the front/sideloader in factory applications. One is the handling of long loads. By swinging the forks to the side, such a load can be carried parallel to the long axis of the truck, and can thus pass through standard-sized

doorways and factory aisles. Indeed, there is no other efficient way to move long loads through a factory doorway. This load-carrying arrangement can be useful in all applications, including to and from loading docks, between workstations, and into trailers and rail cars.

A second advantage is space savings in storage areas. A conventional, sit-down, counterbalanced lift truck requires access aisles approximately 12-ft (3.7-m) wide, while a standard reach truck needs about 9 ft (2.7 m) of aisle space to operate. But a sideloader, with an articulating mast, can store and retrieve 48 × 40-in. (122 × 102-cm) pallet loads within aisles as narrow as 4.5 ft (1.4 m), because the truck itself does not need to turn within the aisle. Typical sit-down, counterbalanced sideloaders for factory applications have load capacities of from 2,200-12,000 lb (998-5,443 kg), and can reach heights of 30 ft (9 m). These trucks can be powered by battery, or engines using gasoline, propane, or diesel fuel.

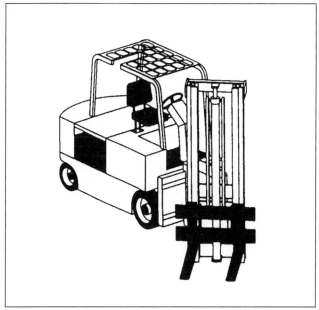

Fig. 8-4 Sit-down, electric, front/sideloader for high-lift pallets. *(Courtesy Industrial Truck Association)*

POWERING FORK LIFT TRUCKS

Fork lift trucks may be powered by batteries, gasoline, diesel fuel, LP-gas, or compressed natural gas (CNG). Most types of trucks are powered by batteries. Of the 26 basic types of powered trucks (as defined by the ITA), 22 of these types are battery-powered. Only classes IV, V, VI, and VII are also offered in gas or liquid fuels (see Table 8-1).

BATTERIES

It is interesting to note that the acquisition of a lift truck battery represents the purchase, in advance, of all the fuel the battery-powered trucks use.

Batteries are electrochemical devices that require an appropriate charger to reverse the electrochemical action and store potential electrical power. Maintenance consists of recharging when 20% of the charge remains.

CHAPTER 8   FLEXIBLE WHEELED HANDLING EQUIPMENT

There are three types of batteries available today. Standard wet-cell batteries, also called *flooded cell batteries*, are the most popular. This type not only requires recharging, but the battery cells require regular filling with water.

A type of battery that is gaining popularity is the *maintenance-free battery*. This type of battery uses gelled electrolyte or electrolyte contained within porous mat separators in the battery cells. This allows the battery to be sealed and thus it does not gas during recharging; therefore, it does not use water. A variation of this battery is the *reduced-maintenance battery* that requires water only about four times per year.

The maintenance-free battery can be recharged anywhere; it does not need a charging room or maintenance. The charger and recharging is much more critical for these batteries than for standard, flooded-cell batteries. Maintenance-free batteries are desirable for walkie truck operation, as well as larger rider trucks that have built-in chargers. Recharging is a simple matter of plugging the battery charger in at the end of the shift. Some batteries recharge from a 110-V AC outlet.

Nickel cadmium batteries are used for some trucks, such as automated guided vehicles. They are recharged during operation as they stop and contact in-floor electrical contacts at dwell points located along their routes.

Batteries come in 6-72 V sizes. The overall size of the cells determines the total ampere hours each will produce. In normal service, a battery charge is usually adequate for a full shift. This means that 80% of the full battery charge is used during an eight-hour shift. If two or more shifts are worked, a second battery is needed for each lift truck, and a battery changing station or battery room is required. This permits one battery to be on charge while the other is being used.

For counterbalanced lift trucks, the weight of the battery is specified on the truck data plate. This is because if the battery is too light, it will change the load-carrying capacity of the lift truck. Each size and type of battery must be recharged with the appropriate charger for recharging to be effective. Depending upon the care provided, batteries may last up to six years before requiring replacement.

Batteries are extremely heavy due to the lead used in the cells. The weight is put to good use in counterbalanced stand-drive and sit-down rider lift trucks. Only the correct battery will provide the correct counterbalance and operating safety for counterbalanced trucks. Battery weight adds to the stability of other types of trucks, also.

Batteries must be handled with either an overhead hoist or a roller bed transfer cart designed especially for switching. Only trained persons should do the battery switching, watering, or charging.

GASOLINE

Gasoline is relatively inexpensive as a motor fuel and, gallon for gallon, contains more energy (123,000 Btu/gal [34,329 J/L]) than any other lift truck fuel. For this reason, it provides the highest lift and travel speeds. On average, 8 gal (30 L) of gasoline will power a 5,000-lb (2,268-kg) capacity lift truck for a full eight-hour shift.

Gasoline engines are well-understood by most mechanics and are relatively easy to service. The carburetor and ignition systems require periodic attention as well as regular oil and filter changes. A few engines have throttle-body fuel injection with microprocessor control similar to automobiles.

Gasoline is highly flammable and toxic. It has the highest potential for water and air pollution. If left uncontrolled, gasoline engines are heavy producers of carbon monoxide (CO). Few gasoline engines are used indoors because of the potential for CO buildup. When used outdoors, gasoline is an economical and efficient fuel. If operated indoors, gasoline-powered lift trucks must operate where there is an adequate air exchange, replenishing 8,000 ft³ (227 m³) per minute for each truck operated. Catalytic mufflers are also recommended.

PROPANE

LP-gas and *liquid petroleum gas* (LPG) are other names for propane. It is widely used as an alternative to gasoline in engine-powered lift trucks. This fuel is a man-made, high-octane, colorless, odorless, nontoxic, noncorrosive compound produced from natural gas, light crude oil, oil refinery gases, and butane. An odorant is added during manufacturing so that leaks will be noticed.

LPG-fueled lift trucks have been operated successfully indoors for about 45 years. Today, there are nearly 800,000 engine-powered lift trucks in operation. More than half are in the 2,000-6,000-lb (907-2,722-kg) capacity load range, and of these more than 80% are LPG-fueled. Current estimates are that 85% of new engine-powered lift trucks use LP-gas.

How LPG Works

LPG vaporizes above the boiling point of propane which is −44° F (−42° C). For handling and storage, propane is transformed into a liquid by compressing the vapor. The liquid is transferred into high-pressure tanks that are mounted on the back of the lift truck. Lift trucks are refueled by exchanging or refilling these tanks. LPG is stored and transported as a liquid in pressurized tanks at 107 psi (738 kPa) and at a temperature of 60° F (16° C). For engine use, the LPG is first piped to a water-heated vaporizer, and once expanded, to an LP-gas carburetor on the engine.

The principal elements in propane are carbon and hydrogen (C_3H_8). The specific gravity of LPG is 0.504. One gal (3.8 L) of LP-gas weighs 4.2 lb (2 kg). A standard 33.6-lb (15-kg) lift truck tank holds 8 gal (30 L) of LPG.

One gal (3.8 L) of liquid propane produces 36.4 ft³ (1 m³) of propane vapor, and a full tank of LPG vaporizes to about 270 ft³ (7.6 m³) of vapor. This is enough to power a 5,000-lb (2,268-kg) capacity lift truck for an eight-hour shift. In average handling applications, lift trucks in the 3,000-6,000-lb (1,361-2,722-kg) capacity range use 0.5-2.0 gal (1.9-7.6 L) of gasoline per hour, or 2-8 lb (0.9-3.6 kg) of LP-gas per hour. One gal (3.8 L) of LPG contains 90,960 Btus (95,962 kJ) of energy, less than gasoline's 123,000 Btus (129,765 kJ). But as a fuel, propane is better than gasoline because it:

- Produces lower exhaust emissions.
- Reduces engine maintenance.
- Lowers engine repair cost.
- Is nonpolluting (even though dangerous) if spilled.

Any gasoline, engine-powered lift truck can be modified to burn LPG. It is easier to convert these engines, because most are made to burn nonleaded gas, so the valve train already has specially hardened valve seats.

It is a good idea, though not necessary, to increase the engine's compression ratio to increase the power lost when converting from gasoline to LPG. Ignition timing is advanced, however. The fuel pump, fuel filter, gasoline tank, lines, dashboard fuel gage, and gasoline carburetor are not required. (This is true unless the truck is to be set up for dual fuel operation, as is the case of many rental fleet trucks.)

LPG Tanks

LPG tanks for lift trucks and other mobile equipment must be manufactured to ASTM standards and meet the specifications set forth by the U.S. Department of Transportation (DOT). These tanks are available in steel or aluminum, and come in 14-lb (6-kg), 20-lb (9-kg), 33.5-lb (15-kg), and 43.5-lb (20-kg) capacities. Aluminum is sometimes preferred because it will not rust or scale on the inside, which can clog the tank exit tube valve or filter.

DOT specifies that tanks must be capable of handling designed pressures with a good margin of safety under normal temperatures. Tanks are filled to only 80% of capacity to allow for increased pressure from liquid expansion. Most LPG tanks are mounted on the rear of the truck, behind the driver, and oriented so the pressure relief valve is in the vapor area of the tank. Most fleet operators have their own refueling stations stocked with full tanks. These may be supplied by the LPG dealer or refilled from bulk supplies on the premises. Some users refuel the tank on the truck.

LPG dealers must fill, maintain, and certify tanks according to DOT specifications. DOT LPG tanks are numbered and must be inspected periodically. The results should be recorded and kept on file for the life of the tank. The pressure relief valve must be replaced with a new one 12 years from the manufacture date of the tank, and at 10-year intervals thereafter. Users filling their own tanks must also do this. Fleet operators must conform to tank tracking and record keeping requirements and train refueling personnel on the equipment required to refuel the LPG trucks.

The National Fire Protection Association (NFPA) has guidelines that are part of most local fire regulations for handling and storage of LPG. Tanks are always stored, exchanged, and filled outdoors. Bulk fuel tanks must be located a specified distance from the nearest building and any kind of refueling facility must be constructed according to regulations. Weather protection is usually necessary.

DUAL-FUEL LIFT TRUCKS

LPG carburetors are relatively small and simple. Some consist of a ring that fits on top of the existing gasoline carburetor. A hose connects this ring to an LPG fuel vaporizer. This permits the user to burn either fuel. A flip of a switch will shut off the LPG and turn on the gasoline.

While only 10-15% of lift trucks are manufactured or converted for dual-fuel use each year, there is a demand for them. However, an engine tuned specifically for gasoline will lack performance with LPG. The reverse is also true.

Rental trucks, particularly those with pneumatic tires that may be used indoors or out, are often equipped for dual fuel. The reason is that these trucks are likely to be used outdoors on construction sites to unload construction materials from trucks and trailers.[2]

DIESEL

In some lift truck lines, there is a corresponding diesel engine available for each size gasoline engine. This is the result of the global use of lift trucks, and the fact that diesel fuel is the cheapest, most available fuel in many parts of the world. Additionally, in many areas buildings are wide open and unheated, and storage is outdoors because of the favorable weather.

Diesel engines are hard-working and long-running between overhauls, but they are more expensive initially, and when repair or a complete rebuild is needed, repairs can be more costly. Diesels get more power from the higher rpms, so they may be geared down when operating heavily-loaded or when working on ramps.

For some trucks, such as the large outdoor container handlers and yard trucks, diesels may be the only choice. They can stand long idle periods between use and are usually unaffected by moisture.

COMPRESSED NATURAL GAS

Compressed natural gas (CNG) is becoming an increasingly popular fuel for a number of reasons.

- A well-tuned CNG engine burns extremely clean with little, if any, CO and no hydrocarbons. It can be used in-plant with no

noticeable change in air quality. In some cases air exchange is not necessary.
- CNG is widely available and can be compressed from the gas mains serving most plants.
- CNG, unlike gasoline or LPG, is dispersed quickly in the air upward, reducing the chance of explosion.
- CNG is low cost, about 40% of the cost of gasoline.
- CNG compression stations are expensive, but not when compared to the cost of operating the plant ventilation, air handling, and heating systems to accommodate other types of fueling systems.
- Natural gas service companies offer help in both financing and servicing customers who convert to CNG. The downside to CNG is the cost of the tanks and conversion of the vehicle (about $2,000). The tanks are made of special high-strength steel, wrapped with fiberglass, and permanently mounted on the truck. They are usually refilled in place. Fleet users install special compression and filling stations. Not as much CNG can be stored in the vehicle tank as LP-gas, so refilling is more frequent. Except for its high pressure (2,300 psi [16 MPa]) state, there are few other hazards to CNG.

EXHAUST TREATMENT

To use lift trucks indoors, gasoline engines should be equipped with catalytic mufflers. LP-gas engines used in confined areas, such as enclosed docks or inside highway transports, should also have catalytic mufflers installed. These are offered as aftermarket add-ons to ensure against CO buildup.

Diesel and gasoline engines can use special exhaust treatment devices that totally eliminate CO by combining exhaust with air and burning it. Catalytic mufflers are available in custom configurations to replace the standard factory-installed exhaust system. Some truck models require removal of the counterweight to install the special converter. Others also require the addition of an air pump and both electrical and air pump connections.

POWER COMPARISON

Propane is the generally accepted fuel of choice when engine-powered lift trucks must be operated indoors. While users do sacrifice some performance in travel and lift speeds, several benefits make up for these deficiencies.

- The application can be the influencing factor in fuel selection. Battery-powered trucks are unbeatable when it comes to emissions, but if the lift trucks are operated two or more consecutive shifts, recharged batteries will be needed. With LPG, only refilled fuel tanks are needed.
- If emissions are a problem, battery-powered lift trucks come out on top again. Gasoline-powered trucks are usually not considered unless the building is wide open or an extensive air exchanging and circulating system is used. LPG trucks operate with low emissions if kept tuned, and if they must be used in confined areas, such as in highway transports, they can be fitted with special mufflers to remove all of the CO and hydrocarbons. It should be understood that for every gasoline-powered lift truck used indoors, the air handling system should exhaust and replace 8,000 ft³ (227 m³) of air per minute. For every LPG truck, the requirement is 5,000 ft³ (142 m³) per minute. Additionally, this means that the incoming air must be heated or cooled and, in special areas, circulated. The trucks themselves may produce sufficient heat to make up for some heat loss in colder climates, but for cooling, the air replacement system must compensate for this increased heat. Battery-powered trucks remain about neutral for these circumstances.

CHAPTER 8   FLEXIBLE WHEELED HANDLING EQUIPMENT

• The octane rating of propane is 100+ which enables it to burn more evenly and efficiently than gasoline. Entering the engine as a vapor, plus a more complete combustion, minimizes the exhaust emissions from LPG and reduces gum, lead, and carbon deposits on the pistons, rings, valves, guides, and spark plugs. Without the dilution effects of gasoline, and the wear caused by carbon buildup, oil life is extended between changes and the oil remains clean. As a result, operating hours between major engine overhauls are increased two to four times. The engine is usually cleaner and easier to work on as a result.

• Fuel cost is a factor. Prices fluctuate and vary by geographic area. Gasoline costs anywhere from $0.95-$1.25/gal while LPG costs from $1-$1.75/gal delivered in tanks. Facilities equipped to fill their own LPG tanks can pay $0.65-$1.25/gal in bulk volumes. Fuel cost studies generally cite $0.90/gal for LPG and $1.25/gal for gasoline. That makes LPG less expensive than gasoline. In any calculation, it should be noted that off-highway use of gasoline or diesel fuel carries federal highway taxes, and this tax is returned as a credit reducing the per gallon cost by the same amount.

LIFT TRUCK ATTACHMENTS

A wide variety of attachments can be installed on various lift trucks (see Fig. 8-5). These *attachments* enable the lift truck to perform additional functions or to perform a standard function more efficiently. The benefits of attachments include:

• Grabbing awkward loads.
• Saving time positioning loads.
• Reducing handling costs.
• Saving labor.
• Reducing product damage.
• Conserving space.

One of the ways that attachments achieve these benefits is by eliminating the need for a platform under the load. Palletless handling is suggested for applications in which loads are suitable for unitizing. The more uniformly weight is distributed in a stack of materials, the better suited that load is for palletless handling.

A familiarity with the attachments most popularly used in factory applications will help determine whether one of these devices can maximize lift truck efficiency. The economic justification of an attachment can be done by determining:

• How often it will be used.
• Attachment cost.
• The time and labor it will save.
• Its impact on safety.

ATTACHMENTS AND SAFETY

If the use of an attachment is economically justified, its effect on the lift truck's load-carrying capacity must be considered. An attachment is generally mounted on the front of the carriage plate. The attachment configuration often extends the load center farther out in front of the truck. This, combined with the added weight of the attachment itself, moves the center of gravity forward, and reduces the capacity of a counterbalanced truck. To offset this condition, either the rated load-carrying capacity must be lowered, or additional counterbalance must be added at the back of the truck.

Attachments should be installed by a reputable lift truck dealer. Major lift truck manufacturers will calculate the extent to which the capacity of a given truck with a particular attachment will have to be down-rated. In accordance with OSHA regulation CFR 1910.178,[3] a new capacity plate must be affixed to the modified truck.

To make installation easier, some lift trucks have hydraulic valves which provide for auxiliary functions required by the attachments. Sectional valve design makes adding spools for attachment functions a simple operation if included in the original design.

Complicated hose reeving has been reduced by mast-mounted spring reels which pay out and retrieve the hose, and by internal mast hose reeving. Quick disconnect hydraulic couplers make attachment interchange possible and easy in some situations.

SIDESHIFTERS

The most popular type of attachment is the *hydraulic sideshifter*. This is a device that moves the fork carriage from side to side a total of about 8 in. (20 cm), 4 in. (10 cm) to either side. Its purpose is to allow the operator to insert the forks into the pallet without repositioning the truck. It also repositions other load-handling attachments when necessary. Because it is a great time saver, the sideshifter is sold on a large percentage of lift trucks and is offered in combination with many other kinds of attachments.

CLAMPS

The *clamp* consists of two pairs of hydraulically-actuated side bars with vertical shoulders connecting them, to which various types of forks, arms, or pads can be bolted or welded. Many clamps are designed to handle specific products. Within the clamp group, the most popular attachments are the carton clamp, drum clamp, and paper roll clamp.

An adjustable pressure regulator can be used with any of the clamping attachments to ensure that suitable clamping pressure is applied to the load. The *paper roll clamp* is generally a combination of two attachments having a rotator at the back of the clamp. While its greatest use is handling large rolls of paper, this clamp also can be used to handle other round products, such as steel cylinders and concrete pipe.

Different kinds of facings are available for the inside gripping surface of the clamp to handle specific loads. Rubber padding is usually used for concrete and steel products.

As the cost of pallets increases, the popularity of the carton clamp rises. This attachment handles cube or unit loads of cartons, usually stretch-wrapped together.

The *drum clamp* is most often used to handle 55-gal (208-L) steel drums without pallets. The drums can be lifted singly, in pairs, or in a group of four. Drum handlers are also available for 30-gal (114-L) and 15-gal (57-L) steel drums, and for all sizes of fiber drums. Many other special purpose clamps, such as bale and cotton clamps, are offered.

ROTATORS

Rotators are usually teamed with clamp attachments or forks. Any degree of rotation desired may be obtained by using stops. If no stops are used, the rotation is continuous in either direction because the fluid drive motor is reversible. Unit loads or containers can be picked up, transported, rotated, dumped, inverted, or up-ended with attachments. Boxes or hoppers equipped with fork channels can be dumped with the hydraulic rotator.

LOAD PUSHES AND LOAD PUSH/PULLS

Widely used in operations that involve warehousing and car or van loading are the load push and the load push/pull attachments. These are used in conjunction with slip sheets or fiberboard pallets. Standard designs have platens instead of conventional forks. With

CHAPTER 8   FLEXIBLE WHEELED HANDLING EQUIPMENT

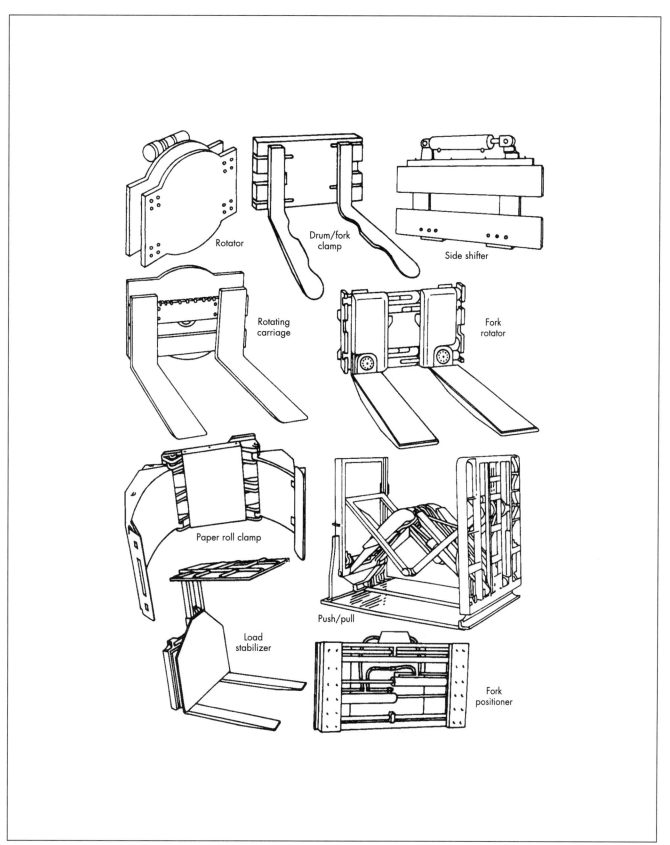

Fig. 8-5 Typical lift truck attachments. *(Courtesy "Material Handling Engineering")*

CHAPTER 8   FLEXIBLE WHEELED HANDLING EQUIPMENT

the *load push models* only, a hydraulically-actuated front frame pushes the load off the platen forks onto the floor or into a storage location on top of another load or pallet.

The difference between the push/pull models and the pull types is that the push/pull model has hydraulically-actuated gripper bars at the base of the front frame. This allows it to grab a slip sheet or paper pallet lip and pull the load onto the polished platens.

The *load push/pull model* is commonly used to handle items such as cartons and sacks stacked on a slip sheet. It is appropriate for use in operations where space can be gained by not using conventional wooden pallets.

FORK POSITIONERS

For operations where a lift truck handles a variety of pallet sizes, a fork positioner adds flexibility. These attachments allow the operator to hydraulically move the forks closer together or farther apart, individually or together. It is particularly popular on larger trucks where the forks are heavy and difficult to adjust by hand.

LOAD STABILIZERS

This attachment is a device with a large square pad that comes down on the top of the load to steady it. This device is designed to ensure safe transport of unstable, palletized loads, such as bags, boxes, drums, barrels, empty bottle cases, or any type of load that might be bounced off while rounding corners or moving over uneven surfaces during transport. In such situations, the stabilizer permits safer, faster handling.

FORK ROTATORS

Also a clamp, the fork rotator is a dual-purpose attachment that handles both palletized and palletless loads. It uses special forks that can be switched from a horizontal to a vertical position. In a normal position, they are used for handling pallets. When rotated 90°, the fork carriage becomes a clamp and can handle such loads as boxes, crates, and bales.

MECHANICAL ATTACHMENTS

There are mechanical attachments that can be installed directly on the forks or carriage of a lift truck. Among these mechanical devices are rams, scoops, booms, crane arms, and drum handlers.

The variety of mechanical attachments is almost limitless. Some of the attachments offered are: die handlers, glass pack handlers, appliance stackers, concrete pipe handlers, tire handlers, vacuum paper roll handlers, fork extensions, maintenance platforms, scales, sweepers, empty container handlers, snow plows, log handlers, boat forks, scrap handlers, and concrete forks.

All of these attachments are standard products. Lift truck users should discuss their handling problems with their dealers. If there are no standard attachments that can be modified to meet a specific need, a custom attachment can usually be designed.

POWERED WALKIE LIFT TRUCKS

Battery-powered walkie lift trucks are primarily designed for moving, storing, and retrieving material on pallets or skids. These trucks are controlled by an operator who walks along with the truck, either beside it or behind it.

With load capacities of up to 8,000 lb (3,629 kg) and lifting heights up to 16 ft (5 m), they offer an economical alternative to rider-type trucks in a wide range of material handling applications.

The situations where walkies can provide efficient performance are characterized by one or more of the following conditions:

- Single shift operation, or multishift where facilities are available for changing batteries.
- Intermittent-duty: the truck is used half of the time or less.
- Indoor usage over smooth, level floors.
- Multistory buildings where floor load or elevator load limits prohibit the use of heavier rider trucks.
- Relatively short travel distances, usually within a radius of 125 ft (38 m).
- Highly congested or heavily populated areas, where their slower movement and added maneuverability make walkies safer than rider-type trucks.
- Transporting in-process material or storing finished goods where load and lift requirements do not exceed 4,000 lb (1,814 kg) and 16 ft (5 m) respectively.
- On shipping and receiving docks, for rapidly loading and unloading transports of up to 6,000 lb (2,722 kg) each.

From a performance standpoint, many material handling jobs can be handled equally well by either a walkie or a rider truck. In such situations, the truck with the lowest lifetime operating expense should be selected.

ECONOMICS

In deciding whether to purchase an electric-powered, sit-down, counterbalanced lift truck or an electric-powered walkie, initial cost should be a consideration. Walkies typically cost about half as much as riders of equal load capacity. Two walkies can be purchased for the price of a single rider truck, which provides added flexibility in work scheduling and eliminates work interruptions caused by the unavailability of a lift truck.

Fuel is another cost consideration. Most walkie trucks will consume about 50% less electricity than a comparably-sized electric rider because walkies use 12-V batteries while the rider trucks use 24- or 36-V systems.

A third part of the overall cost picture is operator expense. A rider truck may require a full-time operator who has no other assignment but to drive the truck. Powered walkie trucks, however, usually do not require a full-time operator. Any production worker can be trained to operate this machine as needed.

Finally, weight and maneuverability also affect overall lift truck costs. A smaller, more maneuverable truck can help economize on valuable floor space in a plant or warehouse, and walkies are typically half the length and two-thirds the width of riders. This allows walkies to operate with a greater margin of safety in narrow aisles and cramped production areas. Narrower pallets or containers can be used. Walkies are also lighter than riders, so they consume less power. In multistory buildings, weight restrictions often make walkies the only viable choice, especially if freight elevators are involved.

MAINTENANCE FACTORS

Powered walkies can save maintenance dollars because their basic design and simple componentry allow quick, easy servicing in the shop. This work can be done by trained maintenance personnel. Moreover, walkie parts are more easily stocked so less downtime is spent waiting for parts on order. Since there are fewer parts to replace on a walkie, the spare parts inventory is reduced.

TYPES

There are three basic types of powered walkie lift trucks: counterbalanced, straddle, and low-lift. Many hybrid designs have evolved for special applications, but these three are still the most fundamental.

CHAPTER 8   FLEXIBLE WHEELED HANDLING EQUIPMENT

- *Straddle walkies* have structural extensions (or straddle legs) mounted parallel to and outside of the forks. This puts the truck's center of gravity directly beneath the load (see Fig. 8-6).
- *Counterbalanced models* balance the load and carriage by adding length and weight to the truck body (see Fig. 8-7). A typical 2,500-lb (1,134-kg) capacity counterbalanced walkie may be nearly twice as long and two and a half times as heavy as a similar straddle model.
- *Low-lift powered walkies* are similar to the nonpowered hydraulic hand pallet truck (see Fig. 8-8). The tips of the forks are tapered for easy pallet entry. Wide load wheels are mounted on a linkage mechanism in the fork tips and are raised and lowered by the mechanical links terminating at the hydraulic lift cylinder. The load is supported at three or more points, including the drive wheel. Typically, the forks are long enough to drive through a double-sided pallet. A fold-down frame is sometimes used to add height to the forks for handling skids or skid-base containers.

SELECTION

In general, high-lift straddle walkies are the best choice for narrow-aisle operations. They cost about 20% less than comparable counterbalanced units. But the size of the pallets they can lift is limited to the distance between the straddles.

For applications where various pallet sizes are encountered, a counterbalanced, high-lift walkie offers versatility. If no stacking is to be done, the low-lift is best suited for load shuttle moves, and capacity ranges can be higher than high-lift straddle or counterbalanced models. So, selecting the right type of walkie for the job at hand involves careful consideration of these trade-offs.

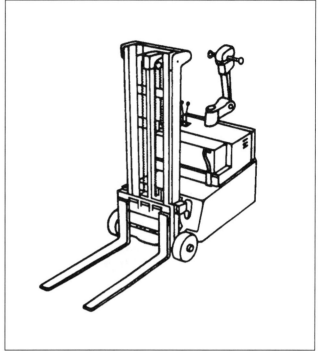

Fig. 8-7 Counterbalanced walkie truck. *(Courtesy "Material Handling Engineering")*

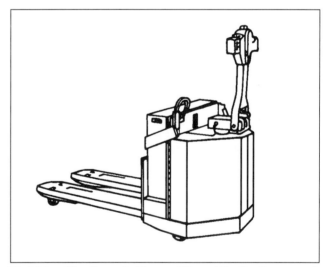

Fig. 8-8 Low-lift pallet truck. *(Courtesy "Material Handling Engineering")*

TWO-WHEEL HAND TRUCKS

One of the most useful and popular pieces of nonpowered, material handling equipment is the two-wheel hand truck. Like a counterbalanced lift truck, this device is also a lever, with wheels used for moving material too heavy or awkward to be hand-carried and too light or small to involve the use of an expensive piece of powered equipment.

Applications for the two-wheel hand truck can be found in every manufacturing and warehousing operation. The truck's cost is low

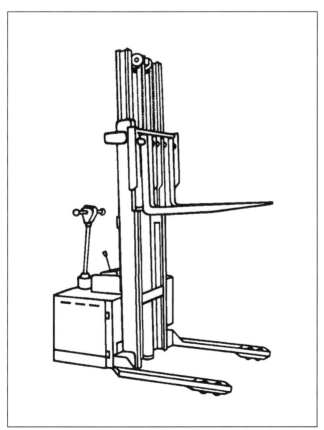

Fig. 8-6 Straddle truck. *(Courtesy "Material Handling Engineering")*

CHAPTER 8   FLEXIBLE WHEELED HANDLING EQUIPMENT

and its maintenance requirements are minimal. These trucks are highly suitable if:

- The cube (area displacement) and weight of the load fits the capabilities of the truck and the operator.
- Travel distances are relatively short (platform trucks are recommended for longer runs).
- Volume and frequency of runs are low.
- Building or terrain limitations (such as narrow doors, ramps, stairs, etc.) preclude the use of other types of equipment.

TERMINOLOGY

A common nomenclature applies to all standard two-wheel hand trucks regardless of size, class, or style. The basic parts are: handles, axle, axle brackets, wheels, nose, frame, leg, and leg braces.

In older style wood and steel two-wheel hand trucks there were two styles, Eastern and Western style. They were differentiated largely by the shape of the handles. The *Eastern style* generally has a tapered frame with wheels located outside of the frame. It has curved or flat cross members and usually has straight handles. The *Western style* hand truck had parallel frame rails with wheels mounted inboard and flat or curved cross members and curved handles. Very few of these trucks are produced today. Most modern two-wheel hand trucks have extruded or tubular frames and a variety of handle and frame styles.

HAND TRUCK TYPES

There are a number of different types of hand trucks that are frequently used in factory and warehouse settings.

- *Utility trucks* are light, inexpensive, general purpose trucks for handling lightweight or awkwardly-shaped materials (see Figs. 8-9, 8-10, and 8-11). Design variations abound and each manufacturer may produce several models. Steel, aluminum, magnesium, and wood are the most widely-used hand truck materials. Several types of one- and two-handle designs are made. Frames are of varied construction, from square tube to channel or flat metal. The prime concern is that these trucks must be lightweight to minimize user fatigue.
- *Warehouse trucks* are designed for the heaviest service. The nose is usually reinforced with extra longitudinal straps permitting secure handling of heavier loads. The frames are of

Fig. 8-10 General magnesium-construction utility truck with a solid nose plate and curved rest for handling square or round loads. Extending ears protect load from wheels. *(Courtesy "Material Handling Engineering")*

Fig. 8-11 Special utility truck with aluminum channel construction. This folding type handles 500-lb (227-kg) loads, collapses to 13 in. (33 cm), and extends to 44 in. (112 cm). *(Courtesy "Material Handling Engineering")*

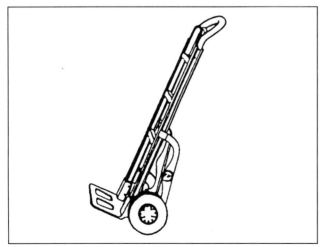

Fig. 8-9 General utility two-wheel hand truck made of lightweight magnesium with large pneumatic or semipneumatic tires, stair skids, and tubular handle. *(Courtesy "Material Handling Engineering")*

CHAPTER 8   FLEXIBLE WHEELED HANDLING EQUIPMENT

wood- and steel-bolted construction and the noses are of forged steel. Warehouse trucks are available in both Eastern- and Western-styles.

- *Barrel or drum trucks* have short prongs instead of a full nose and most of them have a special hook mechanism that attaches to the top chime of the barrel (see Fig. 8-12). Others have chains or straps to secure the barrel to the handle. Many of these trucks have a floating axle design that aids in tilting the load back and moves the balance point back, easing the load stress on the user.
- *Cotton trucks* can be either Eastern- or Western-style designs, and are of conventional configuration with one exception. Instead of a nose, they have short, tapered prongs that dig into the bale instead of under it.
- *Bag trucks* may be of either Eastern- or Western-style designs (see Fig. 8-13). The distinguishing feature is the design length of the nose. Various designs, from a basic elongated open nose to spatula shapes, are common. All are designed for handling different bagged materials.
- *Grain trucks* are standard Eastern-style trucks with a longer nose and wheel guards. These guards are welded to the frame and prevent the wheels from damaging sacks of material. The ends of the axles are usually covered with hubcaps or made in such a manner to prevent snagging of the sacks.
- *Cylinder trucks* are unlike any of the trucks already mentioned (see Fig. 8-14). They are used for carrying welding cylinders and have large wheels to negotiate rough terrain. They have a right-angle plate nose, a chain for holding the cylinders on the truck, and usually have a tool tray mounted between the handles for welding tips, torches, etc.

SPECIAL DESIGNS

Adaptations of the basic two-wheel hand truck were made for unique loads to be moved. *Appliance trucks*, for example, have short noses, extended handles, a web belt, and a ratchet for securing the load, and most have roller bearing-type, stair-climbing devices. Some are equipped with a balance frame and casters so the load can be rolled easily in the tilted position.

Lifting hand trucks have a large platform nose that can lift the load to preferred heights by hydraulic or mechanical devices. They are useful for transferring loads from floor level to a work table.

Another hand truck design is used expressly for hauling 5-gal (19-L) pails (see Fig. 8-15). The nose is of a special design that engages the ridge under the top chime of the pail resting on the floor. This enables the user to carry from one to four pails without wrestling them onto a standard nose.

Another specially-designed utility truck incorporates a set of casters and a fold-out push handle, turning the hand truck into a four-wheel floor truck (see Fig. 8-16). This convertible design permits

Fig. 8-13 Slat frame, Western-style bag truck with malleable iron nose plate has no sharp bends or corners and is able to handle irregular items. *(Courtesy "Material Handling Engineering")*

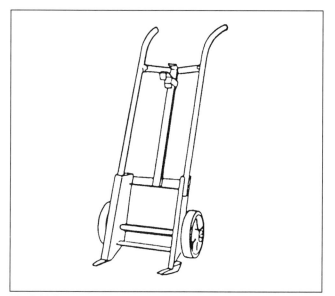

Fig. 8-12 Steel construction drum and barrel truck with small chime hooks for easy chisel-under and pick up, and a top chime hook. *(Courtesy "Material Handling Engineering")*

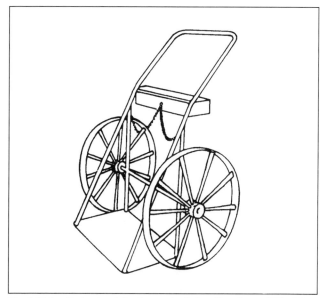

Fig. 8-14 A cylinder truck has large wheels to roll easily on difficult terrain and a tool box mounted between the handles for welding tips, torches, and accessories. *(Courtesy "Material Handling Engineering")*

CHAPTER 8   FLEXIBLE WHEELED HANDLING EQUIPMENT

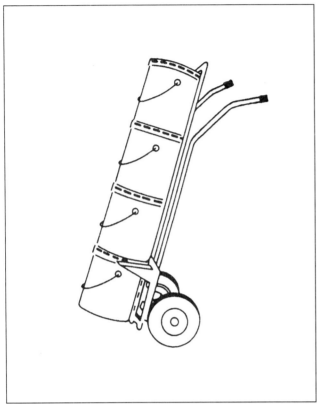

Fig. 8-15 A pail truck can handle 500 lb (227 kg) on 10-in. (25-cm) semipneumatic tires. *(Courtesy "Material Handling Engineering")*

Fig. 8-16 Handle pulls out of side tubes and fits upright into tubular pockets on swivel wheel end of truck to make a hand platform combination truck with 800-lb (363-kg) capacity. *(Courtesy "Material Handling Engineering")*

two-in-one versatility for handling loads that are slightly heavier and higher in cube.

WHEEL SELECTION

There are several types of wheels available for use on two-wheel hand trucks. Careful selection of wheels should include such considerations as flotation, size, tread composition, and types of surfaces on which the truck will be used.

Depending on these considerations, the truck wheels could be of the molded on, metal, plastic, or hard rubber types. Semipneumatic and full pneumatic tires are also available.

Even on hand trucks, tire wear is a problem. Neoprene could be used where chemical or petroleum contamination of rubber would lead to rapid deterioration or wear. Polyurethane wheels show excellent wear resistance, and some compositions are chosen because they do not mark floors.

WEIGHT AND BEARINGS

The capacity of two-wheel hand trucks varies. They may carry 1,000 lb (454 kg) or more, but this is not to say that any one person can manage this much weight safely. Once the truck is tipped and the weight shifts toward the operator, it can become dangerous. Even 500 lb (227 kg) can become unmanageable, and certainly it would be dangerous to move heavy weights up and down ramps or steps.

The capacity of certain wheels can limit the uses of the hand truck. Hand trucks can be overloaded and overworked, and heavy loads can break welds or bend structural members. Bearings should be incorporated in the wheel if overloading is more than occasionally encountered.

Bearings used in the wheels could be ball, roller, or plain bushing type. Except in extremely light-duty applications, ball or roller bearings are recommended. If these antifriction bearings are used, the balls or rollers are hardened and can take more stress than the plain bearing.

ATTACHMENTS

Extra devices added to the basic two-wheel hand truck can increase its usefulness. Simple options may enable these trucks to do double duty in some instances.

- Height extensions, when attached to the upper handles, increase the handling capacity of the truck for light, high-cube loads.
- Barrel forks can be used on some hand truck models, especially those with curved cross members. These forks are folding cradle-type attachments fixed to the top cross members of the truck. They keep the barrel contained within the handles and prevent it from rocking.
- Safety brakes fit the frame and stop the wheels. The user can step on a bar and lock the wheels as an aid in tilting the load. Some specialty trucks have hand brakes to aid in stair climbing.
- Center straps, running longitudinally between the handles, also increase the usefulness of hand trucks. They prevent small cartons from falling through the handles. In some cases, the strap can be integrated with the nose for added strength. This is particularly true of the warehouse truck used for moving very heavy dies and castings.

WORKER PREFERENCES

Years ago, the basic warehouse truck was the ideal means of moving small amounts of material quickly. It was sufficient for its time, and using it was easier than hand-carrying the load. Weight was of little consequence and fatigue was not a consideration.

Today, workers favor lighter-weight trucks made of aluminum and magnesium alloys. These trucks have the same strength as the old heavyweight devices and are less demanding to use, because the

CHAPTER 8   FLEXIBLE WHEELED HANDLING EQUIPMENT

total load (truck plus the product) is less tiring on the worker. Moreover, the harder wheels used with the right floor conditions offer very little start-up resistance, further easing total work effort.

HAND PALLET TRUCKS

The *hydraulic hand pallet truck*, also referred to as a *pallet jack*, represents the most elementary and economical device that, when used with a reasonable degree of manual effort, can effectively lift, transport, and deposit heavy palletized loads (see Figs. 8-17 and 8-18).

This truck enables an operator to lift a palletized load a maximum of about 5 in. (13 cm) off the floor via a manually-actuated pump and hydraulically-powered lifting mechanism. Once raised, the pallet may be manually pulled or pushed to a desired location.

The truck consists of a frame; steering handle and grip; pallet entry forks; hydraulic pump with raise and lower mechanism; mechanical lifting mechanism; steering wheels; load wheels; and entry/exit assisting wheels, rollers, or metal skid runners.

The hydraulic hand truck has been used to some degree in the U.S. since around 1935. The first ones were all mechanical and handled skids, not pallets. Today, these trucks are available in load-carrying capacities of from 2,500-4,500 lb (1,134-2,041 kg). In fact, many of the top trucks have such large, built-in safety factors that they can handle loads in excess of 4,500 lb (2,041 kg). However, it is important to note that a 4,500-lb (2,041-kg) load is extremely difficult to push or pull manually. Thus, the hand pallet truck is safer and more efficient when carrying loads well below its capability.

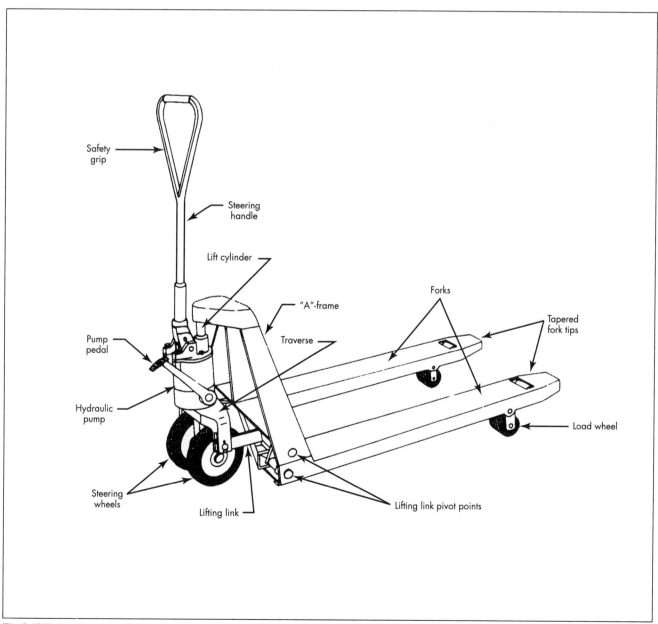

Fig. 8-17 Hydraulic hand pallet truck. *(Courtesy "Material Handling Engineering")*

CHAPTER 8 FLEXIBLE WHEELED HANDLING EQUIPMENT

FORK DIMENSIONS

Forks are available on a standard basis in many popular lengths, widths, and spreads. Less common fork dimensions are usually available on a custom basis. The two most popular fork spreads are 22 in. (56 cm) and 27 in. (69 cm), and the most popular fork lengths are 41 in. (104 cm) and 48 in. (122 cm). The most frequently used configuration is 27-in. (69-cm) wide and 48-in. (122-cm) long.

WHEELS

Most pallet trucks have two 8-in. (20-cm) steer wheels and one 3.25-in. (8-cm) load wheel (roller) under each fork. They can be specified with a variety of wheel materials and hardness, depending on user preference and floor conditions.

Generally, steel wheels or rollers are the easiest to pull, but they are the hardest on floors, especially concrete and tile. Nylon steering wheels are the next easiest to roll and the easiest to steer, particularly with heavy loads. The most commonly used wheel tread material is polyurethane. It is the third easiest material to roll, is long-lasting, resists flat spots, and is impervious to oils and caustic liquids.

The choice of wheels depends on the condition of the plant floor, the weights and loads to be carried, and the severity of the work environment. As a general rule, it should be kept in mind that hand pallet trucks require relatively smooth floors for easy rolling.

PALLET ENTRY DEVICES

It is important to choose a hand pallet truck that enters the pallet with ease and without damage to the pallet deckboards. To preclude this problem, pallet entry devices can be located at the tip of the forks, directly in front of the load rollers. They can be welded metal runners, canted disks, and nylon or polyurethane wheels or rollers.

MAINTENANCE

Hand pallet trucks are designed to require minimum maintenance. Due mainly to their simplicity of design and function, these trucks are usually trouble-free with a working life of up to 20 years or more. Barring gross abuse, the component that would most likely need occasional repair would be the hydraulic pump. Most seal replacement and minor repairs can be done at the user's facility. In the case of a major failure, most dealers offer a pump exchange program.

Most standard trucks use permanently-sealed and lubricated wheel bearings that require no servicing.

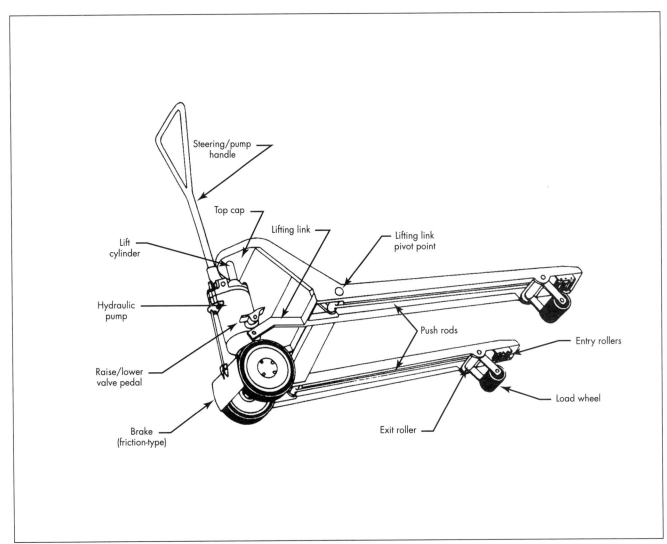

Fig. 8-18 Hydraulic hand pallet truck. *(Courtesy "Material Handling Engineering")*

CHAPTER 8   FLEXIBLE WHEELED HANDLING EQUIPMENT

The hand pallet truck frame is available in painted steel, stainless and galvanized, or plated finishes. These are used when trucks must be steam- or water-cleaned or are susceptible to chemical attack.

APPLICATIONS

There is no cheaper way to effectively handle a unit load than with a hydraulic hand pallet truck. It can be found in industries of all types and in operations of all sizes. Pallet trucks are designed to move relatively light loads horizontally, but have been known to handle heavy ones in places such as grocery stores. They are used most productively when trips are limited to light loads over short hauls. Hand pallet trucks interface well with fleets of electric- or engine-powered lift trucks, freeing the more expensive units for long hauls of heavy loads that require stacking and unstacking. For example, on the production floor, machine operators often need to reposition containers of finished or semifinished parts and assemblies. It is neither productive nor economical to have to wait for an available lift truck or to have a lift truck waiting around for such an assignment. The hand pallet truck is made-to-order for this type of work. Hand pallet trucks also work well on the loading dock where their ability to raise the load over 5 in. (13 cm) allows them to clear the crown on dockboards at the point of trailer contact.

FLOOR TRUCKS

In many applications, material can be moved most efficiently and economically with nonpowered equipment. Among the most popular of such equipment are floor or platform trucks and trailers, which can be either manually propelled or pulled by a tow tractor (see Fig. 8-19). Basically, these are trucks with a load-carrying platform with four or six casters or wheels. An application may be best handled by a platform truck or a trailer if:

• Travel distances are short; a towed trailer is better for longer runs.
• Few maintenance requirements are desired.

• A load is awkward or hard-to-handle.
• Volume is low.
• A vehicle must be tied up with the load.
• Building limitations may not allow the use of heavier or bigger equipment.
• The handling equipment will be used for live storage or display.
• Low-cost flexibility is required.

Platform and trailer trucks find wide usage in manufacturing, warehousing, and shipping operations. They are often used in production areas, moving materials among workstations, from production line to storage, or to the shipping dock. In addition, they can be used for order picking and to supply assembly lines with component parts.

Trailers, which are commonly propelled along a towline by tractor or overhead conveyor, are an economical means of moving materials longer distances. Often, trailers not being towed have the added advantage of being maneuvered manually so they can be brought close to a workstation.

RUNNING GEAR

Perhaps the most important part of the floor truck is the running gear, consisting of the wheels, casters, axles, and mountings. This running gear may be either the nontilt or balance-tilt variety.

The *nontilt floor truck* is equipped with two swivel casters at the push handle end, and two larger load wheels (or two rigid casters), usually mounted on an axle, at the other end.

Balance-tilt trucks have two, slightly larger, fixed wheels mounted on an axle midway in the length of the truck. With swivel casters at both ends, the truck turns around its exact center, and can turn in its own length. The caster wheels under the greater load bear on the floor. The truck is easy to maneuver in tight places and it can be tilted to clear door sills and other obstructions.

WHEEL SELECTION

An important consideration when buying a floor truck is wheel selection. Always select the largest diameter wheel feasible in an application, because it will roll more easily and provide the greatest load capacity. On the other hand, while large-diameter wheels are

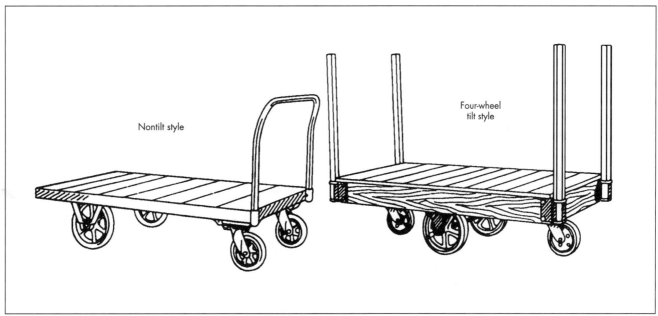

Fig. 8-19 Two styles of floor trucks. *(Courtesy "Material Handling Engineering")*

CHAPTER 8 FLEXIBLE WHEELED HANDLING EQUIPMENT

desirable, it is also important to keep the deck of the truck as close to the floor as possible. This will keep the center of gravity low to the ground and make the truck more stable and safe.

Other factors to consider in choosing wheels suited to the application are: relative capacity; quiet operation; floor protection; shock absorption or resilience; oil, chemicals, and dilute acid resistance; and relative cost.

FRAMES

The most commonly-used material for frames is steel. The all-welded steel frame is less expensive to manufacture, makes a stronger truck, and is maintenance-free.

Some truck frames are made of hardwood. These frames are generally joined together at the corners with nuts and bolts, which can eventually work loose and require maintenance. Wood frame members will crack on impact, while steel members will bend. The wood frame truck is best suited for loads under 2,000 lb (907 kg).

Aluminum or stainless steel frames are also available for applications where sanitary conditions must be maintained through frequent steam cleaning. They also may be desired because of their light weight.

DECKS

Like the frame, the deck can be made of steel, aluminum, or wood. The deck on a steel frame truck is designed to be flush inside the frame. On a wood frame truck, the deck is nailed on top of the hardwood frame, sometimes with a slight overhang along the sides.

Hardwoods are often chosen for durability and, where required, are finished with paint or varnish. Wood decks are the most popular for several reasons:

- Strength.
- Will not scratch most loads.
- Resistant to impact damage.
- Not subject to attack by most corrosive atmospheres, compounds, or fluids.
- Resistant to sliding.
- Easy to repair if damaged.

Steel decks are used when a smooth surface is needed, especially for sliding loads on and off. Some steel decks are made of nonskid or diamond plate. But they are noisier than wood and will usually dent when subjected to sharp impact. The advantages of metal or steel decks include:

- Will not expand or contract on exposure to dry heat or excessive moisture.
- More attractive and, with fewer cracks and crevices, are easier to keep clean than wooden decks.

SIZE AND CAPACITY

There are many styles, models, and sizes of floor trucks available to fit any appropriate material handling task. In standard sizes, the smaller units measure about 24-in. (61-cm) wide by 48-in. (122-cm) long. The largest standard truck is about 48-in. (122-cm) wide by 96-in. (244-cm) long. Generally, size increases in increments of 6 in. (15 cm).

For nontrailer trucks, load capacities range from about 500-5,000 lb (227-2,268 kg) and capacities of trailer-type trucks can reach 20,000 lb (9,072 kg) or more.

There has been a tendency, in recent years, to go to lighter-duty floor trucks. While the 5,000-lb (2,268-kg) truck was popular, it is difficult to move by hand.

Not only are more trucks sold in lighter weights, but greater attention is being paid to the rollability of wheels and casters. Be-

cause starting resistance on smooth concrete floors with molded-on rubber wheels is about 40 lb/short ton (20 kg/metric ton), including the weight of the truck, users are specifying harder types of wheels—such as plastic and polyurethane—that are easier to push. For optimum rollability, rubber-tired truck capacities should be reduced by about 50%, a desirable load for manual pushing.

FLEET MANAGEMENT

One to three or more brands and styles of fork lift trucks is called a *fleet*. To keep these vehicles available for work, they must be managed when they work and when they break down. This falls under the purview of fleet management, which involves:

- Selecting equipment.
- Purchasing, renting, or leasing equipment.
- Maintaining equipment.
- Scheduling internal and external equipment maintenance.
- Operator training—the trained operator does most of the day-to-day maintenance that keeps the truck running.

The past decade has seen lift trucks attain new levels of productivity. State-of-the-art machines in use today feature efficient fuel systems, sophisticated electronics, operator-friendly controls, and ergonomic cab designs. These advances mean greater efficiency at reduced life-cycle cost.

To achieve maximum benefit from this equipment, industrial truck owners must utilize the best techniques in fleet management. Their goal must be to maximize the return-on-investment to get the greatest possible production from the money spent on purchase, operation, and maintenance of the fleet. Companies that manage their fleets with this goal in mind can save a lot of money. However, such companies are in the minority.

Industry sources say many lift truck users pay up to twice as much as they should to operate and maintain their fleets. For example, it has been estimated that almost one quarter of the more than one million lift trucks in use in the U.S. are operated beyond their economic lives, with another one quarter approaching economic obsolescence (see Fig. 8-20).[4]

It also has been estimated that U.S. companies could save more than $1 billion per year by replacing their trucks at the end of their economic life cycle. Clearly, better lift truck fleet management can help a company boost profits and gain a competitive edge.

Effective fleet management starts with the involvement of everyone who deals with lift trucks: financial managers, purchasing agents, material handling and manufacturing engineers, maintenance staff, and vehicle operators, as well as the material handling equipment dealers who sell and service these fleets.

STANDARDIZING THE LIFT TRUCK FLEET

Lift truck cost control begins with fleet standardization. Today, more than 90% of lift truck-owning companies operate fleets containing multiple makes and models of trucks, often with different fuel systems.

Mixed fleets are often a consequence of buying equipment strictly on price, and ignoring other important factors. The short-term benefits of price-shopping are soon dwarfed by the long-term costs of maintaining an assortment of vehicles. A company can save 12-21% (16% on average) on parts and labor alone by sticking with one or two manufacturers and fuel types.

CHAPTER 8   FLEXIBLE WHEELED HANDLING EQUIPMENT

Fleet standardization saves in several ways:

- It reduces parts inventory. A mixed fleet requires a mixed inventory of spare parts ranging from hoses, belts, and filters to expensive starters, alternators, and water pumps from various different lift truck suppliers. For a large fleet, standardization can cut the value of parts inventory tremendously.
- It saves labor. Maintenance personnel are more productive if they can concentrate on one type of truck.
- It reduces accidents and boosts output. Operators spend less time learning different sets of controls and can react immediately and instinctively in situations calling for quick stops or maneuvers. This saves on training, too.
- It adds pricing leverage. Dealers and manufacturers may offer substantial discounts for large fleet purchases.

Although the case for fleet standardization is compelling, some lift truck users resist it for fear of depending on one source. For such companies, a workable alternative is to buy 90% of their lift trucks from one manufacturer and 10% from another, while still standardizing on one fuel system. This arrangement provides most of the benefits of pure standardization, while keeping both suppliers competitive on pricing and service.

TRACKING FLEET MAINTENANCE COSTS

Over the life of a lift truck, maintenance costs can account for more than twice the purchase price. Yet, some 85% of lift truck-owning companies do not know the maintenance costs of the brands of trucks they buy (see Fig. 8-21).[5]

Furthermore, 95% fail to routinely record the three kinds of information they need to track their expenses: labor costs, parts costs, and lift truck hour meter readings. Consequently, fewer than 5% know their maintenance costs per operating hour by truck. Without that information, it is impossible to manage fleet expenses.

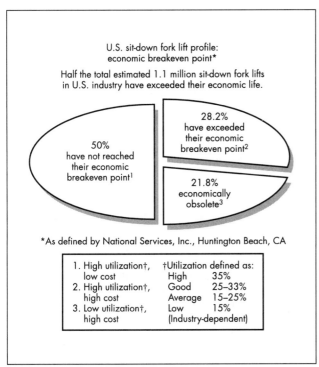

U.S. sit-down fork lift profile:
economic breakeven point*

Half the total estimated 1.1 million sit-down fork lifts in U.S. industry have exceeded their economic life.

28.2% have exceeded their economic breakeven point[2]

50% have not reached their economic breakeven point[1]

21.8% economically obsolete[3]

*As defined by National Services, Inc., Huntington Beach, CA

		†Utilization defined as:	
1. High utilization†, low cost		High	35%
2. High utilization†, high cost		Good	25–33%
		Average	15–25%
3. Low utilization†, high cost		Low	15%
		(Industry-dependent)	

Fig. 8-20 Sit-down fork lifts in use in the U.S.: economic breakeven point.
(Courtesy Nissan Fork Lift Corp., N. America)

Companies that develop good maintenance cost data gain a powerful decision-making tool that can help them:

- Budget accurately for spare parts and labor.
- Fine-tune scheduled maintenance programs.
- Allocate trucks cost-effectively, by using units with low hourly cost for the bulk of the work, while reserving those with high expense for sporadic duty.
- Anticipate when a truck is no longer economical to operate, and therefore, replace rather than repair it.

Data gathering involves nothing more than fitting each truck with an accurate hour meter and recording parts costs, labor costs, and the hour meter reading at each maintenance interval. With these data available, it is easy to track each truck's accumulated maintenance cost per hour. This, in turn, becomes a potent tool for making sound repair or replace decisions.

WHEN TO REPLACE TRUCKS

There are several erroneous rules of thumb for replacing lift trucks that are often followed:

- Replace after seven years.
- Replace at 10,000 operating hours.
- Replace when annual maintenance cost equals resale value.

Following these rules can cause companies to waste money because they may trade a truck in too soon and give up low-cost operating hours, or they may trade too late and spend excessively for maintenance and repairs.

Rules of thumb fail because they are not rooted in an objective, site-specific analysis. It is hard for fleet managers to gain approval for new purchases without solid cost justification. Yet, only 3% of companies have formal fork lift replacement programs.

Lift truck maintenance and repair costs escalate as trucks age. An engine-powered truck is relatively low cost to maintain in its first year. But by the seventh year, maintenance costs may increase 10 times, and by the eighth year, 20 times—nearly 40% of the price of a new unit.

A planned replacement program helps the fleet manager replace trucks before they become money losers. One widely-used method utilizes a company's own maintenance cost data to locate each truck's economic breakeven point.

The *breakeven point* is the time in a truck's life cycle when it reaches its lowest total cost per hour, which is the sum total of ownership cost per hour (as shown in Eq. 8-1). Beyond the breakeven point, the truck becomes a drain on profits (see Fig. 8-22).

$$B_{ep} = \frac{\Sigma_0}{h_{op}}$$
(1)

where:

B_{ep} = breakeven point
Σ_0 = purchase price minus resale or scrap value
h_{op} = hours of operation

The fleet manager who knows how to calculate the end of a truck's economic life can cut maintenance costs, trim fleet size, and use operator time more productively.

LIFT TRUCK SELECTION

The maintenance cost of a lift truck is largely decided the moment it arrives on site. There are two reasons for this.

First, there are marked differences in quality and performance among models. Data suggest that ICE lift truck maintenance costs may differ by as much as 38% from one model to another at the economic breakeven point.[6]

CHAPTER 8   FLEXIBLE WHEELED HANDLING EQUIPMENT

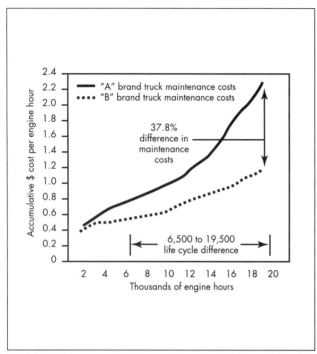

Fig. 8-21 Maintenance costs. *(Courtesy Nissan Fork Lift Corp., N. America)*

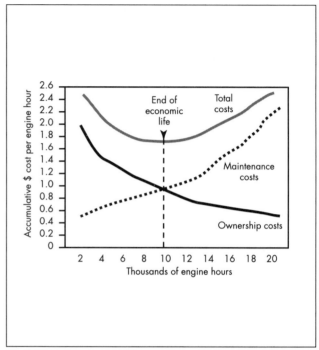

Fig. 8-22 Breakeven point. *(Courtesy Nissan Fork Lift Corp., N. America)*

But maintenance costs also depend on how well the truck fits the application. A truck that has inadequate capacity, or is otherwise ill-suited to its workplace, will break down early and often and spend too much time in the shop.

Before standardizing on a make, model, and fuel system, the fleet manager should conduct a thorough site survey with help from an experienced material handling equipment dealer familiar with the company's industry and the specific application.

The analysis should cover every aspect of the operation including, but not limited to:

• Type, weight, and dimensions of loads.
• Maximum loads to be handled.
• Maximum lifting heights.
• Typical travel distances.
• Height of lowest overhead obstructions.
• Narrowest aisle widths.
• Maneuvering requirements, if any, inside transports.
• Indoor or outdoor operation, or both.
• Number of shifts trucks will operate each day.
• Number of loads trucks will handle each shift.
• Environment, including air quality, temperature, and potentially explosive agents.
• Floor surfaces (smooth, semi-improved, woodblock, asphalt, gravel) and their load-bearing capacities.

A thorough site survey will point to a true material handling solution: a truck, fuel system, tires, attachments and accessories, and even operator training, that provide the most productive operation and reduced life-cycle cost.

MAINTENANCE

There are no more crucial factors in the performance and longevity of industrial trucks than the care with which these machines are operated and the level of preventive maintenance that they receive.

Lift trucks are among the most rugged and reliable of machines. They are designed to operate under the most punishing conditions and provide years of reliable service. They do not have to be babied, but they do have to be regularly serviced.

Regardless of how well-built they are, the only way to get the most out of them and to operate a thrifty fleet, is through a planned program of preventive maintenance. Preventive maintenance is meant to prevent future, serious, costly repairs. Minimal or improper maintenance will inevitably lead to unscheduled downtime, costly, unnecessary repairs, and premature retirement of a vehicle.

A U.S. material handling research study revealed that the number one concern of lift truck owners and users was having better service and parts support for their equipment.[7] Purchase decisions, they said, were based not only on product quality and price, but equally on the buyer's confidence that the dealer would support its products with first class service and prompt availability of replacement parts. Lift truck users cannot tolerate excessive downtime. A nonoperating fork lift truck means lost productivity, idle workers, and perhaps, lost business.

There is no substitute for good maintenance:

• It keeps trucks performing at optimum levels.
• It can detect and rectify minor problems before they affect productivity.
• It will prolong the productive life of a truck.

Lift truck manufacturers know this, and all the major firms provide maintenance services through their dealer networks. An effective maintenance program is designed to match the kind of work performed by the truck, that is, more frequently for trucks performing demanding jobs in hostile environments, less frequently for lighter applications in cleaner conditions.

A maintenance schedule should specify tasks to be performed daily, monthly, quarterly, semi-annually, and annually.

Daily maintenance should be performed by the truck operator. This is a simple procedure he or she can perform at the beginning of

CHAPTER 8   FLEXIBLE WHEELED HANDLING EQUIPMENT

each shift, taking only a few minutes. The operator should visually inspect for leaks and obvious damage, tire condition, and the operation of safety lights, service and parking brakes, horn, and steering. He or she should then check mast operation by raising and lowering the forks both with and without a load, and finally check the levels of engine oil, fuel, radiator water, and hydraulic fluid. (On an electric truck, the oil, fuel, and water check is replaced with a battery check.) Any deficiencies detected should be reported.

Monthly maintenance (after every 200 hours of operation) is performed by a trained mechanic and includes:

- Lubrication of chassis and mast components.
- Replacement of engine oil.
- Cleaning of the air filter element.
- Adjustment of engine idle speed and ignition timing on engine-powered trucks.
- Inspection of lift and tilt cylinder operation, drive belt tension, and, for engine-powered trucks, spark plugs, distributor point, cap, and rotor.

Quarterly maintenance (every 600 hours) includes:

- Inspection of pedal free play, hand brake, lift chain tension, mast operation, carriage rollers, lift and tilt cylinder operation, hydraulic oil pump, differential and transmission oil, fuel filter, positive crankcase ventilation (PCV) valve, and hoses on engine-powered trucks.
- Cleaning the radiator exterior and replacing the fuel filter.
- Replacement of the hydraulic filter.
- Draining of the water separator on diesel trucks.
- Adjustment of intake and exhaust valve clearances.
- Lubrication of the clutch release bearing (standard shift trucks), mast support bushing, tilt cylinder pins, and chassis links.

Semi-annual maintenance (every 1,200 hours) includes:

- Inspection of mast rollers and testing of battery electrolyte.
- Replacement of torque converter and transmission oil, hydraulic oil, the hydraulic oil filter, and the air cleaner element.
- Cleaning of the transmission filter.

Annual maintenance (every 2,400 hours) includes:

- Inspection of the brake booster operation.
- Cleaning the inside of the distributor.
- Torquing the engine head bolts and manifold nuts.
- Replacement of brake fluid, wheel bearing grease, engine coolant, fuel filter, fuel strainer element, and water separator on diesel trucks.

Careful attention also must be paid to the forks. As they wear, they lose strength. It is important to measure fork wear annually in normal, one-shift operations, and more frequently in multishift and severe applications. Forks should be replaced when wear reaches 10% of its original thickness. Such a reduction in fork thickness reduces lifting capacity safety by 20%. This wear cannot be detected with the naked eye. Fortunately, an inexpensive caliper for making this measurement is available from most lift truck dealers.

The importance of this fork inspection cannot be over emphasized. For example, a lift truck with a rated load capacity of 3,000 lb (1,361 kg), with forks worn by 10%, can safely lift only 2,400 lb (1,089 kg). Lifting a 3,000-lb (1,361-kg) load could lead to a serious accident.

Clearly, adherence to a maintenance program like this will help keep a lift truck in good condition, prolong its useful life, and minimize downtime and costs associated with major repairs. Refer to Chapter 6 of this handbook for more information on maintenance.

Cutting the Cost of Maintenance

Plants with sizeable fleets will have maintenance personnel on staff who can perform all or most maintenance procedures. As long as the work gets done, it does not matter whether all or part of it is done in-plant or contracted out to a lift truck dealer. For fleet managers who wish to manage their maintenance programs via computer, software programs are available from some dealers that are designed to keep track of a broad range of maintenance data, including lift truck inventory, service histories, parts inventory, maintenance schedules, and maintenance costs, including parts and labor.

Most lift truck dealers offer preventive maintenance programs, the benefits of which include reduced in-plant parts inventory, freedom from internal maintenance scheduling and labor costs, and regular inspection by factory-trained technicians. Although these services can amount to several hundred dollars a year over the life of a lift truck, they compare favorably with the cost of replacing a poorly-maintained engine or transmission.

Under a rental and maintenance agreement, the user leases the trucks for a specified period. The dealer then adds all costs (lease payments and maintenance expenses) into a single fixed fee. Often, the term of the lease is set to match the economic life of the trucks so they are replaced at the most advantageous time in their life cycles.

For companies that service their fleets in-house, dealers experienced with a specific manufacturer's equipment can:

- Help determine maintenance schedules based on specific operating conditions.
- Investigate and solve application-specific problems with manufacturer-engineered truck modifications.
- Provide service training for company technicians.
- Recommend lists of spare parts to stock.

Fleet managers and dealers can work together to keep repair costs and unscheduled downtime to a minimum, thus ensuring the most economical management of the fleet.

CONDUCT OPERATOR TRAINING

Powered industrial trucks of all kinds require operator training. More than one hundred people are killed each year by fork lift trucks alone, and hundreds more are injured. More than 34,000 injuries per year involve fork lifts, more than 13,000 workers' compensation claims are filed annually because of fork lift accidents, and some 70-90% of fork lift accidents are caused by operator error. An untrained operator is a menace to both himself and anyone walking or working in the vicinity of a fork lift truck. More potential hazards exist in a manufacturing company, than perhaps any other environment where fork lift trucks operate.

To reduce the costs of workers' compensation, damage to loads, injury to pedestrians and other workers in and around operating lift trucks, and to protect against damage to the building structure and the vehicles, a comprehensive lift truck operation and safety training course must be developed and implemented.

Trained operators can sharply curtail lift truck accidents that can injure people and damage product and equipment. Trained operators can also extend vehicle life and reduce maintenance expenses by using lift trucks properly. For example:

- Correct brake use can extend brake life by 25%, saving up to $250 annually per truck.
- Proper procedures for backing out of truck trailers and over dockboards can prevent tire damage and reduce wear on steer axles, ball joints, and tie rods.
- Proper maintenance can extend battery life to seven years or longer, while neglected maintenance can lead to failure in one year or less.

CHAPTER 8 FLEXIBLE WHEELED HANDLING EQUIPMENT

Every lift truck driver should be trained in the basics of lift truck care and operation, including daily maintenance checks, basic operating principles, and load-handling procedures. Operators should also receive site-specific instruction tailored to the kinds of trucks they will use and the special challenges of the workplace.

A wallet card stating the equipment that an operator has been trained for and is authorized to operate makes good sense. It keeps unauthorized operators off equipment they have not been trained to use. All supervisors should receive the same training as the operators reporting to them.

The following recommendations on lift truck operator training are not intended to be complete. Only an in-depth program, of which there are many available from safety sources, will satisfy the need. Lift truck distributors usually have training programs or can recommend a good one that will satisfy management requirements.

Training Program Elements

Lift truck styles differ in stability and how they carry a load. Training programs must be tailored to the lift truck being used to explain the intricacies of the particular type of vehicle.

An adequate lift truck operator safety training program must contain these elements:

- Specific training about the controls and their adjustability and use, by specific type, model, and brand of fork lift truck that the operator is assigned to use.
- Specific training on the dynamics and handling characteristics of the loaded fork lift truck.
- Specific understanding of the shape, balance, and construction of the loads that are likely to be encountered.
- General safety training for equipment and situations that will likely be encountered by the lift truck operator.
- Specific training in the environment where the operator and lift truck will function.
- A test evaluating the operator on the understanding and retention of the subjects taught.
- A wallet card stating that the operator has been trained and what equipment the operator is authorized to operate.

Equipment specific. There are many types and styles, as well as ages, of lift trucks available to industry. These may be further customized with a variety of options and attachments, such as sideshifters and fork positioners. Some battery-powered electric trucks have extremely sophisticated drive controls. These may include a keypad where the operator inserts his own personal authorization code, or where a supervisor sets the maximum speed that the truck may attain in travel or lift. These controls are not intuitive.

Load stability. Straddle trucks and reach trucks operate differently. Among reach trucks are rolling mast reach trucks, adding still more complexity. The pantograph or scissors-type reach trucks may have single- or double-deep reach mechanisms that change the load handling parameters and characteristics of the truck.

Each kind of truck has a separate stability triangle, and for many trucks this changes during operation depending on the height of the lift, and the tilt, forward or back, of the mast. Counterbalanced trucks are a good example. There is a lot to stability training. This subject should get classroom, blackboard, and instructor explanation to be fully understood.

All loads are not the same. Wire baskets and metal tubs are often used in manufacturing. These containers may be filled with items that are stacked unevenly, or at the outside edges of the container throwing off the balance. This can change the handling dynamics of the truck. The operator might be able to see imbalance in an open top container, but it will be completely hidden in a closed container.

Environment and safety. General safety training for equipment and situations is important. It includes such areas as refueling for both liquids and gaseous fuels. Spilled gasoline can cause a fire or explosion. Leaking liquid propane gas can do the same. LP-gas can also cause severe freezing burns if the operator does not use gloves during refueling. Use of seat belts, hard hats, and safety shoes should be part of training.

Safety training also includes instructions about blocking exits, stretcher and fire cabinets, extinguishers with loads, and observing sprinkler heads when stacking loads.

Specific training in the operating environment is crucial. Each environment presents different challenges to an operator. Docks are an especially hazardous area and present many hidden dangers not apparent, even to skilled operators. Inspection of operating doors, dock levelers, placing dockboards and ramps, chocking transport wheels, and dozens of other safety-related tasks are part of lift truck operator training. An empty truck or trailer is an unknown surface and should be inspected by the lift truck operator before a truck is driven onto it.

- Operating in and around machine tools is different from operating in a storage or dock area. The operator must be trained in assembly line supply and maneuvering in and around fixed equipment.
- The operating areas for fork lift trucks, whether in the dock area or in production areas, should be plainly marked and aisles kept clear. Pickup and drop off points should be noted.
- Pedestrian areas should be marked with warnings on the floor and inside office doors that lead to the production floor.
- Parking areas for fork lift trucks should be marked.
- Overhead obstructions that could be hit with an elevated mast should be marked with black and yellow tapes or paint.
- Areas that exclude lift trucks also should be plainly marked.

Operator testing. A test evaluating the operator's understanding and retention of the subjects taught must be part of the training program. The test should be part of the trainee's personnel file and should be updated when lift trucks are changed or modified, when the operating environment changes, or when an operator is transferred from one department to another. The employer must determine how much retraining is necessary in these cases.

It also should be noted that formal operator training presents a forum during which company policies can be restated and reinforced. Use of alcohol, drugs, sexual or racial harassment, and other topics can be made part of the training program and specific to facilities, departments, or operations. Such subjects also can be included in the tests or examinations at the end of the training.

Maintenance performed by operator. If operators are responsible for some vehicle maintenance, such as engine or fluid level checks at the beginning of each shift, training programs should include these procedures.

For battery-powered lift trucks, it is usually the operator's job to connect the battery to a charger at the end of the shift or to exchange batteries when one runs low during a shift. The correct and safe procedure for this must be part of operator training.

To safely operate within the Occupational Safety & Health Administration (OSHA) regulation, lift truck users should order a copy of the latest regulation from the Department of Labor or from a lift truck distributor.

OSHA oversees the operation of powered industrial trucks. It publishes federal regulations covering the manufacture and use of these trucks, and any user of powered industrial trucks should be fully familiar with them. As part of a training program, fleet managers and operators of powered industrial trucks should be made thoroughly familiar with all safety requirements contained in OSHA Standard 1910.178.[8]

PURCHASING USED FORK LIFT TRUCKS

In the purchase of powered material handling equipment, the option of acquiring used units should not be overlooked. In the case of lift trucks, there can be some very compelling reasons for purchasing used machines for special material handling applications. In fact, more than 70,000 used lift trucks are purchased annually in the U.S. The primary advantage of buying a used lift truck is, of course, financial. An astute buyer can save as much as 35% or more over the cost of a new one.

Used machines do not have the power and endurance of new ones, nor can they take on sustained, heavy-duty tasks. The criteria for choosing a used vehicle are as follows:

- The truck should be used for less than five hours per day and no more than five days per week.
- It should not be used on a multishift basis.
- It should not be used in a heavy-duty production application.

Every manufacturing operation has some light-duty material handling tasks and it could be wasteful to employ a new machine when a used one will serve the same purpose. Such tasks as hauling scrap and trash, filling in for trucks undergoing maintenance, hauling unanticipated loads, etc., are useful activities for a used machine.

In purchasing a used lift truck, a buyer should look for a machine that:

- Is in sufficiently good condition to perform and operate for a minimum of three years.
- Comes with a reasonable written warranty that is fully explained.
- Comes with a full history of all maintenance and repairs performed on it.
- Is available from a reliable dealer that can be depended on for prompt, reliable service and timely parts replacement.

To make a wise used truck purchase, it helps to understand the used lift truck business. Most new lift trucks bought by companies are used for an average of seven years, then traded in on new models. Most of these trucks are operated for about 1,500 hours per year on a one-shift basis. A truck that has been under a preventive maintenance contract during this time is a good purchase candidate.

Many manufacturers lease trucks for four to six years and then turn them in, regardless of hours. The lessor has made certain that the truck was maintained. Depending on where these trucks were used, they can be good used truck candidates.

Many new lift trucks are not sold to end-users, but to franchised dealer rental fleets and equipment rental firms. These trucks are well-maintained and their average annual usage is only about 1,000 hours. Most of them have received maintenance in accord with factory recommendations, and maintenance records are usually complete and available for review. These rental fleet trucks generally represent the most consistently good values.

Moreover, rental fleet trucks are replaced every three to five years, which means they are equipped with the latest improvements in lift truck design and engineering. For these reasons, rental fleet trucks generally sell for 10-15% more than those that have spent their initial years in a manufacturing plant or a warehouse.

REBUILT TRUCKS

About 5% of used lift trucks are rebuilt. This means they have been completely disassembled down to the bare frame, cleaned, inspected, repaired, put back together with new or rebuilt parts, and completely repainted. What results is an almost new vehicle.

Rebuilding is expensive, however, and a rebuilt lift truck will cost between 80-85% of the cost of the same model new. For this reason, rebuilding is generally performed only on larger engine-powered lift trucks with capacities of 15,000 lb (6,804 kg) or higher, or on trucks that have some special features or attachments. This is because the dollar difference between the cost of a new truck and a used one becomes significant only when one is dealing with these larger, more expensive, or custom machines.

"AS-IS" TRUCKS

The second largest category of used lift trucks are the "as-is" units which, after many years of service, may have received little in the way of care, and are badly worn. Of all used lift trucks retailed, about 40% of them are sold in the "as-is" condition. They sell for about 35% of the price of a new one and come without any kind of warranty. Within a year, buyers of "as-is" trucks can expect to spend between 25-60% of the purchase price just to keep these trucks running.

RECONDITIONED TRUCKS

The third, and largest, segment of the used lift truck pool is comprised of reconditioned trucks, which represent about 55% of all used lift trucks available. These are the most popular, and represent the best bargains because they are generally in very good shape.

To qualify as reconditioned, a lift truck has received a thorough inspection, with special attention paid to all safety features. Parts and components that are in good working order remain on the truck, while major components that do not operate properly, such as the engine, transmission, drive and steer axles, and masts are rebuilt or replaced with new or rebuilt parts. The truck is cleaned throughout and, in some cases, repainted and equipped with new tires.

WHERE TO BUY

The reconditioning of used lift trucks is carried out by two types of organizations. The first is a large, fully-staffed, well-equipped, franchised lift truck dealer that maintains a permanent tie with a major lift truck manufacturer. The second is a relatively small, independent, used lift truck shop that performs reconditioning (and some rebuilding) on a small number of used trucks each year, and also sells many "as-is" units.

Though there are about twice as many small, independent shops as franchised dealers, they account for only about 35% of all retail used lift truck sales. The franchised dealers sell about 50% of used lift trucks, and the remaining 15% of used lift truck sales are carried out privately between one end-user and another or through auctions.

WARRANTIES

Warranties on used trucks vary considerably between dealers, independents, and different sections of the country.

- Rebuilt trucks generally carry a 90-day or longer warranty, including parts and labor.
- Rental fleet trucks usually carry a 30- to 90-day warranty with parts and labor included.
- Reconditioned units are covered by a wide variety of warranties, ranging from a 30-day warranty where the buyer and seller split the cost of repairs, to a full 90-day warranty including parts and labor.
- "As-is" trucks have no warranty.

CHAPTER 8   FLEXIBLE WHEELED HANDLING EQUIPMENT

Extended drive train insurance is sometimes available for a period of up to two years. The cost for a six-month drive train warranty is usually about 1.5% of the sale price of the machine. It is unwise to buy a used lift truck without some type of basic warranty.

In purchasing a used truck, the buyer must make certain that it meets OSHA and ANSI Standards.[9] The buyer may request that the seller guarantee compliance by writing on his invoice that the truck meets these standards.[10, 11]

References

1. Kulweic, Raymond A., ed. *Materials Handling Handbook*, 2nd Edition. New York: John Wiley & Sons, Inc., 1985.
2. "Evaluating Propane-powered Lift Trucks." *Plant Engineering* July 10, 1995: 66.
3. U. S. Department of Labor. Occupational Safety and Health Administration (OSHA) Standards-29 CFR, Part 1910, Occupational Safety and Health Standards, Subpart N-*Materials Handling and Storage*, Standard Number 1910.178-*Powered Industrial Trucks*. Washington: U.S. Department of Labor, 1996.
4. National Services, Inc. Huntington Beach, CA.
5. Ibid.
6. Ibid.
7. Caterpillar. Lift Trucks Survey. Houston, TX: 1989-1990.
8. U. S. Department of Labor. OSHA Standard Number 1910.178-*Powered Industrial Trucks*. Washington: U.S. Department of Labor, 1996.
9. Ibid.
10. American National Standards Institute (ANSI)/American Society of Mechanical Engineers (ASME). Standard B56.1-1993-*Low-lift and High-lift Trucks*. New York: ANSI/ASME, 1993.
11. Thompson, Larry. "Used Fork Lift Trucks: A Look at What's Available, With Some Tips on Evaluation." *Plant Services,* December 1989: 91.

Bibliography

Adams, Nicholas D., ed., Firth, Rowland V.D., Brown, Terry W., and Misenheimer, Laura P., coauthors. *Warehouse & Distribution Automation Handbook*. New York: McGraw-Hill, Inc., 1996.
Bowman, Daniel. *Lift Trucks, A Practical Guide for Buyers and Users.* Boston: Cahners Books, 1972.
Cohan, Bud. *Lift Truck Fleet Management and Operator Training.* Washington: International Thomson Transport Press, 1988.
Lindkvist, R.G.T. (translator). *Handbook of Materials Handling.* Compiled by Swedish Transport Research Commission. West Sussex, England: Ellis Horwood, Ltd., 1985.
Mulcahy, David E. *Warehouse Distribution & Operations Handbook.* New York: McGraw-Hill, Inc., 1994.
Rosaler, Robert C., PE, ed. *Standard Handbook of Plant Engineering*, 2nd Edition. New York: McGraw-Hill, Inc., 1995.
Tompkins, James A., and Harmelink, Dale, eds. *The Distribution Management Handbook.* New York: McGraw-Hill, 1994.

CHAPTER 9

CONVEYORS FOR UNIT LOAD HANDLING

CHAPTER CONTENTS

When Henry Ford built the first mass production assembly line in the early 1920s, the impact of powered conveyors on American industry was immediate and profound. In fact, so dramatic was the increase in manufacturing efficiency, that Model T cars seemed to almost race along the chain conveyor assembly line at Lincoln Motor Car Company.

Unit load handling conveyors form the backbone of a wide range of manufacturing and assembly applications. The number of conveyors to choose from is as diverse as the material being handled. Mr. Ford would have been astonished at the speed and efficiency with which these systems operate. Moreover, the advent of computer control has made it possible to use conveyors not only to transport products, but also to automatically buffer, merge, singulate (separate), scan, sort, and deliver each item to a specific destination.

This chapter addresses the general classes of unit load handling conveyor systems that support manufacturing and assembly applications and is limited to those conveyor systems that support the product from below (that is, in-floor) rather than from above (overhead). It provides essential information on conveyor design features and operating characteristics. Selection guidelines and design considerations will aid the manufacturing engineer in the evaluation of unit load handling conveyor equipment for a specific application. Key management issues are also addressed in sections on cost estimating and conveyor safety.

A point to keep in mind is that there are few applications where a single type of handling technology is the obvious choice. This chapter provides the manufacturing engineer with a working knowledge of the various options for unit load conveyors (in-floor) used in manufacturing and assembly applications and some of the key design considerations, maintenance requirements, and technology developments. The material included here is intended as a basic framework to assist the engineer in the conveyor equipment selection process.

DESIGN CONSIDERATIONS

Every good engineer knows that you cannot take a solution and go looking for a problem. The same applies to conveyor applications. The selection process cannot begin until the problem at hand has been defined.

This section discusses the key parameters used to define a potential conveyor application, including physical requirements, logical requirements, and site requirements. Figure 9-1 provides a checklist summary of the key requirements for each category. Define as much of this information as possible in the beginning of the design process. This will ensure that the right handling equipment is selected for the application. The information also can be used as a basis for the functional requirements document.

One of the first steps in defining a conveyor application is to describe the complete range of products to be handled and their physical requirements. This includes not only the geometry of the products (height, length, width, and weight), but also a judgment about their relative conveyability. If the product's bottom is not a flat surface, the area of contact should be described.

With regard to conveyability, the orientation of the product to the direction of travel is an important consideration. Also, every item has unique characteristics. Some items have a high center of gravity, some have a high surface friction, others are extremely lightweight or fragile—all of these factors influence conveyability. A thorough examination of these characteristics will help determine whether or not a conveyor offers the most suitable method of transportation. Different conveying methods may be required at different stages of the process, since many items change as they move through the various steps of a manufacturing process.

Defining the application also involves estimating the throughput rates for all sources and destinations within the system, as well as the overall throughput. Many engineers make the mistake of simply using averages that can lead to invalid conclusions about a system's ability to meet capacity requirements. Engineers also need to know the maximum rate per day, the peak sustained rate, and most importantly, the *burst rate* (the throughput rate for the peak interval of the peak hour). An important point to remember later on in the analysis is that the actual capacity of a conveyor in a design may be lower than rated capacity. Limiting factors include diverters, merges, lifts, or other devices.

Historical data are often good sources for these physical requirements. Valuable information can be gleaned from the archives—even paging through old packing slips or invoices may be enlightening. However, problems with data collection typically arise when forecasting is involved. Designers often deal with the uncertainty inherent in forecasting by performing a sensitivity analysis. In this way, a range can be defined within which the performance of the system

The Contributors of this chapter are: Paul Moews, Account Manager, HK Systems; **Brian Sanford,** Director of International Marketing, Rapistan Demag; **George A. Schultz, PE,** Vice President, Siebert Engineers, Inc.
The Reviewers of this chapter are: Roger Alderink, Past President of the Conveyor Equipment Manufacturers Association and Vice President, Product Development, Alvey, Inc.; **Mike Brown,** Chairman, The Conveyor Product Section of the Material Handling Industry of America and Vice President of Sales and Marketing, Alvey, Inc.; **Michael Cornelia,** Regional Manager, Jervis B. Webb Co.

CHAPTER 9   CONVEYORS FOR UNIT LOAD HANDLING

Physical Requirements
  Production rates
    Rate per day (average rate): _____
    Rate per h (sustained rate): _____
    Rate per min (peak rate): _____
    Maximum rate over short time period (burst rate):* _____

Product Profile
  Weight
    Light (bottles, cans, filters, etc.): _____
    Medium (weighs less than 100 lb [45 kg]): _____
    Heavy (100-4,000 lb [45-1,814 kg]): _____
    Dimensions (length, width, height): _____
    Center of gravity: _____
    Conveying surface: _____
    Content:† _____

Logical Requirements
    Instructions to the conveyor (by data point): _____
    When, why, how items are accumulated, released, sorted: _____
    Data collected from the product: _____
    Disposition of data by the system: _____

Site Requirements
    Aisle widths: _____
    Turn radii: _____
    Overhead clearances: _____
    Location of fire doors: _____
    Noise requirements: _____
    Clean room requirements: _____
    Safety requirements: _____
    Environmental requirements: _____

  * Burst can never exceed peaks.
  † A bowling ball in a box is a different problem than a box of soap.

Fig. 9-1 Defining some of the key parameters of the application will aid in the conveyor selection process. *(Courtesy Rapistan Demag)*

can be evaluated. A good designer will also perform a sensitivity analysis on the product profile, because no matter how stable the industry may seem to be, the time cycle to introduce new products is shrinking. What a designer should know is how much the weight or size of the product can be changed before major modifications to the system are required.

A primary function of a conveyor system is transporting items. However, conveyors can also perform accumulating, merging, sorting, and diverting processes. Designers should keep these capabilities in mind as they consider the product flow for the application.

Defining a conveyor application also requires complete information about the plant's characteristics and site requirements. Specific operating parameters include aisle widths, turn radii, overhead clearances, and fire doors. Other factors include clean room, low noise, or safety requirements. Also, the designer should understand what kind of an impact the plant's environment will have on conveyor equipment. A manufacturing process that produces abrasive dust will shorten the life expectancy of bearings, shaft seals, roller chains, sprockets, and other conveyor components.

The definition of the application should also include system control requirements. Essentially, this is a description of the physical product and data flow within the system and the means for accomplishing those flows. Data elements to be considered include instructions to the conveyor system, information collected from the products, and the strategy for accumulating, releasing, and sorting items.

Without good input data, the chances of selecting the right equipment for a potential conveyor application (or meeting the requirements) are slim. An important point to remember is that selecting the best transport system is an iterative process. Early system planning should always include "what ifs." Questions to ask include:

- What if the mix of product changes?
- What if the product footprint changes?
- What if maximum product weights change in the future?
- What if throughput is more than expected?
- What if throughput is less than expected?

After the application has been defined, the data collected can be compared against the characteristics of the equipment candidates. This will help reduce the number of choices to a manageable few that can be taken to the detailed analysis stage.

Sequential elimination is a useful technique for screening and reducing the number of equipment options. This method involves specifying and comparing the degree to which different alternatives satisfy a set of performance objectives or requirements. Some typical attributes that are desirable in a conveyor system include maintainability, flexibility, economy, and throughput. In selecting these

CHAPTER 9   CONVEYORS FOR UNIT LOAD HANDLING

attributes, it is important to be as specific as possible. Does flexibility mean the ability to modify the system easily? Or does it mean the ability to handle a wide range of products?

The degree to which a particular solution satisfies this criteria is then judged on some arbitrary scale—from one to ten, for example. This rating is then compared to a baseline value. If a candidate solution meets or exceeds this value, it will remain under consideration. The ratings of the various alternatives also can be compared. Another variation is to take into consideration the values of each of the requirements by weighting them.

After collecting the data and the system flow is established, simulation is a good method for testing concepts. Using simulation software, engineers can build a 3D model of the system under investigation and test various operating conditions. It is an extremely powerful tool for performing sensitivity analysis and evaluating alternative designs.

NONPOWERED CONVEYORS

Nonpowered conveyors enjoy widespread use in many types of low- to medium-throughput assembly applications where powered conveyors cannot be justified. One of the easiest classes of equipment to incorporate into the manufacturing environment, they offer an economical means of moving materials through the manufacturing process or supplying parts to an assembly line.

One typical application for a nonpowered conveyor is the progressive assembly line. As each sequential operation is completed, an operator manually pushes the product along the conveyor to the next assembly point. Often, lift tables or ball transfer tables are used to transfer finished product from the line to inspection or test stations. Flow racks equipped with gravity feed lanes are a popular way of supplying fast-moving parts to the assembly line. Parts are replenished from the rear side of the flow rack as necessary.

Simple in design, the maintenance requirements of nonpowered conveyors are minimal, and operation is usually trouble-free. When the conveyor is pitched, gravity moves the load, and when it is level, an operator pushes the load. By sharply reducing the amount of bending and lifting required, nonpowered conveyors are a simple

method of reducing the potential for worker injury. While nonpowered conveyors offer an economical means of handling material, the low cost is offset, to some extent, by the difficulty in determining just how much pitch (slope) is required to transport a product at the desired speed. Often, experience is the only reliable method of making this determination.

This section reviews the two main categories of nonpowered conveyors, skate wheel and gravity roller. While similar in some respects, each category is particularly well suited to certain types of applications as shown in Table 9-1.

SKATE WHEEL

Comparatively lightweight, skate wheel conveyors are ideal for use in portable conveyor lines requiring frequent setup and teardown. The conveyor weight itself can be reduced by using aluminum frames and wheels. When not in use, these conveyors can be wheeled out of the way of pedestrians or other traffic. Although ideal for carton handling, skate wheel conveyors are less forgiving of products with uneven footprints. Fixtures, drums, and pallets are not suitable for transport on a skate wheel conveyor, nor are loads with rims or picture frame bottoms, or runners in the direction of travel.

The basic skate wheel conveyor consists of steel or aluminum wheels mounted on axles with multiples of 1.5 in. (38 mm) centers. The top of the wheels extend over the top of the frame that is normally formed from 2.5 × 1.0 in. (64 × 25 mm) channels. Conveyor widths of 12, 14, 16, and 24 in. (305, 356, 406, and 610 mm) are commonly available. Standard wheel sections come in lengths of 5 and 10 ft (1.5 and 3.0 m). Spacer tubes assembled onto the axles form the various wheel patterns.

Skate wheel conveyors are ideal for handling light to medium loads. Aluminum sections and wheels, preferable because of their lighter weight, will have less capacity than an all-steel construction. Wheel density should be sufficient to support the loads to be handled, although overall weight capacity is typically limited by the frame, support spacing, or characteristics of the load. The distance between the floor supports also influences load capacity. However, about 90% of all skate wheel conveyors currently in service are supported on 10 ft (3.0 m) centers.

The *pitch* of a skate wheel conveyor relates to the downward slope required to start a stationary load moving, and the slope required to

TABLE 9-1
Comparison of Nonpowered Conveyors

Characteristics	Conveyor Type	
	Skate Wheel	Gravity Roller
Load capacity	Low	Low
Cost	Low	Low
Throughput	Low	Low
Handle irregular shapes?	No	Yes
Portability	High	Medium
Average pitch	0.5 in. (13 mm) per 10 in. (254 mm) of conveyor	0.5 in. (13 mm) per 10 in. (254 mm) of conveyor
Initial rolling resistance	Low	Medium
Ideal application	Portable assembly lines requiring frequent setup and teardown Not recommended for side loading	Work areas Short accumulating lines where manual assistance is available

CHAPTER 9   CONVEYORS FOR UNIT LOAD HANDLING

sustain that movement. Pitch, a function of the load weight and the characteristics of the load's bottom (carrying) surface, will vary from application to application. Generally, firm carrying surfaces require less pitch than softer surfaces. As a general guideline, the average pitch for cardboard cases is 6 in. (152 mm) per 10 ft (3.0 m) of conveyor length; the average pitch for a cloth bag is 15-20 in. (381-508 mm) per 10 ft (3.0 m) of conveyor length.

Curved sections (45 or 90°) extend the range of a skate wheel conveyor. The average pitch of a 90° curved section should be the same as that of a 10-ft (3.0-m) long straight section. The inside radius of the curve should be equal to or greater than the longest load. In general, the larger the radius, the better conveyance of loads. Because of interlocking, loads should not be accumulated in curves. Skate wheel conveyors also should not be used if parts are to be loaded from the side.

GRAVITY ROLLER

A primary advantage of a gravity roller conveyor is its great versatility. A nonpowered roller conveyor has a higher load capacity than a skate wheel conveyor and better tolerance of products with uneven carrying surfaces. But these advantages do not come without a cost: initial roll resistance on a gravity roller is higher than that of a skate wheel, which means greater force is required to start a stationary load moving. And, as is the case with a skate wheel conveyor, determining the right amount of pitch is more of an art than an exact science.

A gravity roller conveyor consists of rollers with an internal bearing and stationary axle mounted on side frames. As with a skate wheel, the rollers are set high on the frame, which can be fabricated of formed steel channels, structural channels, or angles.

The size and weight of the roller tubing will be a function of the load capacity, application, and bearing seat requirements. The majority of conveyor rollers used today are either 1.9 or 2.5 in. (48 or 64 mm) diameter. Most rollers are steel, although aluminum, stainless steel, plastic, or brass rollers are available. Most suppliers offer electrogalvanized steel as the standard roller, providing a greater degree of protection against rust.

Most suppliers also recommend low-cost, commercial-grade roller bearings with oil lubrication for all gravity rollers, except in unique environments. Semiprecision or precision bearings avoid the problem of possible contamination (due to the open construction of commercial grade bearings) and produce lower noise levels. But there are tradeoffs: the cost of precision bearings is more per roller, and the conveyor pitch must be increased due to the seals used to protect these bearings.

The load capacity of a roller conveyor depends on the components. All products should be considered fully to determine whether the capacity is sufficient for a particular application. A minimum of three rollers should support the load at all times.

Although the specific loading must always be checked, a general rule of thumb for calculating roller spacing is to subtract 1 in. (25 mm) from the longest load length and divide by three. Center spacing should be no greater than 3 in. (76 mm) for objects with heavy, machined surfaces, 6 in. (152 mm) for wooden pallets, and 2-6 in. (51-152 mm) for corrugated cartons. Allowances must be made for products with nonflat carrying surfaces, as the weight will not be distributed evenly over the roller bed.

The pitch of a gravity roller conveyor is the downward slope required to start a stationary load moving and to sustain that movement. Pitch is impacted by the size of roller and type of bearing, the load weight and its surface condition, and in some cases, the environment. Although testing and experience are the best methods for determining the required pitch, the average pitch of a gravity roller

conveyor is approximately 0.5 in./ft (42 mm/m). Typically, lighter loads and loads with soft or irregular surfaces require more pitch; heavier loads and loads with hard, flat surfaces require less pitch.[1]

When long, uncontrolled runs cannot be avoided, make the pitch to the minimum required. Retarding devices control the speed of the loads, but they do not reduce the forward force or the line pressure, and may not be effective when handling products of varying weights. Some type of load containment device at the end of the conveyor also may be necessary.

BALL TRANSFER TABLES AND OMNIDIRECTION WHEELS

Ball transfer tables and omnidirection wheels are a common sight on assembly lines, providing an ergonomic assist in transferring assemblies from a conveyor to a workstation. They are also recommended for use in applications where product must be transferred at right angles without being rotated.

A *ball transfer* is a large-diameter steel ball supported by a spherical dish containing small diameter balls. A series of these ball transfers are mounted to a flat steel surface to form the table. As the name implies, ball transfer tables are used to move a rigid-surface load in any direction on a horizontal plane with minimum manual force. An excellent ergonomic assist device, a ball transfer table reduces the force required to move the load by approximately 85-90%.

Although a ball transfer table can be tilted up to 30° for gravity flow, in most applications it remains level. The force required to slide the product on ball transfers is a function of the weight of the product and its conveying surface. Hard surface loads require less force to move than soft surface loads. Ball transfers should not be used for loads with soft or irregular-shaped bottoms, such as bags, pallets, drums with rims, or baskets. Also, the finished surface of a product should never be moved across the table, as the ball transfers can leave tracks or marks.

POWERED CONVEYORS

Belt conveyors and roller conveyors form the two major types of powered conveyors for handling unit loads weighing 25-2,500 lb (11-1,134 kg). These conveyors handle a wide range of products and assemblies, including computers, household appliances, and motors. In-floor conveyors for handling large and very heavy unit loads are covered in the following section.

When determining whether a powered conveyor can be justified for a particular manufacturing application, throughput is obviously an important consideration. But while long production runs are usually a prerequisite, powered conveyors do much more than move materials in a horizontal path. Powered roller conveyors can be designed to automatically buffer, merge, divert, and deliver each individual assembly to a specific destination. In a progressive in-line assembly application, for example, a single conveyor system performs many of these functions. With in-line assembly, all work is performed directly on the conveyor transport system. Workstations that may feature in-line stops and a lifting device to raise the assembly fixture off the conveyor, are located at various points along this line. Depending upon the cycle times for various assembly operations and the distance between workstations, accumulation-type conveyors can be used to queue items upstream of particular operations. When more flexibility is required, product movement can be asynchronous.

Selecting the proper choice of powered conveyor requires precise definition of the application requirements. The selection will

CHAPTER 9   CONVEYORS FOR UNIT LOAD HANDLING

primarily be a function of the product being handled. In many cases, products travel along the assembly line on a pallet or in a fixture. The conveying surface should always be flat and sufficiently large. Product application information should include:

- Weight.
- Length.
- Footprint.
- Flexibility of bottom surface.
- Reaction to line pressure.
- Accumulation requirements.

POWERED BELT

While typically best suited for warehousing applications, belt conveyors are commonly used to deliver bulk materials and light to medium loads of parts or packages between assembly operations, departments, or levels within the manufacturing environment. Noise output is low, and the conveyor provides a smooth ride with easy tracking of items. Belt conveyors handle a wide range of products (including those with irregular bottoms). Maximum load capacity is approximately 150 lb/ft (223 kg/m).

There are two basic types of powered belt conveyors: slider bed and roller bed. On a *slider bed conveyor*, the belt is supported on a metal bed set high in channel frames. Slider bed support is used for handling loads with irregular conveying surfaces on declines or unstable loads, and along sections of the conveyor with operator workstations. Because of the high coefficient of friction of the slider bed, more horsepower is required to move the belt. As a consequence, slider bed is not used for heavy loads.

On a *roller bed conveyor*, the belt is supported by evenly-spaced rollers, as shown in Fig. 9-2. The return run of belting is also supported on return rollers attached to the frame, typically on 5-6 ft (1.5-1.8 m) centers. With a lower coefficient of friction, the roller bed requires less belt pull and lower power requirements. Although the cost of a roller bed conveyor is higher, belt life is longer and the operating cost is lower. The use of a roller bed also permits the design of longer conveyor sections per drive unit and operation at speeds of 500 ft (152 m)/min or more. Rollers should be spaced so that a minimum of two rollers is under the load at all times. When the height of a load exceeds its length, a minimum of three rollers should be used for added stability.

Many rollers feature low-cost, commercial grade bearings. Although this type of bearing will tolerate moderate impact loading, noise levels will be higher. Semiprecision or precision bearings avoid that problem, and should be used when the conveyor is operating at speeds of over 150 ft (46 m)/min. However, the cost of precision bearings is more per roller.

A wide variety of conveyor belting is available. Typical belt widths range from 6-120 in. (15-305 cm). Belt selection requires experience and an understanding of the characteristics of the product's conveying surface, particularly if inclines are involved. Belt pull is generated by wrapping the belt around a pulley of sufficient diameter and coefficient of friction to move the heaviest load. At the tail (entry) end, sufficient belt pull energy must remain to pull the return run of belting from the drive pulley to the tail pulley and maintain wrap tension on the drive pulley itself. A snub pulley just behind the drive pulley helps the belt maintain contact area with the drive pulley. The residual tension in the belt also must be sufficient to keep the belt from slipping on the drive pulley under maximum load. A snub pulley in the drive and the tape-up pulley adjustment creates and maintains this tension.

An adjustable belt take-up is required on all belt conveyors to compensate for the normal elongation of the belt that typically oc-

curs during the first three months of use. The take-up also must have enough travel to compensate for changes in the belt length due to seasonal changes in temperature. This device can be located anywhere along the return run, although the preferred location is close to the drive unit on the slack side of the belt.

The location of the drive itself will depend on the type of drive, type of conveyor, and the angles of inclines and declines (if any). Typically, the drive should be located such that a minimum amount of return belt is under primary tension. End drives are used for shorter conveyor lengths, single direction travel, and lighter loads. Center drives are ideal for medium- to heavy-duty applications and for reversible service. To facilitate smooth transfers when several belt conveyors are linked together, the speed of all belts should be about 5 ft (1.5 m)/min or approximately 10% greater than the speed of the preceding belt. Variable speed drives will help tune these varying speeds. For duty cycles of more than eight cycles per minute, a heavy-duty drive unit, cycle motor, and reducer should be used.

Inclines and Declines

As shown in Fig. 9-3, one of the great advantages of belt conveyors is their easy navigation of inclines and declines, which can be expensive to accomplish with other types of unit load handling conveyors. The maximum incline angle of the conveyor is a function of product characteristics, such as dimensions, center of gravity, and conveying surface, as well as the type of belting and method of feeding the incline. Typically, the stability of the load and its contact with the belt are limiting factors.

Load stability is an important factor in managing inclines and declines. For the load to remain stable, a vertical line drawn through the center of gravity must pass through the riding surface of the package. Best practice design is to limit the incline to an angle that keeps this vertical line through the center of gravity within the center half of the length of the load base. The angle should not exceed 20°. Although the typical carton does not normally slip at even 25°, the risk of slippage is greater as the angle increases. Plastic totes with a smooth bottom can slip at only 15° of incline. To help reduce slippage, belting typically has a top cover with a rough surface texture that increases the coefficient of friction. Cleats also can be molded into the belt or attached by ultrasonic welding or bolts.

As the load makes the transition to the incline, it is temporarily supported only by its leading and trailing edge. Longer loads with hard, sharp corners tend to accumulate at this point. This situation can be avoided by installing a straight, horizontal belt feeder that is equal in length to the longest load at the entry point. As a general reference, corrugated cartons that are less than 24 in. (610 mm) long do not require a feeder for inclines of 15° or less; metal and plastic totes almost always do. It is desirable to run the feeder at a speed 10% faster than the speed of the upstream conveyor, generating a gap between two packages traveling together before the incline. At the top of the incline, a "nose-over" section of rollers under the belt is typically used to return the packages to the horizontal plane before transfer to the next conveyor. Declined conveyors follow this same principle, only in reverse.

Smaller packages with a length or width less than 8 in. (203 mm) require special consideration when it comes to inclines and declines. Transition plates, support rollers, special belting, or end pulleys can be installed to avoid upending at the transition point.

Belt Turns and Spirals

Belt turns are typically required when changing the direction of the belt conveyor path. The standard belt turn is a 90° horizontal curve with either a left or right hand pitch (direction of turn relative to the direction of travel). The shape of the belt resembles a truncated cone

CHAPTER 9   CONVEYORS FOR UNIT LOAD HANDLING

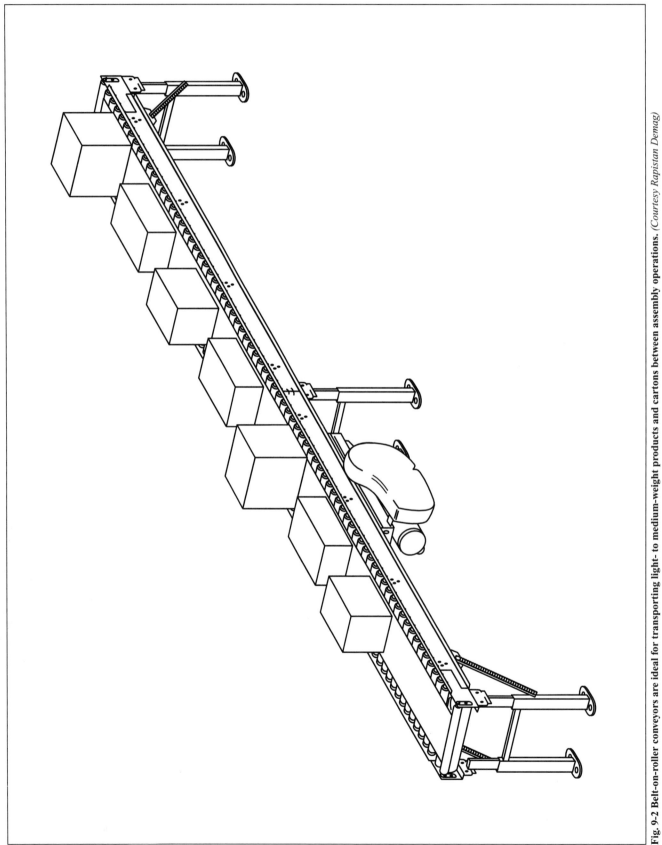

Fig. 9-2 Belt-on-roller conveyors are ideal for transporting light- to medium-weight products and cartons between assembly operations. *(Courtesy Rapistan Demag)*

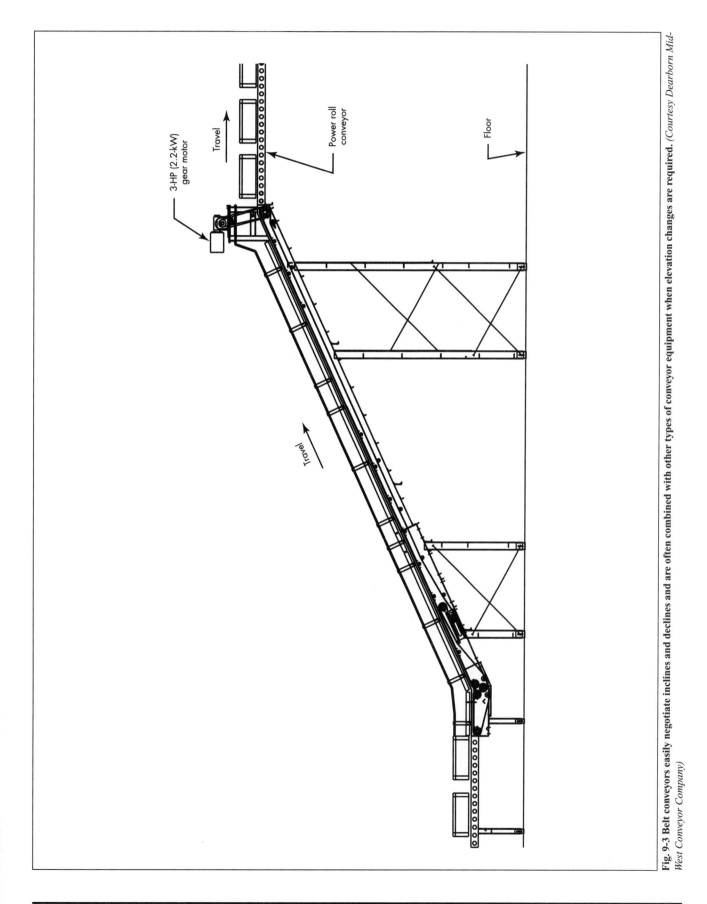

Fig. 9-3 Belt conveyors easily negotiate inclines and declines and are often combined with other types of conveyor equipment when elevation changes are required. *(Courtesy Dearborn Mid-West Conveyor Company)*

CHAPTER 9   CONVEYORS FOR UNIT LOAD HANDLING

when assembled, while the end pulleys are tapered. Together, they provide the correct speed for the belt section entering or exiting the carrying surface. A small diameter transition roller or transfer plate may be required between the end rollers of the belt turn and the adjacent belt conveyor to assist small items across the gap.

Belt turns are also available as spiral inclines or declines. Depending on the particular model, the angle of incline ranges from 16-20° on centerline. Spirals are built around a pivot frame, with individual segments linked to provide a continuous spiral up to 720°. Although more costly than flat curves, they are an ideal solution in applications where floor space is scarce.

LIVE ROLLER

More versatile than a powered belt conveyor, a live roller conveyor is ideal for a broad range of assembly and manufacturing applications. (A comparison of the characteristics of these types of powered conveyors is shown in Table 9-2.) The low friction relationship between roller and load, and the roller's ability to accept thrust loading, enables the roller conveyor to perform many more functions than just transporting product. Live roller can be used as the conveyor bed for pusher diverters, fixed diverters, merges, skewed roller edge alignment, and load or unload stations. In fact, a live roller is the primary method of accumulating product on a powered conveyor. But a live roller does have its limitations: it can manage only slight inclines and declines, and cannot handle products with an irregular bottom surface.

There are four basic types of live roller conveyors, classified by the type of drive used to turn the rollers: belt-driven, chain-driven, line shaft-powered, and internally-powered. Various models are designed to handle different weight capacities.

Belt-driven

Similar in design to a belt conveyor, a flat-belt roller conveyor has one obvious difference: the carrying rollers are on top of the belt. This type of power roller conveyor is used for light- to medium-duty loads and applications.

A narrow width of belt, running between the carrying rollers and the pressure rollers underneath, powers the rollers. Sufficient pressure is applied to the belt to overcome the roller and load resistance, causing the rollers to rotate. Assemblies and parts move in the direction of travel at the belt speed. The appropriate pressure roll setting is the minimum amount of pressure that will move the maximum weight load.

The load shortest in length should ride on at least three powered carrying rollers at all times. Maximum recommended incline on a belt-driven live roller conveyor is 5°. For declines over 4°, the belt pull should be calculated both with the conveyor empty and fully loaded. The larger of the two calculations will determine motor horsepower.

Another variation of this type of conveyor is the V-belt roller conveyor. The only difference in this design is that the V-belt replaces the flat belt and pressure wheels are mounted on one side of the frame. Because the V-belt can flex around the radius of curves, this type of conveyor is ideal for applications with many direction changes. Because the strength of the splice in this type of belt is uncertain, an endless belt should be used if possible. V-belt conveyors are best suited for light loads and short runs.

Line Shaft-powered

Ideal for light- to medium-handling applications, a line shaft-powered, live roller conveyor uses a rotating line shaft mounted on one side of the conveyor frame. The rollers are driven from the line shaft via plastic spools that ride on the carrying roller and plastic drive belt loops on the line shaft. As the line shaft rotates, the belt loops drive each roller. The spools are designed to slip on the line shaft when the roller rotation is stopped, allowing minimum pressure accumulation. Individual line shaft segments can be fitted with universal joints to transmit power through curves. A line shaft can also provide power to drive right angle transfers, feeders, pop-up transfers, and other components.

TABLE 9-2
Comparison of Powered Conveyors for Assembly

Characteristics	Conveyor Type	
	Powered Belt	Powered Roller
Load capacity	Light to medium	Light to medium
Cost	Medium	Medium
Throughput	Medium to high	Low to medium
Ease of interfacing with manual operations	High	High
Handle irregular bottoms?	Yes	Yes (without accumulation)
Accumulation/merge/sort?	Requires enhancements	Yes
Bidirectional?	No	Yes
Ease of reconfigurability	Medium	Medium
Required maintenance	Low	Low
Negotiate curves?	Requires enhancements	Requires enhancements
Negotiate inclines/declines?	Yes	No
Noise level	Low	Medium
Ideal application	Delivery of product between assembly operations	Assembly operations requiring accumulation

CHAPTER 9   CONVEYORS FOR UNIT LOAD HANDLING

An obvious advantage of using a line shaft to power the rollers is that only a single motor is necessary to run the entire length of conveyor. Maintenance requirements are relatively minimal. However, a line shaft-powered conveyor does not endure the rigors of abrasive environments, extreme temperatures, and wet or oily environments very well. Product slippage is also a possibility.

Chain-driven

The sturdy chain-driven, live roller conveyor is the most popular choice for applications requiring high speeds and capacities, and is ideal when the speed of the conveyor must be synchronized with other equipment. Figure 9-4 illustrates a chain-driven, live roller conveyor for handling heavy unit loads.

A chain-driven, live roller conveyor tolerates adverse environmental conditions and has relatively low maintenance requirements. For added protection, the frame, roller assemblies, and sprockets can be galvanized and a stainless steel chain used. On the downside, the chain-driven roller does not manage incline well and product slippage is a possibility.

The continuous chain-driven, live roller conveyor uses a single strand of precision roller chain to deliver power from the motor to each roller. Sprockets that are atttached to the rollers mesh with the chain to provide a positive means of rotation. Because the chain only contacts the teeth at the top of the sprocket, this design is not appropriate for stop and start applications.

Each roller has two sprockets on a roll-to-roll, chain-driven live roller conveyor. A loop of roller chain connects the outer sprockets on the first and second rollers. Another loop connects the inner sprockets on the second and third rollers. A third loop connects the outer sprockets on the third and fourth rollers, and so on. Rotating any one roller causes all rollers to rotate in the same direction at the same speed. Power is introduced by positioning the sprocket on a gear motor above or below one of the drive chain loops near the center of the conveyor, and using a longer chain loop to wrap around all three sprockets. Roller chain transfers, like the one shown in Fig. 9-5, help to extend the versatility of this class of conveyor system.

A variation of the chain conveyor is the *sliding chain*, or tabletop conveyor. These conveyors consist of a roller chain with an

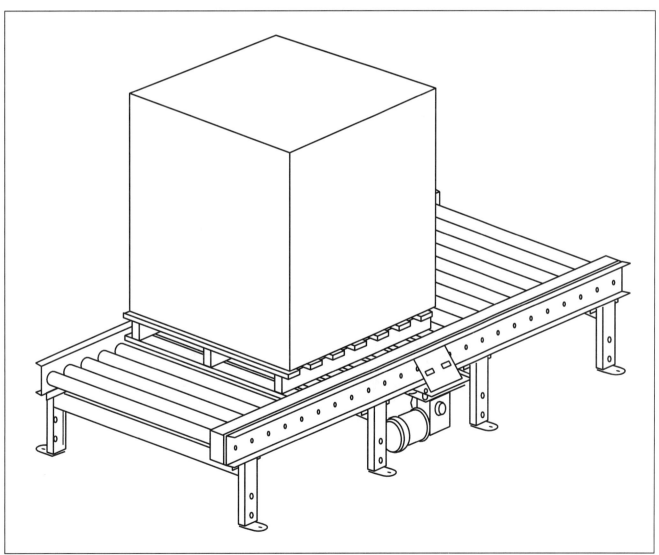

Fig. 9-4 Used for a much wider range of applications than a belt conveyor, a live roller conveyor consists of rollers that form the conveying surface. *(Courtesy Rapistan Demag)*

CHAPTER 9   CONVEYORS FOR UNIT LOAD HANDLING

attached top plate mounted on a frame above the floor. Numerous types of plates are available, including stainless steel and plastic. Chain type will depend on the particular application. Operating at speeds of up to 300 ft (91 m)/min, the sliding chain is used extensively to transport lightweight parts between assembly operations. The ability to travel long distances and negotiate horizontal turns extends the number of potential applications.

Material developments in the area of powered conveyors continue. One offering is a polyurethane belt that rides on rollers fitted with molded plastic sprockets. Unlike chain, the belt does not stretch (eliminating tensioning devices) and requires no lubrication. Maximum load capacity is approximately 350 lb (159 kg).

Internally-powered Rollers

Another development in the live roller conveyor category is the self-powered, electric conveyor roller. These rollers have an internal, direct current (DC) motor that drives a gear reducer, producing about 3.5 lbf-in. (0.4 Nm) of torque. The conveyor frame serves as the negative conductor.

Self-powered rollers are placed at intervals on the roller bed with idlers in between. O-ring drive belts are used to transmit power from the powered roller to between one and five adjacent idlers (slaves).

Depending on the application, as many as 25 rollers can be powered and controlled by a single power supply. A particular advantage is that individual zones can be powered only as required, reducing noise levels and component wear and tear.

Designers are finding numerous conveyor applications for internally-powered rollers. In workstation transfers, for example, powered rollers at the transfer point are raised, straddle the belts to support the load, and are then powered left or right to complete the transfer. On powered curves, internally-powered tapered rollers can help ease products around a tight radius without additional hardware. These rollers are also proving valuable in preventing runaway that occurs when product continues to move until it is mechanically stopped.

ACCUMULATION

Providing product accumulation is one of the most challenging aspects of a powered conveyor application. This is because the steps in a manufacturing process typically do not have equivalent cycle times. Accumulation allows upstream operations to continue while a downstream operation catches up.

All types of roller conveyors can provide what is known as *zero pressure* or *minimum pressure accumulation*, which essentially means

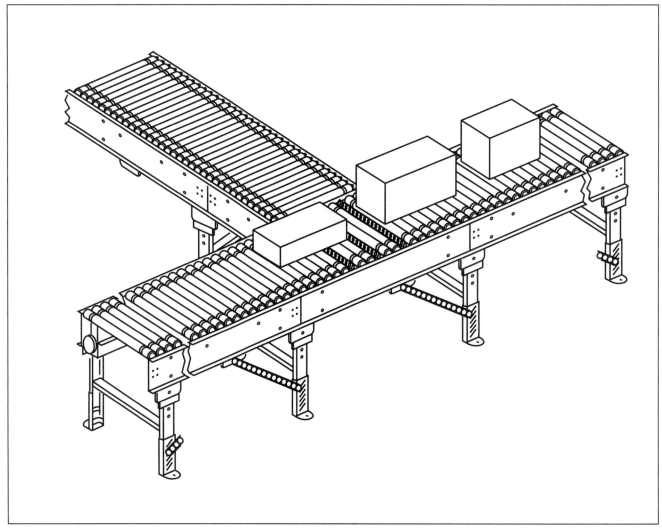

Fig. 9-5 Specialty components like this chain transfer extend the versatility of roller conveyors. *(Courtesy Rapistan Demag)*

CHAPTER 9   CONVEYORS FOR UNIT LOAD HANDLING

that the driving force from the accumulated product is eliminated or reduced. If it is not, several things can happen: the lead item can be damaged with the concentrated pressure; several adjacent, lightweight cartons may collapse under the pressure; or cartons may be pushed off the conveyor. Typically, as more products are accumulated, the line pressure is compounded.

Some types of belt-driven and chain-driven live roller conveyor can provide zero pressure accumulation by automatically lowering the drive belt away from the carrying rollers. When the rollers lose frictional contact, the load is no longer driven forward.

A belt-driven, live roller conveyor generally divides the pressure rollers into 2-3 ft (0.6-0.9 m) zones per 10 ft (3.0 m) section of conveyor. When accumulation is not required, the conveyor operates normally. When accumulation is required, a load sensor device immediately deactivates the upstream zone, causing product entering into this zone to slowly stop. This signals the pressure roller in the next zone to deactivate. As a result, product is accumulated with no line pressure or carton damage. To release the product (a process known as *singulation*), the first zone empties. This allows the pressure rollers in the next zone upstream to engage, permitting product to move. Metering belts are another way of accomplishing singulation.

The line shaft conveyor uses air brakes to stop a group of rollers in a particular zone. To start accumulation, an external signal triggers a proximity sensor in the first zone. When product arrives at the zone, a brake is actuated, triggering the proximity sensor in the next zone. Carton release occurs when an external signal releases the brake in the first zone. As product clears each zone, the brake under the following carton is released, and so on.

Chain-driven, live roller conveyors accumulate products through the use of slip or clutch mechanisms built into the rollers. Self-powered rollers offer another means of powered accumulation. By coordinating control of the roller rotation, products can be accumulated and released as required.

Accumulation conveyors have some unique limitations. They are limited to operation in a level configuration or only at the slightest incline or decline. Products handled must have a smooth, rigid base.

Though products can vary in width and length, drastic differences in product weight and size may cause cartons to jackknife.

Many designers tend to overlook this final point concerning accumulation: when the operating rates of upstream and downstream equipment are identical, the entire length of the accumulation lane is not available to manage unplanned downtime; only the spacing between products can provide the required buffer.

SORTATION EQUIPMENT

Belt-driven and live roller conveyors also form the basis for sortation systems. Used almost exclusively in distribution warehouses and having some application to warehouses tied to manufacturing operations, these systems are used to consolidate orders after batch picking and for product sorting to the appropriate shipping lanes. Some sorters for return products run in reverse at the receiving end.[2]

Following is a brief description of the major types of sortation systems. Table 9-3 presents a comparison of the characteristics of each type of system.

- A pusher diverter is air-operated and diverts product at right angles from a live roller or belt conveyor. Throughput is approximately 40 cartons per minute.
- A pop-up wheel sorter has an air-operated, pop-up wheel located at each divert point on a belt conveyor. Normally in a position flush with the conveyor surface, this mechanism pops up to divert a product. Skewed wheels direct the package toward the take away spur.
- A steerable roller, similar to a pop-up wheel sorter, uses powered in-line rollers at the belt conveyor level that can be switched to a skewed position for diverting. Bilateral sorting is possible.
- Deflectors and diverters use a stationary or movable arm to sweep the product laterally onto a take away conveyor. Power diverters or case pushers use a flat surface to sweep the carton from the conveyor.
- A sliding shoe slat sorter is configured from a two-strand chain conveyor fitted with tubes or slats. Each slat has a pusher shoe

TABLE 9-3
Comparison of Sortation Conveyors

| Characteristics | Deflector | Diverter | Conveyor Type | | | | |
			Pop-up Wheel	Steerable Roller	Sliding Shoe	Tilt Tray	Cross Belt
Sorting speed	Low	Low	Medium	Medium	High	High	High
Load range	Low	Medium	High	High	Medium	Medium	High
Handling of product	Medium to rough	Medium	Gentle	Gentle	Gentle	Gentle to medium	Gentle
Cost	Low	Low to medium	Medium	Medium to high	High	High	High
Maintains product orientation?	Yes	No	Yes	Yes	Yes	Yes	Yes
Type of products handled	Cartons	Cartons	Cartons/totes	Cartons/totes	Cartons/totes/envelopes	Cartons/break pack goods	Cartons/break pack goods
Bidirectional sort?	No	No	No	Yes	Yes	Yes	Yes
Ideal application	Parcels and freight baggage	Parcels and freight baggage	General merchandise, cartons, and totes	General merchandise, cartons, and totes	General merchandise, cartons, and totes	Catalog, postal parcel, and freight	Catalog, postal parcel, and freight

CHAPTER 9   CONVEYORS FOR UNIT LOAD HANDLING

that slides laterally across the width of the slat. As a carton approaches its destination, the shoes move along an angled path across the slat, sweeping the item into the divert spur.

- A tilt tray is a series of hinged trays mounted to a continuous track. Products are inducted, one per tray, into the system. When the tray reaches the appropriate sort destination, it tilts, and the product slides off onto the sort chute. The tray can tilt in either direction for bidirectional sorting.
- A cross belt sorter is like a tilt tray sorter and employs reversible belt conveyors (with belt travel perpendicular to product travel) instead of trays. When the product approaches, the cross belt powers up, directing the product onto a delivery chute or conveyor.

POWERED CONVEYORS FOR LARGE UNIT LOADS

In many cases, powered conveyors for the assembly of large unit loads can be the backbone of the factory. Since manufacturing ap-

plications can range from a simple paint line to a fully integrated system for assembly, a wide range of conveyors are available, including multiple strand chain, slat, flat top, in-floor towline, and inverted power-and-free.

Rarely is one type of conveyor the obvious choice. In some applications, two or more conveyors may meet all of the requirements. In other applications, multiple types of conveyors may be combined. A common example is the skid conveyor system. The skid conveyor is a combination of floor conveyors. Skidded car or truck bodies are conveyed over two-strand chain conveyors, roller flight accumulation conveyors, chain-driven power roller beds, and two-strand cross-transfers, with various stops along the way at lift tables, turntables, and hydraulic lifts.

To select the appropriate (and most cost-effective) conveyor type for a given assembly application, the specific material handling requirements of the application must be defined.

- What are the load capacities?
- What are the throughput requirements?
- Is asynchronous or bidirectional operation required?
- Will the application involve elevation changes?

TABLE 9-4
Comparison of In-floor Conveyor Systems for Assembly of Large Unit Loads

| Characteristics | Conveyor Type | | | |
	Inverted Power-and-free	Towline	Automated Electrified Monorail	Spinning Tube
Asynchronous operation	Yes	Requires enhancements	Yes	Yes
Ease of interfacing with manual operations	High	High	High	High
Load capacity	Medium to low	Heavy	Medium	Light
Throughput	Moderate to high	Low	Low to moderate	High
Buffering capability	Yes	Requires enhancements	Yes	Yes
Zero pressure accumulation	Yes	No	Yes	Yes
Bidirectional travel	Yes	No	Yes	Yes
Ease of reconfigurability	Low	Low	Low	Low
Required maintenance	Low to moderate	Low	Moderate	Moderate
Negotiates curves	Yes	Yes	Yes	Yes
Negotiates inclines	Yes	Requires enhancements	Requires enhancements	No
Cost	Moderate to high	Low	High	High
Load tracking capability	Yes	Yes	Yes	Yes
High positioning accuracy	Requires enhancements	No	Yes	Yes
Compatability with adverse environments	Good	Good (with enhancements)	Poor	Poor
Ideal application	Medium duty assembly with moderate throughput and elevation changes	Heavy assembly with low throughput requirements	Long travel distances where speed and precision accuracy are essential	Manufacturing processes with high throughput and positioning accuracy

CHAPTER 9   CONVEYORS FOR UNIT LOAD HANDLING

These requirements should then be compared against the capabilities of the conveyors under consideration. Although this process should narrow the list of alternatives, no one conveyor may emerge as the single solution. Attributes that a standard conveyor may not have can sometimes be "designed in." For example, the standard two-strand chain conveyor is not designed to provide load accumulation, but this can be accomplished by installing transfer devices or lift tables.

Table 9-4 compares some of the key operating characteristics of this class of unit load handling conveyor. But when it comes to powered conveyors for assembly, keep in mind that rarely is there a best solution or right answer. What matters is that the conveyor system ultimately selected meets the application requirements and performs as expected.

MULTIPLE STRAND CHAIN

As one of the most versatile and economical types of powered conveyor, chain conveyors make up a majority of the material handling equipment in manufacturing, painting, and assembly facilities. Typically used for long horizontal runs or short transfer stations, the rugged chain conveyor is capable of operating under severe conditions, including freezers, ovens, furnaces, and corrosive atmospheres. They can handle a wide range of loads, including very heavy loads weighing over 10,000 lb (4,536 kg) and operate at a variety of speeds. Maximum speed for light loads is about 200 ft (61 m)/min; for loads weighing more than 4,000 lb (1,814 kg), travel speeds are more in the range of 30 ft (9 m)/min.

Chain conveyors use many different types of chain, including roller, drop-forged, brushed, cast, and other specialty chains. Two chains (or more, depending on the application) ride in a track with a wear strip in a chain-on-flat orientation. In two strand, the most common type of chain conveyor (see Fig. 9-6), the two chains are located 2-3 in. (51-76 mm) inside the load edges. In a *chain-on-flat configuration*, the chains are used in an over-and-under mode, primarily for travel in a straight line and horizontal plane, although slight elevation changes and some horizontal turns can be negotiated.

In light-duty applications, chain conveyors can be used as inclined or declined conveyors at any angle where the load remains stable and does not slip on the chain (typically less than 7.5°). Any type of product capable of being supported by two or more strands of parallel chain may be handled. Typical products include pallets, cartons, tires, fixtures, appliances, coil stock, etc. However, the product must have bottom runners perpendicular to the direction of travel. With enhancements, a chain conveyor also can be designed to handle heavier loads at inclines. For load tracking, magnets with lead switches can be installed in the floor.

The simplicity of the standard chain conveyor is also its greatest drawback. Flexibility, in particular, is a limitation of chain conveyors. For example, nonsynchronous operation or buffering between sequential process steps is not possible without special enhancements. In the chain-on-flat configuration, turns or curves cannot be negotiated, limiting the conveyor's use to straight runs. However, both attributes can be designed into a chain conveyor by incorporating transfer devices. Because any enhancements add cost to a conveyor system, this is not always a practical strategy. However, it is a common solution when accumulation is needed at only a few points.

A variation on a *single-strand chain conveyor* that can navigate horizontal turns is the *chain-on-edge (COE) conveyor* (see Fig. 9-7). This type of conveyor also navigates vertical curves, freeing up floor space in the plant. In the chain-on-edge configuration, a drop-forged chain with assembled rider plates and pusher dogs transports four-wheel trucks through body, paint, and trim operations in a typical assembly plant.

A mainstay of automobile paint shops for years, chain-on-edge conveyors suffered from the tendency for paint to build up on their rider plates, along with the lack of any easy method for accumulating product. The advent of inverted power-and-free (discussed later in this section) has solved these problems. But for nonpaint applications, the chain-on-flat conveyor—at one third the price of other conveyor systems—continues to be the dominant technology for handling a wide range of heavy loads.

SLAT

Another variation on the chain conveyor is the *slat conveyor,* which provides a semirigid conveying surface capable of handling a wider variety of products, such as drums and coils. As shown in Figure 9-8, the typical slat conveyor consists of two strands of fabricated chain operating on support tracks. These chains are connected by a slat. The spacing of these slats will vary, depending on the type of product to be conveyed. Slats come in a variety of forms, including channel and pipe types. A special adaptation is the roller slat, that allows accumulation of product on the conveyor with low back pressure. Products that can be handled on a traditional roller conveyor also can be handled on a roller slat conveyor.

FLAT TOP

A *flat top conveyor* is a type of chain conveyor that is flush with the floor. The conveying surface is a flat plate. As shown in Figure 9-9, virtually all of the equipment is below floor level (in a pit), making it ideal for cross-conveyor access and movement. With an average operating speed of 10-30 ft (3-9 m)/min, this type of conveyor is typically used for slow speed production assembly. Smaller versions with fabricated chain also have been applied for high speed aisle transfers between multiple chain conveyor systems. This type of conveyor is commonly used in the auto industry to transport completed vehicles through final trim, repair, and wash operations.

A variation of the flat top conveyor is the *over-and-under pallet conveyor* or *fixture conveyor*. By blending the features of a flat top conveyor with the fixturing capabilities of a slat conveyor, a compact, large capacity fixturing conveyor is created without a pit. The horizontal over-and-under movement always maintains the fixturing in a relatively stationary position, keeping loads stable in a more compact conveyor structure.

IN-FLOOR TOWLINE

Another version of the chain conveyor, the *in-floor towline*, takes up a minimum of floor space, requiring only a single trench for the channel or U-shaped track section. The conveyor uses a chain-on-edge configuration. This drop-forged chain with attached four-wheeled pusher dogs or a special fabricated steel chain, provides the towing force. The towline transports four-wheel dollies or tow carts with chain engagement. Although the path is fixed, carts can typically be disengaged and handled manually, adding flexibility to the system.

A special feature of this type of chain conveyor is the ability to transport carts horizontally around turns and through multiple switches and spurs. A towline addresses the need for buffer accumulation in the assembly process to a certain extent by allowing the cart to transfer from a line with a slow production rate to a line with a faster production rate. Top speed of a towline conveyor is about 120 ft (37 m)/min.

The rugged towline conveyor has found a particular niche in heavy-duty assembly applications with relatively low throughput requirements. This conveyor also provides a good interface with automated staging systems on the factory floor.

CHAPTER 9 CONVEYORS FOR UNIT LOAD HANDLING

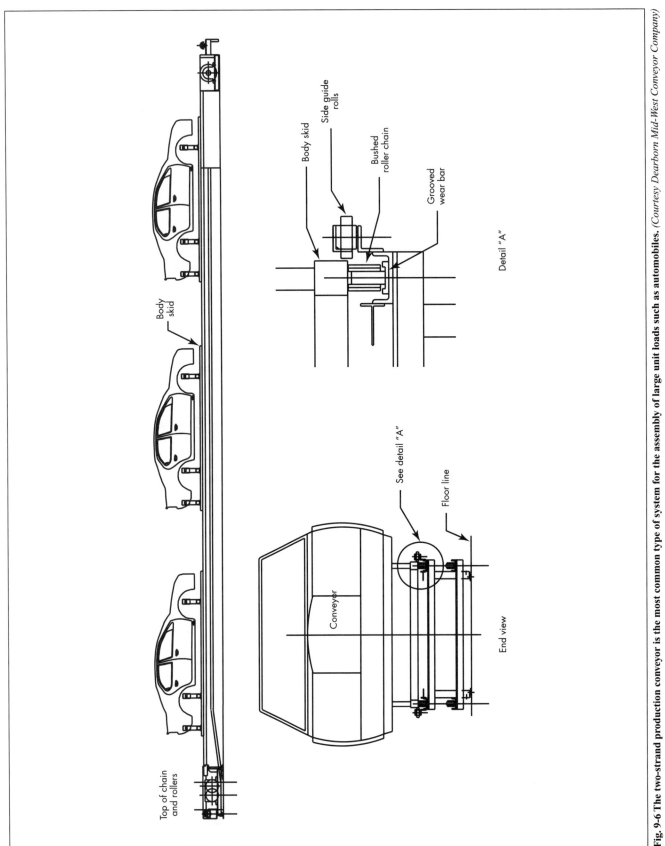

Fig. 9-6 The two-strand production conveyor is the most common type of system for the assembly of large unit loads such as automobiles. *(Courtesy Dearborn Mid-West Conveyor Company)*

CHAPTER 9   CONVEYORS FOR UNIT LOAD HANDLING

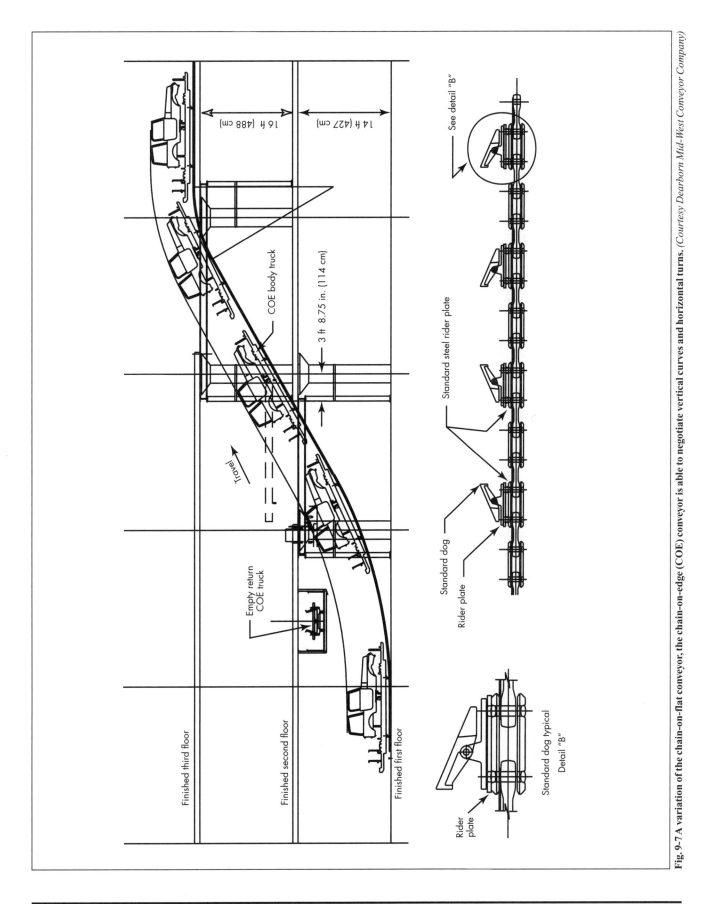

Fig. 9-7 A variation of the chain-on-flat conveyor, the chain-on-edge (COE) conveyor is able to negotiate vertical curves and horizontal turns. *(Courtesy Dearborn Mid-West Conveyor Company)*

CHAPTER 9 CONVEYORS FOR UNIT LOAD HANDLING

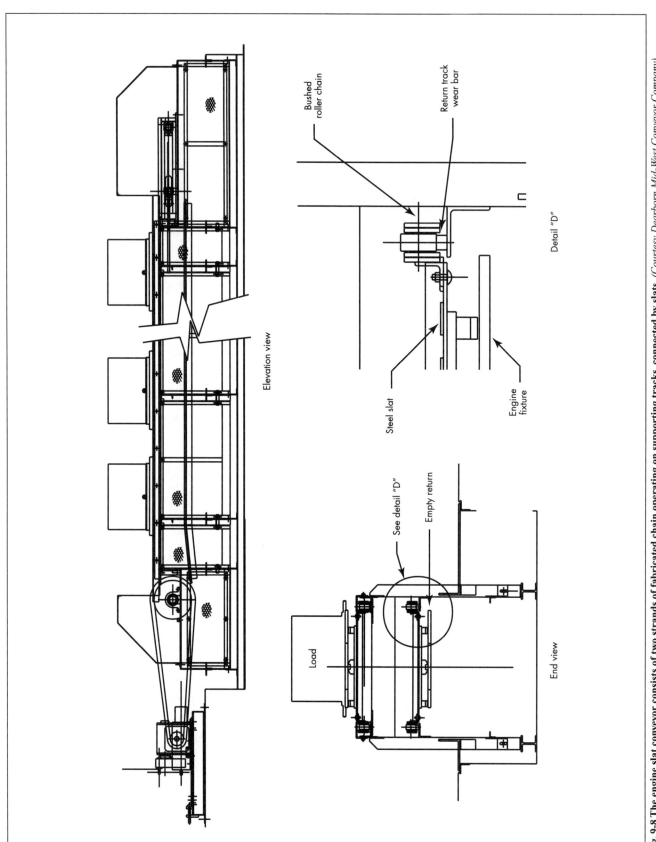

Fig. 9-8 The engine slat conveyor consists of two strands of fabricated chain operating on supporting tracks, connected by slats. *(Courtesy Dearborn Mid-West Conveyor Company)*

CHAPTER 9   CONVEYORS FOR UNIT LOAD HANDLING

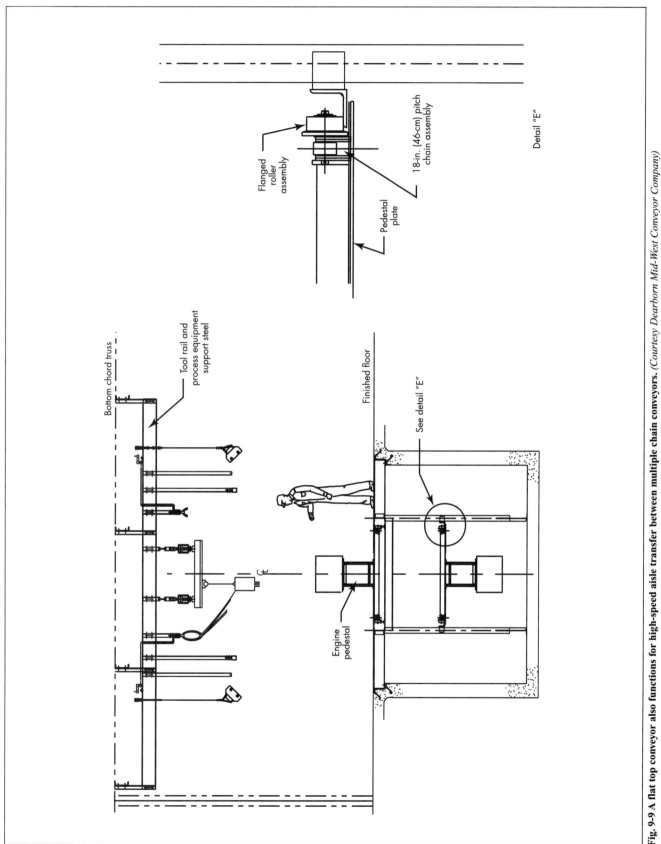

Fig. 9-9 A flat top conveyor also functions for high-speed aisle transfer between multiple chain conveyors. *(Courtesy Dearborn Mid-West Conveyor Company)*

CHAPTER 9   CONVEYORS FOR UNIT LOAD HANDLING

INVERTED POWER-AND-FREE

A special type of chain conveyor featuring a dual track, power-and-free systems for auto, appliance, and large equipment assembly plants and have gained acceptance in other light- to medium-manufacturing industries. A major advantage of power-and-free, when compared to its chain-based predecessors, is the ability to provide buffering and high-density storage between sequential processes—an integral requirement of most assembly strategies. This capability provides tremendous flexibility because individual carriers can be independently started, stopped, and accumulated for assembly work, maintenance, testing, etc., without interrupting the flow on the main assembly line.

Power-and-free conveyors were designed with the specific feature of accumulation in mind. The configuration consists of unpowered or free trolleys that ride on a power track incorporating a continuously-driven chain, as shown in Figure 9-10. This drive chain is linked to the "free" track by pusher dogs. Product carriers, typically custom-designed, can be automatically or manually switched off of the power track into spurs as required. Individual carriers also can be operated at a variety of speeds. Although the maximum speed is only in the range of 60 ft (18 m)/min, power-and-free systems are a proven conveyor technology with an extremely rugged construction.

In a power-and-free conveyor system, the load can be floor-supported (inverted) or supported overhead. A primary advantage of the inverted style is that it provides 360° access to a part, albeit at the cost of floor space. Particularly in paint shops where quality is a must, the inverted power-and-free also keeps lubricant and debris from falling onto the car bodies. With its smaller, under-the-body type carrier and sealed track, power-and-free avoids the problem of build-up on the rider plates associated with the chain-on-edge conveyor. To further ease maintenance requirements, an automatic lubrication system can be easily installed on a power-and-free system.

Power-and-free carrier design is an important consideration. Engineers have been able to significantly reduce the price and space requirements of a power-and-free system through intelligent design of the carriers. Consider, for example, a 9-ft (3-m) long assembly. If the assembly runs parallel to the direction of travel, 9 ft (3 m) of conveyor (at least) would be required to accumulate each part at a storage point. But, by designing an automotive side aperture (that is narrow with regard to its length) and locating it on a bias at a 45° angle, only a fraction of the space is required to accumulate parts or empty carriers. This results in a significant reduction in the number of structural members and amount of floor space required to operate the system.

Since the early 1930s, power-and-free conveyor systems continue to be important in manufacturing. A unique strength of power-and-free lies in its ability to easily perform elevation changes and, with enhancements, operate in harsh environments. Technology developments are also extending the range of power-and-free systems. For example, the high-speed chains on any type of conveyor system can be notoriously noisy. At least one manufacturer now offers a special package for power-and-free conveyors that reduces noise levels, even at high speeds. The package includes a special nylon tire for the chain wheels, a plastic operating link used on the chain drive, and a coating for the track that helps to dampen noise. The package is available on new systems and can be retrofit to older systems.

Despite its advantages, power-and-free technology has its limitations: its fixed path is difficult to change and the cost is significant for the relatively moderate throughput (maximum speed is about 60 ft [18 m]/min as compared to 150 ft [46 m]/min or more for a chain conveyor). Power-and-free is also limited in its ability to handle extremely heavy parts: load capacity is approximately 10,000 lb (4,536 kg). Although typically reliable in operation, when the chain

or a major drive component fails on a power-and-free conveyor, the entire system stops.

Without enhancements, power-and-free conveyors do not have extreme positioning accuracy for critical applications, such as interfacing with welding robots. However, if positioning accuracy is only required at a few points in the system, it can be achieved by installing hydraulic cylinders or some type of auxiliary positioning device. While these devices add cost to the system, they still may be the most economical solutions.

The reason for the continued popularity of the power-and-free conveyor in the U.S. may be its important historical significance: power-and-free gained a foothold in the early days of the auto industry and is a proven technology. Apparently, companies continue to use a technology they perceive to be more reliable and less costly than the alternatives. Overhead power-and-free conveyors are covered in detail in Chapter 10.

SPECIALTY IN-FLOOR CONVEYING SYSTEMS

Because of their distinctive designs, several types of systems are considered specialty conveyors. They include the automated electrified monorail, spinning tube, walking beam, and automated guided vehicle systems. Although they are not classified as conventional conveyor systems, these specialty systems compete against traditional conveyors in some applications. Often, they are best-suited to very specific types of applications. Linear induction motor (LIM) technology, that uses magnetic fields to produce thrust or linear motion, is also being applied in some specialty conveyor applications.

INVERTED AUTOMATED ELECTRIFIED MONORAIL

Although an alternative to the power-and-free conveyor, the inverted *automated electrified monorail* (AEM) is not really a conveyor system at all. In the basic AEM configuration, individually-powered carriers ride on top of a single, extruded aluminum track containing bus bars that supply power and a communications network. The friction created between the drive wheel and the fixed track provides the motive force. Carriers can switch paths, negotiate horizontal turns, and manage track sections with slight inclines, making the AEM one of the most versatile conveyor technologies available.

AEMs can also provide on-board power for carrier-mounted devices such as lifts and test fixtures, as well as reversing carrier movement for dead end spurs or areas. Unique strengths of the AEM are its extremely high travel speed (up to 600 ft [183 m]/min) and low-noise operation, making it an ideal system for applications involving long runs and rapid delivery requirements. With no moving chain and recent enhancements such as urethane wheels, an AEM operates at very low noise levels.

These features, along with the ability to position carriers within critical tolerances, have led to the growing use of AEMs in automated and flexible assembly applications. Although AEM systems were used for some time, standardization of the track size and clearances for drives and other components has helped repopularize the technology. Applications run the gamut from the delivery of heavy rolls of newsprint to presses, to the handling of circuit boards in a clean room.

AEMs themselves have a proven record, particularly in Europe, where the technology is more universally applied, however, they are

CHAPTER 9   CONVEYORS FOR UNIT LOAD HANDLING

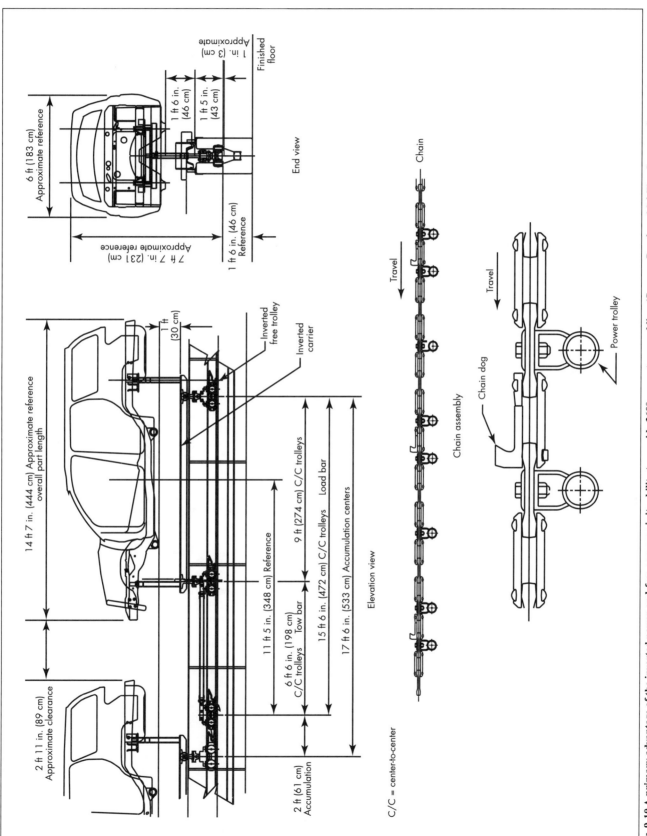

Fig. 9-10 A primary advantage of the inverted power-and-free conveyor is its ability to provide 360° access to assemblies. *(Courtesy Dearborn Mid-West Conveyor Company)*

CHAPTER 9   CONVEYORS FOR UNIT LOAD HANDLING

beginning to be used more in the U.S. Overall, AEMs actually require less hardware maintenance than conventional chain conveyor systems, but have a need for more sophisticated electronics knowledge.

One shortcoming of AEM is the apparent perception that it is a costly, high-tech conveying technology. With self-powered carriers and a higher degree of computer control, it is certainly true that AEM technology is more sophisticated than some other types of conveyor solutions. However, many people contest the idea that AEM is the most expensive technology. Nonetheless, whether the cost issue is real or merely perception, many industry observers believe that it has been an impediment to the greater use of AEM.

Efforts are being made to simplify AEM technology and lower the cost. For example, several technologies recently have been introduced that assist carriers with light to medium payloads in managing large differences in conveying elevations. The benefit is the elimination of costly auxiliary conveyors or vertical lifts. One such technology involves locating a special rail above the track that forces the second wheel against a spring pressure. The friction achieved is sufficient to overcome an angle of incline up to 30°. Another design features a special gear and rack design on the motor, combined with a rack in the design.

AEM carriers, too, are getting another look. Due to their high cost, the early vision of fully autonomous, intelligent AEM carriers has never fully materialized. In many cases, designers are keeping costs down by limiting the amount of on-board electronics; some carriers have nothing more sophisticated than a speed controller and a photocell detector to prevent collisions.

Overhead AEMs are covered in detail in Chapter 10.

SPINNING TUBE

A higher-speed alternative to power-and-free, the *spinning tube* (also known as car-on-track) is a specialized type of assembly conveyor consisting of carriers that ride along two parallel tracks. A spinning tube that contacts a drive wheel on the bottom of each carrier provides the power. This tube essentially acts as a screw to transport the cart, having an angled bottom, along a fixed path. The drive speed is varied by changing the angle of contact between the roller and the tube. Carts can accumulate on the conveyor and travel at different speeds along the path.

Although more costly than alternative technologies, spinning tube conveyors achieve a very high throughput rate with controlled acceleration and deceleration. The high positioning accuracy of the spinning tube conveyor also makes it an ideal choice for manufacturing processes involving robotic welding or automated assembly. However, load capacity of the spinning tube is not as high as some other unit load conveyor technologies, and this type of conveyor cannot be used in adverse environments such as painting operations.

WALKING BEAM

A *walking beam conveyor* consists of assembly fixtures that oscillate or index along a "beam" rather than moving continuously. Because of the fixture design, a walking beam conveyor has excellent positioning accuracy. Lacking the accumulating capability of other conveyor systems, walking beam conveyors are somewhat limited in use for assembly. However, they are frequently used in applications where the environment would adversely affect other types of systems.

AUTOMATED GUIDED VEHICLES

Automated guided vehicles (AGVs) represent another alternative to in-floor conveyor systems. Essentially driverless automated carriers, the early systems followed a guidance path embedded in the floor. The trend, however, is toward free-ranging vehicles, with sales of wireless systems now outnumbering wire-guided systems. Nonwire guidance can be accomplished in several ways: optical guidance, laser triangulation using reference points, floor-grid referencing, and gyroscopic guidance. These wireless technologies give AGVs a unique characteristic among all conveyor technologies—elimination of the fixed path.

Depending on vehicle design, the cost of an AGV system can be significant compared to alternative conveyor technologies. But with high precision accuracy and significant routing flexibility, AGVs have found a niche in a number of totally automated assembly applications, such as flexible manufacturing systems (FMS). One current trend in AGV design is systems having fewer carriers and less complexity, with some new systems now performing simple dispatch and delivery functions.

AGV systems are covered in more detail in Chapter 13.

LINEAR INDUCTION MOTORS

Linear induction motor technology works by electrically controlling the strength and timing of voltage to a series of flattened motor stators laid end-to-end along a given distance, creating an electromagnetic field that propels a flat plate (the rotor) along a horizontal plane. The rate of acceleration and deceleration is a function of the voltage applied to the motors.

The number of conveyor applications using linear induction motor (LIM) technology is few. But interest in the technology for conveyor applications is growing, due to its ability to smoothly move loads quickly, using less energy than conventional drive systems. Because the LIMs and carriers do not mechanically connect, operation is quieter and maintenance requirements are lower. Positioning accuracy is also extremely high—within approximately 0.04 in. (1 mm).

LIM technology is used today in some cross belt and tilt tray sortation systems, and in a number of specialty conveyor applications, including baggage handling systems.

SOFTWARE AND CONTROLS

Software and controls play an increasingly important role in conveyor design, extending the equipment's functionality well beyond mere transportation. With the appropriate hardware, software, and communication networks, conveyors can be designed to perform a variety of functions, including moving, tracking, buffering, merging, singulating, scanning, and sorting products.

The control system for a conveyor consists of a hierarchical structure of computer systems. As shown in Figure 9-11, which is a simplified version of a typical control system, a host (or main) computer resides at the top level. The equipment controllers, including programmable logic controls (PLCs), sensors, radio frequency (RF) devices, etc., reside at the lowest level. Software applications that execute on a mainframe or distributed personal computer (PC) create an integrated process by performing control functions, such as scheduling material movement, tracking material movement, and monitoring conveyor equipment functions, including induction, merging, and sorting. A communications network connects the peripheral devices, such as PC terminals, printers, PLCs, etc., to the host.

Although software and controls have greatly extended the functionality of conveyor systems, it is not without a cost: owners of new conveyor systems frequently complain that they failed to anticipate the maintenance requirements. Maintenance personnel must be well-versed in mechanical issues and have a good understanding of con-

CHAPTER 9   CONVEYORS FOR UNIT LOAD HANDLING

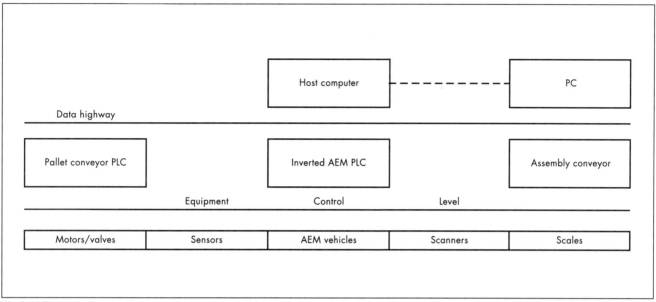

Fig. 9-11 The control system for a conveyor consists of a hierarchical structure of computer systems. *(Courtesy HK Systems)*

trols. Often, this requires additional training or the hiring of experienced personnel.

Because there is no one best approach, designing the control architecture for a conveyor system is a challenging undertaking. Some of the important characteristics of a well-designed control system are that it:

- Has well-defined interfaces.
- Uses standard components and software applications, if possible.
- Is maintainable.
- Has design flexibility.
- Uses decentralized control, if possible.
- Meets throughput, reliability, and data requirements.
- Provides feedback on material flow.
- Queues data records at the proper levels.
- Provides the required response at all levels.
- Includes detailed, up-to-date documentation.
- Has the resources and support of major vendors.

EQUIPMENT CONTROL DEVICES

Conveyor equipment controllers include PLCs, sensors, and scanners. This section describes the typical functions and design considerations associated with these components.

Programmable Logic Controllers (PLCs)

In a conveyor system, a PLC is responsible for all functions associated with equipment control and product data tracking. The memory of the PLC is organized in a logical manner that allows a modular approach to program development and troubleshooting. In general, the conveyor PLC will:

- Provide safety interlocks (in addition to hard-wired safety circuits) to ensure the safety of all personnel and equipment.
- Perform start and stop sequencing of conveyor motors and associated equipment to ensure collision-free movement and a smooth, efficient flow of product on the conveyor.
- Provide a level of load tracking that will ensure product data integrity during movement on the conveyor.
- Provide fault detection, alarm annunciation, proper recovery procedures, and conveyor status information as required.

Device control and load tracking controls software is the main and often largest portion of the PLC program. In this module, the PLC monitors all inputs and controls all outputs for conveyor devices such as motor starters and solenoids. The PLC monitors and commands load movement and transfers tracking data from one logical zone to another as required. This tracking scheme allows for the proper diversion of loads to the destination locations on the conveyor systems.

In the fault and status logic routines module, the PLC monitors inputs and outputs such that if a specific event is not received within a preset time frame, a fault condition is set. This condition may then be used in the load movement logic section to inhibit motion for the faulted piece of equipment. Status information is also located in this section of logic. Typical conveyor faults include:

- Zone fault—a load did not move from one conveyor zone to the next within a preset time period or a load is detected in a zone when no load is expected.
- Conveyor equipment fault—a transfer device output is on and its associated position indicator does not turn on within a preset time period.

The PLC also executes the logic necessary to communicate to the host computer system. The type of information communicated includes PLC-initiated messages (load arrivals and departures, fault information), as well as host-initiated messages (such as load releases). These routines enable the PLC to receive important pallet information, such as load identification and destination from the host, at critical decision points throughout the conveyor system. This information is then used to make control decisions and route the loads to their final destinations. Because these routines only interact with the host at specific points on the conveyor, once pallet information is passed down, the PLC can control the movement of the pallet until it encounters another PLC and host computer interface point. However, the capacity of a PLC and the exact functions it performs will depend on the type and complexity of the system.

Sensors

Sensors play an important role in conveyor operations. They provide the ability to detect the presence of an object at a specific

CHAPTER 9   CONVEYORS FOR UNIT LOAD HANDLING

location, sort or count products, and in some cases, provide a means of data transmission by light. Often, a conveyor incorporates a combination of contact and noncontact sensors to accomplish these functions.

A limit switch is a type of mechanical sensing device that contacts the object. This low-cost sensing technology has a long, reliable track record in conveyor systems and is easy to apply. Although limit switches typically enjoy a long operating life, their misapplication can result in premature failures. For example, it is important to use these devices only within their specified contact ratings and in the operating environment for which they were designed. Limit switches also should be rigidly mounted with suitable clearances in an accessible location. The cover plates on the switch should be facing out.[3]

There are several basic types of noncontact sensors, also called *proximity switches*, used in conveyor systems. These sensors are able to detect an object without contact by the presence of a magnetic field, changes in dielectric characteristics, the propagation of sound, or reflected light. One major advantage when compared to mechanical switches is that noncontact sensors have no moving parts or electrical contacts that can wear out.

The most common type is the *photoelectric proximity sensor*. Consisting of a light source (typically LED-generated infrared light) and a receiver or reflector, these optical sensors use a light beam instead of a lever arm as the sensing device. There are several different modes of this sensing technology. *Retroreflective sensors,* which send out an infrared beam that is reflected back to the photo detector, are the most common type of photoelectric. A *diffuse reflector sensor* works in much the same manner, although it reads the light reflected back from the object rather than the retroreflective target. This type of sensor is ideal for applications where there is access to only one side of the target. A *through-beam photoelectric sensor* that uses a remote receiving unit is also ideal for applications having access to only one side of the target. The receiving device reads the signal generated by the transmitter unless the beam is broken as an object passes by.

Two major advantages of photoelectrics are their greater range and faster operating speeds (approximately 2,500 pulses per second). They also excel at sensing small objects. On the downside, photoelectrics are sensitive to dirt and dust. While frequent cleaning or a pulsed signal can help overcome this problem, a clean operating environment is desirable. Photoelectric sensors also can be tricky to align during setup.

An *inductive proximity sensor* uses an oscillator to produce a radio frequency (RF) signal that is partly absorbed by the object. This type of sensor is fast (operating at about 1,000 pulses per second) and resistant to electrical noise, as well as harsh environments. A limitation of this technology is that it is designed to detect metal objects. While these sensors can detect nonferrous metal objects, their range is more limited. A shielded construction may increase the sensing distance and will concentrate the electromagnetic field to the front of the sensor face.

Although more expensive than other sensing devices, *ultrasonic sensors* have potential application in conveyor systems. A major advantage is their great versatility. Because this type of sensor uses sound as the sensing medium rather than light, it is impervious to dust and dirt, variations in color, and targets with reflective surfaces.

Data transmission sensors are a relatively new class of devices. An alternative to hard-wired systems, these sensors use infrared light to transmit data from a host station to mobile carriers on AEMs, power-and-free conveyors, and other types of conveyor systems.

Some considerations when selecting the appropriate sensing device for a conveyor application include:

- Type of operating environment.
- Type of load (open or closed structure).
- Spacing between targets.
- Metal or nonmetal target.
- Operating speed of the conveyor.
- Accuracy level required.
- Response time required.
- Two-sided access to the target.
- Distance between target and sensor.

In any conveyor system, each sensor has a specific role in tracking product. Although exact placement will be a function of package size and spacing, sensors should be strategically located at points where information on product location is desired.[4]

Scanners

Fixed position laser scanners are the basic means of collecting bar-coded information on assembly conveyors. They can be mounted on the side of a conveyor, above it, or beneath it, depending on the location of the bar code to be scanned. (For a bottom read, the space between rollers or the gap between belts provides a scanning window.) The scanner sends the bar code signal to a decoder that interprets the signal and activates control conveyor mechanisms that route the product to a particular workstation or other destination.

Variations of the bar code scanner include the read only and read and write system. Read and write systems employ tags containing product information, including build options, product identification (ID) number, and process destinations.

Conveyor sensors frequently work in tandem with bar code scanners. In fact, photoelectric sensors are the most common method of enabling a scanner. The photoelectric sensor initiates the enable by sending an input signal that an object is passing through the scanning area. Enable continues until the sensor is no longer blocked by the object.

One of the advantages of scanners is that they now feature many of the controls that once had to be designed into the conveyor system. In selecting a scanner for a conveyor application, conveyor speed and width should be considered. Also, the conveyor design should incorporate a lane for no-reads and misreads.

SYSTEM CONTROL SOFTWARE

PLCs control the individual functions of a conveyor system separately, creating isolated islands of information and data. A variety of software applications are available that integrate these islands by providing a real-time interface to equipment level controllers and the host computer.

System control software, when executed on distributed PLCs or PCs, perform data acquisition and information processing functions. This includes the monitoring of loading areas and equipment functions such as jam status, subsystems or panel on/off status, diagnostic data collection and reports, jam detection, and sequential load routing and optimization. They also perform various command and control functions, including scheduling of material movement, tracking of material movement, communicating order information to conveyor systems, and in the case of PC-based applications, performing other complex tasks that may not be appropriate for PLCs.

Many of these functions can be customized to an application's exact requirements. With additional hardware, they can also communicate with other monitors and host systems.

One of the major benefits of software applications is the availability of data. Conveyor owners can now monitor and report almost any aspect of their system's performance. This data can be extremely useful for troubleshooting and maintenance activities. Some in-

CHAPTER 9   CONVEYORS FOR UNIT LOAD HANDLING

novative users also use the data to compare actual to expected system performance.

A truism with all conveyors is that changes will be made throughout the life of the system. When it comes to software in particular, concise documentation of all modifications (even the most basic details) is critical to the continued successful operation of the system. Unfortunately, many companies underestimate the power of the written record until they cannot locate the original source code for an upgrade project.

EMULATION

Emulation testing allows the conveyor designer to test out all control functions before field installation, reducing equipment start-up costs and integration activities, and minimizing risk. Emulation involves developing a detailed, graphical computer model that mimics the technical hardware to be controlled. Specific conveyor-related parameters that can be specified in the model include exact conveyor section length and width, speed, and sensor actuation timing. System inputs, such as limit switches or photoeyes, can be instructed to turn on or off at specific times to detect events such as pallet presence or pallet transfer position. Information sensors, such as bar code scanners and RF tag readers, also can be replicated by placing a unique data string within each emulated pallet entity.

An emulation model can be used to test multiple "what-if" scenarios that would prove costly or dangerous if done in the field. This scenario testing provides for safer and more robust conveyor control programs before field implementation. Emulation also greatly reduces the amount of time needed for software debug. Another significant benefit is the ability to obtain a realistic estimate of throughput. By having control of conveyor length, width, speed, and sensor positioning, system throughput can be roughly tested before system implementation.

JUSTIFICATION

Financial justification may be the most challenging aspect of a conveyor project. The reason is twofold. Hardware progressively accounts for less of the total conveyor system cost, making it more difficult to estimate true costs. At the same time, the benefits are increasingly for a conveyor system regarding intangibles such as greater flexibility or higher product quality. This makes it more difficult to come up with the actual savings.

Some people believe that a conveyor system will never be justified unless the throughput requirements demand it. While that may be true in some cases, many a conveyor system that provides a desired function, eliminates an undesirable condition, or fits into the firm's overall strategic plan has been justified. Some conveyor projects even get justified because they head off a potential disaster, such as total system failure. "Telling a compelling story," says one financial manager, "is the easiest way to justify anything."

To that end, this section examines how to generate and effectively communicate the expected return on a proposed conveyor project. It offers guidelines for calculating the costs and savings (both hard and soft) of a proposed project. It also reviews four popular methods for calculating a project's return on investment that incorporate the notion of the time value of money.

COSTS

Basing price on length is misleading because the complexity and functionality of a conveyor greatly influence its cost. A gravity skate wheel conveyor is very simple; an inverted power-and-free conveyor can get very complex, due to the controls, accumulation stations, carriers, etc. Some estimates for the cost of the software and controls in a conveyor system, as a portion of total cost, can range as high as 40%.

One way to develop a more accurate cost estimate is to break the conveyor system down into individual components. (Cost data can be obtained from a variety of sources, past projects, conveyor manufacturers, or consultants.) Obviously, the finer the breakdown, the higher the accuracy of the estimate. Also, it allows the engineer to explore the impact of changes to the design. Typically, this breakdown consists of the following categories:

- Materials.
- Installation (labor, supplies, equipment).
- Mechanical and electrical.
- Software and controls.

Taking the concept one step further, each of these categories can then be broken down into individual components. For example, some of the mechanical components of a monorail would include vertical curves, turns, straight rail sections, and a conveyor guard.

To ensure a valid return on investment (ROI), an accurate estimate of these costs is crucial. When estimating cost, be aware of hidden costs. For example, if the new conveyor system is going to require significantly more maintenance time, that cost should be included in the estimate. Finally, be wary of any low-ball bids. If a vendor is bidding a job with no margin for profit, the company may not work very hard to ensure the project's success.

SAVINGS

The savings associated with a new conveyor system can be tangible or intangible. *Tangible savings* are the benefits that are easily identified and quantified. They typically include items such as the savings in direct labor, elimination of overtime hours, lower maintenance costs, less production downtime, and reduction of scrap. The salvage value of the new system at the end of its life is also included as part of the cash inflow.

Intangible savings are elusive. One problem is that automated manufacturing plants have less direct labor content. Indirect labor is often lumped into a large overhead category, making it difficult to sort out the actual costs associated with a conveyor project. Another problem is that it is notoriously difficult to quantify certain benefits, such as increased safety, greater flexibility, or improved ergonomics. Coming up with the actual dollar savings will require some good detective work. If safety is increased, do workers' compensation records reflect the cost of accidents? Does greater flexibility eliminate downtime due to line changeovers? If product quality will be higher, what is the current cost of rework or returns?

RETURN ON INVESTMENT

In considering whether or not a proposed project should be funded, most companies use a combination of net present value, the payback method, the profitability index, and internal rate of return. These methods all incorporate the notion of the time value of money. In other words, that a dollar today is worth more than a dollar tomorrow. This requires that costs or savings that are expected in the future be discounted. The discount rate is typically the desired rate of return.

Net Present Value

Net present value (NPV) takes into account the time value of money by discounting the expected cash flows from each year of a proposed project (see Eq. 9-1). These individual cash flows are then

CHAPTER 9   CONVEYORS FOR UNIT LOAD HANDLING

added together to obtain the project's NPV. An NPV of zero (break-even) or a positive number is typically considered a good investment opportunity.

$$NPV = -C_o + \sum_{t=1}^{n} [C_n \div (1 + r)^n] \qquad (1)$$

where:

NPV	=	net present value
C_o	=	initial investment
n	=	time period over which project is evaluated
C_1 through C_n	=	expected cash flows
r	=	company rate of return

The Payback Method

The payback method looks at how quickly a project pays back the initial investment or breaks even. This involves constructing a table of the NPV of the project by year, until it reaches zero or becomes positive (see Eq. 9-2). In general, the shorter the payback period, the more attractive the investment opportunity. Two years is considered the threshold for many investments.

$$NPV = 0 = -C_o + \sum_{t=1}^{n} [C_n \div (1 + r)^n] \qquad (2)$$

where:

NPV	=	net present value
C_o	=	initial investment
n	=	time period over which project is evaluated
C_1 through C_n	=	expected cash flows
r	=	company rate of return

Profitability Index

The profitability index (PI) is closely related to NPV (see Eq. 9-3). Projects with an index greater than one are considered desirable.

$$PI = D_i \div D_o \qquad (3)$$

where:

PI	=	profitability index
D_i	=	discounted cash inflows
D_o	=	discounted cash outflows

Internal Rate of Return

The internal rate of return (IRR) can be used to calculate a project's expected return at the breakeven point. To calculate IRR, the NPV is set equal to zero and the discount rate is solved for in the NPV equation (see Eq. 9-4).

$$NPV = 0 = -C_o + \sum_{t=1}^{n} [C_n \div (1 + IRR)^n] \qquad (4)$$

where:

NPV	=	net present value
C_o	=	initial investment
n	=	time period over which project is evaluated
C_1 through C_n	=	expected cash flows
IRR	=	internal rate of return

DEALING WITH UNCERTAINTY

Uncertainty is part of any project. Given this fact, contingency estimates should always be included as part of the NPV calculation, particularly with line items that are historically problematic, such as software debugging. Examining how a project's ROI will be affected over a range of conditions is another way of managing uncertainty. This type of sensitivity analysis is often done by specifying a range. This range is bounded at the top by the best case (everything goes perfectly and all forecasts are accurate) and at the bottom by the worst case (everything that can go wrong, will, and the forecasts are all wrong). Some of the factors that should be considered in the worst case scenario are: wrong forecasts of expected throughput (both high and low), project delays, and unexpected design changes.

Hopefully, a project engineer will never have to deal with a worst case situation, but the prudent one will have considered all of the possible scenarios. This exercise should also help the project manager answer the following questions, typically asked by senior management:

- Can we wait and do nothing?
- Is the schedule realistic?
- What unique risks does this project pose?
- What is the impact on the project's NPV if start-up is delayed?
- What alternatives did you evaluate and why is this the best?
- What is the impact on the project's NPV if forecasts of throughput are too high?

CONVEYOR SAFETY

Each year, more than 9,000 conveyor-related accidents are reported in the U.S., and in 1995 accounted for 12% of all equipment-related fatalities (Fig. 9-12). Although most accidents are typically the result of several contributing factors, the most common causes of conveyor accidents are: the lack of appropriate safety devices; the removal or disabling of equipment safety devices; the altering of equipment, such that safety devices are rendered ineffective; and the failure to enforce or comply with conveyor safety rules.

Also problematic is the fact that a variety of people interface with a conveyor system, from the conveyor manufacturer, contractor, and designer, to the operators, maintenance personnel, and even other workers in the facility. Not everyone receives the appropriate safety training. A particular challenge is training for assembly workers. Although assembly workers typically interface with conveyor systems, they do not actually operate the equipment, as do lift truck drivers, for example. This can lead to the incorrect assumption that training is not necessary. Conveyor training is required for all plant personnel, whether they install, maintain, operate, or merely work in the vicinity of a conveyor system.

ESTABLISHING A SAFETY PROGRAM

Experts agree that most of these accidents could be avoided through the diligent efforts of plant management to develop and enforce a conveyor safety program, and a willingness to take disciplinary action if safety rules are violated. In general, a safety program consists of the following elements:

- Compliance with the ANSI B20.1 standard and Occupational Safety and Health Administration (OSHA) rules relating to the proper installation and operation of conveyors.
- Identification and elimination of potential hazards.
- Use of warning signs as required.
- Emergency training in operational, maintenance, and stop procedures.
- Enforcement of safety rules.

CHAPTER 9   CONVEYORS FOR UNIT LOAD HANDLING

A starting point for establishing a conveyor safety program is to become familiar with the relevant standards. The ANSI B20.1, "Safety Standard for Conveyors and Related Equipment," is a performance standard that relates to the proper installation and operation of conveyor systems. This standard has been issued periodically since 1947. The Conveyor Equipment Manufacturers' Association (CEMA) is also a good source of conveyor safety information. Also, federal regulations issued by the Department of Labor's Mine Safety and Health Administration (MASA) make reference to conveyor guarding, as well as operational methods and procedures.

COMMON HAZARDS

Conveyor safety can be dramatically improved by the identification and elimination of potential hazards. Most conveyor accidents happen at an action point, such as the infeed or outfeed, exposed edges on the conveyor, or at a point of power transmission. Common hazards include the following:

- Nip points generally encountered in conveyor usage are incident to the transmission of power or the application of motion. A *nip point*, by definition, is where two moving or rotating elements of the conveyor operate in proximity such that objects (fingers, long hair, clothing, etc.) contacting this area can be nipped, pinched, squeezed, sucked in, or trapped. An ex-

ample is the contact point between the conveying belt and drive pulleys. Pinch points are also created by the exposed edges of a conveyor, such as chain and sprocket transmissions. Nip points can also occur at the interface between a conveyor and another type of process equipment or at a transfer mechanism.

- Unlike a nip point that involves two moving elements, a *shear point* or *shear line* is created when a moving part of the conveyor passes close to a stationary object, leaving just enough clearance to trap an object. An example of a shear point is the area between the take-up on a belt conveyor and the frame. Shear points also can be unintentionally created by people installing the conveyor equipment. When a conveyor is not properly located, the building structure, equipment operating in conjunction with the conveyor, and even equipment not related to the conveyor's operation but located in proximity to it, can form a shear point.

- A *spill point* occurs at a location where material could fall or slip off the conveyor. Overhead conveyor sections are of particular concern, though care should be taken with conveyors located at or near a level grade to guard against products falling off the conveyor and striking workers in the vicinity.

- *Counterweights* are used to balance or oppose a load and are supported overhead by belts, cables, chains, or similar means. Failure to carefully check the counterweight protection against

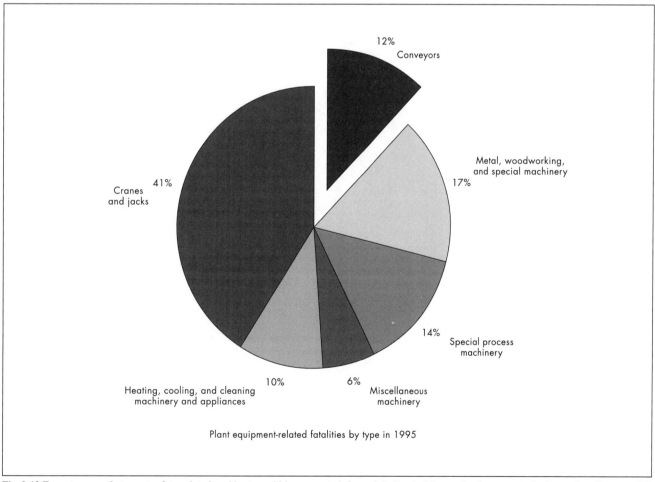

Plant equipment-related fatalities by type in 1995

12% Conveyors

17% Metal, woodworking, and special machinery

14% Special process machinery

6% Miscellaneous machinery

10% Heating, cooling, and cleaning machinery and appliances

41% Cranes and jacks

Fig. 9-12 Experts agree that most safety-related accidents could be prevented through better training and enforcement of safety rules. *(Courtesy U.S. Department of Labor, Bureau of Labor Statistics, Fatal Injuries by Primary Source)*

CHAPTER 9   CONVEYORS FOR UNIT LOAD HANDLING

location could pose a safety hazard, as changes in the location of conveyor components can result in varying degrees of counterweight guarding being required.

• Falling materials from elevated sections of conveyor that are situated over pedestrian walkways, vehicle lanes, and workstations pose an obvious safety hazard.

SAFETY DEVICES

The first priority in conveyor safety is to eliminate potential hazards whenever possible. One of the most common strategies is to install guarding on all sections of a conveyor that have exposed, moving parts. As shown in Figure 9-13, conveyor guarding is typically constructed of solid sheet or perforated metal, but in some cases may be fabricated out of wire mesh or plastic. The guard is securely fastened to the building or conveyor frame to provide a covering or barricade. Sometimes special designs are required for adequate edge protection. On a belt-driven, live roller conveyor, for example, paddle guards may be used to protect the area between the rollers and belt on radius curves. On the straight sections, pop-out rollers are commonly used. The axle on this type of roller floats freely in the bed frame, popping out if fingers, hands, clothing, or other objects become wedged between the roller and drive bed.

Spill guards, of either solid sheet or open construction, prevent material from falling off the conveyor. The sides and ends of the guard should be of sufficient height and strength to retain materials. As an alternative, the guard may be angled so that spillage will be directed into a discharge lane or container.

To meet the requirements of a particular application, guards for overhead conveyor sections are generally fabricated in the field. These guards are typically constructed of wire mesh panels, expanded metal, or solid steel sheet material. The size of the carrier or load will determine the required height and width of the guard opening. Curved sections should be designed to allow sufficient clearance.

A conveyor can be guarded by location or position if all moving parts are remote from a floor, platform, walkway, or workplace, or protected from accidental contact by their relationship to a frame, foundation, or structure. In general, a conveyor is considered guarded if it is located 7 ft (2 m), above the floor (9 ft [3 m] in the case of potential nip points).

Mechanical guarding is often combined with electrical safety devices. For example, guards may be put up around the exposed edges of a conveyor, and an emergency pull cord run parallel to the conveyor and fixed to one end of the actuating arm on a stop switch.

A conveyor owner "...shall furnish to each of his employees employment and a place of employment which is free from recognized hazards that are caused or likely to cause death or serious physical harm..."[5] While general industry standards contain no direct references to conveyor safety, it is incumbent upon the conveyor owner to comply with the information set forth in these rules.

The design of the workplace should provide safe access to and from work areas, emergency exits, reasonable noise levels in work areas, and adequate safety protection. Safe access to maintenance points, such as drives and take-ups, also must be provided. For overhead conveyor sections, additional site-specific safety features in-

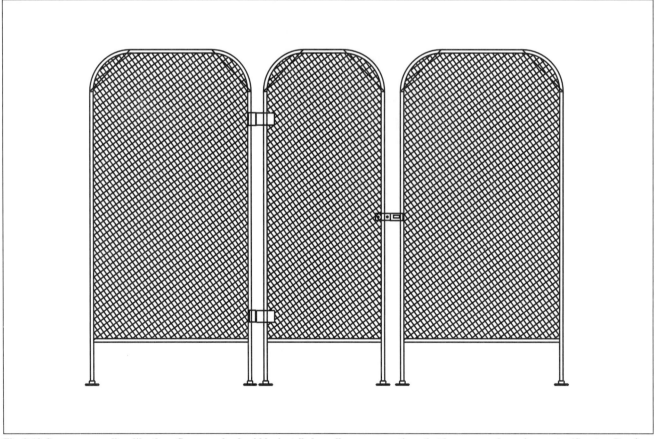

Fig. 9-13 Conveyor guarding, like these floor panels, should be installed on all conveyor sections that have exposed, moving parts. *(Courtesy Dearborn Mid-West Conveyor Company)*

CHAPTER 9   CONVEYORS FOR UNIT LOAD HANDLING

clude walkways, crossovers, low headroom protection, railings, and large service platforms.

Conditions can prevail where guarding or other protection may not be practical. One example is on assembly lines that use overhead or slat conveyors. Where the intermediate sections of a conveyor are not guarded and there is even a slight chance of accidental contact, the owner is responsible for posting adequate warning signs or personnel barriers.

The goal of warning signs is to enhance safety by modifying human behavior. These signs rarely deal with hidden dangers. Mostly, they warn against hazards that are obvious. In general terms, the law requires that warning signs:

- Must catch the attention of a prudent person.
- Must be comprehensible to the average user and convey the extent of the danger.
- Warn with a degree of intensity that would cause the prudent person to exercise appropriate caution.
- Tell the user how to avoid the danger.

CEMA offers a series of conveyor warning labels. These labels contain a cautionary message and a graphic illustration of the hazard at hand. Figure 9-14 provides a checklist for the selection of appropriate conveyor safety labels.

TRAINING

OSHA requires training in conveyor safety for all employees. This training should include instruction on emergency stop and lockout and tagout procedures. Most experts believe that many injuries could have been prevented if the power to the conveyor had simply been shut off. The lockout and tagout provision, intended to prevent an unintentional start-up during the maintenance of powered equipment, requires that all power switches be lockable or key-operated. Training should also cover the written information appearing in the operations and maintenance manuals for the conveyor system. It is the owner's responsibility to distribute and upgrade this information and make copies of these manuals available to employees.

NOISE CONSIDERATIONS

Conveyor systems can be a major source of noise in a busy manufacturing plant, particularly if they are operating at high speeds or there are multiple lines operating in proximity. OSHA's maximum permissible exposure limit for noise is 90 decibels (dB[A]), measured as an eight-hour, time-weighted average (TWA). OSHA also requires a hearing conservation program if workers are subjected to a noise level that equals or exceeds 85 dB(A) for more than eight

hours daily as a TWA. Typically, a doubling in perceived loudness requires a six decibel change; the smallest change the human ear can detect is approximately three decibels. Figure 9-15 shows how conveyors compare to other noise sources.

Speed has a significant influence on conveyor noise. A line shaft conveyor operating at 60 ft (18 m)/min, for example, has a level of between 69-70 dB(A). If that same conveyor is operating at 150 ft (46 m)/min, the noise level increases to 78-80 dB(A). Even in the electronics industry, where a conveyor operating at 60 ft (18 m)/min would be considered fast, there is an increasing desire to not only meet, but significantly beat OSHA's noise requirements. The motivation is twofold: assembly workers are typically exposed to conveyor noise for extended periods, and there is a growing recognition that a better working environment leads to healthy, more productive workers.

Attention has naturally focused on identifying sources of conveyor noise and developing strategies to reduce or eliminate them. In a live roller conveyor, the rattle of commercial-grade bearings is a primary source of noise. Replacing commercial bearings with precision bearings that are enclosed in plastic and use separators can reduce noise levels by about 5-10 dB(A). As the cost of precision bearings increases per roller, many designers use precision bearings only in those conveyor sections that are near work areas.

Shaft clatter that occurs when a hexagonal roller shaft moves up and down in the mounting hole is another irksome source of noise. Strategies to retain the axle in the bearing (thereby eliminating the noise) include special, spring-loaded, tapered axles and wedges or clips. A steel chain passing over the sprockets also generates noise. Substituting fiber composite belts for the chain or including jump chains, right angle slave drives, and other accessories, will reduce noise levels.

The electric motors that provide the power for conveyors are another source of noise. When drives cannot be located away from work areas, placing them in an enclosure lined with sound deadening material will help to muffle the noise. Precision gears and motorized pulleys also reduce noise.

Often, the product itself is a source of noise. Generally, the contact of steel pans or even plastic totes moving on a roller conveyor is noisier than a steel pan on a belt conveyor, or corrugated boxes on any type of conveyor. One noise reducing strategy is to line the roller tube with some type of sound deadening material.

One of the frustrations in conveyor design is that overall sound levels cannot be determined in advance. The actual noise level will be a function of the environment where the conveyor operates. Building acoustics, and particularly the ceiling height and construction materials used in walls, ceilings, and floors, are major factors in determin-

Is the label:	Does the text:
☐ Clearly visible?	☐ Identify the hazard?
☐ Readable?	☐ Indicate the degree of risk?
☐ Attention-getting?	☐ Indicate the consequence of exposure?
☐ Scaled in size to the equipment?	☐ Identify means of avoiding hazard?
☐ In proximity to hazard?	☐ Identify actions to be taken if exposure occurs?
☐ Appropriately color-coded?	☐ Conform to standards, regulations, and practices?

Fig. 9-14 This checklist contains some of the elements that should be considered when selecting safety labels for a conveyor system. *(Courtesy Siebert Engineers)*

CHAPTER 9   CONVEYORS FOR UNIT LOAD HANDLING

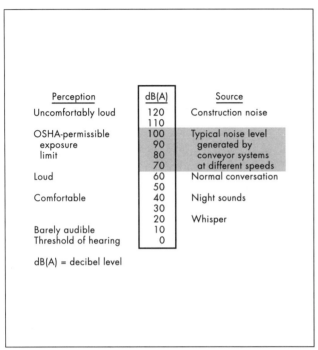

Perception	dB(A)	Source
Uncomfortably loud	120	Construction noise
	110	
OSHA-permissible	100	Typical noise level
exposure	90	generated by
limit	80	conveyor systems
	70	at different speeds
Loud	60	Normal conversation
	50	
Comfortable	40	Night sounds
	30	
	20	Whisper
Barely audible	10	
Threshold of hearing	0	

dB(A) = decibel level

Fig. 9-15 Conveyors operate within a large range of the decibel scale. Typically, a doubling in perceived loudness requires a six decibel change.

ing the overall noise levels. Heavy materials such as concrete absorb sound, while a tin roof may actually amplify it. Powered equipment operating in the vicinity of the conveyor also influences noise levels. However, because decibels are logarithms of noise levels, they are not additive in the usual way. In fact, it may not be worthwhile to worry about reducing the noise of a conveyor operating next to a punch press or other equipment that is substantially louder.

If taking the steps to reduce conveyor noise does not seem worthwhile, keep in mind that a conveyor that is quiet also performs better, needs less maintenance, and has a longer equipment life.

References

1. Material Handling Institute. *Application Guidelines for Gravity Roller and Wheel Conveyors.* Charlotte, NC: The Conveyor Product Section of Material Handling Institute (MHI), 1993.
2. Material Handling Institute. *Considerations for Conveyor Sortation Systems.* Charlotte, NC: The Conveyor Product Section of MHI, 1989.
3. Material Handling Institute. *Considerations when Planning and Implementing Integrated Material Handling Systems.* Charlotte, NC: Integrated Systems and Controls Product, A Council of the Material Handling Institute, 1992.
4. Material Handling Institute. *Sensors: Terminology and Application Within the Material Handling Industry.* Charlotte, NC: Integrated Systems and Controls, A Council of the Material Handling Institute, 1994.
5. Occupational Safety and Health Administration (OSHA). *General Duty Clause, Section 5(a)-1.* Washington: OSHA.

Bibliography

American National Standards Institute. ANSI B20.1. *Safety Standard for Conveyors and Related Equipment.* Washington: American National Standards Institute, 1947, 1972 (www.ansi.org).
Conveyor Equipment Manufacturers Association (CEMA) Standard No. 401. *Roller Conveyors—Nonpowered.* Manassas, VA: CEMA, 1985.
CEMA Standard No. 402. *Belt Conveyors.* Manassas, VA: CEMA, 1985.
CEMA Standard No. 403. *Belt-driven Live Roller Conveyors.* Manassas, VA: CEMA, 1985.
CEMA Standard No. 404. *Chain-driven Live Roller Conveyors.* Manassas, VA: CEMA, 1985.
CEMA Standard No. 405. *Slat Conveyors.* Manassas, VA: CEMA, 1985.
CEMA *Conveyor Terms and Definitions 102.* Manassas, VA: CEMA, 1988.
Federal Regulation Code 30, Parts 0-199, Subparts M and Q. Washington: Department of Labor, Mine Safety and Health Administration (MASA).
Kulwiec, Raymond A. *Materials Handling Handbook,* 2nd Edition. New York: John Wiley & Sons, 1985.
White, John A. *Production Handbook,* 4th Edition. New York: John Wiley & Sons, 1987.

CHAPTER 10

OVERHEAD HANDLING AND LIFTING DEVICES

CHAPTER CONTENTS

This chapter reviews and describes the major types of overhead handling equipment and lifting devices that are used in industrial applications. Although this chapter does not cover many custom-designed or hybrid types of equipment, it does include all of the designs commonly encountered today.

INTRODUCTION

In a broad range of industries, overhead handling equipment provides the muscle to move and position loads varying from auto bodies and heavy steel fabrications to delicate computer components. The use of overhead handling equipment frees up valuable floor space in manufacturing and assembly plants, as well as in supporting warehouses, maximizing the efficient use of these buildings. When properly selected for the application, overhead handling equipment serves as a safe and efficient material handling solution.

Overhead handling equipment can be simply defined as equipment that can lift, transport, and lower loads (or only transport loads) while suspending them by some overhead device. The various types of overhead equipment range from simple manual cranes and hoists to sophisticated, fully-automated production, sortation, and transport systems.

Overhead handling equipment is capable of efficiently handling loads of many different sizes and weights in a wide variety of industries. This type of equipment is found in plants that manufacture or perform final assembly work on automobiles, aircraft, appliances, marine equipment, lawn equipment, farm and construction equipment—the list is almost endless. With the move toward increasing use of outsourcing, this equipment is also seen in factories that manufacture components and in subassembly plants that produce items such as axles, engines, seats, and instrument panels.

In addition to defining and describing the various types of overhead handling equipment, this chapter outlines the main equipment fundamentals that should be considered when choosing between the different types of equipment.

Several major overhead equipment groups are reviewed in general terms, and specific details are given for many of the types of equipment that fall within these main categories. The major equipment groups include:

- Manual and powered overhead cranes.
- Overhead trolley conveyors (OTC).
- Overhead power-and-free conveyors (OHPF).
- Automated electrified monorails (AEMs).
- Drop/lift section transfers (DLT).

EQUIPMENT SELECTION

Selecting the optimum type of overhead handling equipment should be a decision that is driven primarily by the performance requirements of a specific application. Other considerations such as cost and maintainability must be factored into the decision-making process as well, but satisfying the material handling needs of the application should always be the primary driver. For some applications, the type of equipment will be self-evident; for others, there may be more than one right answer. Let the unique requirements of the specific application point the way.

Manufacturing and Production Flexibility

Manufacturing or production flexibility is the initial consideration in the selection process, while equipment costs are generally the last factor in the mix. Ultimately, the cost of the equipment may force a decision that is at odds with the selection conclusion based on the other factors. The final selection decision, then, may be driven by factors other than the material handling requirements of the specific application.

Maintainability and Reliability

Equipment reliability is generally related to cost. Certain types of overhead handling equipment are more robust, and therefore more reliable in typical industrial applications than other types. They are usually more costly as well.

Reliability is directly related to maintainability. Equipment must be properly designed and maintained to be reliable. The equipment should be carefully designed for ease of maintenance or the necessary maintenance work may not get done.

Product Quality Issues

One school of thought suggests that high quality does not add cost in the long run, but this concept does not necessarily hold true in the case of initial equipment costs. The same load that can be handled by a precision-engineered device that protects the product from damage might also be handled by a simple hook and sling. While the overall cost of quality may well be negligible when the manufacturer achieves zero defects due to a properly-designed carrier, the initial cost of that carrier may be a real issue. Smart firms, however, focus on life-cycle costs.

The Contributors of this chapter are: Brian Jaynes, Project Manager, Dearborn Mid-West Conveyor Co.; Bernard Licari, CAD Engineer, Dearborn Mid-West Conveyor Co.; Wes Paisley, President, Dearborn Mid-West Conveyor Co.; Russell Polgar, General Manager, Unified Industries, Inc.; Robert Short, Director, Industrial/Automotive Group, Dearborn Mid-West Conveyor Co.
The Reviewers of this chapter are: Peter Kerrick, Vice President, P&H Material Handling; Dan Sullivan, PE, Vice President, Advanced Technologies Group, Electromotive Systems, Inc.; Howard Zollinger, PE, President, Zollinger Associates.

CHAPTER 10   OVERHEAD HANDLING AND LIFTING DEVICES

Operator Safety Issues

Operator safety can add to the initial cost of a piece of overhead handling equipment, but as is the case with quality, the long-term cost of unsafe equipment will be much higher than the initial cost of safe equipment.

Equipment Cost Considerations

The main question that must be asked is how much manufacturing flexibility, equipment reliability, product quality, and operator safety is required? After all of these fundamentals have been reviewed and analyzed, then the task is to balance them against an equipment budget (see Fig. 10-1).

At each decision point, it is important to be comfortable before moving on in the selection process: identifying the optimum choice is a building process.

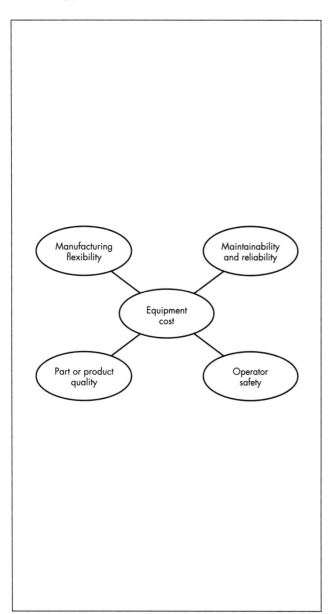

Fig. 10-1 When choosing equipment, several factors must be weighed against the cost. *(Courtesy Dearborn Mid-West Conveyor Co.)*

MANUAL AND POWERED OVERHEAD CRANES

Although there are many special-purpose, custom-designs of overhead cranes available, these are the most frequently encountered:

- Structural-beam underhung cranes.
- Patented rail underhung cranes.
- Enclosed-track underhung cranes.
- Top-running bridge cranes.
- Gantry cranes.
- Jib cranes.
- Ergonomic manipulator cranes.
- Automatic cranes.

The first four categories are frequently collectively referred to as "bridge cranes"; whereas only the top running bridge crane is referred to as a bridge crane by the Crane Manufacturers Association of America (CMAA). For the benefit of covering all of the common attributes of the three underhung cranes and one top-running crane category, the term bridge crane is used.

A *bridge crane* can be defined as one or two horizontal beams, rails, or girders suspended overhead by two or more end trucks capable of moving the beam horizontally in two directions. The resulting bridge assembly is equipped with a hoist and trolley to accommodate four horizontal and two vertical movements of loads.

Bridge cranes move horizontally along two or more overhead or building-supported runway beams. A complete crane system gives the operator full *X, Y* and *Z* motions for handling loads as small as car axles and tires or as large as aircraft assembly modules.

Bridge cranes used in industrial applications can be manually propelled or powered by electrically-, pneumatically-, or hydraulically-driven end trucks, trolleys, and hoists. Electrically-powered cranes may be designed with either AC or DC power systems.

The operation of these cranes can be controlled manually via an operator in a control cab or by an operator on the floor with a pendant. Alternatively, bridge cranes can be controlled through radio frequency or infrared remote cordless controllers. The operation of bridge cranes also can be controlled by computers in semi-automated or fully-automated applications.

Bridge cranes are used in a wide range of applications from standby service to high production. Bridge cranes, jib cranes, and ergonomic cranes are designed to reduce worker fatigue and improve product quality.

Bridge crane equipment costs vary widely depending on load ratings, span, crane styles, etc. Users should consider more than the initial cost when selecting a new, upgraded, or replacement crane system. Other factors to be considered include increased production, reduced downtime, and improved safety.

BRIDGE CRANE FUNDAMENTALS

The proper design, engineering, construction, installation, and operation of bridge cranes in industrial settings is an engineering science all unto itself and requires a specialist.

Bridge cranes range from standard to highly custom-designed units. Competent manufacturing professionals can apply many of the different types of standard cranes to provide the functions and requirements for a specific application. The application strengths and weaknesses can be reviewed and costs are easily obtained.

The more specialized applications are different. Competent manufacturing professionals cannot be expected to know as much as the application and design engineers employed by crane manufacturers.

CHAPTER 10   OVERHEAD HANDLING AND LIFTING DEVICES

The manufacturing professional would be wise to focus on precisely defining the performance requirements of the application. The application engineers can handle the detail work involved in the actual design and installation of the crane.

All bridge cranes, hoists, and monorails carry a rated load or capacity as defined by the manufacturer. When determining the rated load of a crane, all accessories below the hook (such as load bars, magnets, grabs, etc.) should be included as part of the load to be handled. Safety factors are not included.

The rated load must be displayed so that it is clearly visible to the crane operator. The capacity should be marked on each side of the crane bridge. Individual hoist units should have their rated capacity marked on the bottom block and on the hoist.

Careful consideration must be given to situations where multiple hoists, bridge cranes, carriers, trolleys, articulating arms, or balancers are operated or stored on the same runways. The combined loads for the multiple pieces of equipment that will be imposed on the runway section dictates the track size of the runway.

Bridge crane equipment must be selected with consideration given to the number of stress cycles, the expected stress range, and the stress category. This requirement applies to the selection of all bridges, runways, track hangers, hoists, balancers, trolleys, and additional equipment that is subjected to repeated lifting of loads.

Building Considerations

The building where the overhead crane will be installed should be designed with the following considerations. The distance from the floor to the lowest overhead obstruction must allow for the required hook lift, plus the distance from the saddle or palm of the hook in its highest position to the high point on the crane, plus clearance to the lowest overhead obstruction. In addition, the distance from the floor to the lowest overhead obstruction must be such that the lowest point on the crane will clear all machinery that has been positioned under the crane. A minimum clearance of 3 or 4 in. (76 or 102 mm) (depending on span) overhead and 2 in. (51 mm) laterally must be provided and maintained adjacent to all bridge cranes, hoists, and similar equipment. More clearance consideration should be given for supply services, festooning, lighting, etc., and their location in relation to the adjacent equipment, structures, supports, and obstructions. Bridge equipment, support steel, hangers, sway bracing, headers, hoists, and all associated equipment should not be connected to, or suspended from, a building jack truss. After the building height has been determined, the crane runway should be located with the top of the runway rail at a distance below the lowest overhead construction that is equal to the height of the crane, plus the required clearance. Lights, pipes, or other objects projecting below the lowest point on the building truss must be considered when determining the lowest overhead obstruction. The building knee braces must be designed to permit the required hook end approaches.

Crane Service Classes

Crane service classes are based on the load spectrum that most closely reflects the actual service conditions. Cranes are classified into loading groups according to the service conditions of the most severely loaded part of the crane.

The purpose of the crane service classification system is to enable material handling professionals to specify the most economical crane for a given application without compromising safety or performance.

The following classes are used throughout industry. In general, Class C and lower-rated overhead cranes are best suited for nonproduction settings unless the production rates are very low and the loads being handled are very large or heavy. Class D and higher are

designed for production settings. CMAA further defines service classes based on load class and load cycles.

Class A. This class is used for standby or infrequent service, and covers overhead cranes that may be used in settings such as powerhouses, public utilities, turbine rooms, motor rooms, testing laboratories, and transformer stations. These applications require precise handling of equipment at slow speeds. Infrequent use is the key defining factor for this class.

Class B. Used primarily for light service, class B covers slow speed cranes that might be used in repair shops, light assembly operations, service buildings, and light warehousing applications. Loads may vary from light loads to rated loads on occasion, with between two and five lifts per hour, averaging 10 ft (3 m) per lift.

Class C. These cranes are used for moderate service and may be used in applications such as machine shops or areas in paper mills. Typically, cranes in this category will handle loads that average 50% of the rated load, with five to ten lifts per hour, averaging 15 ft (4.6 m) per lift, and not over 50% of the lifts at the rated capacity.

Class D. For heavy service applications, this class contains cranes that are used in settings such as heavy machine shops, foundries, fabricating plants, steel warehouses, container yards, and lumber mills, where heavy-duty production is the norm. In this type of service, loads approaching 50% of the rated load will be handled constantly during the working day. High speeds are acceptable with 10-20 lifts per hour, averaging 15 ft (4.6 m) per lift, with no more than 65% of the lifts at the rated load.

Class E. Severe service requires a crane that is capable of handling loads approaching the rated load throughout its service life. Applications may include magnet, bucket, or magnet and bucket combination cranes used in scrap yards, cement plants, lumber mills, fertilizer plants, and container handling operations. Cranes in this category will typically perform 20 or more lifts per hour at or near the crane's rated load.

Class F. Continuous severe service demands a crane that is capable of handling loads approaching its rated load continuously at high production rate conditions throughout its life. Applications include custom-designed specialty cranes that perform critical work tasks, such as hot metal ladle cranes in a steel mill. Class F cranes must offer a high level of reliability, ease of maintenance, and operator safety. For fast or frequent cycles, a duty cycle calculation needs to be made to ensure that the motors will not overheat.

Maintainability and Reliability

Cranes and their components are manufactured with ease of maintenance and reliability in mind. A reputable manufacturer will provide components which have been successfully tested for function, strength, and longevity.

Overhead cranes are generally provided with all necessary lubrication and instructions. Before putting a crane in service, all bearings, gears, etc., should be properly lubricated according to the manufacturer's recommendations.

Regularly scheduled maintenance and inspection, performed according to the schedule recommended by the manufacturer, is the best way to ensure that the crane remains reliable. Failure to adhere to such a maintenance schedule can endanger employees working beneath and near the crane. With properly trained maintenance crews and operators, manual and motorized overhead cranes can be expected to perform safely and reliably for years. If any questions arise concerning crane maintenance and inspection, the crane manufacturer should be consulted for guidance.

It is the end-user's responsibility to maintain a properly trained maintenance staff or arrange for the equipment to be serviced by a qualified outside service. However, it is the crane manufacturer's

CHAPTER 10   OVERHEAD HANDLING AND LIFTING DEVICES

responsibility to supply adequate information to the user in the form of manuals and training in proper maintenance and inspection of the crane system.

Operator and Crane Safety Issues

Extreme caution must be exercised in all areas of manufacturing, production, and warehousing where overhead cranes are used. Managers, supervisors, and employees must realize that because there are often people working underneath these cranes, any failure of the overhead crane system could result in a serious accident.

The best protection for proper crane maintenance and operation is a properly trained operator. Operators should always perform a visual inspection of the crane system, along with a functional inspection, prior to using the equipment.

To ensure operator safety: choose a reliable supplier, apply the crane system properly, provide comprehensive operator training, and implement a preventive maintenance and inspection program.

A crane system must be selected for the specific application for which it is intended. Manufacturers can supply the technical expertise required to ensure that the crane is properly matched to the application. In addition, companies whose core business is designing and manufacturing cranes have safeguards in place to ensure that the equipment shipped to customers is safe.

Operators should be properly trained prior to the crane being put into service. They should be trained in all aspects of the crane system by instructors who are fully qualified in crane design, maintenance, rigging, and operation. They should know the limitations of the system, as well as the indications that maintenance work is required.

MAJOR TYPES OF OVERHEAD CRANES

To assist in identifying the best crane for a given application, the following major types are discussed in this section:

- Structural-beam underhung cranes.
- Patented-rail underhung cranes.
- Enclosed-track underhung cranes.
- Top-running cranes.
- Gantry cranes.
- Jib cranes.
- Ergonomic manipulator cranes.
- Hoists.

Structural-beam Underhung Cranes

Structural-beam underhung bridge cranes are overhead cranes that use mill-run structural steel (that is, American standard shapes of I-beam and wide-flange beams) as either the runway or bridge girders, or as both. The lower beam flanges are the weight-bearing flanges that the trolley carriers or end trucks ride on.

Structural-beam cranes should be used only in moderate service applications due to the possibility of excessive flange wear. Common applications include a small manufacturing area, shipping and receiving areas, and other settings in which the crane is not in continuous use. These cranes are normally used in applications that handle only light- to medium-duty loads. Structural-beam overhead cranes can offer users a very cost-effective, safe, and reliable means for lifting and transferring loads when they are used in appropriate applications.

These cranes can be purchased as a complete assembly from the manufacturer or as a kit with the customer supplying the structural steel and fasteners. A kit will contain trolleys or end-truck assemblies and end stops. In the case of a crane kit, it is the responsibility of the user to correctly assemble and install the crane. While taking

the kit approach will result in cost savings, users should bear in mind that proper assembly and installation are critically important.

Patented-rail Underhung Overhead Cranes

Patented-rail underhung overhead cranes use a fabricated steel rail with a high-carbon/alloy bottom T-section for the lower flange as either the runway or the bridge girder, or as both. Patented-rail is manufactured by joining cut steel plates for the top flange and web section to the high-carbon hardened-bottom T-section lower flange. The rails are welded using an automatic continuous welding machine to ensure precise weld penetration of the dissimilar metals. The rail is then straightened and cut to length, and prepared to match the customer's specifications.

Patented-rail cranes can be used in light- to heavy-duty load applications. The hardened lower flange section will provide long life and minimal wear even in very heavy-duty applications.

The bridges are usually supplied completely assembled. Typically, all of the runway hardware is supplied (for example, end stops, hangers, splice assemblies, fasteners). The rails are normally supplied true, straight, and cut with all required holes drilled.

Due to their uniform lower running flange, patented rail cranes provide the interlocking of cranes running on adjacent runways or with a monorail spur line. This allows transfer of the hoist carrier and load from crane to crane or to a fixed location under the monorail.

Patented-rail cranes come in both manual light-load and motorized heavy-load versions, and adapt easily to existing building support structures. Although more expensive than structural-steel cranes, the longevity and proven reliability can more than offset the initial added cost. The motorized version with a hoist is found in manufacturing plants throughout North America and Europe (see Fig. 10-2).

Patented-rail underhung cranes are one of the most widely-recognized, reliable, and versatile types of cranes available for medium- to heavy-duty applications. Typical applications range from low-weight, high-throughput automotive operations, such as semi-automatic body decking transfers, to high-weight, large-piece, low-throughput work, such as the manual building and assembly of aircraft.

Enclosed-track Underhung Cranes

Enclosed-track underhung cranes are cranes that use hollow or tunnel-type rail made of extruded aluminum or cold-rolled steel for either the runway or the bridge girders, or both, with the load wheels travelling on the internal running surface.

Enclosed tracks, bridges, monorails, and track sections are generally made of cold-rolled carbon steel or extruded aluminum as shown in Fig. 10-3. Typically, a crane assembly will use lightweight aluminum-cast trolley housings with wear-resistant plastic wheels. This combination produces a smooth, easy push, as well as precise travel of the crane along an aluminum runway.

The ease of movement of these cranes can be attributed to the lightweight materials used in their construction, the reduced rolling resistance of the plastic wheels, and the unique end truck/bridge rail connection that allows the system to skew or articulate as needed.

Enclosed-track underhung crane systems adapt easily to already-existing building support structures, and due to their light weight, small freestanding structures can be used when overhead steel structures are not available. Because these cranes are available in a variety of sizes and load capacities, the crane system must be carefully selected to match the performance requirements of the application.

Enclosed-track underhung cranes may be manually-powered or motorized. It is common to have motorized hoists with manual push trolley and bridge functions. Motorized trolley and bridge functions are becoming more common as the loads handled increase and the bridge spans become larger. The motors run on an AC power system.

CHAPTER 10   OVERHEAD HANDLING AND LIFTING DEVICES

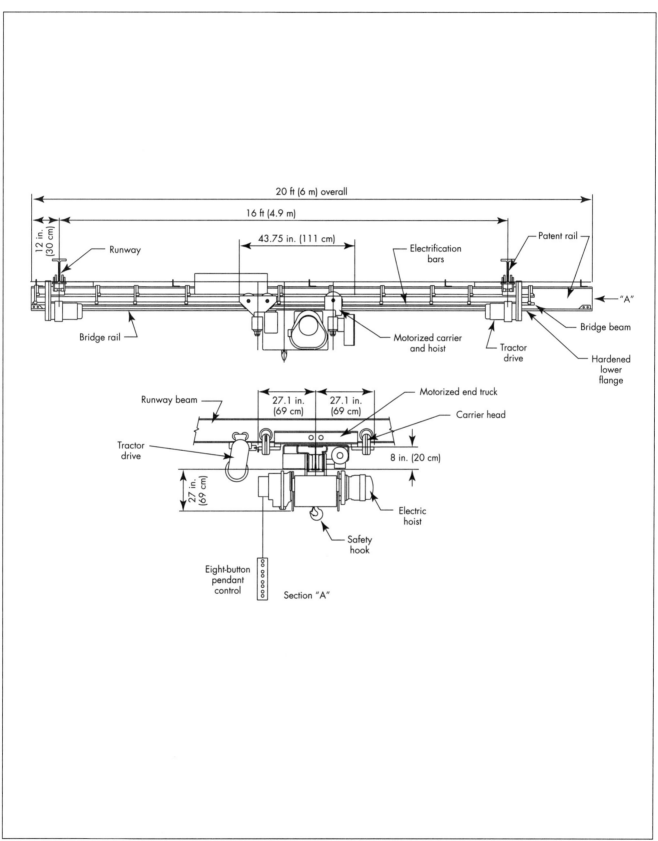

Fig. 10-2 Motorized patented-rail underhung crane with hoist. *(Courtesy Trambeam Corp.)*

CHAPTER 10   OVERHEAD HANDLING AND LIFTING DEVICES

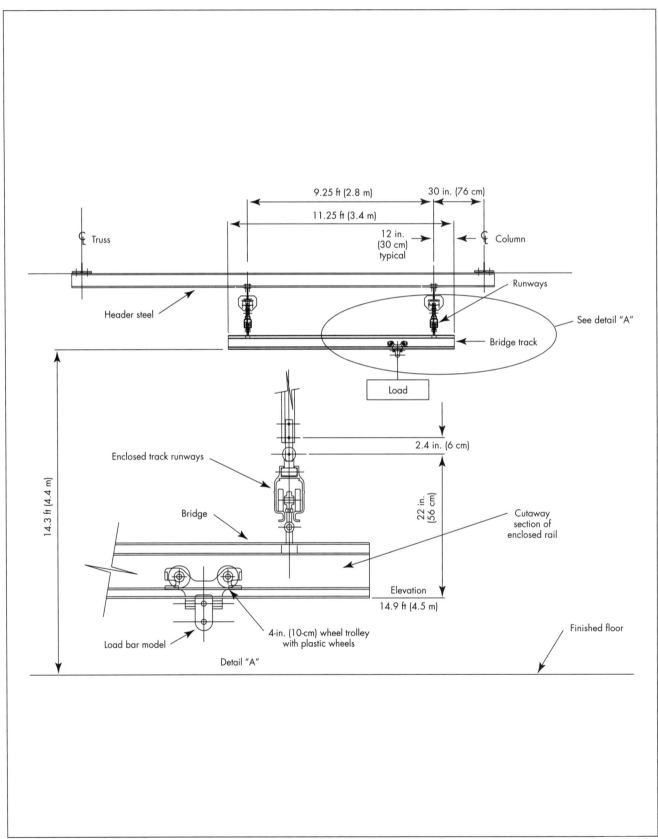

Fig. 10-3 Enclosed-track aluminum crane and runway. *(Courtesy Unified Industries)*

CHAPTER 10   OVERHEAD HANDLING AND LIFTING DEVICES

This type of crane is becoming more popular due to the increased importance of workplace ergonomics and the increasing weight of the loads being handled. If the application calls for the quiet, clean, and efficient movement of loads, an enclosed-track underhung crane is often a good choice. Typical applications are those that require repetitive motions and high-duty cycles.

Enclosed-track underhung cranes are available in custom-made, pre-assembled versions or as kits with the user assembling the crane and hangers.

Top-running Cranes

Top-running overhead cranes use either runway rail or hoist traveling rail (or both) according to the specifications of the American Society of Civil Engineers (ASCE), the Association of American Railroads (AAR), or the American Railroad Engineering Association (AREA). Rail and girder material will vary by manufacturer and application. The rails are mounted to the top flange of a structural shape and the trolleys ride on top of the rails.

Typical applications include those that involve very heavy loads and large spans, such as steel mills, heavy machinery handling, aircraft manufacturing, and tool and die shops. Rated loads vary from 1-3 ton (907-2,722 kg) and higher. Top-running cranes are almost always motorized and equipped with either an operator cab, traveling pendant station, remote controls, or automatic controls. In most cases, the support structure for a top-running crane is designed and installed when the building is built. The bridge girders for top-running cranes are either structural steel for medium loads and short spans, or fabricated box girders for heavy loads with wide spans.

Automatic overhead cranes have been in use for over 25 years for container handling, pulp logs, bucket cranes, and steel coils, and are used increasingly more in basic manufacturing industries. The majority of automatic overhead are top-running cranes, with some of the most recent applications using structural beam underhung cranes (see Fig. 10-4). Their use ranges from delivery and removal from conveyor stands at machining areas and press shops to automatically transferring large rolls between overhead cranes and automated guided vehicles.

Some of the earliest automatic cranes required the load to be lifted up to the underside of the trolley for stability when traveling. With the advent of "anti-swing" controls, the duty cycles can be shortened by lifting only high enough to clear the machines or jib cranes on the floor. The controls have the contour of the transport area in memory, enabling the most efficient path selection.

Gantry Cranes

A *gantry crane* is a freestanding, movable overhead crane that uses floor-mounted track or base-mounted tires or casters instead of overhead-mounted runway rails. Gantry cranes are well-suited for buildings that do not have load-bearing walls or columns that can be used to support structural steel members and runways.

Floor-mounted gantry cranes are used for heavy load conditions in which there are insufficient load-bearing structures for other types of cranes. They are also used as retrofits into existing buildings. Floor-mounted cranes use end trucks traveling on an embedded track as shown in Fig. 10-5. The gantry follows a pre-established travel path that is defined by the position of the tracks.

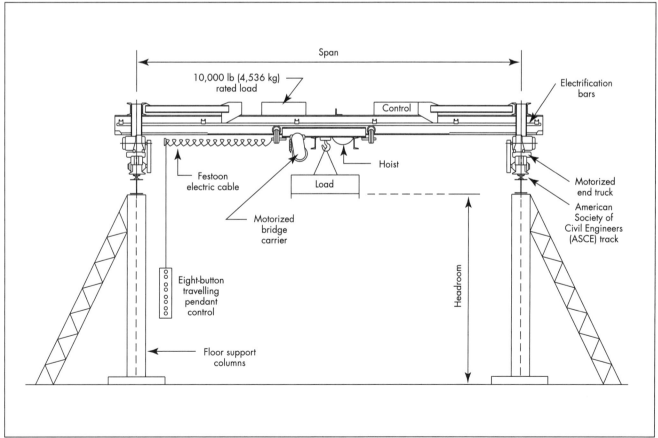

Fig. 10-4 Top-running crane. *(Courtesy Trambeam Corp.)*

CHAPTER 10   OVERHEAD HANDLING AND LIFTING DEVICES

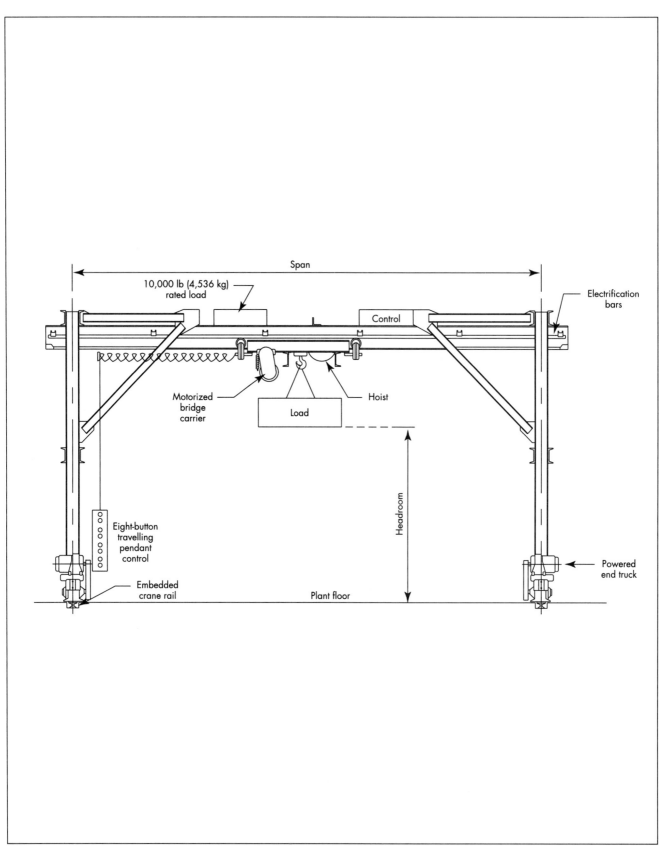

Fig. 10-5 Gantry crane. *(Courtesy Trambeam Corp.)*

CHAPTER 10   OVERHEAD HANDLING AND LIFTING DEVICES

Floor-mounted gantry cranes are typically used in assembly aisles, fabrication shops, power generation dam sites, and other industrial and steel mill applications.

Base-mounted gantry cranes are typically used in marinas, boat yards, and other outdoor settings that do not have overhead support structures, and that require free-ranging mobility, rather than a fixed track. For light and moderate loads, base-mounted, caster-type gantry cranes may be the most versatile crane system available. As soon as one of these cranes is assembled, it is ready to go to work. There is no installation cost or work to be done.

Both the floor-mounted track style and the base-mounted tire or caster style are available in manually-propelled and motorized models. Costs vary according to capacities and options.

Jib Cranes

Jib cranes have the virtue of simplicity. They use a single horizontal rotating load rail or boom suspended on one end from a vertical support or mast to carry loads overhead. The boom can be diagonally braced for additional load capacity if needed. The boom may be a structural shape, a patented rail, or an enclosed rail. Freestanding, wall-cantilevered, and mast-type jib crane designs are all common.

Freestanding jib cranes are available in three styles: base-plate mounted, insert mounted, or sleeve-insert mounted. All of these use a similar mast pipe head-assembly boom, but the difference is found in the base arrangement. A hexagonal base plate is welded to the base of the mast pipe, and is reinforced with six gusset plates equally spaced around the circumference of the mast. The base plate is secured with anchor bolts to a reinforced foundation capable of handling the load.

An *insert-mounted jib crane* uses a square base plate welded to the mast. Each side of the base plate is 3 in. (76 mm) longer than the diameter of the mast. The base is secured in place by anchor bolts positioned below floor level before the first pour. A second pour is then made to bring the finished floor up to the correct level and to support the mast pipe. In the sleeve-insert mounted version, the mast is inserted into a sleeve that has been secured in the foundation. The sleeve can be lined with friction-reducing material if desired.

Wall-cantilevered jib cranes combine quality, safety, stringent design criteria, ease of installation, and ease of rotation. This type of jib crane is wall-mounted, enabling it to provide at least 180° of rotation. A wall-cantilevered jib crane consists of an I-beam for the mast and two fabricated rotation brackets that are bolted to the structural support on the wall. The wall-cantilevered jib crane provides a versatile and cost-effective solution for applications that involve handling loads in a small area.

Mast-type jib cranes are floor-supported and stabilized at the top; top and bottom bearing assemblies enable them to revolve through an arc of 360°. Therefore, this type of crane permits full use of a work area, provided that there are no obstructions. In addition, the mast-type jib crane exerts less force on its supporting structures than do other types of jib cranes. Generally, special foundation preparation is not required. The component parts include top and bottom bearing assemblies, a wide-flange mast, and a boom with removable trolley stops. For applications that require maximum lift and up to 360° of movement, the mast-type jib crane is a good choice.

Ergonomic Manipulator Cranes

Ergonomic manipulator cranes are designed to support manipulators, articulating arms, vacuum lifts, and other types of ergonomic devices. They can be manufactured using enclosed rail, patented rail, or structural steel. A typical enclosed aluminum rail unit is shown in Fig. 10-6. The double bridge girder shown is commonly used to produce the stability required, as well as ease of motion.

This type of crane was originally developed in response to increasing awareness of the costs incurred as a result of on-the-job injuries and lost time, especially in the case of tasks requiring repetitive motions or manual lifting. As production rates and the weight of items being handled increases, so does the frequency of this type of worker injury. By replacing conventional material handling equipment with ergonomically-designed devices, the incidence of handling-related injuries can be reduced.

Switching to ergonomically-designed equipment also can have a positive effect on product quality by reducing the amount of handling-related product damage. The controls for the ergonomic manipulator cranes have improved and are more user-friendly by sensing the desired direction of movement and actuating the drive to move in that direction. This type of device is called a *balancer*, requiring only a small amount of manual force to set the crane in motion in the desired direction.

In calculating the payback period for an ergonomic manipulator crane, the formulation must include the reduction in handling-related worker injuries, as well as increased productivity, reduced product damage, and improved material handling efficiency.

A specialized version of the ergonomic manipulator crane is the *modular workstation crane*, which is designed to be freestanding and easy to install. These specialized systems, which can be manually-operated or motorized, provide overhead handling capability for workstations or process equipment clustered within a defined area. Because they occupy a small segment of the overall crane market, they are not included as one of the seven main categories of cranes.

In a typical application, a modular workstation crane system might be installed over an area that contains machine tools, workbenches, and test stands. The crane would be used for vertical positioning and horizontal transport from workstation to workstation.

Modular workstation cranes are supplied as modular units in standardized dimensions, ready for assembly. The layout and overall size of a system can be easily altered by bolting on new sections. Because these systems are usually not building-supported, they lend themselves well to retrofit situations. They can be easily dismantled and relocated at a later date.

In most cases, a standard hoist is suspended from the bridge, with the hoist being controlled by a pendant. Modular workstation cranes also can be equipped with ergonomic handling devices, such as vacuum lifts, in which case they could be classified as a kind of ergonomic manipulator crane. Chapter 14 discusses the use of ergonomic assist devices in more detail.

When combined with linear actuators, these systems can be used in semi-automated operations. Load capacities typically vary from as light as 250 lb (113 kg), up to about 4,000 lb (1,814 kg).

Hoists

Although hoists are typically one component of an overhead crane system (the component that handles the vertical lifting and lowering), they also can be used as stand-alone equipment in some industrial applications. For example, a hoist might be suspended from an overhead beam in a transfer area where an item is lifted off of a transport vehicle, such as an automated guided vehicle (AGV), and then lowered onto another carrier. Hoists can be electrically-, pneumatically-, or manually-powered. They use either a chain or wire rope to raise and lower a load.

COMPARISON OF OVERHEAD CRANES

Information on the most common types of overhead cranes is contained in Tables 10-1 and 10-2. Table 10-1 lists typical selection parameters; Table 10-2 rates the cranes in six areas, with one standing for high, two standing for moderate, and three standing for low.

CHAPTER 10   OVERHEAD HANDLING AND LIFTING DEVICES

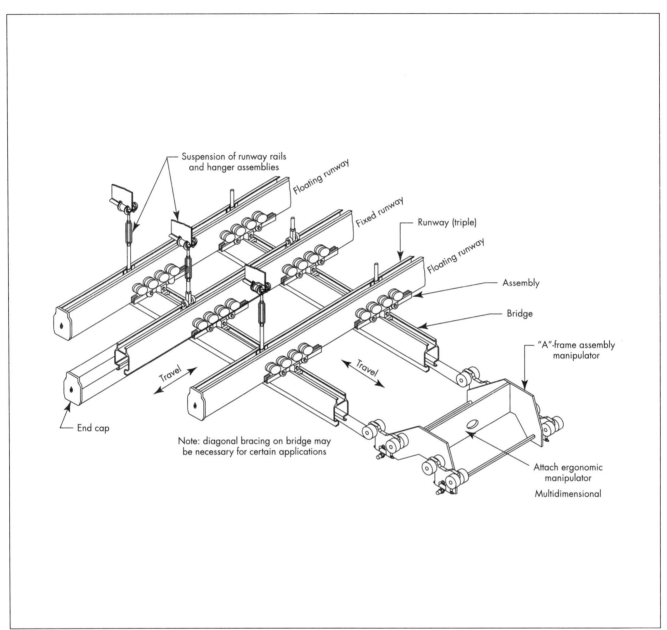

Fig. 10-6 Ergonomic manipulator crane. *(Courtesy Unified Industries)*

TABLE 10-1
Overhead Crane Selection Parameters

Overhead Crane Type	Rated Load ton (kg)	Typical Bridge Speed Range fpm (mpm)	Hoist Speed Range fpm (mpm)	Operations Mode	Typical Industry Usage
Structural	0.5-10 (454-9,072)	60-150 (18.3-45.7)	10-40 (3-12.2)	Motorized	Industrial
Patented rail	1-15 (907-13,608)	60-300 (18.3-91.4)	10-40 (3.-12.2)	Motorized	Auto and industrial
Enclosed-track	0.25-1.5 (227-1,361)	60-600 (18.3-183)	5-30 (1.5-9.1)	Hand push	Auto and industrial
Top running	2-100+ (1,814-90,720+)	100-400 (30.5-121.9)	15-80 (4.6-24.4)*	Motorized	Industrial
Gantry	0.5-25 (454-22,680)	60-400 (18.3-121.9)	15-60 (4.6-18.3)*	Motorized	Ship yards/industrial
Jib	0.25-3 (227-2,722)	30-60 (9.1-18.3)	5-30 (1.5-9.1)	Hand push	Machining
Ergonomic	0.25-1 (227-907)	30-60 (9.1-18.3)	10-30 (3-9.1)	Hand push	Automotive and assembly

*Hoist speeds for magnet and bucket cranes are much higher, that is, 160 feet per minute (fpm [48.8 meter per minute (mpm)]).

CHAPTER 10   OVERHEAD HANDLING AND LIFTING DEVICES

TABLE 10-2
Overhead Crane Equipment Comparison

Overhead Crane Type	Production Flexibility	Maintainability/ Reliability	Operator Safety	Relative Cost	Ergonomic Rating
Structural	2	2	2	3	2
Patented rail	2	2	2	2	2
Enclosed-track	1	1	2	3	1
Top running	1	1	1	1	1
Gantry	2	2	1	1	2
Jib	3	1	1	3	2
Ergonomic	1	1	1	2	1

Note: this information may be subjective and is comparable, but is relative to this group only. Verification should be done by a qualified equipment supplier.
Ratings 1-3:   1-High   2-Moderate   3-Low

OVERHEAD TROLLEY CONVEYORS

An *overhead trolley conveyor* consists of a system of trolleys that hang from or nest in a track supported by overhead steel structures. The trolleys are linked together and driven by a continuous chain, or in some applications, a cable.

In most cases, loads are suspended from attachments that are bolted directly to the trolley brackets. In applications involving lighter loads, the loads may be suspended from clevis attachments that are bolted directly to the chain.

However, different carrier, hook, and tray arrangements are specifically designed and fabricated to suit the parts being transported. This ability to be custom-designed for the task makes the overhead trolley conveyor a very simple handling system.

OVERHEAD TROLLEY CONVEYOR SELECTION

These conveyors are most commonly used as a production conveyor within a manufacturing process or as a delivery conveyor that travels from one production zone to another. They are well suited for transporting loads through hazardous environments, such as those found in painting or plating operations or in foundries.

With this type of conveyor, the loads are supported on fixed centers that are typically between 1 ft (3 m) and 20 ft (6 m), depending on the part configuration and the production rate required. An overhead trolley conveyor should not be selected if the application requires accumulation or buffer zones. However, this type of conveyor can serve an accumulation or buffering function when it is used as a separate handling system and not tied into other operations, such as production.

The most productive use of this type of conveyor is for applications where tasks are performed while the loads are in transit. If the operation requires that the parts be stopped or indexed, production cycle time could be a problem.

The loading and unloading of overhead trolley conveyors is usually performed manually while the conveyor is moving. Stopping the conveyor to load or unload an item will affect production all along the line since it stops the entire conveyor. Although loading and unloading can be automated, it involves considerable expense.

Manufacturing and Production Flexibility

An overhead trolley conveyor can be used to carry almost any type of load through a series of manufacturing operations. These conveyors are used in most areas of manufacturing plants from product preparation and painting to final assembly.

The path of an overhead trolley conveyor can be designed for a high degree of production flexibility. The loads carried within the conveyor's path travel horizontally in a closed loop at predetermined elevations, with the help of horizontal turns and vertical curves. The routing of the conveyor's path is highly dependent on building layout and influenced by the requirements of adjacent processes. However, this type of conveyor is usually flexible enough to avoid interfering with other operations. When additional synchronized drives are added, a trolley conveyor can extend for lengths of several thousand feet (meters).

Because overhead trolley conveyors are endless, their entire length can be used to recirculate parts when called for by the application.

Overhead trolley conveyors can be dismantled and moved to new locations. Because they are supported from overhead, relocation work is simplified. In addition, this type of conveyor requires a relatively small amount of space.

Conveyor paths can be altered, shortened, lengthened, combined, or divided into new configurations as needed. If the loads change, they can be accommodated by adding or respacing the trolleys.

Maintainability and Reliability

Overhead trolley conveyors require very little maintenance, and over the years, they have earned a reputation for being extremely reliable. In an industrial application, it is not unusual for this type of conveyor to log a 99% uptime record while being operated on a multishift basis. However, accumulating this kind of a performance record depends on a well-run maintenance program. Fortunately, this type of conveyor is designed for easy maintainability.

Lubrication is the primary focus of the maintenance program. Conveyor chain and trolleys, roller turn rollers, and traction-wheel bearings all require regular lubrication, either by manual lubrication or by automatic lubricators. Conveyor drives and take-up units are commonly installed at higher points and may require ladders and platforms when maintenance is due. See Chapter 6 for more information on maintenance.

Overhead trolley conveyors are made of modular, standardized components. For this reason, if a part fails, the downtime required to fix it should be minimal. However, because these conveyors operate as a closed loop, any downtime for repair at one point shuts down the entire conveyor system.

Product Quality Issues

Manufacturers offer a wide variety of load-supporting devices for these conveyors. Hooks, baskets, trays, fixtures, jigs, and bins

CHAPTER 10   OVERHEAD HANDLING AND LIFTING DEVICES

can be custom-designed to firmly position and carry products in such a way as to reduce the likelihood of handling-related product damage. As additional insurance, coatings or padding can be added to the appropriate parts of the carrier. The use of plastic carriers lessens the likelihood of damage caused by contact between the product and the carrier. At the same time, the use of plastic carriers will reduce the overall weight of the conveyor for drive calculation purposes. However, because loading and unloading is almost always performed manually, repeatability may be a problem and increase the risk of product damage.

Lubrication is another factor that can have an impact on product quality. Depending on the types of products handled, drip pans may need to be installed on the conveyor to prevent oil on the chain or trolleys from falling onto the products and their carriers. Containment pans installed around automatic lubricators will also help prevent oil spillage.

Operator Safety Issues

Overhead trolley conveyor systems generally allow for a safe interface between the worker and the product. In production areas, the conveyors move at fairly slow (40 ft [12.2 m]/min) speeds. The carriers are hung on fixed centers, and when adequately spaced, they permit employees to move freely around products and from one side of the conveyor to the other. However, because the conveyor operates at a constant speed, the worker needs to mimic this rate of movement to synchronize the work task with the movement of the product. This need to match the employee's movement with the conveyor's could potentially result in poor ergonomics. However, the fact that the conveyor path elevation can be altered to bring the products to the ideal height for the workers on the line makes this type of conveyor ergonomically-friendly.

Given the low speeds that are typical for overhead trolley conveyors, noise is not usually a problem. Even when trolleys are equipped with open wheels and bearings (as compared to completely sealed wheels), the noise levels remain acceptable.

When installing an overhead trolley conveyor system, be sure to install wire mesh guards beneath the carrier running the full length of the conveyor in the sections that are elevated to guard against falling parts reaching the floor level. Mechanical backstops and antirunaway devices are needed to help prevent a load runaway if the chain should break. Light screens, safety mats, and accessible emergency-stop buttons are necessary as well for safety.

Equipment Cost Considerations

Because overhead trolley conveyors are a relatively mature type of equipment with a long history, there is little risk involved in choosing to install one and many conveyor suppliers have good experience with the installation process. The risk of installation cost overruns should be low, and the chances of on-time completion and start-up are high.

Maintenance and training costs are minimal due to the simplicity of these systems—provided that a good maintenance program is put into place. With the large installed base of overhead trolley conveyors already in the field, technical support is readily available.

The use of standardized components adds to the cost-effectiveness of these conveyors.

MAJOR TYPES OF OVERHEAD TROLLEY CONVEYORS

Although custom-designed and special-purpose overhead trolley conveyors are available, the major types of systems commonly available will satisfy most handling requirements. The types most often seen in industrial applications include:

- Cable conveyors.
- Enclosed-track chain conveyors.
- 348, 458, and 678 chain conveyors.
- Overhead tow conveyors.

Cable Conveyors

Cable conveyors are specifically designed for handling light loads. The trolleys are linked together and driven by individual steel cables instead of by a chain, as shown in Fig. 10-7. The cables can be steel, galvanized steel, or stainless steel.

Cable lugs are attached to the cables using jigs to ensure uniform lug spacing. This spacing determines the trolley centers, which are generally 12, 16, or 24 in. (30, 41, or 61 cm) for this type of conveyor. The cable assembly is completed when the trolley brackets are bolted over the lugs. The track that the trolleys nest in is a 2.25 or 3 in. (6 or 8 cm) I-beam or a junior T-section, depending on the supplier's standard. Note: metric dimensions in this chapter are for approximate comparison.

The drives used on cable conveyors closely resemble those of power chain conveyors. Instead of a sprocket, a cable conveyor uses a fabricated wheel or sheave with cast iron or forged shoes that are correctly spaced to mesh with the lugs and propel the trolley and cable assembly. The cable trolleys nest in the gaps between the shoes on the drive wheel that propels the conveyor. Traction wheels are used for horizontal cable movement and vertical curves are used for elevation changes.

The maximum load per trolley varies with system size, but in general, loads of 75 lb (34 kg) or less are recommended.

In a typical installation, a cable conveyor might use a 0.3-in. (8-mm) diameter cable that has a maximum working load of 500 lb (227 kg), and an ultimate strength of 5,000 lb (2,268 kg). The cable itself must offer the least amount of stretch possible. Otherwise, the relationship between the trolley spacing and the spacing of the shoes on the drive wheel might be compromised.

A single-drive cable conveyor system should have a maximum length of not more than 1,000 ft (305 m) and a maximum pull of not more than 500 lb (227 kg). Values greater than these would call for multiple drives, which are generally not recommended for these conveyors due to the added cost. If the application requires a longer conveyor, selecting another type of overhead trolley conveyor might be a more cost-effective solution than adding multiple drives to a cable conveyor.

When properly selected and installed, cable conveyors run very smoothly without the surging and pulsating experienced with some types of conveyors. In addition, the initial equipment cost for a cable conveyor system is relatively low.

When reviewing possible equipment options, bear in mind that cable conveyors have load capacity limitations and require a good maintenance program, especially in the areas of shoe adjustment and cable lubrication. Cable conveyors are not recommended for high-temperature applications due to the tendency of the cables to dry out and become brittle.

Enclosed-track Chain Conveyors

The unique component of an *enclosed-track chain conveyor* is the chain itself. These conveyors use a universal link-type chain that is designed to provide maximum flexibility and smooth operation in all directions, including when operating around horizontal turns and vertical curves. In operation, this chain performs as if there was a universal joint at each pitch. Built-in chain rollers take the place of separate trolleys. Side guide-rollers, which are spaced along the chain assembly between each pair of vertical load wheels, help guide the chain through the steel-enclosed track, eliminating the need for

CHAPTER 10   OVERHEAD HANDLING AND LIFTING DEVICES

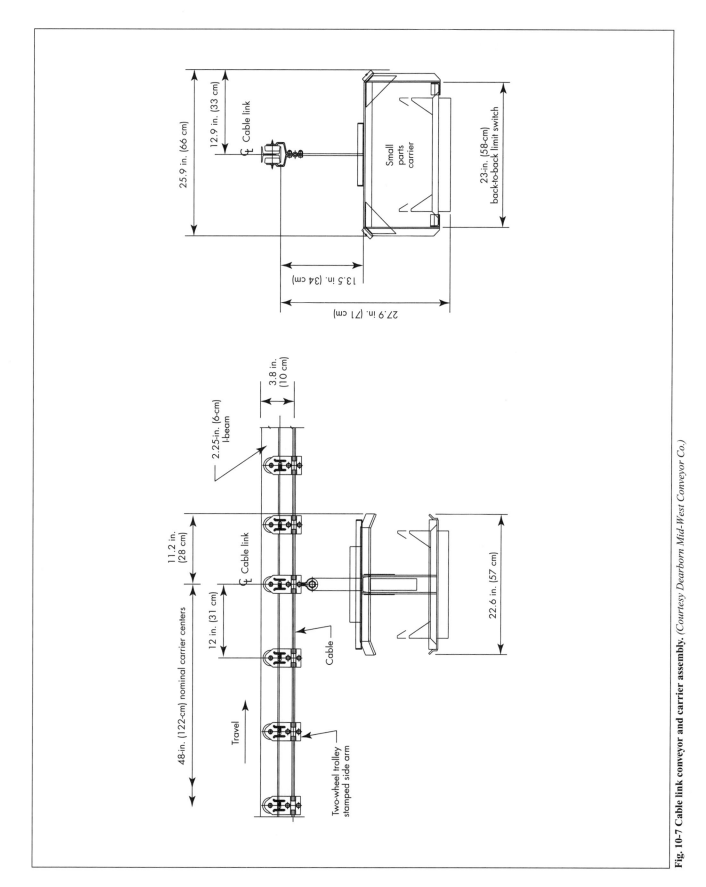

Fig. 10-7 Cable link conveyor and carrier assembly. *(Courtesy Dearborn Mid-West Conveyor Co.)*

CHAPTER 10   OVERHEAD HANDLING AND LIFTING DEVICES

separate roller or traction wheel turns in the system. An ultimate chain strength of over 10,000 lb (4,536 kg) is common.

The track is a square tubular section, typically formed with 0.16-in. (4-mm) high-strength steel. This choice of material results in lighter weight construction, which simplifies installation and puts a lighter load on the building's steel members.

As with the cable conveyor, the enclosed-track chain conveyor is designed for applications involving light loads, such as small parts handling. The design of the chain and track enables it to negotiate a path through tight spaces. Installation of this type of conveyor is fairly simple: standard threaded rod hangers and clamps are used to suspend the system from overhead grid steel (see Fig. 10-8).

Depending on the system design and application, both constant-speed and variable-speed drives may be available. These drives are the caterpillar chain-type, and are typically designed to handle a maximum of no more than 600 lb (272 kg) of chain pull. Exceeding this amount of pull will require a multiple-drive system.

Proper lubrication is vitally important for all chain conveyors, and enclosed-track chain conveyors are no exception. Automatic lubricators are a sound investment. But bear in mind that they only lubricate as long as they have oil in their reservoirs—checking lubricant levels should be a part of every regular preventive maintenance program.

To compensate for chain stretch due to normal wear and to permit adjustments in the amount of tension, spring or counterweight take-ups are usually included in the system. The optimal location for a take-up is on the slack side of the drive unit.

Suppliers offer a wide variety of standard load attachments. These attachments may suspend the load directly from the chain or suspend a carrier that has been designed for a specific load.

348, 458, and 678 Chain Conveyors

If an application involves loads that are beyond the capabilities of either cable conveyors or enclosed-track chain conveyors, the next type of overhead trolley conveyor might provide the answer. This group of overhead chain conveyors uses a structural I-beam section rail and drop-forged, bolted-on rivetless chain. These conveyors typically use a 3-, 4-, or 6-in. (8-, 10-, or 15-cm) I-beam, with 348, 458, or 678 rivetless chain as the conveying mechanism. These conveyors have been around for years and are still a mainstay for overhead handling applications.

The numbering system (348, 458, or 678) describes the chain's dimensions in U.S. customary units. The first number is the pitch in inches and the last two numbers are the pin diameter in fractions of an inch. In the case of 348 chain, the chain has a 3-in. (76-mm) pitch, and a 0.5-in. (12.7-mm) pin diameter. The 678 chain is reserved for heavily-loaded or severe-duty systems.

If the weight of a load exceeds the rating of a single trolley, the load can be hung from a load bar connected to two trolleys, as shown in Fig.10-9. Load bars also may be necessary on steeply inclined vertical curves to hold the suspended loads away from the chain and prevent the chain from kinking. Another advantage of load bars is the protection they give to the loads being conveyed.

The caterpillar drive design is the one most commonly used to propel 348, 458, and 678 chain conveyors. It employs a short loop auxiliary drive chain, with forged dogs attached alongside and parallel to the conveyor chain. The driving dogs on the caterpillar chain engage the side links of the conveyor chain to drive the conveyor. Back-up bars on the caterpillar chain side and rollers on the conveyor chain side confine the two chains, preventing them from separating. A caterpillar drive can be located on any straight run of conveyor. A maintenance platform also may need to be installed for access to the drive.

The method used to support this type of conveyor depends on the track loading and the construction of the building. The load imposed on the building includes the track loads and the weight of the supports. The track loads include the track weight, trolleys, chain, carriers, and the conveyed loads.

As is true with the other types of overhead trolley conveyors, the service life and performance of I-beam chain conveyors are greatly enhanced by regular maintenance. The chain pin bearing areas require regular oil lubrication; trolley wheels, whether open or sealed, need regular oiling or greasing; and drive components may need lubrication as well. Although this maintenance work can be performed manually, using an automatic system will probably prove to be more practical. In the case of heavily-used chain conveyors, automatic lubricators with variable controls enable the amount of lubrication to be matched to the rate of production. In addition to regular lubrication, slack chain inspection, drive belt inspection, and the investigation of abnormal noises should all be part of the preventive maintenance program. When correctly maintained, bolted-on, rivetless chain conveyors are extremely reliable and offer users a long service life.

Carrier designs for these conveyors have few limitations. The essential design requirement—other than the ability to carry the load safely—is to keep the weight and size of the carrier to a minimum. The optimal carrier design keeps excess weight to a minimum, enhances worker safety, and protects product quality.

Although a 678 I-beam chain conveyor follows the same basic specifications and requirements as 348 and 458 systems, the difference in load carrying abilities is substantial. Typical applications for 678 chain conveyors are auto assembly plants where engines, chassis, or complete car bodies are conveyed through production processes such as painting or final assembly.

An I-beam chain conveyor costs more than either a cable conveyor or an enclosed-track chain conveyor, but the advantages of increased load capacity, speed, durability, and longer conveyor lengths must be factored into the cost-justification equation.

Overhead Tow Conveyors

The term "overhead tow conveyor" can be misleading. Even though the conveyor track, trolleys, and chain are all suspended from overhead, these conveyors require a substantial amount of floor space as well. Any of the types of overhead trolley conveyors just described can be used as an overhead tow conveyor. The choice will depend on load and pull requirements.

Overhead tow conveyors are commonly used to convey four-wheeled carts through warehouses or freight terminals. They are also used for production line work. Sets of hanging chains attached between the overhead chain and the tow carts allow the loads to be towed in synchronized movement with the overhead trolley conveyor. Switching systems can be used when the carts have a tow mast.

These systems are flexible in a horizontal path. However, caution and special provisions are required when inclined or declined paths are involved. The use of this type of conveyor has decreased with the increasing use of automated guided vehicles (AGVs), which require the same amount of floor space, but are more flexible and do not require any overhead conveyor equipment.

COMPARISON OF OVERHEAD TROLLEY CONVEYORS

When evaluating the suitability of any monorail-type overhead conveyor system, such as chain conveyors, load and speed capacities are two major considerations. Table 10-3 gives an overview of the differences in capacities and performance among the different

CHAPTER 10   OVERHEAD HANDLING AND LIFTING DEVICES

types of trolley conveyors. Table 10-4 rates the conveyors in six areas, with one standing for high, two standing for moderate, and three standing for low. The figures in these two tables apply to single-drive systems. These drives are commonly available with ratings from 1.0-10.0 hp (746-7,460 W), and in either constant-speed or variable-speed versions. If the application requirements exceed the values that are shown in the tables, additional synchronized drives may be needed.

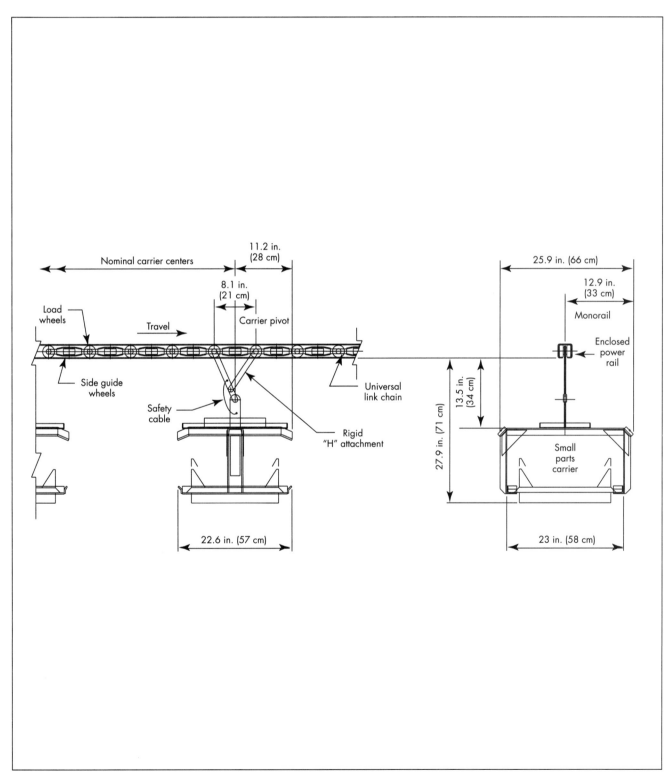

Fig. 10-8 Enclosed-track monorail and carrier assembly. *(Courtesy Dearborn Mid-West Conveyor Co.)*

CHAPTER 10   OVERHEAD HANDLING AND LIFTING DEVICES

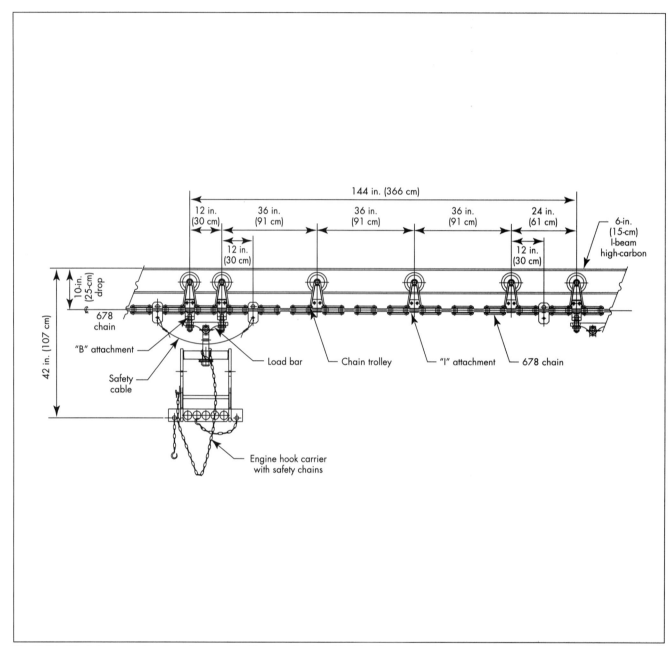

Fig. 10-9 A 678-chain monorail and carrier assembly. *(Courtesy Dearborn Mid-West Conveyor Co.)*

TABLE 10-3
Overhead Trolley Conveyor Selection Parameters

Overhead Trolley Conveyor Type	Maximum Capacity/Drive lb (kg)	Speed Ranges fpm (mpm)	Maximum Power Trolley Load lb (kg)	Industry Usage
Cable	500 (227)	20-60 (6-18.3)	75 (34)	Light industrial
Enclosed-track	600 (272)	20-60 (6-18.3)	100 (45)	Industrial/automotive
348 chain	2,000 (907)	0-70 (0-21.3)	200 (91)	Industrial/automotive
458 chain	3,000 (1,361)	0-70 (0-21.3)	400 (181)	Automotive
678 chain	6,000 (2,722)	0-70 (0-21.3)	1,200 (544)	Automotive
Overhead tow	See above	0-40 (0-12.2)	See above	Industrial

CHAPTER 10   OVERHEAD HANDLING AND LIFTING DEVICES

TABLE 10-4
Overhead Trolley Conveyor Equipment Comparison

Overhead Trolley Conveyor Type	Production Flexibility	Maintainability/ Reliability	Product Quality	Operator Safety	Relative Cost	Ergonomic Rating
Cable	2	2	2	2	3	1
Enclosed-track	2	2	2	2	3	1
348 chain	2	1	2	2	2	2
458 chain	2	1	2	2	2	2
678 chain	2	1	2	2	1	2
Overhead tow	2	2	2	2	2	1

Note: this information may be subjective and is comparable, but is relative to this group only. Verification should be done by a qualified equipment supplier.
Ratings 1-3:   1-High   2-Moderate   3-Low

OVERHEAD POWER-AND-FREE CONVEYORS

An *overhead power-and-free conveyor* (OHPF) consists of a continuously-moving powered chain, which when engaged, moves a free (nonpowered) load-carrying trolley along through the conveyor system. The powered chain can be either a universal-link type or one of the standard chains (such as 348).

The power-and-free conveyor design can be thought of as a hybrid between a standard overhead trolley conveyor and the four-wheel free trolley of a typical crane system. In fact, the power-and-free conveyor design represents an evolutionary step that began with simple, hand-pushed monorail-type conveyors and cranes.

Power-and-free conveyors offer one performance characteristic that sets them apart from the overhead trolley conveyor family. Power-and-free conveyors have the built-in flexibility to move products individually or in groups, to stop in place for load and unload operations, or to accumulate products or empty carriers for high-density storage, all within the same system and without affecting operations in the rest of the system. This type of conveyor is used to move product through production areas on specific job centers. In addition, the product carriers are able to start, stop, sort, accumulate, and change speed as required to maintain a specific production rate or to create a buffer zone before or after a production area.

POWER-AND-FREE CONVEYOR SELECTION

The power-and-free conveyor design offers considerable flexibility in layout, as well as on-the-job performance. These systems can be designed to move a product in a simple monoplane loop or they can carry products through a variety of elevations and complex layout configurations. They easily accommodate extreme changes in elevation, which can help to maximize use of floor space. The overhead configuration, with the product suspended below the power-and-free track, offers excellent product access. This ease of access enables workers to perform many different types of operations, whether the products are moving or stationary.

Power-and-free systems offer a wide range of load capacities, sizes, and operating speeds. Speeds range from extremely slow, 1-2 ft (0.3-0.6 m)/min, up to 60 ft (18.3 m)/min and higher for special transfer applications.

In a power-and-free conveyor system, force is applied to the free load-carrying trolley via a retractable dog, which is contained within the front free trolley. This retractable dog engages another dog on the continuously-moving powered chain and power is then trans-

mitted to the trolley. The retractable dog on the free trolley can be engaged and disengaged through the use of a blade-type stop mechanism, or by the mechanical reaction of load carrying trolley accumulation in the free track.

A typical carrier arrangement is supported by two or more free trolleys using pivoting king pins. The trolley that leads is the front (accumulation) trolley. The rear or trailing trolley is equipped with a ramp or beaver tail that provides the means to begin the accumulation process.

Manufacturing and Production Flexibility

The ability of a power-and-free conveyor to accommodate load-carrying free trolleys on minimal centers provides a great degree of system flexibility. Loaded carriers conveyed on production centers may be completely purged from certain work areas and accumulated in a much smaller space. The carriers can then be allowed to re-enter the production process in sequence, if required.

The accumulation feature permits high-density storage, which can be used for storing empty carriers when not in use, creating product sortation and sequencing banks, or storing product in production surge banks. With the added dimension of the free trolleys to the overhead conveyor, sophisticated systems can be created using multiple chains to transfer product endlessly throughout the plant from process to process.

Maintainability and Reliability

An OHPF conveyor is an inherently simple and reliable method of transporting products. A minimal basic maintenance program will result in many years of trouble-free service. Special attention must be paid to monitor the load-carrying free trolleys—they are the essential part of the system. The free trolley's moving parts must be maintained for proper accumulation to occur, and require regular lubrication. The wheels, side guides, and pivot points all require lubrication to prevent premature wear. As is the case with overhead trolley conveyors, power-and-free conveyors can be easily equipped with automatic lubrication systems.

A large percentage of the components used in the fabrication and installation of these systems are standard. Examples include valves, the structural steel shapes used for track, steel plate, air cylinders, motors, gear reducers, and electrical control devices. Replacement components are usually easily available.

System components such as powered chain, free trolleys, track switches, stops, and drives have been designed for extremely heavy-duty usage. This rugged construction makes for a highly reliable system that requires only basic maintenance. In addition, with its simple operating principles and rugged components, the overhead

CHAPTER 10   OVERHEAD HANDLING AND LIFTING DEVICES

power-and-free conveyor design is easily understood by maintenance technicians. If an equipment breakdown does occur, in most cases it can be repaired by the plant's own in-house maintenance staff.

Product Quality Issues

If needed, specially-designed carriers can be used to protect product quality. However, having a system that can be stopped at load and unload areas without affecting other areas of production also enhances product quality. Carriers can be transferred and lowered at different speeds to ergonomically adapt to work as well.

Overhead power-and-free conveyors are generally supported using pivoting king pins from two free trolleys. In situations where more accumulation space is required between the loads, a tow bar and trailing bar can be added. With the use of these additional spacing bars, the carriers can have a free trolley arrangement that encompasses three, four, or more trolleys to suit the needs of a specific application. The carriers themselves can be fixed or rigged in construction, or they can have moving parts to adapt to a product. The design of these product-specific carriers can improve product quality while also increasing the flexibility of the load, production, and unload functions.

Operator Safety Issues

Because these conveyors suspend products below or to the side of the power source, workers do not normally come into contact with any of the components of the drive mechanism. The continuously-moving power chain and the load carrying trolleys are elevated away from the normal traffic flow on the work floor; only the product and its carriers are positioned at working height. The products being conveyed through the production area are conveyed at a predetermined spacing, which maintains adequate clearances between the moving products.

The accumulation of products and empty carriers usually takes place in high-density storage areas located away from traffic flow. (To maximize building cube or space availability, this accumulation often takes place overhead.) Using spacing bars, a safe distance is normally added between accumulated products to eliminate possible pinch points. To protect workers from a falling product or piece of debris, safety guarding should be installed beneath the elevated portions. In addition, drip pans also may need to be installed in certain areas to catch lubricant drips or bits of debris.

Equipment Cost Considerations

An efficient, rugged design, coupled with low manufacturing, installation, and maintenance costs, and a high degree of system layout flexibility, makes the OHPF conveyor a cost-effective material handling option. Minimal close tolerance machining processes and standard manufacturing practices contribute to the relatively low manufacturing costs of these conveyors, as does the use of off-the-shelf materials and components. During installation, contractors typically use standard construction materials and practices, which also helps to keep equipment costs down.

When evaluating equipment costs for power-and-free conveyors, flexibility should probably be placed at the top of the list of benefits. However, this benefit comes at a price. Generally, a power-and-free conveyor costs more than an equivalent overhead crane solution or standard overhead trolley conveyor. Ultimately, the selection decision must be based on a good cost justification analysis.

MAJOR TYPES OF OVERHEAD POWER-AND-FREE CONVEYORS

There are three types of power-and-free conveyor systems that are found throughout industry in the U.S. and Canada. Two of these designs use standardized inch dimension chains. In addition, manufacturers also offer a number of hybrid designs for handling special products, special production processes, or unusual performance requirements. Grouped together, these designs include:

- Enclosed-track power-and-free conveyor.
- 4-in. (10-cm) power-and-free conveyor.
- 6-in. (15-cm) power-and-free conveyor.
- Special hybrid power-and-free conveyors.

Enclosed-track Power-and-free Conveyor

An enclosed-track power-and-free conveyor, while operating on the same basic overhead power-and-free principle discussed previously, is usually used for light load applications of up to approximately 150 lb (68 kg) per free trolley. This type of conveyor is also used for comparatively small material handling systems.

In Figure 10-10, the powered chain track is shown as an inverted U-shaped formed section approximately 2.75-in. (7-cm) wide and 2.75-in. (7-cm) high. This formed section encloses the moving universal-link-type power chain on three sides. The powered chain is usually a 4-in. (10-cm) pitch link chain with guide rollers positioned at 4-in. (10-cm) centers, alternately on horizontal and vertical planes. The free trolley track is a conventional configuration of two toe-to-toe formed 2.75-in. (7-cm) channel sections, or a 3-in. (7.6-cm) high-carbon structural channel for heavier loads.

The powered chain dog is a pivoting type, which eliminates the need for moving accumulated parts on the free trolleys. Parts accumulate when the front trolley nests into the rear trolley, forcing the power dog to pivot up and disengage from the front trolley.

The enclosed powered chain and roller design used in this type of system provides for a great deal of flexibility in the layout of light-duty systems. Vertical curves with a 60° incline may be used, as well as small radius (that is, 24 in. [61 cm]) horizontally- and vertically-curved track sections. This feature can be very useful in plants where space is at a premium. Product can be moved into and out of load and unload areas with minimal use of floor space.

Given their light weight and compact size, parts and components lend themselves to dealer stocking, as well as easy installation and modification. The enclosed-track power-and-free conveyor offers a cost-effective means for transporting, positioning, and storing small production parts efficiently.

Four-inch Power-and-free Conveyor

This design of power-and-free equipment consists of a powered chain track of 4-in. (10-cm) structural I-beam, and a free trolley track consisting of two 4-in. (10-cm) structural channel sections mounted toe-to-toe. The powered chain is a standard drop-forged, rivetless-link 4-in. (10-cm) pitch chain, supported by trolleys that ride on the lower I-beam flange. The load-carrying free trolleys are captured in the two-channel free track and propelled along as needed by the continuously-moving powered chain pusher dog.

The term "444 power-and-free" is derived from the structural and mechanical components of the system: the high-carbon 4-in. (10-cm) I-beam powered track, the 4-in. (10-cm) pitch chain, and the 4-in. (10-cm) double-channel free trolley track. The industry standard dimensional drop from the top of the I-beam to the centerline of the chain is 7.2 in. (18 cm).

This type of system is used for medium load applications. The 4-in. (10-cm) load-carrying free trolleys have a nominal load capacity of approximately 800 lb (363 kg). However, because the product is typically carried from a load bar that links two or more trolleys in tandem, the actual load capacity may be 1,600 lb (726 kg) or more.

The accumulation action of the 4-in. (10-cm) power-and-free is achieved using a fixed powered-chain dog, as shown in Fig. 10-11.

CHAPTER 10   OVERHEAD HANDLING AND LIFTING DEVICES

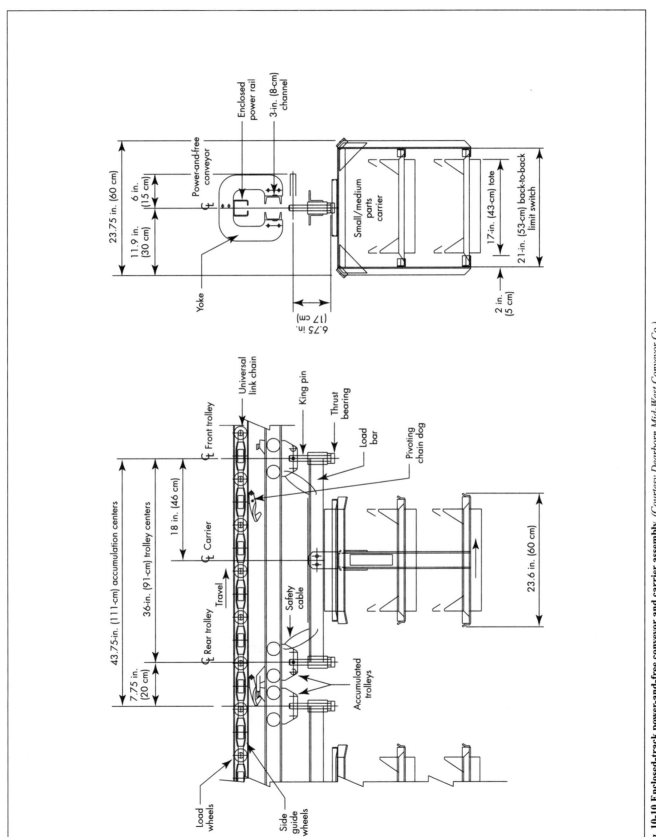

Fig. 10-10 Enclosed-track power-and-free conveyor and carrier assembly. *(Courtesy Dearborn Mid-West Conveyor Co.)*

CHAPTER 10   OVERHEAD HANDLING AND LIFTING DEVICES

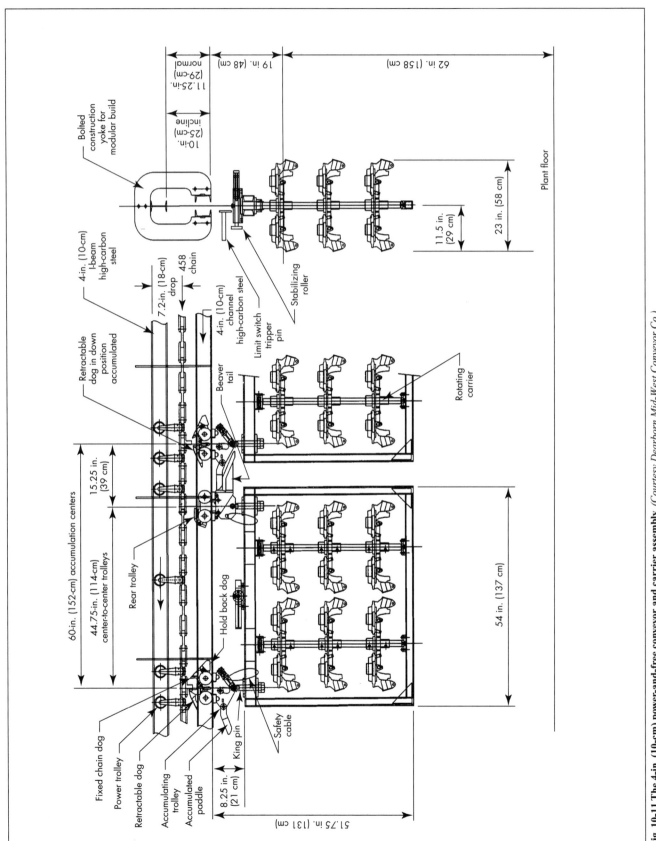

Fig. 10-11 The 4-in. (10-cm) power-and-free conveyor and carrier assembly. *(Courtesy Dearborn Mid-West Conveyor Co.)*

CHAPTER 10   OVERHEAD HANDLING AND LIFTING DEVICES

The free trolleys have the moving parts to create the disengagement mode. The pivoting paddle on the front trolley engages the beaver tail of the rear trolley. As the front paddle pivots up, an internal linkage pulls the retractable dog down. This action disengages the retractable dog from the fixed powered-chain dog, enabling products to accumulate.

With the extremely-high working strength of the powered chain and the rugged simplicity of the conveyor components, this type of power-and-free conveyor lends itself well to longer powered chains and more cost-effective system layouts. These systems should have a typical chain pull of approximately 3,500 lb (1,588 kg) and an average length of powered chain of about 2,500 ft (762 m). Typical applications include building and sorting automobile engines, body sides, marine equipment, axles, or trimmed doors. The 4-in. (10-cm) power-and-free conveyor system is one of the most commonly-used systems on the market today.

Six-inch Power-and-free Conveyor

For applications involving heavy product loading and large system layouts, a 6-in. (15-cm) power-and-free conveyor is often the right choice. This heavy-duty system uses a 6-in. (15-cm) pitch, forged powered chain supported by trolley wheels that ride on the lower flange of a 4-in. (10-cm) high-carbon, I-beam, powered-chain track. The load-carrying free trolleys are captured in the free track section consisting of two 6-in. (15-cm) high-carbon structural channels mounted toe-to-toe. The accumulation mechanism and method of operation are identical to the 4-in. (10-cm) power-and-free.

As was true in the description of the 4-in. (10-cm) design, the term for the 6-in. (15-cm) design—"466 power-and-free"—is derived from the track member sizes and the pitch of the powered chain. The industry standard dimensional drop from the top of the I-beam to the centerline of the chain is 7.4 in. (19 cm). The carrying capacity of each free trolley is approximately 3,000 lb (1,361 kg). However, as with the 4-in. (10-cm) design, the free trolleys are usually used in tandem, effectively doubling their load-carrying capacity.

For material handling applications that require very high load-carrying capacity, long, complex multi-level layouts, and automated sortation, the 466 power-and-free design is often the best choice. These systems usually have a maximum chain pull of 6,500 lb (2,948 kg) per drive and an average chain length of approximately 4,000 ft (1,219 m), and are similar to the full body, final assembly system shown in Fig. 10-12.

Special Hybrid Power-and-free Conveyors

For applications where the production process or the products require long systems, and in which the products themselves are relatively light, special hybrid power-and-free conveyors can be the right choice. Such hybrid systems may use a 458 chain in conjunction with 3-in. (7.6-cm) free trolleys, or a 678 chain with 4-in. (10-cm) free trolleys. These hybrid combinations increase the chain-pull capacity of the system without incurring the cost of increasing the size of the free trolleys.

A cost analysis should compare this option to that of adding another chain and transfer to the system or adding multiple drives to reduce chain pull. These types of conveyors are not widely used, but they do offer another material handling option.

COMPARISON OF OVERHEAD POWER-AND-FREE CONVEYORS

Tables 10-5 and 10-6 give an overview of the performance characteristics of the major types of overhead power-and-free conveyors. Table 10-6 rates the conveyors in six areas, with one standing for high, two standing for moderate, and three standing for low.

AUTOMATED ELECTRIFIED MONORAILS

An *automated electrified monorail* (AEM) is an overhead conveyor or monorail system in which each carrier is equipped with its own electric drive and controls, making it self-powered. Conductor bars mounted on the track supply electric power to the individual carrier's motors, and control and communication data to its controls.

AEM systems are well-suited for flexible production requirements. These systems have the ability to operate at a wide range of speeds from slow to very fast, and they can precisely control acceleration, deceleration, and braking. The AEM's greater flexibility of speed and controls bring performance advantages to transport and delivery applications and to assembly operations. AEMs also perform well in buffer and storage applications, but the high cost of the individual motorized carriers may offset this advantage.

AUTOMATED ELECTRIFIED MONORAIL SELECTION

In the early days of AEM development, the carriers (or "mono-tractors" as they were called) ran on a steel patented rail or a structural I-beam. The preferred material for AEM tracks today is extruded aluminum, due to its cleanliness, light weight, and dimensional accuracy, and because it can be easily sawn, drilled, and tapped.

With its self-powered carriers and integrated computer control systems, the AEM offers a degree of flexibility that other fixed-track material handling systems have difficulty emulating. For example, sliding or rotating switches allow carriers to transfer horizontally from one track to another, or from one process to another.

Vertical drop and lift stations, which take up very little room, permit AEM carriers to move vertically. Unassisted and assisted incline and decline track sections let the carriers make more gradual (and less expensive) changes in elevation. Inclines and declines provide a steady flow of carriers, rather than the individual cycling of vertical lifts. Either method may be used. The selection decision should be based on layout, throughput requirements, and cost.

The AEM has few process limitations, and it offers a highly flexible material handling solution for the right applications. However, on any technological spectrum showing the full range of different types of overhead handling systems, the AEM would be labelled the most sophisticated. AEM systems rely on sophisticated control logic and software. However, the many existing AEM installations are creating a history of proven performance on the job and their use will continue to grow.

Due to the AEM's high speed capabilities and flexibility, it is compatible with a variety of manufacturing and assembly processes. The ability to run at high speeds can be a great advantage when cycle times are critical.

Sortation, scheduling, and broadcasting requirements lend themselves well to the AEM because of its high speed and ability to switch tracks. When production operations require longer dwell times for a carrier at a critical machine interface point, an AEM can accommodate that need. An AEM carrier can enter and exit stop stations at higher speeds when necessary to help ease machine cycle time requirements.

AEMs are used in a broad range of industries, both in North America and overseas. They do have some application limitations, based mostly on the workplace environment. Applications such as paint booths, ovens, wash booths, and water tests all require special considerations. Chapter 19 discusses this area in greater detail.

CHAPTER 10   OVERHEAD HANDLING AND LIFTING DEVICES

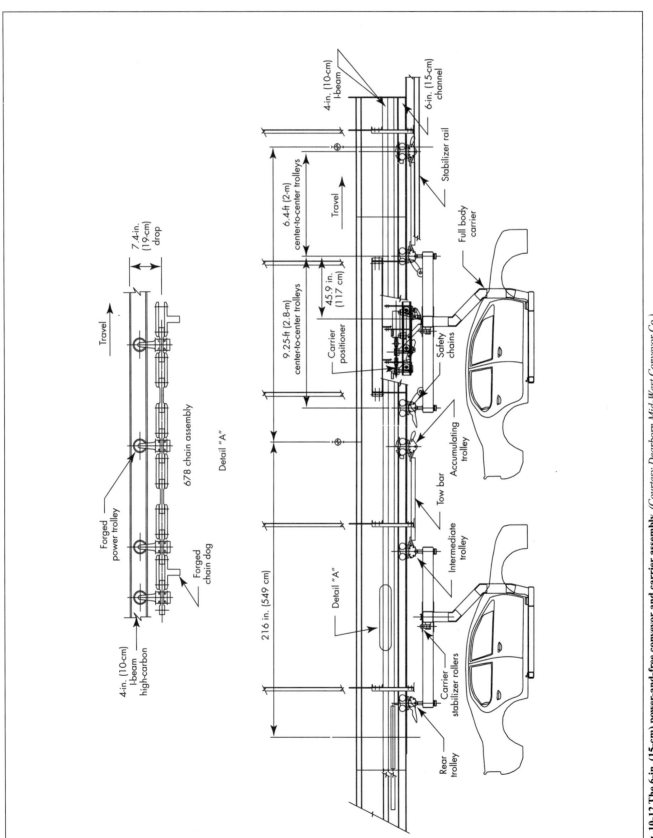

Fig. 10-12 The 6-in. (15-cm) power-and-free conveyor and carrier assembly. *(Courtesy Dearborn Mid-West Conveyor Co.)*

CHAPTER 10   OVERHEAD HANDLING AND LIFTING DEVICES

TABLE 10-5
Overhead Power-and-free Selection Parameters

Overhead Power-and-free Conveyor Type	Maximum Capacity/Drive lb (kg)	Speed Ranges fpm (mpm)	Maximum Free Trolley Load lb (kg)	Plant Usage
Enclosed-track (light-duty)	300 (136)	4-40 (1.2-12.2)	250 (113)	Industrial
Enclosed-track	600 (272)	6-60 (1.8-18.3)	700 (318)	Body and trim/industrial
4 in. (10 cm)	3,000 (1,361)	6-60 (1.8-18.3)	800 (363)	Paint body and trim
6 in. (15 cm)	6,500 (2,948)	6-60 (1.8-18.3)	3,000 (1,361)	Paint body and trim
Hybrid	Varies	60 (18.3)	Varies	Paint body and trim

TABLE 10-6
Overhead Power-and-free Equipment Comparison

Overhead Power-and-free Conveyor Type	Production Flexibility	Maintainability/ Reliability	Product Quality	Operator Safety	Relative Cost	Ergonomic Rating
Enclosed-track (light-duty)	2	2	1	1	3	1
Enclosed-track	2	2	1	1	2-3	1
4 in. (10 cm)	2	1	1	1	2	1
6 in. (15 cm)	2	1	1	1	1	1
Hybrid	2	2	1	1	1	1

Note: this information may be subjective and is comparable, but is relative to this group only. Verification should be done by a qualified equipment supplier.
Ratings 1-3:   1-High   2-Moderate   3-Low

Manufacturing and Production Flexibility

AEM systems make good use of available building space. As with other overhead handling systems, an AEM requires very little floor space. With the use of sloped track and vertical lifts, the AEM path can be laid out on multiple levels. As production layouts change, the AEM path can change as well. Switches, tracks, and carriers can be easily added or removed. Similarly, additional carriers can be added to provide greater throughput.

Another attribute of the AEM is its flexible cycle time. One of the goals of flexible assembly is to allow time for a job to be done right the first time, or at least to have the part correctly repaired and ready to go to the next step before it is released. In addition, stationary workstations give workers a better chance to perform tasks correctly. Inventory and work-in-process control are simplified due, in part, to the flexibility of the AEM. Because each carrier is outfitted with its own identification, such as a bar code label, the carrier can carry vital process and product information specific to that carrier. This data can be tracked by a programmable logic controller (PLC). If the process requirements change, the carriers can be reprogrammed appropriately.

One of the specific benefits of the AEM when compared to overhead trolley and power-and-free conveyors is the ease of expansion or rerouting at model changeover time. The track can be installed in advance of changeover at all the free locations, leaving only the switches to be cut during a shutdown. Likewise, subsystems can be tested before the overall system is tested. This has often reduced installation downtime from one to two weeks to two to three days.

Another benefit of AEM is the ability to cross two paths. When required or beneficial, overhead trolley and power-and-free conveyors require twice the height of the track and load to pass one under the other. This also requires the distance to decline and incline the

path before crossing. The AEM solution is a motorized cross with normally one track on a turntable. Added to this are the controls for the cross rate to stop any oncoming vehicle carried on the other path until it is free.

Maintainability and Reliability

On average, an AEM system requires less mechanical maintenance than a conventional overhead chain conveyor. In comparison to a chain conveyor, an AEM requires minimal lubrication other than for trolley wheels and possibly the drive motor. However, as with all automated systems, a far greater level of expertise in electronics is needed by maintenance technicians.

One important aspect of AEM maintenance is the regular inspection of the carriers. A typical AEM system may have over 100 carriers, their motors, and other electronics. Repair spurs offer the best means for inspecting and servicing the carriers. Such spurs can be installed overhead and fitted with service platforms for easy access. Because AEMs are designed to communicate with PLCs, carrier diagnostics can be a part of the maintenance program. The PLC can isolate problems with a specific carrier and thereby minimize downtime. Track switches and vertical lifts also should be part of a regularly scheduled maintenance inspection program.

Many AEM production systems with 60 carriers or more have automatic checking stations that check for braking, collector shoeware, slowdown controls, and proximity sensing.

The performance history of the AEM in North America shows that these systems have accumulated good records of reliability, like those in Europe, which have been in use for over 25 years. AEM system downtime has typically not been a limiting factor to overall production. A fairly simple AEM can operate for long periods with

CHAPTER 10 OVERHEAD HANDLING AND LIFTING DEVICES

minimal attention. However, a full-time technician with a sufficient skills base would be needed in the case of a large, complex AEM.

Regardless of the type of material handling system, if the system is an automated one (for example, an AEM, overhead crane, or an automated guided vehicle system), and if that system interfaces with other handling systems, those interfaces will rarely perform flawlessly for long periods of time. The best maintenance and skilled supervision are needed to keep such interfaces in action.

Product Quality Issues

An AEM may improve the quality of a part that it is handling and can go a long way toward preventing quality from degrading. The smooth operation of an AEM during acceleration, deceleration, and vertical transfer greatly lessens the likelihood of handling-related product damage. Because an AEM is virtually dirt-free, it maintains the quality in final trim operations where preserving paint finish is extremely important.

Operator Safety Issues

AEMs help to create a positive, user-friendly work environment. They integrate well with ergonomically-designed workstations and give employees 360° access to parts. Workers can put their feet and knees under AEMs safely and comfortably. In comparison to most overhead chain conveyors, an AEM is virtually silent, which can help to reduce worker stress and fatigue.

As with other types of powered industrial equipment, the AEMs depend on electrical power and this poses a safety hazard. Covered bus bars and low-voltage power systems are ways of protecting production workers. Proper training of all production workers, supervisors, and maintenance staff that work with AEMs is essential.

Equipment Cost Considerations

Costs incurred for an AEM system are directly related to what the system is asked to do. In general, the more flexibility that is required, the greater the cost. A system that requires accumulation and sortation capabilities will cost more than one that just requires quick transport from one work area to the next. The main reason is the relatively high per-carrier cost when compared with either overhead power-and-free systems or overhead trolley conveyors.

The benefits of increased throughput and the lower cost of production labor need to be analyzed and weighed against the cost of the system. Higher training costs should be factored in as well.

ALUMINUM-ALLOY TRACK AUTOMATED ELECTRIFIED MONORAILS

Aluminum-alloy track AEMs are the standard design throughout the world, but there are many structural-beam and patented-rail powered monorails in service.

In its early stages, the AEM was simply an automatic dispatch monorail system that was used primarily for the point-to-point delivery of loads. The monorail track itself was either a steel I-beam or a patented track with steel wheels as shown in Fig. 10-13. These track designs were initially developed for manual pendant-controlled monorail systems.

As electrical control hardware technology advanced, so did attempts to further develop the AEM concept. However, the new control hardware often proved to be unreliable. With the later advent of solid-state electrical components, the reliability problem was solved, resulting in the development of more complex steel track AEM systems. The automotive industry then began using these steel track AEM systems for final assembly, engine, chassis, and decking operations, first in Europe and then in the U.S. and Canada (in many cases, as a replacement of power-and-free conveyors).

With recent advances in industrial computer technology, AEM systems have grown in sophistication and size. The evolution of the technologies used in AEM drives and controls has been paralleled by a similar evolution in track design and componentry.

Current AEM Design

In terms of automated overhead material handling systems, AEMs are a technology that is on the leading edge. AEM technology has evolved at an impressive rate and is continuing to evolve. While much of that evolution is now taking place in the realm of software, drives, and controls, some advances have been purely mechanical.

For example, wheels made of urethane and special plastics replaced steel wheels, resulting in higher travel speeds, reduced noise, and more precise braking and positioning. As speeds increased, the track itself became outmoded. European AEM manufacturers replaced rolled steel track with track made of extruded aluminum, and also introduced cast-aluminum trolley housings, setting a new standard worldwide (see Fig. 10-14).

Today's AEMs offer controlled acceleration and deceleration rates that make higher running speeds more practical. In most applications, a top speed of about 300 ft (91 m)/min is considered practical.

Extruded-aluminum track offers many clear advantages when compared to steel construction. Aluminum track is clean and maintenance-free, and never requires painting. It is also easier to bend and form than steel. Aluminum track sections are light enough in weight to be hand-carried during installation. The extrusions have superior dimensional accuracy as well, permitting precise fits and alignments for smooth carrier travel at high speeds.

With aluminum track, precision locators for the electrification can be extruded into the rail. The result is a tight fit for the bus bar installation, which results in longer system service life, less maintenance, and better integrity of communication.

European automotive engineers recognized the need for system standardization. Working in concert with AEM manufacturers, they developed a standard set of specifications that covers areas such as track size, track configurations, and drive and idler clearances. North American manufacturers have now joined the Europeans in adopting large parts of these standards.

The part of the standard that applies to track covers both light-load and heavy-load track applications. The two main tracks now in use throughout North America and Europe are 2 × 7 in. (51 × 178 mm) for loads up to 1,100 lb (499 kg), and 3 × 9 in. (76 × 229 mm) for loads up to 6,000 lb (2,722 kg) on double-trolley setups. However, the move toward standardization does not extend to all of the different parts of the electrical system because of the differences in voltages and cycles between North America and Europe.

The bus bars transmit electric power, control signals, and communications data to the individual carriers. A typical AEM arrangement might use eight bus bars arranged as follows:

1. 480-V electrification.
2. 480-V electrification.
3. 480-V electrification.
4. 480-V ground.
5. Travel permit.
6. Carrier present.
7. Control common (110-V ground).
8. Auxiliary control.

The configuration of the bus bars varies considerably with system complexity and specifications. For safety reasons, the higher voltage is positioned at the top.

A programmable logic controller (PLC) usually functions as the master controller for the carriers. In a typical computer system

CHAPTER 10   OVERHEAD HANDLING AND LIFTING DEVICES

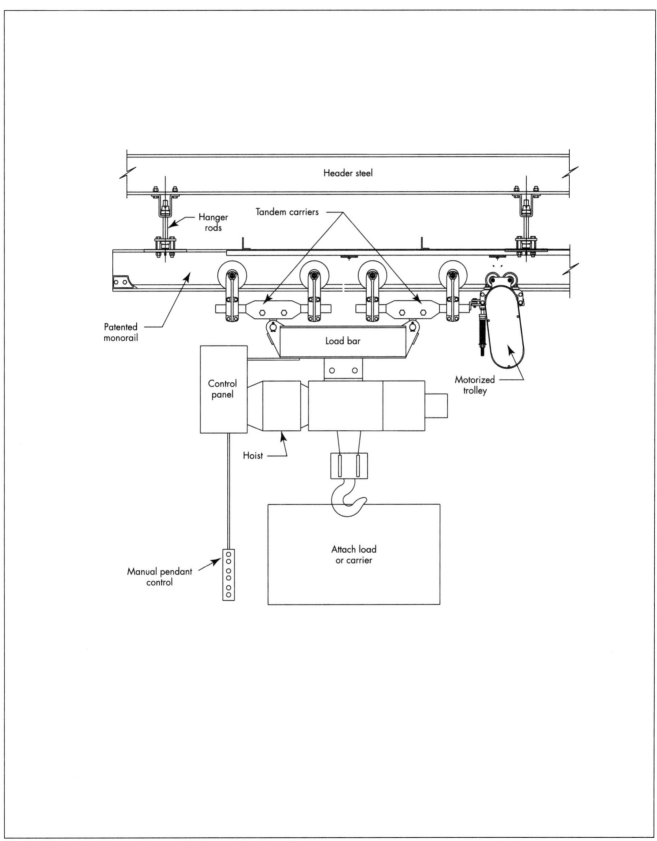

Fig. 10-13 Patented-rail powered monorail. *(Courtesy Trambeam Corp.)*

CHAPTER 10 OVERHEAD HANDLING AND LIFTING DEVICES

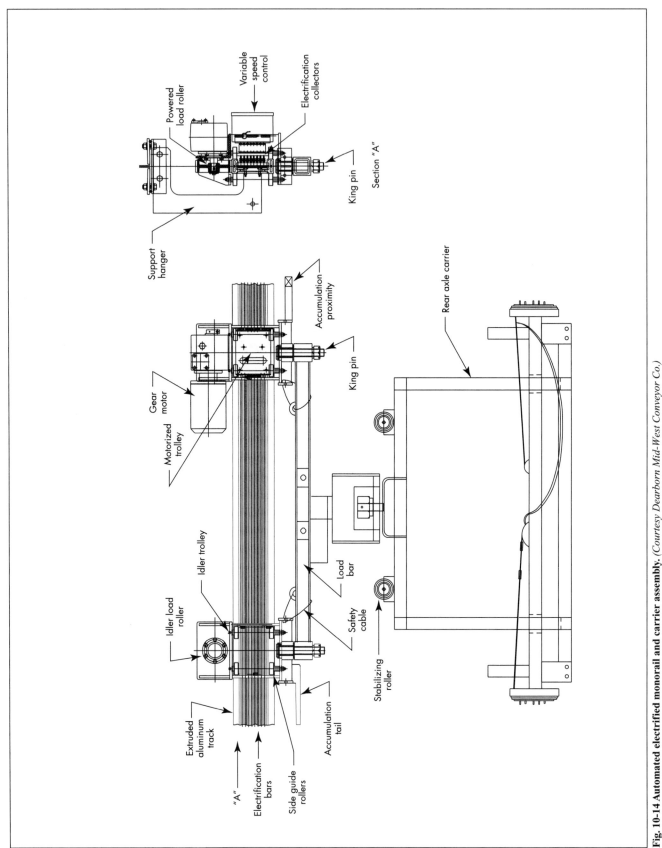

Fig. 10-14 Automated electrified monorail and carrier assembly. *(Courtesy Dearborn Mid-West Conveyor Co.)*

CHAPTER 10   OVERHEAD HANDLING AND LIFTING DEVICES

hierarchy, this PLC will operate beneath a host computer, and the host computer will operate under a main computer system, which can be company-wide, division-wide, or facility-wide. The capacity of the PLC will vary with the complexity and size of the system. A controller onboard each carrier handles the speed control function under the direction of the PLC. These onboard controls can be single-speed, two-speed, or variable-speed. Individual components or sections of the system, such as switches, lift stations, and sortation banks have their own lower-level controllers, which operate under the direction of the PLC.

In all but the most simple AEM systems, specific carriers must be identified for routing, control, and other functions. AEM systems use two basic types of identification systems for carriers: "read only" and "read/write." "Read only" systems are actually variations of bar code readers. "Read/write" systems use tags mounted on the carriers to hold complex data, such as vehicle identification numbers, options, and destinations. The data held on these tags can be read and then erased and new data recorded.

AEM Performance Characteristics

One of the performance benefits offered by AEMs is the ability to accumulate loads. Many different methods can be used to control accumulation on an AEM, for example, proximity devices, zone blocking, limit switches, photoelectrics, and ultrasonics.

The *proximity device* is the most popular. It works well on straight sections but not as well on curves. Carriers are equipped with a down-looking proximity sensor in the front and a reading plate on the rear. As a moving carrier approaches a stopped carrier, the moving carrier's front proximity device senses the rear plate of the stopped carrier and slows down. As the down-looking sensor sees the plate, the power to the drive is disengaged and the brake is set. With this type of accumulation, operation at the correct speeds is critical. If high approach speeds are needed, then the proximity method may not be the right choice.

Zone blocking incorporates two methods of zone control, the PLC method and the jumper method. In the PLC method, every zone must be wired back to the PLC. As it monitors the movement of each carrier from zone to zone, the PLC either gives the carrier permission to move to the next zone, or it instructs the carrier to remain where it is. The PLC always knows which zone each carrier is in at any given time. With the jumper method, zone blocking is accomplished by connecting the "travel permit" (TP) bar of each zone to the "carrier present" (CP) bar in the zone ahead of it. In operation, the carriers effectively block each other without needing any direction from the PLC.

AEMs offer the ability to perform sortation operations using a combination of the AEM's speed capabilities, positive control, accumulation, and reversibility. Two of the most common sortation methods are lines and loops. Sortation loops require only two switches. This method becomes cost-effective when loads are seldom very far out of sequence, or when the production rate is relatively low. The limiting factor is that the entire bank must travel through the loop to resequence a single part.

The sortation method that uses lines or spurs is similar to a railroad yard. As more lines are installed, it becomes easier to select a single load without having to wait for resequencing. These two sortation methods are also used with overhead power-and-free conveyors.

As described earlier, aluminum-track AEMs also have the ability to change elevation quickly. These AEMs can negotiate vertical curves quickly, changing levels within a plant with ease. Drop/lift section transfers were specifically designed for the AEM (as shown in Fig. 10-15). These electric-powered, chain-driven transfers move

a section of rail and an AEM carrier with its load vertically from elevation to elevation as needed.

For high-throughput manufacturing and assembly operations that can take advantage of a fully-automated system, an AEM can be a state-of-the-art solution. The AEM concept has been widely embraced in Europe, especially in the automotive industry. AEMs have been installed in many automotive plants in North America and are now used by an increasing variety of industries, including textile, computer, and appliance manufacturing.

COMPARISON OF AUTOMATED ELECTRIFIED MONORAILS

Tables 10-7 and 10-8 provide basic information on the two common extruded-aluminum AEM systems now on the market and on the older structural-steel design. Table 10-8 has a rating scale for the three types of AEMs in six areas, with one standing for high, two standing for moderate, and three standing for low.

LINEAR INDUCTION MOTOR SYSTEMS

Although linear induction motor (LIM) systems are not new, their entry into the material handling field is more recent. They are currently used in some power-and-free conveyor systems as well as in tilt tray conveyor sortation systems.

Simply put, a LIM is configured as a linear device, rather than as a rotary device like a conventional electric motor. LIM systems basically use two different methods to get the power to the moving carrier or vehicle. In the first situation, the stator is located in the track and the cart or carrier contains the "rotor" or reaction plate. These systems have either continuous carriers or reaction plates in contact with the stator. In the later case, the carriers are propelled by the "slingshot" method where the power and control is applied only when the cart is over the LIM. Both approaches have been used successfully, but the control techniques must be thoroughly understood to gain the reduced cost, high speed, and low power requirements that are characteristic of these devices.

In the second situation, the power is provided through collectors on sliding shoes to the car or vehicle stator and the reaction plate is continuous along the track. This is typical of people mover applications.

DROP/LIFT TRANSFERS

Drop/lift transfers are a specialized type of material handling equipment designed to move loads vertically between different handling systems or within a single multilevel system. Although drop/lift transfers can add flexibility to any standard overhead conveyor, they offer the greatest benefits when paired with either overhead power-and-free conveyors or automated electrified monorail systems. Power-and-free systems and AEMs allow loads to be stopped and positioned during the transfer cycle, which enable them to integrate well with drop/lift transfers. For continuously moving conveyors, this transfer process is more difficult to perform smoothly.

Drop/lift transfers add an impressive degree of flexibility and efficiency to material handling systems. They can function as the mechanism that changes two separate handling systems into a single integrated one.

DROP/LIFT TRANSFER SELECTION

The operation of drop/lift transfers can be fully-automated, semi-automated, or manual. These units come in a wide range of electrical, mechanical, and hydraulic designs. Chains, cables, and belts have

CHAPTER 10   OVERHEAD HANDLING AND LIFTING DEVICES

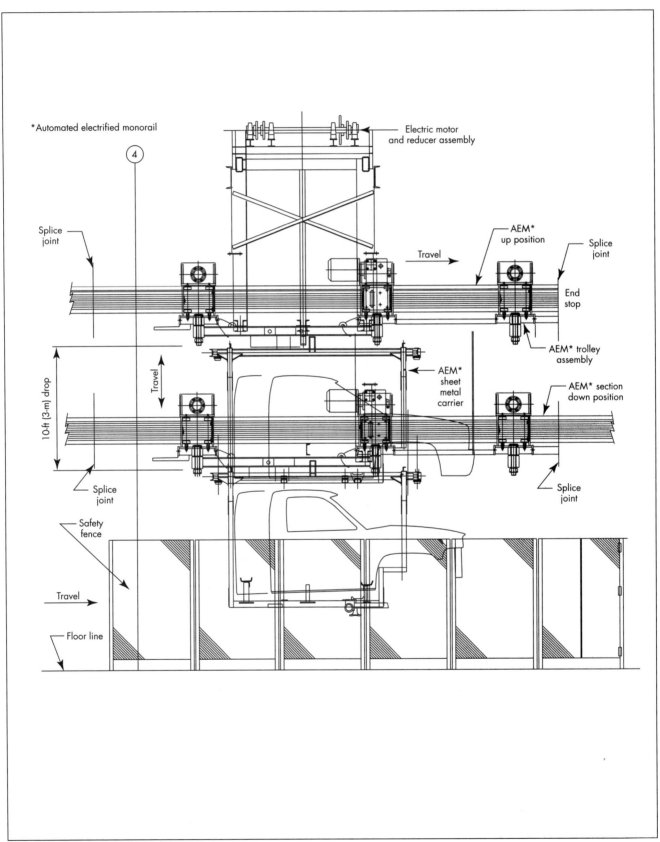

Fig. 10-15 Electrical chain drop/lift. *(Courtesy Dearborn Mid-West Conveyor Co.)*

CHAPTER 10   OVERHEAD HANDLING AND LIFTING DEVICES

TABLE 10-7
Automated Electrified Monorail (AEM) Selection Parameters

Automated Electrified Monorail Type	Track Dimensions in. (mm)	Speed Ranges fpm (mpm)	Maximum Trolley Load lb (kg)	Plant Usage
Structural	Varies	15-300 (4.6-91)	Varies	Body and trim/industrial
Aluminum	2.3-7 (58 ×178)	40-400* (12-122)	1,100 (499)	Body and trim/industrial
Aluminum	3-9 (76 × 229)	40-400* (12-122)	3,000 (1,361)	Body and trim/industrial

*240 fpm (73 meter per minute [mpm]) for AC drives, 400 fpm (122 mpm) for DC drives.

TABLE 10-8
Automated Electrified Monorail (AEM) Equipment Comparison

Automated Electrified Monorail Type	Production Flexibility	Maintainability/ Reliability	Product Quality	Operator Safety	Relative Cost	Ergonomic Rating
Structural	2	2	3	2	2	2
Aluminum	1	1	1	1	1	1

Note: this information may be subjective and is comparable, but is relative to this group only. Verification should be done by a qualified equipment supplier.
Ratings 1-3:   1-High   2-Moderate   3-Low

all been used to support and transfer loads from one conveyor or AEM to another.

While drop/lift transfers can move loads from one overhead handling system to another, they are more typically used to transfer loads from an overhead system to a floor-mounted system, or vice-versa. A typical application will help to illustrate how these transfers are used in manufacturing settings. In an automobile assembly plant, there may be assembly procedures at one point that need to be performed on the vehicle from underneath, but the vehicle is being handled on an in-floor chain conveyor. A drop/lift transfer can be installed at this point to lift and transfer the vehicle to an overhead conveyor system or AEM allowing workers at the next assembly station unimpeded access to the vehicle's underbody.

Drop/lift transfers are usually designed to handle a specific type of load, application, production problem, or plant layout consideration. The major types of these transfers differ in the way in which they support loads during the transfer cycle, but their overall mission remains the same.

Maintainability and Reliability

Drop/lift transfers are designed to be reliable and easy to maintain. However, sophisticated automated equipment, such as these transfers, requires properly trained technicians who stay ahead of maintenance and inspection needs. The same technicians must ensure that the equipment stays correctly calibrated.

Product Quality Issues

During the transfer cycle, the load is positioned and held firmly to prevent any handling-related product damage. Although most transfers run in an automated mode, employees can override the automated mode with manual controls if needed to deal with a potential product quality problem.

The end-user can influence product quality as well by providing perch or contact points on the products to help with the transfer process. These perch points are generally cradled in plastic mounts

on the transfer mechanism for additional product protection and quality assurance.

Operator Safety Issues

As with other forms of automated material handling equipment, drop/lift transfers need to meet a very high standard to ensure employee safety. Transfers must be equipped with complete guarding, light screens, warning lights, E-stops (emergency stops), electrical/mechanical lockout devices, and in full compliance with the applicable safety codes and standards. These transfer units, with their quick transfer speeds and automatic operation, require extremely stringent safety measures, and thorough employee training.

Equipment Cost Considerations

Incremental improvements in production flexibility almost always require accompanying increases in cost, and drop/lift transfers are no exception to this principle. They are relatively expensive pieces of equipment. In fact, it is not unusual for these transfers to account for a major portion of the overall cost of a system. But, the alternative of handling loads manually may be even more costly as a result of inefficient manual labor, poor product quality, inefficient product flow, or work-related injuries. Given the custom-built nature of most drop/lift transfers, comparing costs among the various types of transfers is difficult to do.

MAJOR TYPES OF DROP/LIFT TRANSFERS

An interesting aspect of drop/lift transfer design is that while the task they perform is a straightforward one, there are many different engineering approaches for getting the job done. Typically, transfers can be assigned to one of six categories:

- Cable hoist-operated drop/lifts.
- Continuous vertical lift conveyors.
- Hydraulic-cylinder drop/lifts.
- Electric-powered chain drop/lifts.

CHAPTER 10 OVERHEAD HANDLING AND LIFTING DEVICES

- Electric-powered belt drop/lifts.
- Automatic fork lift and transfer.

Cable Hoist-operated Drop/Lifts

Cable hoist-operated drop/lifts were the first designs developed for use in manufacturing settings. Their primary use was to move products from one conveyor to another and they were commonly controlled with manually-operated pendants. Controlling one of these early transfers without damaging the product or the equipment itself took a skilled operator. An early application in the automotive industry involved moving engine decking from conveyors to autobodies. In fact, some of these installations are still in use today.

The design of these first transfers was fairly simple, which made for good reliability. However, their track-record in the area of maintaining product quality during the transfer cycle was not very good until automation was introduced. Automating these early transfers improved operator safety and reduced product quality problems, but as production speeds increased, some of these older units had difficulty keeping up.

The cost of a typical cable hoist-operated drop/lift is very reasonable when compared with other, more highly-automated designs, but its use is limited to low-throughput applications in which the operator and products can be properly protected.

Continuous Vertical Lift Conveyors

A *continuous vertical lift conveyor* is a lift and carry device that transports loads in one direction only—either up or down. Its movement is continuous throughout the entire product transfer cycle. It is this continuous movement that separates the vertical lift conveyor from other types that have programmed starts and stops during their transfer cycles. The vertical lift conveyor is used where elevation changes are great, and where quick production rates require the continuous movement of multiple jobs simultaneously.

A continuous vertical lift conveyor uses multiple lengths of chain that wrap around an assortment of sprockets to produce the desired transfer lift or drop. Crossbars are attached to the strands of chain at intervals spaced for specific product centers or other job requirements. The continuously-moving matched chains and support bars deliver loads to the required elevation quickly and smoothly.

Generally, continuous vertical lift conveyors are used to transfer loads between two floor conveyors located on different levels. However, with the addition of an auxiliary lift, they can transfer loads from floor conveyors to overhead handling systems. As shown in Fig. 10-16, loads enter the conveyor on one floor, are conveyed continuously to the next floor, and are then automatically transferred to an overhead power-and-free conveyor. The accumulation of loads prior to the vertical lift conveyor, and the accumulation of empty carriers that are ready for loading, contribute to the smooth, efficient operation of the conveyor.

As with other types of chain conveyors, continuous vertical lift conveyors need a preventive maintenance program. From the maintenance perspective, the fact that these conveyors are in continuous motion can make it easier to spot potential trouble areas before they become critical.

Product quality issues can be a concern with a continuous vertical lift conveyor. Loads must be adequately supported and protected during the transfer cycle. The use of chains near the loads could also present quality concerns because of oil and grease.

Hydraulic-cylinder Drop/Lifts

Figure 10-17 shows a *hydraulic-cylinder drop/lift*, a type of transfer that uses a powerful hydraulic cylinder installed in the plant floor to move loads up or down. A carriage that is specifically designed to match the perch points on the load being transferred is attached to the rod end of the cylinder. Carriage guides are built into the supporting structure to prevent carriage twisting during the transfer cycle. This hydraulically-controlled transfer has built-in acceleration and deceleration functions for accurately positioning the loads at both the pickup and discharge points to avoid product damage.

When these units were initially installed in industrial settings, there was some concern raised over the inaccessibility of the cylinder itself. But hydraulic-cylinder drop/lifts have developed a good reputation for reliability in the field, and the addition of stand-by hydraulic pumps and controls have made them even more reliable. Typical performance in an automotive assembly plant would be 70 car bodies transferred per hour over a 25-ft (7.6-m) vertical distance.

A common application involves loading or unloading products from an overhead power-and-free conveyor or from an AEM to a floor conveyor. The overhead carrier is moved into position above the transfer unit. An electrical interlock control then signals the hydraulic cylinder transfer to cycle up. The transfer lifts the product just high enough to allow the conveyor system to cycle the empty carrier out of the way. After the transfer receives a carrier-clear signal, it lowers the product onto the waiting floor conveyor. This process could be performed in reverse as well.

The unload control logic sequence—that is, loaded carrier in the transfer zone, lift load, empty carrier clear of transfer zone, lower load to new conveyor—is typical of many of the drop/load transfers previously described.

Electric-powered Chain Drop/Lifts

Electric-powered chain drop/lifts use a series of electric-powered chain drives to lift and lower loads. The example shown in Fig. 10-18 is transferring a van body from a floor conveyor to an overhead power-and-free conveyor. This same transfer could be servicing an overhead AEM as well.

After all the interlocks have been properly engaged, the chain transfer carriage raises the load to the pickup point. The overhead power-and-free carrier cycles into position and stops. The transfer then lowers the van body into the carrier perches and cycles back down to its home position to await another load. The power-and-free carrier then cycles out of the transfer area, carrying its load into the main conveyor system.

The electric-powered chain drop/lift, like the hydraulic-cylinder drop/lift, features acceleration, deceleration, and braking functions. The speed control is typically either variable-speed DC or variable-frequency AC. The use of electric control systems with conventional chain drives produces a reliable, smooth load transfer at precisely controlled speeds. Throughput rates run about 75 to 80 transfers per hour over a vertical distance of 20 ft (6 m).

The use of electric-powered chain lifts is not restricted to heavy manufacturing. Lighter load capacity designs can be used in assembly operations that handle items such as PCs. Regardless of the application, though, the transfers must be properly safeguarded with safety cages, light screens, alarm systems, and similar safety devices.

Electric-powered Belt Drop/Lifts

In Figure 10-19, the basic design of this unit closely resembles that of the electric-powered chain drop/lift. The control logic is also extremely similar. Both types of units can accomplish the transfer cycle quickly and reliably. The central difference between the two designs is in the use of special belts, rather than chain. These high-strength, wear-resistant belts are quieter, without sacrificing speed or load capacity.

In addition, the electric-powered belt lift design eliminates the lubrication requirements of chains and sprockets, as well as the

CHAPTER 10   OVERHEAD HANDLING AND LIFTING DEVICES

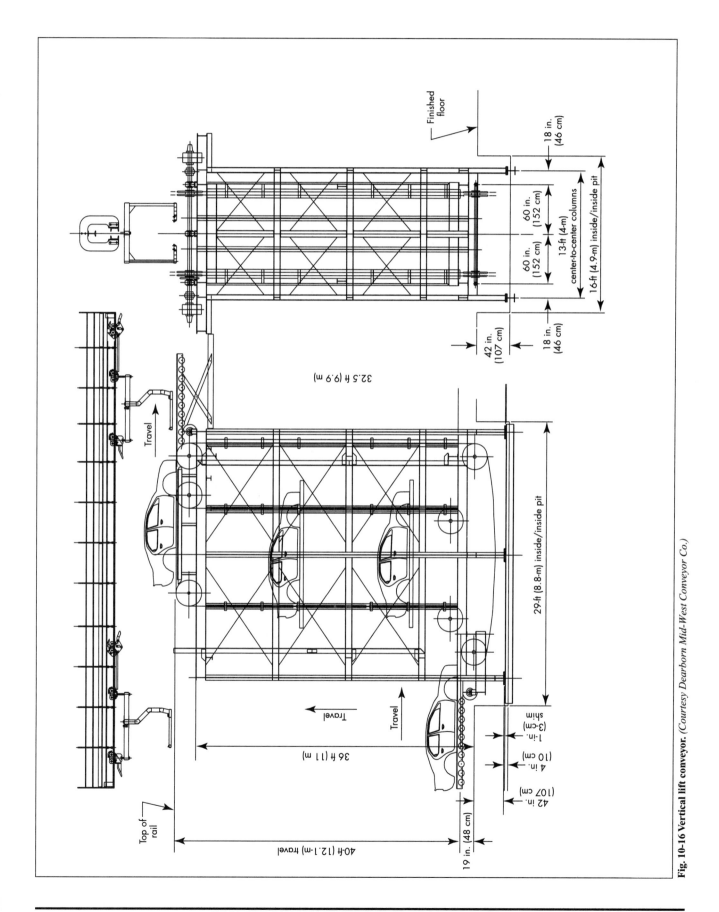

Fig. 10-16 Vertical lift conveyor. *(Courtesy Dearborn Mid-West Conveyor Co.)*

CHAPTER 10   OVERHEAD HANDLING AND LIFTING DEVICES

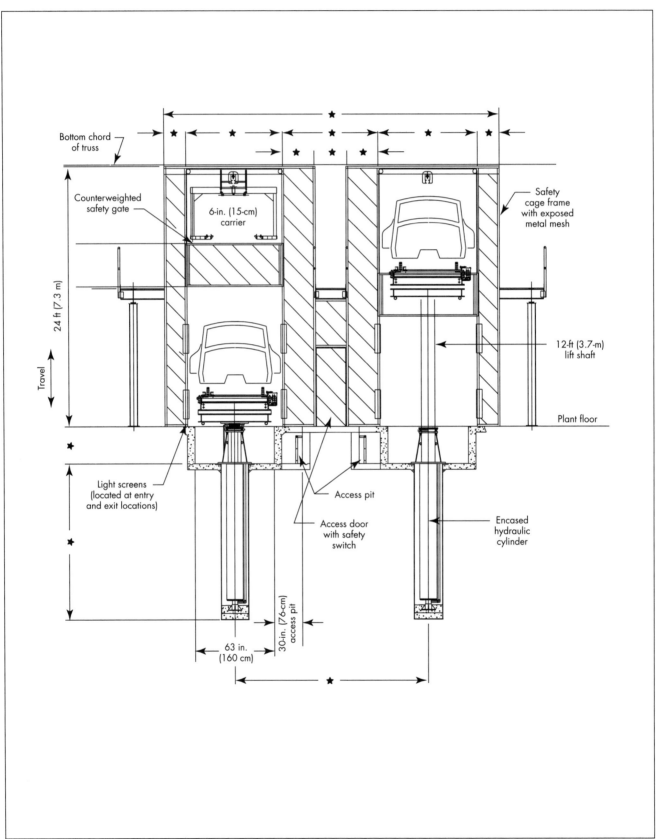

Fig. 10-17 Hydraulic-cylinder drop/lift. *(Courtesy Dearborn Mid-West Conveyor Co.)*

CHAPTER 10   OVERHEAD HANDLING AND LIFTING DEVICES

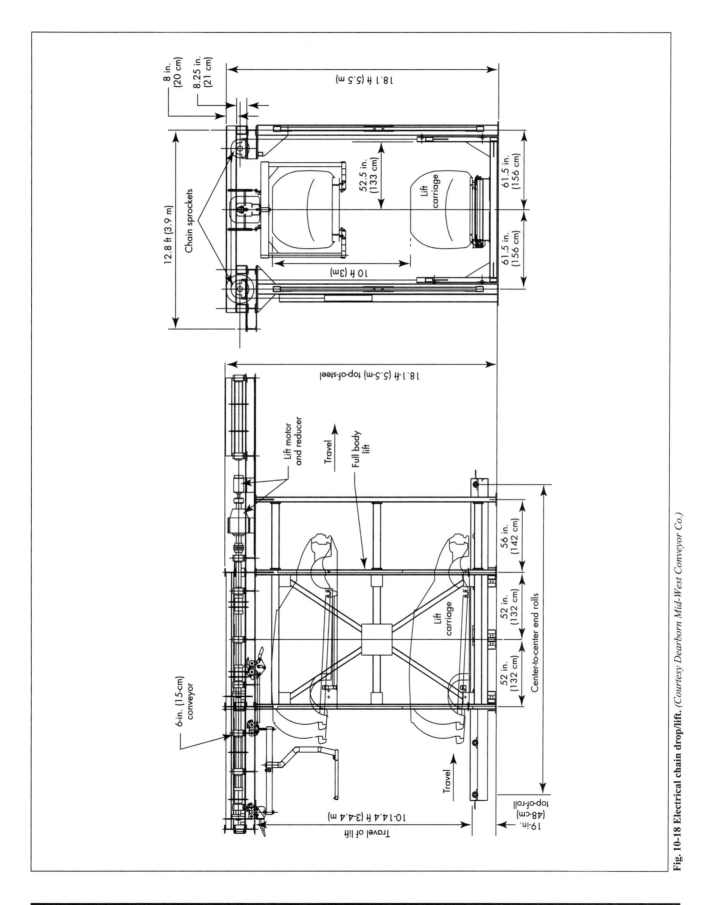

Fig. 10-18 Electrical chain drop/lift. *(Courtesy Dearborn Mid-West Conveyor Co.)*

CHAPTER 10   OVERHEAD HANDLING AND LIFTING DEVICES

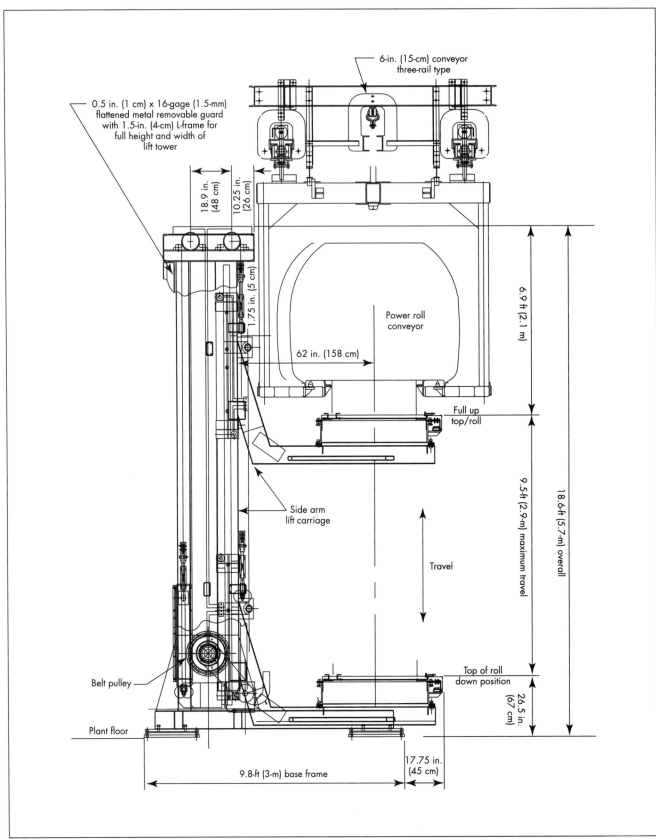

Fig. 10-19 Electrical belt drop/lift. *(Courtesy Dearborn Mid-West Conveyor Co.)*

CHAPTER 10   OVERHEAD HANDLING AND LIFTING DEVICES

problem of normal chain wear and alignment problems. By eliminating the need for chain lubrication, these transfers eliminate a potential source of quality problems.

Automatic Fork Lift and Transfer

Automatic lift and transfer devices, commonly referred to as "fork transfers," are designed to not only transfer loads vertically, but to also move them horizontally. Figure 10-20 shows a typical fork transfer that was built for an automotive application.

Fork transfers can accommodate virtually any unit load that can be handled with forks, but their load capacity is limited to approximately 2,000 lb (907 kg). This load limitation is due mainly to the low-profile design of their forks and the cantilevered positioning of their loads.

Fork transfers equipped with telescoping forks can move a load from one conveyor to a home position and then across to the other side for loading onto another conveyor. A telescoping fork is a precisely-machined steel rack-and-pinion device that can move loads horizontally from the center about 7 ft (2.1 m) in each direction. Two or more forks may be used in tandem, depending on the load size and weight. Specially-designed perches help ensure that the load is carried securely and accurately during the transfer cycle.

Fork transfers also move loads vertically. The transfer shown in Figure 10-20 is a low-lift model, offering a vertical movement of just 2.75 ft (0.8 m). But, when one of these transfers is mounted to a carriage arrangement similar to an electric-powered chain drop/lift, its vertical range can reach 20 ft (6.1 m).

By offering both horizontal and vertical movement, the fork transfer adds a great deal of flexibility to manufacturing processes. In some applications, the precise horizontal and vertical travel of a fork transfer may make it the only practical handling solution.

When transferring loads from a floor conveyor to an overhead power-and-free conveyor, or from a power-and-free system to an AEM, a fork transfer can handle about 80 transfers per hour. Variable speed controls for both vertical and horizontal movement enable users to match the transfer speed to the needs of the specific product being handled. Product quality is not usually an issue with these units.

The precision-built forks used by these machines require proper lubrication and regular inspection for wear and alignment. The transfer's chains and sprockets will require standard maintenance. Based on their track record in the field, fork transfers offer good durability.

Considering that they offer both horizontal and vertical travel, fork transfers are generally more expensive than standard vertical lift designs. However, fork transfers can offer unique material handling solutions for production flow problems.

COMPARISON OF DROP/LIFT TRANSFERS

Tables 10-9 and 10-10 provide basic information on six popular types of drop/lift transfers. Table 10-10 rates these six transfers in six areas, with one standing for high, two standing for moderate, and three standing for low.

CONCLUSION

The material presented in this chapter is intended to serve as an overview. Tables 10-11 and 10-12 present a quick summary of some of this information. For more detailed and technical information, consult either an overhead handling equipment manufacturer or a material handling equipment distributor.

Manufacturing or production flexibility, maintainability and reliability, product quality, operator safety, and cost are only some of the relevant issues that must be considered when selecting overhead handling equipment. The parameters of each material handling application are different, which means that a system that works well in one plant may be a poor choice for another plant, even though the two facilities are similar.

During the selection process, several possible solutions may emerge. Trying to stay within a budget may further confuse the matter. Acquisition cost is not the only cost to consider: increases in employee efficiency, product quality, maintenance, and production rates must all be factored in. The goal of the selection process should be to find the optimum, cost-effective, overhead handling system— one that can handle the needs of production and of the employees.

CHAPTER 10   OVERHEAD HANDLING AND LIFTING DEVICES

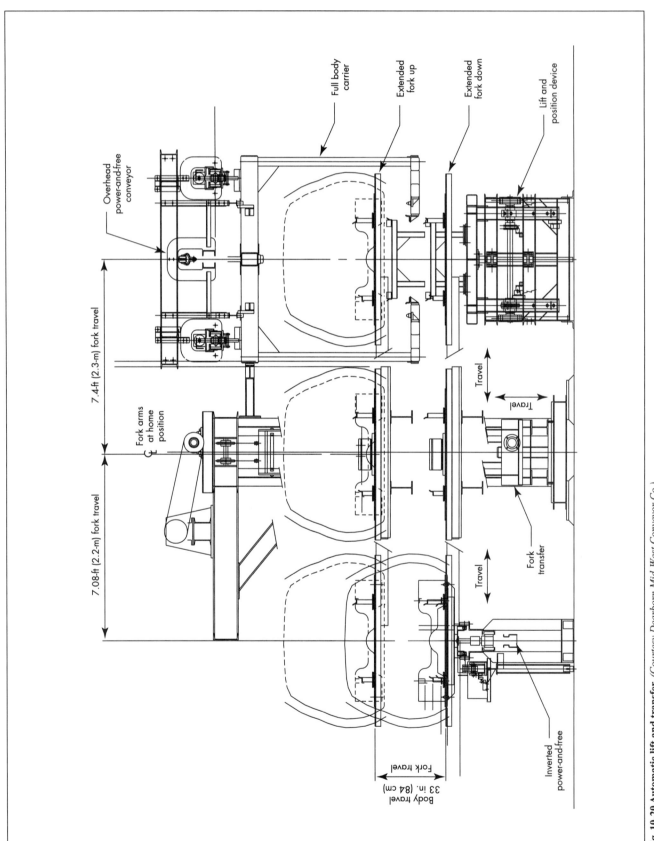

Fig. 10-20 Automatic lift and transfer. *(Courtesy Dearborn Mid-West Conveyor Co.)*

CHAPTER 10   OVERHEAD HANDLING AND LIFTING DEVICES

TABLE 10-9
Drop/Lift Transfer Selection Parameters

Drop/Lift Transfer Type	Typical Lift ft (m)	Product Cycles/h	Usual Loads lb (kg)	Plant Usage
Cable	10/20 (3/6.1)	50	4,000 (1,814)	Body/trim/industrial
Continuous vertical	20-50 (6.1-15.2)	80-85	2,500 (1,134)	Paint/trim/industrial
Hydraulic	15-35 (4.6-10.7)	70	5,000 (2,268)	All areas
Electrical chain	10/20 (3/6.1)	75-80	3,000 (1,361)	All areas
Electrical belt	10/20 (3/6.1)	75-80	3,000 (1,361)	All areas
Fork transfer	3/20 (0.9/6.1)	80	2,000 (907)	All areas

TABLE 10-10
Drop/Lift Transfer Comparison

Drop/Lift Transfer Type	Production Flexibility	Maintainability/ Reliability	Product Quality	Operator Safety	Relative Cost
Cable	2	2	3	3	3
Vertical	2	2	2	2	1
Hydraulic	2	1	1	2	2
Electrical chain	2	2	2	2	2
Electrical belt	2	1	1	2	2
Fork transfer	1	1	1	2	1

Note: this information may be subjective and is comparable, but is relative to this group only. Verification should be done by a qualified equipment supplier.

Ratings 1-3:   1-High   2-Moderate   3-Low

TABLE 10-11
Overhead Crane Equipment Selection Parameters

Overhead Crane Equipment Type	Rated Load or Capacity lb (kg)	Hoist Speed Ranges fpm (mpm)	Bridge Speed Ranges fpm (mpm)	Start-up Time Required	Main Industry Usage
Overhead crane	500-200,000+ (227-90,720+)	5-60 (1.5-18.3)	30-400 (9.1-122)	3	Automotive/ industrial
Overhead trolley conveyor	500-6,000 (227-2,722)	—	20-70 (6.1-21.3)	3	Automotive/ industrial
Power-and-free	250-6,000 (113-2,722)	—	6-60 (1.8-18.3)	2	Automotive/ industrial
Automated electrified monorail	50-3,000 (23-1,361)/trolley	*	15-400 (4.6-122)	1	Industrial
Drop/lift transfer	2,000-5,000 (907-2,268)	10-90 (3-27.4)	—	1	Automotive

*Some are equipped with hoists.

CHAPTER 10   OVERHEAD HANDLING AND LIFTING DEVICES

TABLE 10-12
Overhead Handling Equipment Comparison

Handling Equipment Type	Production Flexibility	Maintainability/ Reliability	Relative Cost	Ergonomic Rating
Overhead crane	2	1	3	2
Overhead trolley conveyor	3	2	3	2
Power-and-free	2	2	2	2
Automated electrified monorail	1	3	1	1
Drop/lift transfer	2	2	1	—

Note: this information may be subjective and is comparable, but is relative to this group only. Verification should be done by a qualified equipment supplier.

Ratings 1-3:   1-High   2-Moderate   3-Low

Bibliography

Design

American National Standards Institute (ANSI)/American Society of Mechanical Engineers (ASME) B30.11. *Monorails and Underhung Cranes.* New York: ANSI/ASME, 1993.

ANSI/ASME B30.16. *Overhead Hoists (Underhung).* New York: ANSI/ASME, 1993.

ANSI/ASME B30.17. *Overhead and Gantry Cranes (Top Running Bridge, Single Girder, Underhung Hoist).* New York: ANSI/ASME 1992.

ANSI MH27.1. *Specifications for Underhung Cranes and Monorail Systems.* New York: ANSI, 1996.

ASME HST-4M. *Performance Standard for Overhead Electric Wire Rope Hoists.* Fairfield, NJ: ASME, 1991.

Association of Iron and Steel Engineers (AISE) Technical Report No. 6. *Specification for Electric Overhead Traveling Cranes for Steel Mill Service.* Pittsburgh, PA: AISE.

CMAA (Crane Manufacturers Association of America) No. 70. *Specifications for Top Running Bridge- and Gantry-type Multiple Girder Electric Overhead Traveling Cranes.* Charlotte, NC: CMAA.

CMAA No. 74. *Specifications for Top-Running and Under-Running Single-Girder Electric Traveling Cranes Utilizing Under-Running Trolley Hoist.* Charlotte, NC: CMAA.

CMAA Specification No. 70, Section 2.8. *Crane Service Class in Terms of Load Class and Load Cycles for Estimate of Duty.* Charlotte, NC: CMAA.

Conveyor Equipment Manufacturers Association (CEMA) Standard No. 102. *Conveyor Terms and Definitions.* Manassas, VA: ANSI/CEMA, 1994.

Conveyor Equipment Manufacturers Association (CEMA) No. 601. *Overhead Trolley Chain Conveyors.* Manassas, VA: CEMA, 1995.

Dearborn Mid-West Conveyor Co. *Cable-link Conveyors Brochure.* Dearborn, MI: Dearborn Mid-West Conveyor Co.

Dearborn Mid-West Conveyor Co. *Power-and-free Conveyors Brochure.* Dearborn, MI: Dearborn Mid-West Conveyor Co.

Jervis B. Webb Co. Bulletin #8020. *Enclosed Track Conveyors Brochure.* Farmington Hills, MI: Jervis B. Webb Co., 1985.

Jervis B. Webb Co. Bulletin #8023. *Enclosed Track/Power-and-Free.* Farmington Hills, MI: Jervis B. Webb Co., 1985.

Kulwiec, Raymond A. *Materials Handling Handbook,* 2nd Edition. New York: John Wiley & Sons, 1985.

Moon, E. "Overhead Trolley Conveyors." *Materials Handling Handbook.* New York: John Wiley & Sons, 1995.

Occupational Safety and Health Administration (OSHA) Section 1910.79. *Overhead and Gantry Cranes.* Washington: OSHA, 1996.

Reibel, S. "Cable Conveyors." *Trolley Conveyors,* 1949: 230-232.

Trambeam Corporation. *Engineering Data Book.* Attalla, AL: Trambeam Corporation, 1995.

Unified Industries, Inc. *Bridge Cranes, Monorails, and Trolleys Specifications Brochure.* Springfield, VA: Unified Industries, Inc.

Maintenance and Inspection

ANSI B30.2. *Overhead and Gantry Cranes (Top Running, Single or Multiple Girder, Top-Running Trolley Hoist).* New York: ANSI, 1996.

CMAA. *Inspection and Maintenance Checklist.* Charlotte, NC: CMAA.

Training

ANSI B30.2 *Overhead and Gantry Cranes (Top Running, Single or Multiple Girder, Top-Running Trolley Hoist).* New York: ANSI, 1996.

CMAA. *CMAA Crane Operator Manual.* Charlotte, NC: CMAA.

Safety

ANSI B30.11. *Safety Code for Underhung Cranes and Monorail Systems.* New York: ANSI, 1993.

ANSI B30.2. *Overhead and Gantry Cranes (Top Running, Single or Multiple Girder, Top-Running Trolley Hoist).* New York: ANSI, 1996.

OSHA. *Safety and Health Standards-29* CFR 1910.179 #2206. Washington: OSHA.

CHAPTER 11
STORAGE EQUIPMENT

CHAPTER CONTENTS

APPLICATIONS AND PLANNING

This chapter focuses on static storage equipment or shelving. The term *rack* defines a variety of devices ranging from bread racks to pallet racks. Using a rack as a specific holding device requires special consideration of its handling or holding characteristics. The rack must maintain the pieces in proper orientation during processing or maintain their relative position during movement and storage. The shape, form, and materials used to make this rack fall into a unique design niche. This design will vary widely from the rack in an automatic dishwasher to a rack weighing 10,000 lb (4,536 kg) loaded with automobile panels.

Shelving and other more conventional storage units are made by a variety of manufacturers. These units generally have a maximum shelf capacity of under 1,000 lb (454 kg) and are usually no more than 8 ft (2 m) high. This type of shelving arrives disassembled and can be erected with unskilled labor using hand tools. It can store books, records, tools, raw materials, work-in-process (WIP), and finished goods.

Pallet racks are large shelving units with single-shelf capacities in excess of 10,000 lb (4,536 kg). They do not usually contain a solid shelf, but use the shipping pallet as the shelf. The pallet is supported in the front and back by horizontal supports running parallel to the traffic aisle. These units are serviced by some type of lift truck whereas shelving is loaded and unloaded by hand. Exercise care when mixing pallet rack brands because the published load tables assume that only one specific brand is used. Pallet racks, as shown in Figure 11-1, are used as shelving in places such as home centers or very large hardware stores.

Uses for static storage equipment or shelving include:

• Tool and die storage.
• Consumables.
• Work queue.
• Finished materials.

As the application of these basic storage devices is discussed, remember their various characteristics. In the case of tool and die storage, tool sets are generally heavy. Often, special die carts are employed to facilitate movement and placement. A lift truck may be used, after the tool set is transferred from the cart to a storage pallet. Often, this intermediate step is skipped to save time. The manual effort to slide the tools from the cart onto a pallet rack with a full shelf is very hazardous. It can only be done at very low-floor levels which limit cube (space) utilization and is not recommended.

Fig. 11-1 Pallet rack used as shelving. Upper areas have full pallets for reserve inventory. *(Courtesy Republic Storage Systems Company)*

Consumables are parts or supplies not usually inventoried and are generally very small. These are best suited for storage close to the point of consumption. Often, shelving is erected in each work area and stock is continually replenished based upon visual inspection of the available quantities. Rotary units may be placed in a corner or some other area with limited access to maximize the available space and take advantage of the limited face (access space) required. In addition to small parts such as nuts and bolts, this classification might include things such as gloves or rags needed by personnel that are not part of the product.

WIP or temporary storage of the work queue is another area requiring some consideration. Gravity or powered conveyors allow minimal material handling. Some parts or containers are not conveyable or the throughput may not justify this level of investment. Carts and shelving are still viable solutions. Their arrangement should keep the work organized so that the production personnel and material handlers understand the storage schemes employed to ensure the required sequencing, etc. When the parts require equipment such as lift trucks for transportation, the manufacturing engineer should use pallet racks instead of shelving.

In finished goods storage, size, weight, and equipment will determine which type of storage unit to employ and moveable shelving can be considered. Records storage might be another area, although it is usually relegated to the use of discarded materials.

Planning is always important and should consider:

• Customer needs (internal and external).
• Supplier (vendor) needs (internal and external).
• Safety.
• Environment temperature and humidity.
• Security (lighting and accessibility).
• Ergonomics (access, lighting, size of opening, weight of items, and type of mechanical assistance available).

The Contributor of this chapter is: William T. Guiher, Vice President, Material Handling, Inflection Point, Inc.
The Reviewers of this chapter are: Winston F. Erevelles, PhD, Associate Professor of Manufacturing Systems Engineering, GMI Engineering and Management Institute; **Robert Lawless,** President, Creative Storage Systems; **Edward Smith,** Vice President/Dealer Sales Manager, Kornylak Corporation.

CHAPTER 11   STORAGE EQUIPMENT

- Operations inventory or production control requirements, response times required, special handling, or procedures.
- Government regulations.
- Fire insurance requirements (sprinklers, etc.).
- Corporate policies, record keeping, etc.
- Space planning.
- Building limitations, square foot loading, and unobstructed heights.
- Building permits.
- Access and egress.
- Funding and budget constraints.

See Chapters 1 and 2 of this handbook for more information on planning and analysis.

GUIDELINES

Choosing the proper type of shelf requires having selection criteria, layout plans, storage specifications, and other equipment considerations.

While most manufacturers will routinely provide strap bracing located at about midheight, locations in moderate seismic activity zones should have this bracing installed as low as possible. Analysis by qualified personnel is required for areas with higher risk of seismic activity, generally resulting in the need for additional bracing. Consult your local building department if you are not sure of the seismic risk for your location. The West Coast generally has the highest risk. Moderate risk exists for the Central U.S. (southeast Missouri) and parts of the Southeast, including parts of Georgia and the Carolinas. Another requirement in moderate- to high-risk seismic areas is the use of floor anchors. Shelving units must be fastened to the floor with a bolt or concrete anchor. Buildings in moderate risk areas may be able to utilize a top tie across the aisles in storage areas if the general layout will permit.

As the weights of materials increase, available choices move from shelving, to package racks, and eventually pallet racks. The only difference from a design viewpoint is that the post capacities are now listed as "frame" capacities. This eliminates the need to take half of the total weight in a unit. This total weight can be directly compared to the frame capacity.

One other difference is the increments of height. Shelving is most often adjustable in 1 in. (25 mm) increments. Pallet racks are adjustable in either 2 or 3 in. (≈50 or 75 mm) increments depending upon the style. (Note: SI conversions are the approximate [≈] metric equivalent and are usually described in mm rather than cm. Therefore, "2 or 3 in. [50 or 75 mm]" should be used.) Pallet racks are made with two standard post depths, 1.6 or 3 in. (41 or 76 mm) deep. Care should be exercised when using 1.6-in. (41-mm) deep posts when powered equipment, such as a fork lift, is operating. When a lift truck is present, floor anchoring should be utilized. The RMI (Rack Manufacturers Institute) specification recommends anchoring when the height to the top load divided by the frame depth exceeds six. If this specification is not used, sound engineering practice would mandate that all units exceeding a ratio of eight be anchored or braced in some manner.

Extremely high single shelf and frame capacities are possible even with standard rack components. Special designs might incorporate three mezzanine levels of storage and sophisticated conveyor systems. Their application as shelving follows exactly the same procedure outlined earlier except that the rack capacities are compared to the design requirements instead of the shelving capacities. The decking is the only questionable area to be investigated by the designer. Decking can be a wood-product sheathing or lumber, corrugated metal, or welded-wire fabric. Wire fabric has the advantage of low weight and permits light to pass through empty shelves. In addition, water can penetrate downward directly through the shelf in the event of a fire. It is recommended that a front and rear "waterfall" design be employed. This design causes the front and rear edges of the fabric to be folded downward over the front and rear beams of the rack. Not only does this provide a smooth edge for sliding packages on or off the shelf, it prevents the beams from spreading and the shelf deck from dropping through or sliding front to rear.

SELECTION CRITERIA

Shelving has either all bolted, wedging type hooks, or loose clip construction. Another style, often referred to as automotive shelving, incorporates a formed sheet-metal side panel with a series of slots that engage and support the shelves. All of these styles are generally provided in an 8 ft (2 m) height. It is possible to double stack them and support a service platform or mezzanine directly from the heavy-duty versions. This has an added advantage because this upper level walkway is part of the shelving and not part of the building. This generally permits a shorter depreciation life—consult your comptroller in this regard. Have the shelving supplier provide necessary documentation from a professional engineer whenever the top height is more than 8 ft (2 m).

Usually, the shelf will have a hole pattern in the flat storage surface. Some facilities will purchase plain shelves or provide their own liquid-tight plugs and install the shelves upside down. The type of shelf that bolts together is the easiest to adapt and is used as a containment pan when storing liquids. Most of these units can be enhanced with appropriate accessories to provide shelf dividers, lockable cabinet doors, and a wide variety of other devices to meet custom requirements.

Most shelving units are not suited for servicing (loading and unloading) by automated equipment. Shelf capacity should be matched to the maximum weight that can be hand stacked onto any particular shelf. Consult your local work rules regarding the maximum weight to be moved by someone from the floor, at waist height, and overhead. Clearly, heavy items should not be stored above waist height.

As discussed earlier, the weight distribution for varying height will permit a calculation of the maximum weight stored in a single bay. This maximum bay weight and vertical distribution is important when selecting the appropriate post designs. If you are located in an area of higher risk of seismic activity, and the shelves are more than 8 ft (2 m) high, then this vertical distribution is extremely important. While not always enforced, building permits are usually required for units more than 8 ft (2 m) high. In higher risk areas, the design must be reviewed by a professional engineer.

Steel shelving makes a nice die rack from the standpoint of service. The steel shelves, especially those where a little lubricant drips onto the shelf, will provide a smooth, slippery surface for moving medium weight dies. The shelf is impervious to the lubricants but build-up of lubricants should be avoided.

There are a couple of other factors to consider before beginning the design cycle. Small parts require special considerations. When allocating space in a drawer or pan arrangement, the minimum recommended opening or compartment size is 4 × 4 in. (102 × 102 mm). When assigning space requirements on a shelf, 5 in. (127 mm) should be the narrowest opening. If the intent is to keep the parts in their original containers, shelf dividers should be considered. If shelves are preferred over drawers for small parts, and spacing is critical, cardboard inserts or shelf boxes are viable options. In areas of low to medium activity, they have been known to last 20 years or more.

LAYOUT PLANS

There are two approaches to the tool room layout. The first approach is to see how much space the manufacturing department is willing to give up and where, and then put as much shelving into that space as possible. This will result in a disorganized area with maximum retrieval times for every request. It usually results in narrow aisles, poor lighting and, when serviced by two or more personnel, a high level of confusion and interference.

The preferred approach is to "soft load" or "planograph" a system. The idea is to begin with an analysis of the tools, goods, or products to be stored, by gathering certain basic information. If you are fortunate enough to have a locator system and a master parts file, you may find the information relatively easy to collect. If guessing must be done, interview personnel working in the existing or a similar environment before making a choice. While not 100% accurate, their intuitive responses will be based on years of experience.

STORAGE SPECIFICATIONS

The data for storage specifications should include:

• Size of stored item.
• Item weight.
• Quantity per carton.
• Total quantity on hand.
• Re-order point.
• Economic order quantity.
• Activity per some time frame (seasonally adjusted if necessary).
• Expected growth in inventory level for this item.

After gathering data for storage specifications, the maximum amount of storage volume is calculated. The parts are grouped together in an appropriate manner with space allocated for future growth. The formation of the groups is somewhat intuitive but there are a few logical considerations.

Before doing a general sort, collect and remove items requiring either a special environment or handling. This might include chemicals, items needing refrigeration, or items that need a secure space. Government or corporate policies or regulations might create segregation by contract usage or final ownership.

The next step is to sort the items in order of descending activity. The first goal is to keep the items that require frequent access close to the point of distribution. They can be organized by size, weight, total volume requirements, part number sequence, etc. Maintaining strict part number sequencing may not be suitable (many computer packages or locator systems are now available). You may need to examine weights and lifting requirements, gather drawers into a single area, etc. When you have finished these other steps, start looking at lighting, fire protection, and other services.

A scan of the dimensions or the cartons and the volumes needed for each item should result in picking a depth of storage. The best space utilization will be achieved when this depth is some multiple of all of the packages or cartons. When small parts must be retrieved from a shelf, the deepest shelf should not exceed 24 in. (610 mm). As the packages grow in size, the shelf may need to be deeper. However, depths exceeding 36 in. (914 mm) should probably be reserved for pallet racks or some solution other than shelving.

After the depth has been selected, the height may be determined. Scan the list for compatible carton heights. Remember that the level-to-level dimension between shelves may vary. However, if the pattern for shelf height differs from unit to unit, the personnel installing the shelves will either ignore the plan, go very slowly, or become confused. Some trial and error efforts may be needed to get the best configuration.

Planning Considerations

Important planning considerations are:

• Do not place shelves (surface-to-surface) closer than 6 in. (152 mm). This results in a 5-in. (127-mm) clear opening and the smallest height in which someone can reasonably insert his or her hand and forearm.
• Do not place the shelving (surface-to-surface) closer than the depth (front-to-back) without special lighting.

• Do not place heavy items above the waist.
• Place the most active items in the "golden zone" between 30 and 48 in. (762 and 1,219 mm) above the floor.
• Do not place smaller items above 66 in. (1,676 mm) from floor.
• The top shelf is usually 7 ft (2 m) above the floor. Because it is unreachable by most people, it is rarely used for storage but provides a dust cover for the shelf below. It is also a vital structural element and should not be excluded.
• Depending upon carton size and weight, the shelf-to-shelf height should be the package height plus 2 in. (51 mm). This will allow for the shelf thickness, deflection of the shelf above it, and the clearance necessary to remove a box.

Many manufacturers have standard shelf, drawer, or divider combinations available. Until some preliminary analysis is done, the choice of the most appropriate mix is almost impossible. Review these options before doing the final calculations for determining the required shelf lengths.

Next, determine the shelf length required for each item including growth space. Only now is it necessary to begin working with the space available. Considering the lengths of shelving that might be utilized, a shelf length of either 36, 42, or 48 in. (914, 1,067, or 1,219 mm) can be selected. Probably the most common length used is 36 in. (914 mm).

After selecting the shelf depth, height, and length required, a front view of each shelving unit could be produced showing the exact space reserved for each item and growth space. This collection of elevations is often called the *planograph*. This process simulates building and loading the shelving system.

The final task is to determine the maximum weight on a single shelf and the total maximum weight for a single unit. Compare the maximum shelf weight to the manufacturer's unreinforced shelf capacity. If the recommended capacity is exceeded, reinforce the shelves. Examine each of the shelf reinforcement options to determine if more than one style in the system is needed. If the shelf weight is under 300 lb (136 kg), special shelf reinforcing may not be needed, depending upon the manufacturer's specifications.

Now, look at the total weight in each unit. Add up the weight on each shelf in each unit. Most manufacturers can provide a single post capacity chart. Compare half of the total weight in each unit to the various posts' capacities (*post capacity* is the amount of weight that the post can support before collapsing). If less than 600 or 800 lb (272 or 363 kg) is stored on each unit, then it should be easy to check each of the various post selections.

Most shelving units will be constructed with angle posts in the rear, and rounded or "beaded" posts in the front (as shown in Fig. 11-2). This rounded post has no sharp edges to scratch personnel when storing or retrieving items. Generally, the most critical post is the single angle post used in the rear of the first or last unit in a line

Fig. 11-2 Shelving unit constructed to suit both container size and weight. *(Courtesy Republic Storage Systems Company)*

CHAPTER 11 STORAGE EQUIPMENT

or "run." If a suitable post cannot be found, then the choices are either to reconfigure the system to spread out the load or change from shelving to package racks or full-size pallet racks.

Using package racks or pallet racks as shelving sometimes requires decking material. These units generally consist of only the metal framework without the storage surface. The supplier generally does not produce the shelves and represents the manufacturer, but can take the responsibility for proper sizing and coordinate delivery of all materials.

Increasing Shelf Height

To see if a shelving-supported mezzanine or second level is possible, determine the unobstructed building height available, weights involved, and slab capacity. For example, it is possible that 1,000 pounds in 18-in. deep shelves with 3 ft aisles might overload the basic slab. Calculate the square footage of the footprint and include half of the aisle width. Use this equation:

$$\text{Footprint} = W \div A \qquad (1)$$

where:

W = weight (pounds or kilograms) per unit area (foot or meter)
A = area = $L \times W$
L = length (foot or meter)
W = width (foot or meter)

It is important to keep all units consistent. That is, all U.S. customary or all metric (SI) when doing the calculations.

For example:

Width = 1.5-ft (18-in.) deep shelf + 3 ft ÷ 2 ft (aisle) =
    (1.5 + 3) ÷ 2 = roughly 3 ft
Shelf length = 3 ft
Area = 9 ft² (3 ft wide × 3 ft long)
Pounds per square foot (psf) = 1,000 (total weight in unit)
    ÷ 9 (the area) = 111 psf

This example was calculated using U.S. customary units but it is just as easy to substitute SI units.

This would not overload most factory floors but might overload a second story floor. Many people will avoid the use of a "foot" or base plate in single-height systems. Base plates should be used in all applications. They are required when the units are located on anything other than concrete or when a second level is used. The decision to use the shelving as the main support for a second level is only a function of the load capacity of the base units. Otherwise, a separate unsupported mezzanine can be provided.

Aisle Space

Aisles should be at least 36-in. (914-mm) wide (as shown in Fig. 11-3). The width should be expanded in high-traffic areas with two-way traffic or if carts are used. Powered equipment should never be used in shelving areas. When only carts are permitted, the shelving should still be inspected regularly for damage. Damage can occur from overloading, personnel stepping or climbing on units, or general rust and corrosion. When damage is detected, unload the shelves and repair damaged parts immediately; do not wait for a regular inspection period.

OTHER EQUIPMENT CONSIDERATIONS

In addition to rack design options, a variety of equipment styles must be examined. Reach trucks or trucks with outriggers present entirely different considerations than conventional counterweighted trucks. Talk with equipment and rack suppliers to be sure the two

Fig. 11-3 Pallet rack has a wide aisle for lift equipment and is used as shelving. Consider cross aisles, particularly at the end of the units. *(Courtesy Republic Storage Systems Company)*

designs are compatible. It is the buyer's responsibility to be sure that the supplier has considered all of these factors.

If there is a need for very high throughput and the user has many requests for retrievals or storage, consider other equipment. Other choices include: an automated storage and retrieval system (AS/RS) or a carousel system (either horizontal or vertical). This equipment comes in a variety of sizes and speeds and the supplier is helped by having the data properly collected when these alternatives are explored.

FIXTURES AND HOLDING DEVICES

This section discusses specialty frames, wire and plastic baskets (with or without drop sides), tubs and skids with crane hairpins, and mobile storage.

SPECIALTY FRAMES

The design of specialty frames or fixtures that hold tool and die sets, inspection gages, or attachments for a particular piece of equipment is beyond the scope of this chapter. However, their design should consider the available space, ergonomic needs, and special requirements of the stored pieces. The frame should hold the pieces at an approximate height and reach or within easy access of appropriate lift assisting devices, and not block access to other work areas. Thus, these fixtures are often wheel-mounted for proper positioning while loading or unloading. This approach also maximizes available space since the fixtures can be moved when not active. The support method for the pieces must consider areas or surfaces that can be easily damaged and how to hold the piece in a stable position. For example, storing drill bits without damage to the tips.

BASKETS

One method for storing and presenting parts in an operation is the use of wire or plastic baskets. These baskets are available from several suppliers in a variety of sizes. Multiple sizes within a single facility create material handling and storage problems. They may have a "drop-down" side or partial side. This, too, can create problems when the basket is moved without this section being properly latched into position. Plan regular inspection for damaged latches or panels that cannot be raised.

These baskets usually have a stacking foot of some special configuration. The feet sit on the top lip of the basket below it and provide a lip or flange to prevent the foot from sliding off. This stacking foot renders this basket nonconveyable. Some manufacturers offer an option consisting of a runner on each side between the feet. This allows conveyance on rollers when the runners are aligned parallel to the direction of travel or on chain conveyors when perpendicular.

For floor stock, use baskets with feet and stack no more than two additional tiers. In addition to wasting the space above the basket, first-in, first-out (FIFO) parts rotation cannot be easily maintained. If care is not taken, parts will stagnate against the wall of the bottom tier. Over time, these parts may deteriorate or be rendered obsolete.

Storing the wire baskets with feet in more conventional pallet racks requires the introduction of a slave or storage pallet. This additional pallet outweighs many of the advantages of using the wire basket. An alternate method would be to provide a flush shelf capable of transferring the concentrated foot load to the pallet rack beams. If the racks are properly sized for the baskets, this can be a relatively inexpensive option. Often, however, the pallet racks are sized to store standard 48-in. (1,219-mm) deep pallets. The baskets may be only 36-in. (914-mm) deep or less. This places the foot closer to the midpoint of the shelf and thus requires the shelf to be significantly stronger. Using a larger basket is not practical since the back of the deeper basket cannot be reached by an operator retrieving parts. The basket with runners can be stored in a pallet rack without the shelf if the basket is deep enough to span the distance from the front to rear beams.

TUBS AND SKIDS WITH CRANE HAIRPINS

A *crane hairpin* is a lifting lug formed by bending a hot-rolled angle into the shape of a hairpin. One is welded to each side of a metal tub or container (as shown in Fig. 11-4). The top of the hairpin is exposed above the tub so that a crane hook can be used to lift the container. Often the loop is over-formed so that the sides are closer together near the bottom. Metal tubs with or without lifting eyes or corner attachments are also available. These tubs generally have solid sides and may be mounted on top of a metal skid. Tubs and skids are specially designed for movement with a pallet jack. The tubs may come with "ears" on the corners that not only provide hooks for lifting from above but also permit stacking as described for the wire baskets. Some metal skids may have posts at the corners or sockets for posts to be added. Care should be taken when skids are stacked with the use of posts. The posts are susceptible to damage or bending and can create very precarious stacks.

Skids or tubs on skids can be modified into four-way devices. *Four-way units* may be handled with conventional fork lift equipment from any principle direction. *Two-way units* are approached from the front or rear and not from either side. The storage of these skids or tubs is very similar to the methods used for the wire baskets with runners. The exception is when a skid is inverted to form a two-sided tray for the storage and handling of long, usually round, parts or stock. The length of the skid is increased to a dimension appropriate for the material, although it may not necessarily be longer than the pieces inside.

MOBILE STORAGE

Moveable storage equipment includes:

- Mobile fixtures.
- Shelving on wheels.
- Tool and die racks.

Mobile fixtures may be employed in either a temporary or permanent situation. Storage is not usually described in terms of wheeled device use, but it is sometimes appropriate. Test equipment is often an excellent candidate. A die cart is usually too expensive to be considered a storage device. However, die sets which are exchanged frequently might be better stored on carts rather than double handling (double handling occurs because the die set is moved into static storage to free the cart).

Shelving units on wheels are another option for improving security or eliminating aisles. When the shelving is on wheels, all of the units are rolled together so that there is no aisle space except at the last row. To gain access to the units in the middle, an appropriate number of units are pulled from the stack by moving them one aisle width away. This scheme can also be applied in a perpendicular direction so that the unit is pulled out of the stack (much like opening a file drawer except that the total height of the unit moves). These units are very efficient in their use of space but quick access is sacrificed.

Tool and die racks or tool room storage may employ everything from very light shelving to full pallet racks. Very small tools may even employ units with drawers to maximize cube utilization yet maintain very quick access. Some of these will approach furniture quality construction on one extreme or can be homemade from erector-set type products depending upon budget, requirements, cleanliness, and a variety of other factors.

Fig. 11-4 Typical metal tub with a hairpin crane hook. The hook is formed to nest in the bottom of another tub to facilitate stacking. *(Courtesy Streator Dependable Manufacturing)*

PALLETS AND RACKS

This section discusses the following:

- Pallet racks.
- High-density storage racks.
- Drive-in racks.
- Drive-through racks.

CHAPTER 11   STORAGE EQUIPMENT

- Push-back racks.
- Flow racks.
- Cantilever-style racks.
- Steel pallet racks.
- Considerations for pallet moving equipment.

PALLET RACKS

When utilizing pallet racks without shelves for the conventional storage of pallets, there are a few different considerations. All material handling and storage designs begin with the most basic question: what is the product to be moved or stored? For instance, European DIN or nine-post pallets are not generally suited for storage in U.S.-style racks. The nine-post pallets do not always have bottom boards, and when they do, they are very thin. (DIN is the European equivalent of the American Society for Testing Materials [ASTM] and is responsible for their international standards and specifications.)

The most common U.S. pallet is the GMA (formerly Grocery Manufacturers' Association) or four-way pallet with three stringers and bottom boards. The usual recommended practice is to provide a frame depth or beam spacing equal to the pallet depth minus 4-6 in. (102-152 mm). This will permit the pallet to overhang the front and rear beams by 2-3 in. (51-76 mm). The first board is usually 5.5-in. (140-mm) wide. Thus, the pallet may be mislocated by about 2 in. (51 mm) without affecting the integrity or safety of the system. It should be noted that the stringers usually run the long dimension of the pallet or from the front to the rear. This means that the bottom board is not stressed in the usual configuration. This also presents the narrowest dimension to the aisle and thus maximizes the number of faces or positions available to an operator storing or retrieving pallets. The DIN pallet has the bottom boards running in the long direction of the pallet. Any mislocation of it results in the bottom board being stressed to the maximum. The result is failure of the bottom board and tipping of the load, a significant hazard. This pallet, along with U.S. conventional pallets of poor quality, is intended as a shipping pallet and should not be used as a storage pallet in conventional racks.

The occasional use of DIN pallets requires personnel to move the product onto a proper pallet, or place the entire unit onto a second pallet. If these types of pallets are encountered on a regular basis, a slave pallet or proper storage pallet provides one answer. Another alternative is to add decking material to each of the pallet rack shelves using the methods previously discussed.

HIGH-DENSITY STORAGE RACKS

Several alternate styles of rack may be considered to increase the cube or volume utilization. If the task is to design or plan the warehouse layout, refer to Chapter 2 of this handbook, texts on that specific subject, or consider engaging a professional material handling consultant.

A selective rack is really a form of overgrown shelving. It is called a *selective rack* because when pallets are used in it, immediate access can be gained to each and every pallet as a single unit. Typically, selective racks are the width of two pallets on each beam pair or shelf. The number of tiers is limited by what can be accommodated by the building and available space. The selective rack category is the most common standard catalog item produced by manufacturers. Some caution should be exercised when choosing the selective rack out of the catalogs, as the members are displayed by the manufacturers in the best possible light. Select an upright unit with as much as 50% more capacity than calculated.

DRIVE-IN RACKS

Drive-in racks and drive-through racks are highly specialized rack designs used principally in the frozen goods industry. A drive-in rack stores product in bay rows similar to the way pallets are stored if there is no racking available. That is to say, a drive-in rack might be located against the wall, with two parallel arms coming out from the wall at 90°, which hold up the load. Loads are then stored in several tiers from floor to ceiling, and the entire face (access area) must be worked outward toward the aisle. The truck must drive into the racks between these two arms to carry a load in and then set it down. When the load is set down, access is denied to any load behind it. This provides for maximum cube utilization but destroys selectivity in the process. The design of a drive-in rack is highly specialized. There is no standard or specification or even standardized approach to its design. So, some care must be exercised when designing and utilizing them.

This type of rack is frequently used for freezer applications where space utilization is the most important concern and controlling energy consumption and temperature maintenance is more critical than quick and easy access.

The drive-in rack is constructed with what might be considered a conventional selective rack, often called the *anchor frame*, in the rear. The difference between a drive-in rack and the standard selective rack is that the shelves are only one load wide. So there is a set of upright frames between every load when viewed in the plan and the loads are extended outward from the anchor frame. The deeper the lane, the less stable the structure, and the more susceptible it is to severe damage or collapse by fork truck impact. It would be recommended therefore, that when designing a drive-in rack, the lanes be kept as short as possible.

DRIVE-THROUGH RACKS

When a drive-in rack becomes deeper than the length of about five pallets, the front end begins to function as if it were a drive-through rack. From a structural standpoint, there is very little bracing provided by the anchor frame, so the design becomes more like a drive-through rack, where there is no anchor frame. The vehicle entering from one side into an empty lane would be able to drive all the way through and out the other side.

These structures can be very unstable and their design is critical. They are generally not a preferred storage solution. Other industries, such as the carpet industry, require specialized considerations as well, in the form of a rack called the "carpet rack." Here, the rack is designed to store long rolls of carpet, 12-15 ft (4-5 m), or longer.

PUSHBACK RACKS

The *pushback rack* is quite popular. This is a rack that consists of a cart, specially designed for use on a pitch. The first load in the rack is placed on the cart. When an operator needs room for a second load, he/she uses a vehicle (a fork truck, etc.) to push the second load. The second load pushes the first load back and up a slight incline. The advantage is that two loads can be accessed very quickly.

When the load in front is removed, the load behind will roll to the front. The operator does not have to enter the rack with his vehicle. The pushback rack can be built to accept two or three pallets (these are the most common) although they have been built slightly deeper. The disadvantage is that the moving process requires a large force to push the second load back. As the lane gets deeper, the amount of force on both the product and the vehicle increases linearly with each depth load. This is not a hardship for the vehicle when the loads are close to the floor, but when moving the load overhead, it is near the top of the fork truck mast. The vehicle's construction and type are important considerations when this kind of activity is expected to be sustained over a long period without incurring major maintenance problems.

FLOW RACKS

A *flow rack* has a pallet conveyor on a pitch located inside the rack. Loads can be entered at the high end, or the input end, and permitted to roll down the conveyor arriving at a stop at the front end of the system. As a load is removed, all the loads in the system will then roll forward. Much care should be taken with these kinds of installations. First of all, racks with long lane depths (greater than two or three pallets), must have some kind of speed retarding system built into them. This is critical. Otherwise, the momentum that is built up as a pallet rolls down an empty lane will be too great, and the load at the discharge end cannot be stopped. The other consideration in designing flow racks is the potential for a product jam. While gravity is a sure thing, the ability of the product to roll down the conveyor lanes is not.

If a loaded pallet is left to sit for a long period of time, it can result in an indented bottom, due to the pressure from the rollers. Then, when the front load is removed, if the indentation is too great, the second pallet will be prevented from rolling downward.

That is only one part of the problem. Broken pallets, bad pallets, nails, splintered boards, and general debris are all things that will not allow pallets to move in the rack. When a pallet hangs up, gets stuck, or when the lane is jammed, it is cleared via access at the discharge end of the system. There is a great temptation for personnel to enter the rack by climbing up the discharge end to the jammed pallet. Freeing the pallet creates a danger because there is no place for personnel to get out of the way when heavy palletized material moves down the lane. One solution is to provide a pair of lanes and a space 2-3 ft (61-91 cm) wide for personnel to gain access to the body of the rack. Then, install another two lanes of storage and another access space, and so on. While this reduces cube utilization somewhat, it does improve safety tremendously. Now, an operator attempting to clear a jam is not standing in the jammed lane, but rather beside it, either to its left or right. These types of product storage equipment require the consultation of an expert in storage and material handling because of the complexities involved. What is gained is good space utilization or minimized need for building to add space. Their use needs to be considered very carefully.

CANTILEVER RACKS

Cantilever racks are special, custom designed racks used for unique circumstances. Cantilever racks will generally fall into one of two varieties. The first consists of a very heavy structure, designed to support long materials, such as bars or rods, carried in a tray. The arms are very short, and the loads are heavy. Everything is kept close to the center. The second can accommodate very large, but light loads. For instance, in the furniture business, a sofa is large but not very heavy. So the furniture rack (cantilever rack) would permit the storage of sofas and armchairs on a continuous shelf running the length of the aisle, unencumbered by the aisle side post. Keep in mind that it is a very wide shelf designed to carry a very light load.

STEEL PALLET RACKS

While most people believe that hot-rolled or structural racks are more resistant to fork truck impact than cold-formed pallet racks, this opinion is not universal. The hot-rolled rack will perform better if the impact is from a sharp object. Most impacts occur from the rear of a counterweighted truck. Neither rack style can survive a serious impact of this type. The truck weighs 9,000 lb (4,082 kg) or more and has no bumper. The counterweight is not sharp and will severely damage or fail either style of steel pallet rack. There is no such thing as a "fork truck-proof" pallet rack. There are many design options such as sloped-leg frames or post protectors. They can provide a wide variety of protection levels from various types of equipment impacts. However, the best protection is to avoid collisions.

CONSIDERATIONS FOR PALLET MOVING EQUIPMENT

In addition to the pallet considerations, evaluate the types of equipment servicing the racks. For instance, if pallet jacks are used at the floor level, what is the height to the first beam? Can the powered equipment safely retrieve a load if the pallet jack is used to place a pallet too deeply into the rack? Single row racks provide many opportunities for dangerous situations. Should they be tied to the wall? Just because there is a wall behind the racks does not automatically mean that this wall is capable of adequately bracing the racks. When used in the central area of the facility, the service aisle needs to be clearly identified. Disaster lurks where this is combined with pallets of varying depths. Operators will place loads based upon relative appearance from their perspective. Loads overextended into the back make it more difficult for servicing the units and more difficult to position the load properly. Aisle space also may be critically reduced.

Often, the aisle widths are not calculated based upon the equipment to be used, but rather upon the building's column spacing. This creates a hazardous condition that will, at least, slow down operations. When planning, building columns are most efficiently buried in the flue space or clear space between back-to-back rack rows. The next best position is in a storage location that is lost to usage. Be sure to have this location clearly identified or marked for the operators. The worst place is in the aisle, even if it is close to the rack posts. This location creates an area of very tight clearances and may require the elimination of the positions directly across the aisle as well as the one behind the column.

Bibliography

Bibliography on Material Handling. Charlotte, NC: The Material Handling Industry and the College-Industrial Council on Material Handling Education.

Bibliography on Order Picking Systems. Charlotte, NC: The Material Handling Industry and the College-Industrial Council on Material Handling Education.

For other resource information see "Appendix B."

CHAPTER 12
TRANSPORT PACKAGING

CHAPTER CONTENTS

There is a growing awareness that the manufacturing process does not stop at the end of the assembly line. Packaging, once thought to be a back-end operation, is now considered an integral part of the manufacturing function. This is because the basic elements of the packaging process—protecting, identifying, unitizing, and securing—play an integral role in ensuring that finished goods get safely delivered to the correct customer on time.

This chapter approaches packaging as a seamless extension of the manufacturing process. In some cases, there is a physical link between the two. Once stand-alone, more types of packaging equipment, including carton erectors, label print and apply systems, electronic scales, dunnage dispensers, palletizers, and stretch wrappers are being integrated directly into the assembly line. In other cases, while the link may not be physical, it creates a smooth flow of products from manufacturing to the shipping dock.

This chapter addresses the basic packaging functions of protecting, identifying, unitizing, and securing as they relate to transport packaging. It provides essential information on protective inner packaging materials, returnable containers, unit load bases, labeling requirements, and the major classes of packaging equipment. It also identifies some of the key management issues associated with transport packaging, including pallet standards and fire protection for plastic packaging.

The goal is to provide the manufacturing engineer with an understanding of the relationship between manufacturing and packaging, as well as an awareness of some of the major design considerations when selecting transport packaging. Packaging must be designed to overcome the following hazards:

- Shock.
- Vibration.
- Various compressive forces.
- Temperature.
- Moisture.
- Time (product shelf life).
- Electrostatic charges.
- Static and dynamic compression.
- Piercing.

- Snagging.
- Deformation (caused by uneven support).
- Light.
- Biological contaminants.
- General contamination.

PROTECTIVE PACKAGING

This section defines the key types of protective packaging, including loose fill, wrapping materials, fabricated packaging, and molded packaging. It also reviews their properties and typical applications and examines the relationship between cushioning and environmental performance, providing selection guidelines.

The majority of products must be protected and secured before they leave the manufacturing plant. The role of protective packaging, which typically is used in conjunction with a primary shipping container, is to absorb the impact forces that products are exposed to during handling, shipping, and distribution.

However, this class of packaging materials does far more than provide cushioning protection. Depending on the material, protective packaging can also provide void fill, interleaving (protection between parts), surface protection, and protection against hazards such as electrostatic discharge, electromagnetic interference, fire, and corrosion.

LOOSE FILL

Loose fill is any lightweight, amorphous packaging material that is packed around a product for void fill and light cushioning protection.

The most popular form of loose fill is the ubiquitous plastic "peanut." Made of expanded polystyrene, the peanut is available in various shapes, including cubes and shells. The most economical form of plastic cushioning on a volume basis, plastic loose fill performs best (in terms of cushioning protection) at lighter loadings. *Loading* is the product weight divided by the area to be supported by the cushioning.

Although polystyrene provides more cushioning than other void fill materials, such as shredded paper or excelsior, it is not recommended for use with heavier products because it may shift and compress during transit. To eliminate the potential for settling, an adhesive-coated plastic loose fill is available. This type of loose fill requires the addition of a layer of plastic film to protect the surface of the product.

One of the primary advantages of loose fill is its inherent flexibility. Loose fill can be used in conjunction with a wide range of lightweight products, eliminating the need to stock custom-size packages. However, loose fill can be messy. Some polystyrene loose fills are electrostatic-sensitive, particularly at low humidities. This creates a tendency for the material to cling to the product, making for a messy unpacking process.[1] Lightweight but bulky, loose fill can also

The Contributors of this chapter are: David Luton, President, David Luton & Associates, Inc.; *John Healy,* Executive Director, National Wooden Pallet and Container Association; *Rob Rothfuss,* Marketing Manager, Buckhorn, Inc.; *Dr. Paul S. Singh,* Associate Professor and Director of The Consortium of Distribution Packaging Research, School of Packaging, Michigan State University; *Dr. Marshall S. White,* Professor and Director of The William H. Sardo Jr. Pallet & Container Research Laboratory, Virginia Polytechnic Institute and State University.
The Reviewers of this chapter are: David Luton, President, David Luton & Associates, Inc.; *Dr. Paul S. Singh,* Associate Professor and Director of The Consortium of Distribution Packaging Research, School of Packaging, Michigan State University.

CHAPTER 12   TRANSPORT PACKAGING

require substantial storage space, particularly for high-volume operations. Overhead hoppers, which double as dispensing devices, help free up floor space and provide for easy handling. In these simple systems, the material flows by gravity through tubes extending from the hopper. To ensure that only the correct amount of material is dispensed, filler lines are often printed inside the carton.

Environmental concerns in the early 1990s prompted many companies to begin exploring alternatives to plastic loose fill. Expanded polystyrene loose fill, with a high recycled content, is now available from several manufacturers (a green dye is sometimes added to distinguish it from standard loose fill). One loose fill product is made from 95% corn starch and synthetic additives. With a performance similar to that of plastic, the material has the added environmental benefit of being water-soluble. However, this also may be a disadvantage: under conditions of high temperature and humidity, the material may unexpectedly shrink or dissolve. It can also become sticky under these conditions, leaving a residue on products. Another starch-based product made of 100% recycled paper does not exhibit this same sensitivity to tropical conditions.[2]

Another type of loose fill is made from a high content of recycled unbleached kraft paper that is cut, folded, and compressed into a Z-shape. Although popular as a void fill to prevent product migration, it only exhibits adequate shock isolation properties for a single impact.[3] Products typically require protection against multiple impacts.

Similarly, corrugated paper, wood shavings, and even popped popcorn have been used for light cushioning protection and void fill. One study compared the shock absorbing capabilities of these so-called "environment-friendly" packaging materials, however, and discovered some drawbacks. Materials such as popcorn and wood shavings require a much larger amount of material (by volume and weight) to achieve the same level of protection offered by other materials. Popcorn and honeycomb are practical alternatives only for rugged products that need void filler, but no cushioning protection. A major conclusion of the study was that polymer-based materials generally provide the best protection for the least amount of material used, meeting two goals of the packaging designer.[4, 5]

Meanwhile, recycling rates for polystyrene are at an all-time high. More than 24.7 million lb (11.2 million kg) of post-consumer polystyrene is recycled annually.

WRAPPING MATERIALS

Various forms of wrapping material are another option for light cushioning and void fill. These materials also provide surface protection as well as protection between parts.

Air cellular packaging, which is a multilayered polyethylene film consisting mostly of entrapped air, is a popular choice. In general, air cellular packaging provides the highest cushioning protection for the amount of material used. The size of the bubbles, the gage of the film, and the number of wrap layers determine the actual level of cushioning.

However, under pressure, all air bubbles will deflate, losing their cushioning ability over time. This can be a particular concern for applications involving unpredictable shipping cycles or long-term storage. In one popular brand, a thin, co-extruded barrier is used to enhance the bubble's air retention capability. Some other products feature only a single layer of polyethylene.

Cellulose wadding is another wrapping material that is made of crepe, consisting of multiple layers of pliable tissue. Flexible and resilient, cellulose wadding is popular for surface protection applications or use with very lightweight parts.

A major disadvantage of any wrapping material is the amount of labor involved in its use, particularly when multiple wraps and tap-

ing are necessary. Manufacturers have responded to this concern by offering wrapping materials in slit-to-size rolls, perforated rolls, and individual sheets. Cohesive sheets are also available, which eliminate positioning and taping activities. Automatic and semi-automatic dispensing equipment is available to help streamline the process. In some cases, this equipment can be integrated directly onto the assembly line.

FABRICATED PACKAGING

Protective packaging can be fabricated from plastic foams, corrugated fiberboard, or a combination of materials. To make parts, fabricators typically cut and glue pieces together into various shapes and configurations. Dies can be produced in a day and are far less costly than molds.

Also called *dunnage*, fabricated parts are ideal for applications ranging from precision cushioning (flexible foams) to blocking and bracing (rigid foams and corrugated). Custom-designed dunnage (both fabricated and molded) is often combined with a returnable container to create a durable shipping container.

Expanded polystyrene (EPS) is the most commonly-used fabricated cushioning material. Low in cost, EPS holds products securely in place and provides light cushioning protection. Although fabricated parts have less detail than molded parts, fabrication is a flexible, economical method of producing foam parts in small- to medium-size lots. One of the most generic cushioning materials on the market, EPS enjoys wide general use despite the fact that other foam plastics have better cushioning capabilities.

Expanded polyurethane is the softest foam, providing excellent cushioning at lighter loadings. Available in a variety of densities, expanded polyethylene is a highly-resilient foam with good cushioning characteristics and performs best at high loadings.

Inserts of fabricated corrugated fiberboard, consisting of a fluted corrugating medium glued between linerboards, are another packaging option. Corrugated fiberboard is used primarily for blocking and bracing applications or to augment the load-carrying capacity of foam packaging materials. Corrugated sleeves combined with four plastic corner blocks are a common type of design. Available in single-, double-, or triple-wall configurations, corrugated inserts can be laminated with plastics and foils for custom applications. Used for high-volume, rugged applications, corrugated fiberboard is rated on the density of the wall facings and intermediate members (the higher the weight, the stronger the board) and bursting strength, determined by the strength of the liners. Corrugated has an advantage when compared to plastic foam. It can be folded for storage and easily baled with other corrugated waste and recycled.

When no additional cushioning protection is required, some products may be simply suspended in the air space between two corrugated frames or secured to a corrugated base. A strong, flexible film holds the product securely in place and provides surface protection from dirt, moisture, and scratches. In addition to the obvious space savings, the transparent film allows for a quick, visual inspection of the contents.

MOLDED PACKAGING

One of the major advantages of molded foam packaging is that very detailed shapes can be produced. However, although it is easy to handle and attractive looking, molded foam packaging is best suited to high-volume, custom applications. Mold tooling can be high ($20,000 or more) with long lead times (up to six months).

Foam-in-place polyurethane avoids the high cost of tooling and long lead times. Although less robust than molded polyurethane, an advantage of foam-in-place is that it can be produced on-site. The cushions are produced by mixing two liquid chemicals (polymeric isocyanate and polyols). As they react, the foam expands to approximately 200 times its original volume, conforming to the product's shape and securing it for shipment. Typical rise time is between 15 and 25 seconds, although longer rise times actually give operators the few extra seconds needed to place a cushion filled with the expanding foam into a mold. Because the cushioning is produced on demand, there is a built-in flexibility that allows a wide variety of products to be packaged. The fact that the chemicals are stored in liquid form also cuts down on storage requirements. Two 55-gal (208-L) drums of chemicals produce approximately enough cushioning to fill a tractor trailer.

Unlike other types of packaging, however, the unplanned molding process requires some type of dispensing equipment. Some systems automatically dispense the chemicals, simplifying handling and increasing productivity. Although the process is usually operator-dependent, systems have been developed that allow an operator to produce several foam-filled cushions simultaneously.

SELECTION GUIDELINES

When it comes to protective packaging, the goal is to provide an adequate level of protection using the minimum amount of material. But with all of the options available, it can be a challenge to determine the best material for a given application. The effort will be worthwhile, however, because a poorly designed package can result in high levels of product damage. Overdesigning a package will incur unnecessary material costs.

To design the most appropriate packaging, the product's fragility and anticipated handling conditions first must be identified. A product's fragility is determined by measuring the maximum deceleration that it can sustain without damage. This measurement, obtained by subjecting the product to a series of impacts, is expressed in Gs, a unit of acceleration equal to the acceleration caused by gravity at the earth's surface. The lower the G-factor, the higher the fragility. Table 12-1 shows the approximate fragility of some common products.

The conditions that a product will be exposed to during handling and shipping are defined by the maximum drop height. Typically, the weight of the product is inversely proportional to the drop height. The typical drop height for one person carrying a carton weighing between 50 and 100 lb (23 and 45 kg) is approximately 24 in. (61 cm). For pallet loads weighing 1,000 lb (454 kg) or more, the typical drop height is 6 in. (15 cm).

After the G-factor and drop height have been determined, dynamic cushioning curves can be utilized to select the strength and thickness of material that will adequately protect the product. These curves, which are generated by dropping objects from a specified height onto a foam sample and measuring the amount of shock transmitted through the foam, are available from material suppliers. The curves are also used to calculate the amount of material required on each surface area of the product.

Other considerations that must be taken into account in the design of protective packaging are environmental conditions, such as humidity and temperature range and the compressive creep characteristics of the material. Buckling also can be problematic if the length of the cushion is disproportionate to the thickness.

It is important to understand what role the protective packaging material is expected to perform. Some products may only require blocking or bracing, while others may need surface protection and light cushioning. Table 12-2 summarizes the key characteristics of some of the most popular protective packaging materials.

After a package design has been established, dynamic testing of prototypes is recommended to determine the potential for vibration damage. If the vibration (impact) is synchronous with the natural frequency at which the package moves in response to that vibration, the response will be amplified. Designers would like to avoid this condition because it produces the kind of rapid motion that can damage products.

TABLE 12-1
Approximate Fragility of Some Packaged Items

Fragility	Typical Products	G-factor
Extremely fragile	Aircraft altimeters, hard disk drives	15-25 G
Very delicate	Medical diagnostic equipment	25-40 G
Delicate	Cathode ray tubes (CRTs), printers	40-60 G
Moderately delicate	Stereo equipment, televisions	60-85 G
Moderately rugged	Household appliances, furniture	85-115 G
Rugged	Table saws, machine tools	115 G and up

(Courtesy Dow Chemical Company)

TABLE 12-2
Protective Packaging Materials Comparison

Material	Material Cost	Static Loading	Typical Applications
Air cellular packaging	Low	Light-medium	Void fill, wrapping
Corrugated	Low	Light-heavy	Blocking and bracing, crush protection
Polystyrene loose fill	Low	Light-medium	Void fill, light cushioning
Molded polystyrene	Low	Light-medium	Light cushioning
Molded polyurethane	High	Light-medium	Precision cushioning at lighter loadings
Polyethylene loadings	High	Medium-heavy	Precision cushioning at heavy loadings

CHAPTER 12   TRANSPORT PACKAGING

CORRUGATED CARTONS

This section describes the properties used to specify corrugated board, including factors that impact its strength and design considerations. It also discusses the performance of corrugated with recycled content and film packaging alternatives.

Despite the growing popularity of packaging alternatives, such as durable plastic containers and flexible film pouch packages, the corrugated carton continues to be a primary shipping container. *Fabricated corrugated fiberboard*, which consists of a fluted corrugated medium glued between linerboards, is the largest material segment of the packaging industry. About 1,600 box plants in the U.S. produce billions of dollars in product annually.

A major advantage of corrugated fiberboard as a packaging material is its great flexibility; it can be shaped into a wide variety of shapes, sizes, and strengths. If the product line changes, there is no expensive die required or inventory of containers that instantly becomes obsolete. The relatively low cost and the high convenience factor of this disposable packaging material (although some containers are designed for multiple trips) have huge appeal. Moreover, many recyclers now pay for used corrugated boxes. The recovery rate for scrap corrugated boxes is estimated to reach more than 75% by the year 2000.[6]

Extremely lightweight, corrugated cartons are a popular choice for overseas shipping applications. Because they contain no live plant material, corrugated cartons are exempt from the U.S. Department of Agriculture's (USDA) Plant Health Inspection Service, which states that all wood packaging materials must be certified insect-free or undergo fumigation upon arrival at U.S. ports.

DESIGN CONSIDERATIONS

Corrugated cartons must perform many functions as product makes its way through the distribution environment. They must exhibit structural rigidity, have good stacking strength, provide light cushioning protection, handle easily in conveyor and rack systems, and survive the rigors of over-the-road transit.

Historically, freight claims have dictated corrugated carton standards, although this has begun to change.[7]

Many material properties are used to specify corrugated board. *Bursting strength* (measured in $lb/in.^2$ [g/cm^2]) is the amount of pressure that a box can withstand before breaking apart. The strength of the liners is the most important factor in determining burst strength. *Edge crush* (measured in lb/in. [g/cm]) refers to the stacking capacity of the carton, determined by measuring the strength of the board in a vertical position. Flat crush, puncture strength, and pin adhesion strength are other properties used to evaluate the performance of corrugated boards.

Several factors can impact carton strength. Uniformity of the corrugating medium and the quality of the glue bond are probably the most critical.[8] A carton also loses strength as the width of the panel is increased. The corners provide approximately 60% of a carton's stacking strength, so strength is highest when the corners of one layer of boxes are aligned with adjacent layers. Misalignment of the corners or overhang of the cartons on a pallet can reduce the strength by as much as 50%.[9]

However, the ultimate performance of a corrugated carton is dictated to a large extent by how the carton is handled and its environment. For example, if cartons are not interleaved in layers or secured by stretch wrap or banding when using a clamp attachment, the problem of "flowering" (carton separation) may occur.

While a corrugated board can support compressive loads up to 500 times its own weight, this strength deteriorates when moisture is absorbed. Under prolonged exposure to extreme humidity, corrugated board may gain up to 20% weight in moisture content, and strength characteristics may diminish as much as 50%. The board also expands slightly as humidity increases.[10] Many different treatments can be applied to produce better performance in humid conditions, including resins and waxes.

RECYCLED CORRUGATED FIBERBOARD

The recycled content of fiberboard has been steadily rising over the past few years, thanks in part to the efforts of papermakers to improve the performance of recycled materials and set up collection programs to recover material. Corrugated material now averages a recycled content of nearly 40%, although some cartons are made from as much as 100% recycled material.[11]

Do corrugated cartons with recycled content perform as well as cartons made of 100% virgin material? Surprisingly, the findings of one study suggest that recycled content is not the primary concern. In this study, researchers examined the performance of corrugated with recycled fiber and concluded that there are many factors associated with the papermaking process that can affect the strength of the board, as much (if not more), than the recycled content.[12]

Another conclusion was that fiber type has an impact on board strength. One effect of recycling is a shortening of the cellulose fibers, which affects carton compression strength. These issues, which are covered in a subsequent section on unit load bases, also affect corrugated pallets.

A FILM ALTERNATIVE

One concept in packaging is the use of stretch film as a primary package. A thin, plastic film typically made from a linear low-density polyethylene resin engineered for high stretch and toughness, stretch film is typically used to wrap and secure pallet loads. When combined selectively with corrugated inserts, stretch film can provide a high degree of surface protection from dirt, scratches, moisture, and dust. Stretch film is also used to unitize large assortments of items into a secure bundle. Products as diverse as metal pipes and bagged clothing have been stretch-bundled successfully.

One potential drawback of stretch bundling is that impact damage sustained in transit is not apparent. With corrugated fiberboard, crushed cartons are an indication that damage has occurred.

RETURNABLE CONTAINERS

This section describes a closed-loop returnable container system and typical returnable container types, and then examines application guidelines and strategies for maximizing the return-on-investment.

In the mid-1970s, U.S. automakers pioneered the use of returnable containers. Containers that last for hundreds of trips now constitute standard packaging procedure and are being adopted in a variety of industries from aerospace to household appliances.

The continued popularity of Just-in-Time (JIT) manufacturing strategies—whereby materials are delivered in lot size quantities directly to the assembly line—is one factor that has helped to stimulate the growing interest in returnable containers. After manufacturers learned that they could use the same container many times over for both in-plant handling and transport packaging, many went to returnables. But even more of a motivating force has been the significant cost savings achieved by making the switch from disposable to reusable packaging.

Returnable containers perform many of the same functions as disposable packaging. Containers can be used to handle products at a single location or to ship materials between multiple locations.

CHAPTER 12   TRANSPORT PACKAGING

Inside a manufacturing facility, containers feed parts on a JIT basis to assembly lines, handle and store raw materials and work-in-process, and support kitting operations. Externally, returnable containers carry materials between multiple locations.

However, returnable containers are not always a perfect substitute for disposable packaging. Unlike one-time use packaging, returnable containers require a substantial capital investment. To protect that investment, some type of control system is necessary to ensure that the containers are recovered and remain captive in the system.

CONTAINER DESIGN

Returnable containers come in different styles and materials, including plastic, steel wire mesh, and composite materials, and perform so many different functions that no single definition applies. Although any type of container that survives multiple trips could be classified as returnable, several popular container types include:

- Stackable containers: available in both straight and tapered-wall versions, these interlocking containers typically come in modular sizes that can be mixed and matched to hold a standard pallet load. Dividers can be added, allowing a single container to handle multiple parts.
- Modular container system: combines stackable containers with a pallet and optional top cap for unit load handling.
- Intermediate bulk container: consisting of a reusable high-density polyethylene bottle and separate outer structure, these containers are designed to handle bulk and semibulk materials.
- Custom interior dunnage: a container consists of a rigid outer frame with removable dunnage. For applications that cannot take advantage of a standard container, custom dunnage can be designed for securing and protecting parts. Dunnage also can be used to orient a part for ease of unloading.

A key consideration in container design is product protection. A container's dimensions, degree of cushioning, and ability to provide surface protection will vary depending on the products handled. When the container is to be handled manually, the weight of the contents is a consideration. Lifting guidelines proposed by the National Institute for Occupational Safety and Health (NIOSH) substantially restrict lifting weights to less than 50 lb (23 kg). The specific size and design of the container—such as two- or four-way entry—will depend on the equipment used to handle the containers and the functions the container will perform. A cleverly-designed container can perform many functions, from consolidating parts in a kitting operation, to fixturing parts for assembly and folding flat for economical return shipping.

Another consideration in container design is standardization. Can a standard container be used throughout the process? If not, are containers modular so that different combinations of containers fit a standard footprint? Some companies have standardized container size and footprint, then designed custom dunnage to facilitate the handling of different types of parts. Figure 12-1 shows a molded plastic dunnage insert that was designed for automobile bumpers.

Developments in container design have helped to extend the life and flexibility of returnables. Many designs feature reinforcing ribs for added stacking strength and weight capacity. Ribbed bottoms are another feature that interlock with shelf wires to prevent lateral movement in staging applications. Quarter-half top lids with locking tabs are available that open in an up-and-back orientation for access through the container top, with a hinged front gate that drops down. Ergonomic handles, with a wide shape and smooth, round edges, also ease the task of manually handling containers. Figure 12-2 highlights some of the features of a returnable container that facilitate the handling of outboard engines.

APPLICATION GUIDELINES

Although many companies have reaped a substantial cost savings with returnable containers, making the switch from disposable packaging materials is not for everyone. The firms that benefit most from returnables typically have a medium to high number of inventory turns annually. The faster that inventory turns over, the more benefits returnable containers can deliver. However, if the product or component mix changes frequently or unexpectedly, a container designed to last for years can become prematurely obsolete.

In an ideal returnable container application, the number of trading partners will be relatively small and preferably located nearby (within a 200 mile [322 km] radius). These characteristics are one reason that returnables have been so successful in the automotive industry. In contrast, when travel distances are long, it takes a container more time to travel the entire cycle. Generally, there is a direct correlation between shipping distance and the number of containers required to keep the distribution pipeline stocked. An easy reference is to multiply the usage requirement—the number of containers shipped in a particular month—by a factor of three. However, the number of days a container takes to travel the complete cycle depends on factors such as the supplier, product, location, and transportation time. If the float quantity increases, then more containers need to be purchased.

As with any type of capital equipment, an important goal of a returnable container program is to keep as many containers in use as possible at all times. To put that goal into context, 408 ft^2 (38 m^2) of floor space is required to store containers carried in a standard 48 ft (15 m) trailer that is 102-in. (259-cm) wide. The involvement of both suppliers and customers decreases container availability.

In general, the fewer standard container sizes, the better. While this may not always be practical from the perspective of cube efficiency, as the number of different-size containers increases, the volume of containers that must be stocked also increases. In addition, container handling and storage equipment may not be capable of managing a large number of container sizes. Too many different container sizes can result in a juggling act, as companies try to ensure that the right size containers are at the right place in the distribution chain at the right time. One way to manage this situation is to buy more containers, but that results in higher costs and greater storage space requirements. Too few containers, on the other hand, may result in the need for costly fill-ins with disposable packaging.

Finally, most successful returnable container programs require the commitment and support of top management. One reason is that returnable containers require a kind of diligence and ongoing effort that can often only be communicated from the top down. A second reason is that the high initial purchase price of the containers is typically a capital expenditure, not an expense, as is the case with most disposable packaging materials. There are, however, strategies for reducing the cash outlay. Some companies are able to spread out their container purchases over several years. This type of phased-in conversion is often recommended by the container suppliers, not only as a way to level out the expenditure, but also as a way to work out problems before a major conversion. Some companies also arrange to share the cost of containers with their trading partners.

The previously outlined factors are intended only as broad guidelines and some applications that do not fit the typical profile have been successfully implemented. Determining just how well returnables fit into a specific application requires a detailed analysis. Some specific factors that should be analyzed include:

- Production rates.
- Material flows.
- Number of parts.

CHAPTER 12   TRANSPORT PACKAGING

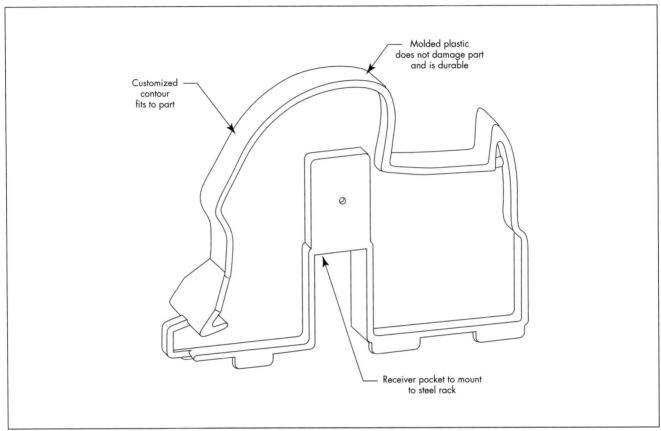

Fig. 12-1 Bumper dunnage.

- Number of trading partners.
- Current types of containers.
- Current size of containers.
- Dunnage designs.
- Handling methods.

A majority of returnable container systems are justified on the basis of cost savings. For the right application, returnables can reap a significant savings, particularly when compared to disposable packaging on a cost-per-trip basis. The obvious savings is the reduction in ongoing material purchases. Other possible savings include a reduction in inventory, greater handling efficiency, better ergonomics, and more efficient use of the cube (storage volume).

Durable returnable containers require a higher initial capital investment and ongoing maintenance costs (washing, repair, and replacement), as well as return transportation and administrative costs. These specific costs and savings associated with a returnable container program are different for every application. Cost justification and various analysis methods are covered more in Chapter 9.

MAXIMIZING THE RETURN-ON-INVESTMENT

There are several strategies for maximizing the payback of a returnable container program. Transportation costs, for example, can be minimized through a strategy, whereby empty containers are picked up at the same time drop shipments are made. Containers that nest or fold flat when empty help maximize the use of trailer space. Some companies have even been able to obtain rate reductions from their carriers for using returnable containers.

Container control and tracking is essential to the success of any returnable container program. Keeping good records on the ordering, accounting, invoicing, and monitoring of containers helps to ensure that containers remain captive in the distribution channel and are available at the right place and time.

"Shrinkage" (losses) can be a problem, because costly containers have an obvious value that disposable packaging does not. Strategies for reducing losses include:

- Minimizing the number of containers held in the system.
- Minimizing the number of carriers used.
- Minimizing the number of locations where containers are stored.
- Color coding the containers or using hot stamp logos and identification marks.

Another strategy for discouraging theft is to customize the container to limit it to a very specific use. The downside, of course, is less standardization and potential premature obsolescence of the container. Many people believe that the best protection is to create a loop so tight that potential thieves are discouraged from even attempting to pilfer containers.

Because repairs or replacements are typically costly, containers should be used only for the intended application and design capacity. Lift truck drivers and other equipment operators should be trained on proper handling techniques. Containers that are exposed to significant amounts of grime or contaminants like oil should be cleaned frequently, possibly after every use. Containers can be cleaned by hand, although environmental requirements may prevent the hosing down of contaminated containers outdoors. For throughputs of more than 150 units a day, commercial washing systems using high pres-

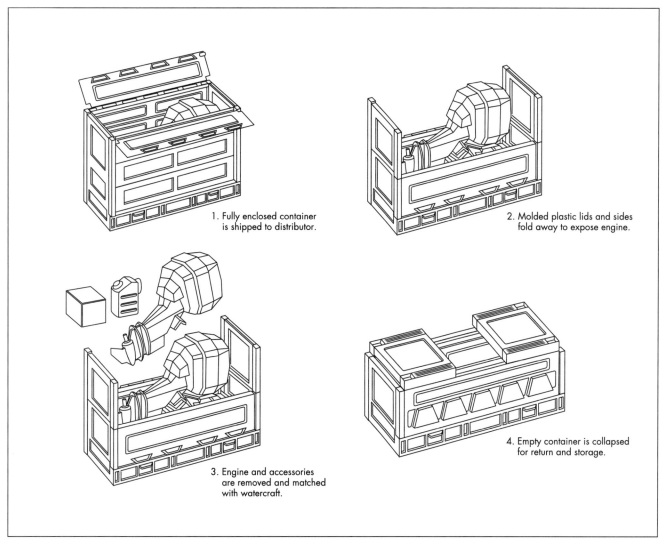

1. Fully enclosed container is shipped to distributor.

2. Molded plastic lids and sides fold away to expose engine.

3. Engine and accessories are removed and matched with watercraft.

4. Empty container is collapsed for return and storage.

Fig. 12-2 Outboard engine returnable shipping container (concept).

sure water or steam to blast containers clean, can reduce labor requirements.

Finally, many experienced users and container manufacturers recommend taking a conservative approach when setting up a returnable container program. Most conversions are planned on a part-by-part, line-by-line, or supplier-by-supplier basis, which is reflected accordingly in the economic analysis. Because a returnable container program requires that companies undergo some basic institutional changes, this kind of phased-in approach is typically more manageable. An important point to keep in mind is that few companies are ever able to achieve a full 100% conversion to returnable containers. Anything more than 90% is considered very good.

THE UNIT LOAD BASE

This section reviews the primary types of unit load bases, including wood pallets, plastic pallets, corrugated fiberboard pallets, and slip-sheets, and the common, controlled pallet standards used today. It also discusses key considerations in pallet design, pallet quality issues, and pallet leasing programs.

A *unit load base* is a portable, rigid platform used to stack, store, handle, and transport individual items as a single unit. The popularity of the unit load concept is evidenced by the more than 1.5 billion pallets used daily. Approximately 500 million wood pallets are sold each year in the U.S. In fact, the ubiquitous wood pallet accounts for the vast majority of unit load bases in use today. But in recent years, alternatives to wood pallets, including corrugated, plastic, and plywood pallets, as well as slip-sheets, have enjoyed a surge in popularity in some niche markets.

As the name implies, the primary function of the *unit load base* is to facilitate the handling of many individual items as a single unit. A well-designed unit load base also protects the load from the rigors of the handling environment, and interfaces smoothly with a wide range of handling equipment, from lift trucks to storage racks to queuing conveyors to automated systems.

Table 12-3 compares some of the key characteristics of the most popular types of unit load bases and Figure 12-3 is a questionnaire for determining the performance requirements for pallets. Each is described in detail in the following sections.

CHAPTER 12 TRANSPORT PACKAGING

WOOD PALLETS

Part of the reason for the popularity of the wood pallet is its great versatility. Enjoying wide general use in industries as diverse as grocery, retail distribution, and durable goods, wood pallets are available in a wide range of sizes and load capacities. Among all of the alternatives, wood pallets are the easiest to repair. In fact, some wood pallets are even graded by the extent of those repairs.

Wood pallets are constructed from the boards of common North American wood species, including hardwoods, softwoods, or a mixture of both. Top and bottom deck boards and supporting members are fastened together into a variety of footprint sizes and configurations, typically determined by the load, support, and handling conditions. Pallets made of composites (a molded mixture of wood fiber and synthetic organic resins) are also available, offering a four-to-one nesting ratio for reduced storage space requirements.

In the U.S., the predominant pallet size is 48 × 40 in. (122 × 102 cm). The predominant design is the *stringer pallet*, which utilizes solid or notched beams called stringers to support the top and bottom deck components. Two to five stringer versions are typical. Stringer pallets feature either two-way entry or partial four-way entry, which restricts the entry of a pallet jack or lift truck. Figure 12-4 illustrates a typical stringer-style pallet.

Block pallets, which are more common in Europe, utilize rectangular wood blocks between the pallet decks. One of the major advantages of this design is that it provides true four-way entry, allowing a pallet jack or lift truck to enter on either the 40- or 48-in. (102- or 122-cm) side. When the bottom deck boards are oriented around the perimeter of the bottom deck, it is called a *perimeter based block pallet*. This is the preferred block pallet design in the U.S. When the bottom deck boards are oriented in only one direction, the bottom deck is unidirectional. The benefit is better sideway transfer and flow on roller conveyors. Figure 12-5 illustrates a typical unidirectional block-style pallet.

Variations of these two basic pallet types include single-wing and double-wing (the deck board overhangs the stringers or the blocks).

Wood pallets have good stiffness and strength characteristics and perform well in racking applications and in automated systems, which make them ideal for general use. They can travel from a manufacturer to a finished goods warehouse, be stored in a racking system, and then used to ship product downstream to retail stores.

One of the most attractive features of wood pallets is their relatively low cost. Prices will depend on the lumber availability, pallet quality, and region. With increased use of pallet and container retrieval and moving systems, high-quality wood pallets are providing pallet users the lowest cost per use.

The versatility of the wood pallet is also its greatest drawback. Wood pallets come in a wide range of sizes and quality—to the dismay of Receiving departments that are striving to control the consistency of incoming pallets. Many purchasing agents buy pallets based on price, not on how the pallet will be used or on its total cost (as determined by an activity-based costing system). Low-price, poor quality wood pallets are particularly problematic for warehousing operations because they can fail under load, damage the product, and wreak havoc with automated handling equipment. The quality of pallets can be assured by compliance with specifications set by the National Wooden Pallet and Container Association.

Panel deck pallets cost more than a comparable all-wood pallet and are designed for long life and heavy-duty service. The solid deck provides a good load carrying surface and resists deflection in racking applications when compared to plastic pallets. Sturdy and durable, the deck's cross-laminated construction helps to distribute impact loads. The greater the thickness of the deck, the greater the stiffness and strength. Stiffer pallet decks can minimize the potential for product damage by reducing the transmissibility of the normal vibrations experienced during over-the-road travel.

Some wood pallets feature structural panel decks, which are typically made of plywood or oriented-strand boards (OSB). In some automated storage and retrieval systems, in which the pallet functions as a slave (captive to the system), the pallet may be no more than a simple plywood deck cut to size.

PLASTIC PALLETS

Although once limited to specialty applications such as pharmaceutical and food processing, which have strict United States Department of Agriculture (USDA) or Food and Drug Administration (FDA) and sanitation requirements, plastic pallets are gaining share in general use applications. Plastic pallets have become an integral part of returnable container programs in the auto industry. There is also increasing use of plastic pallets in the downstream loop—from distributor to retailer—in the grocery industry. One desirable characteristic of plastic is the ability to mold unique shapes and features such as drains and lips. Some plastic pallets are also nestable, making for efficient use of storage space and more economical returns.

TABLE 12-3
Unit Load Base Comparison

Unit Load Base	Price	Durability	Repairability	Typical Applications
Corrugated pallet	Low	Low	Low	One-way shipping applications Lightweight products Export shipping
Wood pallet	Low-medium	Medium-high	High	Wide general use, automated capture or closed-loop systems
Plastic pallet	Medium-high	Medium-high	Low	Captive or closed-loop systems Medical and food processing applications Grocery (downstream loop)
Corrugated slip-sheet	Low	Low	Low	One-way shipping applications Export shipping
Plastic slip-sheet	Medium	High	Low	Captive or closed-loop systems

CHAPTER 12   TRANSPORT PACKAGING

PERFORMANCE REQUIREMENTS FOR PALLETS QUESTIONNAIRE

Load Conditions

1. List the container types and objects to be placed on the pallet (bags, cases, bulk containers, barrels, blocks, machinery, etc.).

_____

2. What are the maximum and minimum unit load dimensions, not including the pallet (length, width, and height in inches [centimeters])?

_____

3. What are the minimum container or object dimensions by type in question 1 (length, width, and height in inches [centimeters])?

_____

4. For each unit load type*, what are the maximum, minimum, and average load levels (in pounds [kilograms])?

_____

5. List the type of load stabilizers used (that is, shrink-wrap, stretch wrap, adhesives, etc.) and the approximate percent bound and unbound.

_____

6. Identify the unit load types that incorporate pallet sheets, spacers, or caps.

_____

7. Describe, for each unit load type, load binders used in transit.

_____

8. Describe any product or package more moisture-sensitive than untreated corrugated, which will be placed on the pallet.

_____

Support Conditions

1. Is the pallet to be placed into racks?

_____

2. Describe the types of racks in use (that is, gravity feed, drive-through, conventional, etc.).

_____

3. By unit load type, what are the maximum and minimum unsupported free spans racked across the 48-in. (122-cm) length and 40-in. (102-cm) width of the pallet?

_____

4. By unit load type, how many unit loads high will pallet loads be stacked (maximum) in the warehouse?

_____

5. By unit load type, what is the maximum length of time a unit load will remain in a rack or stack?

_____

6. How many unit loads high will pallet loads be stacked (maximum) in shipping?

_____

7. What are the maximum allowable deflections (in inches [centimeters]) permitted for pallets and pallet parts for each support condition (stacking or racking)?

_____

Handling Conditions

1. Will the pallets be handled with fork lifts? If yes, what is the range of fork length, width, and spacing between the forks?

_____

2. Will the pallets be handled with wheeled pallet trucks or walkies? What is the range in length and width of the forks, spacing of the forks, and lowered fork height (in inches [centimeters])?

_____

3. Will the pallet be handled in a sling mechanism? If so, what is the width of the support bar and bar spacing (in inches [centimeters])?

_____

Fig. 12-3 Performance requirements for pallets questionnaire.

CHAPTER 12   TRANSPORT PACKAGING

4. Will the pallet be subjected to roller conveyors during horizontal transport? If yes, what is the range in roller diameters and roller spacing? Are the rolls parallel, perpendicular, or both with respect to pallet length (48 in. [122 cm] direction)?

_____

5. Will the pallet be subjected to chain conveyance? If yes, what is the range in chain width and unsupported free span between the chains? Is pallet movement on the chain conveyor parallel, perpendicular, or both with respect to pallet length (48 in. [122 cm] direction)?

_____

6. Will the pallet be used in automatic palletizers and pallet dispensers or other automated equipment (for example, AS/RS)?

_____

7. Is the pallet to be two-way, partial four-way (notched stringer), or full four-way accessible to handling equipment?

_____

8. Are there any situations or flammability performance requirements?

_____

9. What are the maximum and minimum temperatures to which the pallet will be exposed? _____

10. Is the pallet for multiple or limited use? _____

11. As returnable, what level of durability in handling† is desirable?

_____

12. Describe any other unusual condition which would stress the pallet beyond the conditions described in completing this questionnaire.

_____

Miscellaneous Conditions

1. What is the maximum allowable pallet weight? _____

2. What is the range of acceptable pallet heights? _____

3. What is the range of acceptable pallet length and width? _____

4. Is the pallet repairable? _____

5. Is the pallet nestable? _____

6. By the percent coverage, list any minimum top- and bottom-deck bearing area requirements.

_____

7. Are deck overhangs or wings desirable and acceptable? How much overhang is acceptable?

_____

8. Are openings required in pallet decks for ventilation? _____

*A unit load type is described as:

    a. Object type, for example, bags
    b. Object size, for example, $16 \times 20 \times 9$ in. ($41 \times 51 \times 23$ cm)
    c. Footprint size, for example, 36×36 in. (91×91 cm)

    To simplify the process, you may wish to use unit load type *classes* or *categories*.

†A *handling* is a single lifting, transport, and setting down of a loaded or unloaded pallet.

Fig. 12-3 (cont.) Performance requirements for pallets questionnaire.

High-density polyethylene is the most popular material used for plastic pallets, although there is growing interest in polycarbonate, rigid vinyl, and composite plastics. The forming and molding methods used to manufacture plastic pallets include:

- Single- or twin-sheet thermoforming.
- Injection molding.
- Structural foam molding.
- Blow molding.
- Compression molding.
- Rotational molding.
- Profile extrusion.

Exhibiting good impact resistance, high-density polyethylene makes for an extremely durable pallet. The design of a plastic pallet can be modified to increase its structural rigidity and strength. A pallet that has ribbing, for example, has almost 50% more rigidity than one that does not. Similarly, impact resistance can be enhanced by rounding out the contours of the pallet to disperse the impact force. The physical properties of the plastic itself, including its coefficient of friction and structural strength, also can be modified through the addition of fibers or plasticizers. Clever design can produce a pallet that exhibits the best performance with the minimum material content.

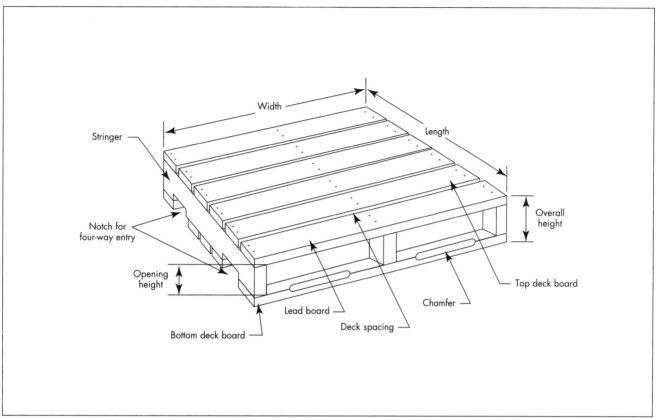

Fig. 12-4 Stringer-style pallet design.

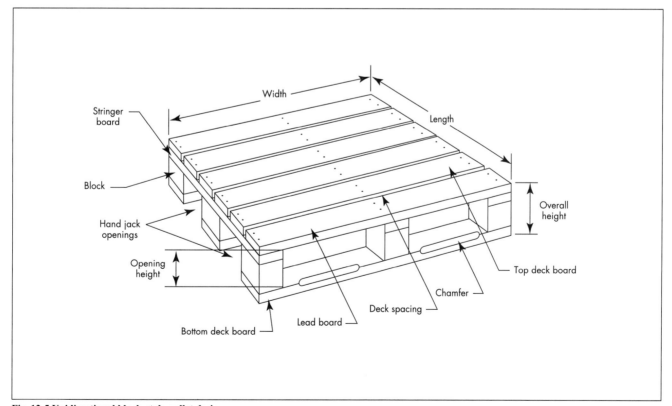

Fig. 12-5 Unidirectional block-style pallet design.

CHAPTER 12   TRANSPORT PACKAGING

However, plastic pallets have low *flexural strength*, which is an indicator of a material's ability to resist bending. Plastic also exhibits a high degree of *creep*, which is a slow strain (or deflection) in response to an applied stress. For these reasons, most plastic pallets must be racked, particularly in applications with large, unsupported spans. Rigid steel tubing can be used to increase racking strength, as shown in Fig. 12-6, but this increases the cost of the pallet and presents problems during recycling.

Resins such as polycarbonate have improved stiffness and several new composites are being developed. Today, however, these strategies add to the cost of the pallet. The question for many users is whether a rackable plastic pallet is worth the additional cost. Even without enhancements, plastic pallets are a more expensive alternative. Although many pallet users like the high dimensional consistency and durable performance of plastic pallets, the relatively high price (depending on design and volumes) typically restricts their use to a closed-loop system. In some cases, the user will keep the pallet captive in his or her own facility and transfer loads to a less expensive pallet for shipping. Other companies have tightly managed programs in place to ensure the pallet's return.

Plastic pallets also present safety and environmental concerns if they are in a fire because of toxic fumes. Contact your insurance carrier for any special requirements. If plastic pallets are to be used in cold environments, special attention should be given to the coefficient of friction for the unit load to the top deck. This factor will determine whether the unit loads will slide off the pallet.

CORRUGATED FIBERBOARD PALLETS

Although fiberboard pallets—in both corrugated and honeycomb forms—have been used for awhile, they have recently experienced an explosive growth in sales. More than half of all corrugated pallets are used in the automotive industry. Fiberboard pallets are used for international shipping applications when the unit load is very light, because they are exempt from USDA regulation stating that all wood packing materials must be certified insect-free upon arrival at U.S. ports.

Less durable but far lighter than other materials, fiberboard is particularly well-suited for pallets used in one-way shipping applications. Its low weight, approximately 10-20 lb (4.5-9 kg), is a particular advantage from an ergonomics perspective.

Corrugated pallets come in a variety of configurations. Containing flat, uniform decks, they are very consistent dimensionally. One popular style resembles a wood stringer pallet, with three stringer members for load support and two- or four-way entry. They can have a solid upper deck. Paper cores can be included at the corners or corrugated inserts added to the stringers for additional strength and stability. Solid corrugated decks are sometimes cross-laminated to give greater strength in both directions.

Another popular design consists of a triple-wall or laminated double-wall corrugated top deck and a double-wall corrugated bottom deck supported by nine wound cores of corrugated fiberboard (Fig. 12-7). In addition to maximizing the compression strength, this design permits four-way entry by lift truck or pallet jack. Honeycomb paper pallets are available in a variety of styles and sizes, including a block style with single- or double-deck facings.

With less structural durability than other materials, fiberboard pallets are more prone to damage from normal handling, although lift truck or hand truck operators should exercise care in handling any type of pallet. Care must be taken to ensure that the load is uniformly distributed across the surface of a fiberboard pallet, particularly in applications involving mixed loads. In addition, while fiberboard pallets can be designed to be strong enough to support loads weighing more than 2,500 lb (1,134 kg), a low stacking strength precludes their use in most warehouse racking applications unless they are double-stacked on top of a more durable base. The strength of fiberboard pallets also deteriorates as the moisture content increases. This phenomenon can be problematic if the pallet is handled in humid or wet environments. For more details on the properties of fiberboard, see the preceding section on corrugated cartons.

Some fiberboard pallets last for multiple trips, but are most commonly used for one-way shipping applications. For a single-use pallet to be economically feasible, it must have a low price and be easily disposable. Currently, fiberboard pallets can simply be baled and recycled along with other paper waste. A major push by papermakers to recover paper for recycling has actually increased the value of worn out fiberboard boxes and pallets.

While fiberboard pallets are attractively priced when compared to other pallet alternatives, they are sensitive to material prices. From time to time, volatility in the paper market has caused fluctuations that have made fiberboard pallets less cost competitive.

SLIP-SHEETS

A *slip-sheet* is a thin sheet of material—typically corrugated fiberboard, solid fiber, or plastic—with tabs. These tabs permit the gripper bars of a front-end attachment on a lift truck, consisting of a face plate that extends by means of a pantograph mechanism and gripper bar, to pull the load onto a platen or set of oversize forks. A typical push and pull attachment is shown in Fig. 12-8.

Although far-outnumbered by the volume of pallets in use, plastic slip-sheets may sometimes be reused within a warehouse in conjunction with a slave pallet, although most slip-sheets are designed for one-trip shipping applications. Slip-sheets are also low priced, but can result in higher costs due to increased product damage to the unit load and the extra cost of equipment needed to use them. Space savings is another advantage because approximately 100 slip-sheets take up the same amount of space as a single pallet. This smaller profile makes for denser product storage. Slip-sheets also weigh a fraction of other unit load base alternatives.

Benefits like these have led to the experimentation with slip-sheets in many industries, including food processing, grocery, paper products, electronics, chemical, and retail, for one-way shipping. Plastic slip-sheets, while more expensive than paper, are reusable and offer some of the same advantages as plastic pallets.

When using slip-sheets, special attention should be paid to load stacking. Cases should be stacked inside the score lines and tabs so that the tabs can be folded up against the unit load for transit. Cases on the bottom layer should be prevented from shifting, particularly onto tab areas, during transit. Interlocking stacking patterns improve stability. Another strategy is to design in extra tabs on the slip-sheet that are used in conjunction with stretch film to unitize the loads.

Disposable fiberboard slip-sheets are prone to the same durability and moisture problems as cartons and corrugated pallets. But the greatest obstacle to their use has simply been the immense popularity of pallets. Receivers must be equipped to deal with slip-sheets, which requires an investment in special equipment. A push and pull attachment can be mounted to any standard ITA Class I or II lift truck carriage. A captive pallet is also required if the slip-sheeted load is stored in a rack system.

PALLET DESIGN

Some people may believe that all pallets are similar. But there is growing consensus that not all pallets are alike. Every pallet must be designed to meet the exact requirements of the intended application, including its load weight and distribution, handling equipment, and storage environment. A properly-designed pallet must be sufficiently strong and stiff to support the load within the specific environment

CHAPTER 12   TRANSPORT PACKAGING

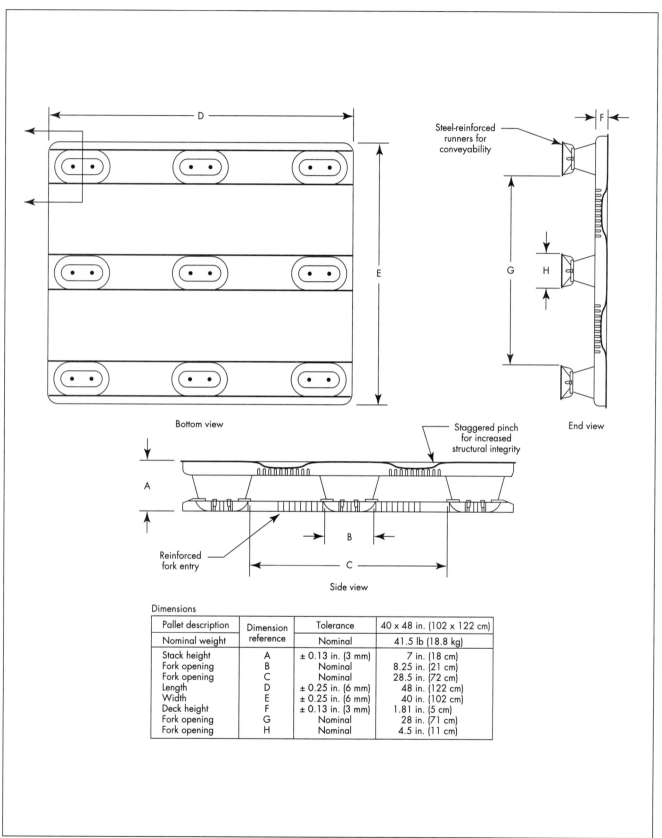

Steel-reinforced
runners for
conveyability

Bottom view

End view

Staggered pinch
for increased
structural integrity

Reinforced
fork entry

Side view

Dimensions

Pallet description	Dimension reference	Tolerance	40 x 48 in. (102 x 122 cm)
Nominal weight		Nominal	41.5 lb (18.8 kg)
Stack height	A	± 0.13 in. (3 mm)	7 in. (18 cm)
Fork opening	B	Nominal	8.25 in. (21 cm)
Fork opening	C	Nominal	28.5 in. (72 cm)
Length	D	± 0.25 in. (6 mm)	48 in. (122 cm)
Width	E	± 0.25 in. (6 mm)	40 in. (102 cm)
Deck height	F	± 0.13 in. (3 mm)	1.81 in. (5 cm)
Fork opening	G	Nominal	28 in. (71 cm)
Fork opening	H	Nominal	4.5 in. (11 cm)

Fig. 12-6 Rackable, conveyable plastic pallet. *(Courtesy Tri Enda)*

CHAPTER 12   TRANSPORT PACKAGING

at minimum cost. It must also have a footprint that prevents underhang and overhang of cartons. Otherwise, the pallet does not fulfill its primary function: to protect the unit load. Without this protection, added costs are realized because of hang-ups in automated handling systems or product damage.

Underdesigned pallets will not perform all of the required functions adequately. Just a few of the costs of an inappropriate pallet design include:

- Purchase of additional pallets to replace damaged ones.
- Product damage—researchers have proven that the design of a pallet can lead to accelerated load motion during transit, resulting in greater product damage.[13]

- Productivity losses caused by hang-ups.
- Workers' compensation costs associated with injuries.
- Equipment downtime.
- Manual restacking of loads.

Designers would like to avoid these situations, but pallets that are overdesigned run the risk of not being economical. How do you design the best pallet for an application? When determining the performance requirements for a pallet, the specific load, support, and handling conditions must be identified (see Fig. 12-3).

One design characteristic of particular interest is pallet stiffness, which refers to the relative amount of deformation of the pallet deck. Designers are typically concerned with the deformation between the

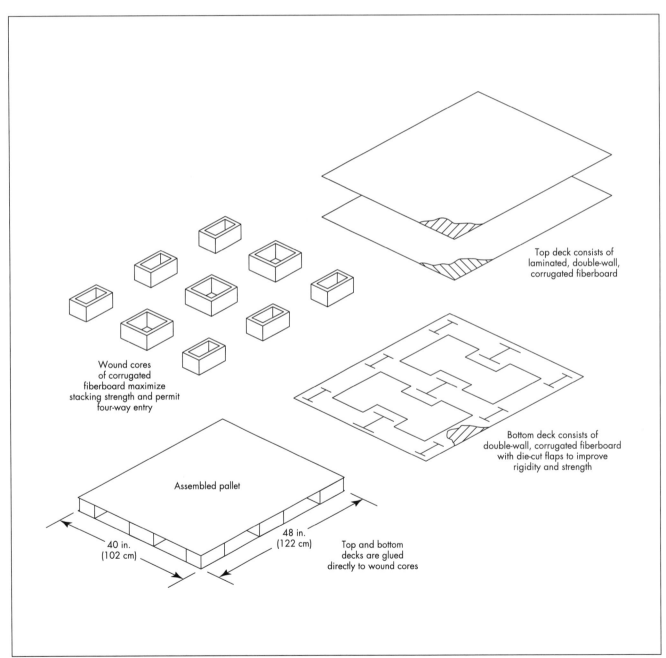

Top deck consists of laminated, double-wall, corrugated fiberboard

Wound cores of corrugated fiberboard maximize stacking strength and permit four-way entry

Bottom deck consists of double-wall, corrugated fiberboard with die-cut flaps to improve rigidity and strength

Assembled pallet

40 in. (102 cm)

48 in. (122 cm)

Top and bottom decks are glued directly to wound cores

Fig. 12-7 Anatomy of a corrugated fiberboard pallet. *(Courtesy Stone Container Corp.)*

stringers or blocks and deflection of the deck, particularly in racking applications. A good reference is to design pallets and pallet decks to deform at a design load less than 1% of free span. These *spans* refer to the distance between supports in racks or between deck support members within the pallet.[14]

PALLET STANDARDS

After the appropriate pallet design has been determined for an application, a detailed specification should be prepared. Pallet standards are important because they provide a common basis for understanding among trading partners.

Many pallet standards have been developed for this purpose and are widely used. Many industries, including automotive and printing, have even established their own specifications.[15] The International Organization for Standardization (ISO) has also published a series of pallet standards.[16]

A performance specification for pallets used in automated material handling systems, including conveyors, palletizers, and automated storage and retrieval systems, has been developed by the pallet laboratory at Virginia Tech, the National Wooden Pallet and Container Association (NWPCA), and the Material Handling Industry of America (MHIA). This specification addresses many of the unique requirements of automated handling equipment, including the extremely tight tolerances between the pallet and equipment frame, load tracking methods, and repair issues.

Metal plates, which are commonly used to repair pallets, can confuse a photoelectric sensing device on a conveyor system. Likewise, a missing or damaged deck board can result in a no-read.

Many of the controlled standards are based on a stringer or block pallet design with a 40 × 48-in. (1,016 × 1,219-mm) footprint. The 40-in. (1,016-mm) face has the added advantage that all conventional lift trucks can be used for trailer loading and unloading. In Europe, the *Europallet*, a unidirectional block-style pallet with a 31.5 × 47-in. (800 × 1,200-mm) footprint, is one of the predominant standards. The other predominant standard is the *ISO pallet*, with a 39 × 47-in. (1,000 × 1,200 mm) footprint. Use varies by region.

Interest in the block pallet is growing in the U.S. Its benefits include four-way entry, allowing a pallet jack to enter on either the 40- or 48-in. (1,016- or 1,219-mm) side with nestability if using the unidirectional style pallet. Interest in both the one-quarter and one-half pallet (based on the standard 40 × 48-in. [1,016 × 1,219-mm]

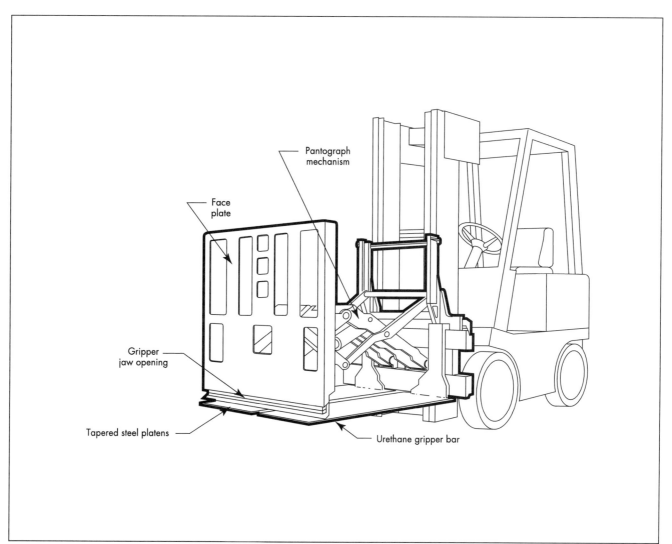

Fig. 12-8 Push/pull lift truck attachment for slip-sheet handling.

CHAPTER 12   TRANSPORT PACKAGING

pallet) is also growing. The rationale for a smaller-size pallet is to allow more full loads to travel intact through the distribution chain because the average order size is decreasing.

The most popular of all standards in the U.S., however, is probably the least understood and the most abused. Known as the *GMA pallet standard*, this standard was developed by the Grocery Manufacturers' Association in the late 1960s. Although perfectly adequate at the time, it suffered almost immediately from a lack of control, which led to a downward spiral in quality. Ironically, the GMA pallet is still enormously popular. But for many people, it is simply a convenient label for any pallet with a 40 × 48-in. (1,016 × 1,219-mm) footprint. The quality of many so-called GMA pallets varies tremendously, with wide inconsistencies in the dimensional tolerances, number of components, and thickness of boards. Some GMA pallets are designed to last only one trip; others may last for years.

The long-standing problem with the GMA pallet is indicative of the problem with pallet standards in general: after a good standard has been developed, the challenge for users shifts from one of dealing with poorly-designed pallets to ensuring compliance with the new standard. As a consequence, companies are often forced to police their pallet suppliers and trading partners.

In a concentrated effort to control pallet manufacturing repair quality, the NWPCA has launched a national pallet quality assurance auditing program (see Bibliography). Called SPEQ (specified pallets, engineered for quality), this program guarantees that new pallets are manufactured to a given standard. It is one of several initiatives intended to directly confront the issue of pallet quality.

Some companies have implemented their own procedures for inspecting incoming pallets from their suppliers, refusing to accept low-quality pallets. Receivers are typically trained to look for protruding nails, missing deck boards, metal repair plates, warped boards, knots in the vicinity of a notch, and other defects. The same kind of inspection process is also used to determine whether a multiple-use pallet is in need of repair or ready to be recycled.

In lieu of institutionalizing pallet inspection and control activities, more companies are outsourcing pallet retrieval or recovery functions to companies that specialize in this or beginning to explore the concept of pallet leasing. In the successful Canadian Pallet Council (CPC) program, participants purchase their own pallets. Under this type of program, which is administered by a third party, all participants throughout the system use a standard, high-quality pallet. Quality and consistency are ensured through rigorous inspection, maintenance, and repair activities. Already a common practice in other countries, pallet leasing is increasing in the U.S. Pallet leasing has grown most notably in the grocery industry.

In the final analysis, the most successful pallet programs in the world have some sort of facilitating mechanism to ensure: a good quality input into the system, good quality output (in terms of control), and a basic method of repair that works.

HANDLING WITHOUT PALLETS

Many problems associated with pallets could be avoided by simply doing away with them and using clamps instead. A popular strategy in several industries, including paper products and appliances, carton clamps work by applying pressure to the sides of the load. Standard clamp equipment, which attaches to a lift truck, can handle load widths from 20-72-in. (51-183-cm) wide and 60-in. (152-cm) tall. An obvious advantage of palletless loads is that they increase storage stacking height. Care must be taken in building the load, however. To preserve stacking strength, a noninterlocking pattern should be used and the load should be stabilized by banding or wrapping. Stabilizer sheets between loads are often employed. Additional packaging, such as partitions or dividers, may help to withstand the clamping forces.

FIRE PROTECTION AND PACKAGING

This section references the key fire protection guidelines, defines fire hazard classifications for wood and plastic pallets and containers, and reviews fire protection strategies.

All types of storage equipment, including pallets or containers made of wood and plastic, are subject to specific fire protection requirements. National and local building codes also publish fire protection standards, typically referencing National Fire Protection Association (NFPA) standards, which are enforceable by law.

While in use during the manufacturing process, pallets and containers are not considered to require any special fire protection. However, fire protection is a major issue when full or empty containers are concentrated in staging or storage areas. To determine the specific degree of fire hazard, the packaging, product, and configuration of the storage medium all must be considered.

The National Fire Protection Association (NFPA) and The Factory Mutual Research Corporation (FMRC) have established commodity classes reflecting the severity of fire hazards. A Class I commodity is the least hazardous, requiring sprinkler protection or another acceptable method of fire protection. The most hazardous is a Class IV commodity. Two factors, however, can increase the hazard beyond Class IV: a high percentage of plastic content in the product or packaging—expanded plastics have a low-density and high-heat release rate, thus producing a high burning rate; and rack storage, which represents a greater fire hazard than other storage configurations because of the increased supply of oxygen from an increased available surface area.[17] Table 12-4 contains a description of the various classes and typical commodities within each class.

Determining the rating for plastic pallets, which come in a variety of resin types and designs, has proved to be troublesome. Currently, FMRC considers wood and fiberboard pallets a Class I commodity and all plastic pallets a Class II commodity. NFPA considers both wood pallets and nonexpanded polyethylene pallets as Class I commodities.

Nevertheless, the onus is on a company using pallets of any sort to demonstrate to the satisfaction of its casualty insurer that appropriate fire protection strategies are in place. Qualified fire protection professionals, sprinkler system contractors, and casualty insurers can all assist companies in navigating the complexity of fire protection codes and requirements.

Automatic sprinkler protection is considered the most effective form of fire protection for stored commodities.

Exact sprinkler specifications will be dictated by the type of product stored, storage rack arrangement and height, product density, and building height. Requirements for sprinkler capacity will vary from state to state. If adequate sprinkler protection is not available in areas where idle pallets or containers are staged or stored, FMRC recommends that they be stored outdoors. Idle pallets and containers also may be stored in an unattached building.

Fire protection requirements for polyethylene packaging may be reduced through the use of special fire-retardant additives. However, these additives may significantly alter the properties of the plastic. Extensive testing and evaluation will determine whether the fire hazard rating can be reduced.

TABLE 12-4
Fire Protection Commodity Classes

Class	Description	Examples
Class I	Essentially noncombustible, products may be in light cartons and on wood pallets.	Glass, mineral, metals, ceramics Unused wood or corrugated pallets
Class II	Class I products with more or heavier combustible wrapping or containers on wood pallets.	Class I products in multiwall corrugated cartons or boxes Unused plastic pallets
Class III	Combustible products in combustible wrapping or containers on wood pallets. May have a limited amount of plastic.	Wood, paper, leather, and some food products
Class IV	Class I, II, or III with considerable plastic content in product or packaging.	Typewriters and cameras with plastic parts
Beyond Class IV	Two factors can increase hazard beyond Class IV: 1. When the plastic content of the product or packaging exceeds 25% by volume. 2. When the storage arrangement is conducive to rapid fire spread.	Class III product on a plastic pallet Hanging garments Large rolls of paper stacked on end

Source: Factory Mutual Engineering and Research Loss Prevention Data Sheet

Finally, steps should be taken for fire prevention. The top sources of ignition (in order of frequency) are arson, cutting and welding, electricity, smoking, and hot surfaces.[18]

PRODUCT IDENTIFICATION

This section discusses shipping label identification requirements and the integration of bar-code printer technology and weighing systems on the packaging line.

For any manufacturing company not currently using bar codes, it is likely that its first application of automatic data collection technology will be on the packaging line. More and more firms are demanding that their suppliers put bar-coded labels on shipping cartons, a process known as *compliance labeling*. Fortunately, shipping labels represent a relatively simple, low-risk way to gain experience with a technology that has extremely wide-reaching benefits. With a proven track record, companies can extend the use of bar codes and automatic data collection technology to manage their production processes, control inventory levels, perform random audits, and support a host of other activities.

An additional benefit of bar code technology is that it operates concurrently with electronic data interchange (EDI). EDI is rapidly becoming a method for communicating the data gleaned from bar code labels in a standard format. Moreover, the Internet's growing impact will increase the number of EDI transactions significantly, as it alters the fundamental ways that trading partners communicate.

LABEL REQUIREMENTS

To a large extent, the information that appears on a bar-coded shipping label and the way that the information is formatted depend on the requirements of the trading partners involved. Figure 12-9 illustrates a typical shipping label for a parts distribution warehouse. Other good sources of information include the American National Standards Institute (ANSI) standard (see Bibliography), which describes the requirements for bar code symbols on unit loads and transport packages, and conveying data between trading partners.

Many industries have also adopted bar code label guidelines, which contain specifications for items such as:

- The data (and format) to be printed on the label.
- Acceptable bar-code symbologies.
- Arrangement of human-readable and bar-coded data.
- Acceptable label size.
- Placement of the label on the shipping container.

BAR CODE PRINTERS

Bar code printers can be grouped into two basic categories, nonimpact and impact. As the name implies, *nonimpact printers*, including thermal transfer, laser, and ink jet, do not physically contact the label. Thermal transfer printers, which transfer ink from a ribbon to the label, produce an extremely high-quality image at speeds of up to 50 in.^{2} (323 cm^2)/sec. These highly-flexible printers accept a wide variety of label and ribbon combinations and can be operated in an on-demand or batch mode. But these features come with a cost: the relative cost of operating a thermal transfer printer is high compared to that of alternative technologies, due in part to the ongoing need to replace the ribbon.

A laser printer operates on the same principle as a photo copier, which uses a laser beam to form a latent image. Toner is applied to this image, which is transferred to the paper via heat and sometimes pressure. While the print image is typically good, a downside of laser printers is that the images produced can fade over time. Although more expensive initially, laser printers cost less to operate than thermal transfer printers in the long run.

Ink jet printers work by spraying a drop of ink onto a label and, in some cases, directly onto a carton. Because the bar code that is produced is a low-density image, it is five to ten times larger than a bar code produced by a dot matrix printer. Because the bar codes are so large, they typically have poor resolution. As a result, scanning equipment can require modifications.[19]

As the name implies, *impact printers* physically contact the label material. Dot matrix printers work by firing tiny pins against a ribbon that impacts the label, leaving a small ink dot on the surface. Because a single dot ranging from only 0.008-0.020 in. (0.20-0.51 mm) in width represents the narrowest possible column width, print

CHAPTER 12   TRANSPORT PACKAGING

Fig. 12-9 Sample bar-coded shipping label.

density is limited. Although print quality is moderate as compared to other printing technologies, dot matrix printers offer the lowest cost of ownership.

Another type of contact printing is *flexographic* or *offset printing*. Requiring a large label printing press and costly printing plates or film masters, this printing technology is most appropriate for long, generic label runs.

Developments in printer technology continue. Although introduced more than a decade ago, in-line printer/applicator systems are becoming a popular fixture on the manufacturing floor, thanks in part to the trend toward smaller lot sizes and JIT operations. Integrated directly into the manufacturing process, these flexible systems print and apply labels in a single step, adjusting to different carton sizes and label requirements as they are needed. Custom applicators that can wrap labels around two sides of a carton, follow the contours of an irregularly-shaped item, or deal with irregular surfaces are also available.

Until in-line printer/applicators grow more in use, some companies may have difficulty finding a software package that is capable of interfacing with their existing manufacturing control system. More software development will take place as firms take the lead in their industries in adopting this technology.

The type of printing method that is appropriate for a particular application depends on a variety of factors, including the required data density, speed, flexibility (are custom labels required?), volume of labels to be printed, and turnaround time. Similarly, the decision of whether or not to produce labels in-house will depend on the diversity of the product line, changes in label information, and type of manufacturing process (batch mode versus made-to-order).

Care should be taken to ensure that the bar codes produced comply with the specifications. Some retailers are levied expensive penalties if bar codes are not readable upon receipt. In addition to specifying the appropriate printing technology and label stock, the majority of companies utilize some kind of verification system to ensure that labels are within specifications.

WEIGHING SYSTEMS

Integrated with automatic identification systems, advanced weighing systems play an important role on the packaging line in providing a final check of products before shipping, and automatically checking and reporting the weight, size, and contents of an order. Linked to a small computer with software and printer for producing bar code labels, a scale can become part of an entire inventory management system. The four major types of weighing systems are: weigh-in-motion, cubing system, inventory management system (not discussed in this chapter), and parcel manifest system.

Integrated directly onto the packaging line, a *weigh-in-motion system* records the weight of a carton traveling along the conveyor and confirms that it is within expected tolerances. To maintain throughput levels, top systems operate at 55 cartons per minute with weighing accuracy to within 0.02 lb (9.07 g). Weigh-in-motion systems also can be programmed to automatically reject a predetermined number of in-tolerance cartons to perform a random audit. Every carton is weighed for accuracy against tolerances, with an additional random audit to catch any other errors and ensure that tolerances stay in tune.

In addition to recording weight, a *cubing system* also measures the height, length, and width of a carton to accuracies within 0.2 in. (5 mm). *Parcel manifest systems* use the information provided by carton scales to manage sender, recipient, and carrier data, and produce shipping-related documents.

Chapter 3 contains information on product identification and tracking technologies as they relate to the manufacturing process.

UNIT LOAD FORMING

This section examines methods of forming unit loads, including ergonomic devices for manual palletizing applications and automated palletizing equipment. Selection guidelines are also described.

From palletizing equipment to load protection devices, new technologies are playing an important role in delivering the right product to the right customer, on time. When deciding what type of equipment and level of automation is appropriate, the unit load requirements of the application should be defined. Some of the information that will assist in the decision-making process includes:

- Size, weight, and quantities of the items being handled.
- Throughput requirements (cartons per minute or hour).
- Actual number of inventory turns per year and number expected.
- Type of pallet.
- Pallet stacking pattern.
- Handling methods (lift truck, conveyor, etc.).
- Any special handling requirements.

PALLETIZING METHODS

To ensure that no efficiency is lost in unit load handling, the methods for forming the load should be selected to meet the exact requirements of the application.

A major question for load forming or palletizing is whether or not to automate. When throughput is low (less than 10 cases per minute) or when building mixed loads, the operation is typically performed manually. However, manual palletizing has come under particular scrutiny from the perspective of ergonomics, because workers are often forced to handle heavy cartons and perform reaching and bending motions as they build the load. The following lists some of the warning signs of a potential ergonomics problem.

- Worker absenteeism is high.
- Workers' compensation claims or other records show a high incidence of injuries.
- Productivity is low or has fallen.
- Workers complain about lifting too much weight.
- Workers cannot keep up with the pace.
- Workers have an awkward posture.
- Workers are doing a lot of bending, reaching, or twisting.
- Jobs involve repetitive lifting from the floor or long reaches.

Table 12-5 compares typical palletizing methods in terms of speed and capacity.

Ergonomic aids, however, are helping to ease the strain and new equipment developments are helping companies automatically palletize hard-to-manage objects.

Ergonomic Aids

Several ergonomic aids have been designed to relieve the stress on workers who build loads manually, by eliminating bending and reaching motions. The popular scissors-lift, for example, can be used to position the load at a comfortable working height and distance from the worker. This extremely versatile device also supports loading and unloading operations on the assembly line. The operator simply selects the height, making manual adjustments as necessary.

Lift tables are ideal for handling products that do not require near side loading, such as sheet or board materials that can simply be slid from one surface to another. If near side loading is required, a turntable top can be added. Load capacities for lift tables can range from a few hundred pounds to many tons. Manufacturers should be contacted to determine the exact capacity required.

CHAPTER 12   TRANSPORT PACKAGING

A variation of the scissors-lift, the automatic pallet positioner is designed specifically for manual palletizing and depalletizing operations. Essentially a lift table with a turntable or rotating ring top, the device has the added capability of maintaining the top level of the load at a comfortable working height. This leveling action is performed through mechanical (spring) or pneumatic pressure. Most pallet positioners are designed to handle load capacities up to 4,500 lb (2,041 kg). Lending itself to a wide variety of palletizing applications, a limitation of the pallet positioner is that it is weight-sensitive. Constant, uniform loads of a single product or products of uniform weight are required. If the application calls for handling mixed pallet loads, a standard lift table is recommended.

Balancers and vacuum manipulators provide a simple, cost-effective means of supporting the weight of the object being palletized. These devices are also useful for handling objects that are lightweight but difficult to grasp, such as bags or bundles. They help to eliminate unsafe lifting motions by supporting and controlling loads. With these devices, a worker supports only a fraction of the load as he or she guides it into place.

Researchers have developed a class of robotic manipulators called *human extenders*, which may someday be used to assist with all types of onerous manual handling tasks. Designed to be worn by the operator, the primary purpose of these extenders is to achieve a scaling down of the load force. A hand linkage performs the grasping function, while the arm mechanisms execute the load manipulations. For every 100 lb (45 kg) of load, for example, a typical extender supports 95 lb (43 kg). For safe manual handling, 50 lb (23 kg) is generally considered the upper limit.

Back belts are used as a simple, ergonomic aid for manual palletizing applications. However, there are conflicting opinions on their effectiveness. Many experts caution that a back belt should not be considered a substitute for proper job design, nor should anyone believe that wearing a back belt will allow them to lift heavier weights. Chapter 7 contains more information on ergonomic principles and Chapter 14 contains data on ergonomic equipment.

Automated Palletizers

There are three basic automated palletizer designs: vacuum head, row-stripping, and robotic. Typically, these units include row and layer makeup areas, as well as infeed conveyors. The major difference is in how they stack a load.

Ideal for applications with 10 to 25 cartons per minute, a *vacuum-head palletizer* forms a complete layer of cartons in a makeup area and uses pneumatically-powered suction cups to lift the layer onto the load. Because products are lifted from the top, they must have a flat, sturdy top surface. Weight capacity is lower than that of the row-stripping palletizer, although some vacuum-head units can handle cartons weighing up to 100 lb (45 kg).

The *row-stripping palletizer* can palletize cartons of different shapes and sizes (although not intermixed) at speeds of up to 120 cartons per minute. These machines work by forming one row of products at a time until a layer is complete. The layer is then deposited as a single unit onto the pallet through the use of an electromechanical or hydraulic lift inside the palletizer. Products can be fed into a row-stripping palletizer either at floor level or at a level above the floor. Commonly used in high-volume operations, the row-stripping palletizer can handle cartons weighing up to 250 lb (113 kg) each.

Robotic palletizers use three designs: Cartesian, articulating arm, and gantry. Cartesian palletizers feature a mast and a cross arm, and maneuver products through four-axis movement. Articulated-arm models also offer four-axis movement, but use a jointed arm. A gantry palletizer provides the robot with mobility by placing it on a gantry or track, allowing access to multiple palletizing stations. Pneumatic cups or mechanical grabs are used to grip the products. Suited for low- to medium-throughput applications, a robotic palletizer is most ideal for applications where carton sizes vary or there are multiple palletizing stations. This capability is key today because of concepts like JIT manufacturing. Orders are smaller, meaning that many more pallets of mixed carton sizes are being assembled.

One type of robotic palletizer can build unit loads from a random assortment of cartons of varying sizes and weights. The most efficient stacking pattern is achieved by presenting the robot with six cartons at a time. The robot then selects cartons from this group, much like fitting together the pieces of a jigsaw puzzle, as it builds the load. One drawback of this palletizer is that it moves at a relatively slow speed compared to other automated systems.

Automated palletizers typically have high-duty cycles. As a result, machines are currently being designed with low maintenance and reliability in mind. New models have fewer moving parts and now feature electronic controls, avoiding the leakage problem associated with hydraulic systems. To ensure high reliability, many of these control systems are based on simple logic, feature built-in diagnostics, and a user-friendly operator interface.

LOAD PROTECTING AND SECURING

This section discusses the major approaches for securing and containing unit loads, including stretch wrap, strapping, and shrink-wrap. Selection guidelines are also discussed.

After palletizing, nearly every unit load is protected and secured in some way. Since its introduction in the 1960s, the consistent growth

TABLE 12-5
Palletizing Methods Comparison

Method	Speed (cartons/min)	Capacity lb (kg)	Notes
Manual	<10	40 (18) per carton	Requires attention to safety and ergonomics
Manual with manipulator assistance	<10	400 (181) per carton	Can handle greater weights, but not necessarily faster
Automated–vacuum head	10-25	100 (45) per carton	Limited to loads with flat surfaces
Automated–row stripper	20-120	250 (113) per carton 800 (363) per layer 6,000 (2,722) per load	Fastest palletizing speeds Best for few stock-keeping units (SKUs) with large volume throughput
Automated–robotic	10-30	50-200 (23-91) per carton 400 (181) per layer	Most flexible, but speed penalty Best for many SKUs with lower throughput per SKU

of stretch wrap is testimony to its great versatility in protecting and securing a wide range of load types. Improvements in both films and wrapping equipment have extended the range of potential applications. Today's films can be stretched further, provide better cling, and have improved clarity.

Tough and durable, shrink-wrap resists punctures and provides five-sided load protection. Unlike stretch, however, shrink-wrap requires heat to form the film tightly around the load. Strapping is another alternative that is ideal for securing heavy loads or loads that have a tendency to shift. Table 12-6 highlights the ideal applications for each unitizing method.

One approach for stabilizing loads involves spraying an adhesive onto the top surface of each layer of cartons. New adhesive formulations cause the cartons to interlock tightly for transit, yet pull apart easily when depalletizing. Another approach in securing loads is a type of pallet with an integrated strapping system. Resembling the seat belts in an automobile, the straps simply retract when they are not being used to hold the load in place.

Stretch Wrapping

It is estimated that U.S. industry consumes 600 million lb (272 million kg) of stretch film each year.[20] Much of this material, which is a thin, plastic film made from a linear low-density polyethylene resin that is engineered for high stretch and toughness, is used to wrap and secure pallet loads. Typical film gages are between 70 and 120 mils (0.07 and 0.12 in. [1.8 and 3 mm]).

The rotary turntable and overhead spiral machine are the two main types of machines for applying stretch film. Both come in a wide assortment of models and prices, from basic, semi-automatic machines to computer-controlled, fully automatic models that are able to wrap 40-120 loads per hour. Throughput, however, depends not only on how fast the equipment operates, but on the number of wraps applied per load, the load height, and the cycle time for load pickup and delivery. Table 12-7 highlights some of the key characteristics of each type of technology.

In the rotary turntable design, ideal for wrapping stable loads at low- to moderate-throughputs, the film dispensing mechanism remains stationary while the load rotates on a mechanically-driven platform. The film can be applied either as a full-web or in a spiral fashion, in which case a powered carriage travels up and down a vertical mast as the load rotates. To keep this type of machine in good working condition, the floor space under the unit must be kept clear and the turntable well-maintained.

Low profile turntables are a popular option on these machines. Standing just 2-3 in. (5-8 cm) off the floor, these devices feature a ramp that allows hand jacks, pallet jacks, or lift trucks to easily pick up and deliver loads.

With an overhead spiral machine, the load remains stationary while the film dispensing mechanism travels around it. This mechanism can either move up and down on a rotating mast or around a rotating ring, applying the film to the load while it moves. Ideal applications include wrapping tall, unstable, or heavy loads (greater than 6,000 lb [2,722 kg]) at medium- to high-volumes.

While the majority of unit loads are wrapped as a single unit, stretch film can be used to wrap the individual layers for greater stabilization. This can be accomplished with a special, horizontal layer-wrapper device incorporated directly into the layer makeup area of a palletizer.

One major development in stretch-wrapping equipment technology is the powered prestretch mechanism. All stretch films have properties that permit them to be stretched while retaining their strength characteristics. This elongation property is important in

TABLE 12-6
Stretch Film, Shrink-wrap, and Strapping

Unitizing Method	Typical Application
Stretch film	Heat-sensitive loads
Stretch film or shrink-wrap	Loads that need to be protected and secured
	Loads that require four- or five-sided protection
	Light, crushable loads
	Loads that are stored outdoors
Shrink-wrap	Loads with sharp or protruding edges
Strapping	Loads that require high compression
	Heavy, bulky, or shifting loads
	Loads that need to be held to the pallet

TABLE 12-7
Wrapping Technology Comparison

	Rotary Turntable	Overhead Spiral
Cost	$4,250-75,000+	$8,000-80,000+
Speed (rpm)*	6-12	12-20
Load stability	Low-medium	High
Weight capacity	6,000 lb (2,722 kg)	Unlimited— capacity of conveyor becomes limiting factor
Ideal applications	Low-medium volumes Stable loads	High volumes Tall, unstable, or heavy loads

* Throughput depends on how fast the turntable or rotating arm spins, as well as the load height and number of wraps. For a 60-in. (152-cm) tall load, assume 60 loads/h at 10 rpm.

pallet wrapping applications, because the further a film is stretched, the less tendency it will have to loosen up on the load.

The goal is to stretch the film well above its yield point until it is close to its maximum holding point. The powered prestretch mechanism available on new stretch wrappers can be retrofit to most installed units and uses two geared rollers to stretch the film. A major advantage is that film tension is kept to a minimum, while allowing film to be stretched to levels of 300% or more. About 20% elongation can be achieved when manually applying stretch film. Another version of the powered prestretch system stretches the film both lengthwise and transversely across the width, requiring even less film to wrap a load. For even higher levels of stretch, one manufacturer offers a device that uses a heated roller to soften the film before it is applied.

For five-sided protection, both the turntable-style and overhead spiral machines can be equipped with a top sheet dispenser. A more elaborate alternative is the stretch hood, a machine designed to pro-

CHAPTER 12   TRANSPORT PACKAGING

vide five-sided protection for uniform loads. Using a gusseted, tubular film combined with a crimping and stretching unit, the machine draws the film around and under the load.

Success with stretch wrapping starts with a good pallet load. Whatever the wrapping technology and film type selected, the best results are obtained with well-aligned loads that are accurately positioned on a correctly-sized pallet.

Strapping

Another method for securing unit loads, as well as closing individual cartons, is strapping. Applied under tension, strapping uses compressive force to secure the load, which makes it suitable for applications involving heavy, bulky, or shifting loads, or when holding loads to a pallet. Strapping is typically made of steel or a variety of plastic resins.

Steel strapping has the greatest tensile strength and is ideal for heavy-duty applications requiring high strength to secure load weights exceeding 4,000 lb (1,814 kg). A major advantage of steel strapping is its dimensional stability. Because it does not creep or stretch after being applied, steel strapping keeps a firm hold on a load. However, this can be a disadvantage with loads that tend to settle or shrink.

Various types of plastic strapping have greater elasticity and are more accommodating to changes in load size. Because of its low cost and flexibility, polypropylene is the most popular type of plastic strapping and is suitable for light- to medium-duty applications. A more durable material, polyester strapping exhibits good resistance to heat and moisture, and retains its tension fairly well.

Strapping can be applied either by hand or automatically with a machine. A simple, manual system consists of portable tools for dispensing, tensioning, and sealing the strap. Semi-automated, powered strapping machines automate some of these steps, but an operator must position the load and place the strapping around it. Fully automated machines, which may be linked by conveyor to upstream and downstream operations, can strap 60 pallets or more an hour.

Because strapping is applied under tension, extreme caution should be exercised when working with it. Operators should not stand over or in front of a strap being tensioned, as a sudden, unintended release of the strap may cause it to snap free. Similarly, when removing a tensioned strap, operators should stand to the side, pressing the strap against the load above the cutting device. Manufacturers discourage the reuse of strapping, because its mechanical properties may have been altered through use.

INTEGRATING THE PACKAGING FUNCTION

As stated previously, packaging is an integral part of the overall manufacturing system. That system may be as simple as a single, nonpowered conveyor feeding a manual palletizing operation, or it may be a fully-integrated system with multiple manufacturing lines feeding a bank of automated palletizers and stretch-wrapping equipment, as shown in Fig. 12-10.

Taking a systems approach in designing transport packaging functions will help to streamline the flow of products through the manufacturing facility, from receiving to shipping. In the end, it is important to remember that the purpose of packaging is to increase handling efficiency. With the right unit load base design, returnable container, and palletizing and securing methods, efficiency and productivity is maximized throughout the supply chain.

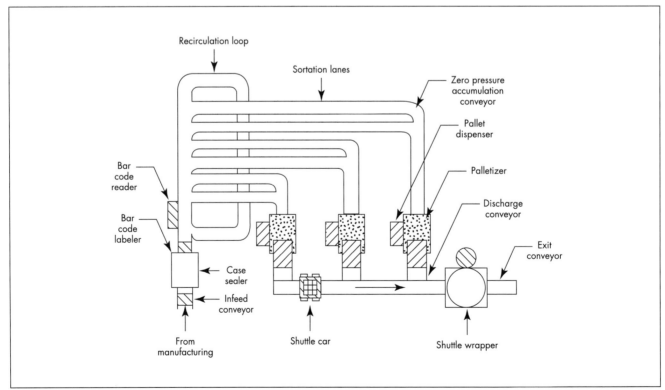

Fig. 12-10 Integrated packaging line. *(Courtesy "Modern Materials Handling" Magazine)*

References

1. Singh, S. Paul, Ph.D., Chonhenchob, Vanee, and Burgess, Gary, Ph.D. "Comparison of Various Loose-fill Cushioning Materials Based on Protective and Environmental Performance." *Packaging Technology and Science*, 7: 229-241. New York: John Wiley and Sons, 1994.
2. Singh, S. Paul, Ph.D., Charnnarong, Nopporn, and Burgess, Gary, Ph.D. "A Comparison Between Various Packaging Cushioning Materials." *Institute of Packaging Professionals (IoPP) Technical Journal*, Winter 1991.
3. Ibid.
4. Singh, S. Paul, Ph.D., Chonhenchob, Vanee, and Burgess, Gary, Ph.D. "Comparison of Various Loose Fill Cushioning Materials Based on Protective and Environmental Performance." *Packaging Technology and Science*, 7: 229-241. New York: John Wiley and Sons, 1994.
5. Singh, S. Paul, Ph.D., Charnnarong, Nopporn, and Burgess, Gary, Ph.D. "A Comparison Between Various Packaging Cushioning Materials." *IoPP Technical Journal*, Winter 1991: 28-35.
6. Singh, S. Paul, Ph.D., Burgess, Gary, Ph.D., and Lee, Julian, Ph.D. "Study Details Performance of Corrugated with Recycled Fiber." *Packaging Technology and Engineering*, November 1996.
7. Item 22 of the National Motor Freight Classification Tariff. Rule 41 of the Railroad's Uniform Freight Classification.
8. Singh, S. Paul, Ph.D., Burgess, Gary, Ph.D., and Lee, Julian, Ph.D. "Study Details Performance of Corrugated with Recycled Fiber." *Packaging Technology and Engineering*, November 1996.
9. Ievans, Uldis I. "The Effect of Warehouse Mishandling and Stacking Patterns on the Compression Strength of Corrugated Boxes." *Tappi Journal* 58(8), 1975.
10. McKinlay, Alfred H., PE. "The Design and Performance of Corrugated and Honeycomb Fiberboard Pallets." National Wooden Pallet and Container Association (NWPCA) Special Value Seminar. Chicago, IL: NWPCA, October 1996.
11. Ibid.
12. Singh, S. Paul, Ph.D., Burgess, Gary, Ph.D., and Lee, Julian, Ph.D. "Study Details Performance of Corrugated with Recycled Fiber." *Packaging Technology and Engineering*, November 1996.
13. Virginia Tech (Virginia Polytechnic Institute and State University). William H. Sardo Pallet and Container Research Laboratory. Blacksburg, VA.
14. White, Marshall S. "The Impact of Pallet Design on the Performance of Unit Loads." *IoPP Technical Journal* 1992, 10(2): 44-50.
15. *Uniform Standard for Wooden Pallets*. Arlington, VA: National Wooden Pallet and Container Association (NWPCA). American Society of Mechanical Engineers (ASME), USA National Standard MH1.8.1. Fairfield, NJ: ASME.
   Other ASME MHI national pallet standards include:
   • MH1.1.2 Definitions & Terminology.
   • MH1.2.2 Pallet Sizes.
   • MH1.4.1 Pallet Test Procedures.
   • MH1.5 Slip-sheets.
   • MH1.6 Pallet Durability.
   • MH1.9.1 Export Pallets.
16. International Organization for Standardization (ISO) 6780. "General-purpose Flat Pallets—Principal Dimensional Tolerances and ISO 8611 Test Methods."
17. Singh, S. Paul, Ph.D., Burgess, Gary, Ph.D., Lee, Julian, Ph.D. "Study Details Performance of Corrugated with Recycled Fiber." *Packaging Technology and Engineering*, November 1996.
18. Schofield, Mark. "Warehouse Fire Protection." North American Material Handling Show and Forum. Charlotte, NC: The Material Handling Institute, 1996.
19. Weber Marking Systems. "How to Stay on Top of Bar Codes." Brochure. Arlington Heights, IL: Weber Marketing Systems, November 1996.
20. Schultz, Whitten, and Reiter, William F. "Stretch Wrap—Should You be Recycling?" Oregon State University, 1997.

Bibliography

"A Report on Pallet Use and Applications Among Buyers of Materials Handling Systems." *Modern Materials Handling*, 1995.
American Paper Institute. *Fiberboard Slip-sheet Manual*. NY: American Paper Institute.
ANSI MH10.8M-1993. "Unit Loads and Transport Packages—Bar Code Symbols." NY: American National Standards Institute, December 16, 1993.
ANSI/UCC6-1996. *Application Standard for Shipping Container Codes*. Dayton, OH: Uniform Code Council, Inc., 1996.
Fibre Box Association. *Fibre Box Association Handbook*. Rolling Meadows, IL: Fibre Box Association, 1992.
Uniform Standard for Wood Pallets. Arlington, VA: National Wooden Pallet and Container Association, 1996.

CHAPTER 13

AUTOMATED MATERIAL HANDLING EQUIPMENT

CHAPTER CONTENTS

This chapter provides a general description of selected automated material handling equipment. Although many systems are included, the presentation is not exhaustive and the depth of information is intended to acquaint readers with these systems and their benefits. Analysis methods and equations presented provide rough estimates and should be used only for preliminary planning. More accurate methods are available for detailed analysis and should be used, along with vendor consultations, before final system selection.

AUTOMATED GUIDED VEHICLE SYSTEMS

Automated guided vehicle (AGV) systems are automated, floor-traveling material handling systems used to move materials throughout facilities. An AGV system is composed of one or more automated guided vehicles, which are battery-operated, driverless vehicles that operate automatically. AGVs follow external dispatching signals and a defined travel path, such as a guide path on the floor, a guide path programmed into a central controller, or a path resident in the vehicle's on-board controller. AGVs can carry loads ranging from less than 100 lb (45 kg) to more than 20,000 lb (9,072 kg) and size can vary markedly in each direction.

First introduced in 1953, AGV systems have gained wide industry acceptance. They have evolved from very simple one- and two-vehicle systems to complex systems with hundreds of vehicles. Most installations today are of moderate size and complexity.[1]

TYPES OF AGV SYSTEMS

A wide variety of AGV systems are available, with an equal variety of capabilities, for solving nearly every type of horizontal transportation problem. Discussed in this section are systems that include one or more of the following types of vehicles: unit-load vehicles, driverless trains, fork lift vehicles, wire-guided pallet trucks, light-load vehicles, module transport vehicles, and specialized vehicles.

Unit-load Vehicles

Unit-load vehicles are one of the most commonly used in industry, and they have been adapted for a wide variety of applications. They are used in applications where loads are picked up and delivered at a fixed station, either a static stand or conveyor interface. Load-bed configurations vary widely, the most common being powered and nonpowered conveyors, lift-lower decks, and shuttle mechanisms. A typical unit-load vehicle, with a lift-lower deck, is illustrated by Fig. 13-1. Generally designed to hold one pallet or two to four totes, it is the most common AGV used to interface with an automated storage and retrieval system (AS/RS). Unit-load vehicles operate in a small floor space, making them suitable for cramped manufacturing facilities. They can be fully automated or designed to require user intervention for vehicle routing.

Typical applications of unit-load vehicles in manufacturing include delivering material to production lines and assembly stations, interfacing with an AS/RS, and providing material to flexible manufacturing and assembly cells. Unit-load vehicles are also used to move loads between manufacturing facilities and warehouses, and within warehouses to move material between storage locations and stage material for shipment.

Driverless Trains

Driverless trains, or tugger vehicles, are composed of a tractor pulling one or more carriers. Compared to other AGVs, trains can generally deliver larger volumes of material over longer distances. The vehicle's versatile design and its ability to pull a varying number of carriers allow it to pick up and drop off loads at several points

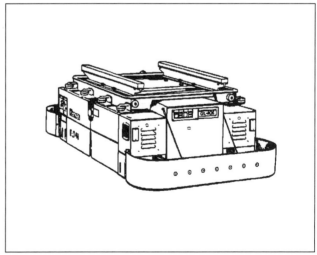

Fig. 13-1 Unit-load AGV. *(Courtesy HK Systems)*

The Contributor of this chapter is: Ann Dunkin, Materials Engineering Manager, Hewlett-Packard.
The Reviewers of this chapter are: John W. Collins, Plant Manager, Burlington Industries; **Rod Farver,** Director, Project Quality Assurance, HK Systems, Inc.

CHAPTER 13 AUTOMATED MATERIAL HANDLING EQUIPMENT

throughout a manufacturing facility in one trip around the guide path. This can be accomplished by loading and unloading from carriers, or picking up and dropping off the carriers themselves, generally at spurs off the main path. The major disadvantage of tugger vehicles is the amount of space required; the trains have a wide turning radius and require a significant amount of space for spurs.

Driverless trains are most efficient for moving moderate volumes of material between two points or in situations where several loads are dropped off or picked up at intermediate points along a route at least 500 ft (152 m) long. They also can operate manually to move loads to areas where a guide path is not available. The long history of driverless train applications in many industries includes moving incoming materials to production operations, moving work-in-process (WIP) from one manufacturing location to another, and transporting finished goods to storage. Specific examples include moving automotive parts, such as green and finished tires, rolls of paper or fabric, and large spools of yarn.

Fork Lift Vehicles

The fork lift vehicle has seen only limited application to date. These vehicles are designed to function similarly to conventional fork lifts and are capable of lifting loads up to 20 ft (6.1 m) high. There are nearly as many types of fork lift AGVs as there are types of fork lifts, including single- and double-load vehicles, side loaders, counterbalanced fork lift AGVs, and straddle AGVs. Their primary purpose is to pick up palletized loads from the floor and deliver them to other floor locations, storage racks, or elevated stations. Fork lift vehicles also retrieve loads from racks or elevated locations and deliver them to floor locations. Moreover, they can be outfitted with many standard fork lift attachments to handle other loads, such as cartons and rolls of paper. Complexities in the application of these vehicles include the tight tolerances required to store material in pallet racks and the guidance challenges of moving inside trailers. These challenges require complex controls, which have proven difficult to perfect and ultimately, have increased vehicle cost. Besides being expensive, these vehicles require a lot of floor space to move through the factory and need more time to pick up and deliver material than other types of vehicles. They are economical for appropriate applications, but extremely expensive if misapplied.

Fork lift vehicles are used in applications where it is desirable to use vertical storage space. Applications include transporting and staging WIP, loading products into trailers for shipment, and moving finished goods into storage. Fork lift AGVs are also used to move and stack assembly fixtures and tools between uses.

Wire-guided Pallet Trucks

Wire-guided pallet trucks are automated versions of walkie pallet jacks. They are manually loaded and then dispatched to delivery locations where they automatically drop their loads at spurs off the main path. For point-to-point deliveries, the vehicles return to their origination point to pick up a new load. For this reason, they are best applied for point-to-point deliveries rather than for making intermediate stops.

Wire-guided pallet trucks are generally used where delivery volumes and travel distances are moderate or long—at least 200 ft (61 m). Although they move independently, wire-guided pallet trucks usually need human intervention to pick up loads and often require assistance during the delivery process and to designate the next destination. Loads generally consist of one or two pallets with a total weight of 4,000-6,000 lb (1,814-2,722 kg). In addition to automated operation, wire-guided pallet trucks can be manually operated in areas that do not have guide paths.

Wire-guided pallet trucks move material from one manufacturing process to the next. For example, to and from assembly and packaging workstations. They are most successful in these applications because an individual is readily available to help load, unload, and dispatch vehicles, minimizing vehicle wait time.

Light-load Vehicles

Light-load vehicles are designed for flexibility. They can move small, lightweight loads—less than 500 lb (227 kg)—at low cost. While some light-load vehicles are manually loaded and unloaded, others deliver loads in a manner similar to unit-load vehicles. Light-load vehicles are used primarily to transport production material between workstations in light manufacturing/assembly applications and to move small parts, baskets, and trays of mail, packages, and other supplies over short and long distances in offices and hospitals.

Module Transport Vehicles

Module transport vehicles are similar to light-load vehicles in size, carrying capacity, and application. Their major difference is that they are low-profile vehicles that pick up loads (called *carriers*), deliver them to their destinations, and automatically drop them off. Module transporters are used in a variety of unique applications: in assembly operations to move WIP from one assembly station to the next; in hospitals and prisons to move linens, supplies, and meals; and in offices to transport mail and office supplies.

Specialized Vehicles

Two general types of AGVs that are categorized as specialized vehicles are assembly vehicles and mobile robots. *Assembly vehicles* are designed to carry specific products during assembly operations and are most often used to move large, heavy products such as cars (Fig. 13-2), construction equipment, and steel coils weighing up to 100,000 lb (45,360 kg). While similar to smaller and standard vehicles because of their tight turning radius and speeds of up to 250 fpm (76 mpm), specialized vehicles have the disadvantage of being custom-designed and therefore expensive and unproven prior to installation. Although suitable for almost any assembly application, they are most frequently used as assembly platforms for large or heavy products such as automobiles.

Mobile robots are actually fixed robots mounted to a vehicle platform. These robots travel to various assembly stations to load and unload materials or perform assembly tasks. Mobile robots are used where robot mobility adds value to an assembly operation, such as

Fig. 13-2 Specialized AGV.

CHAPTER 13   AUTOMATED MATERIAL HANDLING EQUIPMENT

where it is easier to move the robot than to move the item that the robot is working on.

GUIDANCE SYSTEMS

Guidance systems are critical components of AGV systems. Inductive guidance was the first guidance system developed, and for many years, it was the only guidance technology available. During the last 20 years, however, several other types have been developed, providing additional flexibility in application-specific systems. The other types include several kinds of passive guidance as well as laser guidance and inertial navigation systems.

Inductive Guidance Systems

While it was the only type of AGV guidance system for many years, inductive guidance remains the most common type. Inductive guidance systems consist of many wires (generally three or more) embedded in the floor throughout the vehicle's travel area. The guide wire carries a signal with low AC voltage and frequency. The current produces a magnetic field above the guide wire that is detected by the vehicle's antennas. If the vehicle starts to move away from the magnetic field, its controller makes the appropriate steering adjustments to bring it back into position over the wire. Each wire operates at a different frequency, and the vehicle's on-board controller selects the correct frequency at decision points such as junctions and spurs. The guide path also includes reference points that allow the vehicle to update its absolute position.

Inductive guidance is a reliable technology and long lasting with minimal maintenance required. But it is also the most difficult type of guide path to install. Installation cost is high, but is usually offset by reductions in the cost of the vehicle control system. A major disadvantage of inductive guidance systems is that they require cutting the floor where the guide path is located. Any path changes require the floor to be recut. Both installation and changes can take several days or weeks, depending on system complexity.

Passive Guidance Systems

Unlike inductive guidance systems, the guide paths of passive guidance systems cannot communicate with the vehicle or its control system. In some cases, no path exists. For multiple-vehicle systems, traffic control is managed by direct communication with the vehicles, with instructions such as start and stop communicated by markers located next to the guide path. These guide paths are generally used in applications where the guide path is less likely to be damaged, such as in offices and light manufacturing facilities. In these environments, guide paths generally last from six months to one year before requiring replacement. Passive guide paths are very flexible and in most applications, can be installed or modified in a few hours or days. The four types include: optical, chemical, metal tape, and grid systems.

Optical. This the most common form of passive guide path, using fluorescent tape applied to the floor. Vehicles illuminate the path with ultraviolet light and then scan it with a photocell to determine whether the vehicle is centered. If it is not, the vehicle makes the appropriate steering corrections. This type of guidance can be unreliable under some conditions, because it is sensitive to other sources of light as well as dirt and changes in guide path background color.

Chemical. Chemical guide paths are a different form of the optical guide path. This technology, which uses fluorescent particles mixed in a liquid and painted on the floor, was developed in the 1970s. As the vehicle passes over the path, its scanning head stimulates the particles with ultraviolet light. Simultaneously, the vehicle scans the guide path to collect light-energy emissions resulting from the action of the scanning head. The vehicle analyzes the informa-

tion collected and makes the steering corrections necessary to stay centered on the path. This technology tends to be more reliable than the use of fluorescent tape because it is insensitive to other light sources, floor conditions, and short sections of path damage.

Metal tape. These guide paths are used in conjunction with metal sensors located on the vehicle. The metal tape guide path is mounted on the floor surface or under carpet or tile and is not affected by floor conditions such as dirt or heavy traffic that might damage surface-mounted optical guide paths.

Grid systems. Grid systems are a variation of optical guidance. They differ from the other passive systems described in that rather than following a guide path on the floor, the vehicle operates in a predefined work area. The area within which the vehicle travels is covered by a grid of contrasting colors, most commonly floor tiles of alternating colors. A map of the entire area to be traversed is in the vehicle's memory. This map includes all pickup and delivery points, obstacles, and paths to be traveled. The vehicle travels through the area using dead reckoning, occasionally verifying its locations from the grid. The vehicle determines its location by measuring the distance it has traveled and checking against the actual location of an edge—the boundary between two different colors of floor tile—and whenever it reaches one and adjusts its location as necessary.

Although passive guidance systems have the advantage of allowing vehicle paths to be rapidly reconfigured, some can be easily damaged and must be repaired occasionally and replaced about every six months. The exceptions to this rule are the metal tape type, which is often placed under carpet or tile, and grid systems, which often use floor tile for their paths. These systems are less susceptible to damage, but still require periodic maintenance and repair.

Laser Guidance Systems

Laser guidance systems use a laser to emit a beam that hits strategically-located reflective targets. The on-board controller then analyzes the angles of the reflections and uses triangulation to determine the vehicle's location. The vehicle must locate three markers to determine its exact position. When it is unable to locate these markers, the vehicle operates using dead reckoning. Laser guidance systems do not require a guide path on the floor, so they can be used in environments where a floor path would not be practical or where frequent changes are made. Markers must be set every 30-50 ft (9-15 m) and they should not be blocked. Vehicles must be able to see multiple markers at once to determine their exact location.

Inertial Navigation

Inertial navigation uses gyroscopic technology to navigate the vehicle over short distances. Magnetic markers are placed in the floor, and the vehicle updates its exact location whenever it passes over one. Inertial systems follow a guide path stored on the vehicle or in the central controller, comparing it with benchmark locations and adjusting the vehicle location on the guide path, or "map," accordingly. These systems allow rapid map changes, although guide path modifications and placement of additional magnet update markers may be required, depending on the magnitude of the change.

AGV CONTROLS

AGV control systems range from extremely simple to highly complex, depending on how the vehicles are used. This section describes both a simple and a moderately complex control system. These should not be considered an exhaustive description of available AGV control systems, but rather an indication of the available range of controls.

The simplest type of control system operates a stand-alone AGV system. These controls operate with a small number of vehicles, generally less than five, routing them directly from one destination

CHAPTER 13   AUTOMATED MATERIAL HANDLING EQUIPMENT

to the next, usually in a loop. Throughput is generally low and collision avoidance is performed by simple forward sensing; the vehicle senses the area ahead and stops if it determines that an object is in its path.

These systems do not use a central controller—all routing is performed on-board the vehicle. As a result, the vehicles cannot be monitored in real time. These systems require that vehicles be manually dispatched, requiring some level of human intervention for every load moved. The vehicles are generally dispatched by an operator on-board using the vehicle's control panel or by a call system where operators request vehicles from a terminal at their workstation.

A moderately complex AGV control system is the *remote dispatch system*. These mid-range systems generally operate as standalones, but have significantly more capability than most basic ones. They generally include at least three, but not more than 20 vehicles, and are not confined to operating over a closed-loop guide path. Instead, they can manage vehicles operating on a complex guide path with multiple loops, spurs, and intersections that require traffic control and complex vehicle routing to the various pickup and delivery (P/D) stations.

These control systems are fully automated and route vehicles throughout the system for automatic load pickup and delivery. All instructions are communicated to the vehicle by the controller, eliminating the need for an operator to use the vehicle-mounted controller to dispatch each vehicle. However, an operator must direct system operation, monitor performance, and correct failures. This operator must be able to see all the vehicles in the system from the dispatching station. Moderately complex control systems also utilize more sophisticated guide path blocking and routing techniques to avoid collisions and limit vehicle waiting time. Because they use a central controller—either a programmable logic controller (PLC) or computer, vehicle locations and system performance can be monitored at all times and reported.

The more complex control systems have central controllers and are integrated with other manufacturing or distribution systems in a facility, most frequently into automated material handling systems, such as an automated storage and retrieval system (AS/RS) and conveyors. These control systems are used when there are many vehicles, when a path is extremely complex or widespread, or when high throughput is required. Besides ensuring that systems operate routinely without manual intervention, vehicle utilization is optimized and real-time system status is available. These systems know the location of every vehicle and every load in the system at all times, allowing the closest available vehicle to be dispatched for load pickup, and enabling dynamic routing to avoid heavy traffic or blockages. Integrated AGV system controls are the most expensive, yet the most common, for all but the simplest applications because they allow AGV technology to be fully utilized without human intervention during routine system operations.

BATTERY REQUIREMENTS

All AGVs operate on battery power. Depending on the weight of the vehicle and the load, they generally use 12-, 24-, 48-, or 72-V DC batteries. Batteries are generally sized to operate over an 8-12-hour shift. The two types of batteries used are lead acid and nickel cadmium (NICAD), although recently some newer technologies are appearing (for example, lithium compounds).

Where lead acid batteries are used, battery charging is scheduled. With scheduled charging, there must be multiple battery sets for each vehicle in the system. Batteries must be removed and charged through a deep charging cycle in which the battery is completely discharged and then fully charged. Each vehicle requires a dedicated charger. The number of batteries required per vehicle can

be estimated using this guideline: for every eight hours working, the vehicle must charge for eight hours and cool for eight hours. Therefore, the number of battery sets required is one set for each eight-hour shift that the system operates each day. The number of batteries per set is at least two, but can be more.

With NICAD batteries, opportunity charging is used. Vehicles can charge their batteries for a few minutes every hour during idle time between operations or during operations while they are in P/D stations or queuing. Opportunity charging does not work well in systems where vehicle utilization is high and regular charging opportunities do not exist. If such opportunities exist, however, the additional cost of replacement batteries and dedicated chargers is saved.

SELECTION CRITERIA

When selecting an AGV system, there are two major decisions to make: type of vehicle and type of guidance system. Vehicle selection depends on the type of material to be moved and the characteristics of the physical devices that the vehicle must interface with. Guidance-system selection is based on the environment in which the vehicle will be installed. Considerations include the hazards that could damage the guide path and the likelihood of the path changing. Tables 13-1 and 13-2 can serve as guides to determine which vehicles and guidance systems should be considered. Further investigation is required to determine the best AGV system for a particular application.

SYSTEM SIZING

After the type of vehicle and guidance system is selected, the number of vehicles required to operate in the system must be determined. There are many ways to calculate this, but the best method is simulation, and it should be used for all but the simplest systems to validate system designs before purchase. This will prevent a number of problems, including system congestion and over- or under-capacity within the system.

Besides simulation, there are various deterministic methods for estimating the number of vehicles. Two fairly simple methods follow.

Method One

Method one can be used to determine the number of vehicles required to meet the hourly throughput for any AGV system. It assumes that there are no equipment breakdowns and that vehicles are not taken out of service for routine maintenance. In this case, the number of vehicles required is expressed as follows:

$$N_V = \frac{T}{T_a} \tag{1}$$

and

$$T = \Sigma V(T_s + 2T_{(p+d)/2})$$
$$T_a = 60\,(T_f)(L_f)$$

where:

N_V = vehicles required to meet hourly throughput

T = total transit time (minutes [min])

T_a = available time (min)

V = volume of loads moving between any two stations (loads per hour)

T_s = time to travel between any two stations (min)

T_p = time to pick up (min)

T_d = time to deliver a load (min)

T_f = traffic factor—percentage of time the guide path is clear for vehicles to move (0.85-1.0% for most systems)

L_f = load factor—percentage of time the vehicle is carrying a load (0.4-0.7%, generally)

CHAPTER 13 AUTOMATED MATERIAL HANDLING EQUIPMENT

TABLE 13-1
AGV Comparison

Vehicle Type	Load Capacity lb (kg)	Degree of Automation	Throughput	Speed fpm (mpm)	Lifting Height in. (cm)
Unit load	500-8,000 (227-3,629)	Moderate-high	Moderate-high	125-250 (38-76)	12 (30)
Driverless train	2,500-50,000 (1,134-22,680)	Low-moderate	High	100-400 (30-122)	0 (0)
Fork lift	4,000-20,000 (1,814-9,072)	Moderate-high	Low	125-250 (38-76)	40-240 (102-610)
Wire-guided pallet truck	4,000-6,500 (1,814-2,948)	Moderate-high	Low-moderate	50-250 (15-76)	8-12 (20-30)
Light load	up to 500 (227)	Low-high	Low-moderate	50-150 (15-46)	0 (0)
Module transport	500-2,500 (227-1,134)	Moderate-high	Moderate	75-250 (23-76)	0 (0)
Specialized	up to 100,000 (45,360)	Moderate-high	Varies	75-300 (23-91)	Depends on design

TABLE 13-2
AGV Guidance System Comparison

Guidance Type	Navigation Reliability	Suitable for Harsh Environment	Path Maintenance	Guide Path Changes	Guide Path Control Required
Inductive	High	Yes	None	Difficult	Simple-moderate
Passive	High-low	Usually not	High-low	Moderate-easy	Simple-complex
Laser	Moderate	Most	Low	Easy	Complex
Inertial	Moderate-high	Yes	None	Moderate-easy	Complex

Method Two

Method two applies only to a specific subset of AGV systems. It can be used for one-directional and bidirectional vehicles without central dispatching. Assumptions are that each vehicle completes a full loop around the system to its starting point without turning around and going in the other direction; there is limited competition for the same piece of guide path; and equipment utilization and acceleration and deceleration factors are 80%. The number of vehicles required is calculated as follows:

$$N_V = \frac{L_t(C)}{48} \qquad (2)$$

and

$$C = \frac{L}{V_{max}} + T_p + T_d$$

where:

N_V = number of vehicles required
L_t = required throughput of loop "L" (loads/h)
C = unimpeded, full-speed travel time over loop "L" (min/cycle)
L = length of travel, returning to starting point (ft [m])
V_{max} = maximum travel speed (fpm [mpm])
T_p = time to pick up a load (min)
T_d = time to deliver a load (min)

If there are multiple loops, the calculation can be performed for each loop and the results are added. Under these circumstances, additional vehicles may be required to allow for travel between loops. Both methods provide good approximations of system requirements for planning purposes.[2]

CHAPTER 13   AUTOMATED MATERIAL HANDLING EQUIPMENT

COST ESTIMATING AND JUSTIFICATION

AGV costs can range from $30,000 to $275,000 for a single vehicle. Guide paths can range from $30-60/ft ($100-200/m), and a single-position P/D station can cost $1,500-7,500. Design, controls, and installation can run from 15% to more than 100% of the combined cost of vehicle, guide path, and P/D station, depending on system complexity.[3]

For an AGV system, a financial justification with the appropriate payback period must be completed. Hurdle rates and justification tools vary for each company.

BENEFITS

Not all benefits of AGV systems can be assigned dollar values; some must be considered qualitatively. AGV systems lower labor costs by replacing fork lift operations with an automated operation. This frees fork lift operators to perform other jobs that use more of their knowledge and skill, thereby increasing job satisfaction. Sophisticated AGV systems also provide more predictable delivery times than fork lift operations, reducing downtime. Generally, AGV systems require less aisle space than fork lifts and have fewer collisions, reducing damage to loads, buildings, and equipment. They are generally easy to install—wire-guided systems can be put in place in a few days, faster than a conveyor system can be installed.

Moreover, AGV systems allow real-time dispatching and control, which is usually not possible with fork lifts because the driver cannot be contacted until the next destination is reached. Although the lack of real-time control is also true for some of the simplest AGV systems, most can be contacted by a central controller at any time and rerouted or warned of traffic at upcoming intersections. In addition, these systems can integrate remote work areas without placing fixed delivery systems throughout a factory or distribution center. This can generally be done without significant changes in building structure or traffic flow. Traffic paths can be changed, vehicles can be added or removed in response to increasing or decreasing throughput, and throughput can be changed dynamically. Capacity can be moved to different parts of the system by redirecting vehicles to different parts of the guide path. Vehicles that fail can be replaced and loads can be routed around path blockages or interface failures.

Unlike conveyors, AGV systems do not have fixed positions, which leave aisles and other areas within a facility unobstructed and allow the vehicles to cross the paths used by other types of traffic. Although it is preferable for safety that AGVs have dedicated aisles, they can share existing aisles with people and manual material handling equipment. Also, systems can be moved within a facility and even to another facility as needs change.

SAFETY CONSIDERATIONS

Because AGV systems often operate autonomously in areas that are also occupied by people and other vehicles, various safety devices are used to prevent personal injury and vehicle or property damage. Most system vehicles are equipped with collision-avoidance systems, such as sonar or optical detection. These look-ahead features spot obstacles and stop the vehicle or slow it down so that it gently nudges the object rather than ramming it. These systems are important in areas with high potential for contact with people.

All AGVs are equipped with front and back emergency bumpers that will stop the vehicle, usually within 2-5 ft (61-152 cm) of contact with any object. Vehicles using a traditional guide path have a monitoring circuit designed to stop the vehicle if it strays too far, usually within 2 in. (5 cm) of the guide path. Other types of guide paths, such as a laser system, utilize a method that occasionally veri-

fies the absolute location. If the vehicle cannot identify its actual location, it will stop. There are also emergency stops on the vehicles and throughout the area where the system travels to ensure that individuals in danger of being struck can stop the vehicle. Vehicles are also equipped with visual warning signals, such as a rotating red light and an audible alarm to alert anyone who may be in the path area. The alarm sound must be at the correct volume for the working environment to avoid being either overly obtrusive or inaudible.

Control systems have safety features to prevent vehicle collisions. Vehicle anticollision systems, generally called *blocking systems,* direct traffic flow and ensure safe distances between vehicles at intersections and turns. There are two types of blocking systems: zone blocking and forward-sensor blocking. *Zone blocking* divides the system into zones. When a vehicle enters a zone, it reserves that zone for itself, and no other vehicles can enter until it leaves the zone. *Forward-sensor blocking* uses a vehicle's collision avoidance system to detect other vehicles in front of it. When within a predetermined range, the vehicle will slow down and travel forward until it touches the rear bumper of the vehicle ahead. After that vehicle moves, the original vehicle will move again. This method is not effective in systems that have many curves because vehicles cannot always see other vehicles ahead when they enter curves.

AGV system owners can help ensure the safety of pedestrians and vehicles. Lines identifying travel areas can be painted on the floor. Adequate right of way, about 18 in. (46 cm), should be maintained between the vehicle's path and fixed objects along the path. Systems with ramps should allow only one vehicle at a time.

SYSTEM MAINTENANCE

Battery maintenance is the most important part of maintaining an AGV system. For systems with NICAD batteries, care must be taken to ensure that the vehicle receives adequate charging opportunities. For systems with lead acid batteries, the batteries must be discharged at least 90% and then fully recharged to avoid battery memory development and premature failure. With good care under normal operating conditions, batteries generally operate for five to six years. Also, because AGV systems operate autonomously and in close proximity to people, it is extremely important that safety systems be checked regularly to ensure that they are always functional.

FUTURE TRENDS

Here are some of the developments expected in the near future:

- Although the capability to increase vehicle speed already exists, better technology to sense obstacles and stop vehicles rapidly will be required before faster speeds can be implemented.[4]
- At present, each AGV system has only one dispatching algorithm and one routing algorithm for use under all circumstances. Although these algorithms optimize overall system performance, they often perform poorly during specific periods of system operation, such as peak periods and periods when most operations are concentrated in one portion of the system. Future systems will have various dispatching and routing algorithms that can be changed, and the capability to automatically select the appropriate one under changing conditions.[5]
- Controls will integrate the vehicle dispatcher with the shop's scheduling system. In more sophisticated systems, the vehicle will be dispatched before the load is ready for pickup, so it will arrive as soon as the work is ready or new material is required.
- AGV system use will continue to be adopted in many environments. More systems will be used for assembly operations, especially where the vehicles serve as mobile robot platforms.

CHAPTER 13   AUTOMATED MATERIAL HANDLING EQUIPMENT

- System maintenance will improve with better on-board diagnostics and rapidly replaceable modular components to speed diagnosis and repair.[6]
- The steady trend toward smaller systems (one or two vehicles) will continue.
- New guidance systems—ones that allow the AGV to visually recognize items around it to determine vehicle location and navigate around new obstacles entering its environment. An improvement in inertial guidance will be a global positioning system (GPS) to find absolute vehicle position. This advance will allow inertial guidance to operate without update markers embedded in the guide path. This advance, however, will require that the GPS provide positioning information with an accuracy of about 0.25 in. (0.64 cm) rather than the current 3.3 ft (101 cm). The number of guidance systems will decline, however, because many of those already developed have been expensive without providing much better performance than traditional ones.[7]
- Research underway to develop new batteries for electric cars will also yield AGV system batteries that run longer between charges, require less charging time, and provide a longer life.
- The autonomous mobile vehicle, an extension of the AGV, which would significantly extend the scope of an automated task. Without any interaction with the control system, this developmental vehicle could determine a route to travel, get to a storage area, pick up parts, take them to an assembly area, and assemble them. This advance, however, will require an advanced sensor array and considerable information about the work environment to be programmed on-board the vehicle.[8]

AUTOMATED STORAGE AND RETRIEVAL SYSTEMS

Automated storage and retrieval systems (AS/RS) are fully or semi-automated systems that store and retrieve material accurately and rapidly. They consist of three major components: a storage rack, pickup and delivery (P/D) stations, and storage and retrieval (S/R) machines. An automated storage and retrieval system also includes a control system; storage containers, such as pallets or pans; transfer carts; and a fire protection system.

The storage and retrieval machine consists of a mast that travels along the aisle and supports a carriage and shuttle. It is supported on the floor by a rail and guided at the top by support from the storage rack so that it maintains alignment at all levels and is able to access all storage locations in the system. The machine moves along the aisle to where a load is to be stored or retrieved, or to a P/D station, usually at the end of an aisle. When it reaches the designated location, it moves its shuttle to the appropriate height and extends to pick up or deposit a load.

Automated storage and retrieval systems, especially large ones, are most commonly used in warehousing applications, but also in manufacturing. Manufacturing systems tend to store smaller amounts of material for shorter periods of time.

AUTOMATED STORAGE AND RETRIEVAL SYSTEM TYPES

Each type of automated storage and retrieval system is best suited for certain applications. The major types of AS/RS are the unit load,

miniload, microload, use-point manager, man-aboard, deep lane, and vertical lift module (VLM).

Unit-load AS/RS

The unit-load type stores and retrieves loads that have been palletized or otherwise unitized. Pallet loads typically measure 40 × 48 in. (102 × 122 cm), but can weigh more than 5,000 lb (2,268 kg) and be as large as automobiles. There are two variations of unit-load machines: single-masted and double-masted. In each case, the mast(s) supports a carriage that transports the load. Double-masted systems (see Fig. 13-3) support the carriage between the two masts; single-masted systems support it on one side of the mast. The carriage has an extraction and insertion device, usually a shuttle, which slides under a load and lifts it.

A unit-load AS/RS can be designed to store loads one or two deep in a rack or to move one or more loads at a time. Those systems that can store loads greater than two deep are considered deep-lane systems and are described later in this chapter. Two-load racks often use, but do not require, a double-deep shuttle. A single-deep unit can be used with these racks either by shuffling front loads to reach back ones or by only storing like loads in a set of storage positions. Of course, the single-deep shuttle must be capable of extending far enough to reach the load in the rear position.

P/D stations are the entry and exit points of the AS/RS. They position loads in precise orientation for pickup by the S/R machine and devices that the unit load interfaces with. These stations range from simple ones with ordinary locating devices to complex ones with features that convey, lift, lower, or rotate loads for positioning. If system volume does not justify an S/R machine for each aisle, transfer cars can be used to move the machine from one aisle to another, reducing cost.

Unit-load systems are the most common type of AS/RS, and they are used in a variety of applications. The largest number of installations is in warehouses where they are used to store finished goods. Other common applications include storing raw material for manufacturing operations, staging WIP, and storing large tools and fixtures between uses.

Miniload AS/RS

Miniload systems differ from unit load systems in several ways. They are used to store and retrieve small cases or individual parts, most commonly small parts. In most situations, several cases or parts are placed in each storage location. Rather than storing the material on a pallet that is introduced into the system with the load, miniloads store material in pans or bins that remain in the system, returning to the same location each time they are stored. Pans generally store material weighing 250-750 lb (113-340 kg), but pan weight capacity can reach 1,000 lb (454 kg). Pans usually measure 24 × 48 in. (61 × 122 cm) with heights of about 6-24 in. (15-61 cm), although sometimes heights may reach 48 in. (122 cm). Each time a pan is pulled, it is delivered to a P/D station at the end of the storage aisle where a picker removes or inserts material.

Miniload S/R machines are similar to those of unit-load machines, but are much smaller in size. They run on a floor-mounted rail and in a channel at the top of the rack system. These two attachment points support and align the machine as it travels along the aisle. Each S/R machine has a carriage that moves up and down, and a shuttle that stores and retrieves pans or bins. Although some shuttles, such as the one in Fig. 13-4, slide under the pan to place it on the carriage, most use the pan lips to pull it onto the carriage and push it off.

Miniloads present pans to the operator at a height appropriate for order picking so that all the material can be seen and reached. Gen-

CHAPTER 13   AUTOMATED MATERIAL HANDLING EQUIPMENT

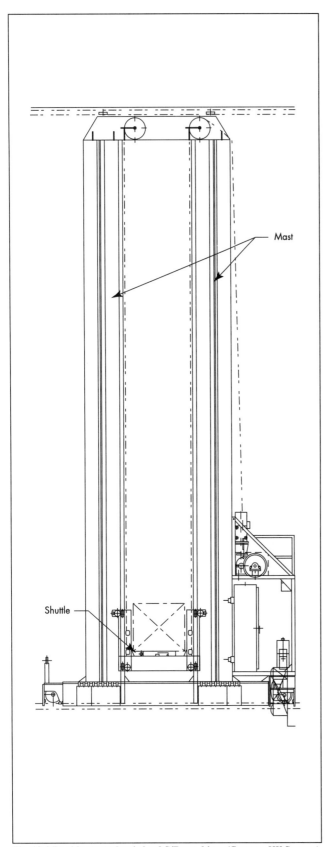

Fig. 13-3 Double-masted unit-load S/R machine. *(Courtesy HK Systems)*

erally, systems include two order-picking positions at the end of each aisle, allowing a worker to pull or store material in one pan as the S/R machine is storing or retrieving a pan for the other pick. Some systems are designed to remove pans from the aisle for order picking and replenishing. In these configurations, the pan is delivered to the P/D station and then transported to a workstation for processing by an operator. When the operator has completed processing the pan, it is returned to its storage location in the miniload. Other miniload systems may be located in production areas, with workstations along their sides. In these systems, rack openings along the length of the rack are used to deliver pans directly to the workstations, such as assembly stations, and retrieve the same pans when the operator is finished using them. P/D stations can also be located on both ends of the aisle and on mezzanines.[9]

A miniload AS/RS is commonly used where small parts are stored or where small numbers of parts are retrieved from a larger stock within a storage location. Common applications include order picking in wholesale and retail distribution, pulling parts for kitting or production operations, and storage and retrieval of WIP. Because miniloads can hold fairly large parts, they are useful for storing large tools and dies.

Microload AS/RS

The microload AS/RS is a smaller version of the miniload. Microloads are generally designed to store and retrieve single totes of material that are about 12 × 24 in. (31 × 61 cm) or about one-third the size of many miniload storage positions. *Totes* are standard containers, generally made of plastic, which store and move material throughout the system. The load capacity of a microload is usually not more than 75 lb (34 kg).

Microloads are generally used to pull entire totes of material from the system and then return those totes or others to the system later. Because the totes often travel to other locations within the facility, they are not customized for extraction unlike many miniload bins. Instead, they are extracted in the same manner used by unit-load systems: the S/R machine moves to a storage location, the shuttle extends under the tote, lifts it out of the rack, and lowers it into position on the shuttle. The tote is delivered to its output point and placed in a similar manner.

A microload AS/RS is generally used where small parts or kits of small parts or WIP are stored for delivery to production lines. They are often located adjacent to production lines to facilitate material delivery to manufacturing locations. These systems are most often used in facilities that manufacture small products, such as consumer electronics, and at manufacturers of electronic parts and companies engaged in remanufacturing.

Use-point Manager AS/RS

The use-point manager (UPM) is a single-aisle, high-volume AS/RS placed close to the center of a manufacturing operation. The UPM stores, sequences, manages, and tracks raw material and WIP buffers. Various workstations, which can include assembly, test, and packaging, are arranged around it. The UPM can be any type of AS/RS, including a hybrid with dual shuttles, but is most commonly a miniload or microload sized to handle an 8-24-hour buffer of materials. Besides serving in this capacity, the UPM is also used as a mechanism for moving materials between the workstations.

Use-point managers are best applied where many manufacturing or assembly steps must be performed, and raw material and work-in-process (WIP) must be stored between operations. Applications include electronic component manufacturing and assembly, assembly of consumer products, such as computers and printers, and manufacture of larger products, such as appliances and automobiles.

CHAPTER 13   AUTOMATED MATERIAL HANDLING EQUIPMENT

Man-aboard AS/RS

The man-aboard AS/RS is considered to be semi-automated because an operator rides on the S/R machine and picks orders. Man-aboard types are both floor and ceiling supported and can work at heights of 40-60 ft (12.2-18.3 m). They have a support member connected to the ceiling or storage rack and travel on a rail or channel in the floor. The vehicles can be dedicated to one aisle or travel to another if throughput is not high enough to justify an S/R machine for each aisle. Man-aboard vehicles that travel to aisles are generally moved by driving the vehicle onto a transfer car. The car is moved to the new aisle and the vehicle is driven off.

An operator rides on the S/R machine and picks parts from storage locations within the rack. Generally, the operator is responsible only for picking the material; a computer controls machine motions. Sometimes, however, the machine is operated manually by the individual riding on it. In either case, safety systems allow the operator to control S/R machine moves and ensure that it does not move during picking. An advantage of the man-aboard over a fully automated AS/RS is that because the operator is raised to the level of the storage location, loads can be positioned with less clearance between them, allowing greater storage density.

Systems using vehicles that are strictly floor-supported are sometimes referred to as man-aboards, but are not the same. The two kinds of floor-supported vehicles work at heights of up to 40 ft (12.2 m). One, the *turret truck*, is used to store and retrieve unit loads. The other, an *order-picking vehicle,* is used to store pallets of material and pick individual parts or cartons from storage locations.

A man-aboard AS/RS is used almost exclusively in warehousing applications where there is a large variety of stock-keeping units (SKUs) and a relatively low volume of picks. These systems are generally applied as a supplement to other storage and retrieval systems, where the other systems pull the faster moving parts and the man-aboards pull the slower moving ones. Specific applications include distribution centers that provide material to many retail stores and mail order companies.

Deep-lane AS/RS

The deep-lane AS/RS stores three or more loads in each rack opening. In these systems, the S/R machine shuttle table is replaced by a deep-lane shuttle car (DLC), or rack-entry vehicle, to move loads in and out of racks. The DLC has two drives: one powers the wheels that move it to and from the carriage and within the storage lane, and the other elevates the load carrier to pick up loads. The rack is a pallet type, modified to accommodate the DLC. Storage beams are modified to have either a *C* or *Z* cross-section, depending on DLC design. The top flange supports the loads as the DLC travels on the bottom flange. Thus, the DLC can move under loads to retrieve them.[10]

There are three types of deep-lane systems. In one, the DLC travels on the S/R machine carriage in the same manner as a traditional shuttle. When the S/R machine arrives at the appropriate lane, the DLC leaves the carriage and using the storage rack as guide rails, travels down the aisle to the closest load in the storage lane. The DLC retrieves the load and returns to the S/R machine carriage. A similar process is used to store loads. In the second type of deep-lane system, each storage lane has its own dedicated rack-entry vehicle. When the S/R machine arrives at a lane, it communicates with the vehicle and dispatches it to store or retrieve a load. The vehicle then returns to the rack face to wait for the next load to be stored or retrieved. The third type of deep-lane AS/RS is uncommon. It does not use a DLC, but has a push back rack and an S/R machine with forks. The S/R machine places the load on a flow-

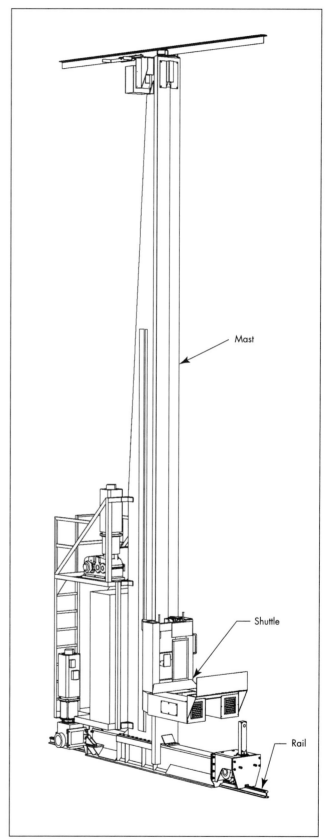

Fig. 13-4 Miniload S/R machine. *(Courtesy HK Systems)*

Mast

Shuttle

Rail

CHAPTER 13 AUTOMATED MATERIAL HANDLING EQUIPMENT

rack face and pushes the load already there back to make room. When a load is needed, the process reverses and the S/R machine removes the load with its forks.

A deep-lane AS/RS primarily supports last-in first-out (LIFO) operations within lanes. Although a load within a lane can be accessed before the material in front of it has been removed, this can require a great deal of load shuffling, depending on the load location. Frequent load shuffling can significantly reduce system throughput. If desired, loads in different lanes can be managed on a first-in first-out (FIFO) basis by retrieving the lanes of material that have been stored the longest first. After a series of loads are stored within a lane, no more loads can be stored in that lane until all the material in the lane has been retrieved. This ensures that no loads remain in the system too long. This requirement decreases system utilization and must be considered when designing such a system.

Deep-lane storage systems are often used in manufacturing or warehousing where large production runs are stored, either as WIP or finished goods. In distribution operations, they are often used for reserve stock of fast-moving items. In this application, orders are pulled from a storage system called the pick area. When the inventory in the pick area falls below a certain minimum, pallets of material are pulled from the deep-lane system to replenish it. Deep-lane AS/RSs are also used in truck-loading operations where products are accumulated in a lane in the order that they will be loaded in a truck.

Vertical Lift Module AS/RS

The vertical lift module (VLM) is a special AS/RS. The crane, which moves down the aisle in other automated storage and retrieval systems, is replaced by a stationary structure that supports the carriage and shuttle. The carriage and shuttle are the only system parts that move. Each VLM consists of one set of storage locations, equivalent to one stop along an AS/RS aisle. Storage locations contain pans similar to those used with miniloads. The pans are moved in and out by a shuttle or powered conveyor in each storage location. They are delivered to and retrieved from P/D stations where operators manually pick and replenish parts. Figure 13-5 shows a VLM with a shuttle and several storage locations.

Although only in use since the late 1980s, VLMs have gained rapid acceptance in manufacturing. They can be used singly or in groups, either back-to-back or side-by-side. Usually, at least two are placed side-by-side and tied together structurally for adequate stability. VLM applications include parts management in stockrooms, tool and die storage near equipment utilizing the tools, and storage of raw material or WIP on the manufacturing floor.

STORAGE RACKS

Storage racks, an extremely important component of an AS/RS, cannot be purchased off the shelf like traditional pallet racks, but must be designed for specific installations. Storage racks must support multiple storage levels without deflection when the rack is either full or empty. If the rack deflects, the S/R machines may not be able to store or retrieve loads successfully.

Factors that must be considered in rack design include the number, size, and weight of loads to be stored, the system throughput, and the characteristics of the existing building or the available building site, such as its seismic zone, foundation construction, soil makeup, and snow and wind loads.[11] Storage racks can provide either structural support for the building or be freestanding within an existing building. Buildings that receive their structural integrity from the rack—or rack-supported buildings—are usually less expensive to construct than conventional buildings. Building cost is further reduced by their tax treatment as equipment rather than buildings,

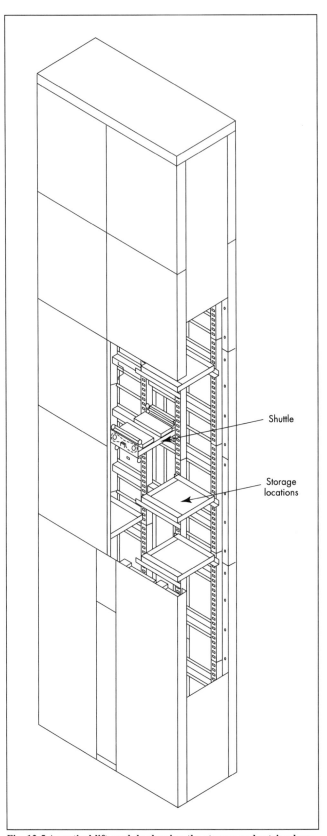

Fig. 13-5 A vertical lift module showing the storage and retrieval machine and storage locations. *(Courtesy Remstar)*

Shuttle

Storage locations

CHAPTER 13 AUTOMATED MATERIAL HANDLING EQUIPMENT

allowing more rapid depreciation. Building codes generally require the installation of sophisticated fire suppression systems for an AS/RS, including sprinkler systems inside the rack system. This issue is discussed in more depth in the section on safety considerations.

PALLETS

Another important component of any unit-load AS/RS is the load platform or pallet. Unless all system pallets remain captive within the facility where the AS/RS resides or the product has a uniform and conveyable base so that it can be moved without a load platform, pallet quality and variability must be considered. Many pallet loads arrive damaged or on pallets designed such that they are difficult to convey. Thus, most unit-load systems utilize "captive" or "slave" pallets. *Captive pallets* are load platforms designed for a specific AS/RS and they remain within the system at all times. *Slave pallets* are generally sheets of 0.75-1-in. (1.9-2.5-cm) thick plywood the same size as the unit-load rack opening, most commonly 40 × 48 in. (102 × 122 cm), but slave pallets can be sized to fit any unit-load storage opening. They also can be plastic or metal, depending on the application, and can include fixturing to secure loads.

CONTROL SYSTEMS

Most AS/RS applications have fully automated control systems. The typical control system is integrated with a supervisory system of some sort: a warehouse management, shop-floor control, or manufacturing execution system. The supervisory system knows which load or material is stored, but not where. When a load is required, the supervisory system sends messages to the control system requesting specific parts. The AS/RS controller then dispatches the S/R machine for retrieval. When the load is brought to the end of the aisle, it is either transferred to a conveyor or delivered to a worker. In the latter case, the operator will complete the appropriate picks and then signal the system to continue with the next operation. Storage is completed in a similar manner. The controller maintains information about where the load is stored, informing the supervisory system only that it has been stored.

When an AS/RS is not fully integrated with a supervisory system, it is controlled by the operator at a control panel located at the end of the aisle. In these environments, a business system, such as a material requirements planning (MRP) system, has an estimate of the amount of material in the AS/RS, but does not communicate directly with the system. The system inventory record resides in the AS/RS controller. The business system or a production system generates a list of material to pick from the AS/RS. An operator at the end of the aisle or at another console directs the S/R machine to pull the required material from the system. For storage, the material is delivered to the AS/RS area, where an operator manually enters information about the material into the system, places it on an input station or in a pan, and a storage and retrieval machine picks it up and places it in the rack.

Other types of control systems also can be implemented. Generally, a control system can be designed to meet the needs and budget of any facility.

SELECTION CRITERIA

Any type of AS/RS may be used for either random or dedicated storage. The unit load is generally used for random storage, and the miniload, microload, and VLM are generally used for dedicated storage. When storage is dedicated, system cycle time can be minimized by storing the fastest moving items at the front and near the level of the P/D station, and the slowest moving ones at the rear of the aisle away from this station.

Factors that should be considered when selecting an AS/RS include load size, space available for a storage system, system through-put, total amount of storage needed, and whether the storage is to be FIFO or LIFO. Some quantitative and qualitative factors appear in Tables 13-3 and 13-4. Other types of storage systems, such as carousels and high-density storage, should also be considered where an AS/RS may be appropriate.

SYSTEM SIZING

The physical size of a unit load, miniload, and microload AS/RS can be estimated using the following equations:[12]

$$H = z(h + c_1) + 4 \tag{3}$$

$$L = y(w + c_2) + r + \left(\frac{p + d}{2}\right) \tag{4}$$

$$W = 3n(l + c_3) + 2 \tag{5}$$

where:

H = system height, including clearances (ft [m])
z = system height in loads
h = load height (ft [m])
c_1 = vertical clearance between loads (ft [m])
L = aisle length, including clearances (ft [m])
y = aisle length in loads
w = load width (ft [m])
c_2 = clearance between loads along rack length (ft [m])
r = system runout (ft [m])
p = space required by pickup station (ft [m])
d = space required by delivery station (ft [m])
W = system width, including clearances (ft [m])
n = number of storage aisles
l = load length (ft [m])
c_3 = clearance between the S/R machine and rack and between loads and aisles (ft [m])

Exact requirements will be influenced by building construction, P/D station design, and fire protection or sprinkler requirements. System runout (r) is influenced by the width of the unit load and whether or not transfer cars are used; values will range from 26-54 ft (7.9-16.5 m). For a conservative estimate, 36 ft (11 m) can be used for systems without transfer cars and 54 ft (16.5 m) for those with them. P/D station space (p and d) is generally between 3 and 8 ft (0.9 and 2.4 m), depending on system size and configuration. If clearances are not known, 10 in. (25.4 cm) can be used for c_1, 9 in. (22.9 cm) for c_2, and 6 in. (15.2 cm) for c_3.

These equations can be simplified to describe a single vertical lift module as follows:

$$H = z(h + c_1) + 4 \text{ (see Eq. 3)}$$

$$L = 3(w + c_2) + \left(\frac{p + d}{2}\right) \tag{6}$$

$$W = (l + c_3) \tag{7}$$

For a deep-lane AS/RS, the equations for length and height remain the same, but the one for width is modified as follows:

$$W = n(l + c_3)(2x + 1) + 2 \tag{8}$$

where x = aisle depth in loads

When it is desirable to know the size of only one aisle without external clearances, the equations for a unit-load, miniload, or microload AS/RS can be stated as follows:

$$H \text{ (rack only)} = z(h + c_1) \tag{9}$$
$$L \text{ (rack only)} = y(w + c_2) \tag{10}$$
$$W \text{ (rack only)} = 3(l + c_3) \tag{11}$$

CHAPTER 13   AUTOMATED MATERIAL HANDLING EQUIPMENT

TABLE 13-3
Quantitative Comparison of AS/RS Types

Type of AS/RS	Load Capacity lb (kg)	Maximum Height ft (m)	S/R Horizontal Speed fpm (mpm)	S/R Speed fpm (mpm)
Unit load	1,000-20,000 (454-9,072)	175 (53)	400-600 (122-183)	100-250 (30-76)
Miniload	250-1,000 (113-454)	50 (15)	400-600 (122-183)	75-100 (23-30)
Microload	Up to 75 (34)	25 (8)	400-600 (122-183)	75-100 (23-30)
Use-point manager	Varies	Varies	Varies	Varies
Man-aboard	500-5,000 (227-2,268)	60 (18)	200-250 (61-76)	50 (15)
Deep-lane	1,000-20,000 (454-9,072)	175 (53)	400-600 (122-183)	100-250 (30-76)
Vertical lift module	100-1,000 (45-454)	30 (9)	—	140 (43)

TABLE 13-4
Qualitative Comparison of AS/RS Types

Type of AS/RS	Storage Density	Load Size	Random or Dedicated Storage	Ease to Install or Move	Ease to Change Storage Configuration	Vertical Cube Utilization
Unit load	High	Large-very large	Either	Very difficult	Very difficult	High
Miniload	Very high	Medium	Usually dedicated	Difficult	Difficult	High
Microload	Very high	Small	Either	Moderate	Difficult	Moderate
Use-point manager	Varies	Varies	Either	Varies	Varies	Varies
Man-aboard	Moderate	Small-large	Either	Difficult	Difficult-very difficult	Moderate
Deep-lane	Very high	Medium-large	Either	Difficult	Very difficult	High
Vertical lift module	High	Small-medium	Usually dedicated	Easy	Moderate	High

For a vertical lift module, width and length are already expressed without external clearances, and the height of the rack only can be stated as follows:

$$H \text{ (rack only)} = z(h + c_l) + 4 \tag{12}$$

For a deep-lane AS/RS, height and length are calculated in the same manner as for the unit-load AS/RS and the width without external clearance is expressed as follows:

$$W \text{ (rack only)} = (l + c_3)(2x + 1) \tag{13}$$

Equations 3 through 13 describe the size of the storage rack for a single AS/RS aisle. The height and length will be used in the cycle time equations that follow.

CYCLE TIME

The cycle time of an AS/RS and the number of loads that can be stored and retrieved in an hour can be estimated through the following equations. These estimates should be used for planning purposes only. Throughput should be verified by the supplier before system specifications are completed. The equations determine the cycle time for an AS/RS where aisle dimensions have already been defined. They apply to the unit load, miniload, and microload.

An S/R machine can make two types of moves: a single-command cycle where it either stores or retrieves a load and returns to the P/D station, and a dual-command cycle where it performs both storage and retrieval before returning to the P/D station. In these cases, the S/R machine is assumed to start and finish the cycle empty at the P/D station. Because an S/R machine can move horizontally and vertically at the same time, the time required to make a move within the rack equals whichever time is greater. Assuming that the P/D station is located at the top or bottom of the rack at one end of the aisle and that storage within the rack is random, cycle time can be estimated as follows:[13]

$$T_{SC} = T(1 + \frac{b^2}{3}) + 2T_{(p+d)/2} \tag{14}$$

$$T_{DC} = T \frac{(40 + 15b^2 - b^3)}{30} + 4T_{(p+d)/2} \tag{15}$$

and

$$T = max\ (t_h, t_v)$$

$$b = min\left(\frac{t_h}{t_v}, \frac{t_v}{t_h}\right)$$

and

$$t_h = \frac{d_l}{V_h}$$

$$t_v = \frac{d_h}{V_v}$$

where:

T_{SC} = single-command cycle time (sec)
T = maximum time required to travel the full rack horizontally or vertically (sec)
b = rack shape—the minimum of the two ratios of horizontal and vertical travel time
T_p = time to pick up a load (sec)
T_d = time to deliver a load (sec)
T_{DC} = dual-command cycle time (sec)
t_h = horizontal travel time from P/D station to opposite end of rack (sec)
t_v = vertical travel time from P/D station to top of rack (sec)
d_l = rack length (ft)

V_h = horizontal velocity of S/R machine (fpm [mpm])
d_h = rack height (ft [m])
V_v = vertical velocity of S/R machine (fpm [mpm])

After T_{SC} and T_{DC} have been determined and the percentage of cycles that will be dual-command cycles has been estimated, aisle throughput can be calculated as follows:[14]

$$L = 3600e\left(\frac{(1-p)}{T_{SC}} + \frac{2p}{T_{DC}}\right) \tag{16}$$

where:

L = total throughput capacity of one aisle, storages and retrievals (loads/h)
e = system efficiency factor, representing the amount of time the S/R machine is actually moving material. This is a value greater than zero, but less than one; 0.85 is recommended.
p = dual-command cycles performed (%)

After the throughput of the aisle is known, the number of aisles needed to meet system requirements can be calculated as follows:

$$N_A = \frac{R}{L} \tag{17}$$

where:

N_A = number of aisles needed to provide required system throughput
R = required system throughput, expressed as the sum of loads in and out each hour. Peak hourly rates should be used to ensure that system requirements can be met.
L = total throughput capacity of one aisle, storages and retrievals (loads/h)

The cycle time equations described earlier can be modified to represent the throughput of a VLM, yielding the following equations:

$$T_{SC} = 2T_{(p+d)/2} + t_v \tag{18}$$

$$T_{DC} = 4T_{(p+d)/2} + \frac{4t_v}{3} \tag{19}$$

Although it was assumed that rack input/output (I/O) points were located at either the top or bottom of the rack, generally these points are several feet from the bottom of the rack. Because VLMs are so much smaller than other types of automated storage and retrieval systems, this simplifying assumption will have more impact on these vehicles and the cycle time estimate should be used cautiously. These equations can be combined so that the throughput expression for a VLM is the same as that for a unit load, miniload, and microload (this is the same as Eq. 16):

$$L = 3600e\left(\frac{(1-p)}{T_{SC}} + \frac{2p}{T_{DC}}\right)$$

Once again, now that the throughput of the aisle is known, the number of aisles needed to meet system requirements can be calculated as follows (this is the same as Eq. 17):

$$N_A = \frac{R}{L}$$

Returning to the general AS/RS cycle-time calculations, those equations can be extended to apply to a deep-lane AS/RS as follows:

$$T_{SC} = T(1 + \frac{b^2}{3}) + 2T_{(p+d)/2} \tag{20}$$

$$T_{DC} = T \frac{(40 + 15b^2 - b^3)}{30} + 4T_{(p+d)/2} \tag{21}$$

CHAPTER 13 AUTOMATED MATERIAL HANDLING EQUIPMENT

and

$$t_d = \frac{d_d}{V_d}$$

where:

t_d = time for deep lane shuttle car (DLC) to travel the length of a storage lane (sec)

d_d = distance from aisle to end of a storage lane (ft [m])

v_d = velocity of DLC in rack lane (fpm [mpm])

Again, these equations (Eqs. 16 and 17) for throughput and number of aisles needed to meet system requirements are as follows:

$$L = 3600e\left(\frac{(1-p)}{T_{SC}} + \frac{2p}{T_{DC}}\right)$$

$$N_A = \frac{R}{L}$$

More complex analysis methods are also available to determine rack size and system throughput within building constraints.

In the cases described, aisle throughput (L) decreases if transfer cars are used. As a general estimate, throughput is divided by the number of aisles that share the S/R machine. For example, if two aisles share the S/R machine, throughput per aisle is one half the throughput calculated for an aisle with a dedicated S/R machine. However, throughput will be further reduced by the time required to transfer the S/R machine from aisle to aisle. Furthermore, each time it is transferred between aisles in an hour, hourly throughput is further reduced. Therefore, to maximize system throughput, it is important to process a large batch of storage and retrieval operations in each aisle before transferring the S/R machine to another aisle.

COST ESTIMATING AND JUSTIFICATION

To determine the cost of an AS/RS, two factors must be considered: initial investment and annual operating cost. Initial investment includes the cost of space that the system will occupy, new buildings or structural modifications to be made, the AS/RS and its interfaces, installation, and capital. Operating costs include operators and support personnel, floor space, utilities, spare parts and equipment upgrades, and insurance and taxes.

Because an AS/RS is custom-designed, it is very difficult to predict cost without detailed information about the system configuration and equipment specifications. For rough estimates: S/R machines, the largest expense, cost $75,000-400,000 per aisle; storage racks, generally $75-200 per location; and aisle hardware, including floor rail, top guide, and sensors, $60-150/ft ($197-492/m). In addition, the cost of a control system must be considered.

BENEFITS

AS/RSs can be adapted to almost any application and have many benefits. With denser storage and efficient use of vertical space, they require 60-70% less space than more conventional systems, reducing storage cost and freeing up space for other manufacturing or warehousing operations. They also provide more predictable storage and retrieval of materials and greater inventory accuracy, improving the productivity of the people and machines they serve. Better inventory accuracy, because only S/R machines can access loads and are unlikely to misplace them, allows tighter production and distribution scheduling with less system inventory.

By automating material storage and retrieval activities, an AS/RS reduces labor for material handling activities. AS/RSs can store and retrieve significantly more loads each hour than a comparable fork lift operation with conventional storage racks. They are safer than fork lifts, reducing personal injury and damage to products, equipment, and buildings. Because they are more ergonomic, AS/

RSs reduce manual intervention and present loads more appropriately. AS/RSs also conserve energy because they require less light and heat than for conventional storage space. Depending on their location and products, many systems require only minimal heating and cooling within the storage rack. In addition, many automated storage and retrieval systems use rack-supported buildings, which are less expensive to construct and maintain than conventional ones and provide a tax advantage through accelerated depreciation.

SAFETY CONSIDERATIONS

Operator interfaces should be carefully designed to ensure that operators do not come into contact with the S/R machine. Many safety devices, such as warning lights and emergency push buttons and pull cords are provided, allowing operators to stop the S/R machine if needed. Safety devices are also included in aisles to protect maintenance workers, and a door at the end of the aisle opposite the P/D station provides maintenance access. Emergency lighting is included in each aisle in case power is lost while a maintenance worker is inside the AS/RS. Workers must be trained in proper lockout/tagout procedures and use a safety harness to reduce the danger of falls when working on the rack structure.[15] Photocells and physical barriers ensure that cranes do not overrun either end of the aisle.

Sprinklers are an important fire protection feature of every AS/RS. Depending on the fire hazard rating and storage density of material in the system, in-rack or ceiling-mounted sprinklers or a combination of the two may be required. Sprinkler systems that are heat activated can be supplemented by a smoke detection system that does not activate the sprinkler system, but does activate an alarm.

SYSTEM MAINTENANCE

With an AS/RS being extremely expensive, maintenance is critical. Because Chapter 6 of this handbook is devoted to the maintenance of material handling systems, only the areas of special concern to an AS/RS are addressed here. These are physical positioning devices, usually encoders, braking systems, and related components. Failure of these devices, such as the S/R machine running into the rack or P/D station, can cause significant damage to the S/R machine and its interfaces. In addition, a serious failure could cause the S/R machine to run into the emergency stop at the end of the aisle at high speed. Care also should be taken to maintain the floor-level guide rail and storage racks because if damaged, S/R machine performance can be adversely affected.

FUTURE TRENDS

Being a fairly mature technology, with many large systems installed during the 1970s and 80s, developments in AS/RS will be primarily in the area of applications, rather than technology. AS/RSs will continue to move from warehousing applications to the factory floor, with the single-aisle, use-point manager (UPM) becoming more common. The AS/RS will also gain acceptance in office and retail operations, with new system configurations being developed to fit these applications as needed. Systems will continue to become smaller, less complex and expensive, and more standardized. Replacing an S/R machine or upgrading a control system will continue to become simpler and faster.

Although technology will not be the primary area of development, systems will continue to take advantage of new technologies, including radio-frequency communications and more sophisticated sensing and control systems. At present, if an AS/RS outlives its application, it is almost always scrapped. In the future, systems will become more flexible and reusable so that they can be moved or reconfigured to support new applications.[16]

HIGH-DENSITY DYNAMIC STORAGE SYSTEMS

High-density dynamic storage systems (HD/DS) are characterized by load movement within a system during storage. Loads are not assigned a storage location as they are in traditional AS/RSs and carousels, but are assigned a path through the system or an output point. Also, system input is independent of system output. Whereas an AS/RS uses the same S/R machine to store and retrieve material, the HD/DS uses one device to store and another to retrieve. These devices are located in different aisles, allowing the system to take advantage of the different input and output characteristics of the devices. In some system variations, the load is constrained to move through the system in one lane and in the same order in which it is stored. In others, it can move between lanes and emerge not only from a different lane, but ahead of another load that was stored before it in the same lane. High-density dynamic storage systems are used primarily in warehousing applications. However, they are useful for staging WIP in manufacturing applications where there is high volume of a limited kind.

TYPES OF SYSTEMS

There are many systems that are described as high-density dynamic storage. The oldest, simplest, and most common systems use gravity to move loads through the system. Others use load carriers and generally, automated input and output devices.

Most applications consist of only one aisle, reducing system cost significantly below that of a traditional AS/RS in the same application, by reducing the number of S/R machines required.

Gravity Flow Rack

Gravity flow racks are slightly tilted so that pallets placed on the higher end can move to the lower end. Loads advance as loads ahead of them are removed, and various methods are used to manage their flow speed. Being contact accumulation systems, the loads ahead are under significant pressure from the loads behind. Gravity flow racks operate exclusively in the FIFO mode and except for the gravity assist, are manual systems.

Modular

The modular HD/DS (see Fig. 13-6) resembles a deep-lane AS/RS divided into three components. Loads are raised to input level by multiple vertical lifts and another device transfers them between lanes, allowing a load to emerge from the rack in a different lane than it was stored in. Each lane has a mobile cart that moves loads within the lane. Output from the rack is in the form of a vertical stack of staged slots and each column of storage lanes serves as an output slot. Multiple loads are delivered to a single output slot timed to match an expected need, such as a truck arrival or production run. Like an AS/RS, an HD/DS can be in either a freestanding rack or a rack-supported building.

The advantage of the modular HD/DS is that three simple components replace the complex crane normally used in an AS/RS for storage and retrieval. A *deep-lane transfer* (DLT) unit moves loads within the lane, a *cross-aisle transfer* (CAT) unit moves loads between storage lanes, and a *vertical transfer lift* (VTL) transfers loads between storage levels and to and from external equipment, such as conveyors and AGV systems. Each of these components is shown in Fig. 13-7. Shuffling loads in storage from lane to lane can enhance staging and order fulfillment. However, a large number of moving parts are involved in the system as each lane must have a dedicated deep-lane transfer vehicle.

The ability to move loads forward and backward in the rack and between lanes allows LIFO or FIFO sequencing for prestaging shipments. For example, shipments can be arranged in the exact order required to load a truck. The extraction system can move large volumes out of the system rapidly. Loads can take many paths throughout the system and many loads can be moved concurrently. While one load is being removed by the VTL, the next load may be brought to the end of a lane by a DLT, while other loads are being shuffled to facilitate retrievals that are scheduled for later.

A modular HD/DS, like other deep-lane storage systems, provides some of the highest-density storage available, typically greater than standard single-deep AS/RSs or manual storage alternatives. The variety of load paths ensures that even when a system component fails, there will still be a path for loads to move on through the system. However, some specific loads may be unable to move until a failed component is serviced.[17]

An HD/DS is appropriate for applications where the number of loads in the system is greater than 2,500 and the mix is in the range of 10-20% of each SKU. Inventory turns should be at least one per week. These systems are often used in applications where material is produced in large lots and depleted over several days, and where loads are sorted and staged for customer orders. They are commonly used in operations requiring buffering or staging, such as cross-docking. The most common uses are in the beverage industry, the grocery industry for cross-docking, for moving rolls and pallets of paper, and in refrigerated environments.

ELVO

ELVO is the trade name for an automated handling and storage technology that uses a "walking beam" to index a series of cases and move them toward an output location by mechanical motion, as shown in Fig. 13-8. The beam lifts a series of cases and moves them forward as a group. Then, the beam drops down and moves back without moving the loads. This cycle repeats, eventually moving loads from the input end of the lane to the output end. This is achieved through the use of an eccentric cam, which raises and lowers the beam as it rotates.

Input and output processes offer various options. All loads are raised by a vertical lift to the desired input level and then travel down an input conveyor. When a load reaches its assigned storage lane, it is pushed into it by a dedicated *stationary pushing device* (SPD), which is dedicated to a specific lane, or by a *movable loading device* (MLD), which moves along the conveyor servicing all loads on one level. Once loads reach the output end of the lane, the same options exist for removing them. Either a *movable unloading device* (MUD) or a stationary pulling device (SPD) pulls the load out of the system. After being pulled, loads travel along a conveyor to a vertical lift, which transfers them to floor level or a palletizing system. The choice between movable and stationary input and output devices is determined by the load mix at the input and output locations. One possible ELVO configuration is illustrated in Fig. 13-9.

An alternative method can be used for either the input or output of any system. Using this method, loads that are to be stored all travel along one conveyor until they reach the lane in which they will be stored. The load (or case) then enters an S/R machine that lifts or lowers it to the appropriate storage level and inserts it into the rack. The process is reversed when the S/R machine is used to remove loads from the rack. Once positioned, this S/R machine can store or retrieve a load very quickly.

ELVO systems can manage any case that is both stable and conveyable. Cases can either be moved singly or in stacks of as many

CHAPTER 13   AUTOMATED MATERIAL HANDLING EQUIPMENT

as five to increase system throughput. Lanes within the system are not dedicated and the system stores only one SKU per lane because loads cannot be moved between lanes within the system. Within each lane, loads are delivered in a FIFO sequence. The SKU can be changed at the end of a run, but that unit will not be available until the previous one has been processed through the lane.

ELVO stores and retrieves cases at high rates, releasing them from the system in the appropriate order to fill customer orders. Orders can be pulled in batches of a single SKU, or various SKUs can be pulled from the system by releasing smaller numbers of cases from several lanes in sequence. The system's compact design, without the aisles required by traditional S/R machines, allows more material to be stored in less space. Space efficiency, however, is achieved by sacrificing the ability to access every load in the system at any time. Walking-beam technology is a zero-pressure accumulation system, making it well-suited to move delicate or easily damaged products.

ELVO systems are appropriate for moving several hundred to several thousand cases per hour where the number of SKUs stored is small. They can be used for case replenishment of flow racks, piece-pick replenishment, and to accumulate, stage, and sequence finished goods before pulling them for shipment. Although their primary application has been in the dairy and airline service industries, they are suitable for any product delivered in uniform cases at fairly high volume, including dry goods, pharmaceuticals, and WIP in manufacturing applications.[18]

CONTROLS

Except for gravity flow racks with manual interfaces, high-density dynamic storage systems require complex controls to route the high volume of material that flows through them. Control systems are generally integrated with the control system for the rest of the facility. The facility control system, or supervisory system, provides

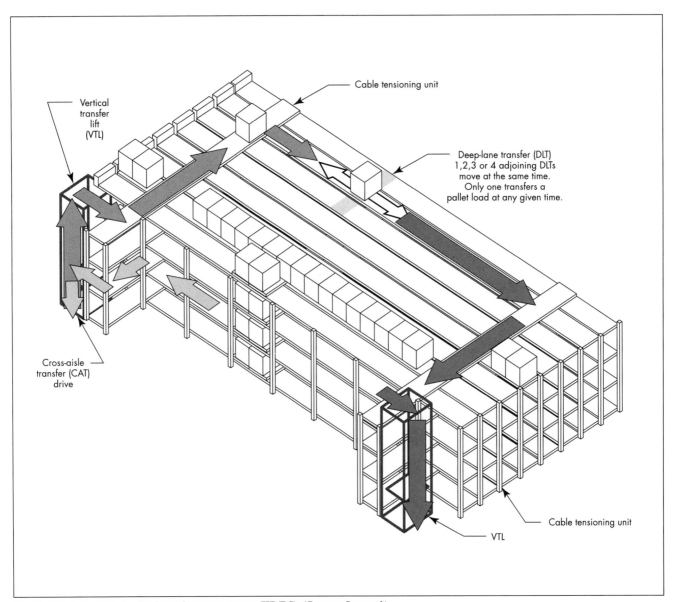

Fig. 13-6 Modular high-density dynamic storage system (HD/DS). *(Courtesy Retrotech)*

CHAPTER 13   AUTOMATED MATERIAL HANDLING EQUIPMENT

information about the contents of containers that are arriving and makes requests for material to be removed from the system. The HD/DS control system assigns storage lanes, determines routing paths, tracks material, and sequences it for retrieval.

SELECTION CRITERIA

Use a HD/DS when there is a large volume of material to be stored and a relatively small number of SKUs. When material must be moved through the system rapidly and sequenced before retrieval, these systems should be used instead of an AS/RS. The major difference between the two automated systems is the type of loads that they generally handle: pallet loads by the modular, and cartons or smaller-than-pallet loads by ELVO.

SYSTEM SIZING

An HD/DS must be sized based on the number of storage locations required, number of stock-keeping units (SKUs) in the system, and the configuration of the space available for storage. Although there is no mathematical expression for accurately determining system size, a rough estimate of the number of lanes required can be made, based on one lane per SKU. However, the assumption that only one lane is required for each SKU is rarely valid. Therefore, the number of lanes determined with this equation should be considered a lower estimate, not an average.[19]

$$N_{SL} = \frac{N_L}{N_S} \qquad (22)$$

where:

N_{SL} = number of storage lanes required
N_L = number of loads stored in system
N_S = number of different SKUs in system

Assuming that there is one input and one output aisle and that the storage lanes are all the same length:

$$L_S = 2A + N_L \frac{(l+c_1)}{N_{SL}} \qquad (23)$$

$$W_S = N_{SL} \frac{(w+c_2)}{N_2} \qquad (24)$$

$$H_S = N_z(h+c_3) \qquad (25)$$

where:

L_S = total system length (ft [m])
A = width of input and output aisles (ft [m])
l = load length (ft [m])
c_1 = clearance between loads in the same lane (ft [m])
W_S = total system width (ft [m])
w = width of the load (ft [m])
c_2 = clearance between loads in adjacent lanes (ft [m])
N_2 = number of lanes in each vertical stack of storage lanes
H_S = total system height (ft [m])
h = height of a single load (ft [m])
c_3 = vertical distance between loads (ft [m])

HD/DS throughput is determined by the number of input and output devices and the speed of each. This allows throughput to be as high or low as needed for the application. For this reason, throughput cannot be expressed mathematically.

COST ESTIMATING AND JUSTIFICATION

Because of the many variations in the number of loads stored in an HD/DS and system configurations, cost is difficult to estimate without information about the specific application, throughput

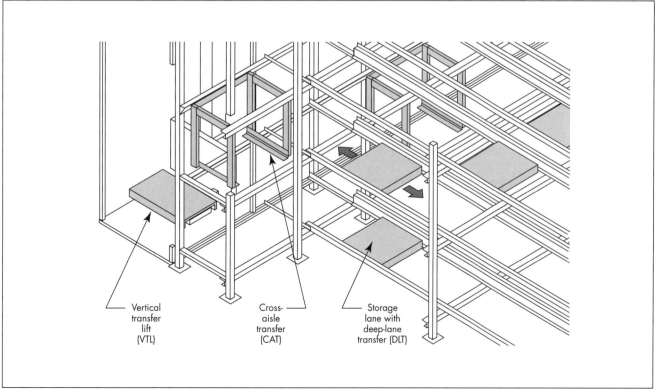

Fig. 13-7 Modular HD/DS. *(Courtesy Retrotech)*

Vertical transfer lift (VTL)

Cross-aisle transfer (CAT)

Storage lane with deep-lane transfer (DLT)

CHAPTER 13   AUTOMATED MATERIAL HANDLING EQUIPMENT

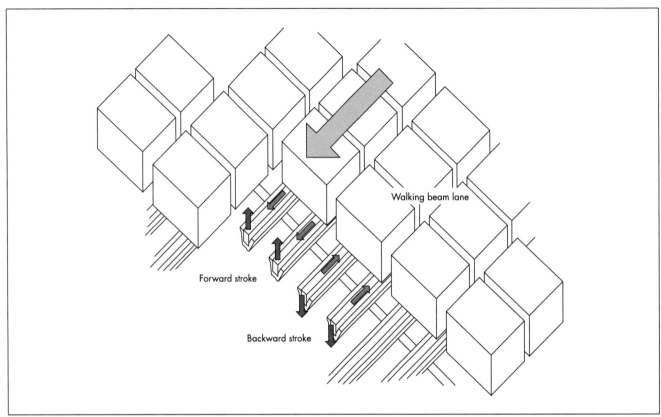

Fig. 13-8 Operation at the output end of an ELVO system. *(Courtesy Retrotech)*

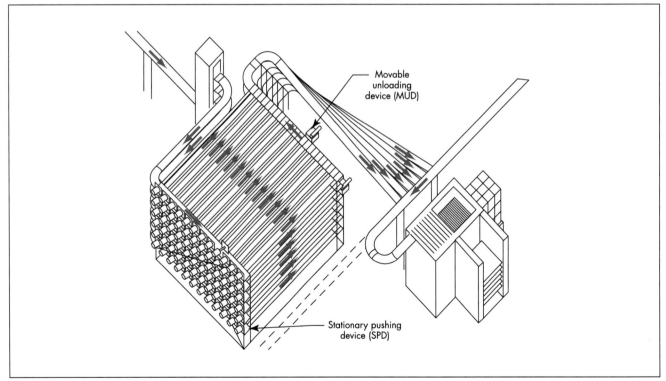

Fig. 13-9 ELVO application. *(Courtesy Retrotech)*

CHAPTER 13   AUTOMATED MATERIAL HANDLING EQUIPMENT

required, and installation space. Cost estimates are best expressed as cost per storage location. For modular systems and ELVOs, the cost can be $400-1,500 per location, depending on the number of SKUs and throughput requirements.[20]

BENEFITS

High-density dynamic storage systems have many benefits. Because all inventory transactions are managed by control systems and inventory cannot be accessed manually, inventory is better controlled than by manual methods. By eliminating all but one input and one output aisle, storage density is high, usually greater than that of an AS/RS, thereby providing more cost-effective space utilization. By being able to store and retrieve high volumes of material without manual intervention, fewer material handlers are required and system operators are more productive.

Flexibility is another advantage. Lanes can be of any length and different lanes within the system can be different lengths. The number and type of input and output devices can be varied to adjust throughput to the level required for an application. Systems can be placed in existing or new buildings, and modular ones can be installed in a rack-supported building. Components are reliable and easily maintained but, should failure occur, most material can be accessed by other components within the system.

SAFETY CONSIDERATIONS AND MAINTENANCE

Operator interfaces should be carefully designed to ensure that operators do not come in contact with any of the input or output devices. Safety devices include warning lights and emergency push buttons and pull cords, allowing operators to stop load movement if necessary. Photocells and physical barriers are used to ensure that load transfer devices do not overrun the areas in which they operate. Depending on the fire hazard rating and storage density of the material in the system, in-rack and/or ceiling-mounted sprinklers are used. Heat-activated sprinkler systems can be supplemented with a smoke detection system that does not activate the sprinkler system, but instead activates an alarm.

Because system components are fairly simple, limited maintenance is required. The most important devices to maintain are those that serve safety. Safety devices must be properly maintained to prevent personal injury and equipment damage.

FUTURE TRENDS

No technical developments for HD/DS are likely over the next several years. Systems using automated input and output devices will gain more acceptance. It is expected that these systems will be heavily used in the growing area of third-party logistics, especially for cross-docking applications.

CAROUSEL STORAGE AND RETRIEVAL SYSTEMS

Carousel storage and retrieval systems (CS/RS), or *carousels* as they are generally called, are a series of linked bin sections mounted on an oval track. Whereas AS/RS storage and retrieval machines move down aisles to collect loads, carousels move their loads to the storage and retrieval machine, called an *inserter/extractor* (I/E), or to individuals who manually remove material from the system. The I/E then deposits the load on the output device, usually a conveyor. When coupled with manual pickers, carousels can remove individual parts from a storage location, whereas traditional AS/RS and automated carousels must remove everything contained in a storage location to present the bin directly in front of the I/E or picker. Carousels are best for random storage because the storage location for any item changes relative to the front of the carousel each time the carousel moves.

TYPES OF SYSTEMS

There are two basic types of carousels: horizontal and vertical. Two variations of the horizontal carousel are the twin-bin and rotary-rack. Although horizontal and vertical carousels have both been in use for many years, the twin-bin and rotary-rack are relatively new. Characteristics of the basic types and variations appear in Table 13-5.

Horizontal Carousels

A *horizontal carousel* is a closed loop of storage bins, each containing multiple storage locations. All the bins in one carousel are connected to each other and rotated by a common drive as they move on a pair of rails, top and bottom, in the horizontal plane. Horizontal carousels bring material to the picker, either an I/E or a person, at the level of each storage location.

TABLE 13-5
Carousel Comparison

Type of Carousel	Storage Density	Size of Load	Random or Dedicated Storage	Ease to Install or Move	Ease to Change Storage Configuration	Vertical Cube Utilization
Horizontal	Medium	Small-medium	Random or dedicated	Easy-moderate	Easy	Moderate-high
Twin-bin	Medium	Small-medium	Random or dedicated	Easy-moderate	Easy	Moderate-high
Vertical	High	Very small-medium	Random or dedicated	Easy	Difficult	High
Rotary rack	Medium-high	Very small-medium	Random or dedicated	Moderate-difficult	Moderate-difficult	Moderate-high

CHAPTER 13   AUTOMATED MATERIAL HANDLING EQUIPMENT

Horizontal carousels are generally 30-50-ft (9.1-15.2-m) long, but length can range from 10 ft (3 m) to more than 100-ft (30.5-m) long. They can be installed singly or in groups, with the groups located adjacent to each other or in stacks of two or three. Upper-level carousels can be accessed by an I/E or by pickers working on a mezzanine. A typical horizontal configuration with automated insertion and extraction is shown in Fig. 13-10. The size and quantity of material to be stored determines the size of individual bins and the carousel's overall size. Bins are generally 12-42-in. (31-107-cm) wide, 6-36-in. (15-91-cm) deep, and 6-18-in. (15-46-cm) high, but systems can be designed to handle larger or smaller loads. Weight, or load capacity, ranges up to 2,000 lb (907 kg) per bin.

There are two basic designs: bottom-driven and top-driven. Generally, bottom-driven units are more versatile. They require less overall space, handle more weight, and distribute that weight over more area. The design is both more reliable and more easily maintained.

With automated picking, the picker is an inserter/extractor that travels along vertical guide rails at the end of the carousel. The I/E interfaces with the carousel, and the input and output devices (generally conveyors). I/Es use various methods to store and retrieve loads. The two most common involve pushing or pulling loads. In one, a gripper on the I/E grabs a lip on the load, generally a tote, and pushes it into the carousel to store. To retrieve a load, the gripper grabs that same lip and pulls the tote out. In the other, a pusher mounted on the I/E is located at each level within the carousel. For storage, the pusher on the I/E pushes the load into the carousel. For retrieval, the pusher behind the carousel bin pushes the load out onto the I/E. The advantage of this extraction method is that it does not require a consistent feature on the load for the I/E to grip. It allows for more variation in containers and storage space for vendor packages.

Horizontal carousels are used in a wide range of applications, the most common being in warehouse operations to store and pick parts or finished goods for orders to be shipped to customers. Other common applications include storing raw material or subassemblies within a warehouse or manufacturing facility. They also can be used to buffer material between production processes. Sometimes these applications involve pulling single parts for manufacturing, but often the systems are used to pull groups or kits of parts to send to a single workstation within the factory. Horizontal carousels are also used in toolrooms and parts cages, primarily the realm of vertical carousels. During the last 10 years, they have also come into use for burn-in testing of electronic equipment and for assembly line operations.

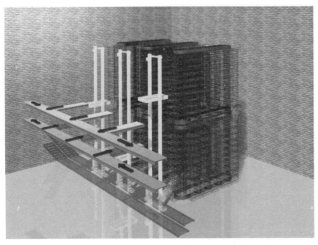

Fig. 13-10 Horizontal carousel system, stacked two high, with automatic extraction and insertion. *(Courtesy White Systems)*

Vertical Carousels

In a vertical carousel (see Fig. 13-11), the series of storage bins connected in a loop rotate together in the vertical plane. By using all of the vertical storage space available in an area, the carousel can store a large amount of material in a very small footprint of floor space. A single unit's footprint is generally less than 50 ft^2 (4.6 m^2). Although most vertical carousels are 12-20-ft (3.7-6.1-m) tall, they can extend above a ceiling and can even move material between floors by using openings at lower and higher levels of the equipment.[21]

Although horizontal carousels deliver material to the picker at varying heights, depending on storage location height, vertical ones deliver all material to the same location—directly in front of the picker for more ergonomic storage and retrieval. This is important because automated picking is not generally used with vertical carousels. Depending on the application, vertical carousels may be located individually or in groups.

Small floor-space requirements allow vertical carousels to be located close to points of use throughout factories and make them useful for WIP storage near manufacturing operations. Vertical carousels are used for generating and storing kits of material to be used in production and for storing tools and dies. Vertical carousels are also commonly used in parts cribs, where attendants can store a large number of parts—both large and small—in a small space and retrieve them quickly on request. In general, vertical carousels are used to store small, valuable material having rapid turnover.

Twin-bin Carousels

A twin-bin carousel is a variation of the horizontal type with bin openings on the side rather than in front. The carousel can present two bins for picking at the same time, on either side of the carousel, rather than one bin at the midpoint. Consequently, more bins can be presented to the picker at any given time, allowing more items to be stored or retrieved between carousel rotations. So far, the twin-bin design has only been applied to manual picking applications, as illustrated in Fig. 13-12.

Twin-bin carousels are best applied in situations where multiple picks can be made each time a pair of bins is brought to the front. Such applications have fewer rotations and system throughput is increased. The most common uses are kitting, where appropriate kits can be placed together; order picking, where fast-moving items and items often ordered together can be stored and pulled together; and WIP storage, where groups of material that will be pulled together can be stored together.

Rotary Rack

Another variation of the horizontal carousel, the rotary rack originated in Japan and was imported to the U.S. Few rotary-rack systems are in operation in the U.S. and very little academic research has been performed in design and control of these systems.

Rotary-rack systems resemble horizontal carousels in appearance, but not in operation. The major difference is that with the horizontal carousel the entire rack rotates to present a tote, whereas with the rotary rack only the level on which the tote is located moves. This means that at any given time any level can rotate except the level from which an item is being picked. This feature reduces I/E idle time to virtually zero on any system with three or more levels. Rotary racks also allow use of multiple I/Es supporting one rotary rack to increase throughput. A system utilizing multiple I/Es appears in Fig. 13-13.

Rotary racks are often used adjacent to assembly lines or flexible assembly systems to feed material. They are effective for high throughput of relatively small parts, allowing the racks to be several

CHAPTER 13   AUTOMATED MATERIAL HANDLING EQUIPMENT

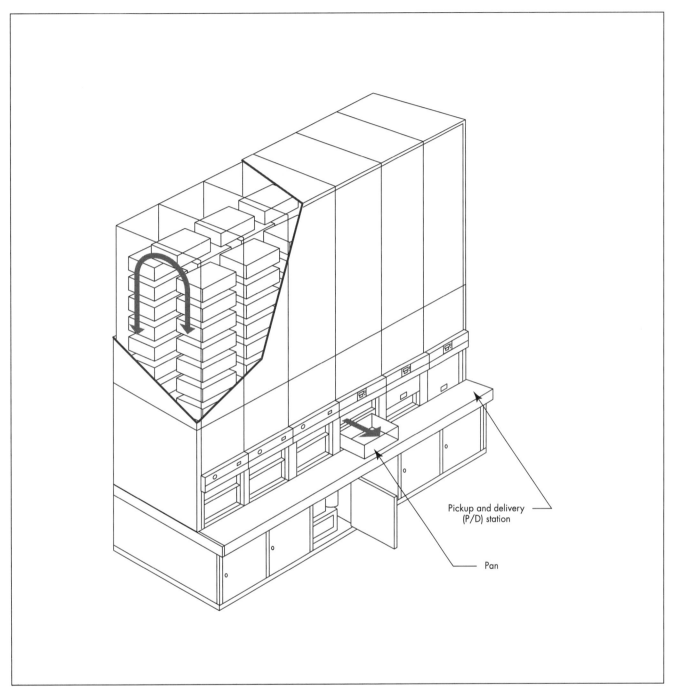

Fig. 13-11 Vertical carousel. *(Courtesy Esscorp)*

levels high and provide sufficient throughput to justify their higher cost. Electronic assembly, test, and burn-in operations generally fit these criteria.

CONTROL SYSTEMS

A wide variety of control systems are available for carousels, the simplest being completely manual: an operator picks and stores material. Manual systems require operators to know which items are to be picked and where they are located. They must use a foot pedal or push-button control console to rotate the carousel. A more sophis-

ticated version only requires the operator to know the part needed; the operator requests it and the carousel automatically rotates to it.

Another common type, also for manual picking, uses a computer to control carousel rotation and the order in which items are picked. A light tree or computer display indicates which bin and how many items to pick or store. When the operator indicates, generally by a push button, that the pick or store has been completed, the carousel rotates to the next location.

The most complex control systems are used with carousels having inserter/extractors. Storage and retrieval actions are determined by

CHAPTER 13   AUTOMATED MATERIAL HANDLING EQUIPMENT

the carousel controller, which is often based on information provided by a supervisory system. Operations are sequenced and communicated to the carousels and I/Es, which then complete the requested operations.

SYSTEM SIZING

The size of a horizontal, twin-bin, or rotary-rack carousel with clearances can be estimated as follows:

$$H = n_h(z(h + c_1) + c_2) + 2 \tag{26}$$

$$L = (w + c_3)\left(\frac{n_b - 2}{2}\right) + 2D + \left(\frac{p + d}{2}\right) \tag{27}$$

$$W = n(2D + w) + c_4(n - 1) + 2 \tag{28}$$

where:

H = system height, including clearances (ft [m])
n_h = number of carousels in a stack
z = system height in shelves or totes
h = tote or storage tray height (ft [m])
c_1 = vertical clearance between totes or storage trays (ft [m])
c_2 = clearance between stacked carousels (ft [m])
L = carousel length, including clearances (ft [m])
w = bin width (ft [m])
c_3 = clearance between bins along carousel length (ft [m])
n_b = number of bins in carousel
D = bin depth, front to back (ft [m])
p = space required by the picker for pickup (ft [m])

d = space required by the picker for drop-off (ft [m])
W = system width, including clearances (ft [m])
n = number of carousels in a row
c_4 = clearance between adjacent carousels (ft [m])

Exact requirements will be influenced by building construction, I/E or manual pick station design, and sprinkler necessities. The space for the picking area (pickup or drop-off) p or d, is generally 4-12 ft (1.2-3.7 m), depending on system size and configuration. If clearances are not known, 4 in. (10 cm) can be used for c_1, 8 in. (20 cm) for c_3, and 18 in. (46 cm) for c_4.

These equations also apply to a rotary rack, provided the pickers are located on the end of the carousel. If they are on the side, the height equation remains the same, but those for length and width are as follows:

$$L = (w + c_3)\left(\frac{n_b - 2}{2}\right) + 2D \tag{29}$$

$$W = n(2D + w) + c_4(n - 1) + n\left(\frac{p + d}{2}\right) + 2 \tag{30}$$

For a single vertical carousel:

$$H = \left(\frac{n_b}{2} + 1\right)(h + c_1) + 4 \tag{31}$$

$$L = 3D + 2c_s \tag{32}$$

$$W = w + 2c_s \tag{33}$$

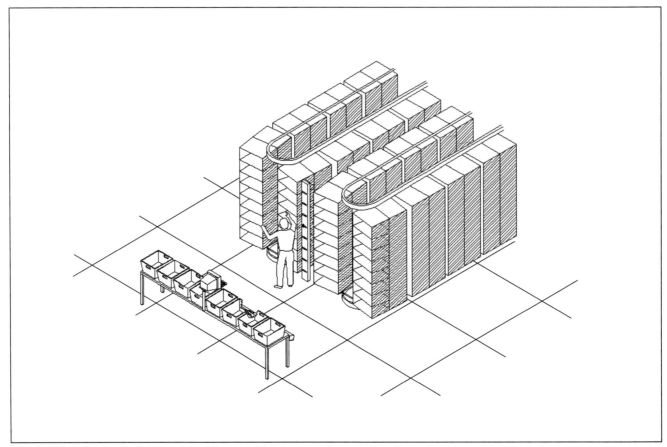

Fig. 13-12 Typical order-picking operation utilizing a twin-bin carousel. *(Courtesy White Systems)*

CHAPTER 13   AUTOMATED MATERIAL HANDLING EQUIPMENT

where:

c_5 =   clearance between storage bins and carousel skin (ft [m])

To determine the size of a horizontal, twin-bin, or rotary-rack carousel without external clearances:

H (rack only) $=$ $z(h + c_1)$ (same as Eq. 9)

$$L \text{ (rack only)} = (w + c_3) \left(\frac{n_b - 2}{2} \right) + 2D \qquad (34)$$

$$W \text{ (rack only)} = n(2D + w) \qquad (35)$$

For a vertical carousel without external clearances, width and length equations are the same as those for the horizontal, twin-bin, and rotary-rack carousels without external clearances, but height is stated as follows:

$$H \text{ (rack only)} = \left(\frac{n_b}{2} + 1 \right) \; (h + c_1) \qquad (36)$$

The single-aisle rack size without clearances described by this equation and the previous ones is necessary for the cycle time calculations.[22]

CYCLE TIME

Carousel cycle time (the number of loads that can be stored and retrieved per hour) can be estimated. The equations presented are for carousels whose dimensions have been defined. When robotic pickers are used with a horizontal carousel, the I/E can move vertically as the carousel positions horizontally. Therefore, the time required to store or retrieve a load from the rack equals the time for the I/E or carousel to complete its move, whichever is greater, plus extraction or storage time. In addition, multiple carousels can be served by one I/E, or multiple I/Es can serve one carousel, depending on throughput required. As the number of carousels served by an I/E increases, cycle time begins to resemble that of a rotary rack. Throughput can be further improved by sequencing picks to reduce system rotation time.

The equations assume that:

- A single I/E serves a single carousel.
- The I/E starts and finishes the cycle empty.
- The carousels can rotate in either direction (clockwise or counterclockwise) to move material over the shortest distance.

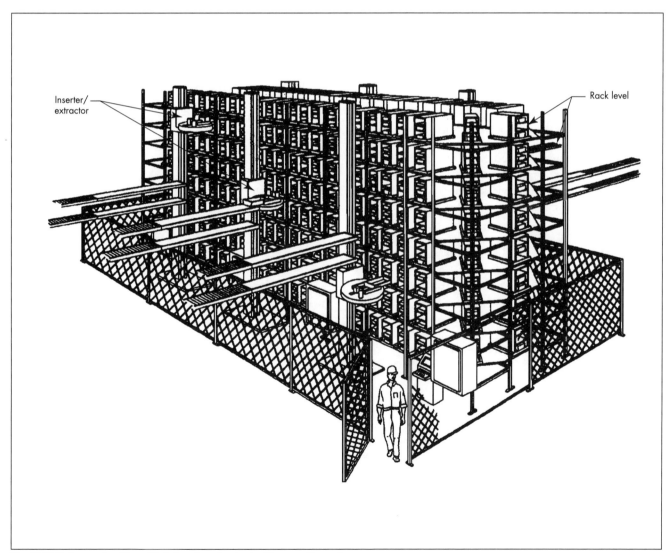

Fig. 13-13 Rotary rack with multiple inputs and outputs. *(Courtesy Esscorp)*

CHAPTER 13   AUTOMATED MATERIAL HANDLING EQUIPMENT

- During any cycle the load is retrieved from the same vertical bin in which it was stored.
- When automated pickers are used, the carousel and picker can perform some of their activities simultaneously, improving overall system throughput.
- The P/D station is located at the top or bottom of the rack at one end of the carousel and storage within the rack is random.

For horizontal and twin-bin carousels:

$$T_{DC} = max \, [(2T_{(p+d)/2} + t_v), + T_{CR}] + 2T_{(p+d)/2} + T_{TB} \tag{37}$$

$$T_{SC} = max \, [(T_{(p+d)/2} + t_v), T_{CR}] + T_{(p+d)/2} \tag{38}$$

and

$$T_{CR} = \frac{t_h}{(p+1)}$$

$$T_{TB} = \frac{t_v}{3}$$

$$t_v = \frac{d_v}{V_v}$$

$$t_h = \frac{d_h}{V_h}$$

where:

T_{DC} = time to complete a dual-command cycle (sec)
T_p = time to complete storage (sec)
T_d = time to complete retrieval (sec)
t_v = vertical travel time from P/D station to top of carousel (sec)
T_{CR} = time for carousel to locate to the next location (sec)
T_{TB} = vertical travel time between two storage locations (sec)
T_{SC} = time to complete a single-command cycle (sec)
t_h = horizontal travel time from P/D station to far end of carousel (sec)
d_v = rack height (ft [m])
V_v = vertical velocity of S/R machine (fpm [mpm])
d_h = rack length (ft [m])
V_h = horizontal velocity of S/R machine (fpm [mpm])

System throughput can be expressed by the same equation used for an AS/RS as follows:

$$L = 3600e \left(\frac{(1-p)}{T_{SC}} + \frac{2p}{T_{DC}} \right) \text{ (same as Eq. 16)}$$

where:

L = total throughput capacity of one carousel, storages and retrievals (loads/h)
e = system efficiency factor, representing the amount of time the carousel and extractor are actually moving material. This is a value greater than zero, but less than one; 0.85 is recommended.
p = dual-command cycles performed, %

The number of carousels needed to meet throughput requirements can be expressed as follows:

$$N_C = \frac{R}{L} \tag{39}$$

where:

N_C = number of carousels needed to provide required system throughput
R = required system throughput, expressed as the sum of loads in and out per hour. Peak hourly rates should be used to ensure that system requirements can be met.
L = total throughput capacity of one carousel, storage and retrievals (loads/h)

When horizontal or twin-bin carousels are used without I/Es, the carousels and pickers do not move simultaneously. In addition, vertical travel time of the picker is set to zero because the vertical travel of the picker is considered negligible. Therefore:

$$T_{DC} = T_{CR} + 2PT \tag{40}$$

$$T_{SC} = T_{CR} + PT \tag{41}$$

and

$$T_{CR} = \frac{t_h}{(p+1)}$$

$$t_h = \frac{d_h}{V_h}$$

where:

PT = time for picker to store or retrieve a tote (sec)

System throughput and the number of carousels needed to meet that throughput can again be expressed as follows:

$$L = 3600e \left(\frac{(1-p)}{T_{SC}} + \frac{2p}{T_{DC}} \right) \text{ (same as Eq. 16)}$$

$$N_C = \frac{R}{L} \text{ (same as Eq. 39)}$$

Because a rotary rack consists of several levels that rotate independently, it can be assumed that the picker never has to wait for the rack to complete rotation even when multiple I/Es are used to serve a single unit. Therefore, rack rotation time can be assumed to be zero, though this assumption will not hold true during all system operations. Thus:

$$T_{DC} = 4T_{(p+d)/2} + t_v + T_{TB} \tag{42}$$

$$T_{SC} = 2T_{(p+d)/2} + t_v \tag{43}$$

where:

$$T_{TB} = \frac{t_v}{3}$$

$$t_v = \frac{d_v}{V_v}$$

System throughput and the number of carousels needed to meet that throughput can again be expressed as:

$$L = 3600e \left(\frac{(1-p)}{T_{SC}} + \frac{2p}{T_{DC}} \right) \text{ (same as Eq. 16)}$$

$$N_C = \frac{R}{L} \text{ (same as Eq. 39)}$$

where:

N_C = number of rotary racks needed to provide required throughput

Vertical carousels are assumed to have manual pickers, meaning that picking and carousel rotation occur sequentially rather than si-

CHAPTER 13   AUTOMATED MATERIAL HANDLING EQUIPMENT

multaneously. The time required to move between the storage locations during a dual command is assumed to be negligible. Thus:

$$T_{DC} = T_{CR} + 2PT \qquad (44)$$
$$T_{SC} = T_{CR} + PT \qquad (45)$$

where:

$$T_{CR} = \frac{t_h}{(p-1)}$$

and

$$t_v = \frac{d_v}{V_v}$$

where:

PT = time required to pick and store or retrieve an item (sec)

System throughput and the number of carousels needed to meet that throughput can again be expressed as (same as Eqs. 16 and 39):

$$L = 3600e\left(\frac{(1-p)}{T_{SC}} + \frac{2p}{T_{DC}}\right)$$
$$N_C = \frac{R}{L}$$

COST ESTIMATING AND JUSTIFICATION

The cost of horizontal, vertical, twin-bin, or rotary-rack carousels can range from $40,000 to more than $600,000, depending on the size of the load and carousel, whether carousels are stacked, whether I/Es or manual pickers are used, and if I/Es are used, how many are used.

Carousels provide high storage density and effective space utilization. Horizontal, twin-bin, and rotary rack carousels are the most appropriate in low-ceiling areas. In high-ceiling areas, vertical carousels are very effective, but horizontals can be stacked to increase their effective use of space. All carousel systems can be placed on mezzanines or have a mezzanine placed above them, although this is less common for verticals than for the other types.

BENEFITS

Generally, carousels require less initial investment than an AS/RS or HD/DS of comparable size, although rotary rack and some large horizontal carousels with I/Es are exceptions, requiring a similar investment.

Unlike an AS/RS, except for larger systems, most carousels are fairly easy to move when required for another application. Those equipped with I/Es or controls that help operators store and retrieve correct amounts of material improve inventory control over manual systems. Because all storage locations are constantly moving, carousel storage is completely random, allowing storage in the closest available location at any time. Carousels also permit high throughput, especially in systems where a large number of picks can be presequenced, allowing fewer rotations between picks.

Carousels are one of the most reliable and durable pieces of automated material-handling equipment, horizontals with manual pickers being the most reliable and durable. They are also flexible as to size and configuration of material to be stored, accommodating items as small as screws and as large as bar stock, carpet rolls, and dies.

SAFETY CONSIDERATIONS AND SYSTEM MAINTENANCE

For horizontal, twin-bin, and rotary-rack carousels, sprinklers are installed at the top of the carousel and sometimes in the flue space between the racks. For verticals, sprinklers are generally mounted on the ceiling above the storage rack, although they can be mounted within the carousel structure, but still above the rack. Sprinkler placement depends on carousel layout and the type of material stored. Carousels should also be equipped with smoke detectors that shut down the system and sound an alarm when activated.

Some systems are equipped with photoeyes or safety cords to ensure that persons are not caught in a rotating carousel. Carousels with I/Es require additional safety devices. I/Es should be surrounded by an enclosure that is interlocked with the controller to ensure that I/E movement stops when the enclosure is opened. Emergency stops should be located around the system where operators or maintenance personnel may be working.

Safety devices are the most important items to maintain. For carousels with automated pickers, it is important to adjust the devices that ensure proper alignment of the I/E and carousel. The rails that carousel wheels travel on must be properly lubricated for operational performance and to prevent rail and wheel damage.

FUTURE TRENDS

For systems with I/Es, the most important trend will be greater reliability and accuracy. Accomplishing this will be a challenge because each storage location moves during rotation. Thus, both the carousel and I/E must be positioned accurately in absolute terms and relative to each other.

Another system advancement will be the development and implementation of automated pickers to interface with vertical carousels. A limited number of these systems have been installed, but no widely-accepted standard system has been developed, interfering with the integration of vertical carousels with fully-automated material handling systems.

SPECIALIZED SYSTEMS

Specialized storage systems range from vending machines with extractor mechanisms to systems used to store golf clubs and park cars. Some of the more common ones for industrial applications are automatic item dispensers, robotic order-selection systems, and tool-dispensing systems.

AUTOMATIC ITEM DISPENSERS

Automatic item dispensers (AID) are intended for picking large bursts of material in short periods of time. The most common is the *A-frame type* (Fig. 13-14) with dispensers on both sides and a conveyor running through the middle. Parts are loaded from the top in vertical stacks, called lanes or channels, and released from the bottom. Individual channels release items onto the conveyor by ejectors located at the bottom of each magazine. Dispensing is timed so that all items for one order end up in a group on the conveyor. When the group reaches the end of the conveyor, it is automatically transferred to a tote. Then, that tote is moved before the next order is placed in the next tote. Grouping items ensures that all the items for one order end up in the same tote.

Replenishment is performed manually by one of two methods. The simplest method requires an individual to walk up and down the aisles looking for lanes that are depleted and replenishing them from a reserve stock area, usually a gravity flow rack adjacent to the AID. With the other method, when a magazine is depleted to a predetermined level, it signals an operator who then fills the magazine.

A-frame systems are modular and can be used singly or in combination with other modules, either in-line or in parallel. Each mod-

CHAPTER 13   AUTOMATED MATERIAL HANDLING EQUIPMENT

Fig. 13-14 Automatic item dispenser.

ule is the same size and has various channels to suit the size of stored products. Each of the dispensers within the module can handle a separate SKU or, depending on volume and product size, one SKU can be loaded in multiple dispensers. The size of an A-frame system is determined by the size and quantity of SKUs to be stored, their pick rate, and their replenishment frequency. These factors dictate the size and total number of lanes, which dictate how many modules are required and their configuration.

Variations of the A-frame system can manage medium- to low-volume products. One variation requires configuring an A-frame with two tiers of storage on either side, one above the other. Although one module can accommodate twice as many channels, only half as much material can be stored in each channel. A second variation uses a traveling dispenser. Whereas a standard A-frame has a dispenser in each channel, allowing any channel to dispense product at any time, this kind has only one dispenser serving a group of channels. The dispenser travels horizontally along the A-frame, stopping at each designated channel and dispensing items. Another style of AID has a single, vertical pick face. Items are loaded into the back of the dispenser and picked from the front. Because the items are dispensed from different levels along the pick face, the conveyor moves up and down to collect them as they are dispensed.

AID systems can be designed to support volumes of 500-1,500 or more orders per hour. Because most orders contain multiple items, some systems can support volume rates as high as six items per second.[23] Suitable items are lightweight, from less than an ounce (28 grams) to slightly more than a pound (0.5 kg); small, lipstick to cigarette-carton size; and low in friction, allowing them to slide away from other items in the magazine. Products of various shapes and texture can be managed, including boxes, bottles, tubes, blister packs, and plastic bags containing soft goods.

AID systems are used in order-picking applications to manage certain fast-moving items, such as the fastest moving 20% of goods with appropriate characteristics in a distribution center. They are most commonly applied in the pharmaceutical industry, where most items are small, easy to dispense, and highly valuable or controlled substances. Other common applications for AID include cosmetics, cassettes and compact disks, auto parts, paperback books, and film.

ROBOTIC ORDER-SELECTION SYSTEMS

As the term implies, *robotic order-selection systems* use robots for picking. The robot is fitted with an appropriate end effector,

usually a vacuum device attached to a small S/R machine. These systems manage material similarly to AID, but pull slow-moving material, generally the slowest moving 50-65% of SKUs in a system. The pick face consists of a large number of items arrayed in a grid. Items in the pick face are at the front of a horizontal row composed entirely of the same item. The picker quickly moves along aisles, picks the correct item, and deposits it into a collector bin. If more than one of the same item is required, the picker can pick all of them at once and deposit them in the appropriate bin or in more than one bin if they are to be used in different orders. The bin dumps material into a waiting carton or tote. After an item is picked, the rest of the items in that row index forward so that an item is always available for picking. Except for retrieving slow- rather than fast-moving items, applications are similar to those of automatic item dispensers.

TOOL-DISPENSING SYSTEMS

Tool-dispensing systems are small cabinets containing small tools or parts, located in the area where these items are used. Of the two basic types, one contains a vertical carousel with small bins. Each bin contains a single part or a small quantity of a part. When a part or tool is requested, the carousel rotates the storage level containing that bin to the output level, and the bin then dispenses it. In the other system, the cabinet has a number of discrete levels, each containing three to six small storage carousels. Each carousel bin stores one part or tool. On an individual's request, the appropriate bin rotates to the front of the drawer and dispenses the item into the output tray. The number of carousels depends on cabinet size, type of carousel, and products stored.

Tool-dispensing systems are completely enclosed and secured. Operators allowed access must enter a password or use a magnetic card to access the items requested. If desired, access can be controlled so that each individual can receive only a limited selection of parts or tools. Systems also keep records of those parts and tools removed by each individual. Products as large as 4.5 × 4.5 × 19 in. (11.4 × 11.4 × 48.3 cm) can be accommodated, but most are small—less than 1 in. (2.5 cm) in all dimensions. Between 1,000 and 5,000 small parts or tools can be stored in one cabinet, which requires about 6 ft² (0.6 m²) of floor space and 7 ft (2.1 m) of vertical space.

Tool-dispensing systems are most appropriate when products to be stored have a high dollar value and need to be tracked, but do not justify a dedicated parts crib. Tool-dispensing systems are best used for consumables, although these systems are capable of returning reusable items to stock. Locations near machining centers, (for example, drill bits) and near maintenance shops, to dispense repair parts and supplies, are good candidates. Other storable products include electronic components, medical and safety supplies, and pharmaceuticals.

CONTROLS

AID and robotic order-selection systems require complex control systems to manage the order in which items are picked, thus ensuring that they are grouped properly and that orders are complete and correct. The controls must be integrated with a supervisory system that downloads orders to the order-picking systems.

Tool-dispensing systems are at the opposite end of the control spectrum. The control system must know only where all the tools in the system are located and manage carousel motions to select single parts or tools. These control systems can stand alone or be linked with other tool dispensers or another inventory system.

SYSTEM SIZING

Determining the size of the specialized system described requires detailed knowledge of the number of SKUs to be stored and the

CHAPTER 13   AUTOMATED MATERIAL HANDLING EQUIPMENT

throughput of each SKU in the system. Thus, accurate mathematical estimates of the number of lanes and storage locations required are difficult to provide.

For AID and robotic order-selection systems, it can be assumed that the minimum number of lanes required equals the number of SKUs in the system, because it is desirable to pick any SKU at any time. For AID systems handling fast-moving parts, the actual number can be double this amount. For tool-dispensing systems, a lower number can be estimated by assuming that only one product is stored in each system. This would require one carousel location for each SKU. However, depending on the type of material stored, this estimate can vary drastically.

BENEFITS

Among the benefits of these specialized systems are product security in a small amount of floor space and reduced product damage due to less handling. Also, these systems reduce order-picking costs by 75% and order-picking and tool-dispensing errors. In high-volume order-picking operations, they allow greater efficiency at peak times than manual systems, necessitating less incremental labor.

SAFETY CONSIDERATIONS AND MAINTENANCE

The most important safety features are sprinkler systems and emergency stops. Depending on system configuration, sprinkler systems can be installed either within or above the storage systems. Emergency stops must be provided in any area where operators are close to the system. It is especially important that emergency stops be located in the replenishment area.

The systems described rely heavily on mechanical mechanisms, such as escapements and grippers. These components must be kept in good working order to ensure that systems function well. If not well maintained, failures can occur causing jams that could result in incomplete or incorrect orders and downtime of the material handling system and other systems it serves.

INDUSTRIAL ROBOTS

Industrial robots are programmable, multifunctional, electromechanical manipulators for moving and assembling materials under a variety of environmental conditions. Work and load capacities vary over a wide range. Unlike most other automated material handling equipment, robots can perform their tasks in varying sequences. They also can be reprogrammed and retooled to perform different tasks or different sequences of tasks. In addition, robots can move objects while simultaneously re-orienting the position of the manipulator. Thus, flexibility is the key difference between the robot and other types of automated equipment.

Robots are comprised of a manipulator and end effector to perform required motions, a controller to direct the motions, and a hydraulic, pneumatic, or electric power source to supply the energy. The manipulator, or arm, which holds the end effector at the wrist, is generally a standard feature, but the end effector is designed for a particular application. They can be grippers for moving and placing objects or tools that perform work. Grippers are used for most material handling applications, such as machine loading and unloading, part positioning, and load palletizing. Tool end effectors are used to cut, weld, assemble, paint, and perform other tasks.

Together, the arm and end effector can have as many as seven axes of motion or degrees of freedom (at least three arm motions to reach any point and wrist motions as required) for the end effector

to manipulate objects. Wrist axes relative to the arm include pitch or rotation in the vertical plane; yaw or rotation in the horizontal plane; and roll or perpendicular rotation.

TYPES OF ROBOTS

Five general classes of robots are based on arm type: Cartesian or rectangular, cylindrical, spherical, jointed or articulated (anthropomorphic), and selective compliance assembly robot arm (SCARA).

The *Cartesian robot,* also called a *gantry robot,* moves in orthogonal coordinates, corresponding to standard Cartesian coordinates *x, y,* and *z.* One of the easiest types to model and program, this robot positions with high accuracy over a limited range.

The *cylindrical robot* has two translational joints and one rotational joint, which correspond to the cylindrical coordinate system's variables. The joints represent the robot's reach, height, and rotation. This type of robot can perform a greater variety of tasks than the Cartesian robot, but with less positioning accuracy.

The *spherical robot* has one translational joint and two rotational joints. As with Cartesian and cylindrical robots, the first three joints correspond to three variables of the spherical coordinates. These axes represent the spherical robot's rotation, rotation about the *z* axis, and reach or radius of the work envelope. The second rotational axis increases versatility, but decreases accuracy.

The *jointed robot* has three rotational joints. Unlike Cartesian, cylindrical, and spherical robots, there is not a corresponding coordinate system. Because of the three axes, the jointed robot is appropriate for complex tasks, including those where the arm cannot extend in a straight line, but must reach around or over obstacles. Though it increases versatility, the additional rotational axis further reduces positioning accuracy.

SCARA is the newest major robotic design. It is the only major category of robot with four degrees of freedom in the arm. All arm joints are rotational, increasing versatility to perform complex tasks, including assembly tasks requiring considerable accuracy.

Each robot has a finite area, or work envelope, in which it can operate. Although most robots are located in one position, some are mobile while operating. In this case, the robot is usually mounted on a gantry, such as for thermal cutting or for moving and positioning objects on a work area. Robots also can be attached to a fixed-path transporter or AGV and moved between work positions.[24]

BENEFITS AND APPLICATIONS

Robots are one of the most versatile kinds of automated material handling equipment. By automating simple or complex tasks previously performed by people, they reduce labor cost and free employees from inhospitable environments and difficult or tedious operations. They are used for traditional material handling activities, such as packaging, part positioning, and machine loading and unloading, but more frequently in traditional manufacturing activities, such as stamping, welding, part assembly, painting, inspection, and thermal cutting.

Robots are good candidates for activities involving a predictive series of operations. The material must be presented in the same position and orientation each time for the robot to grasp and lift it. Robots are generally appropriate for applications requiring less than 15 repetitions of an operation per minute.[25] They are also ideal for hot, noisy, or toxic environments and those with high concentrations of fumes; where high positioning accuracy is required; where vision systems are used to sort material; and where the product to be handled is hot or the operation is a safety or ergonomic risk, such as moving heavy parts or palletizing.

Specific applications include spot and arc welding, spray painting, and assembly. Besides welding, assembly applications include

CHAPTER 13   AUTOMATED MATERIAL HANDLING EQUIPMENT

placing and holding parts, inserting pins, snapping parts together, and fastening screws. Material handling tasks include loading and unloading machines, transferring parts from one location to another, and packaging and palletizing products.

CONTROL SYSTEMS

A controller, often a programmable logic controller, manages all robotic operations, interfacing with the power source to initiate and terminate motions in the appropriate sequence at the correct time. It stores programmed information on past, current, and upcoming sequences and can also send signals to other equipment that the robot interfaces with, such as conveyors and AGVs. The controller can be integrated in the robot or located nearby.

Robot motion can be controlled in two ways: by servomotor or by a nonservo technique. Servo control uses feedback to track and respond to changes in the location of the robot's joints. The simpler nonservo technique uses mechanical stops to mark the range of motion required. When the controller activates the joint, it is driven until the stop is reached. This technique, however, allows for limited control and is rarely used.

SYSTEM SIZING

Sizing involves determining the robot's reach, load it will have to carry, and number of robots that will be required for an application. Reach is the furthest point that the arm must extend to perform its operations. The load is the maximum weight that it must lift with the arm fully extended. The number of robots that will be required can be expressed as:

$$N_R = \frac{T(N_{cy})}{60e} \qquad (46)$$

where:

N_R = number of robots required
T = total robot cycle time (min)
N_{cy} = number of cycles required (cycles/h)
e = system efficiency, representing the amount of time the robot operates each hour. This is a value between 0.0 and 1.0, usually 0.6-0.9.

SAFETY CONSIDERATIONS AND MAINTENANCE

Care must be taken to ensure that people do not come in contact with a working robot. Very specific safety requirements exist, and a risk assessment must be completed for all robots before they are put into use and whenever the application or work environment changes significantly. A safety enclosure must surround the work envelope, and any opening in the enclosure must have appropriate safety devices, such as an array of photoeyes, called a light curtain. The safety enclosure must be located at least 18 in. (46 cm) outside the work area to ensure that any individual caught within it during operation can still avoid the robot. To prevent injury, all entrances to the work envelope must have interlocks, which shut the robot down when someone enters the enclosure.

Because a robot can be dangerous, the most important maintenance activity is periodic checks of its safety devices. Additionally, air hoses and conduits should be checked regularly to see that they are not overly worn from rubbing at the robot's joints, and the arm also should be well maintained.

FUTURE TRENDS

Over the next several years, robot technology and applications will continue to develop. Programming techniques will become more powerful and easier to implement and modify. Hardware and software developments will give robots the capability to navigate in more complex environments and position themselves more precisely. They also will be applied in many applications where they had not been considered previously.

AUTOMATED PACKAGING EQUIPMENT

Automated packaging equipment transforms finished goods into packaged goods, using cartons, pallets, bags, rolls, bundles, and other kinds of packaging.

TYPES OF EQUIPMENT

The equipment covers a wide range, from palletizing systems to bag-filling equipment, and much of it is custom-made for each application. In many applications, the equipment is an extension of the manufacturing process. Described are a few items that are used in the final steps of the packaging process—unitizing and sealing—specifically palletizers and depalletizers, stretch wrappers, shrink-wrappers, strappers, and case-sealing systems.

Palletizers and Depalletizers

Palletizers are used to stack individual products or cases of products in predetermined patterns, creating unit loads. Depalletizers receive the loads, stacked in a predictable pattern, and remove them from the pallet.

Many palletizers and depalletizers are specialized robots. Robotic palletizers can load one or several pallets at a time in the robot's work envelope or the robot can be mounted on a rail and moved to various locations. Depalletizers can unload in the same way.

Most palletizers and depalletizers, however, are not robotic. Although these systems tend to be less flexible, they are less expensive and have higher throughput capability. Nonrobotic systems use a variety of mechanical devices to transfer loads from conveyors to pallets or from pallets to conveyors.

Palletizers and depalletizers primarily handle goods of uniform shape and size, such as cartons, cans, and bottles. They are used where high volumes of products are processed, most commonly to palletize finished goods at the end of a production operation or prior to shipment. Palletizers and depalletizers are also used to handle large or bulky loads that would be awkward to handle manually.

Stretch-wrappers

Stretch-wrappers are the most common equipment used to unitize loads in manufacturing applications. Used to hold unit loads together during shipment, stretch-wrapping is performed by wrapping plastic film around a load tightly enough to stretch the film. Generally, several layers of film are applied to each load to ensure that the loads are stable. Various systems are used, including spiral rotary, dual-roll rotary, overhead rotary, full-web rotary, mobile-platform rotary, and pass-through.

The *spiral rotary system* is the most automated method. Unit loads are placed on a conveyor for transfer to a turntable or directly on a turntable. With the load on the turntable, the end of the stretch film is placed against the load. The turntable rotates and the film-dispensing mechanism moves up and down the height of the load, wrapping the film around the load in a spiral fashion. The film is dispensed

CHAPTER 13   AUTOMATED MATERIAL HANDLING EQUIPMENT

either through a friction-braking system or two rollers, with the second roller rotating faster than the first to stretch the film. Either way can provide appropriate tension to stretch the film, but the roller method is preferred as it applies tension more evenly and consistently, ensuring more uniform stretching and reducing the risk of film breaks. The throughput of a single spiral rotary system is generally 35-65 loads per hour.[26]

The *dual-roll rotary system* operates identically to the spiral rotary system except that it uses two rolls of film and two film-dispensing mechanisms, one moving up the load and the other moving down at the same time. This significantly increases system throughput, allowing volumes of up to 100 loads per hour.

The *overhead rotary system* is similar to other rotary systems. However, the load is stationary while the film tower, or the film and the dispenser, rotates around it, stretching the film and placing it in a spiral fashion. This system is especially useful for wrapping unstable loads, such as cartons of various sizes that have been combined onto a pallet. System throughput is 35-60 loads per hour.

Unlike the other rotary systems described, which use a film width much narrower that the load, the *full-web stretch-wrapper* uses a film width, or web, that is the same height as the load. This allows the load to be wrapped in fewer passes, significantly increasing throughput to as many as 100 loads per hour.

Mobile-platform rotary systems are located at floor level and use a fork lift for loading onto the turntable. Except for wrapping by the spiral rotary method, they are manual systems. An operator attaches the film end to the load, starts the system, and detaches the film when the load is wrapped. The wrapping is completed using the spiral rotary method.

Pass-through systems are among the fastest stretch-wrapping systems available. Although loaded and unloaded in the same manner as rotary systems, they do not have a turntable. Two film supplies, fed from either side of a conveyor, form a vertical sheet of film the height of the load across the conveyor. As a load passes through, it pulls the film around. After the load is fully covered, seal bars extend from either side of the conveyor, meet and melt the film, forming a seal between the two film supplies and separating the film around the load from them. This method is extremely fast, yielding throughputs of more than 100 loads per hour. However, because it unitizes the load with only a single layer of film, the load will not be as stable as if rotary stretch-wrapped.[27]

Stretch-wrappers are the most widely-used load-unitizing equipment because most loads are stretch-wrapped for shipment. They can stand alone or be integrated with other material handling equipment. More sophisticated systems can have conveyor interfaces and fully automated operation. Stretch-wrapping is commonly used for packaged parts and goods, including perishables, that are shipped to manufacturers, retailers, and consumers.

Shrink-wrappers

Automated shrink-wrappers most commonly apply film from a supply reel above the load. The film is expanded into an open tube, pulled over the load without touching it, then pulled until it is the height of the load. The tube is then separated from the rest of the film on the reel, sealed, and pulled down below the bottom of the load.

After the load is covered, there are three ways to shrink the plastic. In the most common method, the load is conveyed into a shrink tunnel where the film, heated by a flow of warm air, shrinks around the load. In the second method, a five-sided chamber, called an *infrared bell,* is lowered from above to cover the load and its infrared heaters heat and shrink the film. In the third method, the load sits on a turntable adjacent to a column of gas jets. As the turntable rotates, each side of the load is exposed to heat from the gas jets.

When the load cools, it is covered on top by a tight film for protection against water, dust, and other contaminants. Thus, shrink-wrapping is suitable for loads that may be stored outdoors.

Shrink-wrappers can be used for many types of palletized loads, including those sensitive to heat and pressure. They are commonly used to completely seal packages for retail display. Often, a shrink-wrapped package will be placed inside a shipping carton, which then is stretch-wrapped with other cartons on a pallet.

Strappers

Strapping prevents unit loads from shifting during transport. One or more steel or plastic straps may be wrapped around the loads, depending on the strength and durability required and the environmental conditions that will be encountered.

Automatic strapping machines wrap the strap around the load and join the ends together by twisting, friction, spot or heat welding, or fasteners, such as buckles, attached to the straps. High-volume equipment can apply as many as 60 straps per minute, securing several hundred loads per hour.

Strapping is generally used for loads that do not require the level of support and protection provided by stretch-wrapping or shrink-wrapping. Usually, these are fully packaged or heavy loads and those that cannot be damaged by the straps, such as steel bars and pipes. Strapping is also frequently used to secure multipart cartons together and to secure cartons to pallets.

Case-sealing Systems

Automatic case-sealing systems apply pressure-sensitive tape, gummed paper tape, or glue to seal cartons. Generally, case sealing is a manual activity, but when volumes are in excess of 30 cartons per hour, automatic case sealers should be considered. There are two types generally used: those that accept cases of the same height and width, and those that adjust, within a limited range, to various heights and widths.

Automatic case sealers are best applied where case sizes are fairly uniform and volumes are high. They are especially appropriate at the end of production lines where high volumes of material flow at a fairly constant rate. Their most common use is in packaging consumer products, such as soft and hard goods and food products. More information on packaging is found in Chapter 12.

References
1. Dunkin, A. "Automated Guided Vehicle Systems Overview." *Industrial Engineering*, August 1994.
2. Ibid.
3. Kulwiec, R.A., ed. *Materials Handling Handbook.* New York: John Wiley & Sons, 1985.
4. Castleberry, G.A. *The AGV Handbook: A Handbook for the Selection of Automated Guided Vehicle Systems.* Port Washington, WI: AGV Decisions, 1991.
5. Conversations with Leslie Interrante (Sandia National Laboratories).
6. Conversations with Randy Winger (HK Systems).
7. Ibid.
8. Castleberry, G.A. *The AGV Handbook: A Handbook for the Selection of Automated Guided Vehicle Systems.* Port Washington, WI: AGV Decisions, 1991.
9. Schwind, Gene F. "Mini-loads: Doing More in Manufacturing." *Material Handling Engineering*, 1991.
10. Dunkin, A. "Automated Guided Vehicle Systems Overview." *Industrial Engineering*, August 1994.
11. National Fire Protection Association (NFPA) 231C. *Rack Storage of Materials.* Quincy, MA: NFPA, 1991.
12. Dunkin, A. "Analysis and Design of Storage and Retrieval Systems for Tote-sized Loads." Atlanta, GA: Georgia Institute of Technology, 1988.
13. Bozer, Yavuz A., and White, John A. *Travel Time Models for Automated Storage/Retrieval Systems.* Report #82-06. Atlanta, GA:

CHAPTER 13   AUTOMATED MATERIAL HANDLING EQUIPMENT

Georgia Institute of Technology, Production and Distribution Research Center, 1982.

14. Dunkin, A. "Analysis and Design of Storage and Retrieval Systems for Tote-sized Loads." Atlanta, GA: Georgia Institute of Technology, 1988.
15. Auguston, K.A. "Integrating Safety with Automated Handling." *Modern Materials Handling,* 1994.
16. Conversations with Jeff Hedges (formerly of Retrotech, Inc.).
17. Ibid.
18. Hammond, P., and Hartman, P. "HD/DS—Planning and Using High-density, Dynamic Storage: Evolving Practices and Systems." *North American Material Handling Show*, 1992.
19. Conversations with Jeff Hedges (formerly of Retrotech, Inc.).
20. Ibid.
21. Sheth, Vijay S. *Facilities Planning and Materials Handling.* New York: Marcel Dekker, Inc., 1995.
22. Dunkin, A. "Analysis and Design of Storage and Retrieval Systems for Tote-sized Loads." Atlanta, GA: Georgia Institute of Technology, 1988.
23. Schwind, Gene F. "Machines that Can Break the Order-picking Barrier." *Material Handling Engineering,* February 1991.
24. Maleki, Reza A. *Flexible Manufacturing Systems: The Technology and Management.* Englewood Cliffs, NJ: Prentice-Hall, 1991.
25. Nnaji, B.O., Rembold, U., and Storr, A. *Computer-integrated Manufacturing and Engineering.* Wokingham, UK: Addison-Wesley Publishing Co., 1994.
26. NAVSUP Publication 529. *Warehouse Modernization and Layout Planning Guide.* OH: Naval Supply Systems Command, Department of the Navy, March 1985.
27. Ibid.

Bibliography

Adams, Nicholas D., Brown, Terry W., Firth, Rowland V.D., and Misenheimer, Laura P. *Warehouse and Distribution Automation Handbook.* New York: McGraw Hill, Inc., 1996.

Apple, James, Dean, James, and Youngs, Peter, eds. *The Professional Materials Handling Learning System.* Charlotte, NC: Material Handling Education Foundation, Inc., 1992.

Tompkins, James A., and White, John A. *Facilities Planning.* New York: John Wiley & Sons, 1984.

CHAPTER 14

WORKER PRODUCTIVITY AND ERGONOMIC ASSISTS

CHAPTER CONTENTS

LIFTING DEVICES

This section discusses the reasons for using lifting devices, lifting tables, balancers and hoists, manipulators, end effectors and tooling, and typical interfaces.

REASONS FOR USE

In recent years, much attention has been given to finding fast, effective ways to maximize the productivity and profitability of the corporation. Phrases such as "downsizing," "rightsizing," and "globally competitive" have become part of everyday language. Today's companies are seeking ways to reduce any costs which adversely affect the bottom line. Staffing is being cut to the bare minimum, requiring those who remain to produce as much or even more with less assistance. Businesses are also reducing medical costs from on-the-job injuries that lead to lost wages, reduced productivity, and workers' compensation claims. They are giving more attention to the Occupational Safety and Health Administration (OSHA), which has recently imposed large fines on many corporations for failing to comply with regulations aimed at reducing employee injuries. Unions are adding clauses to their contracts addressing "ergonomics," or the design of work, to fit worker capabilities. Corporations that do not take these items seriously can find themselves losing both profit and productivity.

With medical costs spiraling upward, OSHA regulations becoming more stringent, and companies trying to do more with less, many businesses have turned to ergonomic assist and lifting devices to aid in bringing expenses under control.

Reduction in Injury and Medical Claims

There are many reasons for companies to provide their employees with ergonomic assist equipment. One of the most obvious is the reduction in job-related injuries, which often lead to workers' compensation claims and substantial medical expenses. Requiring an employee to physically handle a heavy object, especially to lift or reposition it, or even repeated handling of lightweight parts, can cause serious injuries or cumulative trauma disorders (CTDs).

CTDs are conditions of the muscles, tendons, bones, blood vessels, and nerves due to repetitive or high impact motions of the body. Carpal tunnel syndrome, tendinitis, and herniated discs are some of the well-known CTDs that occur in the workplace. OSHA considers CTDs to be illnesses, not injuries, when they are workplace-related, and is making this area a high priority for investigation.

Lower back injury is another ailment resulting from material handling. Many say it is the most costly of such injuries. Lower back injury results from repetitive activities, as well as acute trauma.

As more disorders are identified, medical costs to treat them continue to rise. This, in turn, causes a rise in costs to companies providing health coverage to employees experiencing such disorders. There are also associated costs resulting from such accompanying consequences as lost production time. With the implementation of ergonomic assist and lifting devices, companies can take a proactive approach to reducing these costs before they start.

A prime example occurs in facilities using high-impact or high-torque wrenches to install bolts or similar fasteners. Operators are required to "absorb" the impact of the wrench as it reaches final torque levels, which in many cases is in the 300-450 ft-lb (407-610 Nm) range. This can cause serious injury to the employee in the form of CTDs due to the high and repetitive impact of the task.

Situations such as this have led to the development of ergonomic assist devices (Fig. 14-1) designed to absorb the impact of the torque wrench for the operator, thus reducing the risk of injury, illness, or loss of productivity. Installing such a device before start-up of the work cell or assembly line is an extremely prudent and proactive way to minimize potential medical costs.

Higher Productivity

Companies incorporating lifting and assist devices in the workplace can expect a reduction in injuries, and higher productivity per worker. This is due to less operator fatigue, especially in repetitive motion tasks with high cycle times. Ergonomic assist devices bear the strain for the worker, allowing more productive time between rest or break periods, freeing the employee to perform additional tasks.

For example, assume a worker is performing an operation picking objects from one area, such as a conveyor, and placing them in another area, perhaps on a pallet lying on the floor. This operator could experience fatigue quickly if there is some distance between the two areas, or if the objects are heavy. However, if this same worker was performing the task with an ergonomic assist device, the object could be picked from the conveyor and placed on the pallet without the operator having to physically do the lifting or the bending, and perhaps not even the walking. This allows the operator to perform more tasks without tiring and thus, work either faster or for extended periods of time.

The Contributors of this chapter are: David J. Cummings, Project Engineer, Positech; Penny English, Project Engineer, Vestil Manufacturing; Rich Gronczewski, Project Engineer, Vestil Manufacturing; Brad Holloway, Product Design Development Engineering Director, Vestil Manufacturing; Mark Krystofik, Manufacturing Manager, Gorbel, Inc.; Hui T. Lau, Design Engineer, Vestil Manufacturing; Dean Love, National Sales Manager, Vestil Manufacturing; Jay B. Stevens, PE, Engineering Manager, Vestil Manufacturing; Jim Stockmaster, Mechanical Engineer, Gorbel, Inc.; Bill Yeakle, Design Engineer, Vestil Manufacturing.
The Reviewers of this chapter are: James I. Galante, Director, Product and Market Development, Southworth International Group, Inc.; Brian E. McNamara, President, Southworth International Group, Inc.; Ursula R. Wright, PhD, Ergonomics Consultant, General Motors.

CHAPTER 14   WORKER PRODUCTIVITY AND ERGONOMIC ASSISTS

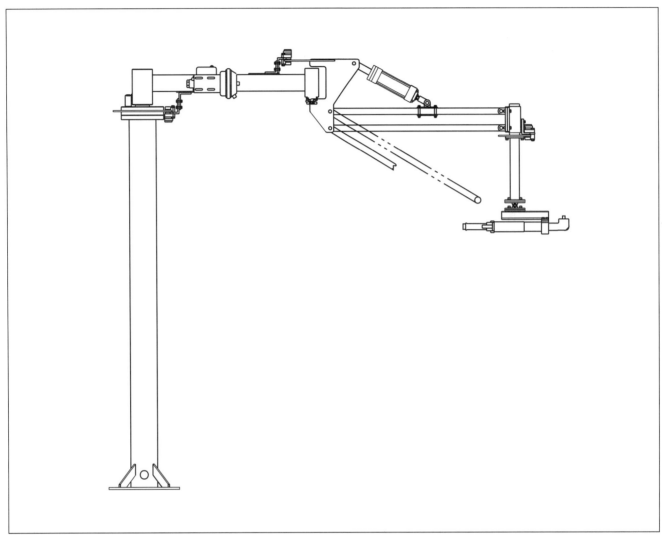

Fig. 14-1 Torque arm with brakes. *(Courtesy Positech)*

Work Force Reduction

Since downsizing is the current norm in industry, employers are looking to do more with less. Ergonomic assist devices can be a valuable asset in this area since they can be used by one operator to handle objects usually requiring two or more workers. The proper device allows a single employee, regardless of physical size or strength (to a reasonable degree), to do the work of multiple employees requiring greater physical ability. A position once requiring a select set of physical qualifications can now be filled by a broader range of people since the physical limitations no longer exist as part of the job description.

For example, suppose a large billet of material is being transferred from a transport cart to a machining center. If it is more profitable to machine a 200-lb (90.7-kg) billet than a 35-lb (15.9-kg) one, the manufacturing engineer must determine a way to transfer such a billet to the machine. This could be accomplished with workers only, requiring a means to grasp the part physically and enough human input force to lift and transfer the billet. Attempting such a feat may be extremely dangerous to the workers, creating the potential for serious injury. It could also require a substantial amount of manpower, with a certain amount of physical strength, and the billet must be altered or specially designed to allow the number of workers required to grasp it.

These requirements may impact the overall profitability of this machining center through workers' compensation claims, increased wages for hazardous duty, and special product design for transfer. Performing the same task with an ergonomic assist or lifting device, however, could produce quite different results. With a device designed for the specific task, to handle the billet as delivered, a single operator could perform the transfer. Use of the device would reduce the risk of injury, the number of workers required, and eliminate the need for a special billet design.

Product that Cannot be Physically Handled

Another advantage of the ergonomic assist device is to handle objects that cannot be moved by purely human physical means. One of the most common limiting factors is excessive weight. Some materials and products are beyond the lifting capacity of the human body and the only alternative is a lifting device. Aircraft skins are a good example of this, because they are manufactured in very large sections, and must be transported from a fabrication area to an assembly area and then positioned on the airframe. Constructing these

CHAPTER 14 WORKER PRODUCTIVITY AND ERGONOMIC ASSISTS

skins in smaller, more humanly-manageable sections would not be cost-effective, and thus a lifting device must be used.

High temperatures are another limiting factor for material handling. Some applications require immediate transport of the product after firing or pouring and cannot be approached by an operator, even in protective gear. Many foundries incorporate ergonomic assist devices to handle freshly poured parts, still red hot, as they are removed from their molds. These devices present quite a challenge to designers since they require special high-temperature resistant materials and extensive shielding for operators.

Ergonomic assist devices can also repetitively provide accurate placement of objects much more effectively than human operators acting alone. As the body fatigues, the senses dull, making it increasingly difficult to place an object in exactly the same place. This type of repetitive motion can also lead to emotional stress and CTDs such as carpal tunnel syndrome. Ergonomic devices allow the operator to translate very small inputs into larger ones, perhaps with the use of joysticks, and devices can be set, or even programmed, to move from exactly point "a" to exactly point "b" at the touch of a button. Many stresses on the operator can be alleviated through such devices, and in cases where placement is critical to assembly of the product, cost of scrap and rework also may be decreased.

The last example is that of lifting or placing objects in areas either too high or too low as to be physically accessible, or operating outside of the human "window." Simple examples of such devices are lift trucks, chain hoists, and scissors lifts. These devices extend the range of the human body, allowing the placement of products and materials to minimize the amount of storage space required.

See Chapter 7 of this handbook for more on ergonomics and manual material handling.

LIFTING TABLES

A simple type of ergonomic assist equipment is the lift table, or "scissors lift," so named because of its scissors-like arm movement when cycling. It raises work to an acceptable level for any worker, regardless of size. The *lift table*, in its basic form, generally consists of the following components: a base to stabilize the unit, a scissors assembly to provide support throughout the travel of the unit, a platform on which the payload is placed, and a means of supplying force to raise and lower the platform.

Most scissors lift bases are designed for stationary use, although many manufacturers offer an optional portable model with casters at the base. Typically, the base serves two purposes. It provides stability to the unit as a whole and contains the rails that guide the scissors assembly. Since this design requires the base to extend upward several inches when fully lowered, some tables are installed with the base recessed into the floor. This type of installation is referred to as a *pit mount* and allows the top surface of the table to be lowered flush to the floor surface.

The scissors assembly of the lift table provides the platform support throughout its range of motion. As force is input to the frame, the "legs" of the scissors are either pushed together or pulled apart. The amount of vertical travel is determined by the length of the legs. A single leg set can provide vertical travel equal to approximately 70% of its length. As payloads increase dimensionally, multiple scissors assemblies can be placed in a common base, either side-by-side or end-to-end to support larger platforms. When higher travel is required in limited space, the scissors assemblies can be stacked.

Some companies offer a variation from the scissors assembly. As force is applied to the table top, the corner posts, basically tube-in-a-tube supports, extend or retract. These are typically used for low-cost, low-payload applications, and cannot reach nearly as close to the floor as a scissors frame system.

The most basic table surface is flat and stationary. However, most manufacturers offer a wide variety of surfaces. Some styles contain rollers imbedded in the surface, which allow horizontal movement about the top of the table. Others are designed to rotate, tilt, and upend payloads, as well as fitted with fixtures to accommodate special load configurations.

Power Sources

Table top units can be powered by many different means. The parameters controlling the type of actuator required are payload, speed, mobility, convenience, and cost. For payloads up to 4,000 lb (1,814 kg), pneumatic, hydraulic, or electric actuators can be used. Although there are special cases, in general, payloads over 4,000 lb (1,814 kg) are normally lifted by means of hydraulic actuators due to their greater mechanical advantage when compared to the size of pneumatic or electric actuators.

For lighter loads and infrequent use, hydraulic lifts can be foot- or hand pump-actuated. Hydraulic actuators for larger payloads are usually driven by pumps powered by electric motors, thus requiring an electrical power source. Some models contain a battery system, allowing the table to be transported and relocated throughout a facility without the need for a readily available outlet. Lifts also can be actuated by air, motor-driven hydraulics, which are well suited for an explosion-proof environment.

Pneumatic actuators are much cleaner to operate and can be easily connected to existing shop air systems. These lifts are well suited for applications requiring two fixed positions, fully lowered or raised. The compressibility of air prevents consistent control of intermediate elevation. These actuators are simply air bags that expand when inflated, containing no moving parts to wear out or fail, and requiring no motors or pumps. They are, however, limited to lift heights of around 24 in. (61 cm) and capacities of 4,000 lb (1,814 kg) or less.

Some lifts use electric motors with drives and ball screw drives, eliminating the need for hydraulic pumps and actuators. These are well suited to applications where precise elevations must be achieved or maintained. They are much quieter than hydraulic lifts, but become very expensive for heavier capacities.

Controls

Lift tables use power to move up and gravity to lower them. Some more sophisticated lifts are powered both up and down. The controls vary widely from hand or foot pumps to elevate, to levers or knobs to lower. Motor-driven lifts may have push button, joystick, or foot-activated controls, or the lift can be automated into a programmable logic controller (PLC). Lift control to specific predetermined elevations can be a matter of choice suitable to the application requirements. Time, pressure, or position logic controls are available to suit individual needs.

Typical Applications and Usage

In its purest form, the lift table is used to lift or lower a payload from one level to another. The best example of a typical lift table application is for "breaking down" palletized goods. A pallet is placed on the table top in its full down position. As the operator unloads the pallet, perhaps onto a conveyor, he or she is normally required to begin bending farther and farther over to reach the next lowest tier of goods. When using a lift table, however, the operator need only raise the table height as he or she reaches the next tier, thus keeping the unload height relatively constant.

Variations of the standard lift table can be used for many different tasks. Tilt tables, for instance, are employed where workers are required to reach into a bin or storage container. Pallet inverters are

CHAPTER 14   WORKER PRODUCTIVITY AND ERGONOMIC ASSISTS

used when damage is sustained to the lower tiers of palletized goods. Instead of unloading the whole pallet to reach the damaged goods at the bottom, the pallet is simply upended, inverting the tiers and allowing easy removal of damaged product.

Ergonomic Benefits

Any device that eliminates the need for the worker to bend, reach, or lift objects from below waist height will most definitely decrease the number of work-related injuries, specifically back injuries, by far the most common CTDs in the workplace.

In the case of tilting tables, since employees no longer need to lean over into a container to remove product, lower back and leg injuries are prevented. Turntables eliminate the stretching and reaching tasks of loading and unloading palletized goods, which saves time (money), as well as worker fatigue and risk of injury.

The lift table is a simple, inexpensive ergonomic assist device designed for certain types of tasks (see Table 14-1). There are, however, many functions and operations in the workplace that cannot be performed with only a lift table. Pick and place operations, for example, usually require devices with larger ranges of motion, as well as specially designed tooling. Some products and materials are too large to be physically handled at any level, and therefore must be handled by other means. The lift table may be used in conjunction with many other devices to provide both vertical and lateral positioning.

BALANCERS AND HOISTS

Balancers and hoists are relatively simple units, designed specifically to lift heavy objects. These devices are generally compact, but capable of lifting large payloads. Most manufactures provide product lines with varying ranges of capacity, allowing consumers the option to purchase enough capacity for the job (see Table 14-2).

The hoist consists mainly of a power source, a drive mechanism to turn a lift wheel or sprocket, and a certain length of chain or wire rope (the lift media). As power is supplied to the unit, the drive mechanism turns the sprocket, which retrieves or extends the lift media, thus raising or lowering the payload. Up and down functions are usually controlled by a hand-held pendant with buttons or levers for each direction (see Fig. 14-2).

A balancer is similar in design, with a slight difference in controls. Balancers are pneumatically-powered, and can be controlled to raise and lower the payload based on physical input from the operator. For example, an operator desires to lower a hook connected to the end of the balancer chain and attach it to a given payload. Instead of having to hold the pendant in one hand and the chain and hook in the other, he or she merely has to pull down on the chain with a small amount of input force. The balancer's controls sense the input and allow the operator to lower the hook. After the hook is attached to the payload, the operator supplies a small amount of up force on the chain and the balancer reacts in similar fashion, raising the payload.

Power Sources

There are mainly two types of power used to drive balancers and hoists: electric and pneumatic.

Electric hoists are the simplest, because they do not require the type of airtight sealing mandatory on pneumatic balancers. Electric input is provided to a motor that turns a gear set, sprocket, or similar mechanism. Gearing can be used to allow small motors with high speeds to generate large torques at slow speeds, ideal for this type of application. Capacities of 2,000 lb (907 kg) and more are commonplace for electric hoists.

Pneumatic balancers are slightly more complex (see Fig. 14-3). Air is input to a cylinder (80-90 psi [552-621 kPa] is standard for most manufacturing facilities) and a piston in the cylinder is forced from one side to the other, exactly as a simple pneumatic cylinder functions. As the piston head moves, a ball screw is turned, which lifts the payload. The capacities of pneumatic balancers are somewhat limited as compared to electric hoists, because the only way to increase the force required to turn the ball screw is to increase the area of the piston head, and thus the bore of the cylinder. Capacities of around 500 lb (227 kg) are typical of pneumatic balancers.

A third type of balancer is the *spring balancer*, so named because its source of lift power is a spring. This type of balancer is usually used for very light loads (about 50 lb [23 kg] maximum). A spring balancer works on the same principle as the common tape measure. As it is extended by a small operator input force, a spring inside the body of the balancer is wound tighter. A locking mechanism holds the lift media in place until the operator decides to retract it, in which case he or she pulls down slightly to release the lock, and then allows the wound spring to retract the lift media.

Controls

The controls differ considerably between the electric hoist and the pneumatic balancer. The pendant control of the electric hoist is a simple electric switch that changes the direction of sprocket rotation to raise or lower the payload. Some controls contain a *rocker switch*, so named because it is rocked by the operator's thumb between the up and down positions, and returns to neutral when released. Others contain separate buttons for the up and down functions. This form of control prevents the operator from activating both directions simultaneously.

Balancers, on the other hand, can be controlled in many different ways. A balancer can be controlled using small operator inputs. As the operator inputs a small down force, the balancer senses the load and decreases the pressure in the cylinder, allowing the operator to lower the lift media with minimal effort.

In similar fashion, when the operator provides a small input up force on the lift media, the balancer reacts by increasing pressure to the cylinder, providing the lift desired by the operator. When the desired height is reached, he or she simply lets go of the lift media, and the balancer stops and holds the payload at that height. Pneumatic circuitry can be designed to allow the balancer to perform this function empty (with no payload) and loaded (with payload attached). This type of control is generally referred to as "balance control" and makes the operator's job much easier, because he or she does not have to hold a pendant and push buttons for up and down control.

Pneumatic balancers also can be equipped with metering controls that regulate the amount of air in the cylinder. This type of control is very similar to the pendant (push a lever for up and down control). As the operator depresses the up lever, the pressure in the cylinder is increased and vice versa for the down lever.

Metering controls are required when the payload weight varies considerably and the same balancer is used. This is because the balancer must be set to handle a certain payload, within a small range of weight. Setting the balance pressure means that when a payload is sensed, the air pressure in the cylinder is automatically adjusted to the set pressure, which is just enough to lift the expected payload. If a payload larger than the one set is used, the pressure sent to the cylinder will not be enough to lift it. If the application requires lifting several sizes of payload in the same work cell randomly, it would be impractical for the operator to set the balancer each time. Metering controls allow the operator to use the same balancer, because the operator must depress the appropriate control lever until the pressure in the cylinder reaches a level that allows the payload to be moved. In other words, the operator controls the amount of pressure in the cylinder, not the pneumatic balance circuitry.

CHAPTER 14   WORKER PRODUCTIVITY AND ERGONOMIC ASSISTS

TABLE 14-1
Lift Tables

Usage	Power	Additional Features	Controls	Range of Motion*	Benefits*	Limitations*
To adjust payload heights and location by raising, lowering, conveying, and/or transferring materials between two or more elevations.	Spring load for light payloads.	Can rotate containers and pallets about a vertical axis to better handle the load.	Foot pedals.	Lifting heights up to a vertical distance of 84 in. (213 cm) from floor level.	Decreases bending, reaching, and lifting objects.	Limited to height adjustments and orientation applications.
	Pneumatic, electric, and hydraulic actuators for payloads up to 4,000 lb (1,814 kg) and lift heights of 24 in. (61 cm).	Table surfaces can be customized to include tilt lifts, personnel lifts, tables for coil transport, roll handling tables, dock use, and powered rotators.	Hand cranks.		Simple to use.	
	Hydraulic power sources for 4,000 lb (1,814 kg) and higher, and lifts up to 84 in. (213 cm).	Floor locks, overload protection, and wheel castors can be added for safety and mobility.	Guarded foot pedals or switches, push buttons, or pendant controls.		Inexpensive.	

*For all types.

CHAPTER 14   WORKER PRODUCTIVITY AND ERGONOMIC ASSISTS

TABLE 14-2
Balancers and Hoists

Usage	Type and Capacity	Controls	Mount	Benefits	Limitations
Balancers: to lift heavy and awkward objects.	Spring balancers use springs as the power source and are used for light payloads of up to 50 lb (23 kg).	Pneumatic balancers: balance control and metering controls available.	Overhead rails for side-to-side and forward and back motions.	Compact.	Pneumatic balancers are limited to payloads under 500 lb (227 kg) and have a slight hesitation when cycling.
				Balancers provide weightless tool positioning for ease of operation and precision positioning.	
Hoists: used for straight lift applications and pick-and-place operations.	Electric hoists are simple and ideal for large torques at slow speeds, usually accommodating payloads of 2,000 lb (907 kg) or higher.	Electric hoists: hand-held pendants with rocker switches and up/down controls.	Without mounts, motion is limited to up and down directions.	Available with different capacities.*	Electric hoists produce excessive heat and may not perform well with faster cycle times.
	Pneumatic hoists are more complex and have a limited payload capacity.		Mobile mounts are available.*	Decrease or eliminate pressure in the lower back and discomfort in the arms and shoulders.*	

*Applies to both hoists and balancers.

CHAPTER 14   WORKER PRODUCTIVITY AND ERGONOMIC ASSISTS

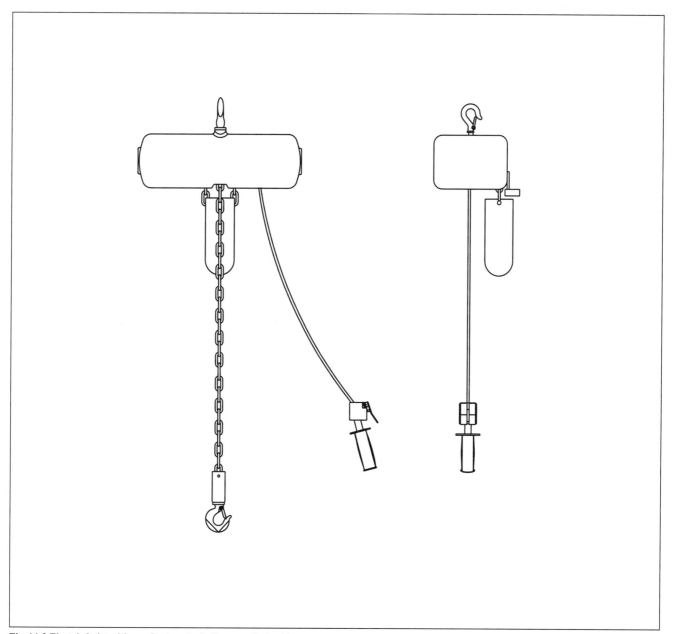

Fig. 14-2 Electric hoist with pendant control. *(Courtesy Positech)*

Typical Applications and Usage

Hoists and balancers are typically used for straight lift applications—lifting a payload from one height to another. They are also commonly used in pick-and-place applications, where they function as part of a tooling and rail system, designed specifically for the application.

Many manufacturing facilities use hoists to lift heavy materials into machining centers, such as lathes or drill presses. In these applications, a sling is usually used to support the material, which attaches to the hook found at the end of the hoist or balancer.

When used as part of a more complex ergonomic solution, the hoist generally provides the lift function only, with special tooling providing the means to handle the payload. It is important to remember in these applications that the hoist being employed must not only be capable of handling the amount of payload, but also the tooling required to handle it.

Ergonomic Benefits

Much money has been spent to educate the work force in the proper ways to lift heavy objects, but it is left to the employee to follow these procedures. By implementing balancers and hoists in the work cell, employers minimize the potential for employees not following proper lifting procedures, because the lifting device now does the task. Employees benefit by a safer work environment and experience fewer accidents and injuries.

Although they do little to eliminate physical problems associated with bending or leaning (unless special tooling is used in conjunction with them), balancers and hoists definitely help reduce lower

CHAPTER 14   WORKER PRODUCTIVITY AND ERGONOMIC ASSISTS

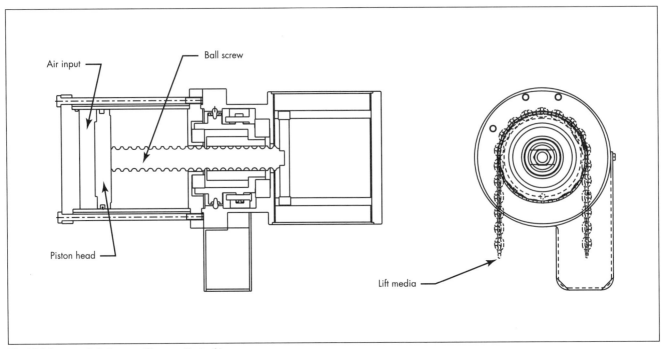

Fig. 14-3 Pneumatic balancer. *(Courtesy Positech)*

back injuries and other common CTDs. The best way to reduce the number of human injuries and accidents is to take the human out of the equation. This is accomplished by substituting the lifting device for physical lifting.

Limitations and Range of Capacity

Electric hoists are employed in many different environments, from manufacturing and assembly to distribution and service. Just as their usage varies greatly, so does their capacity. Many large hoists and cranes are capable of heavy payloads. However, electric hoists have a tendency to generate excess heat when cycled continuously, and do not perform well in areas where high cycle times are required.

Pneumatic balancers are somewhat limited due to the size of the lift cylinder required to generate large forces. Most readily available balancers have a maximum capacity of about 500 lb (227 kg). Balancers have a slight hesitation when cycling, because the cylinder must be pressurized before lifting can take place. This makes them less responsive than their electric counterparts, but unlike the electric hoist, the balancer does not have a tendency to overheat.

The hoist and balancer uses chain or wire rope as the lifting media. However, chains and wire ropes can be reeved, like a block-and-tackle, to increase the capacity of the unit (see Fig. 14-4). For example, an air balancer with a lift capacity of 300 lb (136 kg) could be double-reeved to increase its capacity to 600 lb (272 kg). Reeving systems are relatively inexpensive, especially considering the increase in capacity obtained from employing them.

Balancers and hoists are somewhat limited as a stand-alone item. Unless mounted to an overhead rail system or similar device, they are limited to straight up and down travel. They also must have special tooling added to them if used to pick and place items that cannot be grasped by a simple hook or sling-type apparatus.

MANIPULATORS

Many material handling applications in the manufacturing environment involve more than a simple part transfer from one height to another, or loading and unloading product and raw materials. In some work cells, operators are required to not only lift the material, but also transfer it a significant distance. Some applications also require rotating, pitching, and otherwise manipulating the material or product. Such operations usually require a more sophisticated type of ergonomic assist device, called a *manipulator* (see Table 14-3).

Manipulators come in many styles, with differing functions, capacities, and power sources. They are mainly used to handle parts too heavy or awkward for human operators to handle physically. They are also used in quite a number of interesting applications and designers are constantly challenged to create new and innovative material handling devices and solutions.

Vertical Lifters

Vertical lifters are similar in function to balancers and hoists, but are very different in design. The *vertical lifter*, or *V-lift* as it is often called, uses a rigid lifting media (shaft) in lieu of a chain or wire rope. In fact, the unit as a whole is rigid, and the shaft extends and retracts to raise and lower the payload. This type of design eliminates the "pendulum effect" experienced with balancers and hoists when side loads are applied to the payload. Vertical lifters also provide more stability for applications that incorporate special tooling to pitch parts vertically.

One disadvantage of the vertical lifter, when compared to a hoist or balancer, is the amount of overhead clearance required for the V-lift to function. When the V-lift is in its fully retracted position, the entire shaft must be contained by the outer casing. The overall length of the V-lift when fully extended must be more than twice as long as the amount of stroke length required for the application.

For example, if the amount of stroke (or travel length) required for the operation is 24 in. (61 cm), the entire V-lift assembly must be more than 48-in. (122-cm) long to allow the shaft to retract 24 in. (61 cm) to its full up position. Instead of the lift mechanism wrapping around a sprocket such as a chain (thus allowing a low profile), it has to remain rigid, requiring a higher mounting position.

CHAPTER 14   WORKER PRODUCTIVITY AND ERGONOMIC ASSISTS

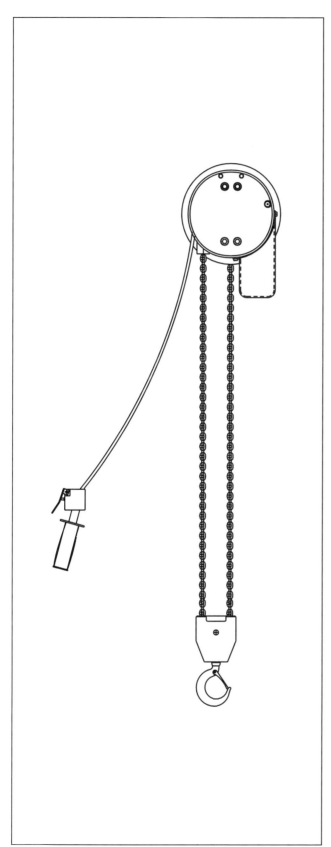

Fig. 14-4 Reeved pneumatic balancer. *(Courtesy Positech)*

Figure 14-5 depicts two common types of vertical lifters. Figure 14-5 (a) shows a *tie-rod style V-lift*, so named because of the tie rods used to hold the two end caps tight against the outer case. This style is similar to a standard pneumatic or hydraulic cylinder, with a few additional components. Inside the lower end cap, a bearing set is inserted. This allows the V-lift's shaft to operate smoothly when actuating, even if moment loads are applied to the shaft. For this reason, tie rod V-lifts are most beneficial when used in applications where tooling or payloads need to extend horizontally some distance from the shaft. Many tie rod V-lifts can handle moment loads of 10,000-15,000 in.-lb (1,130-1,695 Nm).

Figure 14-5 (b) illustrates a style commonly referred to as a *linear thruster*. This type of vertical lifter contains an "off-the-shelf" cylinder mounted in a housing. Bearing sets are imbedded in the housing and guide rods run through the bearings as the cylinder is actuated. The purpose of the guide rod is to provide lateral support, so the cylinder itself does not experience excessive moment loading. Most manufacturers offer linear thrusters with two or four guide rods. Linear thrusters are more readily available than tie rod style vertical lifters, and most can be specially ordered to exact specifications without long lead times. They do not perform as well as their tie rod counterparts, however, when subjected to moment loads in excess of 5,000 in.-lb (565 Nm), at which point they experience binding between the guide rods and bearings.

Both styles of vertical lifters are typically powered by pneumatics or hydraulics. Electrical systems may exist, but are the exception. They would not be very practical for most material handling applications. Pneumatic systems are much cleaner and easier to maintain than hydraulic systems, but the cylinder bore size required to lift large payloads is much larger than hydraulic units. This makes hydraulic V-lifts the most common choice for payloads in excess of 1,000 lb (454 kg).

Linear thrusters have a distinct advantage when it comes to power sources, as pneumatic or hydraulic cylinders can be used interchangeably in the bearing housing. The ability to interchange cylinders allows for greater flexibility in the field with less expense incurred.

Jibs

A *jib*, in its most basic form, is a simple beam, usually extending from a pedestal mounted to the floor. It could be an "I"-style beam fixed to the pedestal, which can be used as a rail for guiding a balancer or hoist mounted on a trolley truck. This allows the operator to translate, as well as lift, a given payload. After the payload is lifted, the operator simply pulls the chain or cable horizontally in the direction he or she would like to move. The unit travels along the I-beam by means of the trolley truck. A simple jib such as this is relatively inexpensive and adds another degree of freedom to the operation.

More sophisticated jibs include a bearing at the pedestal and jib beam interface, allowing the beam to be rotated around the pedestal. This adds still another degree of freedom to the system, enabling the operator to translate in two directions. Some jib arms are composed of enclosed tracks in lieu of an I-style beam, so that the trolley truck can travel without being exposed to the environment. A few manufacturers offer such jibs as off-the-shelf items, made to a predetermined length of arm and height of pedestal.

The most complex of jibs is the *articulated jib*. This type contains a rotation point at the pedestal and jib interface (referred to as the main post) and a second rotation point (called the middle joint), which essentially splits the jib beam into two parts (see Fig. 14-6). The parts of the split beam are commonly referred to as the "first" and "second" arms of the jib.

An articulated jib functions like a chicken wing in that the arms can be bent at the middle joint as well as rotated about the main post.

CHAPTER 14   WORKER PRODUCTIVITY AND ERGONOMIC ASSISTS

TABLE 14-3
Manipulators

Usage	Type and Capacity	Power and Controls	Benefits	Limitations
V-lifts: lifting, transferring, and lowering materials or products.	Tie-rod style can manage moment loads of 10,000–15,000 in.-lb (1,130–1,695 Nm).	Tie rods and linear thrusts are powered by pneumatic and hydraulic systems, however, electric power sources are available.	Eliminates the pendulum effect when side loads are applied to payloads. This effect is seen with hoists and balancers.	Larger overhead clearance is required to operate V-lifts when compared to hoists and balancers.
		Hydraulic V-lifts are recommended for payloads in excess of 1,000 lb (454 kg).	More stability for applications that incorporate special tooling to pitch parts vertically.	V-lifts bind between guide rods and bearings when experiencing loads in excess of 5,000 in.-lb (565 Nm).
		Pneumatic systems are cleaner and easier to maintain than hydraulic systems.	V-lifts are most beneficial where tooling or payloads need to raise horizontally some distance from the shaft.	
			Pneumatic and hydraulic cylinders can be used interchangeably in the bearing housing for linear thrusts.	
			Linear thrusts can be ordered to exact specification without long lead times.	
Jibs: beam extending from a pedestal mount allowing operators to transfer and lift payloads.	Articulated jib: complex due to rotation points at the main post and middle joints. Used when large motions are needed between pick and place operations.	Pneumatic power source available.	Beam can rotate around the pedestal providing increased degrees of freedom.	As payload increases and reaches within the work cell become farther, the jib arm and bearings used at the joints also become larger. This results in more operator input needed to articulate the larger arm.
	The arm length can be as long as 10 ft (3 m) based on the payload amount and type of arm material used.		Payload can be moved around the work cell with ease.	Several design considerations should be made before selecting a jib: reach desired, payload, cycle time, etc.
			Any given point within the overall radius of the arms can be reached when the arm is fully extended.	
			Folds away from work area when not in use.	

CHAPTER 14   WORKER PRODUCTIVITY AND ERGONOMIC ASSISTS

TABLE 14-3—(continued)
Manipulators

Usage	Type and Capacity	Power and Controls	Benefits	Limitations
Balanced manipulators: lifting, transferring, and lowering materials or products.	Capable of handling over 500 lb (227 kg) with a reach capacity of up to 144 in. (366 cm).	Electric or hydraulic power systems are available using either balanced or metered controls.	Table or pedestal mounts available.	Hesitation as the lift cylinder takes time to pressurize in pneumatic manipulators.
		Most units can handle up to 70,000 in.-lb (7,909 Nm) of moment at the main post.	Offers more degrees of freedom than a simple jib or vertical lift, and would otherwise require a combination of two simpler machines.	As the moment increases, the size of the overall unit will increase.
			Can perform lifts and transfers simultaneously, which would otherwise require a combination of two simpler machines.	More expensive than a simple jib or vertical lift.
Positioning arm: complex lifting, transferring, and handling operations.	Can handle from 500-1,500 lb (227-680 kg).	Hydraulic handling capacities of 500-1,500 lb (227-680 kg) at the base.	Units are smoother and easier to control than a pneumatic-powered manipulator.	Hydraulic systems are more difficult to maintain and clean, limiting usage in clean room and food processing applications.
	Moment capacities up to 150,000 in.-lb (16,948 Nm) at the main post.	Controls: electronic push buttons.	Provides fast, easy lifting, and precise positioning of heavy objects. Moves easily to exact location. Folds away from work area when not in use.	
	Reach capacity is less than 100 in. (254 cm) to keep the moment loads within capacity.			
Torque arm: relieves many stresses caused by torque tool operations by absorbing the torque and supporting the weight of the tool for the operator.	Torque arm can handle moments between 5,000-20,000 in.-lb (565-2,260 Nm).	Powered by springs for smaller units.	Take the weight and torque away from the operator.	Braking mechanism is needed at every joint of the torque arm to absorb mount forces.
		Balanced controls available for pneumatic systems.	Allows operators to input very small forces to raise or lower the arms.	Careful design consideration needed before selection.
		Pneumatic for larger units.	Table and pedestal designs available for generating torques of over 20,000 in.-lb (2,260 Nm).	

CHAPTER 14   WORKER PRODUCTIVITY AND ERGONOMIC ASSISTS

This type of articulation allows an operator to easily move a payload within the work cell and reach any point within the overall radius of the arms when fully extended. Articulated jibs are very beneficial in work cells requiring large translations between pick and place operations, because the arm lengths can be as long as 10 ft (3 m) or more, based on the amount of payload and type of arm material used.

It is important to note that both first and second arm lengths on articulated jibs are usually limited by the maximum moment loading capacity of the bearings at the two "joints." For the jib to articulate freely and to extend the life of the bearings, moment loads must be kept lower than the actual capacities of the bearings. For this reason, as payloads get larger and reaches get farther, the jib arms and the bearings used at the joints also become larger (some units are built to handle up to 300,000 in.-lb [33,895 Nm] of moment loading at the main post). This, in turn, leads to more operator input required to articulate the larger arms. Factors such as reach desired, payload, and operator cycle time must all be considered, and sometimes compromised, to reach the best solution for material handling applications.

Balanced Manipulators

Figure 14-7 shows a typical style of balanced manipulator. Most balanced manipulators contain:

- A pedestal for floor mounting (overhead mounting is an alternative option offered by many manufacturers).
- A rotation bearing or similar assembly to allow the main section to rotate.
- A lifting mechanism.
- Counterweights.
- Lift arms for vertical and lateral movement.
- An end joint for mounting special end effectors or tooling.

This type of unit is the standard from which the word "manipulator" has emerged. It combines the articulation of the jib with the lifting capability of the vertical lifter. As the lifting mechanism is activated, the entire main section is raised. This motion creates an upward force on the horizontal or main arm of the manipulator, which pivots about a pin.

Due to the location of the applied force and the length of the horizontal arm, a small stroke movement by the lifting mechanism translates into a large vertical movement of the arm. The second, or down, arm usually consists of a parallel linkage, allowing the tooling attached at the end joint to remain horizontal and level in all arm positions. Counterweights aid in balancing the system at any given point and reduce the overall moment loading at the main post.

Balanced manipulators are mainly powered via pneumatic cylinders, with bores ranging from 6 in. (15 cm) to more than 11 in. (28 cm), depending on the payload capacity of the machine. Airflow to the cylinder is controlled with the same principles used to control pneumatic balancers. Balance controls or metering controls can be incorporated. These controls are normally attached to some type of handles mounted to the tooling for easy operator access.

Electrically-powered, balanced manipulators have been developed by some manufacturers, but higher costs, as compared to their pneumatic counterparts, have limited their widespread use in industry. One distinct advantage of the electric manipulator, however, is its responsiveness. Pneumatically-controlled devices, as illustrated earlier with balancers, tend to have some hesitation because the lift cylinder takes time to pressurize.

The reach of a balanced manipulator can be as long as 144 in. (366 cm), with a payload capacity of over 500 lb (227 kg). Since these units, like articulated jibs, contain bearings at the main post

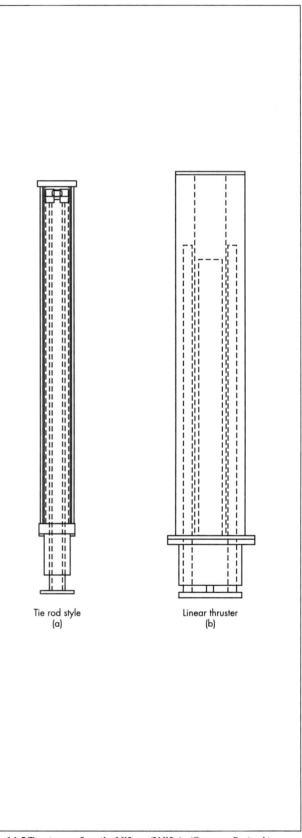

Tie rod style
(a)

Linear thruster
(b)

Fig. 14-5 Two types of vertical lifters (V-lifts). *(Courtesy Positech)*

CHAPTER 14   WORKER PRODUCTIVITY AND ERGONOMIC ASSISTS

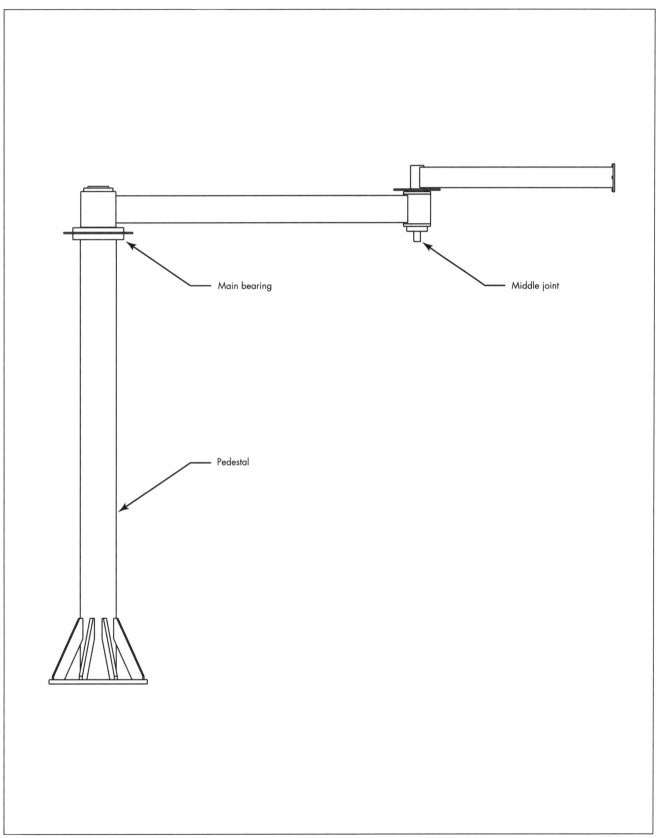

Fig. 14-6 Articulated jib. *(Courtesy Positech)*

CHAPTER 14   WORKER PRODUCTIVITY AND ERGONOMIC ASSISTS

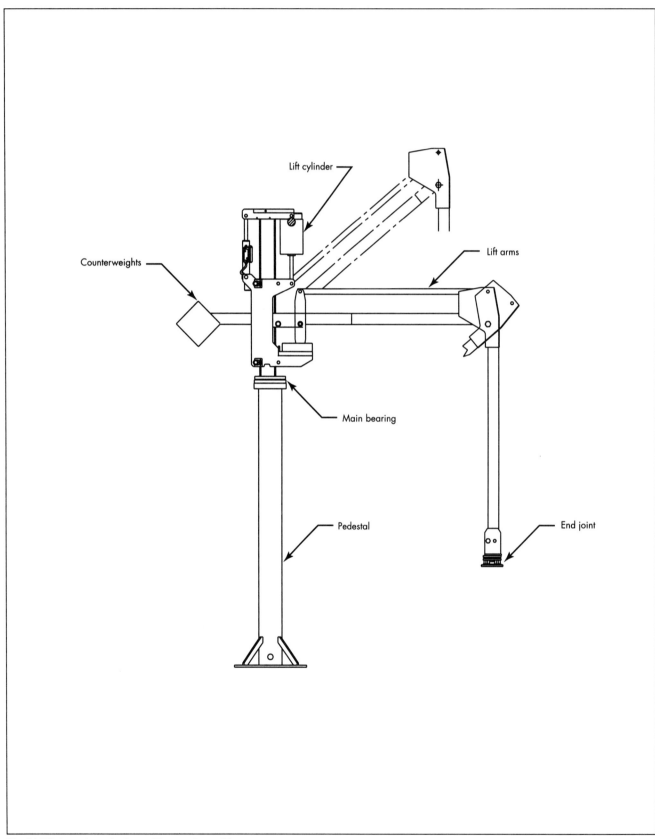

Fig. 14-7 Balanced manipulator. *(Courtesy Positech)*

CHAPTER 14   WORKER PRODUCTIVITY AND ERGONOMIC ASSISTS

for rotation, they are also subject to certain moment loading conditions. As the moment capacity required increases (through longer reach or heavier payload), the size of the overall unit required also increases. Most units will handle moments of up to 70,000 in.-lb (7,909 Nm) at the main post. Many manufacturers offer a line of machines with differing moment capacities, which allows consumers to closely match a unit with the requirements of the application.

A balanced manipulator is usually much more expensive than a simple jib unit or vertical lifter, but offers more in terms of degrees of motion. A single balanced manipulator can perform lift and translation functions simultaneously, something which would take the combination of two simpler machines to accomplish. This makes the balanced manipulator a very attractive system for applications requiring both lifting and transferring payloads.

Positioning Arms

One of the most complex and powerful units of the manipulator family is the positioning arm. This machine articulates quite like the human arm, with joints at three, and sometimes more, locations. Figure 14-8 illustrates a positioning arm which consists of:

- A main post.
- A power unit enclosure.
- A lift section.
- A second arm and downshaft.
- An end joint.

Special tooling is usually attached at the end joint, specific to the application.

The positioning arm is hydraulically-powered, which is why the power unit enclosure exists at the main post. This enclosure houses the hydraulic pumps, reservoirs, and electrical systems required to actuate the lift section and any special tooling functions. Hydraulics are used because the positioning arm is designed to handle payloads from 500 lb (227 kg) to over 1,500 lb (680 kg). Loads of this magnitude make the use of pneumatics or other sources impractical or cost-prohibitive. Hydraulic systems present additional problems from a maintenance standpoint, as well as for clean room or food processing applications.

Positioning arms are also subject to moment loading limitations, due to the bearings at the points of rotation. Moment load capacities of up to 150,000 in.-lb (16,948 Nm) at the main post are possible. Since the payloads associated with positioning arms are usually quite high, the overall reach of the units is usually less than 100 in. (254 cm) to keep the moment loads within capacity.

Electronic push-button controls are standard on positioning arms, because they are required to control hydraulic systems. This makes the unit much smoother and easier to control than a pneumatically-powered manipulator, although it is slower to cycle. Control stations are usually mounted near the end of the arm in close proximity to the end effector or tooling specific to the application.

Positioning arms can cost up to three times as much as pneumatic balanced manipulators. This is mainly due to the increased size of the unit to handle much larger payloads and the complex hydraulic systems required to power them. For material handling applications involving extremely large parts, however, the cost of this type of unit is definitely justified by the reduced risk of injury to employees.

Torque Arms

Torque arms are application-specific manipulators. They have been developed to relieve the many stresses affecting torque tool operators. As previously mentioned, many operators in industry are required to use torque tools capable of generating over 450 ft-lb (610 Nm) of torque. Torques of this magnitude put operators at risk for serious injury.

Torque arms reduce this risk and alleviate stresses by absorbing the torque for the operator. They also support the weight of the torque tool, which can be more than 35 lb (16 kg). This reduces operator fatigue and the potential for CTDs.

Most torque arms are similar to an articulated jib, however, the second arm consists of a set of parallel arms that actuate vertically to raise and lower the torque tool. The parallel arm system allows the tooling to stay horizontal and level at all points of vertical travel.

Moment loading due to weight is generally not a concern as compared to other manipulators, because the only payload at the end of the arm is the weight of the torque tool. However, moment loading due to the torque generated by the tooling becomes an important issue when large torques are involved (> 5,000 in.-lb [565 Nm]). The torque arm must be designed to withstand the amount of torque input by the tooling.

Another concern arises when torque tools with right-angled heads, or in-line torque tools mounted vertically, are used with a torque arm. In these applications, the torque generated by the tool creates moments that must be counteracted by each point of rotation in the system. As Figure 14-1 illustrated, the tool torque is translated to each joint, instead of simply being translated into the tool holder. For this reason, some type of braking mechanism must exist at every joint of the torque arm, with enough braking force to keep the arms from rotating while operating the tool.

Many torque arms, especially for smaller units, are powered by springs. Most larger arms, however, utilize pneumatic cylinders to provide balance to the system. This system operates on the same principle as the pneumatic balancer with balance control. The cylinder provides enough force to allow the operator to input very small forces to raise or lower the arms. When the operator reaches the desired height, he or she lets go of the tooling, and the arm automatically balances at that height. In essence, the tooling is weightless to the operator, who no longer has to support the weight of the torque tool as it is positioned on the job.

Torque arms come in sizes ranging from table-mounted units capable of holding very small torque tools and drill motors, to pedestal-mounted arms reaching 10-15 ft (3-4.6 m) or more, handling tools generating torques of over 20,000 in.-lb (2,260 Nm). They are definitely beneficial for reducing such CTDs as carpal tunnel syndrome and for minimizing the risk of serious injury to operators.

END EFFECTORS AND TOOLING

The manipulators and lifting devices described so far, with the exception of the lift table, are considered by most material handling manufacturers as base machines. That is, they provide the means of lifting and translating the material or product, but cannot hold or grip it. This leads to another area of ergonomic assist and lifting devices: end effectors and tooling (see Table 14-4).

A majority of material handling solutions require the ability to actually grasp the product to lift and transfer it. Many applications also require re-orientation of the part, such as pitching or rotating. Special tooling must be designed to accomplish such tasks in a safe manner for the product and the operator. This special tooling or *end effector* can be any part of the system below the end joint of a manipulator or vertical lifter, or anything attached to the end of a balancer or hoist. End effectors can be as simple as a hook or fork, or can become extremely complex with many degrees of freedom.

Simple Tooling

Simple tooling is classified as containing few, if any, moving parts. Some examples are hooks, forks, or pokes, as illustrated in

CHAPTER 14   WORKER PRODUCTIVITY AND ERGONOMIC ASSISTS

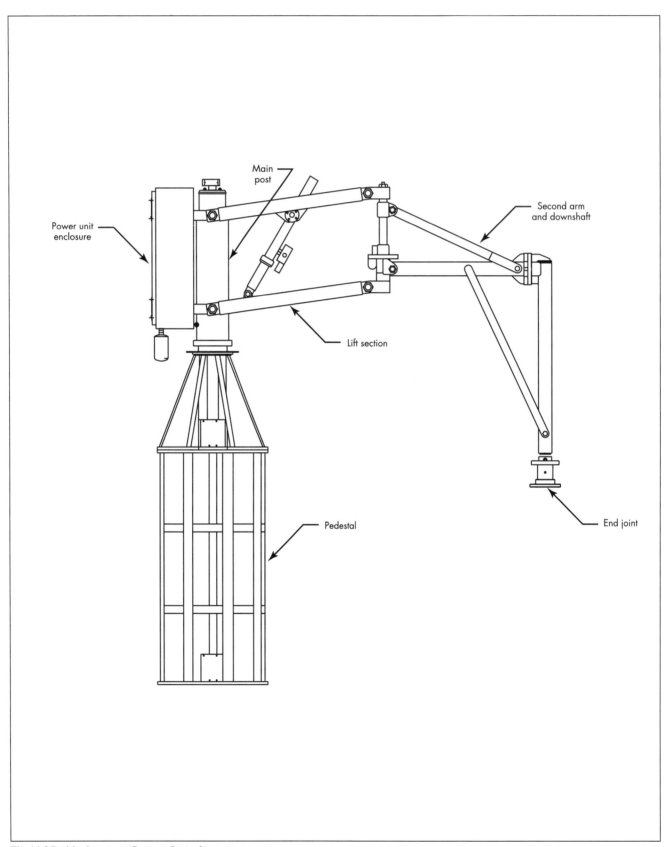

Fig. 14-8 Positioning arm. *(Courtesy Positech)*

CHAPTER 14   WORKER PRODUCTIVITY AND ERGONOMIC ASSISTS

TABLE 14-4
End Effectors

Usage	Type	Power	Controls	Benefits	Limitations
Provides holding, gripping, and re-orientation of an object when using manipulators and lift devices.	Simple: hooks, forks, slings, vacuum cups, pokes, ladles, tongs, grabs, and magnet tooling.	Generally power selection is based on payload weight.	Used with electric hoists: hand-held pendants with rocker switches and up and down controls.	Available with various degrees of freedom and capacity.	Power sources should be the same when mating the end effector with the lifting device or manipulator.
	Moderate: grippers powered by pneumatic, electric, and hydraulic cylinders.	Simple: electric. Moderate: pneumatic. Heavy: hydraulic.	Used with pneumatic balancers: balance control and metering controls.	Decrease the operator's risk for injury in the lifting task.	Proper selection is crucial for efficient end use.
	Complex: re-orientation of the part using pitch and rotation. Bearing sets, steering wheels, and rotation levers are available for re-orientation.				

CHAPTER 14   WORKER PRODUCTIVITY AND ERGONOMIC ASSISTS

Fig. 14-9. Most balancer or hoist applications can use simple tooling because they are usually employed for straight transfers. Tools such as these are also generally lightweight, which is desirable when using balancers or hoists.

Also considered to be fairly simple is vacuum tooling (Fig. 14-10). These tools usually consist of a frame that holds the desired amount of vacuum cups and control handles to operate the tooling functions and guide the payload around the work cell. Vacuum tools can be used to lift almost any amount of payload. Each vacuum cup is capable of a certain amount of pull force, based on the effective area of the cup and the amount of air pressure supplied to it. For lifting payloads with nonporous surfaces, it is a simple matter of providing enough cup area and air pressure to provide more pull force than the payload weight. Porous surfaces, such as cardboard, require more pull force, as a significant amount of force is lost due to leakage through the material.

Payloads that need to be pitched from a horizontal plane to a vertical plane present quite a challenge to vacuum tools. Vacuum cups provide excellent pull force when applied to the top surface of a payload. If the payload is pitched after the cups have been engaged, shear forces are introduced. Since most vacuum cups do not contact a surface with a large amount of area, their ability to support loads in the vertical plane is lower than in the horizontal plane. For this reason, most manufacturers use a 10:1 ratio of vacuum cup force versus payload weight for applications involving pitching.

Vacuum tools are limited by surface irregularities or holes and cutouts. Small variations in the desired lift surface, such as chemically-milled recesses, can be overcome by using a bellows-style vacuum cup (Fig. 14-11). Large variations, however, require alternative methods. If the payload contains areas open to the air, the vacuum cups must be placed in such a manner as to avoid them.

One alternate method would be to incorporate a magnet tool. Magnetic tooling is simple in design, and magnets are available in a wide variety of shapes and sizes, designed to handle many different types of payloads. However, these tools require electrical power and some additional components, which can be quite large.

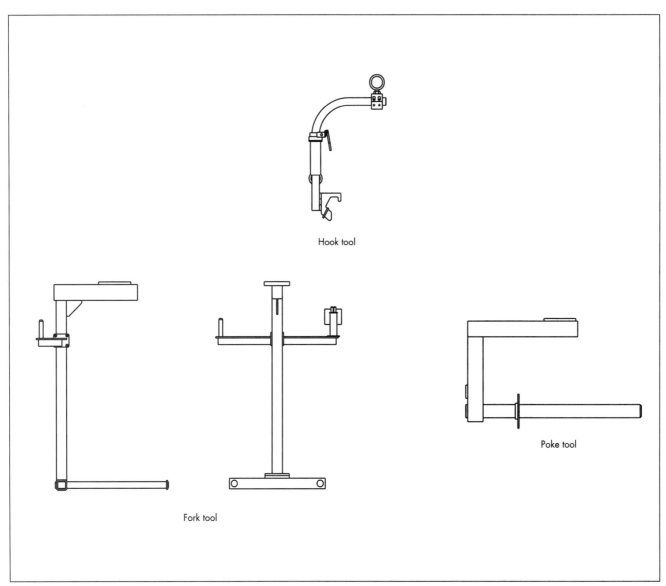

Hook tool

Poke tool

Fork tool

Fig. 14-9 Simple tooling. *(Courtesy Positech)*

CHAPTER 14   WORKER PRODUCTIVITY AND ERGONOMIC ASSISTS

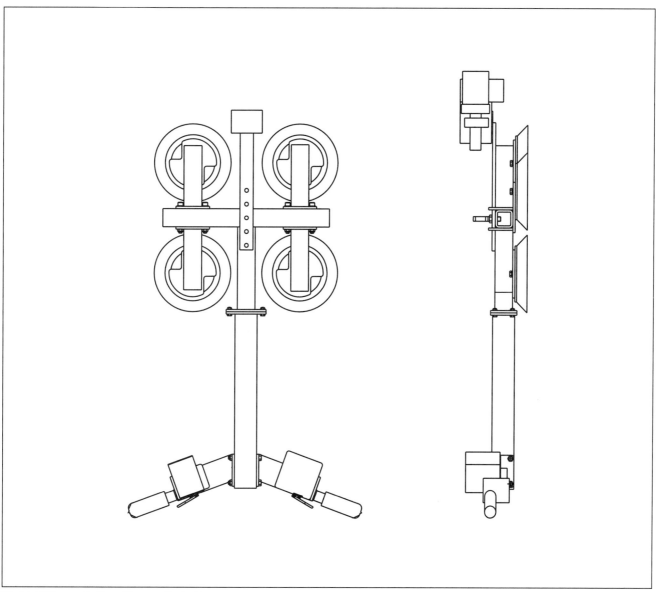

Fig. 14-10 Vacuum tooling. *(Courtesy Positech)*

The advantage of the magnet is that surface penetrations do not pose a problem, provided they are not too excessive. Magnets also provide better holding force when used in shear. They are not susceptible to leaks and are much quieter to operate than vacuum tools.

However, magnets do have a few drawbacks. Most applications require the use of a controller/rectifier that controls the electrical supply to the magnets. This component is normally contained in an enclosure and is too large to be mounted on the end effector. It is generally mounted on the base machine or remotely mounted. Controller/rectifiers also add expense to the overall system. Magnets are much heavier than vacuum cups. Therefore, tooling designed to incorporate magnets is usually heavy, often requiring a larger lifting device to handle the additional payload. The cost of the magnets alone is usually greater than that of vacuum cups by at least a factor of 10. These associated costs make magnet tooling a much more expensive alternative to vacuum tooling. Magnet tools are generally used only for applications where no other option is available.

Grippers

Some payloads cannot be handled by either vacuum or magnetic means. Large surface variations, nonmagnetic materials, and irregular shapes make many products impossible to lift with these systems. Such payloads must be handled by a *gripper*.

Grippers are special tools designed to actually grasp the payload, as the human hand grasps an object. Figure 14-12 illustrates a typical gripping mechanism composed of plates or similar media, usually called "jaws," which provide surface contact with the payload; a mechanical slide device, such as a keyway or tube-in-a-tube, which allows one or both jaws to actuate; and a power source to actuate the mechanical slide.

The principle of operation for the gripper is straightforward. The jaws are spaced at some distance from each other, usually at least 1 in. (2.5 cm) wider than the surface to be gripped. When the power source, such as a pneumatic cylinder, is activated, the jaws are forced together. Single actuating grippers are designed so that one of the

CHAPTER 14   WORKER PRODUCTIVITY AND ERGONOMIC ASSISTS

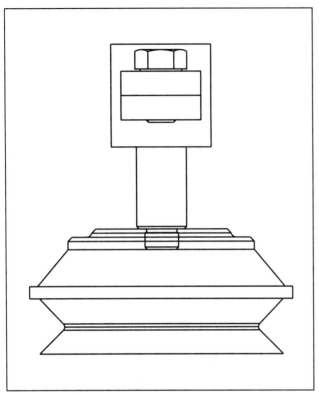

Fig. 14-11 Bellows-style vacuum cup. *(Courtesy Positech)*

jaws remains static at all times and the other is forced toward it. Double actuating grippers allow both jaws to move simultaneously toward each other. As the jaws make contact with the desired gripping surface of the payload, the actuating mechanism continues to input force to the system, creating a certain amount of pressure between the jaws and the payload surface. When this pressure reaches a determined level, usually a few times greater than the weight of the payload as a minimum, the payload is gripped and ready to be lifted and transported.

The simplest of gripping mechanisms operates by use of a manual clamping device. The jaws or gripping surfaces are placed at the desired location for grasping the payload. The clamping device is then manually actuated via a lever to close on the payload, squeezing the payload with enough force to hold it in place while lifting and transporting. Many such clamping devices can be purchased off the shelf from a variety of suppliers. Some employ pneumatic cylinders to actuate the lever, eliminating the need for the operator to physically perform the gripping function.

More complex grippers use a power source to generate the gripping force and contain components similar to those illustrated in Fig. 14-12. The power source can be pneumatic, electric, or hydraulic, based on the size of the payload being gripped. As the payload increases, the amount of grip force required to hold the part in the jaws also increases. This is especially true for payloads pitched down after gripping, as the force of the jaws on the payload becomes the sole means of supporting the entire weight of the part.

Each power source has its own set of characteristics, and each needs to be considered when choosing a source for gripper actuation. For example, pneumatics are much cleaner and require less maintenance than hydraulics, however, they cannot generate nearly

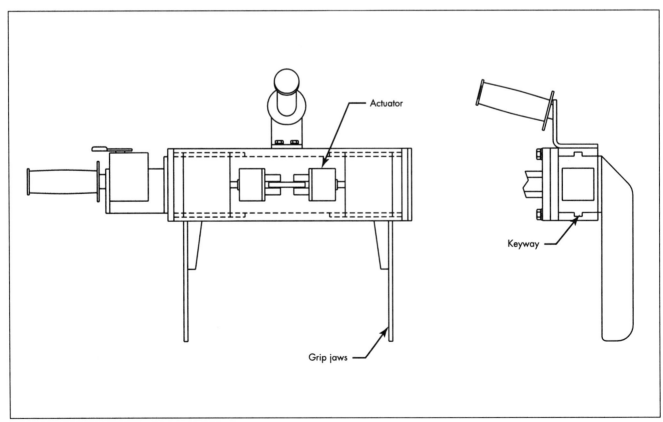

Fig. 14-12 Gripper tooling. *(Courtesy Positech)*

CHAPTER 14   WORKER PRODUCTIVITY AND ERGONOMIC ASSISTS

the magnitude of force of hydraulic systems. Hydraulics, though capable of supplying high grip forces, must be supported by a system of pumps and motors. This adds a significant amount of weight to the overall lifting device. These characteristics must be considered carefully when determining the proper power system.

Complex Payload Handling

When the number of motions required to re-orient the payload increases, the complexity of the lifting device also increases. Many manufacturing processes handle materials and products that must be rotated, pitched, or re-oriented after they have been gripped and lifted. Applications with these requirements present many challenges to the designers and manufacturers of material handling equipment.

Pitch and rotation are the two main types of re-orientation. Pitching involves changing the payload's angle by changing the angle of the arm or device supporting the payload. Rotation is usually accomplished by turning the payload itself, at or near its center of gravity, either manually or mechanically. Typical examples of both types of re-orientation devices are shown in Fig. 14-13.

There are some important factors to consider when pitching a payload. If the payload is gripped in a certain orientation and pitched to another, the height at which the payload is held does not remain constant. In fact, the longer the lever arm between the center point of pitch and the center of gravity of the payload, the greater the change in height. This can be an advantage where the lifting device may not require as much stroke length if the payload is pitched.

As the payload extends farther from the center point of pitch, the force required to pitch the payload also increases in some cases. This requires a large actuator to provide enough force to pitch the payload, adding weight and cost to the tooling. Pitching also changes the amount of moment loading experienced by the tooling, which creates additional design challenges.

Rotation of a payload involves special issues as well. Rotating payloads about their center of gravity requires minimal input force, as the payload is always balanced about its axis of rotation. Manual mechanisms, such as steering wheels or levers, are great devices for rotating payloads under this condition. If the axis of rotation does not pass through the center of gravity, however, more force is required to rotate (or stop the rotation of) the payload. Rotation in this condition must be accomplished by using some type of actuator.

Bearing sets are the most common means employed to rotate a payload. These consist of a housing containing a set of bearings spaced some distance apart. One housing is typically required at each end of the payload to accomplish the rotation. This can add a

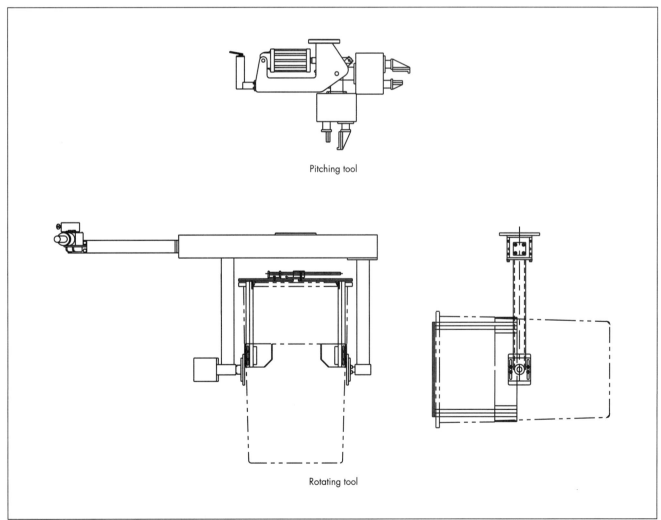

Pitching tool

Rotating tool

Fig. 14-13 Pitching and rotating tools. *(Courtesy Positech)*

CHAPTER 14 WORKER PRODUCTIVITY AND ERGONOMIC ASSISTS

significant amount of width extending from each side of the payload, causing potential interferences in limited space applications. Adding an actuator to the end of one of the housings to provide rotation force can complicate this situation even further. Bearings, housings, and actuators also add a large amount of weight to the overall tool.

Additional degrees of freedom come at a price. Tools required to perform more functions take longer to design, fabricate, and assemble. They also add weight to the overall system, sometimes requiring larger lifting devices or base machines to carry the increased load. For this reason, it is prudent for those creating new work cells to study the flow of the part as it enters and exits the cell. In many cases, a work cell can change the way it presents a product or material to the next consecutive cell. This may eliminate the need to reorient the product, greatly simplifying the material handling device required in that cell.

TYPICAL INTERFACES

Matching the correct lifting device or manipulator with the proper tooling to handle a given payload is a very involved process. Many parameters must be investigated, evaluated, and resolved if the ergonomic assist device is to be successful. If an inadequate tool or lifting device is installed, the operators will be unhappy, the machine will not be used, and the number of injuries associated with the application will not be reduced.

When mating end effectors to lifting devices, it is always best to keep power sources the same. If the manipulator or lifting device is pneumatically-driven, the tooling should be too, provided it contains functions requiring actuation. Likewise, hydraulic systems should be matched, as the same motors and pumps used to drive the lifting device can be used to drive the tooling functions.

Some lift device and tool combinations can create additional challenges. For instance, if a pitching tool is used in conjunction with a balancer or hoist, there is difficulty in keeping the payload level in all positions. It is the natural tendency for the center of gravity of any system hanging below a wire rope or similar lift media to align itself vertically with the lift media. Since the pitching motion changes the center of gravity of the overall system below the hoist, it is difficult to hold the payload level.

In general, any payload required to be offset from the lifting device should be handled by a manipulator or positioning arm. Special vertical lifters also exist to handle such cases, but should be considered the exception rather than the rule. Payloads in excess of 500 lb (227 kg), especially those requiring gripping, are best handled by hydraulically-powered systems. Articulated jibs are best for handling light payloads that need to be transferred over distances greater than 12 in. (30 cm).

ENCLOSED-TRACK WORKSTATION CRANES

Enclosed-track workstation cranes, when used in conjunction with a lifting device, allow the user to relocate a load anywhere within a rectangular work area. They made their debut in Europe and entered the marketplace in the U.S. as an alternative to I-beam, patented track, and jib cranes. Enclosed-track workstation cranes offer several advantages in many applications.

A study conducted by the Rochester Institute of Technology compared manually-operated, traditional I-beam cranes to one manufacturer's enclosed-track workstation cranes. The study found that enclosed-track workstation cranes offered a 27% average produc-

tivity increase for users and are three to four times easier to move than I-beam cranes. The study also revealed that the sustaining force required to keep a load in motion was substantially lower for the enclosed-track workstation cranes than for I-beam cranes.

Enclosed-track workstation cranes are lighter than I-beam cranes of comparable carrying capacity, which results in enclosed-track workstation cranes exerting lower hanger loads than I-beam cranes on the supporting structure.

CONFIGURATION

Workstation cranes exist in a large number of variations, but most have a basic structure consisting of a trolley, a pair of end trucks, a bridge, a pair of runways, and a method of supporting the runways as illustrated in Fig. 14-14. The lifting device attaches to the trolley on the bridge and allows vertical movement. The trolley moves along the bridge and allows the load to be moved laterally. The end trucks attach the bridge to the runways and allow the bridge (and, subsequently, the load) to be moved longitudinally. The runways can be supported either by hangers suspended from the building overhead structure or with a freestanding structure, as shown.

Most of the time, the bridge length is limited to 34 ft (10.4 m) and the runway length can be very long. The load is moved from one position to another manually by the user. This is practical because enclosed-track workstation cranes have a productivity ratio of approximately 100:1 (for example, a 1,000-lb [454-kg] load can be moved with only 10 lb [4.5 kg] of force). Enclosed-track workstation cranes are available for loads weighing up to 4,000 lb (1,814 kg).

The enclosed track used in workstation cranes is cold-rolled steel, stainless steel, or an extruded aluminum shape (see Fig. 14-15). The enclosed track can be reinforced to permit longer spans when frequent support points are not available. Enclosed-track workstation cranes made of steel are usually more economical than stainless steel or aluminum workstation cranes. However, the environment in which the crane is to be used is a major factor in determining the material make-up of the crane. For example, moist environments or washdown applications may require a stainless steel or aluminum workstation crane.

Enclosed-track workstation cranes can be freestanding or ceiling-supported. Both methods are common and should be considered when specifying a crane. Freestanding supports are usually easier to install and offer greater flexibility for future relocation of the crane, but they introduce columns into the work area. Ceiling supports, on the other hand, put additional loads on the overhead building steel, but do not introduce columns in the work area.

APPLICATION

There are many factors to consider when specifying an enclosed-track workstation crane. These include size of the work area and weight of the load.

Size Specification

Enclosed-track workstation cranes perform best when the crane is properly sized for the application. Keeping the bridge length, bridge capacity, and trolley saddle height (the distance from the floor to the trolley) to a minimum ensures optimum performance.

Optimizing Weight

Since workstation cranes are operated manually, it is very important to minimize the dead weight of the bridge. The weight of the bridge and lifting device is a fixed weight apparent to the operator whenever the bridge is moved along the runways. To minimize the weight, the length, size (available capacity), and material for the

CHAPTER 14   WORKER PRODUCTIVITY AND ERGONOMIC ASSISTS

bridge should be evaluated. The following example includes other considerations when specifying an enclosed workstation crane, such as: dimensions, capacity, structural material, support method, and duty cycle. Two short case studies are also presented.

Dimensions. The weight of the load can vary from 100-400 lb (45-182 kg) and the work area is 14-ft (4.3-m) wide by 25-ft (7.6-m) long. The bridge specified for this example would be 14-ft [4.3-m] long and the runway length would be 25-ft [7.6-m] long. The shorter dimension was selected as the bridge length because the

runways are immobile, while the bridge weight must be moved manually. Choosing the smaller dimension minimizes the bridge dead weight that has to be moved.

Capacity. Enclosed-track workstation cranes are generally available for rated capacities at discrete intervals, such as 250 lb (113 kg), 500 lb (227 kg), 1,000 lb (454 kg), 2,000 lb (907 kg), and 4,000 lb (1,814 kg). Since the load for this example can be up to 400 lb (181 kg), the 500-lb (227-kg) capacity bridge is selected because it is the minimum discrete capacity rating available that is equal to or

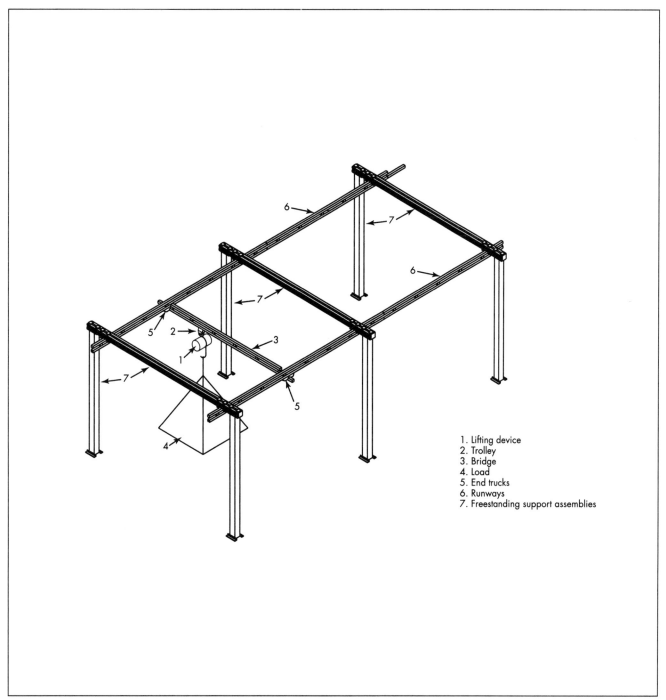

1. Lifting device
2. Trolley
3. Bridge
4. Load
5. End trucks
6. Runways
7. Freestanding support assemblies

Fig. 14-14 Structure of an enclosed-track workstation crane that is freestanding. *(Courtesy Gorbel, Inc.)*

CHAPTER 14   WORKER PRODUCTIVITY AND ERGONOMIC ASSISTS

greater than 400 lb (181 kg). Choosing a bridge capacity of 1,000 lb (454 kg) or higher would increase the dead weight of the bridge and increase the force that the user must exert to move the bridge.

Material. To determine the bridge material, compare the weight per foot of a steel bridge versus an aluminum bridge. In almost all cases the aluminum bridge will weigh less than a steel bridge.

Support method. The building has supporting steel at 30 ft (9.1 m) intervals. Since our runway length is 25 ft (7.6 m), which is less than 30 ft (9.1 m), freestanding supports appear to be a better option than ceiling supports. To ceiling-support the crane, several modifications would have to be made, whereas freestanding supports are readily available from the manufacturer.

Duty cycle. The duty cycle for the crane will be 5-10 lifts per hour. The Crane Equipment Manufacturers' Association (CEMA)

guidelines indicate that this is a moderate service level and they do not require any modifications to the enclosed-track workstation crane.

Case studies. For example, one manufacturing facility was looking for an alternative to jib cranes, which were designed for handling heavier loads than the loads of pump castings and machine fixtures handled at the facility—usually less than 300 lb (136 kg). Also, personnel were experiencing lower back injuries when struggling to use the bulky jib cranes. Freestanding, enclosed-track workstation bridge cranes proved to be the solution.

In another instance, one company that fabricates pipe for commercial heating and cooling systems went looking for a better system than their fork lift trucks for moving odd-shaped pipe through work cells. The fork lift trucks were awkward and dangerous for the purpose. The company considered motorized I-beam cranes and jib

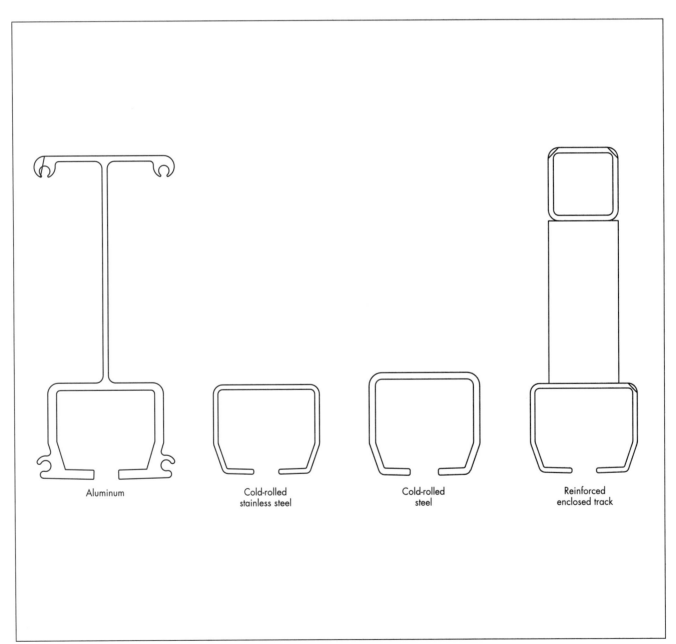

Fig. 14-15 Profiles of enclosed track. *(Courtesy Gorbel, Inc.)*

CHAPTER 14   WORKER PRODUCTIVITY AND ERGONOMIC ASSISTS

cranes, as well as enclosed-track workstation bridge cranes. Enclosed-track workstation bridge cranes were selected since they offered a cost-effective, simple, and flexible method for workers to move workpieces within and between work cells.

Summary

Enclosed track workstation cranes offer an economical ergonomic solution for applications involving lifting and moving loads up to 4,000 lb (1,814 kg) within rectangular work areas.

POSITIONING DEVICES

This section describes a lifter, tilter and dumper, turntable, lift and tilter, lift and turntable, load leveler, and how to choose the right equipment.

LIFTER

The lifter is a positioning device that moves a load vertically (for example, palletizing boxes for shipment and on-loading or off-loading product from a machine or conveyor).

The most common lifter is the scissors-style lift table (see Fig. 14-16). Scissors lift tables are available in various platform sizes and capacities. The scissors lift offers a compact lowered height with a vertical travel of several times the lowered height, and provides a safe, stable platform. Typically, the platform size will dic-

tate the amount of vertical travel available with the scissors lift table. The scissors lift table can be offered with a ground-accessible platform for use with pallet trucks.

The post-style lift table utilizes guide tubes to provide stability and vertically-mounted actuators for height adjustability. The vertical travel is relative to the collapsed height because the length of the guide tubes at the lowered height is the constraining element and must have a minimum engagement to provide stability. Because of the simple design and limited travel, the post-style lift table is usually more economical than the scissors lift table. Applications include adjustable-height work benches and loading dies into machinery and storage shelves. Many sizes and configurations are available, but some stability may be sacrificed for larger platform sizes.

Cantilever-style vertical lifters are offered with a platform guided by rollers in a track. The majority of the cantilever-style lifters are portable, allowing the worker easy maneuverability to accomplish the task. The cantilever-style lifting device is divided into two classes, light-duty and heavy-duty. Light-duty cantilever positioning devices (Fig. 14-17) are manufactured for capacities of up to 1,500 lb (680 kg) and typically have a flat surface platform. The heavy-duty cantilever positioning device (Fig. 14-18) handles capacities of up to 4,000 lb (1,814 kg) and has forks for lifting heavy-duty pallets. Applications for the cantilever-style positioning devices include loading dies into machinery or storage shelves, transporting small packages in a warehouse, moving machine parts for maintenance, and palletizing a shipping skid. In general, most lifters are offered portable to allow more flexibility in the work environment (see Table 14-5).

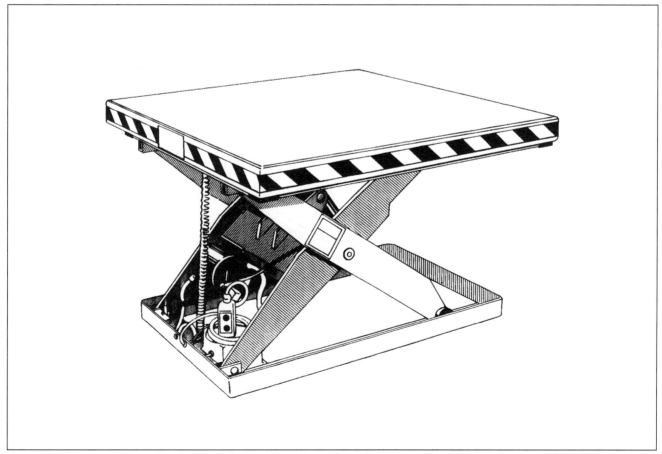

Fig. 14-16 Single scissors lift. *(Courtesy Vestil Manufacturing)*

CHAPTER 14 WORKER PRODUCTIVITY AND ERGONOMIC ASSISTS

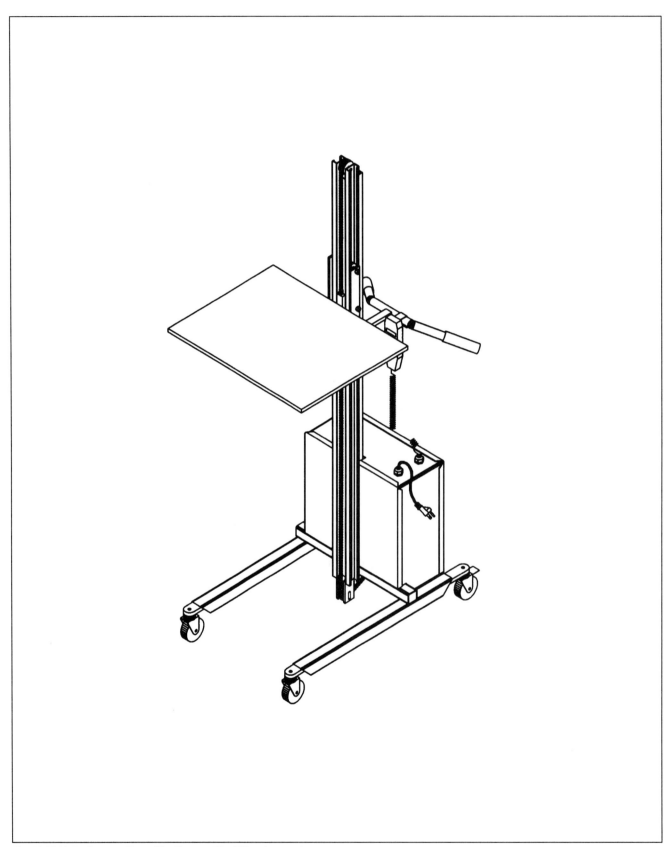

Fig. 14-17 Light-duty cantilever lift. *(Courtesy Vestil Manufacturing)*

CHAPTER 14   WORKER PRODUCTIVITY AND ERGONOMIC ASSISTS

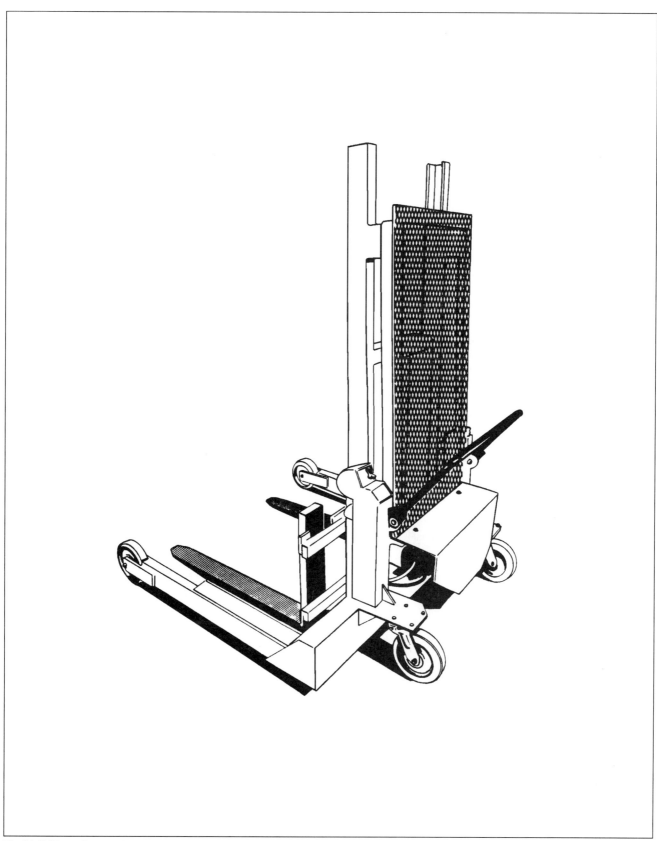

Fig. 14-18 Heavy-duty cantilever pallet lift. *(Courtesy Vestil Manufacturing)*

CHAPTER 14   WORKER PRODUCTIVITY AND ERGONOMIC ASSISTS

TABLE 14-5
Positioning Devices

Usage	Types	Benefits	Limitations
Lifter: positioning device to move loads vertically.	Scissors lift.	Various sizes, capabilities, and platform styles.	Table stability may be sacrificed in larger platform sizes.
	Post-style lift.		
	Cantilever-style: a platform guided by rollers in a rack.	Portable models allow more flexibility in the work area.	
Tilter: used to rotate loads about a horizontal axis to aid in manipulating parts.	Tilters can rotate to angles up to 145°.	Portable models allow for mobility and flexibility in the work area.	Load stabilization must be considered when rotating over 90°.
	Laterally moving pivot points and control links aid in flexibility and safety of design.	Various sizes and design configurations offer more stable positioning while occupying less space.	
Rotators: turn containers or pallets about a vertical axis to aid in manipulating a load.	Manual rotators can be used with limited spaces and directional changes.	Various sizes and capacities are available.	Load stability should be considered in the design.
	Powered rotators can be used when rotations are frequent and beyond the worker's capacity.	Accessible with pallet truck platform configurations.	
Combinations of two mechanisms.	Lifts and tilters.	See individual equipment mechanisms above.	Combination mechanisms may not have as much range of motion as two separate mechanisms.
	Lifts and rotators.	More economical.	
		Decrease space requirements.	

TILTER AND DUMPER

The tilter is a positioning device that rotates a load about a horizontal axis. Rotation angles of up to 90° are available, depending on the application requirements. Rotation angles of up to 45° (Figure 14-19) are generally used to maneuver a load to a more ergonomic position for optimum interaction with the worker. The platform pivot point can be located in the manufacturing process to yield different rotated heights for specific applications.

Another device utilizes a laterally-moving pivot point. This device will tilt along the load, moving it toward the center of the positioning device. The design occupies less work area. The fixed-pivot point tilter is another type manufactured with a pallet truck-accessible platform. The 90° rotation enables the positioning device to also be used as an upender or palletizer. Since the load rotates up to 90°, consideration must be given to stabilizing the moving load.

Dumpers are typically considered for rotation angles beyond 90°. Two main categories are the drum or barrel dumper (see Figure 14-20) and the box dumper (see Figure 14-21). Both styles dispense the contents of the container. Numerous sizes and capacities are available for specific applications.

TURNTABLE

A turntable is a device used to rotate a container or pallet about a vertical axis. Manual and powered turntables can be used in several applications to provide the worker with improved access to the load. Manual turntable (see Fig. 14-22) applications range from palletizing for shipping to performing limited space directional changes required in a conveyor line. A powered turntable should be used when the load is too heavy to manually rotate or the frequency of rotation is beyond the capability of the worker. A common example is the powered stretch wrap rotator that turns a pallet of small boxes for easy application of packaging film. Many sizes and capacities of the manual and powered rotator are available, along with pallet jack-accessible models or models that mount on a lift table.

CHAPTER 14   WORKER PRODUCTIVITY AND ERGONOMIC ASSISTS

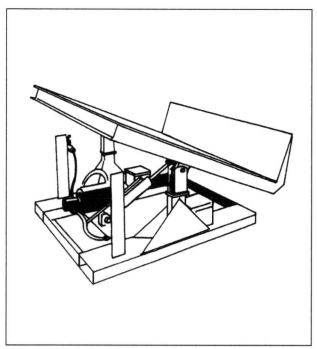

Fig. 14-19 Forty-five-degree tilter. *(Courtesy Vestil Manufacturing)*

LIFT AND TILTER

The lift and tilter is a combination of the two positioning devices integrated into one design. This can be accomplished by utilizing two separate mechanisms or one mechanism providing both the lifting and tilting functions (see Fig. 14-23). The latter can provide a more economical positioning device, but does not render as much range of motion as two separate mechanisms. The lift and tilter comes in many sizes and capacities, along with the capability of pallet truck-accessible platform configurations.

LIFT AND TURNTABLE

A lift and turntable is a combination of the two positioning devices. The turntable can be either manual or powered to enable access to the load. The applications for the lift and turntable can range from palletizing shipping skids to multilevel conveyor transfer stations. The sizes and capacities are based on the shape of the rotating load. Rectangular-shaped loads may require special platform configurations to reduce the amount of load cantilevering beyond the platform during rotation.

LOAD LEVELER

Automatic load levelers, although similar in appearance to scissors lifts, have an entirely different function. Automatic load levelers respond to the load, not the operator and automatically maintain the top of the load height to 30-38 in. (76-97 cm), ideal for most workers when palletizing or de-palletizing. Available in mechanical or pneumatic, load levelers are usually equipped with manual turntables to eliminate stretching.

Some manufacturers can modify the positioning device to tailor the specific application. Simple modifications made to the positioning device during the fabrication process are usually much more economical than after the positioning device has been installed in the manufacturing work area. Be sure to thoroughly evaluate the application criteria and select the most adaptable positioning device for the given requirements.

CHOOSING THE RIGHT EQUIPMENT

Selecting a positioning device can be overwhelming. By analyzing the application criteria in discrete parts, the selection process can become less arduous. Taking a problem-solving approach to selecting equipment will produce better results with a smaller investment of resources than the more typical trial and error method. Purchasing equipment without carefully analyzing all aspects of the task at hand can result in an unsatisfactory solution that may not address all ergonomic and productivity issues. In today's competitive environment, the long-term cost of an inefficient workplace can be devastating. Employee injuries result in medical costs, increased insurance premiums, lower morale, and loss of investment in worker training. More subtle is the everyday loss of production due to wasted time and motion. Utilizing human intellectual skills instead of human muscle power is the essence of an ergonomic workplace.

Selection criteria can be divided into five categories: load parameters, delivery and retrieval methods, load positioning requirements, safety, and power and controls. Each attribute of the intended application is an important piece of the puzzle. The more information available concerning the requirements, the better likelihood of developing the most efficient working environment. Designing the workplace with these considerations in mind will yield the most productive solution.

Load Parameters

Consider the load or container requiring the manipulation. What are its physical attributes? Size, shape, and weight are important and easily measured characteristics when discussing ergonomic positioning devices. The composition of the load is sometimes even more important. It can be difficult to predict the effect of the composition on the equipment's operation. Liquids, powders, or small parts in a large container impose a new set of dynamic constraints. These can lead to hazardous situations, resulting in worker injury, damaged product, and production delays. Constraining or moving the load in a controlled manner can reduce the hazard to an acceptable level.

Delivery and Retrieval

The delivery and retrieval methods should be evaluated. The two main categories are manual and automatic. The manual processes include hand loading by the worker or the use of pallet trucks, fork trucks, and overhead lifting devices. The difference between these methods is the height required to load or unload. An ergonomic height of approximately 30-38 in. (76-97 cm) is usually required to enable a worker to load or unload while standing. The reach required across a pallet should also be considered. In most cases, a rotating device is required when manually palletizing to reduce the strain on the worker. Pallet jacks require a ground-accessible platform or a ramp for loading and unloading. Some applications will have the capability of mounting the positioning device in a pit for access with a pallet jack. Consider the capacity of the pallet jack and the physical effort required to push the jack onto the lift platform. Platform heights above a few inches may require more work than is available from the personnel. Typical ground-accessible platforms are 0.5-in. (1.3-cm) high (or thick) and are relatively easy to traverse using a pallet jack.

Another common means of delivery and retrieval is the fork truck, which can load and unload at any height. This provides greater access to the load and simplifies the positioning device required, but may require additional investment in equipment and labor. Overhead lifting devices also afford better access for delivery and retrieval of loads. The picking and placement of product is virtually unlimited when using the overhead lifting device. The automatic delivery and retrieval methods will usually have much more specific positioning requirements to interact with the delivery and retrieval

CHAPTER 14   WORKER PRODUCTIVITY AND ERGONOMIC ASSISTS

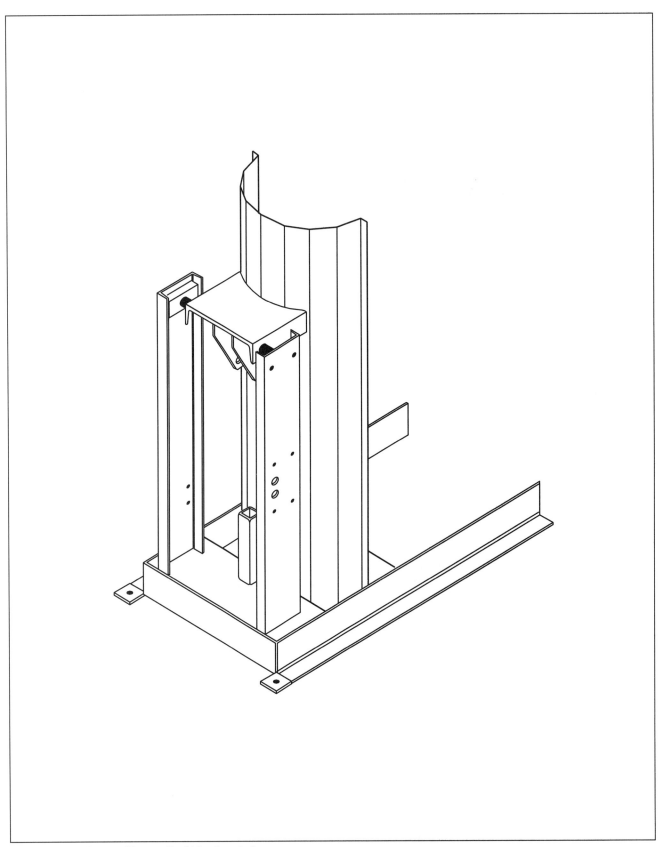

Fig. 14-20 Drum dumper. *(Courtesy Vestil Manufacturing)*

CHAPTER 14   WORKER PRODUCTIVITY AND ERGONOMIC ASSISTS

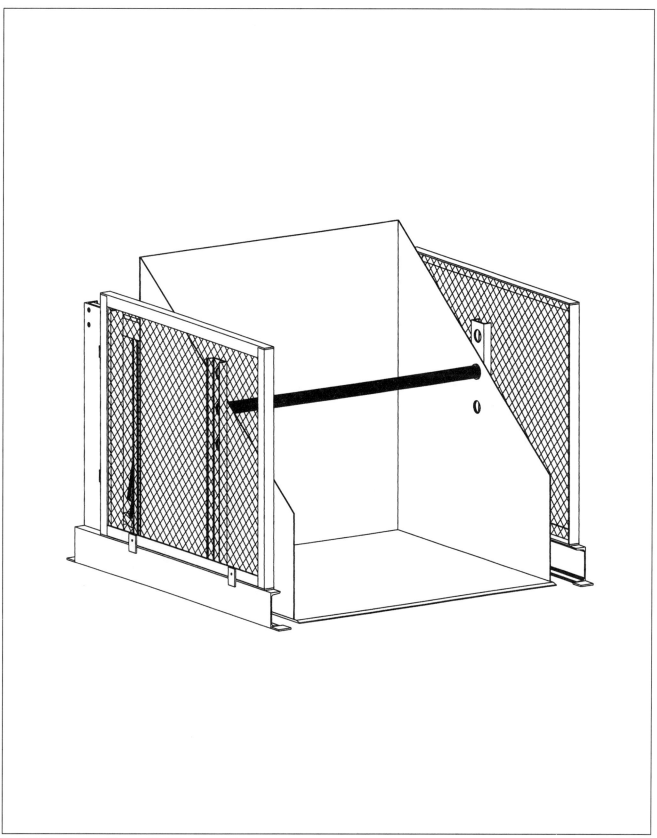

Fig. 14-21 Box dumper. *(Courtesy Vestil Manufacturing)*

CHAPTER 14   WORKER PRODUCTIVITY AND ERGONOMIC ASSISTS

Fig. 14-22 Manual turntable. *(Courtesy Vestil Manufacturing)*

CHAPTER 14 WORKER PRODUCTIVITY AND ERGONOMIC ASSISTS

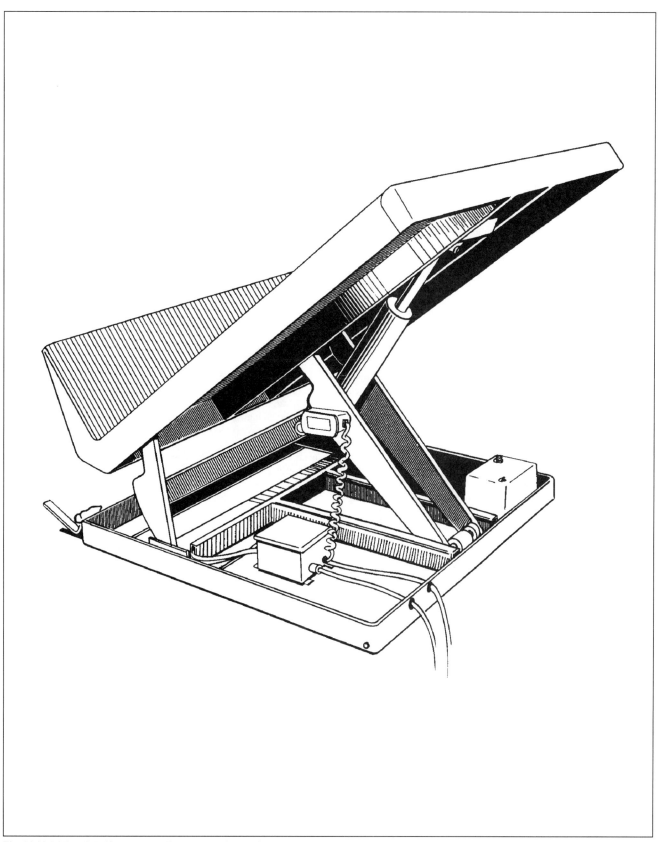

Fig. 14-23 Sliding link lift and tilter. *(Courtesy Vestil Manufacturing)*

CHAPTER 14   WORKER PRODUCTIVITY AND ERGONOMIC ASSISTS

device. A conveyor will demand a specific height for a smooth transition to the positioning device. Also, a brake or stop to limit the travel of the load when moved onto the positioning device may be required. Using a robot to deliver or retrieve the load will require precise feedback as to the location of the load. Three-axis position may need to be measured for accurate placement by the robot.

Load Positioning

Positioning requirements of the load must be considered, with two main factors being space and time. The orientation of the load and the worker can be the most important criterion in achieving an ergonomic workstation. The interaction between the load and the worker is paramount.

To analyze the situation, first consider the load's range of motion. Determine the vertical, horizontal, and angular motions required to position the load in the worker's ergonomically-correct envelope. This can be done by drawing the load and the worker in space without regard to what positioning device may be required.

Also consider the amount of space occupied by all components of the workstation. Floor space can have economic concerns. An efficiently designed positioning device can save valuable floor space, as well as increase worker productivity.

The adage "time is money," points to the second positioning requirement. The speed of the positioning device directly impacts the nonproductive time spent by the worker. Moving the load at a high rate of speed can save time, but also introduces safety concerns. Stopping and starting fast moving loads not only adds to the wear on the positioning device, but can damage the load. Gradual transitions to and from full speed movement may be required to reduce inertial effects. The machine design and specifics of the application will determine the number of cycles between required maintenance. Careful consideration at the design stage will aid in scheduling maintenance time to have the least impact on production. Systems that depend on a high rate of product movement can easily justify the additional cost of positioning devices designed to yield long intervals between maintenance. Planned maintenance is always more cost-effective than unplanned maintenance. Attention to time constraints will result in a productive interaction between the worker and the components of the work cell.

Safety

Safety designed into a workstation can potentially save a company more money in the long run than any other application criterion. The costs of high insurance premiums, litigating liability suits, and productivity losses can have a catastrophic impact on the viability of a business. To evaluate the safety of a positioning device, follow three steps. First, identify the worker's exposure to danger. Second, evaluate how the proposed equipment minimizes the worker's exposure to the identified hazards. Finally, specify safety devices to protect against unavoidable hazards. Sudden shifting of a load or interference between the load and surroundings can result in an unstable condition. Pinch points can be created between the elements of the positioning device or between the positioning device and its surroundings. A general reference suggests that two members approaching closer than 3 in. (76 mm) constitute a pinch point. A well-applied positioning device will minimize the possible pinch points.

Environmental constraints, availability, and costs are the criteria used to determine the power required for a specific application. Various environmental constraints will be found in an industrial atmosphere, including explosion resistant and clean room applications. Flammable vapors, dusts, and gases require special provisions to prevent the motor and electrical components from introducing sparks or high-temperature surfaces to the atmosphere. Reference the Na-

tional Fire Protection Association (NFPA) for ratings on the safe operation of electric components in specific environments. A clean room environment usually involves a positioning device designed with a pneumatic or mechanical system of actuation to eliminate the use of hydraulic oils that can contaminate the atmosphere.

Structural failures can be avoided by careful design, testing, effective quality control, and proper application. Structural components should be designed with adequate safety factors to provide durability and substantial life to the positioning device. The positioning device should be thoroughly tested at the manufacturer's factory and have a proven safety record in the field. The manufacturer should have a quality assurance checklist available to the customer for each positioning device produced to ensure their commitment to building a quality product. Inappropriate application of a positioning device can lead to premature failure and worker injury. Be sure the application has been thoroughly investigated and all feasible types of positioning devices have been evaluated.

The interface between the worker and positioning device should be considered when evaluating the probability of electric shock and exposure to high-pressure hydraulics. Exposed electrical wires from the worker control stations and the main input power can be extremely hazardous.

The use of low-voltage control and careful attention to proper protection of the power components can significantly reduce the electrical hazard. Specify low voltage for all controls used in the interface between the worker and the positioning device. Because the worker usually physically handles the controls, the possibility of an electrical shock is prevalent. Low-voltage controls (24 V) will reduce the magnitude of injury if the worker should be exposed to a shock.

Severed hydraulic lines can result in injuries from the hydraulic fluid and uncontrollable movement of the load. Velocity fuses (valves that control excess flow) will stop movement of the load by closing if fluid velocity exceeds a safe predetermined limit due to a damaged hydraulic system. Velocity fuses must be integrated into the hydraulic actuator instead of being externally located, thus preventing damage to the hydraulic lines which render the fuses ineffective. Pressure-compensated flow controls should be utilized to maintain safe operating speeds and control the flow of hydraulic fluid at a constant rate regardless of load on the positioning device. This will prevent unsafe high-speed movement when the positioning device is fully loaded. Velocity fuses are required for the safe operation of a hydraulic-actuated positioning device and will stop load movement by closing if fluid velocity exceeds a safe predetermined limit due to a damaged hydraulic system. Machine protection can be provided by pressure relief valves and electric limit switches. Pressure relief valves are required to prohibit the use of the positioning device over the rated load capacity. Electric limit switches stop the hydraulic system from generating pressure after the hydraulic actuator is fully extended, and thereby prevent damage to the mechanical, electric, and hydraulic components. Mechanically-actuated positioning devices also require redundant systems to reduce the hazards of power transmission component failures.

When a pinch point cannot be alleviated by the type or orientation of the positioning device mechanism, an appropriate means of reducing the hazard is required. An electric perimeter pinch point guard, accordion skirting, and beveled-style platform edges are common methods of reducing the risk. Objects in the working environment such as carts, pallets, and bins also can be an obstruction to the safe operation of a positioning device.

The electric perimeter pinch point guard (toe guard) is a device that stops the platform's downward travel if there is an obstruction under the platform. The guard should be integrated into the positioning device's electrical circuit to provide a self-checking circuit.

CHAPTER 14 WORKER PRODUCTIVITY AND ERGONOMIC ASSISTS

The guard switch and downward travel circuit should be normally closed, thus prohibiting the downward travel of the platform if the circuit should become open.

Accordion safety skirting will provide a barrier between the working environment and the positioning device mechanism. The skirting alone will not stop the movement of the positioning device, but provides a visual or tactile warning of a possible hazard.

Beveled platform edges are generally found when a positioning device platform travels below floor level. The angled edge is moderately effective at pushing an obstruction laterally to prevent pinching between the floor and platform. The most effective pinch point guard is a semipermanent physical guard. This guard should prohibit the worker or an obstruction from entering a pinch point area. Preferably, the guard should be interlocked into the electric circuit of the positioning device, which requires the guard to be in position before operating the positioning device.

The availability of adequate power is an important factor in determining the proper unit to drive the positioning device and the amount of work required by the positioning device to manipulate the load will dictate the power requirements. Power can be supplied by human, pneumatic, or electrical means. Hand- or foot-pump hydraulic and mechanical crank are typical methods of operating a positioning device.

The most important consideration for a human-powered positioning device is to be certain the worker can do the work required to position the load. The safety requirements and the worker interface are parallel considerations in determining the specific control requirements.

Internal controls, such as flow controls and pressure relief controls for the hydraulic system, are important in specifying a safe positioning device.

Integrating the positioning device into a manufacturing system requires location feedback of the positioning device. Electric limit switches, infrared beams, and reflective light sensors can provide the input required by the manufacturing system controller. If a positioning device will be integrated into a manufacturing system, verify that the power unit and controls will be compatible with the feedback component requirements. Consult with the manufacturer of the equipment to select the appropriate control options for the specific application.

Bibliography

Allegri, T.H. *Material Handling: Principles and Practice.* New York: Van Nostrand Reinhold, 1984.

Apple, J.M. *Material Handling System Design.* New York: The Ronald Press Company, 1972.

Eastman, Robert M. *Materials Handling.* Meier Jr., Wilbur, ed. New York: Marcel Dekker, Inc., 1987.

Friendrich, Peter. "Enclosed-track Bridge Cranes Reduce Injuries." *Modern Materials Handling* Mid-September, 1995: 33.

Kroemer, K.H.E. *Material Handling: Loss Control through Ergonomics.* Chicago, IL: Alliance of American Insurers, 1979.

Lahey, J.W. "Overhead Safety." *National Safety News* 1980, 122 (5): 20-24, 60-63.

Stibitz, Wendy, and Shealy, Jasper. *Comparative Study of Force Requirements and Productivity for the I-Beam and Workstation Overhead Bridge Cranes.* Rochester, NY: Rochester Institute of Technology, 1992.

CHAPTER 15

METALCUTTING

CHAPTER CONTENTS

INTRODUCTION

Four subsystems, all of which could be considered material handling in the broadest sense, are required for metalcutting operations. Workpiece or raw material transport is considered first for material handling in metalcutting. The major subject of this chapter is the automated feeding of different material types to the metalcutting machines and the options to accomplish that. The other three subsystems are the basic material streams involved in metalcutting operations: cutting tools, chips, and coolant, all of which are discussed at the end of the chapter.

When high-speed metalcutting machine tools are involved, there are considerable demands made on the delivery and removal of parts. The material handling equipment, controls, and software must ensure that production goes smoothly and the required material reaches the right place at the right time.

A comprehensive range of work transport systems and equipment exists. The kind of production determines which equipment is chosen in each case. Connection to existing information and communication systems in a factory is generally possible.

The general transport of work materials around a plant, via such devices as fork lifts and conveyor systems, are treated in other chapters. This chapter focuses on the loading and unloading of workpieces from metalcutting machine tools, and peripheral systems linked to the metalcutting operations.

Metalcutting operations in this chapter are primarily divided into two major classes: parts of rotation for turning operations, and prismatic parts for machining center operations. Forming considerations for sheet and plate are discussed in Chapter 16.

Part washing, that is, washing parts between operations to clear chips and coolant, and washing the parts after machining is concluded, is one material handling issue common to many metalcutting operations, but will not be discussed here. However, many part moves within a manufacturing plant may consist of moving the parts from a machining operation to a cleaning operation, into the cleaning machines or lines, and then back to other machining stations.

Material handling suppliers are providing stillage arms and transfer tables, magazine loading, storage and retrieval systems, cut-off part sorting, other handling devices, and the sensor technology to support them. Chip handling is getting more attention. Builders are creating systems that integrate parts washing, deburring, bar coding, and related activities.

CONSIDERATIONS FOR AUTOMATED MACHINE LOADING

The goals of material handling automation in metalcutting are much the same as in other operations: to minimize the nonvalue-added handling of the part from the raw state to the finished machined part and deliver the finished machined part without damage. Several forces may drive the decision to automate the loading and unloading of machine tools: labor reduction, job enhancement, cycle time reduction and throughput improvement, and quality improvement. Unless the application yields more output for less cost with less scrap, it is difficult to pay for the material handling automation. For most companies, the so-called intangible benefits of automation are difficult to justify.

Labor Reduction

Automating the machine load and unload operations replaces a machine operator who might spend 20% of his or her time loading the machine tool with raw parts and unloading finished parts. The other 80% of the operator's time is spent watching the machine tool make chips and performing finished part gaging. Setup production people have a broader range of responsibilities, including fixturing changes and part program modifications. For today's manufacturing in developed industrial countries, retaining a machine operator whose primary responsibility is loading and unloading the machine tool is too costly. Therefore, the drive to reduce labor is strong.

Job Enhancement

Automation has another impact on employees in metalcutting operations. Many metalcutting job shops find it difficult to find and train good machinists. For such shops, one option is to get more production from their present work force by adding automation. When the machine operators get more training and the work gets more challenging, the shop gets more product out the door with the same staff and lower cost. All this depends on the operator advancing to more responsibilities, with the basic machine load and unload functions becoming automated. For example, workers in automotive plants who have spent years moving crankshafts or body panels from machine to storage bin, now typically operate computer numerical

The Contributors of this chapter are: **Edward J. Early,** *Project Executive, Comau-North America;* **John Fredericks,** *Sales Engineer, Liebherr-America, Inc.;* **Dennis Kriesen,** *Vice President, Machine Tool Products Group, Mayfran International;* **David Kuhl,** *Tooling Manager, Motoman, Inc.;* **Steve Leiding,** *National Sales Manager-Horizontal Machining Center Business, Cincinnati Milacron;* **Frederick Mason,** *Editor, "Machine Shop Guide";* **Nicholas Trick,** *Technical Writer, Motoman, Inc.;* **Yusuf Venjara,** *General Manager-Engineering, Hitachi Seiki;* **Bob Weskamp,** *President, Westech, Inc.*
The Reviewers of this chapter are: **Michael Bomya,** *Engineering Manager, Nachi Robotics;* **Steve Brown,** *Vice President, SMW Systems, Inc.;* **Carl Folz,** *General Manager, FMB Machinery, USA;* **Hans Geppert,** *President, Eimeldingen Corp.;* **James Joseph,** *President, Joseph Marketing;* **Wayne Oliver,** *Manager of Sales Engineering, Production Machinery Sales, Ingersoll Milling Machine Co.;* **Marty Plute,** *President, ITC Integrated Systems;* **Jerome A. Raschke,** *National Sales Manager, Erowa Technology, Inc.;* **Randy Sparks,** *Sales Manager, Feedall Automation;* **Mark C. Tomlinson,** *Vice President of Engineering, Lamb Technicon Machining Systems, a Division of Unova;* **Klaus Voos,** *Technical Director, Index Corp.*

CHAPTER 15   METALCUTTING

control (CNC) machine controls. They perform quality checks or handle other vital tasks while the automated material handling system tirelessly handles the task of moving raw and finished parts from point A to point B.

Cycle Time Reduction and Throughput Improvement

Most automated material handling systems that are flexible enough to be used over a broad range of parts, such as gantries and robots, have cycle load and unload times that are slower than a typical machine operator working at peak efficiency. However, human operators do not maintain peak efficiency for a full shift, day after day, and week after week. When the process engineer considers the certain inefficiencies of lunch time, coffee breaks, and some personal time, an automated system catches up with and surpasses the human operator in production per shift, week, or month. This translates into more throughput per time period and possibly lower cost per part for the automated system.

Quality Improvement

When human machine operators make a mistake in loading a part, the result is commonly a scrapped piece. Automated loading also has failures, but these typically result in an alarm condition. This generally allows the problem to be caught and the cause of the problem eliminated. The desired end result of automated material handling is that it performs the operator's load and unload tasks, but in a more consistent manner. A promise of automation is that it leads to parts that are produced with more consistent dimensions and tolerances.

AUTOMATION ISSUES

Before any operation can be considered for robotics or other material handling automation, some features of the application must be considered to ensure that the operation is suitable for automation. Machining issues must be resolved before material handling issues. Material handling automation will not yield a good part if there is a machining problem. Automatic loading and unloading introduces more tasks that have to be taken care of automatically, replacing manual handling by the machine operator.

One machining issue is tool life. A second is the handling of chips adhering to the part when the part is turned from the first side to the second side, as in a two-spindle turning operation. A third consideration is chip disposal, which is treated at the end of this chapter and in Chapter 20.

Tool life must be considered before an application is considered for automation. *Tool life* is the cutting insert longevity before it has to be changed. The main reason for automatic loading and unloading is to get extended runs with minimum operator attendance. But if a cutting tool wears out after every piece that is machined, this can defeat the purpose (for example, machining nickel-based alloys, where tool life may be short).

Another issue, one that arises in turning, is how to handle part turnaround successfully. Turning automation is usually considered when workpieces are turned on both ends, which typically requires some turnaround or, in the case of vertical turning, turnover operation. When a human operator loads and unloads a workpiece, human senses are used to make adjustments if the part is not located properly. If an operator turns a part around in the lathe chuck, he or she removes the chips from its surface and then locates the part in the chuck by feel, before clamping it. A robot or automated load device cannot do that—the robot only works on switches and signals and does not have the ability to check for chips around the workpiece or sense if the piece is seated properly in the chuck.

Ease of access is an issue to consider. The machine tool should offer relatively easy access to the workholding or fixturing to make automated loading feasible. Too complex a situation leads to long load and unload times, when the goal is to maximize the spindle run time. For example, gantry loading of machine tools is typically limited to machines with access from directly above, such as lathes and some grinders. The loading device, such as a gantry or robot, must be able to quickly travel in and out of tight machine tool work areas, known as the machine tool's *load path*. Load paths on machines designed initially for manual load and unload are generally narrow and restricted. Occasionally, machine tools must be modified to create a clear, unobstructed load path. Sometimes a machine's auxiliary features, such as operator safety guards, chip disposal units, or dust and mist containment systems, may complicate the issue of a clear load path. Many modern machining centers, lathes, and grinders are available with automated load and unload doors, hatches, or sliding guide doors that facilitate gantry or pedestal robot loading.

Cycle time is an issue that determines application feasibility in many cases. The time-in-cut must be more than the time required to drop off the finished part and get a raw part to load for the next cycle.

BANDSAWING

Bandsaws are frequently the first step in a machining or fabricating process. Saws cut many varieties and sizes of stock to length for subsequent machining, forming, or fabricating. Bandsaws traditionally received little attention as a machining process or challenge for material handling automation, but this is changing. Manufacturing engineers are more frequently specifying saw productivity and looking at integrated material handling automation options.

AUTOMATING INFEED AND OUTFEED

When bandsaws move into production, they need to move material in and out fast enough to keep up the pace set by machines and processes further down the line. In some cases, such as cutting 6-ft (1.8-m) pieces from a 20-ft (6.1-m) piece, if the cut itself takes two minutes, loading time rather than the cutting speed determines the production rate. Automated infeed and outfeed represents a growing business for several saw manufacturers. With extensive flexible automation options, sawing is now in the era of cell technology.

As with other CNC equipment, dozens or hundreds of jobs with shape, dimensions, and coolant requirements may be programmed into a controller or PC-based computer. Programming an individual job then just becomes a matter of entering the job number, cut length, piece count, and bin position. Sometimes color graphics are available to indicate machine functions, bar cross-section dimensions, and sawing parameters.

Automating the infeed may use a variety of techniques, including an inclined magazine with an automatic bar feed that feeds bars to a powered input roller conveyor. In CNC sawing cells, the output sorting gripper can discharge the cut lengths to preprogrammed positions, either a bin or a pallet.[1]

APPLICATION EXAMPLES

Some automated storage and retrieval systems (AS/RS) automate the movement of material completely. A custom sawing system can include powered roller conveying, cross-transporting, bundle clamping, cutting to length, ejection, and sorting. Such an automated system, although it takes considerable floor space, can cut labor costs substantially and quadruple throughput. One system has a magazine at the back for loading bars of different sizes and materials. The machine retrieves the material, does the cutoff, and dumps the parts in one of 27 different locations.

Sometimes large output and input tables have special importance. One structural fabricator uses 75-ft (23-m) input and output tables on a vertical tilt-frame bandsaw because 60 ft (18 m) lengths of material can be bought from the mill, instead of two 30-ft (9-m) sections.[2] This means they get the material earlier, cut it themselves, and do not have to pay the cutting charge.

A turnkey custom sawing installation, at a manufacturer of steel racks for automotive stampings and subassemblies, has a complete material handling system with a huge L-shaped feed table assembly around a heavy-duty, twin-column, automatic bandsaw. The basic material cut is lengths of 2 × 2-in. (51 × 51-mm) welded steel square tube. The system features a bundle staging area for up to seven bundles and cross-transfer units with powered rollers, which load bundles of the welded square steel tube onto the feed table.[3] The feed system pushes bundles with some force into the feed vise on the input side. The feed stroke goes up to 108 in. (274 cm). Bundles are typically 14 × 14 in. (356 × 356 mm) in cross-section and 24-ft (7-m) long. Sorting and ejection features assist on the output side. Off-loading of cut-offs is speeded by power rollers and a shuttle push device.

BAR WORK

Automating the material handling function in turning operations has been a trend for a long time because of its proven economies and efficiencies. Turning is divided into horizontal and vertical types. *Vertical turning* is confined to chucking work—involving handling single slugs of material or castings. *Horizontal turning* operations are divided into chucking work and bar work, or shaft work. Primarily manual approaches to material handling, such as the loading of heavy workpieces into lathes with the aid of hoists, are not considered in this chapter.

Early bar holding devices, still in use, consisted of no more than a hollow tube or a V-shaped channel in line with the lathe spindle and only supported the bar sticking out of the back end of the head-stock. The bar feeding was done with feed fingers inside the machine spindle and operated by the machine. Most multispindle automatics still operate with feed finger systems, using a stock tube to support the rotating material.

A simple method of loading short bars into a CNC lathe employs a bar puller with spring-loaded fingers to pull the bar to a specified position. Such a device takes up one position on the lathe turret and uses the motion of the turret in the *Z*-axis to pull the bar through the spindle when the chuck releases the bar. The only equipment required to use this method is a spindle liner for reducing the spindle bore size. This prevents the bar from moving back and forth inside the spindle. Bar length is restricted to the length of the headstock.

One of the most common forms of automated material flow for turning machines is bar feeding standard 12-ft (3.7-m) lengths of barstock through the lathe spindle and into the chuck or collet using an *automatic bar feed*. While round bar is by far the most common material handled, hex and square bars also may be run on certain types of bar feeders. Hex and square bars vibrate and must be run about one-third or more slower than round bar. The modern bar feeder performs several functions: feeding the bar into the lathe, supporting the bar while it is rotating, and in some cases automatically loading new bars from a bar magazine, so the machine runs continuously, possibly for a complete work shift or longer. Some use the terms

automatic bar loader or magazine bar feed to refer to those units with such a magazine.[4]

Bar feeds and bar loaders work with turning machines, including fixed headstock CNC lathes, single-spindle automatics, and CNC Swiss-style, sliding headstock automatics. They are typically used for production of standard turned products in medium- to high-volumes. Bar feeders also feed bars into through-feed centerless grinding machines, used for straightening a wavy bar or sizing it prior to sending it to another operation, such as turning or thread rolling. Multispindle automatics may be equipped with bar loaders, which offer the ability to keep large volumes of bars ready in storage. Bar loaders for multispindle automatics replace the stock reels that were supplied with the machine tool and run at the slower speeds typical of that class of machine. This section discusses the aspects of bar feeding and loading systems, cut feeding, and bar loading of centerless grinders.

BAR FEEDING AND LOADING SYSTEMS

Most bar feeders for lathes feed from the left side of the turning machine into the headstock. However, on CNC Swiss-style automatics, the bar feed to the sliding headstock may be positioned on either side of the machine tool, depending on which side of the lathe the headstock is mounted on. Also, bar feed units for Swiss automatics must accommodate the changing home position of the sliding headstock when different length parts are machined, and be able to retrieve and eject the long remnants often found in this class of turning machines. With one bar loader model for Swiss-style machines, the loader may be ordered for loading from either the right or the left, and the barrel is equipped with a retract mechanism to give it 23 in. (584 mm) of travel to compensate for the changing home position of the headstock.

Generally, bar feeds and bar loaders support bars from about 0.06-in. (1.5-mm) diameter up to about 4.5-in. (114-mm) diameter and in lengths from about 3-13.7 ft (0.9-4.2 m), although any one bar loader model handles a much smaller range than that. The bulk of bar work is for material up to about 2.5-in. (64-mm) in diameter.

Bar feeds and loaders may be rated for the maximum revolutions per minute (rpm) they will accommodate, with the maximum rpms permitted depending on the bar lengths and diameters. Rated top speeds of modern bar loaders for CNC machines are typically in the 3,500-7,500 rpm range, with a few capable of effectively supporting smaller diameter bars at 10,000 rpm. Since the bar diameter range is large, it is important to also state the surface feet per minute (sfpm) limits. The upper limit for a single hydrodynamic system is 2,000 sfpm (610 surface meters per minute [smpm]). Most applications with straight, properly prepared bar, can run at 2,000 sfpm (610 smpm), but consistent production is usually run at 1,500 sfpm (457 smpm). A dual hydrodynamic bar feed with one tube free to spin inside the other, and the barstock spinning inside the inner tube, can achieve 2,500 sfpm (762 smpm) or more. In a single hydrodynamic system run above the 2,000 sfpm (610 smpm) limit, the oil shear effect breaks down the support and the hydrodynamic bearing effect fails.

Bar Remnants

During machining of the last piece from a bar, a remnant is required for the chuck to hold it. Consequently, this short piece is left over. The bar end is ejected by the bar feeder into either the lathe working area, where it falls into the chip bin at the base of the machine, or back through the tube to a collection bin at the rear of the loader. Then, a fresh bar is loaded into the feeding mechanism. On some units, there is a device for retracting the remnant and disposing of it in a different manner.

CHAPTER 15   METALCUTTING

Bar Support

The difficulty with feeding barstock into a turning machine is usually not the feeding, but the support. Unsupported or inadequately supported bar moves around and oscillates, creating problems with the lathe workholding and machining operations. Because centrifugal force increases with the second power of the rpm, the bar support becomes critical with the high rpms capable of modern turning machines.

$$\text{Centrifugal force} = r_o \times \omega^2 \times m \qquad (1)$$

where:

r_o = distance of gravity center point from center of rotation
ω = speed
m = mass

Because modern CNC turning machines have fast top rpms, the bar loader must be able to prevent bar deflection and vibration for the machine to utilize its speed. In many cases, component surface finish, dimensional accuracy, and part production rate are limited by the support system capability of the bar loader, rather than any deficiency of the modern lathe. By reducing the vibration to a minimum, a good bar handling system enhances the gripping power of the workholding device on the lathe, assuring good precision and surface finish on the workpiece.

Compromises may have to be made to deal with the vibration of 12-ft (3.7-m) bars rotating at high speeds. One method is to program a lower rpm in the part program of an NC lathe during the time when the bar is long and then reprogram for a higher rpm after the bar is partly consumed.

Bar support mechanisms are built to prevent deflection and some of them accomplish secondary functions, such as noise reduction.

Among the techniques to support rotating bars at high speeds are: ball bearing support, roller or rotating bushing support, hydrodynamic support in an oil-filled stock tube, and support with plastic or metal inserts or tube liners. Interchangeable tube liners will accommodate a range of bar diameter sizes and shapes within the size capacity of a given bar loader.

Support to eliminate bar sag is good for bars even when they are not turning. For example, when a workpiece is stopped in the spindle and is machined with power-driven drills or mills, close support of the bar helps maintain accurate feature spatial relationships, including concentricity.

The ball bearing is a reliable method for supporting a rotating body, including a bar. It allows close support of the bar for high speeds (see Fig. 15-1). The gap between the support bushing and the bar is only a few thousandths of an inch (hundredths of a millimeter), enough to feed the bar through. The ball bearing bushing must be exchanged to accommodate different bar diameters. This method accommodates hex and square bars.[5]

Hydrodynamic Bar Feeders

Hydrodynamic bar feeders, the most common type used with CNC lathes, support the bar on a film of pressurized oil within the tube, with no metal-to-metal contact. The film of oil is about 0.08 in. (2 mm) on a side. The oil support allows for high rpms and quiet operation. A hydraulic pusher runs the length of the bar feeder, feeding the stock into the lathe. The excellent bar support allows high spindle speeds.

The tube-type hydrodynamic bar feeder uses the motion of the spinning bar to generate hydrodynamic pressure to support the bar (see Fig. 15-2). Oil is continually pumped in from the back of the feeder to keep the bar suspended and fill the space resulting from the loss of oil and air that moves out the front and onto the lathe.

The oil is not lost, but is usually caught at the end of the bar feed tube and recirculated back into the oil reservoir of the bar feed unit. Only the oil that adheres to the part in the turning machine is lost to the bar feed unit. This type of bar feeder is manually loaded from the machine end. The tube must be swung away from the machine's headstock so that a fresh bar can be loaded.

This type of bar feed is used for either a single bar size or for multiple bar sizes. The multiple bar type is sometimes called the *Gatling gun style* (see Fig. 15-3); it allows rapid changeover from running one bar diameter to another by indexing the barrel to the next tube size required. When the bar material is used at a given lathe, it is often changed within the size range of that lathe. As in job shop environments, bar feeds with multiple tubes in the Gatling gun style, having three to 11 different diameter tubes within a larger barrel, are suitable. In this style of loader, the barrel or drum is indexed to the desired tube diameter and the hydraulic lines are connected, manually or through an automatic device, to the active tube for the next job. An alternate design, with six or eight channels of different diameters in two mating guide drums of highly wear-resistant plastic, can be operated with or without a film of oil.

The bushing-type bar loader uses multiple close-tolerance bearing blocks spaced along the length of the bar to hold the barstock. The bar is supported during turning by a film of oil injected under pressure through these bearing blocks, so the bar does not contact the bearing blocks during turning operations. In these units, sometimes called *hydrostatic bar loaders*, the bar rides on oil only within the bearing blocks, rather than along its entire length. The main reason for the split bushing type is to accommodate automatic bar loading from the side, while retaining the advantage of running on a film of oil. The bearing blocks split in two to allow this. The design will support an automatic loading bar magazine and very high rpms. A trade-off is that this design does not allow easy indexing of the multitube Gatling gun design for diameter changeover; instead the bearing blocks must be converted to the new bar diameter. Materials such as wood, plastic, or fiberglass, which are harmed by contact with oil, would not use an oil-based loader design.

Short Bar Feeds and Bar Loaders

A full-size loader for 12-ft (3.7-m) bar typically takes 15-19 ft (4.6-5.8 m) of space unless it is equipped with a two-stage pusher, which is more compact than the standard pusher. A short bar magazine, pusher-style bar loader, about 6-8-ft (1.8-2.4-m) long, has no problem supporting a rotating bar, because the rotating bar is supported directly in the spindle of the machine (see Fig. 15-4). However, the bar must be replaced more often. This is accomplished with a bar magazine, which feeds a new bar into the feed tube once the previous bar is consumed by the lathe. One big advantage is space savings, since a full-length bar feed unit connected to a lathe typically more than doubles the floor space requirement.

Short bar pushers most commonly advance the bar through the lathe spindle by intermittent pneumatic pressure. They are simpler to use than the oil-operated hydrodynamic or hydrostatic types and handle shorter bar lengths, up to about 5-ft (1.5-m) long. Some bar pushers are not pneumatic, but are hydraulic-, electromechanical-, or gravity-driven. A pusher saves the lathe turret position for a bar puller device, since the pusher advances the bar through the spindle.

In hydraulic units, all the motions of the pusher are regulated by the hydraulic system. In pneumatic units, pusher speed and force are governed by air pressure, and this technique is generally limited to the short bar loading units. Electromechanical units use a motor connected to the pusher by chain or a toothed belt. There is no oil, and feed speed is constant. Economical, old-time, gravity-based units get their force behind the pusher from weights on the feeding rope

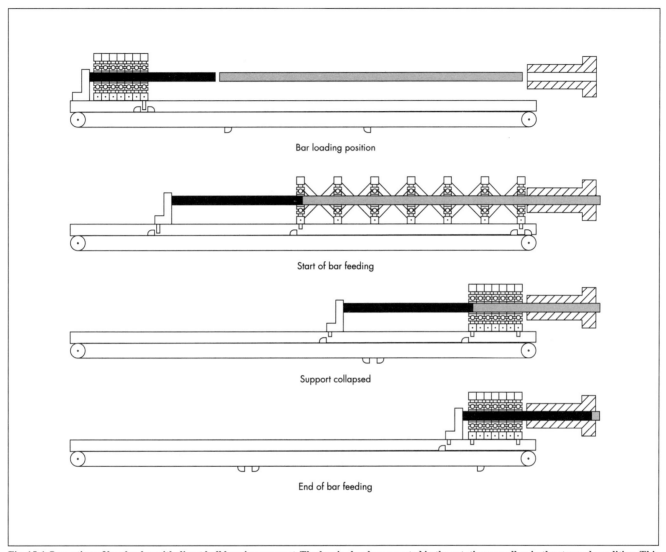

Fig. 15-1 Operation of bar loader with direct ball bearing support. The bar is closely supported in the rotating as well as in the stopped condition. This eliminates bar sag when machining a nonrotating part with power-driven tools. *(Courtesy Index Corp.)*

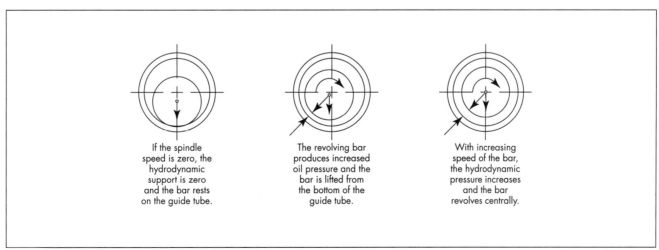

Fig. 15-2 Basic principle of a hydrodynamic bar loader. *(Courtesy LNS America, Inc.)*

CHAPTER 15   METALCUTTING

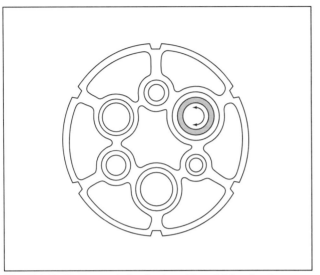

Fig. 15-3 Gatling gun-style bar loader with multiple tubes to cover a range of bar diameters. *(Courtesy SMW Systems, Inc.)*

and the force transmitted over pulleys. They work in speeds up to 2,400 rpm and are suited to automatic screw machines.

In some models, the feed rate may be programmable. Single-tube and multitube designs are available in some of these types.

Material Considerations

The straightness of the bar governs the attainable spindle speeds, the attainable workpiece accuracy and surface finish, and the amount of noise the rotating bar will generate. For best results, bars should not deviate from perfect straightness by more than 0.02 in. per 40 in. (0.5 mm per 1 m) of bar length.

Both ends of the bar must be burr-free. The corners at the start of a polygon bar must be chamfered; on round bar this may or may not be required, depending on the bar feeder. On hydraulic bar feeders, the back end of the bar must usually be chamfered or pointed to the angle on the bar pusher, often 60°, so that the pusher may provide adequate support and concentric performance.

Additional Considerations

Bar feeders must have the right interface to the machine tool. The microprocessor controller or programmable logic controller of

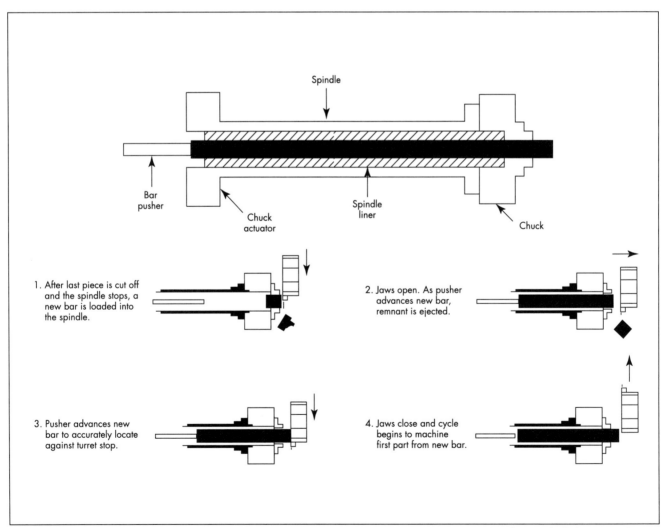

1. After last piece is cut off and the spindle stops, a new bar is loaded into the spindle.

2. Jaws open. As pusher advances new bar, remnant is ejected.

3. Pusher advances new bar to accurately locate against turret stop.

4. Jaws close and cycle begins to machine first part from new bar.

Fig. 15-4 Short-bar bar feeder has an uncomplicated construction with a liner tube and a simple operating cycle. *(Courtesy SMW Systems, Inc.)*

the bar feed unit must interface with the machine tool control to monitor bar presence and length, bar position, bar feeding to stop position, bar remnant rejection, etc. Most CNC lathes have a bar loading program in their control. On the mechanical interface side, the inside diameter of the tube or tube liner in the bar feeder must match the inside diameter of the spindle liner in the lathe.

Many older automatic screw machines have an internal bar feeding mechanism and do not require the bar feeder to feed the bar, but only to support the bar, as mentioned earlier. Such an internal bar feed mechanism typically uses a feed finger in the spindle. This type can feed material faster—approximately one-half second versus three seconds or more for most pusher-type bar feeds.

Newer model bar feeders for multispindle automatics may use hydraulic pressure to feed the bar. This eliminates the need for adjustment and changeover of the feed fingers. In models with a split-tube design, the bars may be loaded from the side rather than the end, saving floor space.

Magazine Loading

Bar magazines carry six to 36 or more bars in a rack, depending on bar diameter, and automatically load them one at a time into the feed tube and feed the bars into the machine (see Fig. 15-5). Magazines, like the bar loaders, are sized for the diameter and length of the bars they accommodate. Magazines have accommodated bars up to 23-ft (7-m) long. Some bar magazines are integral with the loader and others are floor-mounted, freestanding units, feeding directly into the loader.

A common arrangement for bar magazines is where the bar gripping or pushing mechanism retracts to an out-of-the-way position at the side or rear, while a fresh bar moves into the bar feed tube from the side. This side-loading feature saves floor space.

On some bar loaders, the bar pusher is equipped with a measuring system allowing the bar loader to measure the length of the bar. The controller can then calculate the number of pieces that can be made from this bar (bar lengths sometimes vary). It then knows when the last piece is being machined and can load the new bar during the last machining operation. As a result, the five to 10 seconds of bar loading time is not added to the nonproductive time on the machine.

Modern magazine bar loaders for multispindle automatics feed bars into the tubes while the machine is cutting and allow the magazine itself to be loaded while the machine runs. Both of these features reduce manual material handling and add to the productivity of the machines.

CUT FEEDING

In bar feeding, the bar is fed through the lathe headstock and spindle. The cutting off of the turned part from the bar material is performed by the cut-off or parting-off tool inside the lathe.

An alternative to bar feeding, in cases that still use bar material rather than precut slugs, is to cut the bar to desired lengths immediately adjacent to the lathe cutting area, and feed the cut lengths or slugs directly into the lathe's chuck with a robotic arm. With this method, the bar of material does not rotate with the lathe spindle. The device that performs this form of material handling of barstock is called a *cut feeder*.

One machine supplier builds such a device and it runs with the company's CNC lathes.[6] The cut feeder acts like a combination of an automated sawing device and lathe-feeding robot. The device pushes a bar past two rotating cutting tools to a stop, cuts off a length of stock during the machining cycle of the lathe, and loads the freshly cut slug to the lathe's chuck from the front. The cutting tools are mounted on a hollow disk around the bar. The finished part may be removed by a second spindle or dropped into a parts catcher. No

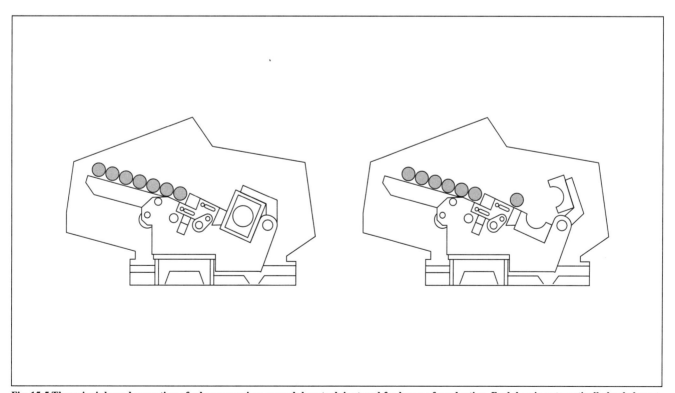

Fig. 15-5 The principle and operation of a bar magazine: enough barstock is stored for hours of production. Each bar is automatically loaded unattended. *(Courtesy FMB Machinery, USA)*

material passes through the lathe headstock or spindle from the left side of the lathe. This device is more complex and more expensive than a bar feeder, but can be effective for larger bars. Also, since the bar does not have to rotate with the lathe spindle and meet specifications for straightness or surface finish, this technique may use less-expensive, hot-rolled barstock and reduce material costs. In addition, larger diameter slugs than the maximum diameter that the lathe's spindle bore accepts can be used.

BAR LOADING OF CENTERLESS GRINDERS

Centerless grinding barstock, for example, in screw machine shops, typically takes one operator to feed the bar and a second one to catch it. Through-feed centerless grinding may be supported and partially automated by a bar feed system, so that one of the two operators is freed up for other work. Such bar feeders are not the standard units used for lathes, but tend to be customized for each application and based on a standard design.[7]

Bar feeders to feed bar or tube stock to centerless grinders, thread rollers, polishing machines, and other operations, can handle bar diameters up to 2.5 in. (64 mm) and bar lengths up to 30 in. (762 mm). In operation, bars, tubes, or shafts are loaded manually into a magazine. Magazines are made in varying sizes and workpiece capacities to fit applications. Some magazines feature adjustable side plates for varying part lengths.

In one design, a mechanical agitator maintains a steady flow of the bars to escapement fingers. In another, a circulating loop carries plastic brackets, which, in turn, carry the bars to the load mechanism. As one part leaves the magazine, a switch is tripped, and another part is released—either to a front-end conveyor for continuous end-to-end feeding, or to a set of rails for diameter-to-diameter feeding. In addition, the material handling for a through-feed, two-grinder installation may be almost fully automated by adding an intermediate conveyor between the first and second grinder, and an exit conveyor, equipped with a pneumatic transfer device and part storage area, following the second grinder. Conveyors for such applications are offered with a nonmarking belt 1 or 2-in. (25 or 51-mm) wide, and are typically from 3-12-ft (0.9-3.7-m) long.

Hopper and Bowl Feeding

Centerless grinders are among the types of metalcutting machine tools sometimes fed by parts hoppers. Other equipment served by hoppers includes lathes, broaches, and a variety of special metalcutting machines, as well as presses and thread rollers, among metal forming equipment. Parts hoppers, bowl feeders, and similar devices are discussed more in Chapter 18, so they are mentioned only briefly here.

Automatic hopper feeding eliminates costly hand-orienting and feeding of a wide range of small parts, most commonly cylindrical parts, which can roll on a track. Parts such as bushings, couplings, rods, shafts, tubes, bearing races, piston pins, valve lifters, and gear blanks can be hopper-fed to centerless grinders and other machining operations via hopper feeders. Hopper capacities are typically 5-15 ft³ (0.14-0.42 m³), but can be as large as 40 ft³ (1.13 m³). The diameters of the vibratory bowls range from 12-40 in. (31-102 cm) and come in a multitude of styles. There are many possible configurations for vibratory feeding systems. Hoppers may be loaded by hand, belt elevator, conveyor, or other means. The hopper orients parts and places them in a chute to feed the machine tool. Or, the hopper feeds a vibratory bowl, which in turn, orients the part. Each application is designed with appropriate controls, timing, feed rate, diverters for incorrectly oriented or defective parts, and special equipment. Some systems, particularly those designed for flexible changeover of the unit when handling more than one part, are equipped with part-recognition technology. This usually consists of a sensitive and high-speed machine vision system designed to reject or re-orient unacceptable parts.

CHUCKING WORK

This section includes gantry loading, gantry applications for horizontal chucking, gantry applications other than turning, robot loading, simple loaders and unloaders for lathes, and vertical chucking.

GANTRY LOADING

The following discussion on gantry loading includes:

- Gantry construction and axes of motion.
- Gantry grippers.
- Suitable part weights and sizes.
- Linear and area gantries.
- Gantry lathe loading.
- Payback calculation for a gantry-loaded turning cell.
- Machine gantry loading other than lathes.
- Machining center gantry loading.
- The machine tool-gantry interface.

Gantry loading for metalcutting machine tools provides flexibility, labor reduction, consistency, continuous throughput, and can be an efficient and cost-effective manner of material handling. Gantry robots or gantries are a very versatile form of material handling equipment and may load and unload turning machines, grinding machines, gear cutting machines, machining centers, and others. They can load workpieces or cutting tool assemblies. Gantry loaders generally do not restrict work aisles and take up relatively little space. Further advantages of gantry loading include an economical use of floor space, easy and unblocked access to the front of the machine tool for tool change, setup, and manual operations. If a gantry loader fails, it can be moved into a position for maintenance that does not interfere with the manual operation of the machine tool.

Gantries may be combined with conveyors and other devices in complex systems, such as production lines for crankshafts or gears. Some gantry systems are designed so that a single gantry robot serves two or more machine tools. While stand-alone gantries may carry very large and heavy workpieces, compact gantry loaders may be built into CNC turning machines, usually horizontal chuckers, so that the machines may run medium to large volumes of parts with minimal operator attention.

The term *gantry* generally denotes an overhead lifting device capable of self-propelled movement, as compared to a *crane*, which is an overhead device that is manually controlled. When a multi-axis control drives the unit, the gantry works as a manipulator to load and unload a machine tool and can move workpieces between operations. Typically, gantry robots use either a programmable logic controller (PLC) or computer numerical control (CNC), which are highly accurate, and fairly expensive. Thus, they can be cost-prohibitive if a given application and its production volumes do not yield a reasonable return.

Gantry Construction and Axes of Motion

A gantry typically consists of a long, straight metal beam that is supported on metal legs securely anchored to the floor. The axis of travel along the beam is commonly referred to as the *X*-axis. A carriage rides along the beam, driven by an electric servodrive motor, and the carriage supports one or more load arms (see Fig. 15-6). Rack and pinion and belt drives are the most common designs for

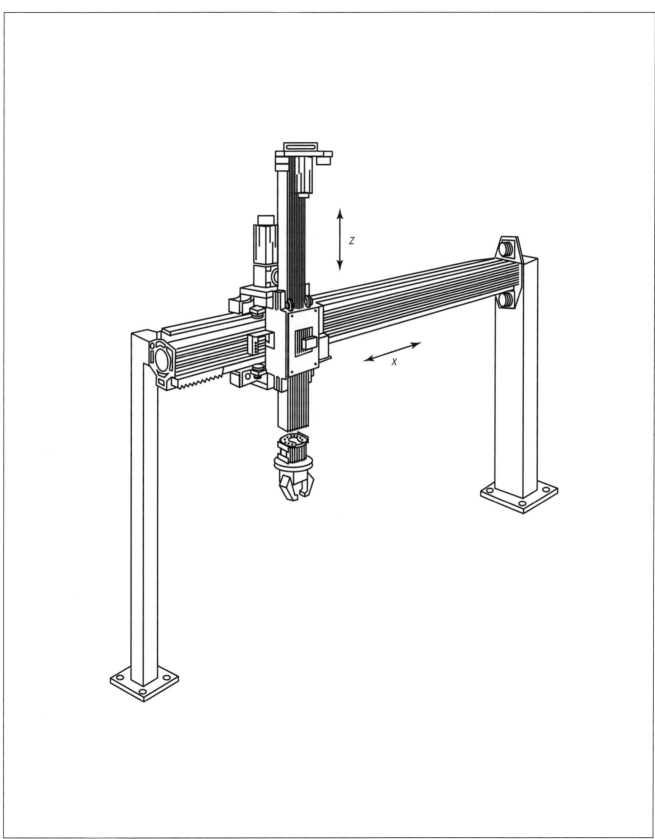

Fig. 15-6 Linear gantry. (*Courtesy Bleichert, Inc./MasTech*)

CHAPTER 15   METALCUTTING

both carriages and load arms, but there are systems that incorporate other mechanisms. Accuracy is maintained by fine-machined and well-aligned guide rails, and highly-accurate linear guide bearings. Multiple carriages may be used. These are either tied together or operate separately with coordinated programming and safety systems to avoid collisions.

The gantry's load and unload arm is usually moved up and down by a separate servomotor. The vertical motion of the load arm is perpendicular to the horizontal beam and designates the Z-axis. A gantry with one carriage supporting one load arm is typically called an *I arrangement*. For particularly heavy workpieces, it may be necessary to provide a counterweight to the Z-axis load and unload arm to prevent deflection.

Many gantries have multiple carriages linked together to provide two or more load arms. The two-arm gantry, called an *H arrangement*, is common. The H arrangement allows one arm to unload finished parts while one arm loads raw parts. This gives the gantry the capability to perform rapid part exchange, often in eight seconds or less, whereas a one-arm gantry would have to make extra moves, thereby taking longer. This would leave the machine tool inactive, waiting for the gantry to complete its part-exchange sequence.

The general form of a gantry or gantry robot provides for movement in a Cartesian coordinate system. Depending on the control architecture and sophistication, multi-axis simultaneous moves, as well as interpolated trajectories, may be possible.

Gantry loading of metalcutting machine tools typically requires machines with access from above, such as lathes, grinders, and sometimes, machining centers. Gantries generally must straddle the machine. Therefore, the gantry carriage must travel at least the width or breadth of the machine tool to get to the part conveying device. Movements are generally linear. Multiple in-line machines may be served by a single long gantry loader, with part cycle time being the limiting factor.

The primary areas requiring guarding are the part pickup point, the drop-off area, and the loading area. Since all these are in line, guard geometry is relatively easy, consisting of mainly straight panels. The use of screen material to cover the traverse path of the gantry above the lathe, when combined with a loading hatch, makes the guarding simple and effective.

Gantry loaders usually are limited to Cartesian moves in three or four axes. Their overhead position may make high ceilings necessary and maintenance difficult. Their positioning capability is dependent upon the parallelism of the gantry's horizontal axis to the machine tool's ways or spindle centerline.

Gantry loaders typically load straight up and down, which implies a requirement for a load path that is clear of all obstructions in a vertical corridor. The dimensions of the load path are typically determined by the workpiece itself, the gantry's gripper unit, and the dimensions of any additional apparatus at the end of the gantry's arm. Machine tools designed for human operator loading must often be modified to be suitable for gantry loading. Many modern lathes, grinders, and machining centers are designed with optional automated load and unload doors or hatches that facilitate gantry or pedestal robot loading and unloading. When a direct vertical load path for a gantry arm to enter a machine tool cannot be established, additional axes of motion are required.

Where there are obstructions directly over the load area, a Y-axis motion may be used. If you think of your leg as the gantry's Z-axis, your foot sticks out in the Y-direction. A Y-axis load assist, as it is often referred to, is also a popular solution for loading traditional orientation vertical spindle lathes and vertical machining centers. The Y-axis, typically achieved by attaching a driven device to the end of the load and unload arm, unfortunately adds weight and bulk to the end of the arm, creating drag. The drag potentially decreases travel speed and the life of the gantry's drive components.

The circular C- and D-axes may be used to change part orientation from conveyor to machine, from machine to machine, or in combination with multiple part grippers (see Fig. 15-7). The part that pivots or rotates around a Z-axis is called a C-axis. However, gantry vendors differ on the definition of axis names. The part that rotates around a Y-axis is called a B-axis (some call it a D-axis). Additional axes of motion on the end of a gantry load and unload arm take up space. Further, machine tool manufacturers and production foremen alike share a fearful reaction when first watching a gantry robot equipped with a combined C and D axis and multiple part grippers move parts inside a machine tool's work area. This feeling disappears after a few thousand cycles.

Cycle times can be a limitation. For example, machine cycles of under 10-25 seconds may be too short to justify a gantry. The gantry must enter the machine work area, grip the finished part, raise and remove the part from the work area, deposit a raw part (if it is carrying the raw part in a second position), then exit the work area to get another raw part to repeat the operation. If the situation is a single arm with a single gripper, then the arm in this arrangement would have to travel to a conveyor for dropping off the finished part, move to a second pickup area or conveyor to pick up a raw part, and then travel back to the machine loading zone to load it. Cycle times that are too short require the machine to wait for the gantry. The ideal situation is for the gantry to complete the exchange of finished and raw parts during the machining cycle.

The speed of the part conveying or queuing device, which brings raw parts to the gantry and takes finished parts away, as well as the device distance from the machining area, are critical factors to determine system cycle time efficiency. It is the gantry robot's travel time that typically allows the part conveying device serving the machine to index, rotate, or robotically transfer another raw part to the gantry pickup point and present an empty station for the gantry to deposit a finished part. The goal is to have a system that can accomplish a finished and raw part transfer between the gantry and the conveying device while the machine is in cycle or in the cut, and index another raw part for pickup during the combined machining and gantry travel cycle.

Systems that incorporate separate conveyors for raw and finished parts are usually more efficient. However, if the machine cycle is long enough, the gantry-to-conveyor transfer of a finished part, and reindexing to present a raw part, may be accomplished efficiently with one conveyor. If a single conveyor is used, it must have safeguards to prevent a raw part from indexing through the gantry pickup point and on to the next operation.

Gantry Grippers

Gantry grippers, or gripper fingers, as they are often called, are the part-touching details on the end of a load arm. Gripper units, which move the fingers to clamp and unclamp the workpiece, are available in a wide variety of styles, shapes, and sizes. They may be driven by a small drive motor or by pneumatic or hydraulic units. Some grippers utilize suction to handle glass. The typical gripper unit moves a pair or multiple pairs of fingers around, under, or into a specified area of the workpiece by actuating a slide mechanism. The fingers are usually machined steel with a profile that mates to the handling area of the workpiece. A V-notched pair of fingers or a dual three-jaw gripper, like a chuck, are common for gripping cylindrical parts (see Fig. 15-8).

If the workpiece surface is sensitive, the gripper fingers can be fitted with an insert or made of softer material, like nylon,

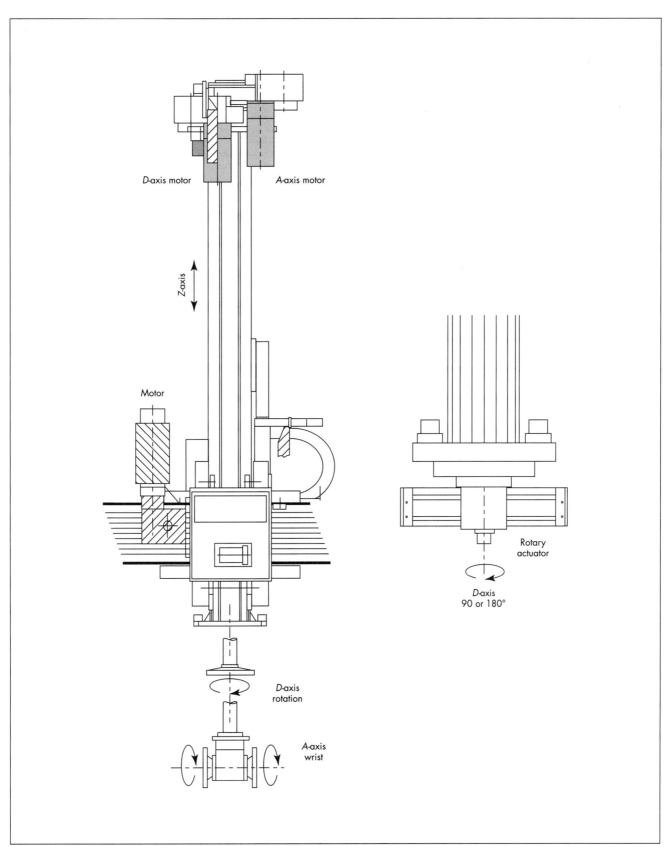

Fig. 15-7 Wrist and rotation axes (*A* and *D*) of a gantry loader arm. *(Courtesy Bleichert, Inc./MasTech)*

CHAPTER 15   METALCUTTING

polyurethane, or ultra-high molecular weight (UHMW) plastic. Even with nylon, the finger tips must be kept clean of chips. In most applications, it is preferable to grip workpieces on a nonmachined, nonsensitive surface.

Suitable Part Weights and Sizes

Gantry robots have been designed to be more lightweight, with aluminum carriages and load arms, driven by lightweight, high-speed servodrive motors. Thus, there are limitations for size and weight on many modern gantries. Some gantries can handle large parts weighing up to 2,200 lb (1,000 kg), such as train axles and turbine shafts. Yet, such large parts generally have long machining times and low-production volumes, so this makes gantry loading economically impractical. At the other end of the size scale, small parts, such as screws and shell casings, have such short cycle times and high volumes that other devices, such as bar loaders, may be the more appropriate form of automation. Between these extremes, the range of part sizes and weights that are suitable for gantry application is fairly well-defined.[8]

Typical gantry-loaded workpieces include camshafts, crankshafts, axle shafts, pump bodies, transmission housings, cylinder blocks and heads, wheels, fan hubs, and similar parts within a size range of 7-35 ft³ (0.2-1.0 m³).

Less typical systems combine a gantry with pedestal robots or devices like a gravity feed magazine, which are dedicated to one machine. Multiple part dunnage may be staged by a gantry serving two or more machines for local, dedicated pedestal robots to load and unload each machine.

Linear and Area Gantries

There are two main types of gantries. They are the linear gantry and the area gantry. The *linear gantry* moves in a single axis (*X*) in the horizontal plane (see Figs. 15-6 and 15-9). It is the most common type because it is the lowest cost configuration for machine tool loading and provides the best solution if the infeed and outfeed parts are not placed in a matrix. The linear gantry can serve one to three machine tools in a line. The loading arm may be equipped with two or three axes of motion. A typical arm uses a vertical axis and a single-axis wrist roll.

The *area gantry* moves in two axes (*X* and *Y*) in the horizontal plane (see Fig. 15-10). The main beam rides on side rails, similar to a bridge crane. While it provides for unlimited freedom of movement within the envelope of the gantry frame, this solution is much more expensive. It requires additional controls and framework, and is complex to install. In machining cells or systems where machining cycles are long, the area gantry, with its additional axis of motion, allows the gantry to be used as the prime material handling device. It can bring parts to machines, gages, wash stations, dunnage, or conveyors. It can thus serve as both the cell's loading system and the material handling system. The costly area gantry can typically only be justified if it is part of an integrated system.

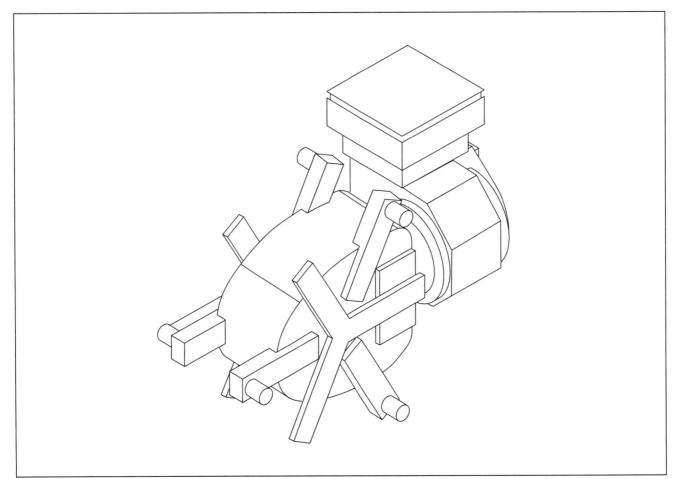

Fig. 15-8 Dual three-jaw gripper, end-of-arm tooling for lathe-loading gantry applications. *(Courtesy Westech Products Group)*

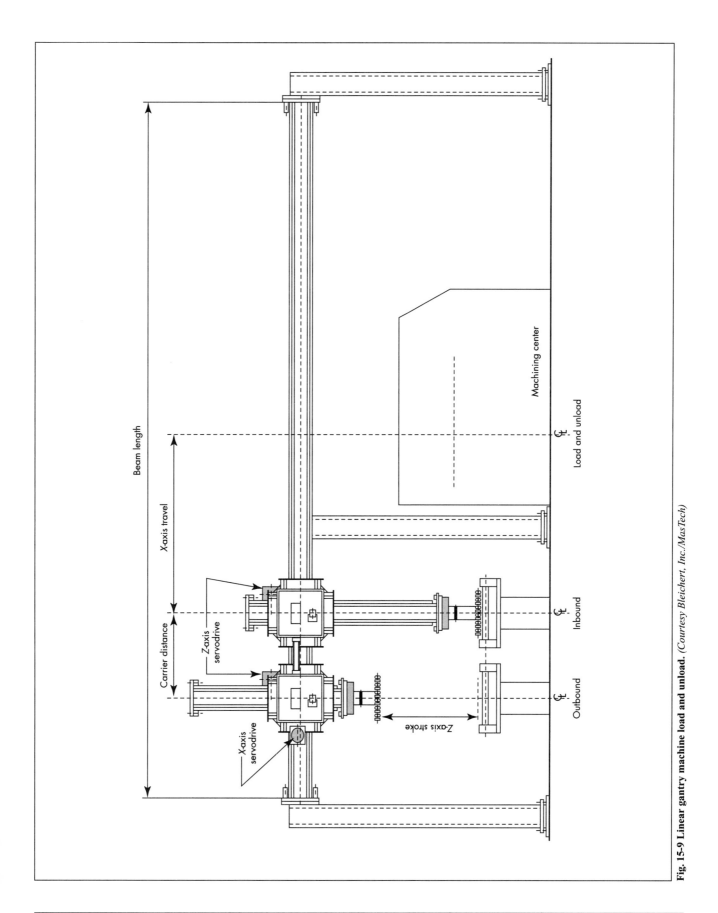

Fig. 15-9 Linear gantry machine load and unload. *(Courtesy Bleichert, Inc./MasTech)*

CHAPTER 15   METALCUTTING

One example of an area gantry application is at a machining line unload area. A single conveyor brings workpieces to an unload area, where they are placed on multiple rail-guided carts feeding 12 different assembly areas, six on either side of the feed conveyor. The area gantry can traverse the area in the X-axis to unload parts from the feed conveyor and load them to carts on either side. It can also traverse in the Y-axis (moving the entire beam as if it is a bridge crane) along the length of the feed conveyor to load multiple lanes of carts positioned side-by-side. In such complex arrangements, one must consider the travel speed of the gantry carriage in the X-axis, the traverse speed of the beam in the Y-axis, and the distances between the multiple load and unload points serviced.

Gantry Lathe Loading

In lathe loading, the horizontal axis of the gantry is installed parallel to the Z-axis of the lathe. The vertical motion of the gantry arm lowers the gripper to the loading zone. A wrist is usually provided to allow for the roll motion required for the exchange of raw and finished parts. Typical applications for chucking and shaft work utilize a double-sided gripper. This saves time by first unloading the finished part into an empty gripper and then completing the cycle by loading a raw part from the second side of the gripper.

Chucked parts can fall into many categories. The simplest is the blank cut from barstock. A second form is the casting. Nonround castings require a special gripper, rather than the basic three-jaw variety, which works so well with sawn round blanks.

Successful material handling automation projects for chucked parts require that the raw parts be relatively consistent in size, geometry, and location of the surfaces gripped. Most gantry loaders are used in turning and the simplest parts to handle and feed are cut slugs of round stock. Round castings or forgings also make good candidates—if the diameter variation does not exceed 0.16 in. (4 mm) where the workpieces are gripped. Larger variations can cause inconsistencies in loading.

Nonround castings with a specific geometry, like valve bodies, rod ends, or clevises, are difficult to fixture and to load. These can

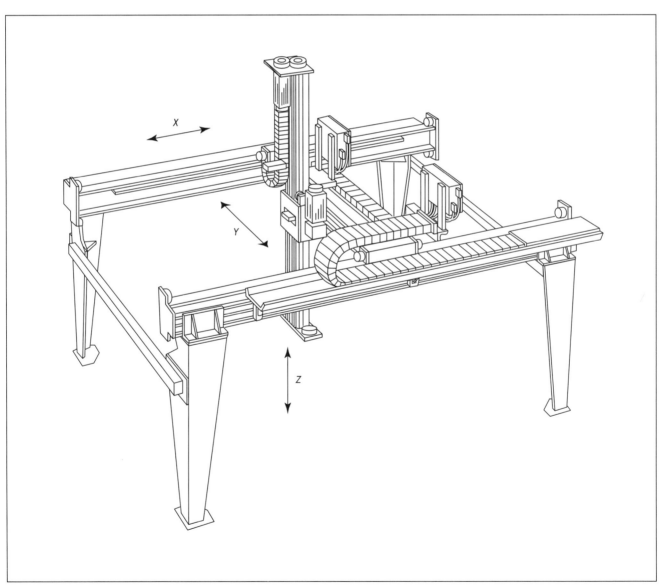

Fig. 15-10 Area gantry. *(Courtesy Bleichert, Inc./MasTech)*

have an excellent payback for automation, but require special grippers and possibly a two-jaw or indexing chuck in the lathe, which add significantly to the complexity of automatic loading. Parts with small gripping surfaces may result in inconsistent loading. One basic reference is that if the gripper holds one-third of the overall workpiece length, the loading will be consistent. If the gripping force is appropriate to the part weight, the part will almost always load into the chuck squarely.

Shaft parts are a second class of turned parts; most of the same guidelines for chucked parts apply here as well. What adds complexity is that there are several methods for holding a shaft in a lathe: chuck, collet, or face driver. If you add the further workholding elements of tailstocks and maybe steady rests, the complexity becomes considerable.

To take the simplest first, consider loading a shaft for a single side turning and facing operation. The easy projects allow the part to be loaded against a step in the jaw, a stop in the bore, or a flange on the part itself. This method will ensure that the loading repeatability is good.

If the part must be loaded into a collet, special attention must be paid to the collet opening. Since a shaft gripper has a tolerance, it is easily possible for the end of the shaft to be eccentric to the gripped location by as much as 0.01 in. (0.25 mm), especially for shafts over 12-in. (305-mm) long. Since many collets have as little as a 0.008-in. (0.20-mm) opening over their nominal size, inserting the shaft into the collet can become tricky. A small chamfer on the shaft, collet, or both, will help. Since the gantry will only move in a straight line, if the part does not start into the collet correctly, a loading crash results.

If a face driver and a tailstock are used in the turning operation, great care must be taken in a material handling automation project. Program subroutines and programming are required to allow the gantry arm to position the shaft to the face driver. The programmed motion must allow the part to stay controlled by the gripper until it is fully seated.

Payback Calculation for a Gantry-loaded Turning Cell

A rough calculation of manual versus gantry loading is shown for an output shaft machining cell at an automotive engine plant.[9]

$$T_P = P \times E \tag{2}$$

where:

T_P	=	total parts production
P	=	production
E	=	efficiency

For example, four parallel turning operations are done on four manually-loaded CNC lathes.

P = 31 parts/h per machine $\times$ 4 machines = 124 parts/h
E = 85%, so 124 parts/h $\times$ 16 h $\times$ 0.85 = 1,686.4 parts/day $\times$ 245 days/yr
T_P = 413,168 parts/yr

and

$$L_C = (W_N \times S_N) + S + B \tag{3}$$

where:

L_C	=	total labor costs
W_N	=	number of workers
S_N	=	number of shifts
S	=	average salary per worker per year
B	=	annual benefits per worker per year

For example,

$W_N \times S_N$ = 4 workers/shift $\times$ 2 shifts	= 8 workers
$S + B$	= $83,753 \times 8$
L_C	= $670,024

The possible automation: two gantry robots, each loading two CNC lathes each. One operator runs the four lathes and the two gantries, but does no part handling.

Investment: 2 gantries @ $632,000	
(amortized over 5 yrs)	= $126,400/yr
Power, air, lubrication (annual average)	= $7,234/yr
Maintenance cost (annual average)	= $5,000/yr

Automated cell labor costs:	
$W_N \times S_N$ = 1 worker/shift $\times$ 2 shifts	= 2 workers
$S + B$	= $83,753/yr $\times$ 2
L_C	= $167,506/yr
Total automation costs	= $306,140/yr

P = 38.3 parts/h per machine $\times$ 4 machines = 153.2 parts/h
E = 97.5%, so 153.2 parts/h $\times$ 16 h $\times$ 0.975 = 2,389.9 parts/day $\times$ 245 days/yr
T_P = 585,526 parts/yr

This calculation shows that this cell is a good candidate for automation. The manual system costs more than twice as much as the automated system on an annual basis ($670,024 versus $306,140). Further, the gantry-loaded cell achieves a 41.7% capacity increase (from 413,168 up to 585,526 parts/yr). Gantry robots can pay for their investment, particularly in situations in which both the labor costs and production volumes are fairly high.

Standard capital expenditure considerations apply: as the value of each part decreases, more volume is required to justify the expense of the capital equipment. As the costs of wages and benefits rise in industrialized countries, gantries (and other automation) become increasingly attractive alternatives to high-volume manual production operations.

Gantry robots for any type of machine loading may be fed parts by traditional types of conveyors, such as palletized chain conveyors, walking beam-type conveyors, and powered roller conveyors. Other options include automated guided vehicles, inverted monorails, and trough feeders.

To illustrate the modularity of much of the material handling automation available today, one hybrid design of gantry robot for a vertical lathe consists of a line gantry standing outside the machine tool that carries a multi-axis robot instead of a typical Z-axis arm and gantry gripper unit.[10] The hanging robot arm picks up work weighing up to 44 lb (20 kg) from a rotary stocker table, feeds it to the first chuck, moves the work from the first to the second chuck while turning it over, and finally removes the work from the second chuck. In some cases, this option might prove less costly than a typical line gantry.

Machine Gantry Loading Other than Lathes

Although the gantry is used for lathe loading, its overhead approach may be used on grinders, vertical and horizontal machining centers, and gear hobbing machines. Gantry loaders are applied to the material handling automation of cylindrical workpieces on cylindrical grinders, through-feed centerless grinders, and center-hole grinders. Such automation may serve single machines, single machines with a gaging station, or multimachine grinding lines. Gear shafts, rotor shafts, and camshafts, as well as such other high-volume applications as spool valves, inlet valves, and outlet valves, lend themselves to such automation. In through-feed centerless grinding,

CHAPTER 15   METALCUTTING

as an alternative to a bar loader, a gantry loader is generally only required to pick up the raw part and deliver it to the infeed track. The gantry input/output (I/O) signal checks if the load position is open, and if it is, the gantry deposits the shaft on the infeed, which usually looks like a small conveyor or a V-shaped chute.

Loading irregularly-shaped prismatic castings, forgings, and other parts into special fixtures in machining centers is a more complex challenge for a gantry than grasping round parts. Such prismatic part situations are most commonly thought of as requiring a system of pallets, rather than a gantry. But, if the machine tool has overhead access, a gantry is at least an option.

Machining Center Gantry Loading

There are two main approaches to gantry loading of machining centers—either load the parts into a fixture on the machine tool table or pallet, or load a tooling plate or fixture carrying one or more parts onto a receiver mounted to the machine table or a pallet.

In the case of loading the part into a fixture, there are as many variations as there are different parts. The gripper, gripper jaws, and fixture must be engineered. The gantry transports the part from a feeding and orienting system to the machine tool. Dual grippers are best to maximize spindle uptime; a raw part can be transported and held while the finished part is removed from the fixture.

Sometimes it is necessary to remove a partially-machined part and re-orient it prior to reloading it into the fixture for further processing. This is usually called *A-side, B-side* processing. The re-orientation can be accomplished inside the machine tool, but it is easier and usually faster to do it in a separate fixture that can flip, rotate, or otherwise re-orient the part outside of the machine. The alternate method is to load and unload fixtured parts. There are many workholding systems available to fixture and clamp parts outside the machining center. The tooling plate is typically equipped with pull-down pins and locators, or sometimes the design incorporates cams on the underside of the tooling plate. A *receiver* is fitted to the machine tool table—or, alternatively, to a pallet. The receiver is powered by air or hydraulic fluid, and through the use of M-codes in the interface, it locks the tooling plate into position. The gantry transports the tooling plate, loaded with a part or multiple parts from some form of feeder, usually a conveyor, to the machining center and back again. The cycle is the same for loading a part, except that the entire tooling plate is loaded at once. This method accommodates complex-shaped or difficult-to-load workpieces. The machinist orients, loads, and clamps the parts onto the tooling plate and fixture. After the parts are located and clamped, the machinist is free to perform other tasks, including loading the fixtures for a different machining center. Typically, one tooling plate at a time is loaded or unloaded. Weight and space limitations generally do not allow handling loaded tooling plates two at one time.

For tooling plate loading, machine table travel is an issue, particularly in vertical machining centers. The gantry works from above, so the table must travel far enough out from under the spindle to give access to the tooling plate receiver, which is not a problem in most horizontal machining centers. If the tooling plate is loaded onto a vertically-oriented receiver, an additional gantry axis is required.

The Machine Tool-gantry Interface

The machine tool-gantry interface or electrical interconnection causes more problems and delays in getting gantry automation projects up and running than any other issue, especially if the application is put together from multiple sources. The hardware and software must talk together in integration projects like gantry loading, yet the interface issues are the most neglected. When these issues are treated lightly or neglected, big projects can sit idle, waiting for the interface to work. The interface prevents crashes between the loader, machine, and parts. An *interface* is a unifier of system elements that lets each important element know precisely what the other is doing. If the gantry arm and its gripper are in the wrong place at the wrong time, the resulting space and time conflict is known as a *crash*. A solid interface avoids this situation.

In its simplest form, a machine tool-gantry interface can be configured from just a few M codes, such as "Load Request," "Fixture/ Chuck Open," "Fixture/Chuck Closed," "Load Cycle Finished," and "Emergency Stop."

In more complex forms, the interface can include everything from signals to open the loading door, to signals that confirm spindle orientation and tailstock position. The more critical that the loading cycle time becomes, the greater the necessity for complex interfaces to track the loading. Typical signals on a reduced-cycle time interface include: "Door Open Confirmation," "Turret Home Confirmation," "Tailstock Home Confirmation," "Spindle Stopped Confirmation," "Spindle Orientation Confirmation," "Chuck/Fixture Open Confirmation," "Chuck/Fixture Closed Confirmation," and "Chuck Blow Off."

When special fixtures are loaded, as in the case of a machining center application, various M-code signals must be passed between the loader and fixture. Typical signals include: "Machine Idle," "Part Present," "Fixture Clear," "Clamps Open," "Clamps Closed," "Loader Clear," and "Clamp Pressure Confirmation."

GANTRY APPLICATIONS FOR HORIZONTAL CHUCKING

The gantry-loading approach to automated turning material handling is illustrated by three examples. These examples employ multiple CNC horizontal chuckers as the core machine tools. Nonturning and complex multimachine gantry examples are also discussed.

Gantry System for Multiple CNC Lathes

An automotive supplier provides high volumes of three different-style poly vee torsional vibration dampers for V-belt drive systems to an auto company. The only way to make the parts at an acceptable price and make a profit is through extensive automation. Several automated twin-spindle, front-loading chuckers, operated by two people per shift, run 24 h/day.[11]

The CNC chuckers have work handling and postprocess gaging with controls for the lathes and their peripheral parts storage and loading systems. Each has a manually-loaded incoming parts storage system, a two-axis servo-controlled gantry, integral postprocess gaging of critical dimensions, and an outgoing parts conveyor. Machining operations include turn, face, bore, and groove. Cycle times are approximately 90 seconds for completing both sides of a part on the lathes.

The disk-shaped, cast gray iron castings roughly 6-8 in. (152-203 mm) in diameter, require turning on both sides. An automated twin-spindle, front-loading chucker is an attractive option. The part stacker feeding the machine can store enough castings for about two hours of production, giving the cell attendant time for tooling preparation and quality control. The lathe chucks are a special three-jaw chuck design, which pull the parts back onto the locator. The lathes plunge-cut poly vee grooves, four at a time, with a special cold-pressed alumina ceramic insert.

The overhead gantry system, integrated with the CNC lathes, picks up a casting from the queue station and waits above the first operation spindle. When the part in the chuck is complete, the gantry unloads the finished part and loads another casting. After the first side is turned, the gantry gripper picks up the part, rotates it 180°, and loads it for the second operation. The gantry also unloads parts from the second operation and deposits them on the outgoing conveyor. If finished parts accumulate to a high level that trips a proximity switch, the system will finish the parts being machined and activate a *hold condition*. A cell attendant then unloads the finished parts from the conveyor for final assembly and normal operation continues automatically. The postprocess gaging system inspects the close-tolerance bore where the part mounts to the crankshaft.

Lathes Supplied with Integrated Gantry Loaders

Gantry-loaded automated turning also provided speed, reliability, and reduced labor input for an auto supplier that manufactured more than 6,000 starter motor housing frames per day for a popular starter motor. In this example, the company installed three compact CNC lathes that came with built-in gantry robots.[12] The three machines are in a U-formation monitored by two operators per shift, three shifts per day, seven days per week. The turret holds redundant tooling, making one full tool change per shift sufficient.

Operators load presawn and preplated tube blanks into a lathe's magazine stack. The tubes then roll down an incline to a pickup point. The gantry robot picks up each one in the identical position and loads it onto an arbor, which grabs the part by the inside diameter (ID). The whole tube is accessible in one operation because the arbor is slightly shorter than the tube blank.

A lathe then turns a register and an undercut on the tube outside diameter (OD), and faces and chamfers both ends. From load to unload is 24 seconds. The part is finished, requiring no secondary machining. The magazine holds enough parts for about eight minutes of operation. Facing, grooving, and chamfering are done with two-headed toolholders, so features on both ends of the part are cut simultaneously.

Gantry-loaded Turning Cell with Multiple Functions

Over the last two decades, an office machine manufacturer has turned to automated turning cells to drive down the cost of producing the rolls that go into its copiers. Associated benefits of the automation are process and product consistency and reliability, and reduced physical demand on machine operators. One of the company's latest automation ventures is a multimillion-dollar cell for making four or more styles of fuser rolls—the rolls that fuse the black toner powder to the paper through heat.

The major components of this cell are: an inertia welder that welds the stainless steel end caps onto the extruded aluminum tubes making up the roll bodies; three two-turret, four-axis CNC lathes;[13] face drivers, programmable tailstocks, and postprocess OD gage; two machining centers for milling and deburring; and an automated parts spray washing system.

Six dual-gripper gantry robots take much of the material-handling labor out of the hands of human operators, and load and unload the five major machine tools and the big parts wash system in the cell.[14] A conveyor system of shuttle carts, with six parts to a pallet, does much of the rest of the material handling in the cell.[15]

The cell process sequence begins with the inertia welder welding the end caps to the aluminum extruded tubes. The first of the two machining centers mills the end caps to length with a face mill and chamfers the roll centers, making the roll ready to load into one of the lathes. A dual-gripper robot grabs turned rolls by the end caps so the aluminum surface is untouched and inserts a new roll into the headstock center. The programmable tailstock center on the right end, and the face driver on the headstock end, grip the roll for turning. With the face driver's pins digging a bit into the end cap, the lathe profile-turns the rolls to a critical profile for proper roll performance.

Each lathe has a postprocess, contact OD gage station loaded by the gantry robot. With the roll held between pneumatically-actuated centers, multiple pencil probes in each gage fixture measure numerous locations on the roll body, as well as both end caps. Using the collected data, which indicate a trend, the gage amplifier compensates the next part via automatic tool adjustments on the lathe. The gage stations also log data for statistical process control (SPC) and communication to the cell data network.

From the lathes, the rolls go to the second machining center, which mills flats or slots for mounting gears. An automatic deburring operation is on the mills, to get the burrs off yet not over-deburr the slots. Finally, the rolls go to the wash plant. Here, the last of the six robots loads them into the wash system.

GANTRY APPLICATIONS OTHER THAN TURNING

This section discusses a gantry-loaded grinder and a crankshaft machining line with gantry loaders.

A Gantry-loaded Grinder

A gantry-loaded ID/OD cylindrical grinder at a second tier automotive supplier uses a linear gantry, a carousel-type parts feeder system, and a special collet-type fixture in the grinder.[16] The tulip (named for its distinctive shape) portion of the constant-velocity (CV) joint is fixtured in a vertical position on the parts feeder pallet. The pallets hold two parts each in a fixture to increase queue time between machine operator service requirements.

The gripper grasps the part inside the tulip portion of the CV shaft. The geometry of the gripper fingers fits the ball grooves of the CV joint when the gripper is opened inside the part. This gives both good orientation and positive gripping. The gripper is double-sided. Room inside the grinder for part rotation was a concern, but prototyping showed it would work.

The interface is a simple design utilizing M-codes for "Gantry Request," "Collet Open/Closed Confirmation," and "Gantry Finished" signals only. The "Tailstock Confirmation" and "Machine Cycle Start" are internal to the grinder.

Crankshaft Machining Line with Gantry Loaders

A machining cell for a diesel engine crankshaft machining line consists of two turning centers and two grinders to perform multiple, serial operations.[17] The first operation is turning the crankshaft main bearing surfaces. This is handled by two turning centers in parallel operation, with an individual machining cycle time of 128.8 seconds. Then, in the second operation, two parallel grinders grind the main bearing journals, each with a 121.5-second cycle time.

The machine cycle times allow the convenient arrangement of pairs of machines loaded by a pair of gantry robots. An automation strategy for such ordered pairs of machines would be based on side-by-side, staggered pairs of palletized chain conveyors running through the center of the area, with one machine tool to either side, and a gantry robot perpendicular to the conveyors and in-line with each pair of machines. One conveyor brings parts from the rough end of the crankshaft line to the first pair of turning centers. Here, a gantry picks up one raw part from the inbound conveyor and transports it to either the A or B turning center. Finished parts are transported by the gantry from the turning center to the outbound conveyor, and from there to the next gantry and pair of machines.

This system requires accuracy. The turning center's chucks require a lateral part loading accuracy of ±0.03 in. (0.76 mm). Although the gantry can maintain a part locating repeatability in the *X*

CHAPTER 15   METALCUTTING

and Z axes of ± 0.004 in. (0.102 mm), the location of the part in the machine tool can be only as accurate as the part that is presented to the gantry by the inbound conveyor. For this reason, it may be necessary to add a part-crowding device to the conveyor at the gantry pickup point. Alternatively, the gantry may have its own compliance device or crowder built into the end-of-arm tooling.

Another issue is the rotational orientation of the workpiece. Crankshafts, being uniquely cylindrical and noncylindrical parts, are notorious for having extremely tight rotational tolerances. In the first cell where the lathe chucks rotate the part, rotational positioning is not an issue. However, in the subsequent grinding process, the single-head indexing pin grinders require a part orientation of pin #1 straight up, to an accuracy of $\pm 0.1°$. A CNC D-axis on the gantry can accomplish this, but the load path of the grinder is narrow and prevents use of this option. Instead, an orientation unit, with a driven wheel that drives the post of the crankshaft as it sits in a V-block until one of its machined counterweight surfaces locates against a hard stop, is added to the inbound conveyor at the gantry pickup point. The gantry's grippers pick up the crankshaft, in the precise, pin #1 straight-up orientation that the grinder requires, and hold it with no slipping until loaded.

To achieve this, the design violates the general gantry rule, "keep the gantry's gripper off machined surfaces," since there is no other place to pick up the part. A microfinishing operation performed later removes the smudges caused by the gantry robot's gripper.

ROBOT LOADING

Multi-axis pedestal-type robots are used in three basic configurations in metalcutting:

- A single robot loads and unloads a single machine, most commonly a lathe.
- One or more robots load and unload two or more machine tools in a cell.
- The robot itself is the metalcutting machine, performing drilling, milling, routing, deburring, laser cutting, plasma cutting, waterjet cutting, etc.

Type three is not considered here, since in those cases, the robot is not engaged primarily in material handling. The most common application of the type one and two robot categories is for loading lathes—to use as an alternative to gantry-based systems, dedicated loading machines, or manual operations. Gantry-type loaders—rather than robots—have become the loaders of choice for lathes and other chip-making machines.

Robots load and unload CNC lathes and some other metalcutting machines, including vertical machining centers.[18] The decision to robotically load and unload parts may be one to remain competitive, increase quality part yield, or address safety or ergonomic issues. Typically, a machine operator can tend two or more lathes when the load and unload function is done robotically.

The operation involves passing workpieces from a parts storage location (parts table) to the spindle and unloading the parts from the spindle to a second storage area or gaging station. In some older dual-spindle horizontal lathes, a stand-alone robot may pass workpieces from the first spindle to the second spindle and reverse the workpiece in the process of that transfer. In newer dual-spindle lathes, these functions are generally performed by built-in robotic arms, gantry systems, or traversing spindle systems, in which either the second spindle picks up the workpiece from the first spindle, or the first spindle delivers the workpiece to the second spindle.

Robots may be used singly or in groups and may be stationary or rail-mounted, all depending on the number of machine tools served and the cycle times of those machines. If part cycle time is long enough, one robot can serve two or three machines. If cycle time is short, as is common with CNC lathes, one robot can serve only one machine. The cycle time for a robot to load and unload through a lathe door is 15-20 seconds when the workpieces are on a conveyor or feed table adjacent to the lathe. Track-mounted robots can traverse 100 ft (30.5 m) or more within a cell.

Machine Integration and Troubleshooting Issues

In CNC lathe and machining center machine-tending applications, robots are reliable choices, but must be properly integrated with the machines. Some robots operate with 32-bit chip technology, while older lathes may have 8-bit or 16-bit technology. This difference means the lathes may run relay logic at slower speeds than the robots, and the machines may require rewiring or new controls. Hard wiring can be replaced with serial communication to the cell controller. The advantage is less wiring and maintenance, and more space saved with serial communication.

Machine integration is important because accurate input/output (I/O) signals between the robot and lathe are critical to the success of automation. Signals from the lathe are designated as inputs and signals from the robot as outputs. A robot brings accuracy to the application, but it needs both send and receive signals to ensure that the machine is ready. Examples include: doors are open, part is loaded properly in spindle, and chuck is in the proper position. The CNC lathe or metalcutting machine needs to receive signals from the robot that it is clear of the machine. Cell logic should be event-driven, not timer-driven. Time is less a factor in tending to CNC lathes than machine conditions, accurate part loading, and other steps.

Troubleshooting and maintenance for the robots are other considerations. Troubleshooting can be a time-intensive job if not performed by properly-trained personnel. Robot users should know about the alarms and troubleshooting procedures. Maintenance is crucial and its schedules must be adhered to. Wear items, such as gripper finger inserts, need to be replaced routinely.

Robots and lathes are just two of the components in a machine-loading cell. A manufacturer needs to ask some questions. How will parts be presented to the robot? Will it be by an automated method or by an operator? If the robot will handle multiple gripper tools (one at a time), will the tool changeover be done by hand or automatically? Other parts of the robot cell can be automated as well, and all those components need to be integrated with the robot and cell controller. With this integration, the robot controller should have adequate allotment for I/O.

Robot Considerations

After deciding to use robots for machine loading, select the features of the robot. Consider the design or type, payload capacity, reach, moment arm rating, and structural design characteristics, such as high rigidity, water and dust resistance, size, and weight.

This section discusses six-axis, vertically-articulated robots. Five-axis robots are also used, but they lack the roll capability on the arm, which is valuable in turning parts over and manipulating them at different angles. Six-axis robots offer more flexibility, which is important if the part requires it (see Fig. 15-11).

Six-axis robot payload capacities range from a few pounds up to 880 lb (400 kg). The combined weight of the gripper and the part must not exceed the robot's payload capacity. Too much weight is taxing upon the robot's motors and structure. A robot's maximum reach typically varies with its payload capacity. Generally, six-axis robots can extend into a metalcutting machine to load and unload a part. Other stations (part conveyor, orientation stands, outfeed chute, etc.) need to be positioned within the robot's reach. If this is not possible, a pneumatic or servo-driven track for the robot is a means to move the robot to different stations.

If the robot's work environment is dusty, dirty, or susceptible to water, the robot may require protection. Wrist and arm protection and cable ducts for wires allow a robot to operate in adverse conditions. Air nozzle blow-off devices can be installed on the robot arm to blast away metal shavings from the lathe bed. Metal shavings create obstructions for chuck clamping and door closing, and can impede the robot's entry into the machine. In applications where there is high voltage or high temperature, the robot may need to be electrically or thermally insulated from the gripper.

How the parts are presented to the robot should be fairly repeatable. If there are inaccuracies in presenting parts or if certain part features, such as a valve stem on a wheel rim, need to be located prior to machine loading, most robots can search for the part feature. It searches for the part feature and automatically adjusts its program path based on the search. Robots can sequentially load different parts. Sensors on the gripper can tell the robot which part it has or the robot can be programmed to find the part by its position on a table or pallet.

How much space does the robot have to operate in? Are there interference areas? If so, the robot may need additional hard stops to restrict its envelope. If the robot's work space is limited, then slimmer designs are beneficial. Some robots can be mounted on a wall or ceiling if an operating zone is not available on the floor. In some situations, the problem of access to the machine tool caused by a pedestal robot in front of it may suggest that the application would be better served by a gantry rather than a robot, since the gantry does not block aisle space and access to the machine.

What to Expect from the Robot

Consistency is a big advantage of robotic machine tending. The robot is consistent over long, sustained production runs. Robots are repeatable, up to ±0.004 in. (0.10 mm) in some cases. Repeatability and payload tend to be in an inverse relationship: the greater the robot payload, the less precise the repeatability. When parts are loaded into a lathe spindle accurately, it ensures proper chuck clamping in the lathe, proper part rotation, and also extends the life of cutting tools. Sensors are important in these cases. They indicate that certain conditions are met so accidents, such as a spindle rotating an improperly clamped part, do not occur.

Robots are flexible units. Costly hardware changes are avoided since new parts can be applied to an existing robot with a new program and maybe a few gripper modifications. Robotic equipment

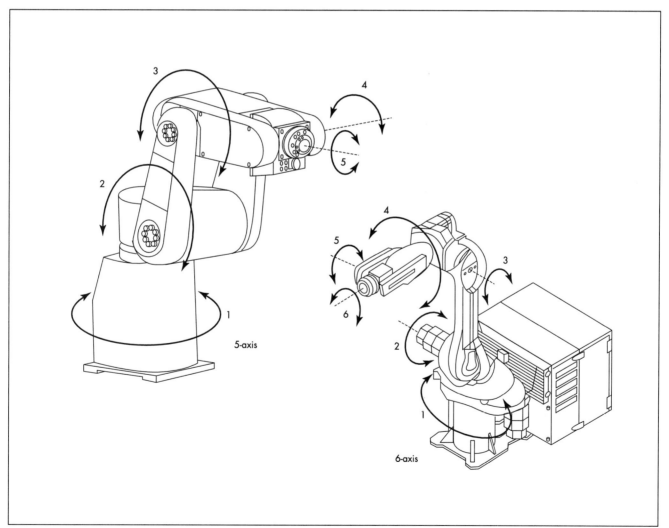

Fig. 15-11 Five-axis and six-axis servo-driven robots for machine load, unload, and other applications. *(Courtesy Fanuc Robotics North America)*

CHAPTER 15 METALCUTTING

does not need to be parallel or aligned with the lathe, unlike gantries or dedicated transfer systems.

Robots remove operators from hazardous working conditions that subject them to dust, part debris, machining fluids, and injuries like carpal tunnel syndrome, cuts from metal shavings, and back strain. While robots perform the repetitive lifting, operators can monitor the robot cell.

Gripper Considerations

There are several choices of how to pick up parts. The most common include pneumatic, electrical, electro-magnetic, hydraulic, or vacuum grippers. Pneumatic grippers offer the most attractive features and are a common choice. They are made mainly of aluminum. This feature allows them to be lightweight, yet durable for machine loading of metal parts. Pneumatic grippers are generally cost-effective because air hoses, valves, and other pneumatic devices are easy to maintain. Replaceable finger inserts for the gripper fingers can be manufactured from a variety of materials to ensure gentle part handling and a firm grip.

The design of the gripper greatly depends on the part itself. The gripper can have a two-jaw, three-jaw, parallel, angular, dual clamp, or pin configuration. The part can be gripped by an outside diameter, inside diameter, or pins can be inserted through holes in the part. Figure 15-12 shows some single and dual gripper configurations that clamp the parts by the outside or inside diameter.

Gripper sensors are essential to robotic machine loading. A *shock sensor* stops the robot in the event that the part or gripper collides with an object. This procedure reduces damage to the part, gripper, robot, and peripheral equipment. Sensors can monitor the gripper for low air pressure level detection so it does not drop the part. *Proximity sensors* confirm gripper and part locations. All signals from sensors should be wired directly to the robot controller.

Other factors for the gripper include part finish, thickness, and cleanliness. Sometimes, the part must be presented to the robot at an angle so the robot can pick it up from either side. Orientation stands are useful in these cases. The force put on the gripper must be considered. Pneumatic controls, valves, and other devices control the force used to handle the part. This force must be consistent and not excessive enough to mar the surface or damage the part. If needed, special adapter plates can extend the reach of the gripper. A *dual gripper* enables the robot to unload and load parts in the same cycle by holding two parts, one machined and one unmachined, resulting in lower overall cycle times.

Other Considerations

Conveyors can serve as part infeed and outfeed mechanisms, and can include part pallets with recessed pockets for accurate location. Parts can circulate on the conveyor pallets, resulting in a part buffer between cells. Conveyors are available in different types: powered roller, gravity, belt, and shuttle-like systems. Part chutes with channeled frames may be another transfer method to move parts to and from the robot cell.

In multiple machine applications, part orientation stands may be placed between each machine. A robot loads and unloads one machine, then transfers the part to an orientation stand, and a second robot picks up the part and places it in another machine for another cutting process. The American National Standards Institute (ANSI) and the Robotic Industries Association (RIA) have established standards for manufacturers installing their own safety equipment. Robot vendors can install safety measures like perimeter fencing, safety mats, photo eyes, and interlocked doors, and provide training.

In multiple cell applications, programmable logic controllers (PLCs) serve as the system supervisor, handling all the cell signals. The PLC processes the diagnostics of the robots, lathes, safety interlocks, and sensors, and displays status and messages to the operator.

Built-in Gantry Loaders and Robots

Built-in gantry or robotic loaders can smoothly handle chucking or between-centers turning work for a limited family of parts. When the user purchases a CNC lathe with a built-in robot or gantry loader from the machine tool builder, the integration issues should be resolved during the robotic cell design.[19] However, it is up to the user to ensure that the elements of the cell have the right size and speed capacities for the application. An integral robot or gantry loader may require 20-30 seconds, depending on workpiece size, gantry speed, and so on, to accomplish its various tasks between cutting operations. So the workpiece must have a cutting cycle that is 20-30 seconds or more per side, or at least long enough to make the automation effective. If the gantry cannot keep up with the cutting cycle, automation may be a costly misapplication. In addition, there are size and weight limitations for built-in gantry loaders, while stand-alone gantries are modular and may be sized to almost any workpiece or application.

The machine tool supplier may offer mechanisms for part turn-around and sensing correct part seating in the chucks, if it is an option. Such turning cells will be more compact than those served by a stand-alone robot, since less space is required for the material handling devices. But, the robot or gantry is dedicated to that machine tool and to parts of a certain configuration. This material handling automation equipment is, therefore, not adaptable to another machine tool or application, unlike the freestanding robot or gantry. In turning cells with built-in material handling, the controller for the robot or gantry may be independent of the CNC unit, or integrated into it. The robot or gantry will have fewer independent axes of motion than a stand-alone robot, since it is equipped with only the axes needed to execute the moves required in the application.

Internal work-handling robots or gantries on lathes for chucking work may have several designs. The simplest serve a single spindle. Some serve two spindles and these may benefit from optional auxiliary devices inside the lathe, which assist in part turnaround between the two spindles. Some are ball screw-driven and travel on a track below the spindle centerline in front of the chuck, while others travel overhead, like a gantry system. They have different speeds and workpiece size capacities. Some of these robots have dual three-jaw hydraulic chucking devices at the end of their arms, designed precisely for chucking two round parts of a certain size range. Axes of motion may include some or all of these: linear traverse, base rotation, hand rotation, and wrist swing.

There are many possible patterns of conveying work to the point where it may be reached by the robot, and likewise there are numerous options for taking the finished part from the robot or unload chute and conveying it away from the lathe. There are many standard and custom-made material handling options.

Work stocker tables. Work stocker tables with 10-20 circular pallets on a moving circular or oval track are a fairly standard device for carrying the supply of parts for the automated lathe. A 10-pallet stocker might, for example, hold work to a 12-in. (305-mm) diameter, while a 20-pallet stocker might hold work to a 6-in. (152-mm) diameter. Sometimes stocker tables stand outside the machine tool and sometimes they are built in. Occasionally, robots and gantries built into the machine tool may operate from either a built-in work stocker table or from one that stands outside the machine enclosure. A work stocker table may load the blanks only, or do both load and unload functions. Or, one work stocker table may be on the left for

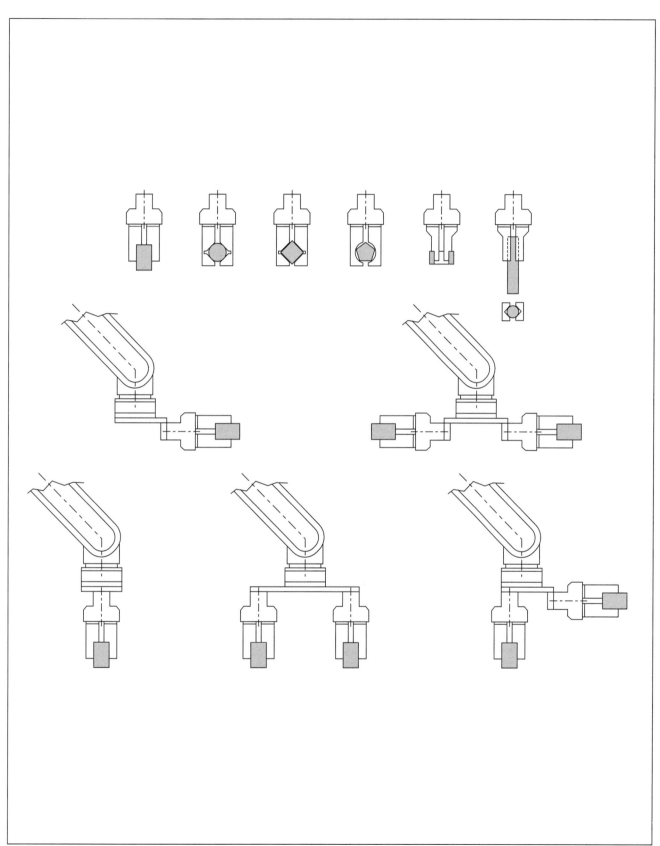

Fig. 15-12 Some robot wrist grippers and positions for machine loading. *(Courtesy Motoman, Inc.)*

CHAPTER 15   METALCUTTING

loading, while a second one may be placed on the right of the lathe for unloading the finished parts. Another option might locate an automated gaging station to one side of the machine tool, with the robot or gantry also loading and unloading that station.

Two robot lathe-loading applications. One example of the application of a stand-alone robot for loading turning equipment is at a major automotive supplier, who was having trouble with a high-precision flywheel-like part that had a lot of error potential. It had been machined on traditional lathes and drills with automatic and manual loading.

The system integrator[20] recommended an automated cell consisting of two conventional-orientation vertical twin-spindle CNC chuckers, a vertical CNC drilling center, a coordinate measuring machine, a jointed spherical parts-loading robot, and associated input and output conveyors.

The part path starts at the roughing lathe. Then, it goes to the finishing lathe, then the drilling station for six bolt holes, and finally, to the coordinate measuring machine (CMM). The CMM not only accepts or rejects the finished flywheel, but when necessary, sends tool correction commands to the lathes and the drill. The combination of the robot, dual-spindle lathes, and feedback to the machines from the CMM reduce part handling time. With the dual-spindle lathe, the robot loads a new part on one spindle while the lathe turns a part on the second spindle, so the loading time is not wasted as noncutting time. The automated cell makes 40 flywheel varieties at a rate of 40 parts/h; a 40% productivity increase over the former arrangement.

The second example of the application of a robot in a compact CNC turning machine is at a parts supplier for automotive and light truck companies.[21] This supplier installed two production lines of turning machines with integral robot loaders to increase production and reduce manual labor for turning aluminum alloy power-steering pumps and components. The ball screw-driven robot traverses on a track above the spindle centerline completely within the lathe enclosure. The 8-in. (200-mm) chuck-size lathe accepts work to 6 in. (150 mm) in diameter.

Two key elements in the pumps are a high-pressure integral plate and the rear half of the pump housing, machined on the robotic turning machines. The high-strength, lightweight housings are made at a rate of 17,000/week on each of the two lines. The turnkey robotic turning cell provides a rotary parts feeder, part orientation, special coolant filtering for fine aluminum particles, and yields a 7-micron (0.007-mm) finish on the side plate with conventional carbide tools.

Each turning machine's integral robot has a resident program that allows restarting the operation anywhere in the cycle without referencing or homing the controller. The robot arm, with two chucks, picks up incoming parts, passes them into the lathe chuck, removes finished parts, and places them in the output area. The outgoing conveyor system carries the parts from the turning cell to cleaning and lapping operations. The robot chucks have a hydraulic jaw stroke of 1 in. (25 mm) to enable shifting from handling one part to another within that size range.

There is no need for a pick-and-place station. Each chuck on the robot arm has an 11-lb (5-kg) capacity. The robot has a travel speed of 4,000 in. (100 m)/min and a 180° wrist-index time of one second. The machines can run unattended and increased productivity by 25% over the previous technology. The robotic turning machines are arranged so that if a major increase in volume is required, other machines can be added without dramatic changes to the cell.

SIMPLE LOADERS FOR LATHES

While gantry loaders and robots are the best known material handling techniques for feeding slugs, castings, or discrete parts to a turning machine, there are alternatives, primarily for single-spindle CNC machines. These options include lathe autoloaders and chutes.

Lathe Autoloaders

Freestanding, pneumatically-controlled and magazine-fed lathe loaders are located outside the machine tool, and typically, but not always, feed sawn slugs, castings or forgings, or semifinished parts in the lathe door. They resemble robots, but are simpler and have a limited range of motion for the dedicated loading function (see Fig. 15-13). The magazine itself is hand-loaded or may be fed from a bowl feeder. The capacity of the magazine determines the time the lathe may run relatively untended. Operators must fill the input queue with raw parts, but are freed from loading a single machine, so they may tend more than one machine.

To pick the right loading technique for an application, the engineer must balance part volume against unproductive machine time caused by loading and changeover. As with robots and gantries, an autoloader's capacity and cycle time must be matched with that of the turning operation. Automation for small lots is difficult to justify.

Dedicated autoloaders are configured for a certain part size range and weight and do not have the range of positioning, including roll and pivot motions, of a freestanding robot. They move the raw material a short distance—from an external position adjacent to the lathe, possibly on a conveyor, directly into the lathe chuck. Load cycles are only a few seconds. These loaders typically interface with the CNC machine via an M-code function. Autoloaders may serve horizontal or vertical chuckers.[22]

One style of low-cost loader stands outside the door of the lathe's cutting zone and uses a gripper on a slide to accept a part from the last position in the magazine and load it through the lathe door and into the lathe chuck.

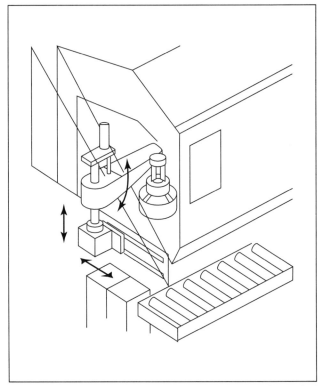

Fig. 15-13 Semi-automatic simple pick-and-place loader for vertical chucker. *(Courtesy Okuma & Howa Machinery/KGK International)*

Another design stands in the position of a bar loader and loads slugs or semifinished parts through the lathe spindle. This style may be adapted to the twin-opposed spindle type of lathe, such that a loader feeds the first spindle from the left side, and an automated unloader takes finished parts on the second end and removes them through a tube, from the second spindle, on the right-hand side of the machine. The unloader may clamp the finished piece from an outside or inside diameter with the appropriate gripper or clamping sleeve.

A third style of autoloader is not freestanding, but attaches to the lathe headstock and takes up no floor space. This servomotor-based design is intended as an add-on to a CNC lathe and can grab a part by an existing internal diameter. There are two parts grippers—unloading at the lower gripper and loading with the upper gripper. Parts or slugs are fed by track into the loader.[23]

Chutes

Simple chutes with little or no mechanization are commonly used to load the front-loading chucker-style of CNC lathe and the double-disk grinder-style of surface grinding machine. Parts roll down an inclined conveyor or are moved by linear transfer to and from the machining zone. The part return chute may exit from the opposite side of the machine or, in certain setups on front-loading chuckers, from the same side.

Finished Parts Handling in Turning

Whether a turning system uses a bar feeder, robot loader, gantry loader, or some other method of feeding material in, some technique of removing the finished piece from the lathe is usually required to round-off the automation of the material handling function. Robotic and gantry systems, including those for both horizontal and vertical chucking, generally make finished part removal from the machine part of their system. But bar-fed lathes need a separate method of finished parts handling. Some form of parts catching device to get the part from the chuck to outside the machine is required. Lathe builders generally offer simple devices to do this, but this may need to be integrated with a material handling solution for getting the finished part onto a table, conveyor, or into a bin.

VERTICAL CHUCKING

Vertical turning for chucked parts that are 8-20-in. (200-500-mm) in diameter has drastically changed in the 1990s, particularly for high-volume production of automotive wheels, rotors, drums, and hubs. High volume calls for automated material handling, and the cost of that automation has been reduced 30-40% by the rise of CNC vertical chuckers with mobile integral spindle motors. The motorized spindle performs workpiece gripping and transport, moves the workpiece to the tools, and rotates the workpiece for turning, drilling, boring, and possibly some milling. The spindle grips the workpiece from above and the clamping force must resist not only centrifugal and cutting forces, but also gravity. These inverted vertical lathes may be employed singly, but are best suited to a cell of two or more units to complete parts on both sides. Since the spindle does most of the work of part transfer, much of the automation costs associated with work handling in traditional vertical turning, such as gantry loaders, can be eliminated.

Many high-volume parts are castings or forgings with a short-cutting cycle time, making it important that the work handling times be reduced to the absolute minimum. This class of mobile-spindle verticals is compact for short traverse distances and offers short workpiece change times as well as quick turret indexing.

The traditional vertical lathe has the rotating chuck, spindle, and motor mounted in a fixed position at the machine base. The turret or tool block moves up, down, and laterally on slides above the table. The traditional design uses gravity to keep the work in the chuck. Single- and twin-spindle vertical CNC chuckers in a variety of sizes with driven tools, part gaging, and automated workpiece handling systems have been available since the early 1980s.

Gantry-type loading devices, in the past, represented the main form of automation for verticals. The gantry loader picks up the workpiece from outside the machine and moves the workpiece to the first chuck, after which it turns the part over and transports it to the second chuck, and then removes the part from the second chuck to pass it out of the work area. Such loaders represent a large investment in automation. For workpieces over 19.7 in. (500 mm) in diameter or for particularly heavy workpieces, this traditionally-designed vertical may still be best.

For workpieces in the mid-size range, the vertical chuckers come in two distinct configurations—the traditional design and newer machines, with a two-axis, linear-travel, integral spindle motor above and tools below, in a turret or tool blocks.

Benefits of Inverted Verticals

The key advantage of inverted verticals is that the motorized mobile spindle can pick up and drop off parts. This eliminates a loader to move the workpiece from the first to the second spindle. Parts may move by conveyor to the point where the spindle picks them up, and likewise move by conveyor from the point where they are completed on the second side. Part turnover methods vary from one design to the next.

Noncutting time is short. Work transfer speed from the pickup point to the start of machining is typically not more than five seconds, which is much faster than gantry work-transfer operations of typically 15-20 seconds. Another advantage is that chips fall away from the work and down into a chip conveyor rather than onto the rotating table and workpiece.

Types of Inverted Verticals

In one model of the inverted vertical, the spindle travels front-to-back on the slide, picking up parts from the conveyor system from the rear of the machine, and bringing them to the 12-station turret at the front of the machine[24] (see Fig. 15-14). After machining is completed, the part is returned to the conveyor. Workpiece change time may be as low as three seconds. Many systems of linked multiple machines have been installed.

Another line of inverted verticals offers an unusual way to address both sides of the workpiece without turning the workpiece over, thus eliminating an additional piece of automation equipment.[25] In a patented configuration, the first operation is performed using an inverted spindle. Following the first operation, that spindle moves the workpiece over to the second spindle, which is fixed in place and oriented in the old way, facing upward toward the tools above it. The inverted spindle positions the part directly in the second spindle without a turnover station and the part is machined in the traditional position in the second spindle (see Fig. 15-15). Following the second operation, a gripper mounted on the vertical slide removes the completed part and places it on the discharge conveyor. Machines may be equipped with 12-station turrets, including live tool capability or block tool holders.

A third design of inverted vertical integrates two vertical work spindles in one machine, with a unidirectional pallet system.[26] If necessary, a turnover station is incorporated in the line. This is cost-efficient because its two machining stations use one control, hydraulic system, chip conveyor, and frame. This model reduces the workpiece load and unload time to four seconds. It may be optionally equipped with a gang-style tool arrangement, a 14-position turret, or both.

CHAPTER 15 METALCUTTING

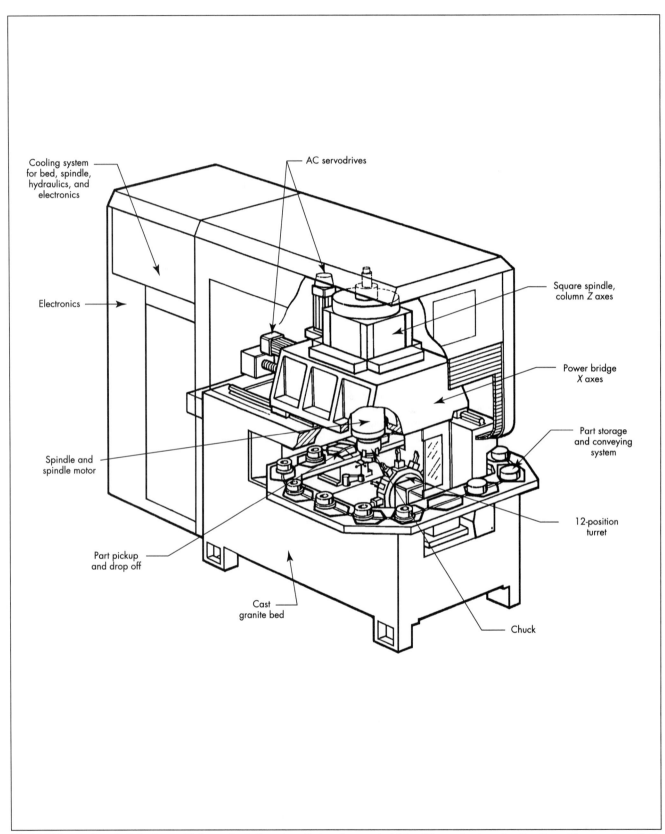

Fig. 15-14 Inverted vertical chuckers with integral spindle motors that perform material handling and automation functions. *(Courtesy Emag Bohle L.L.C.)*

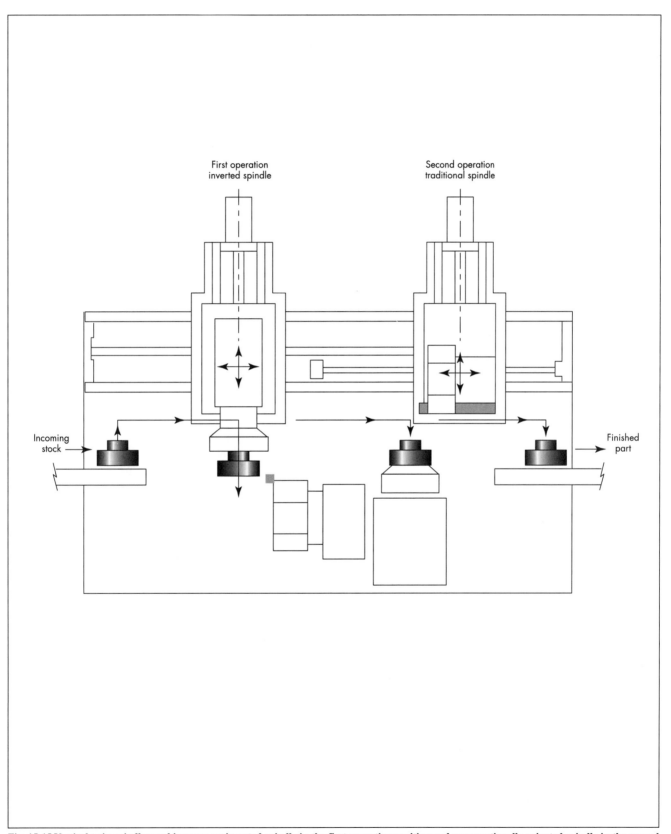

Fig. 15-15 Vertical twin-spindle machine uses an inverted spindle in the first operation position and a conventionally-oriented spindle in the second operation position. *(Courtesy Hessap/Thyssen Production Systems)*

CHAPTER 15 METALCUTTING

A fourth design of a single or twin-spindle, vertical motor, self-loading chucker picks up parts from a variety of feeder systems and moves them to the working position.[27]

There are several options for transporting parts to and from machines. A belt conveyor can carry any part—small or large diameter, short or long—provided it can stand upright on the transporting conveyor. It permits extensive part storage in a compact space. A circulating pallet system consists of two rows of 15 pallets each, for parts up to 8-in. (203-mm) long.

Limits to the Hanging Spindle

The workholding power of the chucks is the major limiting technology in traveling-spindle vertical turning. Smaller chuck sizes, up to 8 in. (200 mm), can handle 5,000+ rpm, but 12-in. (300-mm) chucks for larger workpieces run at much lower speeds. The other limit is weight: some experts do not recommend heavy parts be targeted for the hanging-spindle design.

Example of Gantry-loaded Vertical Turning Lathe (VTL) Application

An automated gantry-loaded, twin-spindle vertical chucking system for turning truck hubs can handle workpieces up to 90 lb (41 kg).[28] Almost a hundred different truck hub designs are machined from seven different castings. This traditional (as compared to inverted spindle), twin-spindle, vertical turning application includes a 26-in. (660-mm) maximum turning diameter, 60-hp (45-kW) spindle drives, and dual 10-station turrets. A fiber-optics system identifies the casting to ensure that the right one is entering the machine. Automated tool management is incorporated in the cell. After turning, a conveyor system carries the hubs to one of two multispindle drills, where dual bolt hole patterns are drilled. All the work handling automation is between the two turning spindles, so access to the work areas is good.

PRISMATIC PARTS

This section discusses pallets and pallet loading systems, and small pallets for electrical discharge machining (EDM) and other uses, for example, a milling machine.

PALLETS AND PALLET LOADING SYSTEMS

Palletizing is for prismatic parts, but not for round parts. For metalcutting machines, a *pallet* is a transportable device, with a top surface designed to securely hold and transport work, and a bottom designed to mate with the machine tool worktable and achieve positive positioning and clamping. A pallet supports one or more workholding or clamping mechanisms, which, in turn carry one part or several parts. Machine tools combined together to form a cell or system are often linked together with a pallet system. Palletizing has changed the way certain types of machining are organized.

Parts palletization provides a known reference point for the machining system. This yields better quality and reproducibility, improved machine tool utilization by setting up work outside the machine, quick job changing and job transfer between different machines, including both metalcutting and gaging machines.

Complex pallet systems are mostly used with linked machining centers. They are occasionally supplemented with other special-function machines. Also, they are used in systems for manufacturing EDM electrodes or other small envelope workpieces transported from one machine to another in a cell for machining, grinding, or gaging. Automotive and truck powertrain systems manufacturers, or other high-volume manufacturing plants with transfer lines for machining, also use pallets extensively.

There are other forms of palletizing not considered in this chapter. These forms include small manually-loaded pallets that have become commonplace in machining center applications, particularly for machining multiples of small parts on vertical machining centers. These devices generally work closely with certain forms of clamping or workholding and may more properly be considered workholding rather than material handling devices.

The material handling options for vertical machining centers (VMC) are typically limited to three options: aftermarket manual pallet-swapping devices and tables, in which the guidance and motive force are supplied by the machinist; the twin-pallet, automatic shuttle-type, pallet changer that loads and unloads from one side of the machine; and the twin-pallet, automatic 180° rotary-type, pallet switcher for high-speed pallet change on the smallest-size vertical machining centers. All three allow the operator to perform load, unload, and fixturing to parts on one pallet, while the second pallet is in the machining zone and parts are being cut. These types of palletizing are not major material handling projects, and the automated ones are more or less confined within the machine tool and under the control of the machine controller.

Pallet System Components for Horizontal Machining Centers

The three major components of a pallet system for machining are the pallets, pallet receivers, and pallet loaders.

Pallets. Pallets are square, rectangular, or round. Common sizes for machining center applications are 400, 500, 650, 800, 1,000, and 1,250 mm². Machining center work capacity is, in part, measured by the pallet size. Round pallets are used in systems for large vertical turning cells and when the load and unload times are lengthy and constitute a large part of the cycle time. The top of the pallet has an arrangement of T-slots for mounting fixtures or parts. The pallet most often holds a workholding fixture, which holds one or more workpieces. Fixtures or parts are located from an edge or a T-slot.

Pallet receivers. These are the portion of the machine tool that receive and clamp the pallet. The precision pallet receiver must both position the pallet accurately and lock it securely before the machining cycle. There is not much standardization regarding pallet receivers; instead designs tend to vary from one machine tool builder to another, with each machine tool builder designing his or her own pallets and pallet receivers.

There are many ways to tell if the pallet is properly registered or located, drawn down completely on the locators, and clamped. The locators usually have a taper to center the pallet as it is pulled down, and a hard stop to eliminate the problem of variations in tapers. The method of locating determines the clamping process used. A sensor is generally used to check on the clamping. Hydraulic clamping is the most widely used, but there are no standards. Consequently, how the hydraulic system is handled varies from one builder to another. This variability in the underside of pallets may be a challenge to retrofitters who add palletizing to existing machines, since a retrofitter must manage both the mechanical interfaces for locating and clamping, as well as the electronic interface to the cell controller.[29]

The time it takes for the pallet receiver to unclamp a pallet after a part is finished to the time it gets the next pallet of parts under the spindle is the only time the spindle is not adding value to the parts. Pallet swap time is only a few seconds on modern systems. Machine builders compete on pallet change cycle time, especially the speed of moving a pallet in and out of the machining center.

Pallet loaders. Pallet loaders transfer the pallet, with or without workpieces fixtured on it, between loading or setup stations, storage positions, the machine tool's pallet receiver, and possibly measuring and washing positions.

Pallet Arrangements

Pallets may be arranged around the machines in several ways. The single machine with two pallets is the simplest and represents no challenge in material handling. In the 1980s, a popular design was the rotary pallet pool, with approximately six pallets arranged in a circle in front of one machine. The drawback was that this cell serviced a single machine and was not expandable (see Fig. 15-16). From the standpoint of material handling, these cells were complex.

A second machining cell design that was used in the 1980s was the multilevel vertical pallet stacker with 24, 30, or more pallets serving multiple machine tools, and intended to run for long periods unattended. Floor space was saved, but the cost of achieving the high degree of automation was prohibitive. Today's cellular machining goals are more modest—to utilize the machining center during breaks, lunch, shift changes, and some after-shift work, but not to try for around-the-clock automated machining.

In the linear cell arrangement, the rail-guided vehicle travels on a linear track, along which are from one to 12 machining centers, the storage racks or park stations for the pallets, the setup station, and the load and unload station (see Fig. 15-16). The storage racks may be single-level or two-level, with 90% being single-level. If two-level, the rail-guided vehicle must have an additional axis of motion—travel up and down. A single pallet loader vehicle is typical. Other forms of pallet loader are possible. The loader picks up the pallet from storage, clamps it, moves it to the setup station, and later moves the pallet with the fixtured workpiece into and out from the machine tool's pallet receiver. Its actions are governed by the machine's CNC or cell controller. The tracks that the rail-guided pallet loader travels are builder-specific rather than standardized and use either a rack-and-pinion drive or a chain drive. One advantage of the linear design when compared to the semicircular pallet pool is that pallets and other cell resources may be shared by more than one machine.

The pallet and machine size selected may not simply be the ones that fit the largest processed part. A manufacturer may wish to process parts in *ship sets*, such as three parts to a set, to make a single subassembly. Then, each time a fixture comes out of the machine, one ship set is completed. In this case, the pallet and machine size

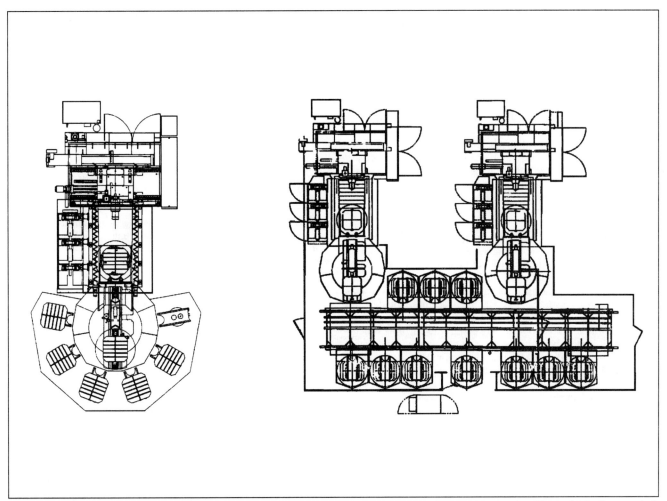

Fig. 15-16 Horizontal machining center with a circular-style pool and dual machining center cell with a linear-style pallet pool. The linear style is expandable; while the circular style is limited to the space in front of the machine tool. Pallets arranged in a linear pallet pool or stocker may serve single or multiple horizontal machining centers. *(Courtesy Cincinnati Milacron)*

CHAPTER 15   METALCUTTING

must accommodate the fixture that, in turn, will clamp the three parts making up the ship set.

For pallets larger than 1,250 mm^2, a wire-guided, rather than a rail-guided vehicle may be used. Very large pallets, up to 8 × 16 ft (2.4 × 4.9 m), are used in the aerospace industry to move huge billets of aluminum and aircraft structural parts.

Cell Design for Palletized Machining

A palletized machining system may be designed that way from the start, or NC machine tools (alike or different) may sometimes be selected to be palletized in a retrofit.

An automated pallet shuttle system boosts machine tool productivity by establishing an automated flow of parts and maximizing mechanical and human resources. A palletized system keeps the spindle turning more hours. The main intent of combining machines into a cell or system is to get workpiece flow, process flexibility, and untended running during the evening shifts. With introduction of the untended operation and multiple machines connected by a pallet system, many new factors arise that were routinely handled by operators and supervisors who ran the stand-alone machines.

Designing a customized palletized machining cell requires information. Information relating to the workpiece includes: kinds of workpieces, quantity to be produced, machining area, accuracy, type of material, and current machining process. Production time issues are manned and unmanned hours available per day and per month. Other information desired includes: objective of the system, range of responsibility between builder and user, level of investment, gradual system development or all at once, and general factory conditions. There has to be constant communication between the user and the builder to ensure that sight of the overall objective is not lost.

Time-study, tooling, and fixturing. This is the first and most important step in building the system. This is where input from the customer defines the pre-automation machining sequence, tooling, and holding. When building a system, the intent is to enhance the knowledge gained by providing linking of machines and automation, not to develop machining knowledge all over again. This step determines the expected time per piece and the overall production. It also helps in determining the options on the machine that will be selected in further steps.

Selection of the core machine and options. This is the central element of the system. The machine selected should have high rigidity and accuracy, and be capable of high-speed operation. Because unattended operation is usually required, tool, workpiece, program, and swarf management should be available on the machine. Then, decide whether or not all the machines should be the same. If not, then there is the pallet compatibility issue for workpiece transfer. If different kinds of machines doing different processes are involved, then other part transfer and part presentation issues have to be considered. With knowledge of the parts and the core machine determined, the options required to handle the part should now be selected for the machine and control.

Number of machines required. The number of machines required will be based on the production requirements, time availability, and machining time calculated for the part.[30]

$$M_N = (M_T \times P_Q) \div (W_D \times S_H \times M \times E) \qquad (4)$$

where:

M_N = number of machines (units)
M_T = machining time
P_Q = production quantity
W_D = work days

S_H = system run hours
M = conversion for minutes
E = efficiency utilization rate (%)

For example:

M_T = 100 min (for 4 position pallet)
P_Q = 700 pieces/month
W_D = 20 days/month
S_H = 24 h/day (including untended operation)
E = 85%

(100 min × 700 pieces) ÷ (20 days × 24 h × 60 min × 0.85) = 2.86 units

In this example, three units are required for the conditions given. When deciding the number of machines, longer machining time should always be considered because of the high probability of process or sequence changes during testing and unforeseen or unaccounted for circumstances.

Number of pallets and setup stations. The number of pallets required has to be calculated for a day's untended operation.

$$\Sigma_P = \frac{T \times M_N \times E}{\overline{M}_T} \qquad (5)$$

where:

Σ_P = total pallets required for day operation
T = untended operation time (min)
M_N = number of machines (units)
E = efficiency or utilization rate (%)
$\overline{M}_T$ = average machine time (min)

For example, using the same values as the previous example and assuming that the untended operation time is 15 h/day, the number of workpieces that can be machined by the system is 23. This number of pallets is for attended running during the day and unattended running during the night.

$$\frac{(15h \times 60 \text{ min} \times 3 \text{ units} \times 0.85)}{100 \text{ min}} = 23 \text{ pallets}$$

The number of pallets required to operate the machine while the completed workpieces from the night's untended operation are unloaded and loaded can be calculated as:

$$\Sigma_P = \frac{T \times P \times M_N}{\overline{M}_T \times S} + P \qquad (6)$$

where:

Σ_P = total pallets required for night operation
T = load and unload time (min)
P = number of day pallets (units)
M_N = number of machines (units)
$\overline{M}_T$ = average machine time (min)
S = number of setup stations (units)

For example, using the answers from Eq. 4 and 5 and a load and unload time of 10 minutes and one setup station:

$$\frac{(10 \text{ min} \times 23 \text{ pallets} \times 3 \text{ units})}{100 \text{ min} \times 1 \text{ setup station}} = 7 \text{ pallets}$$

The total number of pallets required for this system would be:

$$23 + 7 = 30 \text{ for a night's untended operation}$$

The setup stations are either generalized stations or process-specific stations. Generalized stations are those where any pallet could come to get loaded and unloaded. Process-specific stations are those where, after a certain process, pallets have to come for loading and unloading. To calculate the number of general setup stations required:

$$S = \frac{M_N \times T}{\overline{M}_T} \qquad (7)$$

where:

S = number of general setup stations required
M_N = number of machines (units)
T = load and unload time (min)
$\overline{M}_T$ = average machining time (min)

For example:

$$\frac{(3 \text{ machines} \times 10 \text{ min})}{100 \text{ min}} = 0.30$$

This indicates that under the preceding example conditions, one setup station would suffice for the system. As can be seen, the number of setup stations is inversely proportional to the average machining time. As the machining time becomes smaller, the number of setup stations becomes larger.

Level of automation. After determining the machine and pallet elements, the degree of required automation must be established. The level of automation relates to the kind of hardware required, software in the system, and the functions that humans and system computers are capable of handling. The software level required is also dependent upon the number of pallets in the system. When the pallets are few and the time per piece is large, visible management by operators can suffice. But when the number of pallets increases, the human mind is not capable of handling the permutations and combinations of pallet and piece scheduling.

Supply of raw material to the setup station. Many times, little thought is given to the input to the system. The system has setup stations, which are the input and output points for the machining system. But raw material has to get to and finished parts have to be taken away from these setup stations. There must be buffer locations near the setup stations to accommodate the overflow and underflow from the system. Material could be supplied to the setup station either manually or by rail-guided vehicle (RGV) or some other method especially designed for the system. If the level of automation is low, then visual management could control the flow of raw material. If the level of automation is high, then an RGV controlled by the central system could deliver the material and take away the finished parts.

Loading method and layout. It must be determined whether the raw material loading on the pallet at the setup station is going to be performed manually or with a robot, according to the size of the workpiece, level of automation, and accuracy of the work to be held. If a robot is involved, then appropriate space has to be allocated near the setup station, with provisions for the necessary hardware and cabling for interconnecting to the central system. The next determination has to be whether the clamping will be manual or hydraulic. Hydraulic clamping with individually-contained power packs in the pallet is becoming the prevalent method. These hydraulic clamping systems make the process faster and less error-prone than manual clamping.

Some other functions in a machining cell that impact the material handling functions are: swarf and coolant management, and peripheral equipment such as stations for gaging, washing, or deburring.

Other information needed to evaluate installation costs include: floor space available, condition of the floor—gutters, pits, holes, weak floor, column locations in the system, entrance size to the factory, electric supply and drop points, and air supply and outlet points. This information greatly impacts the final cost calculation.

With the information described earlier, including the number of machines, pallets, and setup stations, a preliminary layout can be made, showing all the necessary dimensions of the system. While doing the layout, the floor, column, and such other information must be taken into account.

Carrier use. If the system happens to be equipped with an RGV carrier, as the system dimensions are collected, the carrier utilization rate can be calculated. A carrier's function is to transport the part between the machines, setup station, and stocker. Carrier speed should be at a rate that does not keep the machines waiting for delivery of the raw material pallet or the removal of the finished part pallet from the machine. Simulation software is used to analyze the carrier's performance and utilizations. If simulation software cannot be used because of different machine arrangements or applications, then utilization is roughly calculated by manual methods. When the carrier's estimated utilization rate is more than 80%, use some form of simulation to confirm it.

When a carrier is involved, it is the machine's utilization that is most important. The responsibility of the carrier is very simple—it should deliver the pallet to the machine before the machine completes its machining on the previous pallet.

The use of the carrier in a system does not make it a flexible system. Sometimes, the carrier is used in a dedicated system. In these cases, the carrier's capacity has to be checked very carefully. Because the whole system is based on specific parts, the total time of each piece is very important.

Considerations for higher level control systems. Higher levels of control include NC program data control, tool condition control, tool resource check, and other such scheduling and tracking considerations. These items and topics have to be dealt with in detail, usually by simulation.

SMALL PALLETS FOR ELECTRICAL DISCHARGE MACHINING AND OTHER USES

Small pallet systems, with pallets in the 50-250-mm² size range, have been designed for use with automated EDM systems, but may be employed for a wide range of machining applications in which the workpieces are smaller than those found in machining center palletized cells.

The manufacture of electrodes for diesinking EDM has long used systems of highly accurate, small workholders to achieve precise and repeatable positioning when moving an electrode from the milling, turning, or grinding machines they are machined on, to the ram EDM machine they are employed on. Electrodes are clamped in the holder and then moved from one machine to another. Each receiving machine tool has a receiver or chuck to accept the pallet and clamp it in a fixed position. Builders of tooling for sinker EDM machines have developed systems of palletized workpieces and work-changing robots to achieve high levels of machine tool utilization with minimal operator attention. The workpiece palletization carries the work from machine to machine, eliminating repeated alignment time at each machine.

Applications include changing workpieces and electrodes in sinker EDM machines, changing workpieces in wire EDM machines, changing workpieces and tools in milling machines, and changing workpieces and wheels in jig grinding machines. A small system might consist of two EDM machines with pneumatically-operated chucks or receivers aligned and ready to accept a pallet. After the work is mounted to the pallets, the work can be moved quickly from machine to machine, or taken out of a machine and brought to a

CHAPTER 15   METALCUTTING

CMM for checking. The chuck on the machine table will allow the operator to immediately bring the work back to its original position.

Small pallet systems have similar hardware, software, and communications components to palletizing systems for machining centers, but are designed for small parts and occupy only a modest amount of space. The chucks or receivers from one manufacturer[31] are from 70 to 250 mm^2. The pallet sizes from another builder[32] are 50, 115, and 150 mm^2. Having receivers in the machine ready to accept and orient a job reduces the time for changeovers.

Pallet magazines and accompanying work-handling robots for 10-150 small workpieces occupy no more space than a compact vertical milling machine, yet can carry enough workpieces to keep a milling machine running overnight. Small pallets may carry a single workpiece, but those approximately 250 mm^2 can carry multiple small workpieces, perhaps up to 25 to a pallet. Of course, customized pallet tops for certain workpieces may be designed, just as with larger pallet systems. Pallet magazines may be rotary disks, shelves, or other designs. A variety of gripping jaws accommodate different pallet sizes and types. Some of these systems, like the versions used for machining centers, accommodate programmable embedded chips or code carriers to identify a pallet and carry any required offset values from the preprogrammed positioning to the machine control. The positioning accuracy is typically better than on the pallets built for machining centers. Workpieces clamped in these devices may sometimes be machined on five sides and transported between machines. These pallets and associated hardware can be applied to palletizing non-EDM metalcutting operations for small-envelope workpieces. For transport outside the machine tool, gantries, conveyors, and other material handling systems may be used.

Shops that use extensive workpiece palletization can benefit from work flow management software and read-only computer chips mounted in the pallet to enable more effective production tracking. Each part or electrode is assigned a unique part number. The read-only code carrier, carrying that part number, traces the pallet.

In a typical system of one builder, parts go through registration, presettting, loading, scanning the magazine, and data transfer and prioritizing.[33] In registration, all jobs are given the unique part number and batch number, if desired. At presetting, the parts are mounted to pallets and the offset values are determined and registered in the database. As long as the part stays on the pallet, the offset values will be valid. After a magazine of parts is loaded, a scanner checks to see which parts are loaded. An optical sensor checks how many are loaded and if that number matches the number of code carriers detected, it allows the multipart machining job to be launched. After the job is released to the system, such essential data as the NC programs, magazine positions, offset values, and data on the transfer of parts among machines can be downloaded to the system. The benefits of this level of palletization plus automation for EDM and other operations is streamlined production and increased machine utilization.

HIGH-VOLUME SYSTEMS

High-volume metalcutting processes, such as those in automotive and truck powertrain machining systems, are specialized and expensive, and are becoming more so. No two are exactly alike. Material handling systems are individually designed to meet the application requirements. Specifying and designing them is different from working with standard machine tools and material handling components. Manufacturing automobile engines consists of machining and assem-

bling hundreds of components, and requires integrating several levels of manufacturing. The most effective system can only be selected after a careful analysis has been made of the general circumstances and the expected results. Knowing the standard components does not, in itself, solve the application problem.

The following are some of the important questions that arise early in the planning process. These questions are applicable to many types of situations.

- What needs to be transported and what quantity is involved?
- How easily are the parts damaged?
- What geometrical shapes do the products to be transported have?
- What is the weight of the products?
- What ambient factors need to be considered: temperature, coolant, chips, chemicals?
- What peripheral equipment is needed for handling and storage?
- What size storage capacity is needed? What are the cycle times?
- Are accumulating systems required to eliminate bottlenecks?
- To what degree are factory operations manual, semi-automatic, or automatic?
- What are the building conditions at the installation location?
- What are the part dimensions?
- What are the height differences of the parts?
- Are there upward or downward inclines?
- What legal regulations must be observed?

After preliminary ideas and target results are incorporated into a system layout, software for detailed process and material handling simulation and modeling is used before finalizing the specifications of large machining systems.

Transfer lines are a group of linked mass-production machines connected by automatic mechanisms and control systems, and may serve machining, testing, or assembly functions. Transfer lines for machining are dedicated to producing one or two parts, most commonly such automotive or truck parts as camshafts, crankshafts, cylinder blocks, cylinder heads, valve bodies, or transmission cases.

Lines may have ten or fewer stations in some applications, but 50-75 stations are not uncommon in automotive production. Lines of medium- and large-size include sections interconnected by a powered conveyor. An average section may have 8-12 workstations. Breaking a line into sections improves the operating efficiency by providing part buffers between sections. This allows accumulation and decumulation while a workstation is down for tool change or normal maintenance.

Because of the number of stations, many workpiece surfaces and holes may be machined. Workpieces are automatically transferred between stations by work transfer devices. Complete processing from castings or forgings to finished parts is common.[34]

The discussion of high-volume systems includes:

- Synchronous transfer lines.
- Asynchronous transfer lines.
- Transfer line flexibility.
- Application: simulating an engine plant.

SYNCHRONOUS TRANSFER LINES

Synchronous transfer lines move parts or pallets at all stations or machines simultaneously, after the longest machining or assembly cycle has been completed. They operate at a constant speed because of their fixed cycle. If a station fails to operate, the entire machine goes down and material movement is blocked at the machine not functioning. Therefore, the efficiency of a synchronous line could be lower than that of its least efficient or weakest machine, because of the direct linkage of all stations or machines in the system.[35]

ASYNCHRONOUS TRANSFER LINES

Asynchronous or nonsynchronous transfer lines allow a single station or machine to not be working for a short period of time without immediately affecting the line production by having extra workpieces in the system. The control of the stations and transfer mechanisms is not strictly time-based, because the workpieces move independently. While a single station is inoperative, the rest continue to operate, working on the parts accumulated from each station. Thus, individual stations are somewhat more independent than in the synchronous system and the negative effect of downtime at a single station is reduced. This means that smaller production interruptions, such as tooling changes, minor maintenance, and parts replenishment impact production minimally. The float (or buffering) of parts in the system means operations do not need to be started or completed at the same time. Troublesome or erratic operations can be somewhat isolated from the adjacent stations by arranging for a greater float of workpieces.

Nonsynchronous systems have some other advantages. Fixtures can be removed for repair without stopping the line. The number of fixtures or pallets may be altered as long as there is at least one pallet in float between stations. Because each station is fairly independent, each is installed and aligned individually, rather than as a group as in the synchronous system. Machines or stations may be added or relocated with much less cost and trouble than in a synchronous system.

Mixed or composite systems, comprised of synchronous and asynchronous segments, may often be the most practical from an economic or space consideration. In such systems, it may be desirable to limit the length of the synchronous segments to no more than ten stations to maintain an overall high system reliability.[36]

Asynchronous System Equipment

An asynchronous or nonsynchronous system depends on pallets that move between machines and stations. The pallets rest on conveyor chains. Depending on the work mode, the pallets will move with the conveyor or remain stationary. Mounted on the pallets, or integral with them, are the fixtures that hold the part in the working position. The conveyor chains move continuously. The pallets move at conveyor speed until they meet an obstruction, then stop. All the following pallets come to rest after the stopped pallet. The obstruction can be a manual station, an automatic station, or another pallet at a station.

In most cases, parts are loaded onto the fixtures at the first station. Then, the pallet is discharged or released, either automatically, by palm button, or foot pedal. The discharge couples the pallet to the conveyor chains, and the pallet proceeds to the next station. If there are no pallets at the next station, it moves directly into working position and stops, positioned for machining using a pallet registry. The required operations are performed and then the pallet is automatically or manually discharged downstream. In the event that there are other pallets at the working station, the pallet will stop in back of the last pallet. The number of pallets that may be in float between two stations is limited only by the distance between the stations, which can be varied as required, throughout the system.

The conveyor chain carries the pallet fixtures through the system. The conveyor in metalcutting systems is a steel frame that houses the continuously moving heavy-duty dual chain. The chain is made of conventional links with hardened-steel crescent plates attached. The conveyor is built in sections that are bolted together to form any desired configuration. The chain is supported and guided by hardened rails. The pallets are moved by resting on the flat top crescent plates. Side rails guide and align the pallet with the flow of the conveyor.

The drive that powers the chain consists of separate motors coupled to reducers, which power a chain sprocket. The typical conveyor speed is 60 ft (18.3 m)/min. The conveyor drive is located on both sides of the line and can be positioned anywhere along a straight run of the conveyor.

The pallet is usually a square plate casting. An accurately-located part-holding fixture sits atop this pallet. The underside of the pallet has a flame-hardened wear area that contacts the top plates of the chain. A self-compensating wedge-type slot on one side of the pallet and a semivee edge on the opposite side provide location. Pallet-to-pallet impact is minimized by polyurethane bumpers on the leading and trailing edges of the pallets.

An *escapement* is a device attached to the conveyor frame which is under the pallets and controls the flow of pallets through a workstation. Escapements are operated by pneumatic controls and automatically stop the pallet in a work position at a station, and when actuated, release the pallet downstream. A hardened-steel pallet latch on each escapement projects upward to engage the pallet in such a way that the pallet is prevented from moving backward and rebounding from the pallet-presence switch.

At manual stations, manual stops, release mechanisms, and secondary stops control the pallets and prevent them from hitting one another. Stops at automatic stations are precision-machined to positively locate and clamp the palletized fixture. The locator enters the pallet wedge slot and positions the pallet both linearly and traversely. It then lifts and clamps the pallet against hold-down rails, which provide the Z-axis location.

TRANSFER LINE FLEXIBILITY

The majority of powertrain machining systems used by North American automobile manufacturers are dedicated to produce one part, or two closely-related basic parts types. However, one small in volume, but technologically significant trend in automotive transfer lines is toward a limited amount of agility, flexibility, modularity, or reusability of the component machine tools within a system. Dedicated metalcutting transfer machines are still the low-cost way to achieve medium- to high-volume production, but some newer and recently revamped transfer systems are more flexible, serving goals beyond lowest initial cost.

The market today requires more flexibility in manufacturing. After the planning, business forecasting, and production simulation are done, flexibility is still needed for the large-scale machining systems. The decision to build a certain capacity of production is based on a product demand forecast and is barely reliable for even three years. There is never enough capacity for the popular models and there is expensive wasted capacity for those models that have lost appeal in the market. Rarely can market forecasts reliably predict the utilization of capacity over the equipment life cycle, which is often in excess of 15 years.

Flexible or modular approaches to building transfer line machining systems, using CNC machining center modules and similar CNC equipment, as well as more flexible uses of traditional machine designs, represent a major investment premium when compared to conventional transfer line machining equipment. Historically, the way to have some flexibility in such transfer systems was to build in extra capacity, but this came with a substantial cost of its own for the over-capacity, sometimes as high as 50%. One long-term option is for automakers to mix traditional dedicated transfer line machining capacity with flexible, agile, or modular machining capacity during the life cycle of high-volume parts and part families.

In the short-term, it is possible that the premium for agile or modular CNC machining technology over that of traditional dedi-

CHAPTER 15   METALCUTTING

cated transfer equipment may decline into the 10-50% range, which may be quite acceptable, given the historical tendency to build-in over-capacity of dedicated equipment. Also, as CNC technology for high-volume transfer line machining evolves, this premium for flexibility or modularity becomes increasingly acceptable.

Traditionally, the retooling of a transfer line meant that the automaker spent 70-80% of the original equipment value on new fixtures, tools, multiple spindle heads, transfer bars, and station rework. This retooling took six to eight months and put pressure on capacity elsewhere to accommodate the turnaround for the new part. Alternatively, installing a new transfer line can take up to two years.

Varying degrees of convertibility or flexibility lessen the impact of part changeover. Systems have been designed initially with enough flexibility to machine two different parts with some family resemblance to each other, but typically even these systems require the parts to have common location points to minimize pallet and workholding costs. With the right flexibility in such systems, the flexing back and forth between two similar parts might be accomplished in a few hours. Although flexible or agile machining systems cost more initially, they can be used to produce multiple products simultaneously and will last over the life cycles of two, three, or more products. In addition, machined parts suppliers have the need for flexibility—to turn out, on a subcontractor basis, a half dozen or a dozen different sizes or styles of one type of engine or transmission or other part on the same machining line. This would have been impossible with traditional dedicated transfer systems.

Flexibility and Agility

Flexibility or *agility* in high-volume machine tools is the ability to produce a range of different parts, within the same work envelope, by changing the tools, workholding equipment, and part programs, but with a minimum of change or no change to the machines. Where machine tools must be changed or stations added to a line, flexible or agile means that all connections such as air, coolant, electrical, and hydraulics are designed for fast disconnect and reconnect on the plant floor. In this way, downtime is slashed from months to weeks or days when retooling.

Flexibility can mean that when a part design changes (for example, the distance between cylinder bores in an engine block) at one or more positions in a transfer line, the stations or equipment may be swapped without having to tear up the entire material handling system. For example, a part design may shift so that a multispindle head in a certain position no longer does the required machining pattern, and either a new multispindle head or a three-axis CNC unit can be substituted for it with minimal disruption. This is a form of modularity or flexibility for the machining system as a whole. In some of the latest modular technology, this takes the form of changing the working upper part of the machine tool, while the base remains unchanged. In either case, the connections and transfer mechanisms through the station are only minimally disrupted and changeover is less painful in terms of downtime and lost production.

Flexibility and agility include family-of-parts flexibility—the ability to work on a family of parts, such as V-6, V-8, and V-10 engine blocks, and process flexibility—the ability of station six or seven in a line to perform a required operation if station five goes down. Multi-axis machining modules with tool changers can help achieve process and family-of-parts flexibility. New concepts are filling the gap between machining centers and transfer machines, while transfer machines get a flexibility-oriented redesign. Three- and four-axis machining modules are increasingly welcomed in high-volume environments, side-by-side with dedicated stations.

The advent of flexibility and agility has brought about a cultural change. In cost justification, for example, systems engineers have to factor into the studies not only the cost to machine the new product, but also the next product, the next retool, and maybe even the product after that. Up-front choices need to be made with incomplete information about future product changes.

Agility means different things to different manufacturers, with some more inclined toward total flexibility and others less likely to take big technology risks. Simulation reduces the risk of a new powertrain machining system. Today, all major machining systems go through a detailed simulation of pallets, cycle times, and parts waiting for machine spindle time. Flexible and dedicated options are tested using software before a commitment is made to a system design. Simulation is a lot more important than when dedicated lines were the only option.

Modular Build and Transfer Line Concepts

The modular build concept of one machining line builder includes the following features:

- Develop common and minimal variations of standard equipment for all components that are not part- or process-related.
- Maximize early release of standard equipment.
- Have quick retool capabilities for fixtures, heads, units, spindle drives, and controls, as well as easy base relocation.
- Create standard drop-in subassembled utilities and minimize wiring and piping at assembly.
- Facilitate individual station run-off so that projects can be assembled as kits.
- Have quick disconnects for all utilities such as lubrication, air, hydraulics, electrics, and coolant.
- Have quick-change capability for all major components, such as heads, units, fixtures, spindle drives, and unit drive.
- Controls and guarding should be standardized for acceptance by all customers.[37]

A modular or flexible transfer line accomplishes flexibility by permitting the swapping or exchange of columns, machining heads, and component carriers.[38] The common configuration interfaces are standardized, so that air, electrical, hydraulic, coolant, and other connections may be quickly disconnected and reconnected. A Y-column with a drive unit may be replaced on a line with an X-Y column with a drive unit, a milling head replaced with a facing or drilling head, or a stationary fixture carrier replaced with a carrier with a 90° or 360° rotary table. Flexible lines are more compact than traditional lines, although cycle times are the same or slightly longer.

The benefit is that when a product life cycle ends after five years, it is a lot simpler to reconfigure the line for the next product. One type of column on a wing base could be replaced with another or the wing bases could be moved to make space for a new unit. Because the electrical connections and other connections are standard, a lot of wiring time and manpower is eliminated.

One transfer line uses the electronic information-carrying capability of embedded memory chips to manage flexible machining—the kind of technology that was developed in the 1980s for flexible manufacturing systems (FMSs). The pallets transporting the parts through a line of flexible machining modules each carry an embedded chip with the information on what part the pallet is carrying and what feature or features need to be machined on that part. A machining station or module has the electronic capability to indicate to the pallet's chip whether it has the cutting tools to do the required machining. If not, the pallet moves to another station. This represents, perhaps, an extreme of the kind of flexibility available.

Machining Modules for High-volume Flexibility

Another builder of high-volume equipment has introduced modular workcells with a highly standardized design and self-contained, plug-in services.[39] A key component in the cell's flexibility is a high-speed, three-axis machining module. Machining center builders offer three-axis modules, with a wine rack-type tool changer for a small number of tools. Such machining center modules have all axes movements under the spindle and are on an ISO standard wing base for transfer line interfaces. Automobile manufacturers or component suppliers can begin with a limited configuration for a limited-volume product and expand with production ramp-up, adding machining stations, and adding to or altering the pallet transport system. Hard wiring and piping have been replaced by plug-in electrical cables and adaptable hydraulic and pneumatic lines. Even duct work and guarding feature modular construction.

The transition point in mid-1990s technology between parallel processing with flexible machining centers and a transfer line with some flexible units is 200,000-250,000 units/yr. Above that, full flexibility is too costly. One builder in the mid-1990s experienced the transition point at 60 parts/h in aluminum and 30 parts/h in cast iron. For steel parts, the number may be lower. Above the transition point, the cost of a flexible system skyrockets. According to another builder, for volumes of 250,000-1 million parts/yr, the better solution is an agile manufacturing system built with serial processing, where each station performs selected operations simultaneously with operations at other stations. This approach combines traditional transfer line machining units with three-axis machining center modules to get the best of flexibility at a reasonable cost. This also keeps expensive tool changing options to a minimum. Stations may be added or changed as product mix changes. Parts travel from station to station with a free-flow pallet transport system, with workpieces fixtured on the precision pallet.

Flexibility Limitations of Transfer Lines

The least expensive way to transport a part from one operation to another is still a dedicated transfer system. When dedicated stations are combined with three-axis CNC modules, head changers and turrets, and quick pallet changeover, flexibility is gained, but at additional cost. Flexible transfer systems are attractive for model changes, but engineers need to consider their life cycle costs.[40]

For example, using 15 spindles in a drill head on a transfer machine is efficient and reliable, but to do this on a flexible system, 15 passes are needed for a single-spindle CNC machine, plus tool changes for different hole sizes. To match the production volume of a dedicated machine, multiple CNC machines are needed, and those CNC machines' axes will be working constantly, resulting in significant wear.

A totally flexible system can cost 150-300% more in the beginning than a dedicated system. When a flexible system is ready to be retooled for a new application, will that user be satisfied with machines that have undergone significant wear and now have obsolete controls? Will all that flexibility at a higher cost really be utilized? In some cases, perhaps not.

Some operations can still only be performed on dedicated equipment, for example, to perform critical finishing operations without moving the machine base. This might include a two- or three-way boring machine or a deep-hole drill.

Processing experience and knowing when to apply certain technology can make or break a system. CNC machining centers have become almost commodity products. There are limitations with this type of machine tool for high volume production, however, and knowledge is important. Part stability, tolerances, and production rate, all interrelated, must be considered. Machining forces and the resulting part deflection are important issues. Fixture stability must withstand deflection. Access to as much of the part as possible is

needed and to gain this, some stability may be sacrificed. Evaluation of thrust loads and the resulting deflection will determine whether this is an appropriate application for a multi-axis machine.

CNC machining centers producing 100 parts/h must run at faster speeds than stations in a transfer machine. Today, many manufacturers are going to thin-walled parts. If all the power of the machine goes into cutting these parts, the part will not take it. It is necessary to slow down, for example, opening up a hole in three passes instead of one. With a transfer machine, this will cost two additional spindles, but on a machining center it will cost time, which will influence production rate. In a transfer machine, there is more time, so it can slow down and use less power.

There are also part-tolerance trade-offs. Tolerances in powertrain components are tightening up. Dedicated machines are sometimes the only solution to holding alignment in operations on opposing sides of a part or where extra support for the workpiece is required. Indexing errors, when the part must be rotated on a machining center, sometimes cannot be tolerated. CNC machining centers are most capable of holding a single datum on the part to close tolerances. However, when two or more points on the part must be held in close relationship to each other, CNC machines may not be the best choice.

APPLICATION: SIMULATING AN ENGINE PLANT

Computer simulation, with its capacity for modeling randomness inherent in systems, is an ideal tool that can aid in designing and planning large machining and assembly systems.[41] At the lowest level, simulation can do micromodeling of individual production lines such as crankshaft production; while at the highest level, it can do macromodeling of the entire engine production system. Any manufacturer using a variety of subsystems to feed a main production line can benefit from such computer simulation. The technology can help make decisions about critical issues affecting productivity, such as throughput, operating philosophies, buffer sizes and logistics, material storage issues, shift patterns and manpower optimization, preventive maintenance and tool change strategies, allocation of material handling equipment, and the use of macrolevel and microlevel simulation.

Throughput

In one application, the automaker and the simulation consultant built a simulation to check whether the equipment could produce the required number of engines per year under current operational parameters. If not, simulation could help in devising alternatives.

Operating Philosophies

Simulation is a good way to determine whether to operate on a Just-in-Time basis or to carry inventory. It can help decide whether components can be moved as required, which would entail dedicated material handling, or if inventories must be held at the final assembly line (by operating the subassembly areas longer than the final assembly areas). The latter option would obviously increase the inventory holding costs, but simulation would permit the comparison of additional holding cost to that of closing the final assembly line down due to a lack of the required parts.

Buffer Sizes and Logistics

Simulation helps determine the levels of subassemblies held in inventory at the final assembly line, where floor space might be more valuable and difficult to manage. Simulation can be a way to plan and improve movement from suppliers of all the hundreds of components forming an engine.

CHAPTER 15   METALCUTTING

Material Storage Issues

Storing components within the facility close to each subassembly or machining line can be compared to storing them centrally within the facility, or outside the facility, and moving them to the lines as needed.

Shift Patterns and Manpower Optimization

Whether operating some or all of the assembly and machining lines for additional shifts will improve throughput can be simulated, measuring throughput as jobs produced per hour on an average, or as the total quantity of engines produced over a period of time.

Simulation also helps evaluate the number of operators required per line. Too many operators add cost, but too few can mean less throughput because they would spend too much time moving between operations. Simulation would not only help estimate the optimal number, but also weigh tag relief against mass relief and optimize allocating skilled labor or technicians over different areas.

Preventive Maintenance and Tool Change Strategies

Software can help evaluate the cost of performing preventive maintenance and tool changes during on-shift or off-shift hours, and investigate the frequency of preventive maintenance and its impact on reliability.

Allocation of Material Handling Equipment

In many engine lines, conveyors serve as a means of transporting and storing components between operations. Simulation optimizes the size and speed of conveyors, and the number and task allocation of gantries, automated guided vehicles, and driven vehicles. It also investigates more complex issues, such as traffic management.

Simplifying the simulation to include only the major systems that make the engine's major subassemblies speeds the process of predicting the system's performance. In this case, the main elements are: piston and rod manufacturing and assembly, cylinder head machining and assembly, cylinder block machining, camshaft machining, crankshaft machining, and final engine assembly. Subassemblies are assembled and machined on separate lines, and the final assembly line puts all the pieces together.

The most important task is defining the objective, which affects the scope of the simulation project enormously, as well as the level of detail in the model. For instance, if the goal is to plan material storage or logistics, model many of the subcomponents. To optimize the material handling system, model all the material handling equipment accurately. On the other hand, if the objective is to determine the system's throughput, it might be justifiable to simplify most of the material handling equipment in the model, include only the major subassemblies, and assume all the small parts will be available.

Macrolevel and Microlevel Simulation

Microlevel simulation involves analyzing machining or assembly lines one at a time, for example, studying the connecting rod machining line separately from the cylinder block machining line. When developing a microlevel simulation, start the simulation analysis early to solve design issues, such as buffer sizes (often in the form of conveyors between operations) and number of pallets as early as possible. One objective of a microlevel simulation would be to determine the system's throughput. In this case, the throughput would be the number of connecting rods or cylinder blocks produced. Throughput is usually measured in terms of jobs per hour, on an average, over a long period of time. Thus, it is possible to evaluate if the total demand for a part type can be met.

Other objectives would include optimizing key parameters, such as the cycle times of stations, reducing cycle times to improve the throughput and the recovery rate when machines go down, determining the number of machines of each type, investigating if duplication of the bottleneck will lead to improved throughput, and optimizing buffer sizes between operations. For instance, there should be greater buffer sizes before and after the bottleneck operation to make sure that it is not starved or blocked. Also, if the system efficiency drops because of frequent downtimes or tool changes, buffers between operations can be increased to ensure smooth operation. The number of pallets used for conveying the part or assembly from one station to the next should be modeled. Too few pallets can cause starvation, but too many pallets can cause jamming and add cost. After these issues for subsystems have been determined, use the results to predict the operation of the entire production system and begin the macrosimulation.

Building the macromodel. The objectives of the macrosimulation model determine its scope—which elements, components, machines, and subsystems to include, and which to exclude. There are several ways to build the macromodel; two options are described.

Option one. Integrate all the micromodels into one large, detailed model. The resulting model includes all details from the microlevel models and will have all the stations, buffers, conveyors, and other resources. Thus, one model will include all downtimes, repair times, and tool changes for all stations. The advantage is that this simulation model will be the closest representation of the actual system. It will have a very high level of detail and merit for validating the system and predicting actual behavior accurately. The high level of detail involves a longer model-building phase, makes verification harder, and slows down the execution time for the model.

Option two. Integrate all the micromodels into one large model, but simplify material handling. This involves simplifying as many material handling elements in the model as possible, because elements used to model material handling devices are more memory-intensive than other elements. For instance, replace accumulation conveyors (or roller conveyors) with static buffer elements. The level of detail captured in this simulation model is still high, although it will not be as close to reality as option one. Eliminating certain material handling devices, such as slow moving, nonaccumulating conveyors and gantries shared by competing parts, can reduce the accuracy of results produced. A benefit, however, is that this model will be quicker to build and will run faster once it is working.

With either option one or two: group all elements of a micromodel together (for example, the connecting rod system or the camshaft production system) as a module. Thus, if the micromodel changes drastically, the module is deleted, as compared to deleting each element in the micromodel. A spreadsheet interface will allow easy access to key parameters (such as station cycle times, frequency of failures, and so on). Save the data presented in the interface to text files (flat file in ASCII format) and the simulation macromodel will then pick up its data from the text files. Updates will be easier for both the simulation analysts and the engineers.

Determining inefficiencies. Building the model helps find the inefficiencies in the engine production system. The most important parameters driving the engine production rate of the entire system are inefficiencies in the subassembly and subcomponent machining lines. These depend on the parameters for downtimes, repair times, and tool-change times for individual operations within the subsystems. There are four methods for capturing inefficiencies, in both the micromodels and the macromodels.

Method one. Model all the inefficiencies based on actual data collected from similar systems in existence. Reliability data from suppliers and manufacturers of equipment can supplement the available data. Such data will be in the form of mean time between failures (MTBF). Although results come from highly accurate data, the method is data-collection intensive, which will significantly increase for developing the model.

Method two. Alter all station cycle times for a system (such as the cylinder block machining system) to reflect the percentage of efficiency. For example, cycle time could be defined for station two to be 20 seconds when running at 100% efficiency and 24 seconds when running at 80%. Such analyses require less lead time and the software can predict average estimates of buffers between subassembly lines and the final assembly lines. No further data collection is necessary from similar systems. The limitation is that such simulations may not accurately reflect fluctuations in buffer levels between the subassembly and the final assembly line or accurately capture the randomness of downtime.

Method three. Estimate the expected efficiencies for all subsystems based on past performance of similar systems. Based on the expected efficiencies, this method will derive and distribute repair time and downtime parameters (such as mean time between failures and mean time to repair) across different operations in the subsystem. Data collection is not as intensive as under method one. Sometimes, this method might be more realistic than all the others because reliability estimates for new equipment might not be accurate. One disadvantage is the need to verify the result of distributing the inefficiencies across operations using simulation. Sometimes, it is necessary to redistribute the inefficiencies, such as when the simulation shows that the efficiency of the system is lower or higher than expected. Lead times will grow because of the increased number of simulation runs.

Method four. Integrate all the micromodels into the macromodel. The basis of this method is to operate models of subassembly systems for shorter times than the final assembly line to reflect inefficiencies. Thus, if the cylinder block line can make 400 parts per 8-h shift, then operate the block line for only six hours in the simulation so that it only makes 300 parts, thus capturing a 75% efficiency level. The simulation model will be more efficient (due to lack of randomness) and will execute faster.

This method is not data-collection intensive, and it cannot capture fluctuations accurately in buffer sizes between the subassembly lines and the final assembly line. The distribution of the production will not be very accurate because a subassembly system will produce continuously for a time and will be continuously down for another period. This might not reflect the actual situation.

Summary. In all simulation projects, support of management and all engineers involved is essential due to the large number of data collection, verification, and validation issues. Communicating the study's objectives and scope to all team members is essential. Approval of the objectives and scope in advance is very important. Frequent updates of project status and simulation model demonstration help to maintain support once the project is underway. Use the micromodels to assist in the design of the manufacturing subassembly systems based on constant feedback from the engineers involved. Start the macromodel study only after the team has addressed the issues related to the micromodels and agreed upon them. Make it easy to modify the macromodel, because changes are constant. Use a spreadsheet interface whenever possible to help the engineers to continue using the simulation after implementation.

CUTTING TOOL MANAGEMENT

While material handling is focused on getting raw materials or workpieces to the machine tools doing the material processing, an-other essential consideration is getting the cutting tools and toolholders, workholding devices or fixtures, and gages, to and from the machines. This task receives much less attention and often becomes a bottleneck. Many times the machine tool, manpower, and raw material are ready to go, but the cutting tool kit or fixture for a job is incomplete and it is held up for want of a tool, disrupting the shop schedule and increasing costs.

Some would consider this a material handling issue and others would not, but from an overall systems point of view, the best material handling system and the best machine tools do not cut metal unless the tools are also present and ready. Tools and tooling, however, are often treated reactively rather than proactively. The bars, slugs, castings, or other materials are actively managed, but tooling is often overlooked.

The major elements in the subsystem for cutting tool handling are tool storage, tool transport, tool inventory control and tracking, and tool gaging and calibration and presetting. The actual physical equipment for tool storage and transport is typically managed satisfactorily, while the tool gaging-calibration-presetting requirements are generally not a material handling concern. Tool inventory control and tracking (or tool management) sometimes causes problems in material flows throughout a factory, maintenance facility, or shipyard (see Fig. 15-17).

COMPUTERIZED TOOL MANAGEMENT

Many commercial software packages for material management and material requirements planning effectively plan and schedule the supply of raw materials or workpieces at a work center, but do not manage the flow of cutting tools. Unless a plant with this limitation in its material management software has a second system dedicated to cutting tool management, problems arise. Either many unfortunate surprises regarding tool nonreadiness will occur at machine tools, or else overstocking of tooling avoids such events. The former evil is endemic in low-volume manufacturing, while the latter is endemic in high-volume manufacturing. Both are inefficient and expensive.

A tool management system for a factory or other facility ensures that the right tools are delivered to the right places at the correct times, with the minimum investment in tools, so that operations run on schedule. A tool inventory and control system should track every tool that comes into the plant or is made in house, and know where it is in the plant, until its useful life is over and it is scrapped. For the manager who wants to control his tooling budget and ship his parts on time, to the machinist who wants the tools he or she needs to be available, a comprehensive tool management system serves the overall production system.

The area within a metalcutting establishment that will have the best computerized management of tools is the flexible machining cell or system, if the plant has one. Flexible machining cells and systems do not work without rigorous management of cutting tools as well as workpiece flow. But, for the rest of a metalcutting environment to enjoy efficient material flows, a computerized tool management system must be provided.

Implementing a computerized tool management system includes building a tool database and doing a comprehensive tool inventory. These efforts will likely reveal such previously invisible losses as: needless proliferation of tool and toolholder types for similar operations, large stock quantities of obsolete tooling, and carbide inventory possibly equal to half the total tool inventory.

Setting up the computerized tool management system can lead to greater savings in materials and their management than the cost of implementing the software system. For example, one manufacturer had a $1.4 million tool crib inventory before implementing a

CHAPTER 15   METALCUTTING

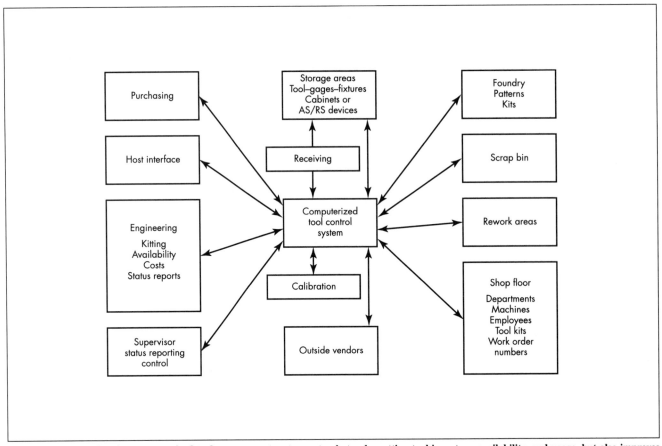

Fig. 15-17 A comprehensive computerized tool management system not only tracks cutting tool inventory, availability, and usage, but also improves control and material flows in many areas of manufacturing. *(Courtesy ITC Integrated Systems, Inc.)*

computerized tool management system. At the end of the second year on the system,[42] the inventory was cut to $600,000. By the end of the third year, the tool crib inventory stood around $300,000. In addition, the tooling budget was cut from $800,000 the year the system was installed to about $300,000 two years later.

After a computerized tool management system is functioning, it aids both the immediate tool inventory situation as well as the larger factory-wide material and data flows. The system provides forward visibility of tooling needs. Cutting tools and fixtures will be available when the raw materials, machines, and manpower are scheduled for a job, ending machine downtime due to want of a tool. This saves a lot of previously wasted machine time. Unexplained tool losses are brought under control. Tool cribs become true service departments to production, rather than a bottleneck and source of aggravation. The totally nonproductive job classification of tool expediter can be eliminated, or if the foremen had been tool expediting, they can give up that task and focus on more productive tasks in managing production. Tool designers and process planners can access the computerized tool database and specify tools which are in inventory for a job, rather than re-invent a new tool. Tool costs, which had been somewhat hidden before and generally not assigned to products or product lines, can be tracked and made available to managers for better manufacturing cost control. Tool purchasing can be transformed, with the cooperation of the parties involved, from being a battleground over competing interests, to being efficient electronic transactions between tool crib and tooling supplier.

AUTOMATIC STORAGE EQUIPMENT FOR TOOLS

Material handling technology applied to other materials is also applied to cutting tools in the modern factory. For example, vertical carousels widely used for the storage and retrieval of parts and supplies, are also suited for storing a large volume of inserts, cutting tools, toolholders, collets, workholding devices, and the many items that make up tooling in a metalcutting shop.[43] Compared to traditional shelves and drawers, vertical carousels use less space for equivalent volumes of material. Differing tray sizes accommodate tool size and type. The shelves move along a track in response to the operator's commands at the control panel. Tool inventory software tracks the storage and retrieval of tools in the unit. These big units can store hundreds of tool types and tooling accessories.

Automatic self-service tool dispensing systems are smaller units stocked only with cutting inserts, drills, end mills, taps, and similar perishable tools—perhaps up to 50 or 70 items per dispenser.[44] The machine typically dispenses one or more at a time of packaged, selected cutting tools, usually in response to a user's ID badge or other identification system. Such tool dispensers may be located in several spots in a plant and sometimes service a shop's machinists 24 h/day, or when no tool crib service is available after a certain hour. In some cases, they have replaced a manned tool crib altogether.

Such units are often stocked directly by the cutting tool distributor and the unit's computer has communication capability with the distributor. Small supply items also could be handled by such units.

Most of them are the size of a soda pop dispensing machine or smaller, with some designed primarily for cutting inserts, fitting on a tabletop. These tool dispensing systems may or may not accept the return of tools. Such units speed access to basic tool types, minimizing the lost productivity that accompanies trips to central tool cribs seeking tools.

AUTOMATED TOOL DELIVERY AND LOADING

Manual tool loading is still the most common way to get cutting tools and grinding wheels into the machine tools. Machining center cells sometimes use such automation devices as robots and tool pallets to bring groups of fresh tools to the machines and replace worn tools in machining center magazines. Elaborate forms of automated tool delivery systems, including large tool delivery pallets on guided vehicles, tool magazine exchange systems, and overhead rail systems with small tool delivery robots were developed in the 1980s for certain flexible manufacturing systems and high-volume operations. That form of large investment in automated tool delivery technology did not grow to any great extent and appears to have somewhat passed out of favor in the 1990s.

APPLICATION: MACHINING CELL TOOL MANAGEMENT

Setting up or reconfiguring a machining cell with linked machining centers is a major exercise in managing tools, as well as other cell resources. This is illustrated by a machine tool builder, which had two flexible machining cells processing machine tool parts.[45] The manufacturing engineers and cell technicians involved in bringing the cells on-line faced the typical concerns: how to put the cells in place, reroute parts into those cells, develop the required tooling packages and programming, and manage cell resources.

One cell includes four machining centers, each with a 170-pocket tool chain, linked by a single-level RGV system with 27 parking stations and three loading stations. A second cell includes three machining centers with a dual-level RGV system, 36 park stations, and three loading stations. Each cell uses a cell controller to manage work load and resources entering and leaving the cell. A preset gage interfaces to both cell controllers to provide on-line access to all preset tools entering the cells. The two cells process parts for standard horizontal machining centers, a line of CNC turning machines, and aerospace and specialty equipment.

The company decided to add more machine cells. Manufacturing Engineering then routed to the cells all parts that could be machined as completely as possible. Rerouting the parts was relatively easy compared to the cutting tool and fixturing changes, and reprogramming. The large quantity of low lot-size parts routed to the cells required a large amount of tools. These had to be built and preset each day. It became clear that if the cell operators were to manage this, the company would have to examine the tooling and programming methods, and particularly, tackle issues of nonproductive tool proliferation.

One problem was that the plant from which two of the machine cells had been moved used a different numbering system for tool assemblies. Also, engineers had attempted to set up for each machine, resident tool packages, that is, tools that stayed permanently in the tool magazine because they were used frequently or across several jobs. However, jobs coming to the machines usually required a large enough number of nonresident and special tools, so they were removing a lot of the resident tools. One reason was that four or five different programmers worked on jobs routed to the cells and did not have standard tool selection guidelines. There are many ways to cut a pocket, for instance. The company needed a system that said: "when cutting this size pocket use this size tool."

To standardize tooling, engineers re-examined every job routed to the cells. They produced a matrix of the tools required for every set of each part and identified the tools used most frequently. Then, they consolidated other tooling. Why use two tools, if one tool will do the job of both? This effort reduced tooling inventory for each cell by 40%. Cell personnel and programmers now work with a standard tool package book that lists the tools to be used. When a new part enters the cell, the cell supervisor reviews all associated programs to make sure that they conform with the book. Engineers have not eliminated all special tools from the cell, but the cell controller helps route all tools efficiently.

This experience demonstrated that companies moving to flexible cellular machining need to rethink their tooling strategy, among other things. Consolidating tooling inventory may not be easy, but not doing it adds unnecessary tool inventory costs to the cell. A key element of cellular machining is knowing what tools are required, their location, and when they need replacing.

CHIP MANAGEMENT

This section discusses:

- Rapid accumulation of chips.
- Stand-alone primary chip handling.
- Chip processing.
- Continuous chip processing.
- Stand-alone chip wringers.
- Central chip handling systems.
- Cold briquetting.

Two material streams in metalcutting operations involve dealing with the chips and swarf and processing the dirty coolant. Additional information about handling scrap and waste from machining operations can be found in Chapter 20.

Two issues in chip disposal are making chips that are easily disposable by automatic methods in the first place, and then keeping the flow of chips moving away from the machine so as not to build up and interfere with the process. Special chip breaking devices may be required to reduce chips to manageable sizes within or near the machine tool work area so the chips may be discharged without a lot of operator intervention.

It is important to consider the matter of chip breaking or chip removal because chip removal is a big issue when robotic or other automated material handling systems are combined with machining operations, particularly turning operations. Chip breaking and chip removal from the machine tool are an integral part of any automated operation. Properly breaking the chip in medium and finish turning, and in drilling and boring operations, is a material handling concern and should be attended to by the process planner or process engineer responsible for the part. It is mentioned here because major machining automation projects may have excellent material handling systems, but when the chips are not broken up enough to get out of the machine tool, they will gum up the works. It will not be satisfactory to solve the load and unload and other material handling issues if the basic machining process is not settled first, and made suitable for automation.

Continuous chip processing systems go from basic $60,000 systems for screw machine shops to much larger factory systems costing over $1 million. The investment is often a combination of the desire to do the right thing environmentally and the incentive to avoid fines or bad press from coolant spills. When the benefits of environmental compliance and having a clean plant are added to the ben-

CHAPTER 15 METALCUTTING

efits of reducing manual chip processing and getting a better price for dry scrap, the investment in continuous scrap handling equipment makes sense.

RAPID ACCUMULATION OF CHIPS

Getting chips out and away from the machine tool is particularly important in such operations as the high speed machining of aluminum, or in any operation where chip volume is dramatic. Chip volumes are perhaps more than one might think. Face milling 1 in.^{3} (16 cm^3) of cast iron yields 7-15 in.^{3} (115-246 cm^3) of chips. Milling 1 in.^{3} (16 cm^3) of steel yields 30-45 in.^{3} (492-737 cm^3) of chips. Drilling 1 in.^{3} (16 cm^3) of steel, in which the resulting chips are long spirals, yields 40-80 in.^{3} (656-1,311 cm^3) of chips. Spar milling 1 in.^{3} (16 cm^3) of aluminum yields 500 in.^{3} (8,194 cm^3) of chips.[46]

STAND-ALONE PRIMARY CHIP HANDLING

In its simplest form, stand-alone primary chip handling consists of a coolant pan or machine sump, a coolant supply pump, and a filter. Chips are manually removed from the pan depending on the size of the chips. The finer chips can cause problems with the supply pump, plug the coolant lines, and require frequent filter changes. Many metalcutting machine tools are equipped with an excellent chip conveyor, which picks up the chips at the bottom of the machine and hauls them out the side or rear quickly, to prevent heat build-up from the hot chips. But, even with the best loading system, such a machine can only run lightly-tended or unattended if the chips are broken up enough to fall into the chip conveyor rather than wrap around the part or the cutting tools.

CHIP PROCESSING

Many technologies for chip processing, including several styles of chip conveyors, crushers, shredders, and centrifugal wringers, vary little from what existed 25 years ago. But there have been changes and refinements. Improvements in reliability and control technology have moved chip processing equipment toward being low-maintenance items. It is important to remember that chip processing is destructive. Chips get into, wear, and generally destroy all processing equipment over time. A major nemesis of continuous chip processing in the past, scrap parts, bar ends, and pieces of tooling which get mixed in with the chips, are being successfully handled automatically by much of today's equipment.[47]

Traditional chip conveyors eliminate the operator from removing chips from the machine by hand. These conveyors also serve as a crude mechanical strainer to remove not only large swarf, but also a percentage of small chips and some fines. The balance of small chips and fines pass through the conveyor and are discharged into the coolant reservoir. There are several types of chip conveyors. A chip conveyor must be matched to the chip carried. Hard alloy chips cause faster wear than softer metals. Powdery chips, such as those from machining cast iron, get into moving parts and cause wear. Stringy turning chips cling to conveyor parts and build up. Aluminum needs more refined equipment to handle the larger chip volumes, larger coolant volumes, smaller chips, and the fact that the chips are often floating. Various types of stand-alone chip conveyors and coolant cleaning separators are available. The basic advantage of these stand-alone primary chip handling units, regardless of type, is that they are flexible—they may be picked up and moved when it comes to plant rearrangements and modernizations. Chapter 20 describes the various types of chip conveyors on the market and contains a conveyor selection chart (Table 20-1).

CONTINUOUS CHIP PROCESSING

A basic continuous chip processing system with a capacity of 2,000 lb (907 kg)/h of steel chips costs about $100,000. Such a system includes a high-torque shredder to break up chip bundles and make them manageable for further processing. The heart of the system is the centrifuge that wrings the chips dry, recovers the coolant, and flings the chips pneumatically to a discharge chute some distance away. An automatic system may cost more than a stand-alone chip wringer, but it is reliable in eliminating scrap parts, bar ends, and tools from the chip stream (see Figs. 15-18 and 15-19). It runs unattended. Chips processed by such a system typically contain under 2% moisture, which should meet dryness requirements. The cost of one person per shift running a chip wringer full time would justify an automatic system.

One key feature of continuous chip systems is that chips must enter the system continuously. Unless a certain volume of chips is present, the system may let through a bundle of stringers. If the pressure is continuous, however, chips break up nicely. Sometimes chip sensors in the input hopper turn on the system only when chip volume is adequate.

Magnetic conveyors may be used to separate ferrous chips, turnings, or small parts from coolant.[48] (See Chapter 20.)

STAND-ALONE CHIP WRINGERS

One of the simplest pieces of equipment to separate chips and coolant is the manually-loaded centrifuge or chip wringer. It uses virtually no automated material handling equipment—chips are carried in barrels from machine tool chip bins to the chip wringer by cart or truck. Chips emerge semidry and ready for shipment, and the coolant can be recycled. Small shops, as well as certain machine tools or cells, use manually-operated batch wringers because they are cheapest in the short run. Although inexpensive for low volumes, stand-alone chip centrifuges require an operator at all times, and that can mean $30,000-50,000 per yr/per worker/per shift. These devices have remained largely unchanged over the last 25 years.

CENTRAL CHIP HANDLING SYSTEMS

Central systems are another approach to primary chip handling. Central chip processing systems serve large areas with many machines. These range in price from $250,000 to several millions and may separately handle two or three different chip materials in large volumes from many machines. These systems have a common chip, swarf, and dirty coolant transportation means, usually in the form of an in-ground flume, either hydraulic flush-type or mechanical push-pull type, for large swarf. In-the-floor flumes can leak and contaminate ground water. Above-the-floor flumes are becoming more commonplace. In some cases, overhead piping can carry wet chips and coolant away from the machines. Complete chip handling systems for major industrial customers require engineering to select the right equipment. A special challenge in recent years has been the handling of small chips produced by high-speed milling and drilling. Smaller chips are harder to filter and transport and are not handled well by some older equipment.

Traditional central chip transport systems are inflexible, because the flume system must be sloped to create enough velocity so that all the chips make it to the central filter or chip processing area. Flushing coolant, often equal in volume to that discharged by the metalcutting machine tools, is sometimes required to guarantee delivery of all chips to the filter without plugging the flumes.

A 1990s design of overhead chip and coolant transport system, using horizontal pipes, is more flexible than in-ground or other above ground systems and does not require large volumes of additional

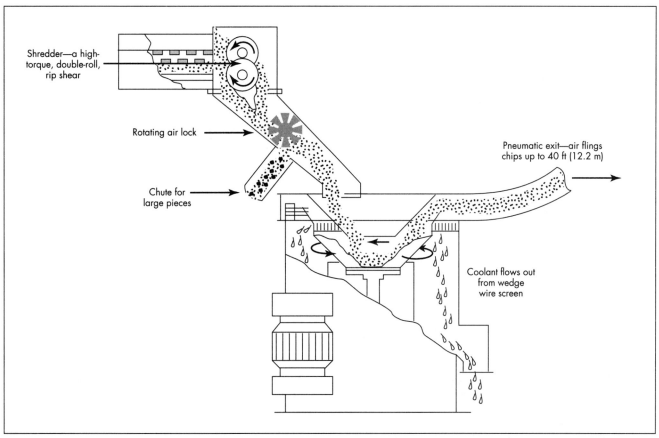

Fig. 15-18 A classic "wring and fling" centrifuge, which separates chips from coolant, is one element in a larger system for continuous chip processing. *(Courtesy Mayfran International)*

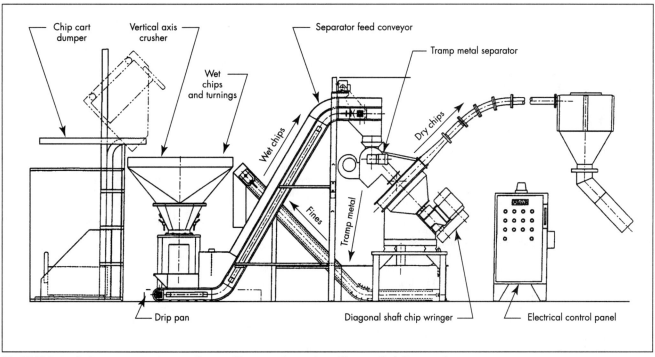

Fig. 15-19 A stand-alone separator-type continuous chip processing system. *(Courtesy Prab Conveyors)*

CHAPTER 15   METALCUTTING

flushing coolant. This technology centers around the creation and control of the right amount of turbulent flow of dirty coolant to keep chips from settling in the pipes. Because no extra flushing coolant is used, the central filter and pumps can be of smaller capacity than in a traditional flume system. In either traditional design or turbulence-based design, overhead chip transport systems require that the chips presented to it be small. If the chips and swarf are large and bushy, then they must be crushed and reduced in size, in chip crushers, before being pumped to the overhead system. Small chips and grinding sludge are often flumed from the machine tool directly to the pumping station, without the need for an intermediate chip conveyor.

Because large amounts of wet chips can be discharged by central filter conveyors, large chip wringers are often used to remove retained coolant. If necessary, large batch-fed crushers may feed the wringers. Wrung chips are typically air blown to a large chip container outside the building.

COLD BRIQUETTING

Chip compacting is another alternative among technologies for chip disposal. Expensive hot briquetting systems—which heat, dry, and compact steel chips into near-solid briquettes—have been out of style for many years, except at scrap dealers.[49] But cold briquetting is making a comeback. Compact cold briquetting units turn wet chips into dry hockey-puck-shaped pellets 3.5 or 5 in. (about 89 or 127 mm) in diameter and reclaim the spent coolant. The pelletized pucks are 98% dense (2% moisture). They offer an alternative to stand-alone chip wringers.[50] Like chip wringers, they may lack a method to separate out bar ends and other solids, for example, a crusher or shredder to chop up packed turnings. Operators can be alerted to look for solid pieces.

Inside, the units have internal augers to break up stringy chips and bird's nest chips, and feed all the chips to a compression unit. One small producer of chips, primarily from a sawing operation, reported getting $90-100/ton per day for compacted steel pucks from his scrap dealer, ($10-20/ton above the price paid for spun dry steel chips), while also saving 90 gal/day (341 L/day) in coolant, valued at $1.40/gal ($0.37 L). Larger manufacturers could use such small cold briquetters to support some of their stand-alone machining cells, separate from centralized factory chip and coolant handling systems.

COOLANT FILTRATION MANAGEMENT

Because chips and coolant are closely linked material streams, chip handling and processing equipment suppliers often work with providers of coolant filtration equipment. However, not all shops that dry chips and reclaim coolant go through the added step of filtering the coolant that is removed from the chips. Oil recycling is less complicated than recycling water-based coolant.

Coolant management affects many aspects of metalcutting. Coolant cools the machine tool, the workpiece, and the chips. It flushes chips out of the cutting zone and into a chip removal mechanism, such as a chip conveyor. On-line filtering at the machining process can keep coolant tanks and supply lines free of clogs from chips and fines, thereby maximizing machine tool uptime. In addition, coolant filtration reduces machine maintenance costs and housekeeping requirements by reducing coolant contamination.[51]

Without a good filtration system, machine tool coolant pumps can be ruined. Filters remove chips and dirt from coolant. They help extend tool and coolant life and improve surface finish. Particles allowed to recirculate into the work area abrade both the tool and the work surface. Less particulate buildup in the coolant limits bacterial and fungal growth.

The size and type of particles requiring filtration varies with the work material and process. For example, high-speed machining generates finer particles. To remove these particles, different techniques are used, depending upon the flow rate and sensitivity of the operation. Separating conveyors, chip conveyors, and filters can be used alone, or in different combinations. That is, in parallel or in tandem.

Filters require the liquid to flow through a barrier (media). Filters may be mounted on a common sump or individual machines, and can use solid elements, such as wedge wire or microscreens, or disposable materials such as paper, cloth, and man-made fibers. Size of the particle to be trapped, automation of the filter cleaning system, and cost determine the choice.

At the end of the flume is a large central filter, which acts as a very large enhanced separator conveyor, although the level of coolant cleaning is much greater because the coolant is actually filtered through a cake by a variety of processes. Coolant is typically cleaned down to the 10-30 microns range and is supplied back to the individual machine tools via large pumps capable of handling the requirements of all the machines. Back-up pumps are a necessity.

Since one of the functions of coolant is to cool, consideration is given to a heat exchanger, which includes a typical plate and frame or shell and tube devices with cooling water. When temperature control needs are below ambient temperature, then a chiller or refrigeration subsystem may be added to the coolant system.

HIGH-PRESSURE COOLANT SYSTEMS

High-pressure coolant systems, with two different applications, may be used. The first application of a high-pressure system is fairly broad, where the high pressure flushes away chips from deep holes or in through-the-tool coolant applications. When using through-the-spindle cooling, fine filtering is important to minimize particle buildup and wear in the lines, valves, rotary connections, and tool channels. The second application uses high pressure to help fracture the chips into manageable sizes (used especially in turning and holemaking). While normal flood cooling (the most common method) operates at 35-150 psi (241 kPa-1 MPa), these high-pressure systems operate at 500-1,000 psi (3.5-7 MPa) or more.[52] The trend is toward using higher pressures to eliminate problems with cutting certain long-chipping materials, and to flush chips out of the workpiece so the coolant is clean for subsequent processing.

SPACE PLANNING

Space planning is an important consideration in chip and coolant filtration management. The floor area for a machining operation grows to considerably more than the space required for the machine tool itself, once coolant filtration, cooling equipment, and chip conveyors are taken into account. This is especially true for machining operations that require very high volumes and pressures of coolant, such as deep-hole drilling and certain grinding operations. The filtration and cooling module with the coolant reservoir may take up more space than the machine tool itself. There is a growing effort to develop packaged systems using less floor space to serve cells.

FUTURE TRENDS

In some industries, such as automotive powertrain machining, the cost of coolants and coolant disposal may exceed the cost of cutting tools and tool management. For cost control, as well as for environmental concerns, there is high interest in moving to total coolant management or where applicable, to dry machining, in which the metalcutting process is engineered to operate completely without coolant.

References

1. Behringer Saws, Inc., Morgantown, PA.
2. Armstrong Blum, Mt. Prospect, IL.
3. Behringer Saws, Inc., Morgantown, PA.
4. Some providers of bar loaders and bar feeders are Hydromat, Inc., St. Louis, MO; Iemca USA, Inc., Suffern, NY; Lexair, Inc., Lexington, KY; LNS America, Inc., Cincinnati, OH; Pietro Cucchi USA, Dayton, OH; and SMW Systems, Inc., Santa Fe Springs, CA.
5. A method used by Index Corp., Shelton, CT.
6. Mazak Corp., Florence, KY.
7. Feedall Automation, Willoughby, OH.
8. Some providers of gantry loaders are: The Bleichert, Co., Sterling Heights, MI; Fibro, Inc., Rockford, IL; Liebherr America, Saline, MI; and Wes-Tech, Inc., Buffalo Grove, IL. System integrators with expertise in gantry loading cells and systems include Creative Automation, Plymouth, MI and MasTech, Troy, MI.
9. Liebherr America, Saline, MI.
10. Okuma & Howa-KGK International, Buffalo Grove, IL.
11. Daewoo Machinery Corp., Plymouth, MI.
12. Hitachi Seiki, USA, Inc., Congers, NY.
13. Index Corp., Shelton, CT.
14. Ventax, Ayr, Ontario.
15. Rapistan, Grand Rapids, MI.
16. Westech Automation, Lincolnshire, IL; CNC grinder from Okuma.
17. Liebherr America, Saline, MI.
18. Some providers of robotic systems for machine loading are ABB Flexible Automation, Inc., New Berlin, WI; Fanuc Robotics North America, Inc., Auburn Hills, MI; Motoman, Inc., West Carrolton, OH; and Nachi Robotics, Farmington Hills, MI, among others.
19. Fuji Machine America Corp., Lincolnshire, IL and Wasino Corp., USA, Wayne, NJ, specialize in this form of turning automation, but several major suppliers of CNC lathes, such as Hitachi Seiki, offer this type of option on their equipment.
20. Giddings & Lewis, Fond du Lac, WI.
21. Fuji Machine America, Lincolnshire, IL.
22. In addition to lathe builders, such as Cincinnati Milacron, Cincinnati, OH; KGK International/Okuma & Howa, Buffalo Grove, IL; and others, who build their own loaders as an option, Indacon, Dayton, OH and Toellner Systems, Inc., Hudson, WI provide such parts loaders for lathes.
23. Drozda, Thomas J., and Wick, Charles, eds. *Tool and Manufacturing Engineers Handbook (TMEH),* Fourth Edition, Vol. 1, *Machining,* Chapter 16. Dearborn, MI: Society of Manufacturing Engineers, 1982.
24. EMAG Bohle VSC Design, Farmington Hills, MI.
25. Hessap DV-Transfer from Thyssen Production Systems, Auburn Hills, MI.
26. The Index 200T, Shelton, CT.
27. Motch Corp., Cleveland, OH.
28. Daewoo Machinery Corp., Plymouth, MI.
29. Such as Eimeldingen, Indianapolis, IN.
30. Each machine builder may use slightly different presuppositions and do these calculations slightly differently. This example has been prepared by Yusuf Venjara, General Manager, Engineering, Hitachi Seiki USA, Inc., Congers, NY.
31. System 3R USA, Fairfield, NJ.
32. Erowa Technology, Arlington Heights, IL.
33. Anders Utterstrom, Manager, System 3R USA.
34. Some providers of in-line transfer line equipment are: Cargill Detroit Corp., Clawson, MI; Ex-Cell-O Machine Tool, Co., Sterling Heights, MI; Giddings & Lewis Integrated Automation, Inc., Fraser, MI; Grob Systems, Bluffton, OH; Heller Machine Tools, Troy, MI; Ingersoll Milling Machine, Co., Rockford, IL; Kingsbury Corp., Keene, NH; Lamb Technicon, Warren, MI; Newcor, Inc., Bay City, MI; Thyssen Production Systems, Auburn Hills, MI; and Zagar, Inc., Cleveland, OH.
35. Drozda, Thomas J., and Wick, Charles, eds. *Tool and Manufacturing Engineers Handbook (TMEH),* Fourth Edition, Vol. 1, *Machining,* Chapter 15. Dearborn, MI: Society of Manufacturing Engineers, 1982.
36. Ibid.
37. Lamb Technicon, Division of Unova, Warren, MI.
38. Heller Machine Tools, Troy, MI.
39. Cargill Detroit, Clawson, MI.
40. The concerns on the economic and technological limitations of flexibility have been raised by Larry Streng, Director of Manufacturing and Engineering, GM Powertrain Group, in "Agile Manufacturing and an Equipment Portfolio Systems Strategy," Technical paper delivered at Society of Manufacturing Engineers Powertrain Machining Systems Technology and Applications Conference, Troy, MI, Nov. 1996, and in an interview with the editor by John S. Klimach, President of Ex-Cell-O North American Operations, Sterling Heights, MI.
41. Jayaraman, Arun, and Agarwal, Arun. "Simulating an Engine Plant." *Manufacturing Engineering,* Nov. 1996: 60-68.
42. Tool management software from ITC Integrated Systems, Cherry Hill, NJ.
43. One provider of this equipment is Remstar International, Inc., Westbrook, ME.
44. Such as those from Vertex Technologies, Cincinnati, OH, or Newcomer Products, Inc., Latrobe, PA.
45. Noaker, Paula M. "Machining Centers, Cornerstones of Flexible Manufacturing." *Manufacturing Engineering,* March 1996: 43.
46. Gough, P.J.C., ed. Data from *Swarf and Machine Tools.*
47. Some providers of chip processing equipment are: Barrett Centrifugals, Worcester, MA; French Systems, Rochester, NY; Intersource Recovery Systems, Kalamazoo, MI; Jorgensen Conveyors, Mequon, WI; Mayfran International, Cleveland, OH; and Prab Conveyors, Kalamazoo, MI.
48. Some providers of magnetic components and systems for chip handling are: Bunting Magnetics, Co., Newton, KS; Eriez Magnetics, Erie, PA; and Storch Products, Co., Livonia, MI.
49. A provider is EMI—Equipment Merchandise International, Cleveland, OH.
50. A cold briquetting unit is built by UHM-Unlimited Horizon Marketing, Apple Valley, MN.
51. Some providers of coolant filtration equipment are: Advanced Filtration Systems, Champaign, IL; Barnes International, Rockford, IL; Filtra-Systems, Wixom, MI; Henry Filters, Bowling Green, OH; Hyde Products, Cleveland, OH; and Oberlin Filter, Co., Waukesha, WI.
52. Two providers of high-pressure units are: Chipblaster, Inc., Loveland, OH; and Cooljet Systems, Brea, CA.

Bibliography

ANSI/RIA 15.06 *Robot Safety Standards.*
Drozda, Thomas J., and Wick, Charles, eds. *Tool and Manufacturing Engineers Handbook (TMEH),* Fourth Edition, Vol. 1. Dearborn, MI: Society of Manufacturing Engineers, 1982.
Gough, P.J.C., ed. *Swarf and Machine Tools.* London: Hutchinson, 1970.
Jayaraman, Arun, and Agarwal, Arun. "Simulating an Engine Plant." *Manufacturing Engineering* Nov., 1996: 60-68.
Joseph, James. *Coolant Filtration.* Williamsburg, VA: Joseph Marketing, Inc., 1985.
Liebherr. *Material Handling Production Systems.* Kempen, Germany, and Saline, MI: Liebherr, 1993.
Mason, F. "Computerized Cutting Tool Management." *American Machinist & Automated Manufacturing* May, 1986: 105-132.
Mason, Frederick, ed. *Computerized Tool Management Systems,* SME Blue Book Series. Dearborn, MI: SME, 1992.
Mason, Frederick. "Chip Processing Gets New Life." *Manufacturing Engineering* March, 1995.
Mason, Frederick. "High Volume Learns to Flex." *Manufacturing Engineering* April, 1995.
Mason, Frederick. "Turnover in Vertical Turning." *Manufacturing Engineering* January, 1996.
Melnyk, Steven A. *Tool Management and Control, Conference Proceedings,* Grand Rapids Chapter APICS. Lansing, MI: Michigan State Univ., Dept. of Management, Oct. 1988.
Owen, Jean, ed. "Profits Through Pallets." *Manufacturing Engineering* January, 1996: 33-42.

CHAPTER 16

METAL FORMING

CHAPTER CONTENTS

INTRODUCTION

This chapter focuses on the importance and cost-effectiveness of reducing the time between entry of material to the manufacturing enterprise and shipment of the final stamped product. Since the largest single expenditure in the manufacture of a typical metal forming process is the cost of the material itself, it is essential that handling material between value-adding operations be kept to a minimum. Studies of material flow through various manufacturing processes indicate that workpieces are idle, waiting, or in storage for a greater period of time than they are worked on. This is unacceptable in today's global competitive environment. This chapter describes and illustrates both basic and unique processes for consideration.

To be internationally competitive, the design and building of a company's metal forming dies and automated material handling equipment must not only comply with corporate standards, but enforce procedures for continual improvement.

Corporate goals must:

- Reduce the influence of direct labor on yield.
- Reduce the number of die operations.
- Eliminate the need for complicated die conditions.
- Enforce a policy of simultaneous engineering.
- Continuously pursue advanced automation technology and computer data analysis.
- Improve throughput while significantly increasing stamping quality through advanced or improved material handling.

In contrast with stamping, sheet metal fabrication uses machines with quickly exchangeable tooling—punch presses, laser or plasma cutters, shears, brakes, and bending equipment. These processes present material handling challenges based on both complexity and economic justification issues. The issues differ significantly from those of high-speed stamping presses and involve, in addition to loading and unloading, issues related to tab breaking, sorting, stacking, and storage.

The first material handling challenge derives from the infinite variety and intermixed sizes, shapes, and weights of the handled parts. This limitless combination of part properties highlights the need for flexibility. Next, there is the question of cost. The addition of automated material handling to a punching or cutting process that already is an insignificant portion of the part cost may be unwise. Bending, welding, grinding, and painting, on the other hand, are more cost-additive because of their complexity, and may justify the cost.

Product flow is vital to a company's productivity and fabricators automate material handling to improve productivity. Not only are significant productivity gains difficult to attain in sheet metal operations, but it is also difficult to determine when further pursuit will result in no return. Automating material handling is like any other strategic company decision. It must be made in response to the customer's continuing need for responsiveness and high quality at the best price.

Usually the rate of production from blanking, to forming, to assembly, decreases. For example, in automotive manufacturing, blanks are produced at 2,000/h, panels formed at 900/h, with assembly producing 50 vehicles/h. Consequently, it is necessary to create a buffer zone—storage capability—between each successive operation to use equipment most effectively. This further emphasizes the need for efficient material handling, particularly when assembly plants schedule their supply Just-in-Time (JIT).

Forging, too, has specialized material handling requirements because of the need to heat the metal billets before they move to the forging machine.

The total life-cycle cost (LCC) of sustaining equipment and purchasing and processing sheet or coil metal to produce a metal stamping must include a thoughtful handling requirements analysis of both material and tooling. Material handling considerations must be proactive, not reactive.

STAMPING PLANTS

Sheet metal stamping plants are among the most capital-intensive of all manufacturing installations in modern industry. The high level of investment and long-term commitment to selected manu-

The Contributors of this chapter are: Jerome Barendt, Supervisor, Ford Motor Company; Michael J. Bleau, Sales Manager, The Schuler Group; Markus Bogener, Marketing Director, SMG Presses; Douglas E. Booth, Director—Application Engineering, Detroit Center Tool Automation Division; Thomas Burke, Marketing Coordinator, Webb Heavy-Duty Roller Conveyor Systems; Carl Corless, Sales Administrator, Prab Conveyors; Jack J. Craddock, General Sales Manager, Webb Triax Corp.; Willi Flick, International Marketing Manager, C. Behrens Machinery Company; Richard Herzfeld, Vice-President—Technical Writing, TechComm Associates; Werner K. Lehman, President, Sesco Corp.; James Lehner, Sales Manager, HMS Products, Inc.; David J. Nelson, Director, Marketing, Verson Division of Allied Products Corp.; Wallace Paprocki, Supervisor, CAD/CAM and Reprographics,Verson Division of Allied Products Corp.; Chris Reed, Program Manager, Fanuc Robotics; Gary Marshall, Director of Marketing Communications, RapidAir Corp.; Kevin Spain, Vice President of Sales, Radyne Corp.; Frank Wennberg, Director of Sales, ABB Olofstrom Automation.

The Reviewers of this chapter are: E. Lee Bainter, Jr., Process Engineer, Chrysler Motors Corp.; Howard A. Bender, Consultant to the Metal Forming Industry.

CHAPTER 16   METAL FORMING

facturing methods and production equipment mean that careful investment and thorough production planning are essential.

Stamping plants are generally comprised of several different types of sheet metal processing equipment, each manufacturing a certain range of parts. The aim of efficient stamping plant configuration is to ensure the most economical operation.

The selection of the individual pieces of equipment depends primarily on the size, shape, and metal forming requirements imposed on the components, as well as planned production batch sizes. Figure 16-1 is an overview of the equipment typically found in a high-production stamping plant.

Sheet metal is supplied from the rolling mill in coils. For larger stampings, such as automotive skin panels, the sheet metal is normally cut into blanks. Subsequent operations to produce the finished stamping are performed in transfer presses or tandem press lines.

Smaller stampings require that the coil stock be fed directly to the forming press using progressive dies with a carrier ribbon designed as the material handler.

The finished parts are palletized either manually or by a stacking device and made ready for downstream processing (welding, painting, etc.). Scrap disposal occurs simultaneously.

STACKERS

Owing to the major material cost of metal stampings, the primary responsibility of the process engineer is to establish the most economical use of the material. Frequently this requires a nesting of blanks within the most economical coil width. Sophisticated software programs register the digital profile of the blank and determine the most favorable nesting.

The blanks are produced at much higher speeds than forming operations and consequently are stored on pallets. Multiple stacks of blanks on each pallet are required for effective use, and multiple stacking heads on blanking systems are often provided to reduce downtime during removal of stacks.

Frequently, left-hand and right-hand (LH and RH) blanks are produced from the same die, requiring stacks to be inverted for the opposite hand in a stack turner. The alternative is to build a separate blanking die for each hand. The cycle starts when the lift cart delivers a stack of blanks on a pallet to the front of the stack turner. An elevator within the lift cart raises (or lowers) the stack to the correct operating height. The fork cart enters the slots of the pallet and the pallet is lowered to leave the stack on the forks. The lift cart retracts to allow the fork cart to place the stack between clamps within the stack turner. After the stack is rotated 180°, the sequence is reversed to deposit the inverted stack on the original pallet.

To achieve favorable nesting of blanks, it is often necessary to blank two parts with each press stroke. One blank is discharged in line with the direction of coil, the other discharged to one side. This requires the use of both an in-line and a side stacker.

Figure 16-2 illustrates a blanking system for trapezoidal blanks. Two blanks are generated with each press stroke, in this example both of the same hand. One blank is discharged to an end stacking system, the other to a side stacker. The die shown has a programmable, oscillating shear blade. Angles can be changed to produce LH or RH blanks, eliminating the need for a dedicated die for each blank profile.

Large blanks, such as those for automotive side panels, are also produced on the same blanking system (a different die for a specific blank), as shown in Figure 16-3.

The side stacker is now used to retain offal (reusable scrap), which is recovered to produce a smaller stamping.

Owing to the wide variety of shapes and sizes of blanks generated in a typical stamping enterprise, flexibility is essential in the handling of both the incoming coil material and the generated blank. Surface quality of the blank must be ensured to avoid scuffing (scratching or marking) to prevent rejects. Disposal of scrap requires equal attention to detail.

DESTACKERS

Feeding precut blanks to a forming operation requires some form of automatic device to utilize the full production rate of the press.

Stacks of blanks can be accepted from the fork lift truck or automated guided vehicle (AGV). The destacker may have a single or double head and can introduce a new stack of blanks without interrupting the press cycle, after the previous stack has been exhausted.

The effectiveness of any automatic destacker is directly related to the condition of the incoming stack. Poorly prepared stacks will cause poor yields from the destacker and press.

With current technology, dies can be changed in minutes. Consequently, destackers must have the same capability, accommodating several blank profiles within the same time frame. Innovative applications combine coil feeding with stacking and destacking blanks, using buffer zones for the time of die and coil change.

Figure 16-4 illustrates a single-head destacker that is feeding blanks to a transfer press after washing. The *short stack support* principle is employed to permit continuous part production (from this short stack), while a new stack of blanks is introduced. Prior to the stack being exhausted, rails extend to support the remaining blanks. Special pallets, similar to that in Figure 16-5, are usually required with this activity. This principle is not suggested for families of small parts because of difficulties in supporting blanks on both pallets and forks.

Magnetic conveyors are normally used for handling ferrous metals. Aluminum and other nonferrous materials require special consideration for handling.

Figure 16-6 shows a double-head destacker, automatically moving from one head to the other when a stack is depleted. No special pallets are required. This is an alternative principle to the short stack support, permitting the press line to stay operating when introducing a fresh stack of blanks.

In this installation, captive carts introduce stacks of blanks beneath the destacking heads and remove empty pallets. Service to and from the blanking area is provided by fork lift trucks. Either carts or pallet conveyors may be used to introduce stacks of blanks to a destacker and serve as "crane savers." The advantage of carts is that they provide greater accessibility around the press entry area.

The destacker usually contains all of the controls within its framework. Power supply and communication connection to the press are the only requirements when installed. The destacker is tested in simulated production conditions prior to being placed in position before the press. Consequently, launch time is minimal.

To reduce production cycle times of new vehicles, policies of simultaneous engineering are executed, requiring machine tool suppliers to design and build equipment long before blank specifications are finalized. Programmable destackers are designed in a range of blank sizes and theoretical blank shapes, but their flexibility and programmability easily and quickly accommodate the final proven shapes. Laser-welded blanks of multiple thicknesses also must be accommodated on destackers, further adding to the need for flexibility.

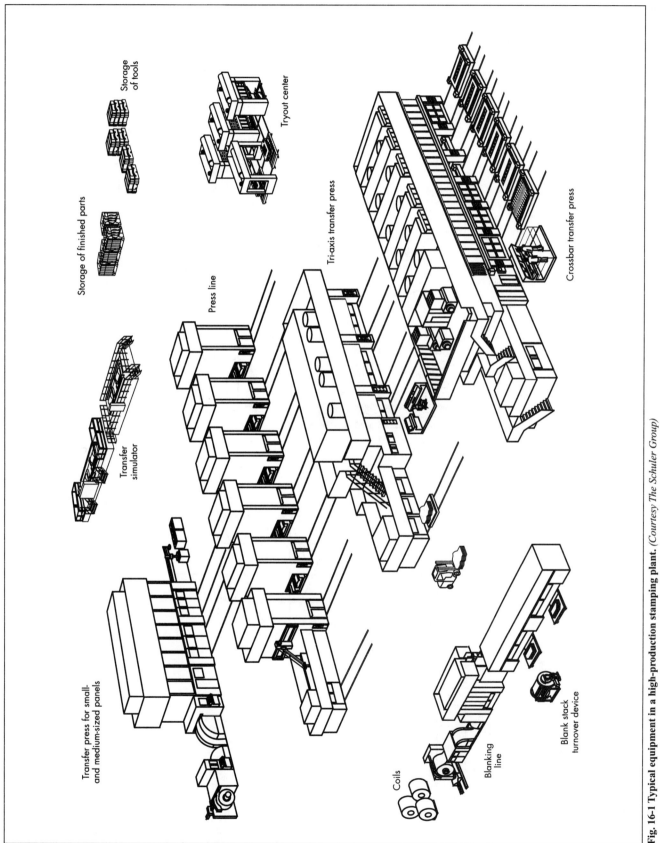

Storage of tools

Tryout center

Storage of finished parts

Tri-axis transfer press

Press line

Crossbar transfer press

Transfer simulator

Transfer press for small- and medium-sized panels

Coils

Blanking line

Blank stack turnover device

Fig. 16-1 Typical equipment in a high-production stamping plant. *(Courtesy The Schuler Group)*

CHAPTER 16   METAL FORMING

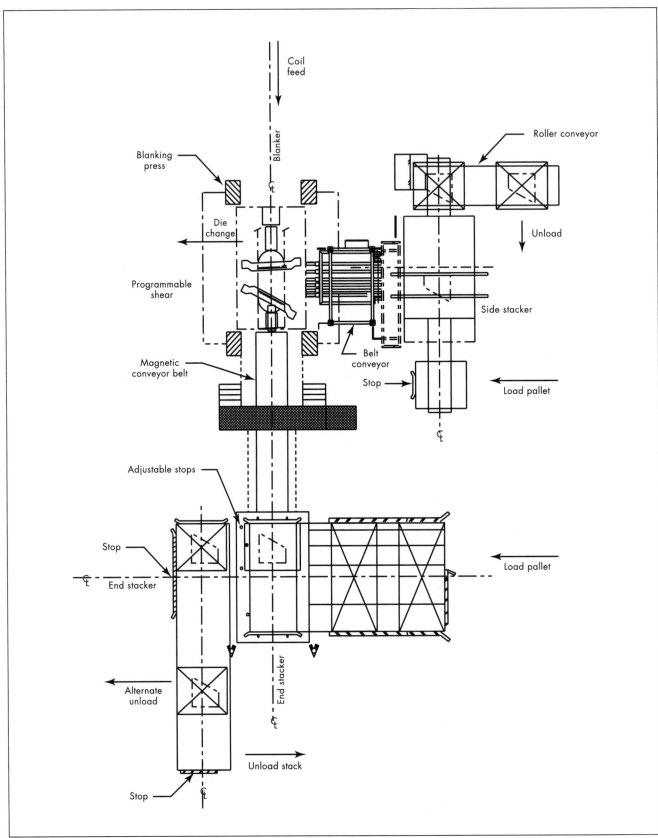

Fig. 16-2 End and side stacker for blanking press producing two blanks per press stroke. *(Courtesy DCT Automation, Inc.)*

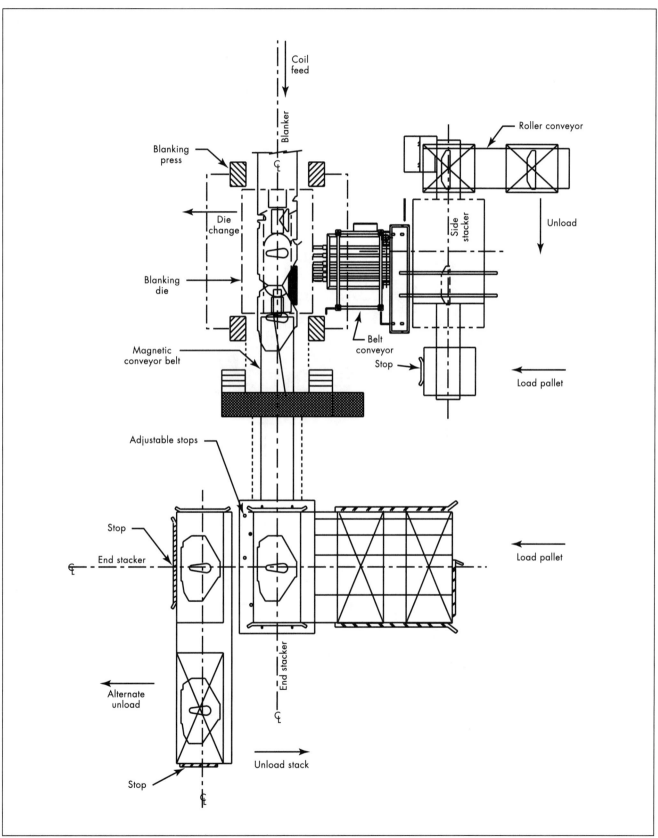

Fig. 16-3 Side stacker used for recovery of scrap from blank of large auto body panel. *(Courtesy DCT Automation, Inc.)*

CHAPTER 16   METAL FORMING

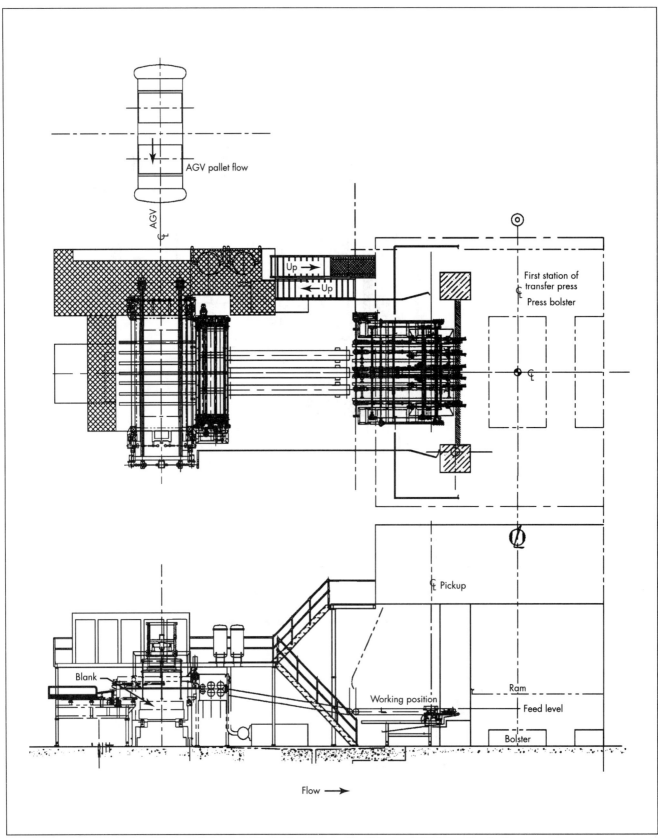

Fig. 16-4 Single-head destacker with short stack support for continuous operation. *(Courtesy DCT Automation, Inc.)*

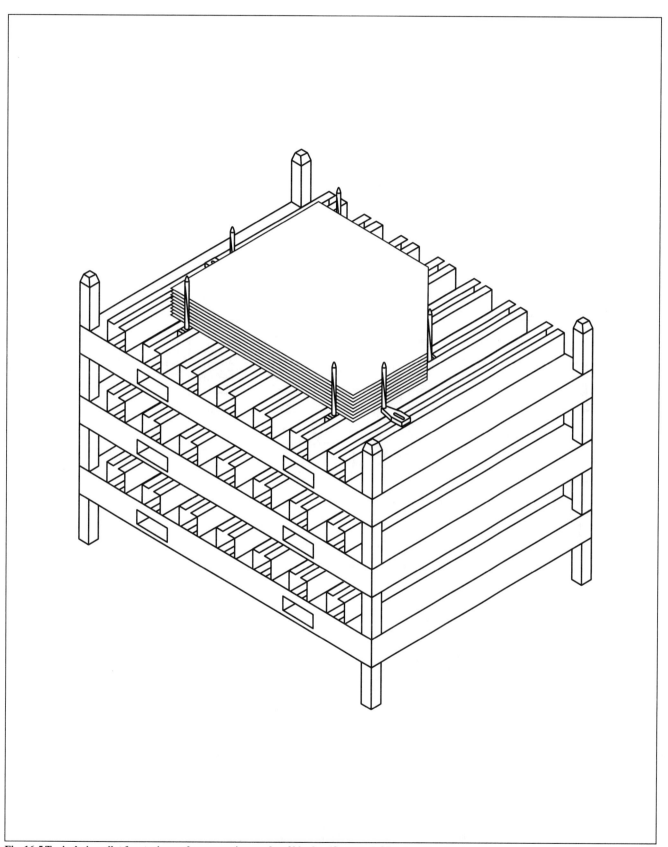

Fig. 16-5 Typical pin pallet for storing and transporting stacks of blanks. *(Courtesy DCT Automation, Inc.)*

CHAPTER 16   METAL FORMING

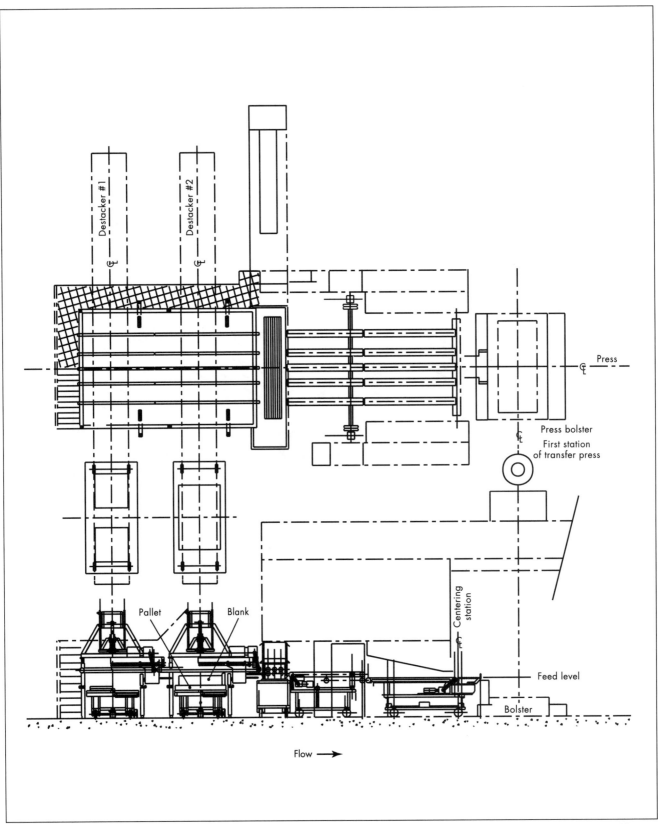

Fig. 16-6 Double-head destacker. Continuous operation is provided by activating one destacking head when the other has depleted a stack. *(Courtesy DCT Automation, Inc.)*

Figure 16-7 illustrates a destacking system servicing a high-speed transfer press capable of handling large stampings. A blanking system located adjacent to the transfer press has the primary responsibility of providing blanks when required. A buffer zone provides a supply of blanks to the blanking area during coil change or service. When open time is available, the blanking system also accommodates other requirements.

Stacks of blanks are usually stored and transported on a pallet made of wood or steel. The stacks are temporarily banded to the pallet for stability. Improved protection of the stack is possible with the use of *pin pallets* (pallets with adjustable pins to trap the stack and prevent movement during transportation). Pin pallets also ensure the position of the stack relative to the pallet profile, which is essential for automatic programmable destackers.

The "comb" profile of the pin pallet (see Figure 16-5) allows space below the stack for fork lift trucks to remove stacks if necessary. Alternatively, the space allows for the arms of a destacker with short stack support or the retrieval forks of an AS/RS.

WASHERS AND LUBRICATORS

The discerning public demands the highest quality and greatest value from products. When a purchase is considered, the appearance of an automobile, for example, is as important as its efficiency.

To obtain the ultimate paint finish on outer skin panels, it is necessary to wash blanks prior to entering the dies. This removes any particles that could cause blemishes. Such blemishes may not cause malfunctions, but would be highlighted by paint and affect the product's appeal.

Most new automated blank or coil feeding systems include washing units. They may be an integral part of a coil feeding line or destacking equipment. The washing occurs as blanks are conveyed between high-pressure nozzles that provide the necessary force to loosen and discharge dirt. During this process, material handling and control of blanks to, through, and from washers are critical to maintaining orientation and control.

Filtration systems are provided to clean and recirculate the washing solution. The necessity for careful handling of the sheet metal and environmental concerns regarding the fluids used make it essential that these units be accessible for periodic cleaning and service. The upper assembly of the unit shown in Figure 16-8 can be power-raised for inspection.

Blank lubricators operate similarly, but are used for the purpose of applying an even coating of draw compound to assist forming the more severe metal shapes.

COIL FEEDING

Whether feeding blanking presses or progressive dies, the handling of 30 tons (27,216 kg) of coiled material requires substantial, efficient equipment to uncoil, straighten, and feed accurately. The emerging trend in the automotive industry is to feed coil material directly to forming presses. Oscillating dies with alternating blank rotation is one of the many innovative ideas developed to address the issue of storing blanks.

Coil feeding for a metal forming system is preferable to blank feeding for the following reasons:

- No blanking press is required.
- Less floor space is required.
- Blank handling is eliminated.
- Blank containers are eliminated.
- Blank separation problems are avoided.
- Poor quality material will be immediately detected.

It is worth the extra time and effort to design a system that employs direct coil feeding, if it can be done without sacrificing material.

TYPES OF COIL FEEDING

The selection of coil feeding is critical to achieving the maximum potential production rate of the press and providing the flexibility to accommodate the family of dies that could be required. Of the various feeds available from many different manufacturers, there are four basic automatic types:

- Hitch feed.
- Air feed.
- Mechanical roll feed.
- Electrical roll feed.

Hitch Feeds

Of the automatic feeds, the hitch-type feed is the oldest and least expensive mechanism. With this type, the material is advanced by a wedging action between a vertically-moving blade and a horizontal slide feed. These units are best at feeding medium-weight material at relatively short progressions. Because of the low cost of some commercially-available hitch feeds, they are often attached directly to a die where the setup can be permanent.

Air Feeds

Because of the simplicity of air and its availability in press rooms, the air-operated punch press feed is probably the most versatile and widely-used unit. It represents a cost basis somewhere between the hitch feed and the roll feed and even has the capability of handling very thin and compressible materials. The air feed is not limited to use in a punch press, but can be mounted on special machines in almost any position and actuated by either mechanical, electrical, or air signals. A typical self-contained unit is illustrated in Figure 16-9.

Adaptability. Air feeds offer the utility of use with a wide variety of presses and machines. Their ease of installation and removal expands their versatility because they can be quickly changed from one die set to another. Often the actuating bracket can be left on the die and the feed can be moved from one job to another within a few minutes. The many available methods of actuation means that air feeds are quite simple to use on impact presses, electric presses, hydraulic presses, wire forming machines, multislide machines, and special machines that bear little relationship to an actual press.

Air feed actuation. There are two basic methods for air feed actuation: internal and external. Internal actuation is by means of a mechanical valve built into the feed. This is normally used with presses having an average stroke and operating under normal conditions. It is the simplest and preferred method of actuation.

If the press stroke is extremely short or long, or if special conditions exist, external actuation may be necessary. External actuation consists of either electric or air actuation, in which the mechanical valve is replaced with an electric or air valve mounted as close as possible to the feed. This external valve must be triggered by a microswitch or air pilot valve mounted to allow operation by a rotary cam on the crankshaft or a linear cam on the ram of the press. This method is most useful on special machines where a slide may not be adjacent to the feed, or in circumstances where long or short stroke presses are being used. A general reference is to allow 50% of the cycle for feeding and 50% for retraction.

CHAPTER 16 METAL FORMING

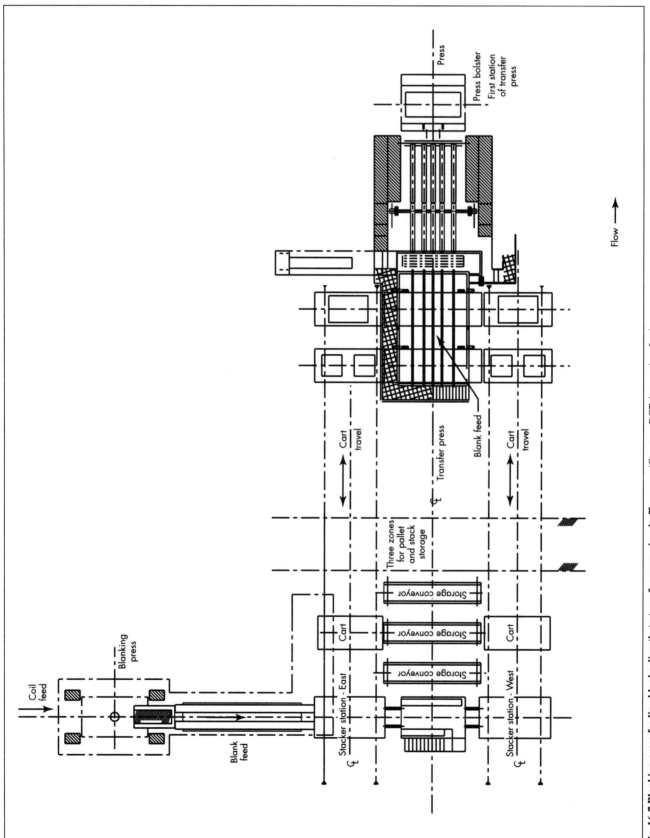

Fig. 16-7 Blanking press feeding blanks directly to transfer press via a buffer zone. *(Courtesy DCT Automation, Inc.)*

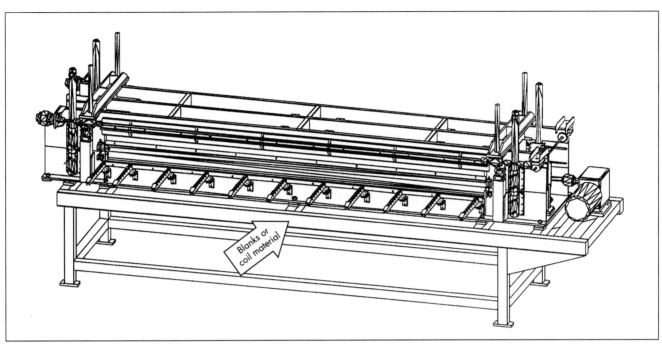

Fig. 16-8 Washing system to clean blanks prior to forming. *(Courtesy DCT Automation, Inc.)*

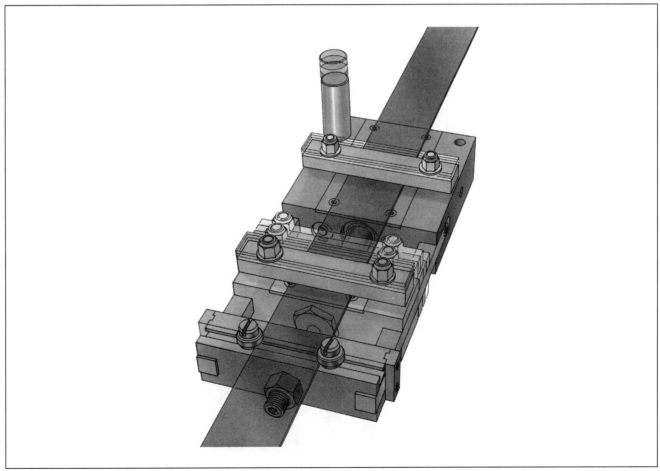

Fig. 16-9 Air-actuated coil feeder. *(Courtesy RapidAir Corp.)*

CHAPTER 16   METAL FORMING

Air circuits. To use machinery effectively, operating principles and functions must be thoroughly understood. Air feeds usually appear complicated because the valve and moving parts are inside of the unit, invisible to view. A few simple principles should be understood to effectively utilize air feed equipment.

The air feed has two separate air circuits. The first is controlled by the main valve, which operates both sets of clamps. The stationary clamp prevents friction of the slide block from dragging the material backward as the feed retracts for a new progression. The movable clamp provides the greatest force to grip and push the material into the die. The clamp portion of the circuit is designed to function sequentially. When the main control valve is depressed, the air exhausts from the clamp circuit. As the pressure falls, the stationary clamp grips the material just before the movable clamp releases. As the main valve elevates, the action reverses and the movable clamp grips the material just before the stationary clamp opens. The clamps move in sequence by a balance between the areas as determined by the designer of the feed.

Motion can be added to the cycle by incorporating a pressure-sensing valve to the circuit. This auxiliary- or pilot-operated valve allows a flow of air into or out of one side of the piston. The area of the pilot-operated valve is adjusted so that the feeding cycle takes place at the appropriate time.

This general principle allows great flexibility in feeding because of the two separate circuits ensuring that the clamping cycle takes place before the feeding cycle. It also helps to separate the two air circuits so that the pressures necessary for clamping are not greatly reduced by the airflow necessary to feed.

Mechanical Roll Feed

A popular type of permanently-mounted equipment is the roll feed. In this unit, the material is advanced by the pressure of two opposed rollers, one or both of which is driven from the crankshaft of the press. These units are generally best for feeding rigid materials of moderate to heavy thickness. Thinner materials can often be handled by using a double roll-feed combination to push and pull the material. In this arrangement, a set of feeding rollers is attached to each side of a press and synchronized by a connecting link. Roll and mechanical slide feeds generally offer the longest life and highest speeds available today, but require a permanent installation.

The rotating motion of the press crankshaft may be used to generate a reciprocating feed motion with fixed timing (180° feed and 180° idle) and adjustable indexing distance.

Alternatively, the rotary motion of the press crankshaft generates rotary motion of cams for increased flexibility of timing. Cams are selected to increase the 180° feed cycle, which permits either a reduction in the feeding coil speed or an increase in the press speed.

Electrical Roll Feed

Improvements in servomotor control, deriving from the need for greater flexibility in metal stamping operations, have accelerated the applications of electronic roll feeds. The principle of operation is illustrated in Figure 16-10. A brushless AC servomotor provides digital control over the feed rolls. Resolver position feedback constantly compensates for any error in motor speed, position, or torque.

By combining advanced electrical controls with standard "user-friendly" operating programs, the roll feed becomes an intelligent accessory without any mechanical interlock to the press, thus providing the flexibility to operate independently of the press. This is particularly useful during die tryout. With little or no programming experience, an operator can easily follow procedures displayed on the key pad of the control console.

Servocontrolled roll feeds have three basic operating modes: manual/jog, job setup, and automatic. Acceleration and deceleration of the rolls also can be programmed for each system.

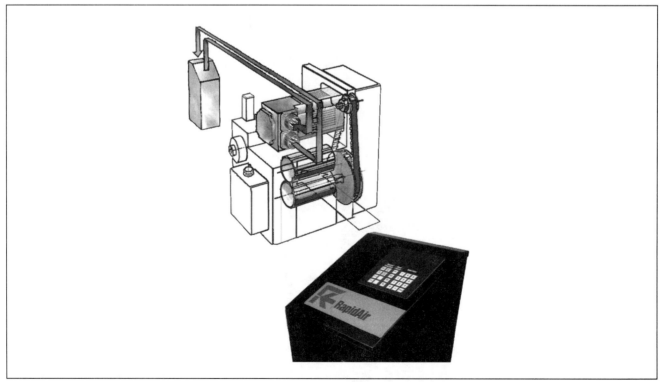

Fig. 16-10 Servomotor-driven coil feeder with controls. *(Courtesy RapidAir Corp.)*

The feed rolls act as powered pinch rolls during setup. Material can be either incrementally moved forward, reversed at slow rates, or jogged to verify precise positioning before the start of continuous operation.

Servomotor feed controls usually include job storage and recall, and self-diagnostic fault capabilities. Any previous job setup can be reviewed prior to production. After a job is programmed, a two-digit entry is all that is required to either store it in memory or recall it for production review or revision. Operating programs include both batch and cumulative counting capabilities.

A computer interface can provide a communication link to virtually any press control and monitoring system. A centralized operator interface (line monitor) can be integrated with the roll feed (and any other supporting equipment having a compatible interface) to allow parameters to be programmed from a remote station.

Electrical cable connections between the servoroll feed and the control console enable the self-contained roll feed to be located in the most suitable position for the press and dies, and with the control console positioned for operator convenience. Programs are established to optimally feed coil material to any die and consider speed and timing relationship to the press.

ACCURACY CONTROL

The two principal reasons for using automatic press feeds are to improve production and provide uniformly accurate progressions. All press feeds have accuracy limitations. Some adapt more easily to these limitations, but generally accuracy can be improved in any feed through the use of automation.

The most common type of accuracy control is that using *pilots*. A hole, generally round, is pierced into the material and, in a subsequent station, a punch with a rounded nose is inserted into the material, aligning it in the proper position. Pilots can be used for both axial and lateral control. To avoid uncorrectable axial errors, it is best for the pilot to engage the material in the station immediately following the piercing operation. When using a pilot with an automatic feed, it is common to feed the material slightly short and allow the pilot to pull the material into the proper position. Thus, any feeding device should have the capability of allowing material to be pulled through the feed with just a slight amount of force. Pilots work well on relatively rigid material, but performance drops considerably when trying to feed thin and compressible materials.

Perhaps the simplest means of controlling accuracy is to rely on the feed itself. Proper attention must be given to the control of various factors that affect accuracy, but with good conditions, repeatability much greater than ±0.001 in. (±0.03 mm) can be achieved.

HIGH-SPEED FEEDING

High-speed feeding is becoming increasingly popular since it is the most obvious and attractive way to shorten cycle time and reduce part costs. Air feeds are capable of speeds up to approximately 500 strokes per minute (spm) at a 0.5-in. (13-mm) progression. Beyond this, it is best to rely on the mechanical advantage of a roll feed or one of the specialized high-speed feeds available. These units are usually costly and should be considered as part of a total package with a reliable, well-built, high-speed press. The problems differ, but for high production the advantages can be rewarding.

FEEDING TECHNIQUES

Some unique ideas have been employed for feeding coil into transfer dies. A frequent requirement is a part manufactured from a trapezoidal blank. Normally, such a blank is produced by an oscillating shear. This is an effective method of obtaining good material utilization. Oscillating shears are generally used with special-purpose presses, with the angle of the shear adjusted to suit the various trapezoidal profiles. Despite the desirable features of this method, some sort of feeding device is required to feed the blanks to the transfer die.

If the required volume of a particular blank profile is sufficient, a special double shear is built as shown in Figure 16-11. Note in this example, that two blanks per press stroke are produced. However, a blank feeder is again required.

It is possible to combine the primary consideration of material utilization and the axiom that "coil feeding is simpler" (see Fig. 16-12). The coil is fed directly to a transfer press, where an oscillating shear produces the trapezoidal blank. A simple rotary table indexes 180° for every other (second) part, so that the fingers of the transfer press receive each part positioned the same way.

Several blank profiles can be generated to produce near net-shape blanks with additional cost savings by:

- Reducing scrap.
- Minimizing die setup time.
- Utilizing economical coil widths.
- Minimizing additional tool costs.

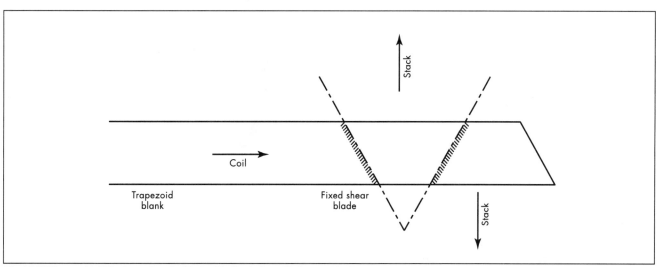

Fig. 16-11 Trapezoidal blank produced with double fixed-shear blade, two blanks per press stroke. *(Courtesy DCT Automation, Inc.)*

CHAPTER 16   METAL FORMING

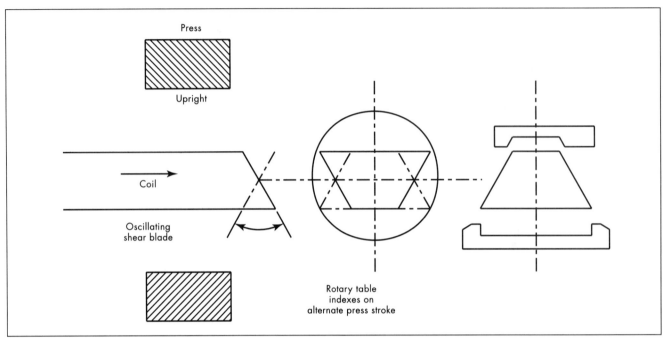

Fig. 16-12 Trapezoidal blank produced with single alternating shear blade, fed directly to transfer press, with rotary table indexing on alternate press strokes to provide the required blank orientation. *(Courtesy DCT Automation, Inc.)*

- Increasing production rates.
- Optimizing productivity.
- Reducing operator work load.

A programmable, oscillating shear die (with a single blade) can be employed on any blanking press. A single, pivoting, straight-cut shear oscillates with each press stroke to produce a rectangular or trapezoidal-shaped blank. Dual-blade shear dies can produce two trapezoidal or rectangular-shaped blanks with each press stroke. Within minutes, two pivoting subdies are positioned to produce any blank size or shape within the limitation of the feeding system.

Chevron-shaped blanks can be produced on dies with two or three connected subdies rotated to programmable positions.

In another shear application, a unique "zee" shear die can cut two rectangular-shaped blanks with each press stroke. The shear blades in this case are adjustable for various pitches of coil.

Other shearing tools, options, and accessories include:

- A three-out blank shuttle tool that punches a variety of blank diameters with one insert. A master die set shuttles across the coil to predetermined positions to produce round blanks forming a three-out circle pattern.
- Variable-gage shears that cut many metal thicknesses by adjusting the gap clearance between the upper and lower trim steels.
- Blank eject conveyors for each tool that usually include belt conveyors with magnetic beds.
- A bump-die feature that requires no clamping of the upper shoe to the ram of the press during operation. This reduces die set time and maximizes run speeds, depending on tool type.
- A bow tie shear that reduces overall die height and press stroke travel while promoting self-centering by shearing from both edges toward the center.

A basic unit to direct coil material to any type of metal forming die is the combination feeder and straightener shown in Figure 16-13. Straighteners are simple to adjust, easy to load, and ensure pre-

Fig. 16-13 Combination roll feeder and coil straightener. *(Courtesy Sesco Corp.)*

dictable flatness without extensive operator training. The entry pinch rolls open to capture irregular or deformed ends of incoming coils. The straightening rolls are mechanically amplified to provide a secure grip of the coil, thus ensuring precise feed increments.

Handling the coil itself requires a reel (Figure 16-14) feeding the inside up or outside up, depending on requirements. An overhead loop press feed system conserves floor space without sacrificing output speed and production requirements.

An expanding mandrel at the center of the reel (Fig. 16-14) securely grips the inside diameter of the coil. To reduce the time to load new coils, two or three mandrels may be mounted on a central column. The load platform may be a cart (or carts) to preload coils of different widths.

An alternative method of supporting the coil is by way of a cradle. This system is recommended for use with heavier-gage materials.

A coil-to-coil welding station enables continuous stampings without threading each leading edge of new coils through the press and dies. Substantial press uptime is achieved and productivity is improved by avoiding the need to stop the press when the end of the coil is reached.

Fig. 16-14 Mandrel support of coil showing expanding arms. *(Courtesy Sesco Corp.)*

IN-PRESS TRANSFER SYSTEMS

Transfer mechanisms (material handling devices), built as integral units of the press, traditionally have been driven by the rotary motion of the crankshaft. Specially-designed cams generate the required movement in mechanical synchronization with the vertical moving ram of the press. Movements of the transfer equipment are usually two- or three-dimensional. Mechanical fingers or air-oper-

ated gripper jaws hold the stamping rigidly as it is moved from one die station to the next.

Developments in electrical servodriven transfer mechanisms have proven effective in providing additional flexibility, without fear of damage caused by malfunction. The advantage is that the transfer mechanism can be moved independently of the press, a valuable feature during die tryout. Advocates of the mechanical drive for the transferring mechanism claim closer synchronization with the dies and, consequently, increased operating speeds.

The possibility of a fourth axis (a wrist action) to either rotate or invert a stamping to favor die conditions is an additional benefit.

The introduction of larger stampings demanded a new motion for the material handling mechanism of the transfer press. Called a *crossbar transfer,* the mechanism for this motion features a series of vacuum cups to support the entire length of the panel during its motion from one die station to the next.

While the basic design of the press structure itself has remained rather constant over the past 20 years, the designs of specific components within the press have changed very rapidly. These changes have resulted in increased productivity of quality stampings.

Transfer presses are considered commonplace and are in widespread use throughout the metal forming industry. This is particularly true in the auto industry where high-volume sheet metal stamping is key to successful production. These presses are assumed to be a primary tool of stamping plants.

Technology advances in transfer presses are occurring rapidly in the area of part flow through the machine. Global competition demands a transfer press that is fast, easy to maintain, and reliable. It must be designed and installed quickly, and produce more quality parts than those in the past. To accomplish this, a transfer press must do as the name implies, faithfully and efficiently move metal throughout the die set. It is control of the stamping (material handling) that governs production rates. The more stable and repeatable the transfer, the closer the press can be run to the limits of the material and part characteristics.

NEW TECHNOLOGY ADVANTAGES

One study compared the operating costs and productive output of one new transfer press to two refurbished tandem press lines.[1] In it, the producer invested in a comprehensive rebuild of older straight-side mechanical presses. The tandem presses were retrofitted with modern electronic controls, new hydraulic and pneumatic systems, and between-press automation, including die handling systems. For purpose of comparison, the presses were examined while running automotive door outer panels. The refurbished tandem lines produced one part every stroke while the transfer press was able to stamp two parts per stroke. Key aspects evaluated were operating costs and productive output, including die change time (see Fig. 16-15). Operating costs included direct labor, utilities, and an assessment of floor space. Part yield was based on the total available hours for machine operation minus a 14% utilization factor and net of die change time. Only five die changes were to occur per week.

The data demonstrated that a single transfer press is more productive, at less cost, than two tandem press lines when running the same part. The findings show the transfer press capable of producing at almost twice the rate of the tandem lines, with operating costs less than half that of the dual tandem lines. The capital invested was roughly equivalent for refurbishing two tandem lines versus purchasing a single, suitably-equipped transfer press.

TRANSFER PRESS SIZE CLASSIFICATION

The stamping industry generally classifies the sizes of transfer presses as *A*, *B*, and *C*.

CHAPTER 16 METAL FORMING

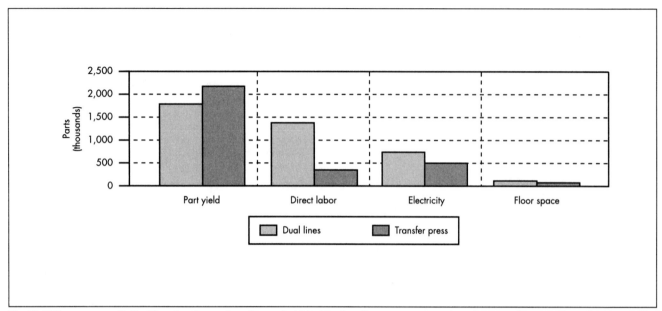

Fig. 16-15 Summary results for 50 weeks of operation of two refurbished tandem lines versus one new transfer press. *(Courtesy Verson Division of Allied Products Corp.)*

Unlike tandem line presses in which the larger die dimension is considered to be in the right-to-left direction of the press, the larger dimension on transfer presses is in the front-to-back dimension (see Fig. 16-16). In both cases, the direction of material flow is in the left-to-right direction.

A-size transfer presses are the largest transfer presses manufactured today. These presses contain dies ranging in size from 156-180 in. (396-457 cm) in the front-to-back dimension, to 96-108 in. (244-274 cm) in the left-to-right direction. This press size generally contains four to six die stations located in presses containing two, three, four, five, or six slides. *A*-size transfer presses are used strictly by the major automotive producers. *A*+ presses are now under construction.

B-size presses typically contain dies ranging from 120-144 in. (305-366 cm) in the front-to-back dimension, to 72-90 in. (183-229 cm) in the left-to-right direction. Like *A* presses, they contain four, five, or six stations, but are generally designed with two or three slides. *B*-size presses are used by the major automotive producers and a few automotive contract stamping companies.

C-size is the dominant size of transfer press used by manufacturers. These presses typically have dies ranging in size from 84-108 in. (213-274 cm) in the front-to-back dimension, to 36-60 in. (91-152 cm) in the left-to-right direction. They contain anywhere from four to eight workstations located under one slide. *C*-size transfer presses are used by many industries, for automotive, appliance, and general stamping.

Table 16-1 lists the typical stampings produced by the three press sizes, the speed range of each system, and an approximate price of the transfer press system for each press classification.

The central objective of transfer presses in today's business environment is maximum quality part output. This applies whether the press is *A*-size, used by a major automotive producer, or a small *C*-size transfer, used by a general contract stamper.

TRANSFER FEED TECHNOLOGY

A *transfer feed* is a material handling device, operating much like a walking beam, that moves stampings through a progression of forming-trimming-piercing operations. Each die or operation in the die set is housed within the same press, hence the term *transfer press*. Transfer feed rails run the entire length of the die space. They are the main structural component upon which the stamping handling devices are attached.

Evolution of the Transfer Feed

The first transfer feeds were developed in the late 1930s. They were mechanically driven off the main press drive using a power takeoff shaft and were designed for the production of stampings that required numerous operations. These systems were usually dedicated to forming a single component, such as pulley rims, wheel covers, and compressor housings.

Initial mechanical transfer feeds were horizontal two-axis types, including clamp and transfer motions. These motions worked well for shallow parts; when necessary, a short lift motion was incorporated using articulating fingers. As deeper and irregularly-shaped parts were introduced into transfer press technology, the necessity of adding a lift motion was created. This third motion allowed raising the part over lower die components, such as binder rings and cam-actuated mechanisms, and provided accurate position at the end of the transfer cycle.

As technology advanced and larger parts were produced on transfer presses, the stroke lengths of each motion increased accordingly. Further, the introduction of Just-in-Time (JIT) manufacturing necessitated the reduction of stamping lot sizes and the time necessary to change dies from one stamping to the next.

Electronic transfer feed (ETF) technology was introduced in the early 1980s. Large stampings historically produced on tandem press lines were now produced on transfer presses at a much higher rate and in very small lot sizes.

Three classifications of transfer feeds operating in stamping plants include mechanical feeds, electronic feeds, and combination feeds (see Fig. 16-17). Mechanical feeds accomplish the task of moving the stamping through the die set by means of direct mechanical connection to the press drive. A power takeoff from the crown transfers energy from the top of the press to below floor level. Large

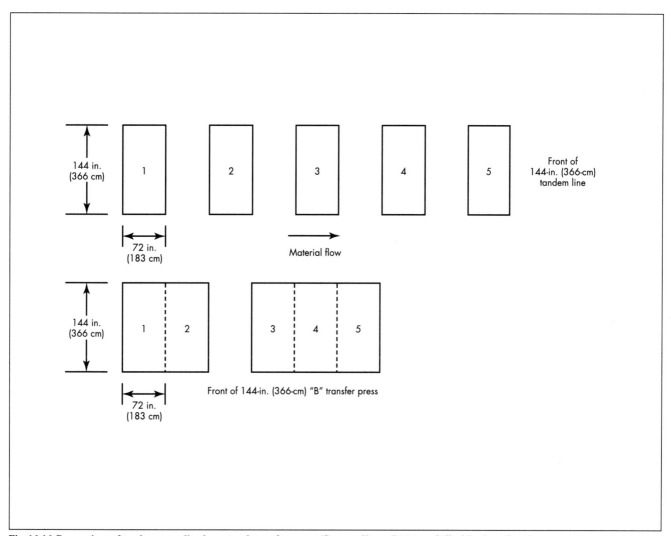

Fig. 16-16 Comparison of tandem press line layout and transfer press. *(Courtesy Verson Division of Allied Products Corp.)*

TABLE 16-1
Transfer Press Size Classifications

Press Classification	Typical Stampings	Speed Range (spm)	Price Range
A	Full doors—two per stroke Side apertures Hood outer Box side outer	7-16	$20 million+
B	Full doors Half door outer—two per stroke Half door inner —two per stroke Hood outer Hood inner	8-20	$15-25 million
C	Gas tanks Hinge pillars Washer tops Dryer tops	12-30	$2-10 million

(Courtesy Verson Division of Allied Products Corp.)

CHAPTER 16   METAL FORMING

mechanical cams are driven by followers attached to the transfer feed unit. As the press drive progresses through the stroke, the mechanical feed motion occurs as prescribed by the configuration of the rotating cams.

ETFs use servomotors instead of a power takeoff. Independent servomotors connected to the feed through gear boxes and drive shafts operate under computer control to effect motion. Coordination with the press is done through electronic signals between the press and feed control. Unlike mechanical feeds, the motion path is defined by a computer program. The ETF's motion can be made to look identical to a mechanical feed or refined to optimize travel paths for a specific part. Combination feeds use mechanical motions in some areas of travel and electronic motions in others.

Several formats of transfer motion are available. *Tri-axis feeds*, as the name implies, use three distinct motions to transfer stampings. Mechanical fingers attached to the front and back transfer rails handle the stamping between operations. A clamp motion moves the fingers into the die cavity so that the stamping can be picked up and moved out of the die. The lift motion removes the stamping from the die and allows it to clear the lower die section. The transfer motion advances the stamping to the next die in sequence. The process then reverses, with the stamping lowered onto the bottom die section and the clamp motion retracting the fingers from the die. Once retracted, the transfer motion returns the feed to the downstream die while the slide is in downward motion and the die is closed. Tri-axis feeds can be either mechanical or electronic (see Fig. 16-18).

Crossbar feeds operate on an entirely different timing diagram than tri-axis feeds. Rigid bars, which travel in a two-axis vertical mode, are suspended between the front and back feed rails. The bars straddle the die space. Outriggers and suction cups are connected to the bar according to stamping geometry. These devices attach to the stamping to allow transfer motion to the upstream die. A lift motion lowers the crossbar into the die cavity so the part can be attached. It then raises the stamping out of the die. The transfer motion moves the part into the next die in sequence. The lift motion lowers the crossbar (with stamping attached) into the die for deposit. The transfer motion then moves the bar out of the die and into a neutral position between upstream and downstream dies. Re-ori-

entation of the stamping can now occur, if required. Only at this time can the slide complete its downward motion and the die close. Since no clamping motion occurs, all part transfer and return must take place while the die is open. For this reason, crossbar feeds must run at higher velocities and accomplish part transfer faster than tri-axis feeds (see Fig. 16-19).

Advances in Transfer Feeds

A notable recent advance in transfer feeds combines both crossbar and tri-axis into a single transfer press, allowing part production using its optimum forming process. Since all motions are programmable, the crossbar mode of operation can be incorporated into the basic ETF with minor mechanical modifications. Simply modifying the motion path of the feed allows the use of either crossbar or tri-axis mode. This is not practical with mechanical feeds, owing to the restrictions inherent with this classification of transfer feed.

Multiple mode tri-axis and crossbar feeds (for large stamping presses) are available in electronic transfer form only. These transfer feeds are a hybrid that combines both formats of transfer motion in one press. One set of transfer feed rails is configured with fingers for tri-axis transfer. A second set of rails is configured with crossbars. The transformation from one format to the other occurs during die change. Computer-controlled motion paths and timing diagrams are revised, as are part programs. Front and back feed rails are interchanged and electrical and pneumatic connections are made. Total hit-to-hit changeover occurs in less than five minutes.

Another advance in transfer feed format is *real-time orientation*, or *dynamic orientation*. Large crossbar transfer presses form stampings which previously were done by tandem press lines. When forming large stampings, it is often necessary to change the part orientation from one station to the next. Traditional crossbar presses accomplish this through the use of idle stations between each working station. These idle stations orient the part before pickup for deposit in the next working station.

A new format for transfer stamping is exclusively electronic and uses a crossbar base of motions with the expanded versatility to orient stampings while the transfer occurs. These real-time orientation systems contrast with other means of orientation. Nonreal-time

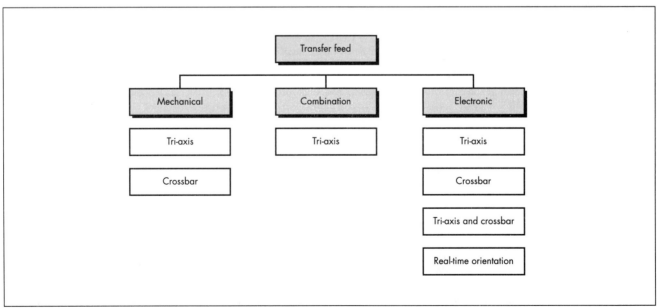

Fig. 16-17 Transfer feed family tree. *(Courtesy Verson Division of Allied Products Corp.)*

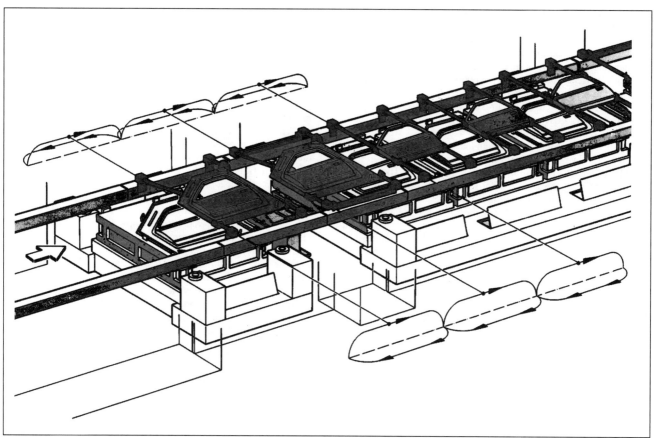

Fig. 16-18 Tri-axis feed primary motion. *(Courtesy The Schuler Group)*

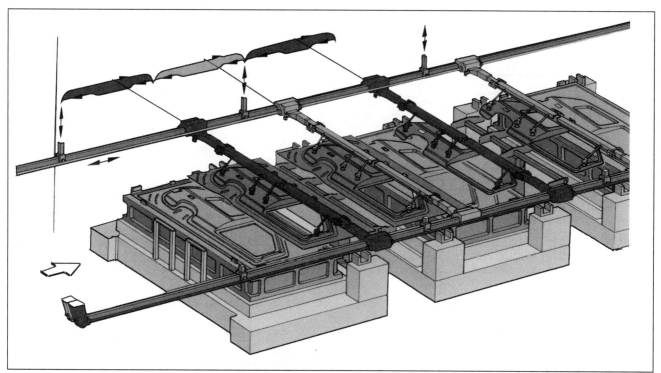

Fig. 16-19 Crossbar feed motion path. *(Courtesy The Schuler Group)*

CHAPTER 16   METAL FORMING

approaches introduce idle stations located between dies or force ram motion to stop while orientation takes place. Real-time orientation is dynamic in the sense that stamping orientation occurs while the part transfers. Idle stations and redundant handling are eliminated. As many as eight degrees of freedom of motion are available to accomplish orientation. All motions are done via servomotors operating under a programmable logic controller (PLC) or computer control. Like conventional ETFs, press synchronization is ensured through auxiliary drive systems and redundant fault detection configurations (see Fig. 16-20).

The real-time system differs from a conventional crossbar system in several ways. First, conventional crossbar systems are not capable of part re-orientation because the bars are affixed to the rails. Second, conventional crossbar systems use one bar between each die—the real-time system uses two bars between each die. Because added motion is available on the rails, the two-bar approach enables spreading the bars apart while handling a stamping, and collapsing together while in the neutral position between dies. The result is greater stability during part transfer and minimal space required while awaiting the next transfer routine. This serves to increase the rate at which a stamping is transferred and reduces the footprint of the press and the associated cost of the machine.

MATERIAL HANDLING CONSIDERATIONS

The tri-axis mode of operation is generally used when producing long, narrow, or rigid stampings or when part geometry allows positive positioning when nested onto locator or form references. The geometry of these stampings allows for pickup at their front and rear edges using shovels or grippers mounted on each transfer

rail. The stamping must be stable enough to be picked up at its outer edges without sagging or tipping.

It is always desirable to keep clamp and lift strokes to a minimum for higher production rates. The clamp motion is often started while the upper die is still ascending. The sooner the stamping can be clamped and lifted out of die, the sooner it can be transferred to the next die station. If these fundamental motions can be accomplished with time to spare, the press speed can be increased, thus allowing higher production rates.

When using the tri-axis mode, a portion of the lower clamp and unclamp strokes and all of the transfer return stroke occur while the dies are closed. The only motions necessary during die open time are those to finish clamping, lift the part, transfer to the next station, and unclamp to clear the die. If a given part can be processed only as one part per stroke (one-out production), it can be processed faster using tri-axis mode than with crossbar mode. However, if more than one part can be produced per stroke (two- or more-out production), crossbar mode should be considered. One added consideration is stamping geometry: if the geometry of the part does not lend itself to being picked up at its outer edges in tri-axis mode, crossbar mode offers a better alternative (see Fig. 16-21).

Crossbar mode transfers the part from one station to the next using only lift and transfer motions. The stamping is picked up by suction cups mounted on crossbars that hang over the die space from the front feed rail to the rear feed rail. This mode of operation is ideal for producing large stampings that would tend to sag if picked up at the outside edges, preventing tri-axis transfer. In addition, crossbar mode is suited for processing two or more parts per stroke, using either single blanks or double unattached blanks. Because the cross-

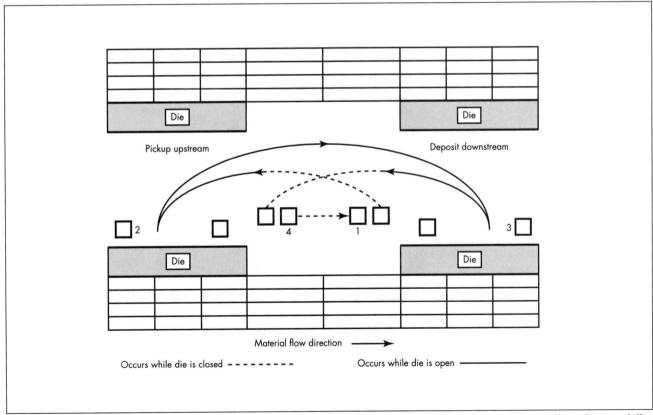

Fig. 16-20 Real-time transfer system sequence of operation and motion path using tow bars between each die station. *(Courtesy Verson Division of Allied Products Corp.)*

bar motion can be completed only while the dies are open, it cannot produce parts at cycle rates as high as the tri-axis mode. In crossbar format, the feed is held motionless at the bottom of the stroke. However, because of its ability to transfer two unattached parts using vacuum cups, crossbar mode can produce more parts per minute than tri-axis, while operating at a slower cycle rate. For example, in one installation, a floor pan is produced at 12 strokes per minute using tri-axis mode. Maximum attainable part yield in this case is 12 parts per minute. By comparison, automotive door outer panels are produced two at a time using crossbar mode at the rate of nine strokes per minute. The derived maximum yield is increased to 18 parts per minute, although the press runs at a slower speed. In this case, the determining factor as to which part is to run under a given transfer format is governed by the size of the stamping.

Because crossbar feeds require clearance space between each die for the crossbars when the dies are closed, the crossbar mode is best suited for transfer strokes of 60 in. (152 cm) or more. Approximately 30% of the transfer pitch is required for crossbar clearance. In the case of a 60-in. (152-cm) pitch machine, 18 in. (46 cm) would be needed for crossbar clearance, leaving a maximum of 42 in. (107 cm) for dies. The part that can be produced within a 42-in. (107 cm) die space would be rather narrow (about 14-18 in. [36-46 cm]). For this reason, press systems with only a crossbar feed are normally quite large and are used for forming large stampings such as automobile hoods, roofs, doors, and apertures.

Factors that Affect Productivity

While there are numerous factors that influence the productivity of a transfer press system, there are several that are common across many part shapes. Die change time is one. The term *hit-to-hit* refers to the total time required to change over from the production of a given part to the production of another part. Global competition mandates an average hit-to-hit changeover time of less than five minutes. This can be achieved if modern equipment is used, proper training is provided, and teamwork among workers associated with the operation is optimized.

Part stability, or the readiness of a part to be picked up and transferred, can have a major impact on how fast a system will operate. If the tooling is not designed properly or the cushion system used does not have dampening features, the part will often bounce upon return to top-of-stroke position. Consequently, the transfer feed must wait for the part to settle before pickup and transfer. This delay can result in loss of productive capacity.

Another factor is scrap disposal. Many parts shed large quantities of scrap at various stations. Transfer presses are provided with scrap chutes to funnel scrap to a central conveyor system located

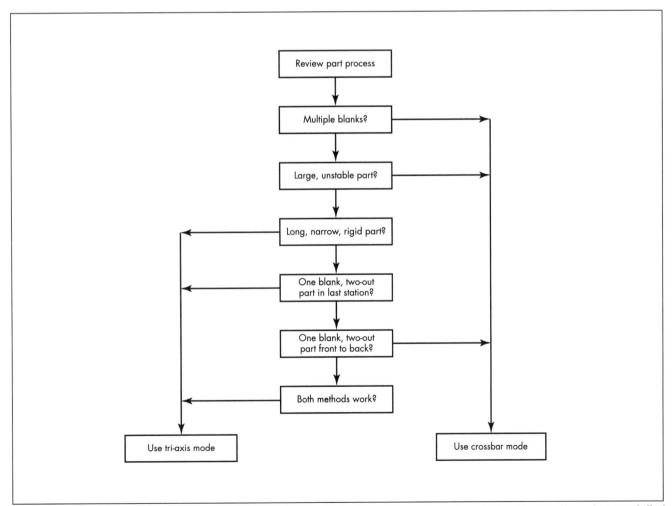

Fig. 16-21 Evaluation process for determining the most effective transfer feed format to use for part production. *(Courtesy Verson Division of Allied Products Corp.)*

CHAPTER 16   METAL FORMING

beneath the press. However, the tooling itself contains deflectors that funnel the scrap to the press scrap chutes located through the moving bolsters, or on the front and rear of the die space. It is imperative that the room allowed and the angle of the deflectors be designed to permit free fall of scrap without material getting trapped. Manually going into the press to break loose scrap buildup often leads to excessive downtime.

Also affecting the overall speed of the system is the level of ease or difficulty of stacking or racking the finished parts as they come off the press. Large transfer presses are capable of stamping multiple parts at speeds exceeding 16 strokes per minute, which necessitates racking 32 or more parts per minute. While automatic racking systems are available, most racking is still done manually. This often results in the system being slowed to accommodate part racking.

Large transfer presses continue to dominate the capital equipment purchases in the large press market. Almost all major automobile manufacturers and many appliance and subcontract stampers are replacing old, less efficient tandem lines with high-output transfer presses. However, it is important that all aspects of the system be thoroughly reviewed prior to the actual purchase to ensure that the system will actually function as planned, and the user will realize the maximum benefit of the investment.

As more sophisticated equipment becomes essential to being internationally competitive, it becomes equally important to provide the technical support to utilize and maintain the manufacturing and material handling equipment. A comparison between the time-motion diagrams of a three-axis transfer movement and crossbar transfer system emphasizes this need (see Figs. 16-22 and 16-23).

Optimized Movement Sequences

The power required for the gripper rail movement could be either electronic or mechanical, transmitted directly from the press drive via cams and cam levers to the rails. Advocates of the mechanical drive claim that the transfer is thus synchronized with the press drive system and is therefore more precisely reproducible. A special computer program optimizes the motion curve of the transfer movements pertaining to mass and acceleration so that the shortest possible cycle times and extremely smooth running are ensured for all stroking rates.

FLEXIBLE UNIVERSAL STATIONS

With the aid of universal stations between the uprights (an alternative arrangement to real-time orientation), it is possible to achieve an optimum degree of production flexibility. Program control of up to five axes allows movement of parts into the ideal position for subsequent operations, thus reducing cost and the likelihood of die malfunctions.

The universal stations also allow the crossbars to assume an asymmetrical parking position during die closure. This means a reduction in the transfer length and, consequently, an increase in the production stroke rate without higher forces during part acceleration. The motion paths and acceleration values are calculated after the part family has been defined. At the idle station, the stamping is placed on a fixture, and the part is manipulated to establish a revised attitude while the die is closed. The transfer feed then picks up the adjusted stamping and moves it to the next operation. The orientation is done in a static state at dedicated stations within the press.

PRESS CONSTRUCTION

A typical transfer press with two synchronized rams and real-time orientation crossbar transfer is illustrated in Figure 16-24.

A typical transfer press with multiple rams (one for each die station) with idle stations in between is shown in Figure 16-25.

The press concept in which every station is equipped with a separate slide offers certain advantages over slides that service several dies. For example, each slide, and therefore each die station, can be individually adjusted as to height, pressing force, and response force of the overload system. The slide is generally subjected to on-center loads, as the individual die stations do not influence each other. Forces are absorbed by the four-point suspension with minimal tilt of the slide.

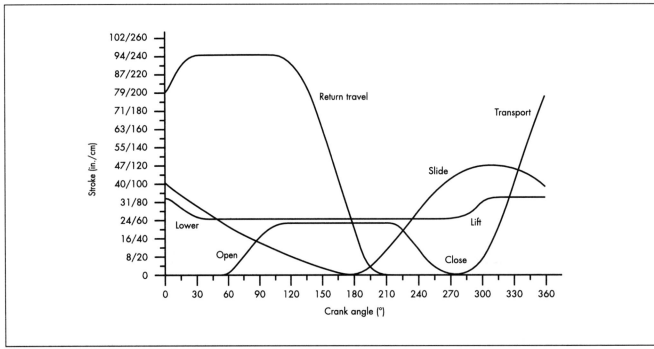

Fig. 16-22 Time-motion diagram for tri-axis transfer press. *(Courtesy The Schuler Group)*

Separate slides also feature greater distance between individual dies. This makes clamping devices, exchange parts from the transfer and universal station, and the dies themselves more easily accessible, allowing more generously dimensioned scrap chutes. Malfunctions are less frequent and easier to locate and remedy.

The multislide crossbar transfer press is designed with individual components such as in-tandem lines (for example, crowns, slides, and beds), but with common uprights between adjacent beds and one common drive system. This arrangement allows multi-axis universal stations between forming stations, providing versatility and easy adaptation of the die designer's needs, such as changes of part location for optimum part quality. More complex and larger panels, as well as light-gage panels, can be produced more efficiently. In addition, this system provides the smallest transfer index for any given die size. Thus, higher production rates are possible.

Special features and benefits of the multislide crossbar transfer press include:

- Elimination of off-center loading. Each die is suspended by an individual slide with four connection rods, thereby effectively eliminating slide misalignment.
- Improved accuracy (given the same length of gibbing), better part quality, and longer die life as a result of eight-way gibbing on each slide, specific to each individual die alignment—the distance between gibs in flow direction is substantially less than with conventional two-slide transfer presses.
- Minimum deviation from designed parallelism, resulting from symmetrical tie rods for each station and shorter distances between tie rods, as compared to two-slide transfer presses.
- Greater die protection. Each slide or station is supplied with an individually-controlled hydraulic overload system, which means each die is protected separately.
- Individual adjustment of each slide.
- A multislide transfer press can be run in a conventional tandem line and vice versa. This offers more flexibility for handling press problems.

- Greater accessibility between carriers for unloading and loading dies, clamping, and setting crossbars when moving bolsters are rolled out.
- Tipping the panels to any slide and separating panels (90° to flow) are easily accomplished, because parallels can be re-oriented at each idle station (one per die set).
- Elimination of deflection and vibration. Due to the idle stations, no moving parts (cylinders) are used on the crossbar itself; therefore, there is no excessive weight to cause deflection or vibration.
- Substantial reduction in die design, die setting, and checkout times. Die height adjustment is individually controlled (to the extent die clearance timing is unaffected). When dies are repaired, varying heights do not have to be matched nor do dies have to be shimmed. Adjustment of each slide will offset any variance within the limits of die clearance timing.
- Capability to try out individual dies in a single-action press independent of the other multislide transfer press dies. Die performance is the same when installed in the multislide press.
- Favorable time-motion characteristics. Transfer index is shorter than comparable two- or three-slide crossbar transfer presses, thus providing potential for greater output.
- Reduced total weight of the system, thus reduced static and dynamic loads on the foundation.

HYDRAULIC PRESSES

Although the majority of transfer presses are mechanically driven, hydraulic presses are increasingly considered owing to their cost and performance characteristics (see Fig. 16-26). In general, hydraulic presses are selected for more universal use than mechanical presses. For example, press capacity up to the rated load is selectable over the entire stroke of the ram. Servovalve technology enables force and path profiles to be programmed for high-approach speed and lower impact speed, minimizing die open timing when work is not being performed (nonvalue-added time). Table 16-2 compares the main features of hydraulic presses and mechanical presses.

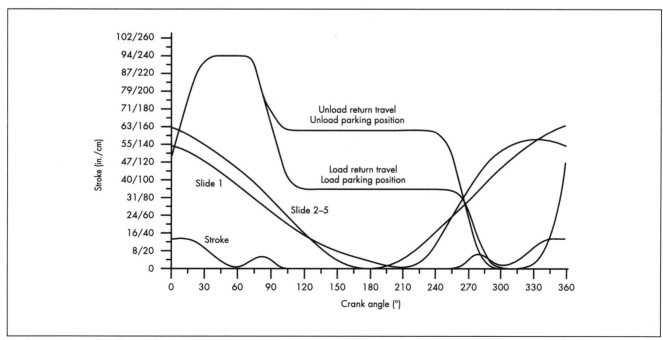

Fig. 16-23 Time-motion diagram for a crossbar transfer system. *(Courtesy The Schuler Group)*

CHAPTER 16 METAL FORMING

Fig. 16-24 Dual ram *A*-size transfer press with real-time orientation transfer system. It features five die stations. Two sets of five moving bolsters permit die changes in minutes. *(Courtesy Verson Division of Allied Products Corp.)*

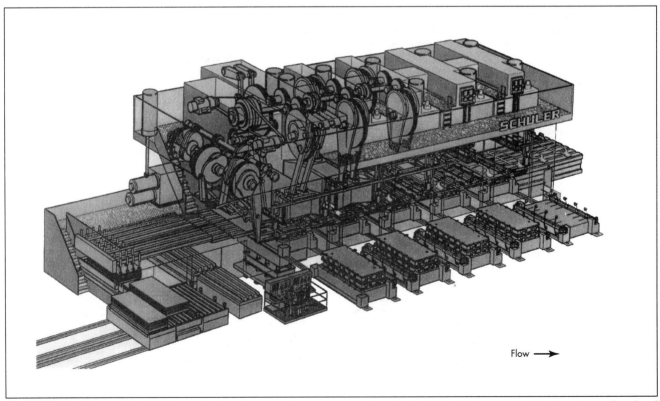

Fig. 16-25 Drive elements of a multislide crossbar transfer press with a separate ram for each die station and a programmable orientation station placed between side-moving bolsters. This permits rapid automatic tooling and die change. *(Courtesy The Schuler Group)*

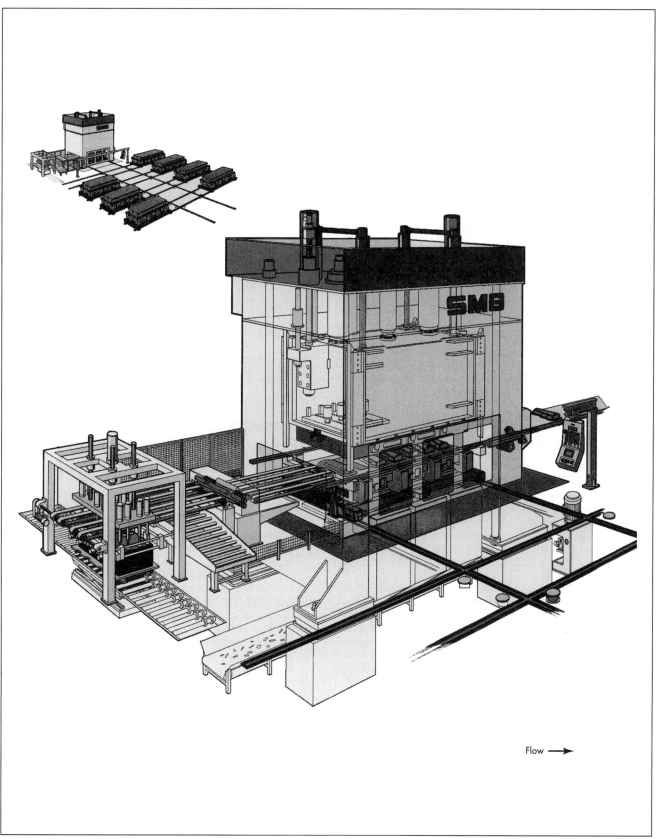

Flow ⟶

Fig. 16-26 Hydraulically-actuated press with transfer mechanism. Destacker is also shown with station for ejected blanks. *(Courtesy The Schuler Group)*

CHAPTER 16   METAL FORMING

TABLE 16-2
Comparison of Mechanical and Hydraulic Presses

Feature	Mechanical Press	Hydraulic Press
Slide stroke	Limited by the mechanics of the drive components.	Infinitely adjustable from zero to maximum stroke, with adjustable hard stops and overload protection that is pressure- and path-related.
Slide speed	Speed profile is determined by the drive kinematics, for example, in the form of a sine curve for crankshaft and eccentric presses.	Can be adjusted to suit the particular task.
Die space	Adjustable only within the range of slide adjustment.	Infinitely adjustable.
Impact speed	Relatively high speed is not adjustable to the die height, thus creating unfavorable effect on the die and die life.	Extremely low since it can be changed over from rapid approach to closing speed at any point of stroke and thus small impact speeds and extended die lives are obtained.
Press capacity	Depending on crank angle, the maximum capacity can be made available only over the effective stroke.	Infinitely adjustable from zero to maximum. The maximum capacity can be made available at any point of the stroke.
Pressure dwell time	Lower than 0.1 second depending on the drive kinematics.	Larger than 0.1 second, may be prolonged infinitely for longer dwell times over timer.
Setup	Depressurized closing is impossible.	Depressurized closing or same capacities and speeds may be used as under production conditions.
Slide in BDC	Slide must be run through bottom dead center (BDC) at any stroke, so there is a risk of overloading.	Slide may be traveled up top dead center (TDC) from any position. Overloading is impossible. Maximum capacity is limited by pressure relief valve.

(Courtesy The Schuler Group)

BETWEEN-PRESS TRANSFER SYSTEMS

Early attempts to provide press automation concentrated on press-to-press requirements for material handling. It was common for four operators to service each of five or six presses in a line. Improvements in operator safety and an increase in press yields were realized with the introduction of press-to-press automation (see Fig. 16-27). Later developments to increase flexibility included servodriven automation equipment and hydraulically-activated presses.

Prior to the introduction of crossbar transfer presses, the accepted method of manufacturing larger stampings was in a *tandem press line*—single presses with individual work cells before, between, and after (see Fig. 16-28). Generally, the lead press would be double (or triple) action, with the following one to five presses used for subsequent operations. This resulted in single-stroke action of the presses, necessitated by waiting for the material handling to complete its motion. Additionally, material handling of the stampings in such configurations could have required re-orientation or rotation to favor die conditions.

A high degree of flexibility is possible with this type of material handling; for example, if all presses are not needed for a particular part, remaining presses can be utilized for other stampings—in a different flow direction, with different automation, if necessary.

However, decisions based on the return-on-investment (ROI) for the purchase of future presses favor single presses with less componentry, needing less floor space, and providing greater yield. Nevertheless, many existing tandem press lines can be made more productive by introducing similar material handling equipment with retrofitted automatic die changing systems.

TANDEM PRESS LINES

Tandem press lines usually are comprised of five or six presses positioned in line with associated electromechanical handling equipment to transfer a blank of raw material from a destacker and automatically (with no manual assistance) move the part in a controlled and consistent manner along the line. Essentially, only three basic designs of equipment are used for transferring the stamping throughout the press line. Special adapters are provided for specific parts or press layout conditions.

The *feeder*, also called the loader or unloader, is a mechanized unit developed to pick up a panel and transfer it either into or out of a press. The loader is used for feeding a panel from a predetermined position into the die of a press. The unloader is used for extracting a pressed panel from a press and delivering it to a predetermined position outside of it. The basic movement of the feeder resembles an elongated, inverted U. The x-axis movement refers to horizontal movement, and z-axis movement to where the feeder is dipped in the vertical direction at either end of the feeder's travel.

The *shuttle unit* is normally a belt-, pneumatic cylinder-, or screw-driven positioning device developed to transport parts between two presses in a press line. Depending on the position of the presses, this distance may be different at each cell. The carriage is designed to accept one of several holding fixtures. (These fixtures are changed manually when dies are changed for a different part.)

The *turnover unit* inverts or rotates parts between two presses. Designed to handle both flat blanks and formed parts, the unit comprises two similar subunits positioned on either side of the shuttle unit. Each arm of the subunit grips the part and rotates it synchronously.

Two presses and subunits serve as the basis for press-to-press automation with a prescribed and programmed sequence: a pallet of blanks is loaded into the destacker, which passes them one at a time

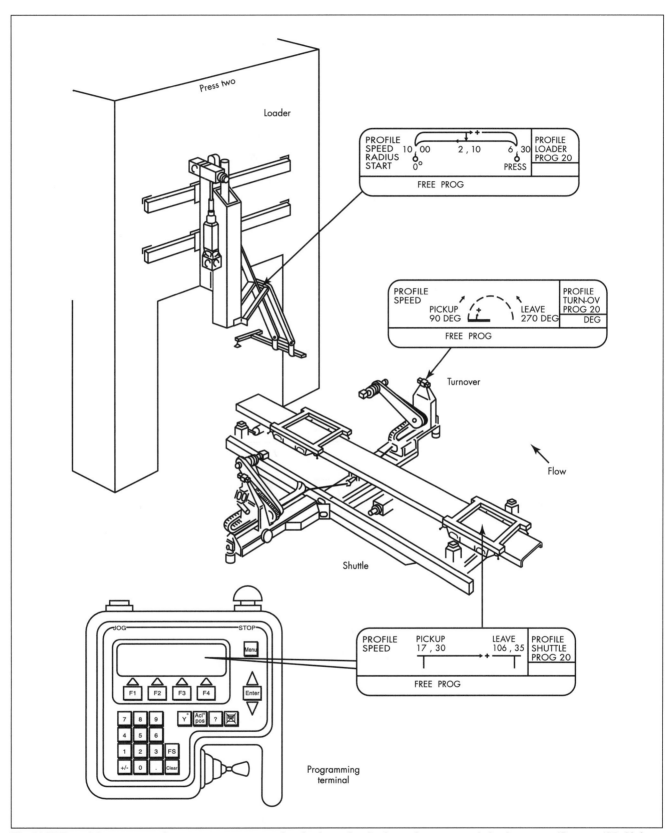

Fig. 16-27 Essential components for press-to-press automation: loader and unloader, and turnover and shuttle system. *(Courtesy ABB Olofstrom Automation, Ltd.)*

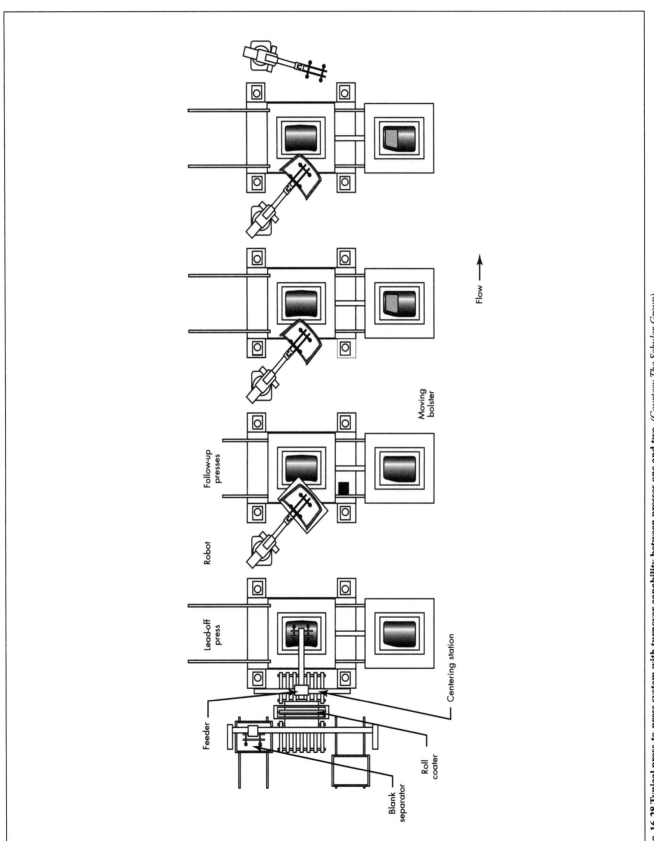

Fig. 16-28 Typical press-to-press system with turnover capability between presses one and two. *(Courtesy The Schuler Group)*

to the lead press via the loading table. A loader mechanism, attached to the front of the lead press, picks up the blank and feeds it into the press. After the press has run through the cycle to stamp the blank as required, an unloader attached to the rear of the press grasps and lifts the panel out of the die and places it onto a shuttle unit, which moves the panel to the second press in the line. In this position, the panel can be inverted by a turnover mechanism (located on either side of the transfer unit) before it reaches the loader attached to the second press. The second loader then picks up the panel and feeds it into the next press. Like the lead press, an unloader removes the panel and delivers it to the next transfer unit. A turnover mechanism is fitted between the first two presses only, so this transfer unit and all others farther down the press line just feed the panel straight to the next loader. This process of transferring, loading, pressing, and unloading a panel continues as the panel passes through the line.

With the exception of the lead press, each press in the line has a loader, an unloader, and a transfer unit. This equipment is collectively known as a *press cell* and is controlled by its own automation cabinet. Each cabinet has two operator panels, one for the loader, transfer, and turnover, and one for the unloader.

When retrofitting existing press lines, it is frequently necessary to remove or relocate this automation equipment for accessibility to dies requiring service or changeover for other parts. To facilitate this activity, the equipment can be mounted on guide rails and powered to one side of the press.

Initially, installations of feeders, shuttles, and turnover mechanisms for press-to-press operations were fixed-path, point-to-point systems. As demand for greater flexibility grew, servodriven, multi-axis equipment became available and was used successfully to improve the productivity of existing presses. In evaluating alternatives for new press installations, press-to-press operation is still considered for its flexibility to rotate or re-orient stampings at idle stations between each press. However, improvements in transfer press technology now allow parts to be re-oriented as they are being transferred from one die station to the next. Improvements in die designs avoid the need to invert the parts between the first draw press and subsequent operations.

IN-DIE TRANSFER SYSTEMS

Many existing presses have the capacity for multiple die stations, but lack the material handling equipment to move the parts between these die stations. Manual movement often results in both short- (hands in die) and long- (ergonomic, repetitive trauma disorder) term safety concerns. Frequently, the transfer equipment can be designed as an integral part of the die. The prime mover may be air, hydraulic, press ram, press crankshaft, electrical/electronics, or a combination.

The danger of material handling through a press and below the ram is damage caused by malfunction. The goal is to improve productivity by more efficient use of resources without jeopardizing the safety of operators, tooling, press, or handling systems.

In evaluating alternative processes to manufacture a metal stamping, a comparison is made between progressive dies and transfer dies. The cost of the excess carrier ribbon serving as the material handler in progressive dies is frequently the reason to select a transfer die, even with a probable reduction in operating speed. For larger stampings, the carrier ribbon principle is not practical and transfer dies are predominant.

A wide selection of material handling (or transfer) equipment is available to suit the product and intended press. The motions may

be two- or three-dimensional, with wrist motions available for a fourth axis to improve die conditions. Mechanical systems driven from the rotary motion of the press crankshaft were originally the preferred method, owing to the positive relationship between dies and transfer equipment. Mechanical systems driven from the reciprocating motion of the press ram were later developed for lower cost and greater flexibility, but sometimes were implemented at the expense of slower operating speed. Because of its speed, flexibility, and safety, the most common method utilizes an independent servodrive for the linear index motion and the press ram to generate the horizontal and vertical finger motion. A typical assembly of dies with integrated transfer equipment is shown in Figure 16-29.

It is impossible to compete without some innovation. Automation plays a critical role in competing in an international manufacturing arena, and several unique material handling systems for metal stamping dies have been developed to make existing equipment more productive. Basic business principles, however, are maintained. Goals of automation are:

- Efficient production (throughput).
- Simplicity.
- Flexibility for growth (agility).
- Proper equipment utilization.
- Increase in material surface feet per minute (sfm) processed.
- Increased profits.
- Die and press accessibility (maintainability).

Things to avoid are:

- Inflated manufacturing costs.
- Downtime.
- Complex systems
- Manual handling of parts.
- Unnecessary inventory.
- Capital expenditure overages.
- Changeover time.

DESIGN OF A THREE-AXIS TRANSFER DIE

Basic design principles refined by continuing practical experience must be followed for a successful operation. Flowchart information needed in preparation for design of any transfer die includes:

1. Description of work to be performed in each station (process). Determine scrap length for proper removal.
2. Transfer information: finger travel, lift (if required), and pitch.
3. Press information: bed size, stroke, shut height, strokes per minute, window size and location, and type of press drive (link-type, direct drive, geared, hydraulic, etc.).
4. How part is lifted off lower die steels.
5. Part gaging on die.
6. Part lifter locations.
7. Part-in-work height, die lifter height, and transfer height in elevation.
8. Dimension part height and attitude in each position listed in item number 7.
9. Stations relative to bolster (plan view).
10. Approximate location of guide pins and bushings shown in plan view, and in elevation length of pin engagement.
11. How scrap is removed (conveyors, chutes, etc.).
12. Incorporation of pilot holes in part, if possible (this will aid in locating part and help check transfer fingers to die station).
13. Stripper pins and their location inside of die lifters.

Guidelines for the design of a transfer die are:

- Part in die lifted position to be shown, dimensioned, and held to ±0.015 in. (±0.38 mm) tolerance in all stations.

CHAPTER 16   METAL FORMING

Fig. 16-29 Typical hydraulic transfer press die with automation mounted to and remaining with die. *(Courtesy The Schuler Group)*

- Part attitude in transfer position is dimensioned in each station.
- The centerline of each die station is to have positive identification. Provide two 0.5-in. (13-mm) diameter construction holes on centerline of station at a specific dimension from centerline of the die.
- Hold distance between centerline of stations at ±0.015 in. (±0.38 mm) tolerance, noncumulative.
- Provide oil breaker stripper pins in all punch steels and spring pads. Stripper pins must be inboard of lower lifter rails.
- Part lifter must operate smoothly and consistently lift part to correct pickup position.
- Die-mounted gages must correctly locate part. Provide minimum of 0.5-in. (13-mm) straight and 0.25-in. (6.4-mm) lead on all gages.
- Provide a minimum of 0.62-in. (15.7-mm) part lift off lower die to clear fingers.
- Show outline of transfer bar assembly (fingers, bars, junction boxes) and provide timing curve in cross-section for each die station (see Fig. 16-30).
- Provide gaging to strip incoming part from transfer fingers or introduce gaging from upper die steels as ram descends.
- Carefully show the relationship of below-ram material handling equipment to the ram position throughout its cycle (see Fig. 16-30 for typical interference curve).
- Standardize transfer movements (finger travel, lift, and linear motion). This will reduce setup times by eliminating parameter adjustments in a trial-and-error mode during tooling setup.

- Locate positively all components such as tooling, transfer mounting, transfer bar and finger positions, part locations, and part lifters to reduce setup time (use puck locators, pull pins, keys).
- Design flexibility into transfer units so that they can be used on multiple numbers of parts and dies, with only the transfer bar tooling changed for different parts (determine operational "envelope" of minimum and maximum travels).
- Design transfer units to allow complete setup off-press in a prestaging area. This allows for the actual change to be made with the least amount of press downtime.
- Engineer and manufacture transfer bars to the part parameters with the tooling processes in mind. This will eliminate the need for adjustments at setup time.
- Provide various transfer mounting designs to allow the stamper to choose the optimum mounting configuration for his or her needs. Standardizing the transfer mounting and interfacing the transfer to the tooling allows for positive setups with no adjustments needed at setup time.

ROBOTS

Improved cycling times, flexibility, reduced cost of tooling, and tool changing capabilities, are making traditional standard robots

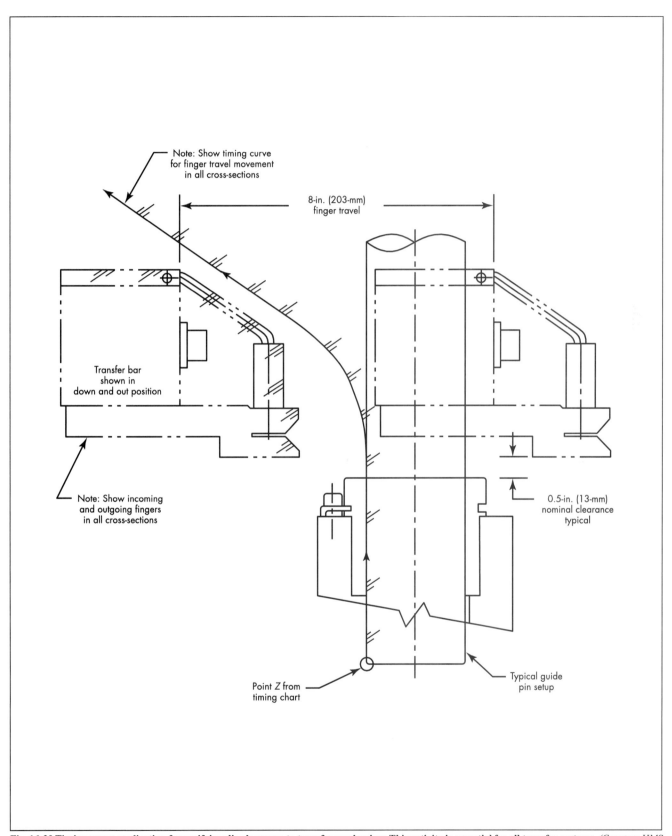

Fig. 16-30 Timing curve application for verifying die clearance to transfer mechanism. This activity is essential for all transfer systems. *(Courtesy HMS Products Co.)*

CHAPTER 16   METAL FORMING

increasingly popular for metal forming automation. The simple definition of a *robot*, that of a "programmable manipulator," defines various types of robots that have been successfully used in the material handling of metal stampings. The evolution of robotics has been from manual feeding, to pick-and-place, fixed-path automation, and now to flexible manufacturing systems, using robots that are quickly and automatically reprogrammed to service one stamping, then another, as unique tooling is also automatically changed.

ROBOTIC SHUTTLE DEVICES

Robotic shuttle solutions attempt to increase flexibility and reliability over the traditional pick-and-place shuttle devices. This concept includes three devices: two press-mounted robots and one floor-mounted part transfer shuttle (see Fig. 16-31). The robots are offered by several vendors in various configurations (from two to six axes of motion) and typically are mounted in an inverted position on the press. Two pickups and sit-downs are required, plus a transfer, increasing the potential for part damage and mislocation of the part in the next press. The robots and part transfer shuttle devices must be relocated during die change unless special side-sliding bolster presses are used.

Robotic shuttle solutions should provide added flexibility, and equipment reliability may be increased slightly over some of the traditional solutions. Disadvantages still exist because these solutions do not reduce the die change time. The two robots and transfer shuttle must be moved out of the die change area. After the dies are changed, the equipment is moved back into position and set up for the next part. These devices can be installed on linear tracks with drives that power the equipment out of the die change area. In certain installations, the robots may have to move out of the way. In either case, this can take hours, reducing press line utilization. The time required to move the equipment in and out for die change, plus the time required to adjust end-of-arm tooling (EOAT), the part of the robot that manipulates the part (sometimes called "end-effector tooling"), and shuttle fixtures for the next part can take from three minutes up to four hours.

SWING-ARM ROBOT

Swing-arm robots can increase flexibility and reliability over traditional pick-and-place shuttle devices for small part applications. The swing-arm robot consists of a six-axis, articulated-arm robot mounted to an auxiliary swing-arm seventh axis. The addition of the swing-arm allows the standard robot to reach the large center-to-center distances of most press lines.

The six-axis, articulated-arm robot mounts to the swing-arm that transports it back and forth between the two presses. The robot is programmable and has a high degree of flexibility to accommodate the variation in parts or die positions. The swing-arm robot is typically mounted to a slide or track, unless special side-sliding bolster presses are used, to allow the robot to be moved manually from between the presses during die changeover.

Swing-arm robots provide a high degree of flexibility, and equipment reliability should increase as a result of just one unit being installed, compared to three units for the traditional solutions. A disadvantage is that this solution does not reduce the die change time. The robots must be moved from between the presses during the die change. After the dies are changed, the robots must be moved back into position and set up for the next part. The time required to move the equipment in and out for die change, plus any time required to change EOAT for the next part can take from two minutes up to four hours. This downtime greatly reduces the press line utilization.

PENDULUM-ARM ROBOT

The pendulum-arm sheet metal transfer robot is a four-axis (with optional fifth axis available) articulated robot. A pendulum motion is applied as the first axis transfers the articulated arm from press to press. This unique design combination of a pendulum, four bar linkages, and rotary axes provides many advantages over existing sheet metal transfer robots and hard automation solutions. The pendulum-arm robot's axis motions are programmable and controlled simultaneously. All axes are driven by AC servomotors coupled to rotary vector reducers.

The pendulum-arm robot (Figure 16-32) is unique, providing single pickup transfer of parts between large press center distances (up to 28 ft [8.5 m]) without the need for the robot to be relocated for die change. Mounting the pendulum arm off to one side of the press line allows it to remain in place during die change, thus reducing the time and labor required during a die changeover. This reduction in time allows the tandem press line to be utilized to its fullest capacity. The increase in reliability, plus the increase in press line usage, provides a substantial net increase in yearly part output when compared to other robotic installations.

When a different part is to be run on the press line, the dies are removed and replaced with different ones. This process must be performed as quickly as possible, so the press line can be put back into production. To accommodate this speed requirement, the pendulum-arm robot moves to a preprogrammed rest position that is outside (above) the die change area. The robot and support structure do not have to be physically removed from between the presses because the support and robot are located off to the side and above the typical die cart exchange height. This allows for the quickest die changeover possible because removal and replacement of the robot is not required.

The EOAT can be exchanged manually by an operator or automatically by a robot. The automatic EOAT exchange is accomplished with the use of an autoboom changer and a tool rack. The robot moves the existing tool into the designated rack position and releases it. The robot receives the location of the next tool from the

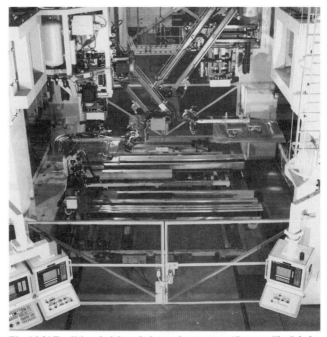

Fig. 16-31 Traditional pick and place robot system. *(Courtesy The Schuler Group)*

next part program and moves to that rack position. The robot then moves into the rack and grasps the new tool, moves clear, and is ready to begin running production. This assumes the dies are located on the bolsters by means of location die pins.

ROBOT SELECTION FOR PRESS-TO-PRESS TRANSFER

When considering an automated transfer system for a tandem press line, manufacturers should investigate how they can improve part yield and quality. To meet overall process needs, goals and objectives should be established and, more importantly, a full understanding of the existing process should exist.

The first step in this investigation is to define a vision statement for the specific tandem line to be automated. This will help define system performance priorities. It is also important in light of the many robotic suppliers, each offering different features and benefits.

The next step is to set key objectives so those involved with the automation plan can stay focused and on track. Goals should be consistent with the vision statement, list key priorities, and state specific achievements that are measurable and realistic. Examples are:

- Increase press line utilization.
- Increase part yield.
- Maintain high flexibility.
- Increase system ease-of-use.
- Reduce part cost.
- Reduce part changeover time.
- Minimize time to add new parts.
- Improve part quality.

Robot Types

There are many robot suppliers and robot configurations, so the selection of vendor and type of robot can be confusing. If a company has not previously used robots in the pressroom, then a vendor that can perform as a full-service supplier may be the best choice. On the other hand, the manufacturer familiar with robotics and press automation may opt to perform some of the tasks in house. The amount of vendor support is variable, but should be considered a key element to a successful system now and in the future.

Fig. 16-32 Pendulum-arm robot positioned to provide greatly reduced obstruction to die changeovers. *(Courtesy Fanuc Robotics)*

AUTOMATED PARTS RACKING

The idea of developing a flexible part racking process is not new. However, many obstacles, such as costly rack designs, fleet management, and the lack of flexibility have kept it from becoming a viable tool for the racking of high-quality outer panels. Recently, the combination of flexible robots, vision systems, and a creative process development has resulted in viable solutions.

Several of the most advanced part racking systems make use of robots loading parts into specially-designed, positively-located racks. These racks employ sophisticated dunnage systems that are costly to produce and maintain. A major problem is maintaining a fleet of such racks because racks incur damage while traveling from the stamping plant to the assembly plant. Thus, use of costly precision racks that ensure consistent dunnage location is not an economical option for most stampers. Consequently, most of these racking systems are installed in integral stamping and assembly plants where the risk of damage is greatly reduced.

A human operator loading a rack can compensate for differences in damaged racks and in changing production from one part to another. However, present these same scenarios to the typical dedicated robotics racking system, and the results are bent parts and broken tooling.

New ventures in this area by the automotive industry make use of vision technology and adaptive motion control. Aggressive system requirements (goals) include a minimum of:

- Producing 500 parts per hour on single parts.
- Supporting up to 14 different parts in the mix, including body sides (see Fig. 16-33).
- Using simple racks and dunnage (see Fig. 16-34).
- Performing unmanned racking and rack replacement.
- Adapting to out-of-tolerance dunnage.
- Reverting to a manual operation (if needed).

Fig. 16-33 Large auto body side panels loaded in a rack and ready for transport to the assembly plant. *(Courtesy Ford Motor Company)*

CHAPTER 16   METAL FORMING

Fig. 16-34 Simple dunnage within a rack to locate metal stamping and prevent damage during transit. *(Courtesy Ford Motor Company)*

A press-mounted robot unloads the last press and deposits the part onto a shuttle transfer. To accomplish high-speed production runs, the system uses a pair of six-axis robots to prequalify racks and a pair of seven-axis robots to rack parts. The racking robots, positioned on either side of the shuttle transfer cart, alternately receive a part from the shuttle and place it into a rack (see Fig. 16-35).

Prequalification is the first step that makes this system truly flexible. As racks come into the system, they are conveyed into a prequalification station. Here, a six-axis robot equipped with a bar code scanner and a laser vision system first identifies the type of rack, then the specific rack by its serial number (see Fig. 16-36). Next, the robot checks a series of predetermined points on the rack and compares this to a set of acceptable parameters stored within a database. This qualifies the rack structure and dunnage within the racks. Conformance or nonconformance variables are then transmitted to the load robot computer.

To accommodate variances, the system adjusts the racking robot's electronic image and loading paths for damaged rack dunnage. In this way, if the dunnage is out of specification, the whole rack is not rejected. The accepted rack is passed onto the next station for loading, and the next rack is advanced for inspection. Dunnage out of place by up to 0.5 in. (13 mm) receives a passing grade. Rejected racks are indexed off line for repair. To aid in rejected rack repair, the system generates a report that identifies where the rack deviates from specified parameters.

The main advantages of this system are that a variety of high quality outer panels can be racked automatically, and the system's ability to actively adapt to new conditions eliminates the need for high-precision racks. This eliminates the costs associated with maintaining a fleet of such racks, and it also allows the flexibility to add dissimilar parts to the production schedule with far greater ease.[2]

CONVEYORS

Conveyors of many different designs for various functions are used throughout a metal stamping enterprise and are described in detail in Chapter 9 of this handbook. The most visible is the typical belt conveyor, transferring completed stampings away from automated presses. Choice of belting material is important for longevity and the prevention of damage to the finished product.

Conveyors of similar design are used on tandem transfer lines between presses to assist in moving stamped panels.

Conveyor products to transport pallets, skids, or containers fall within several categories, depending on size, weight, etc. (see Fig. 16-37). In addition, standard components are available in a broad range of sizes and weight capacities to meet specific load, space, and operation requirements. Typical of the conveyors used by stampers are the following:

- Gravity roller conveyors (Fig. 16-37a) are widely used because of their simplicity, low unit cost, and ease of maintenance.
- As the cornerstone of unit load conveying systems, the chain-driven live roller conveyor (Fig. 16-37b) provides a positive drive for single or bidirectional transportation of large, heavy loads. It is also capable of low-pressure accumulation with the use of plastic slip sleeves on the rollers.
- Pallet accumulation conveyors (Fig. 16-37c) consist of separate zones of chain-driven live roller conveyors, each powered through a mechanical clutch. The clutch-controlled zone allows loads to advance to the farthest downstream zone. Each zone is signaled and disengaged in succession, providing accumulation with zero line pressure. The loads never contact. This accumulation method is more cost-effective than individually-powered and -controlled sections of chain-driven live roller conveyor.
- Loads on the multistrand chain conveyor (Fig. 16-37d) are transported on two or more strands of double-pitch roller chain. This conveyor is ideal for handling loads that cannot be conveyed on roller conveyors, such as containers with feet, wire baskets, pallets with bottom boards running perpendicular to the direction of flow, and pallets with poor integrity.
- Chain transfers are short runs of two or more strands of a double-pitch chain conveyor incorporated into a chain-driven live roller conveyor. The transfer chains rest below the rollers. When activated by an air-operated lifting device, they move beneath the load and provide right-angle transfers off the conveyor. Roller transfers are small sections of roller conveyor built between the strands of a multistrand chain conveyor and work in the same manner as chain transfers (Fig. 16-37e).
- Magnetic conveyors are used with ferrous material to move components vertically or in suspension. Small pieces of scrap (for example, perforations) are frequently moved more efficiently with magnetic conveyors.

Less visible, but critical to the efficiency of a metal stamping operation, is the conveyor system that handles scrap material. Below the dies, or below the press floor, it is essential that the performance of the presses not be affected by the disposal of scrap.

In a normal production year, an automotive stamping plant spends a lot of money for steel. The scrap rate is about 25%. Approximately 2% of the material becomes offal (reusable scrap) for producing smaller stampings. The remaining material recovers only a small percentage of its cost when returned to the supplier. Consequently, the efficient handling of scrap and speedy return to its source is critical to the profitability of a stamping operation. Chapter 20 of this handbook discusses scrap handling in greater detail.

Current state-of-the-art control systems include integrated diagnostics, programmable scrap distribution, automatic level sensing, and safety interlocks. Cameras are usually provided for visual check through monitors positioned conveniently at floor level.

CHAPTER 16   METAL FORMING

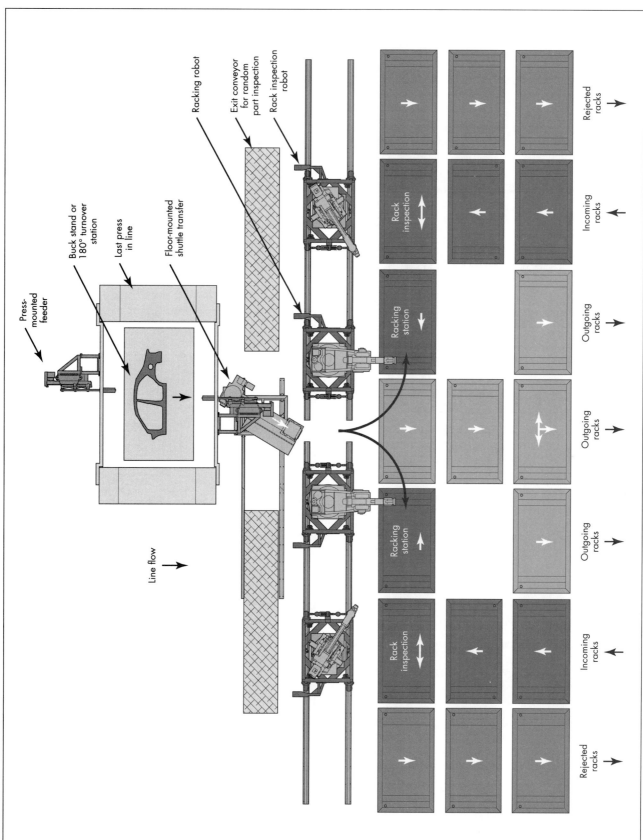

Fig. 16-35 Work cell for automatic panels racking with two robots; two other robots are equipped with vision systems to verify rack integrity before use. *(Courtesy Ford Motor Company)*

CHAPTER 16   METAL FORMING

Fig. 16-36 Robot with vision system checks a series of predetermined points to acceptable tolerances. *(Courtesy Ford Motor Company)*

FLEXIBLE HANDLING SYSTEMS

In contrast to the examples of material handling in the manufacture of automobiles prominent in the earlier section of this chapter are the material handling requirements in a lower-volume manufacturing enterprise.

Definitions of high- and low-volume production vary with the industry. High-volume suggests dedicated automation and hard tooling, for example, that used in canning industries. Low-volume demands prudent material handling and flexible tooling, for example, that found in aircraft industries.

In low-volume production, the percentage of time devoted to handling the part—and the tooling—will likely be greater than that needed to work on and add value to the part. Therefore, the emphasis must rest equally on flexible handling systems (FHS) and flexible manufacturing systems (FMS).

Total automation is probably not practical or economically justifiable for low production, for example, as it may be in a "lights-out" factory where computer programs govern manufacturing processes in response to, or in anticipation of, customer requirements. In low production, material handling will generally require some manual intervention. The goal must be to reduce the manual influence on the projected yield of the production facility.

One of the original golden rules of automation was, "never let go of the part." By way of extension, a basic rule of FHS is, "never lose control of the part."

This section emphasizes the processes at the start of the manufacturing cycle, from the raw material delivery through the completion of the finished blank. For consistency, these are referred to as sheet metal operations.

It is important for manufacturing managers to remember that when contemplating upgrading their plants, automation will not always be the logical choice. The decision to automate depends upon order sizes and the frequency of order changes. With two similar

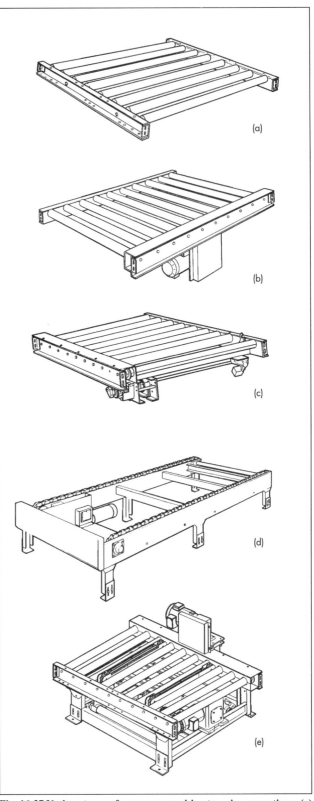

Fig. 16-37 Various types of conveyors used in stamping operations: (a) gravity roll, (b) chain-driven live roller, (c) pallet accumulation, (d) multistrand, and (e) chain and roller transfer. *(Courtesy Webb Heavy-Duty Roller Conveyor Systems)*

machines, it often is better to automate only one. This retains the flexibility to handle single-sheet orders and one-offs. In some situations, it is inefficient to prepare the machine for automatic operation when the complete job takes only two to three minutes. Flexibility may be greater with a human-operated machine.

Planners should determine at the outset exactly what they expect from automation and establish the scope of automation. Sheet metal material handling has both philosophical and mechanical issues. The former relates to the why of material handling, and the latter pertains to the how of automation decisions.

AUTOMATION ECONOMICS

As an issue of technology, manufacturers might purchase automation to gain a sense of prestige among peers, to improve their staff's technical experience, or to cut costs. It is quite possible that the resulting automated system is neither faster nor less expensive than the former manual system. As an issue of necessity, however, automation is required when the material consists of heavy sheet metal.

As an issue of economics, automating material handling must have a logical justification. The twin purposes of reducing costs and improving production flow must be set to ensure that the ultimate manufacturing costs are less than those that existed before.

Material handling must be universal, fast, and reliable; yet, it may be too costly, since the value-added in the first steps of a sheet metal operation and the material cost is quite small. However, it is only with savings in this area that the investment in material handling can be compensated. Introduction of the raw material to manufacturing for small production runs necessitates its frequent return to inventory. Material handling, therefore, becomes a significant contributor to the final part cost. Care must be taken when automating not to increase the part cost: the objective is to reduce it. The primary concern of sheet metal automation is to avoid exceeding the savings with the investment.

AUTOMATED MATERIAL HANDLING BENEFITS

Material handling in sheet metal forming shops focuses on automating the total system, as compared to using fork lifts and manually handling sheets, skeletons, and finished blanks (see Fig. 16-38). Automating a machine usually requires software, and that requires knowledge of the precise location of sheets, parts, and skeletons at every moment.

Such automation can produce savings in material handling before, during, and after the process through:

- Elimination of extra, individual blank loadings by nesting parts.
- Reduction of turret index time and table travel time by using efficient sheet layout and fewer loaded blanks (sheets).
- Improving parts and scrap unloading by way of scrap unloading systems, small part trapdoors, and removal of cut parts and skeletons from laser cutting machines.

Automating the loading process for each machine eliminates many of the invisible costs of the hidden factory, such as manual handling, wait and transport times, and the potential for damage to the material (including material stored on the shop floor). It can also reduce employee injury rates.

By reducing work-in-process (WIP) time through efficient material handling, a 25-30-day product cycle time might shrink to a three-day cycle time with a reduction in WIP itself. Material handling systems must be as inexpensive as possible. An off-the-shelf system would imply low cost; so does modularity (see Fig. 16-39).

Even at the investment breakeven point, automated loading and unloading is more reliable than an operator over the long run.

Organization of the work before going to the shop also has an influence on material handling. Parts scheduled in carefully planned sequence, and consideration for material types requires far less resetting for different gages and materials. Careful organization reduces unnecessary setup time.

Automation planned and carefully implemented can significantly reduce the variable costs of the hidden factory. For example, automated loading and unloading, combined with laser cutters and decentralized storage can cut scrap levels substantially. Damage from manual movement of parts through the plant also can be dramatically reduced.

BULK MATERIAL HANDLING

Automated storage and retrieval systems (AS/RS) have been developed to accept incoming skids of predefined shapes and sizes of material. Skids never rest on the floor, but go directly to an AS/RS. When needed, the central storage area retrieves skids automatically.

In nonautomated systems, fork lift trucks bring the skid from a warehouse storage area and load it into an intermediate storage tower beside the machine. Or, fork lift trucks bring the skid from a warehouse storage area and place it next to the machine where simple sheet loaders feed the material to the turret punch from the pallet. There is also hand loading of sheet metal.

For loading and unloading, the skid must be unpacked and brought to the raw material station of the loading device with the fork lift. The fork lift driver deposits it in the reference position. Often, vendors will recommend some means of moving the skid in the load station (for example, on an air table or ball rollers).

JUST-IN-TIME

Just-in-Time (JIT) raises the issues of short- and long-term buffering of parts, as well as matching one machine's output speed to another's input handling capability. Storage and buffering are important aspects of intermediate and advanced material handling.

With JIT, the focus is on producing a part only when needed. This focus is often considered as only the parts needed in the short-term, perhaps one day. This is difficult, but reducing WIP also reduces product lead time. Conversely, the greater the variety of products, the easier it is for lead time to increase.

While the goal of flexible manufacturing systems (FMS) is to improve operations, misuse of the FMS concept can create chaos. A good example is dynamic nesting. By adding extra parts to nests, excessive scrap or untimely runs are avoided. However, this can create problems of parts misidentified or lost, and more potential for adding to hidden factory costs.

SHEET METAL OPERATION

There are few standard automation solutions prior to cut pieces becoming formed parts, though there are standard methodologies. This is a result of the infinite variety of physical properties challenging sheet metal material handling systems.

The basis for efficient sheet metal operations is agility. In today's manufacturing environment, every parameter can change from one job to another. The basic parameters for handling sheet metal give clue to the variety with which the stamper must deal:

- Standard raw material sheets range from 4×4 to 5×12 ft (1.2 $\times$ 1.2 m to 1.5 $\times$ 3.7 m) and can weigh as much as 880 lb (399 kg) each.
- Finished blanks can be less than 1 in.^{2} (6.5 cm^2) or nearly as large as a full sheet.
- Shearing sheet metal occurs at the final operation upon what becomes a finished blank, but it might also occur before punching or cutting on full-sized sheets.

CHAPTER 16   METAL FORMING

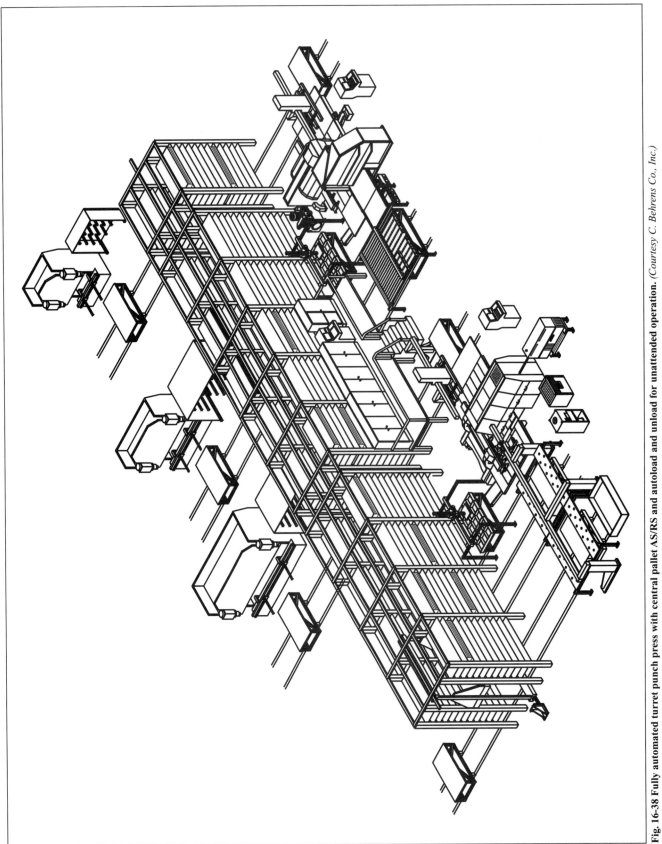

Fig. 16-38 Fully automated turret punch press with central pallet AS/RS and autoload and unload for unattended operation. (*Courtesy C. Behrens Co., Inc.*)

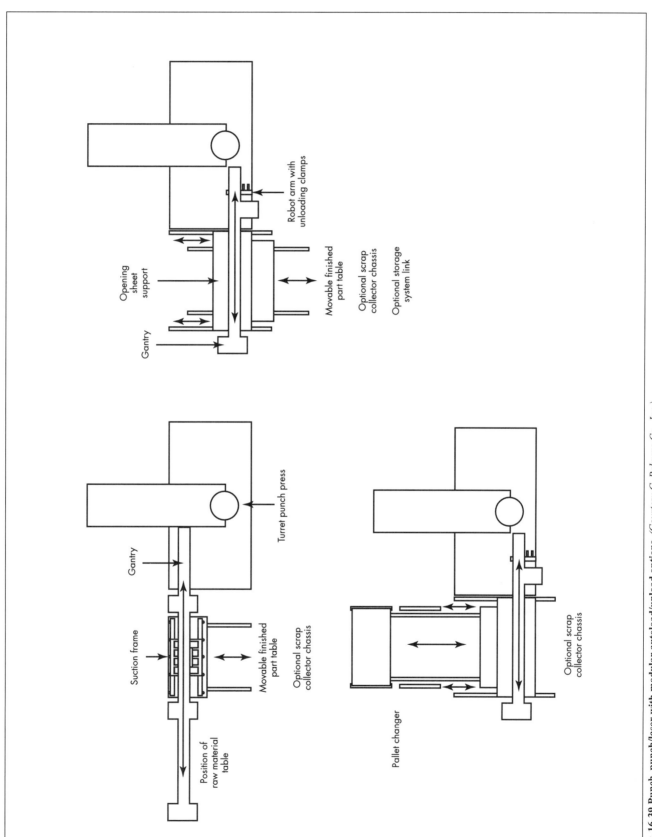

Fig. 16-39 Punch, punch/laser with modular autoload/unload options. *(Courtesy C. Behrens Co., Inc.)*

CHAPTER 16   METAL FORMING

- Forming or bending finished sheet metal blanks can involve one or many simple or complex bends.
- A typical, completed sheet metal part could involve any combination of cutting, shearing, braking, bending, coining, extruding, necking, or stretching.

Obviously, handling must be able to accommodate small, medium, and large sheets of different material of various thicknesses, weights, etc. Thus, handling raw material in sheet metal nearly always results in similar considerations:

- Central storage (inventory).
- Loading devices.
- Retrievers to handle material stacks on system pallets.
- Suction frames to handle single sheets for machine loading.
- Parts and scrap sorting.
- Unload systems.
- Transfer of parts to following processes.

Despite the challenges of designing an automated sheet metal material and parts system, there are significant advantages: unlike metalcutting, sheet metal systems need no workpiece-specific fixtures; and in sheet metal, an unlimited number of geometries of various thicknesses and sizes can be accommodated simply by writing programs and changing some tooling.

Typical Process Equipment

The sheet metal process equipment discussed in this section can be classified as either handling-friendly or handling-unfriendly. In handling-friendly equipment, the sheet has a defined, clamped position. Sheet movement is possible relative to both the process tool and to defined handling positions.

Handling-friendly equipment includes turret punch presses, combined process machines (punch and laser cutters, punch and shears, or punch and plasma cutters), and shears. Laser and plasma cutting processes, as well as bending processes, are handling-unfriendly.

Shears (preshearing). Material is loaded directly onto the punch press, where the blank generation is performed. Some companies continue preshearing batches of sheets to accommodate smaller sizes. Automatic loading of the punch press from the shear, however, is not a common practice, although there are exceptions.

Turret punch press. During the punching process, reduced indexing and positioning times can result from better planning and the ability to use larger sheets. Optional tab breakers and trap doors enable the part sorting and removal process to begin during the punching process. Use of a laser, however, often saves time by eliminating the need for tool changes.

Press brakes. Press brakes are the standard shop method of metal bending. The workpiece lies on top of a V-shaped die, as a knife-shaped tool mounted above forces the sheet into the die.

With rare exception, press brake operation is a manual and labor-intensive procedure. The complexity of the parts, and the fact that part shape changes during the process, greatly restricts the application of automation technologies. Therefore, the possible improvement of material handling for these types of machines generally is limited to blank delivery and part removal.

Folding machines clamp the workpiece to a table, half of which can swing upward to a preprogrammed angle.

Roll forming (profiling) is a bending method found in automated, high-speed transfer lines.

Combination machines. Combining different manufacturing processes that belong together from the workflow point of view, contributes to automation. The combined machines can save time, increase precision, eliminate handling, and avoid accidents.

Punch and laser cutter. The idea behind development of the punch and laser cutter is to save tools—eliminate tool purchases and reduce tool administration, maintenance, and machine setup. Reduced indexing and positioning times can result from better planning and the use of larger sheets. On the punch and laser cutter, tab breakers and trapdoors enable the part sorting and removal process to begin before completely processing the sheet. This is because the laser or the workpiece can typically be manipulated in the x-y plane to produce an infinite number of geometries.

Punch and shear. The integrated turret punch press and right-angle shear (punch and shear) offer a good study of setup time savings. There is no tool change on the shear. The CNC program adjusts for material thickness and blade clearance. To fully comprehend the process, a distinction between punching and shearing is needed: a punch and a shear, though they both provide the same type of metalcutting action, are different in shape.

The concept of the punch and shear is to combine small run production. Sorting identical parts is not typically a problem. The advantages of combining these two machines to form a single unit are:

- Lower material consumption through the shearing process (waste-free separation).
- Reduction of processing times through separation with the shear.
- Improved product quality from the coaxiality of punched and sheared edges, as well as the relative positions of the punching and shearing processes.

Moreover, the punched workpiece does not need realignment and it does not require clamping into another coordinate system for the shearing operation. Both punching and shearing operations take place in the same workpiece clamping position.

Punch and bending. The punch press's automated unloading system links the CNC turret punch press and a bending center. This moves the punched workpieces to an intermediate station for transfer via a robotic loading device to the bending machine.

The system is cost-effective, requiring only one loading system and one unloading system. It requires less space than stand-alone solutions and reduces the number of operators needed.

Punch and shearing/bending. The next logical step in the interlinking of processing machines is to combine three machine processes to form an automated, integrated production line.

The constituent components of the system are a standard turret punch press, right-angle shear, and bending cell. Developing a fully automated line means combining these components with additional material handling modules (including a new sheet turnover device) and an automated raw material supply system.

A single processing cycle punches and shears the blanks (without relocation to another coordinate system), and places them on a roller conveyor for transfer to the sheet turnover device. This device flips the workpiece as required by the bending machine. The parts need to be in a particular position (burr side facing up) for the subsequent bending operation. Once turned, a roller conveyor transports the parts to a transfer station. In this station, parts that do not require bending get sorted and stacked automatically by size and shape.

In this combination of processes, the advantages of a modular handling system are clear. Parts that need bending move to the bending cell's input station, where they feed automatically into the machine. The end product is a finished part that the system stacks according to part type. Other systems and cells can combine with this system to form a production line.

A cell controller regulates this complex manufacturing procedure, including the administration of raw materials and finished products. The controller interfaces to the machine's CNC only for the exchange of essential signals. This enables it to control the complete automatic processing sequence almost independently of the individual part processing programs.

Tooling

Where material handling automation supports unattended operation, tooling needs particular attention. *Multitools* often extend the tool capacity of CNC turret punch presses. Though a variety of these miniturrets are similar in use, the design and versatility of the tools vary considerably. While these differences may not be important, the features could change the efficiency and capability of the entire operation. For applications needing extensive tooling, the multitool capability should be factored into the buying decision. An optional multitool feature known as *drop-in holders* allows storing a family of parts permanently in extra multitool holders to speed job setup.

Modular Systems

By the mid-1990s, machine tool builders began addressing the issue of replacing costly equipment with modular fabricating and handling components (see Fig. 16-39, shown earlier). The concept describes predefined modules that link the process machines and material handling devices logically, based on the individual customer requirements.

The idea of predefined, adaptable automation modules enables the production of tailor-made systems at relatively short notice and at lower costs than with complete one-off solutions. Each modular element is self-contained and already proven. Exact definition of the machine interfaces, and adaptable, upgradable automation modules for loading, unloading, and transport of both raw material and finished parts, allow a high degree of flexibility and optimum fail-safe operation.

Automated storage. Current centralized, automated storage systems are more than simple warehousing systems. Rather, they are designed and built as integral and dynamic manufacturing modules. Their designs acknowledge a higher activity frequency than warehousing systems, or even early AS/RS systems.

Distributing and retrieving material pallets to and from machines has become as programmable, controllable, and reliable as machine tools, and AS/RS devices today serve as buffers for connected shears, punch presses, laser cutters, and bending machines.

Automated storage and buffering systems enable:

- The automatic and controlled handling, storage, and buffering of raw material and work-in-process.
- The allocation of material or parts to machines and assignment of raw materials and components.
- Last-minute changes of run sizes.
- Job optimization, as required.

Pallet storage. Central storage racks for incoming material pallets can consist of a vertical rack and loading elevator that runs parallel to, and at the rear of, the storage rack. Automated central storage designs also contain two parallel racks. The elevator system runs on tracks between the racks and telescopes forward and backward to serve both central racks. The pallet retriever is at the machine side of the single or dual rack configuration. Systems like these support the need for both manned and unmanned operation of multiple machines.

Decentralized automated storage. Today's high-speed production machines with automated load and unload require more than one type of material for short-run production. For such requirements, small, decentralized storage towers are a cost-effective solution.

Similar systems can be part of a fabricating cell. While these typically consist of one or two towers, they can extend to multiple towers, supporting multiple cells. Additional information about racks and storage equipment appears in Chapter 11.

Loading and Unloading

One of the simplest loading automation concepts is an overhead system equipped with suction cups. It picks the uppermost sheet of raw material from a stack of sheets and transports it to the machine.

Sophisticated supply and loading systems select sheets of raw material automatically from an automated storage and retrieval system, transporting them directly to the punch press. These loading modules automatically position and align the workpiece in the coordinate system.

Choices. A single tower with a vertical retrieval system in front (see Fig. 16-40) is an example of a minimum tower configuration. Adding a second tower is an option that allows loading from both towers. Adding towers and a traveling axis to the retriever (which moves only vertically in one or two tower configurations) allows more storage. With the additional left and right motion, the manufacturer is likely to install more than simply a double-double tower with 5-10 racks. The additional cost of the steel structures (after adding the travel axis control) is minimal. It is simple to accommodate hundreds of pallets of readily loadable material in this manner.

Loading laser machines. Loading any turret punch press-based machine presents the same issues. Laser cutting machines require different approaches. In fact, some unloading schemes often include loading, due to their similar, closely-integrated nature. These combined loading and unloading methods, designed as low-cost solutions, work well in small floor-space applications.

To transfer pallets to the laser cutting machine, a pallet-handling device takes a pallet with a raw sheet from the tower and moves it using the gantry robot principle to the changeover table of the laser cutting machine. There, the gantry robot lays the pallet in the frame of the changeover table. Afterward, the handling device waits for the other changeover table to drive out with the cut workpieces. It lifts the pallet out of the frame, places it in the pallet tower, and brings the next pallet to the machine.

Removal of the pallets from the tower to unload workpieces and the skeleton begins with the pallet handling device placing the pallet with the workpieces on a wheeled table. The table then travels through a light barrier in a free area in which the parts are commissioned.

Loading press brakes. Press brakes cannot easily address different part profiles in sequence. Typically, a brake is set up to produce a specific part and is applied to that part as a batch run. Considerable downtime is then incurred as the machine is set up again to produce the next batch of parts.

Parts typically are delivered and staged for the press brake via a fork truck with a pallet. Because bending typically is slower than upstream punching or cutting operations, considerable stagnant work-in-process (WIP) is incurred.

The enhancement of press brake material handling is necessarily application specific. Part size, lot size, part configuration, and weight must be considered, as well as the nuances of particular facilities and procedures. A fork truck may be the most efficient delivery method in some applications, while other situations may benefit from conveyor delivery.

If a system producing dissimilar, nested parts feeds a press brake, some means of sorting and staging the blanks is necessary. An FMS system that sorts blanks may offer its sorting bins themselves as a staging and delivery system.

Enhancement of unloading or dismissal of parts after the bending operations will again require consideration of site and product nuances. Formed parts typically are difficult to stack. Small, structurally-sound parts sometimes can be deposited casually into bins.

CHAPTER 16   METAL FORMING

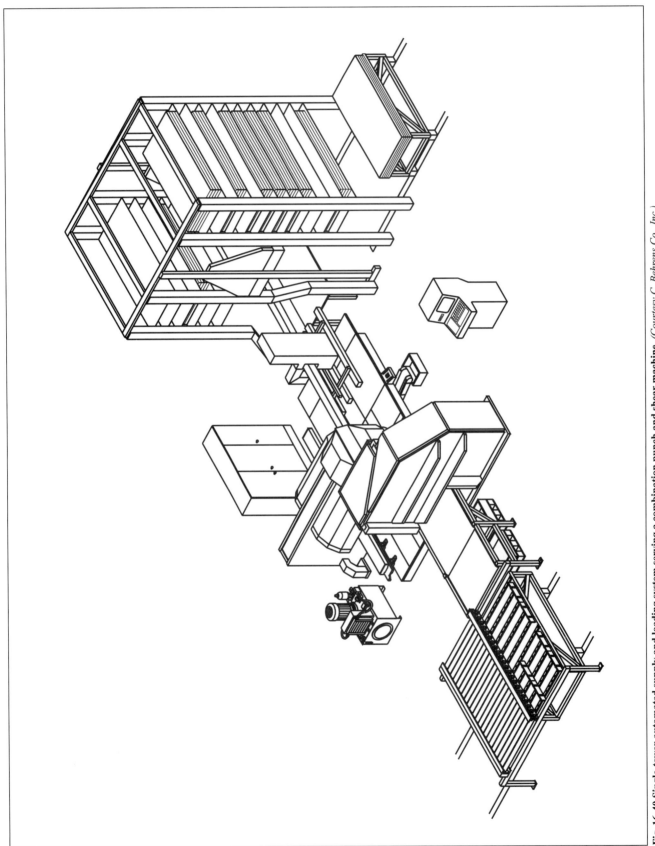

Fig. 16–40 Single-tower automated supply and loading system serving a combination punch and shear machine. *(Courtesy C. Behrens Co., Inc.)*

Larger or more fragile parts often require single-piece handling, including racking or nesting on specially-designed storage devices. The variables are too diverse for any singular handling method to address. In a short-run or contract facility, any one press brake may produce a wide spectrum of parts, and it is unlikely that an automated parts removal system can be fully functional or justifiable. A long-run facility may dedicate a press brake to a specific part or part family. In such a case, automation or an enhanced material handling system may be feasible.

Loading bending machines. Though not yet commonplace, successfully-designed bending systems with automated material handling are available. Any discussion of automated loading for bending machines must begin with the upstream process, from which the finished blank comes. That may be a punch press, laser cutter, or any combination machine.

A system linking a punch and shear to a bending cell, perhaps also including manual press brakes, will form a production line. By combining these components with additional material handling modules—including a sheet turnover device—and an automated raw material supply system, plants can realize a fully automated line for flexible production.

Since bending equipment may require an inserted part's burr side to be face up, finished blanks from the punch and shears will go automatically to a rotating device (flipover table). There, each panel is unloaded and sorted for direct, automatic loading to the bending machine. The stacks of flipped and sorted parts located on a pallet can be picked up by crane and brought to a movable stack table, which automatically positions itself under the bending machine's loading equipment.

Sheets. Normally, when laser cutting, the maximum size of the raw sheet is used for the nesting of parts. To avoid the need for a second person on the machine, some loading help or an automatic loading system is employed. Usually—due to the size and weight of the sheet—its position on the cutting table is not precise enough. Exact positioning can be made in any of several ways.

Initially, the sheet rests on ball rollers and can be easily pushed against reference stops before the ball rollers retract. When the rollers retract, the sheet rests on the sheet support in the correct position. The same actions can be automated.

Systems without support rollers do not allow any corrective movement of the heavy sheet. An optical detection system can determine the actual position of the sheet and correct the x and y commands of the laser cutting program accordingly.

Separation. With the increasingly common practice of using standard stock sheets on machines without preshearing, parts often are punched in multiples out of the individual sheets. Microtabs can be left on processed sheets by the laser, the punch press, and the combination machines. This requires manually breaking out the parts and sorting them after completing the sheet processing. Microtabs will get the parts off the machine faster, but require manual separation and sorting.

One method of automating tab breaking for either turret punch or combination machines is with a trimming tool or by laser cutting the circumference of the part. After the final hit, the part is free and must be removed manually. To avoid this, instead of cutting the part completely free, the trimming tool can leave two 0.125-in. (3.18-mm)-wide tabs between the part and the skeleton. The table then moves the tabs under either of two tab-breaking stations adjacent to the turret, a trapdoor opens, the tabs are broken away by the tab breakers, and the parts drop into a bin or onto a sorting conveyor.

When parts are separated and discharged from a machine prior to completion of the entire sheet, it will take longer, but the total process cycle—including separation and sorting—can be significantly shorter.

Turret punch presses. A straightforward unloading system on turret punch presses uses clamps to draw the finished part away from the area of the machine, and stack it onto a pallet or into a container (see Fig. 16-41).

Punch and laser machine combinations. Because sorting of laser-cut parts is necessary, the combination punch and laser machine offers the only cost-effective results. After cutting or punching the part, the punch and laser machine senses the part's location, and removing the skeleton is easy.

Unloading from punch and laser machines is advanced in comparison with other fabrication processes. It takes no process time for the slugs to drop through the die, and inner laser parts (from within the full sheet) to drop through the trap door when the tab breaker separates the microtabs. This is not currently possible with the laser-only process.

When considering material handling options, fast processing and the need to sort parts are necessary. With net processing time on laser cutters rivaling the turret punch press, sorting becomes the added benefit of the punch, or punch and laser. Laser cutting machines do nothing but process the sheet: the cut parts are in the skeleton or lying on the table. The combination machine, in addition to automated material handling, unloading, and slug and workpiece removal, interrupts the process. The punch and laser process appears longer than the laser's, but at job's end, the punch and laser machine's parts are in their proper places.

Laser cutters. Part sorting on lasers may involve a variety of manual operations: retrieving small parts from the table, separating parts by shaking from the cut sheet, and removing the skeleton.

In automated unloading, parts generally remain in the sheet after cutting. For example, it is sometimes preferable to offload a laser-cut sheet with its parts and return it to an automated storage system. From there, equipment from the next operation retrieves the sheet and an operator shakes the parts loose.

One particular material handling challenge has been the design of satisfactory and efficient methods for separating and sorting laser-cut parts. To separate the parts at the laser machine means material handling systems must address the unloading of both parts and skeletons. Several automated sheet unloading methods are now available. Few, however, also address part sorting, though some solutions are beginning to appear.

The increasing popularity of laser-only solutions has caused renewed attempts to automate laser system unloading. Automated and economical unloading and sorting on laser machines are not yet convenient. While there are designs for truly automated sorting, they have yet to be implemented and proven cost-effective.

An integrated load and unload station with fork stacking mounted to a laser's shuttle table provides automated sheet unloading. Such a station is shown in Figure 16-42. After delivering the pallet of material to the laser, the loading, processing, and unloading of cut parts and skeletons runs automatically. The entire loading and unloading process occurs while cutting the next sheet.

Automated Press Brakes and Bending Machines

Even with a fully-automated bending cell, short-run production can be of such manifold geometry that an operator is still needed. Automated unloading and stacking simply is not practical.

Press brakes address a much wider spectrum of part configuration and present serious material handling challenges. Using robots for press brakes has only recently become a practical material handling option. Current limitations in applicable part complexity and

CHAPTER 16   METAL FORMING

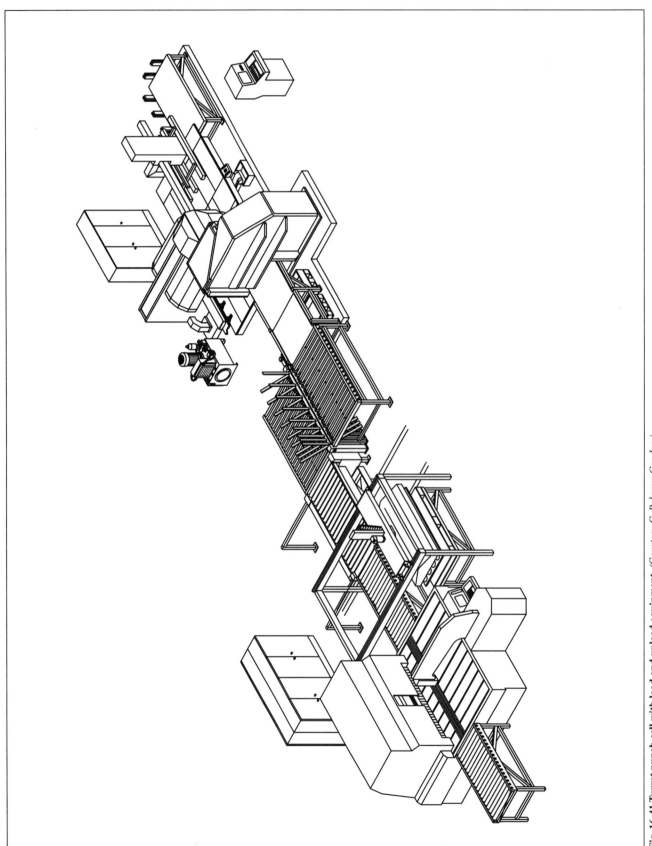

Fig. 16-41 Turret punch cell with load and unload equipment. *(Courtesy C. Behrens Co., Inc.)*

Fig. 16-42 Integrated sheet loading/unloading station with fork stacking designed for laser cutting system with shuttle table. *(Courtesy C. Behrens Co., Inc.)*

size prohibit the automation of many operations. Robotics do, however, offer great potential for addressing material handling needs in press brake operations.

Press brakes outfitted with CNC-controlled robots are available to automatically handle part bending at the brake (see Fig. 16-43). While one robot handles part bending at the brake, a second robot loads material in and out of the cell from a storage or transport device. The second robot also performs movement of material and parts to and from the bending robot. By providing six-axis movement for parts, the material handling robot uses a combination of air-suction and gripper hands to load and unload sheets for the cell. Operator setup is required to deliver the material to the automated brake, select the CNC program, and start the machine process. The robot-automated brake offers a solution when set up for many parts in a long run. It will also likely require automated parts removal.

Sheet thickness is an important consideration in bending. Automatic bending is usually limited to certain classes of products, such as steel furniture, small appliances, cabinets for office equipment and switchgear, and metal doors. Press brakes are used for parts that do not fit the limited profile for bending machines.

Fig. 16-43 Robot-automated CNC brake. *(Courtesy Amada Cutting Technologies, Inc.)*

Automated Material Handling Cells

The trend of automated metal forming technology is shown in three approaches (see Table 16-3).

TABLE 16-3
Progression of Automated Metal Forming

Typical Approach	Alternate Approach	Emerging Approach
• Punch and shear	• Punch and shear	• Punch and shear
• Bending	• CNC brake	

A small number of automated punch and shear-bend lines (automatic bending with automatic tool change) exist today and may be one of the next steps in the evolution of sheet metal forming automation.

Transporting, transferring, and buffering materials automatically. The FMS inherently transports material to the cell, then moves the workpiece between processes, automatically transfers it to buffer storage where needed, and continuously transfers manufacturing-relevant information within the FMS to a controlling system. The storage system's controller typically is responsible for these material logistics.

Adding bending to an FMS line. Adding the automatic bending operation to the FMS line substantially reduces setup and continues the flow of parts by removing one additional floor-storage. Automatic tool change reduces bending machine setup to 30 seconds.

Accommodating bending time, as compared to punching and shear times, presents a challenge when adding CNC bending to FMS lines. Such a connected solution must include a buffer—a storage system for finished blanks from which the bending system calls parts. A part rarely needs the same bending time as punching time.

If a material handling system links punching and bending processes, then both machines should be autonomous, each with its own control and operating independently of the other. The strength of the system becomes the ability to balance the flow.

Transferring to subsequent processes. Without transfer or transmittal of material logistics information, the material handling functions could not occur. These functions are information-based, with system response resembling that of a CNC axis with a resolver or rotary sensor. For every command, feedback is required to determine that the command was properly executed prior to another command being issued. With no feedback signal, no subsequent signal can be sent. This permanent comparison of command with feedback is the heart of FHS and FMS control.

Automated Forging Cells

The majority of sheet metal stampings are formed at normal temperatures, without the need for consideration of heat in the material handling requirement.

A cold or warm extrusion process is also common for stampings manufactured from bar stock (for example, wrist pins, stub shafts, etc.). The handling of these bars in a traditionally vertical position requires a critical timing relationship with the press (see Fig. 16-44).

The introduction of heat, however, is frequently required for a forging environment for several reasons (for example, lower tonnage, to form more intricate shapes, or because of material properties). Forging requires a separate work area or work cell and special consideration for material handling.

A forging cell contains all the items necessary for the extrusion process, from the receipt of raw material to the final product, including shearing, sawing, and automated in-feed. Parts are transferred to a conveyor, an in-feed device, or in-feed placement position next to a heater. Parts are then transferred through the heater, heated to forging temperature, forged, and finally trimmed. The equipment

CHAPTER 16 METAL FORMING

needed to forge, heat, and transport material must be arranged with integrated control to continuously forge a single product or family of products at a predetermined rate.

Utilizing a work cell generates certain benefits: increased productivity, lower unit costs, higher quality, greater adaptability to JIT, and greater capability to meet the needs of the customer. A system that is flexible and generally automated has maximum uptime and flexibility.

The idea of adding induction heating in a working environment started in the period following World War I. The equipment at that time consisted mainly of a motor generator producing power to an induction coil, used to rapidly heat the steel billets prior to the forming operation. One of the most important criteria in the heating of components to be forged is that they be heated evenly throughout the cross-section to ensure that the material has sufficient plasticity to correctly and evenly fill out the die or form.

Induction heating is not a panacea, however. There are times when it does not fit a specific forging environment. In the case of forging preforms of specially-shaped billets, oil- or gas-fired furnaces are probably much more productive. The billet or steel components to be heated are generally regular in shape, being square, rectangular, round, or triangular.

The fixture of a forging cell provides a means of billet conveyance and an out-feed arrangement for the material handling system. Other system components can include an automated billet or bar feeding mechanisms for both the cold and hot billet transfer.

When the system is heating billets end to end, they pass through a *helical coil* (one that surrounds the complete periphery of the part).

Fig. 16-44 Heavy-duty gripper transfer for heavy parts. *(Courtesy The Schuler Group)*

The part is within the coil for a specified period of time. During the process, a series of different material handling systems can be used. In the billet heating phase, material handling can be accomplished by a pneumatic pusher, a cat track, or a twin opposed pinch-wheel drive. Where the heating bar ends, it can take the form of a channel coil or spaced induction coils and operates so that one part of the bar is always outside of the induction coil assembly. Automated handling of cold billets and bars is accomplished by using a bin tipper, for example, to feed billets into a vibratory mechanism comprised of an external or an internal bowl feeder system. Another option is a hydraulically-actuated step feeder that feeds the billets in steps up to an in-feed conveyor. Hot billet and bar out-feed mechanisms include hydraulically-actuated, automatic, or manual transfer mechanisms to move the hot component to a forging machine pickup position, sometimes incorporating over-and-under temperature billet reject positions. Finally, robotics may be used for both cold and hot billet and bar transfer.

References

1. Bleau, Michael J. *Flexible Robotic Part Racking*. Flint, MI: Baker College, 1996.
2. Nelson, David J. *Large Transfer Press Technology*. Chicago: Verson Division of Allied Products Corporation, 1996.

Bibliography

Forming and Fabricating 4 (6). Dearborn, MI: Society of Manufacturing Engineers, 1997.

Forming Technologies Association of SME. *Progressive Dies*: *Principles and Practices of Design and Construction*. Dearborn, MI: Society of Manufacturing Engineers, 1994.

Hosford, William F., and Caddell, Robert M. *Metal Forming: Mechanics and Metallurgy*. Englewood Cliffs, NJ: Prentice Hall, 1993.

Kulweic, Raymond A., ed. American Society of Mechanical Engineers and the International Material Management Society, sponsors. *Materials Handling Handbook*. New York: John Wiley and Sons, 1985.

Lange, Kurt, ed. *Handbook of Metal Forming*. Dearborn, MI: Society of Manufacturing Engineers, 1995.

Phillips, Edward J. *Manufacturing Plant Layout*: *Fundamentals and Fine Points of Optimum Facility Design*. Dearborn, MI: Society of Manufacturing Engineers, 1997.

Schuler, GmbH. *Handbuch der Umformtechnik*. Berlin, Germany: Springer Productions, 1996.

Smith, David A. *Fundamentals of Pressworking*. Dearborn, MI: Society of Manufacturing Engineers, 1994.

CHAPTER 17

PLASTIC MANUFACTURING

CHAPTER CONTENTS

As much as 40% of injection molding processing cost can come from handling material and parts. Because of the nature of the raw material, many methods of material handling used in plastics processing are different from those used in metalworking. Choices can range from completely manual methods to full automation for either (or both) raw material and processed parts. Automatic bulk material handling systems, in-press grinders, parts removal robots, product handling conveyors, automatic take-off equipment, parts and runner separation systems, and equipment for automatic part assembly may be used. The equipment chosen must match the productivity of the primary processing equipment. Conveyors can be the in-press type, take-out type, or special stacking or orienting machines. For long-run products, the mold or die, primary plastic-processing machine, and parts handling equipment are designed to function as a system. Figure 17-1 shows a material flow chart for a typical injection molding operation. This chapter describes material handling as it relates to injection molding. However, much of this information is relevant for other plastic processes as well.

Figure 17-2 shows a typical layout for an injection molding plant. Raw material is moved to one end of each machine for loading into its hopper. It is processed through the machine into the mold, where the part is created. From there, part handling equipment moves the finished pieces to the next stage of manufacturing or packaging. This chapter is broken up into two parts: The first covers the equipment and options that bring the material to the machine, and the second describes methods to automatically or semi-automatically move the parts from the machine.

RAW MATERIAL STORAGE AND HANDLING

Design of the raw material system has a major impact on the plant's manufacturing costs and housekeeping. It is based on the different materials used, annual volume of each raw material, number of different colors, number of primary plastic-processing machines, and average production run length. A raw material system that employs automatic high-volume resin unloading systems, intermediate storage silos, a blending system, cooling and drying equipment, and storage for compounded pellets is illustrated in Figure 17-3. Plastic raw materials take the form of pellets, flakes and fillers, plastic sheet, powder, liquid, or paste. Pellets are the most widely used.

MANUAL METHODS

Resin may be supplied in bags, drums, or "gaylords" rather than in bulk because of high resin costs, low volume of usage, or the tendency of the material to absorb moisture. (The *gaylord* container is a cardboard box, usually lined with plastic sheet, holding about 1,000 lb [454 kg] of material.)

In the smallest applications, material is typically handled in bags of 50 lb (23 kg), or cans of about 25 lb (11 kg). If mixing of colorant or additives is required, it is done by hand. The bags and cans are transported to the machine using hand trucks or manual labor and then opened and dumped into the hopper. This method, while often used, is not desirable overall—there are concerns about worker safety (carrying, opening, lifting, and dumping bags) and material contamination from dust, dirt, and airborne contaminants.

While the gaylord container is the most popular, it is infrequently employed by high-volume users. Bulk bags (also called super sacks, super bags, or jumbo bags) offer a larger lot size, while still offering portability. These fabric sacks, holding approximately 2,000 lb (907 kg), are equipped with slings that fork trucks can handle, and a sewn-in discharge spout. To use the bag, a free-standing, specially-built handling unit with an automated or manual hoist suspends it over a material distribution device, and the spout is connected.

SEMI-AUTOMATIC MATERIAL CONVEYANCE METHODS

The varied needs of processors, such as large or small volume runs, long or short process runs, or quick material changes required for Just-in-Time supply of products, can usually be satisfied by modifying the following simple conveying methods.

The Contributors of this chapter are: Ronald T. Bankos, Regional Sales Manager, Universal Dynamics, Inc.; George P. Colbert, President, George Colbert and Associates, Ltd.; J.G. Fleischer, Regional Sales Manager, Universal Dynamics, Inc.; James Forrester, Vice President, Sales and Marketing, CBW Automation; Terry Godwin, Manager of Marketing, Universal Dynamics, Inc.; William B. Goldfarb, Manager, Material Handling Systems, Universal Dynamics, Inc.; Dan Graville, Industrial Sales Manager, Translogic Corporation; Henry Lardie, Marketing Manager, Translogic Corporation; Kent Leininger, Manager of Engineering, EMI Corporation–Plastics Equipment; Thomas D. Moran, PE, Engineering Manager, Automated Assemblies Corporation; Lance Neward, Senior Partner, Achievement Resources; David Preusse, General Sales Manager, Wittman Robot and Automation Systems, Inc.; James Rodrigues, Product Specialist, Robotics Division, Husky Injection Molding Systems, Ltd.; D.V. Rosato, Marketing Manager, Fallo Plastics.

The Reviewers of this chapter are: Douglas M. Bryce, Chief Consultant, Texas Plastic Technologies; George P. Colbert, President, George Colbert and Associates, Ltd.; David A. Meeks, Vice President, Imperial Tool and Machine Co., Inc.; Lance Neward, Senior Partner, Achievement Resources; Brian Read, Vice President, Engineering, Horizon Plastics Company; Thomas M. Roder, President, Roder Associates; D.V. Rosato, Marketing Manager, Fallo Plastics; Henry J. Wojtaszek, Jr., Vice President of Operations, Key Plastics.

CHAPTER 17 PLASTIC MANUFACTURING

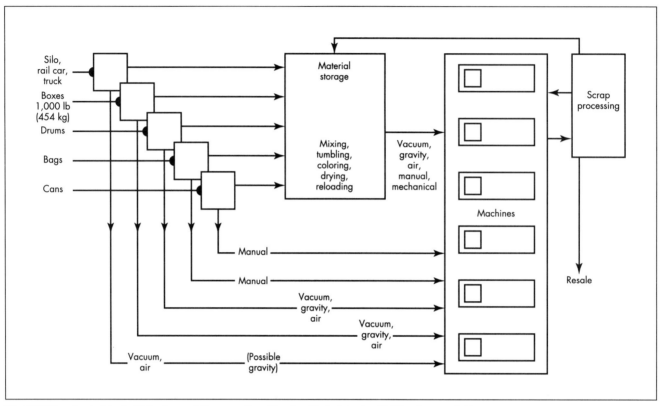

Fig. 17-1 Flow chart of typical injection molding operation. *(Courtesy Husky Injection Molding Systems, Ltd.)*

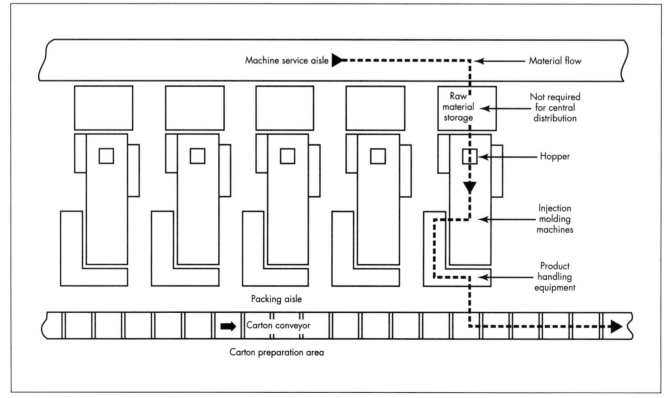

Fig. 17-2 Side-by-side machine layout in one or more parallel rows.

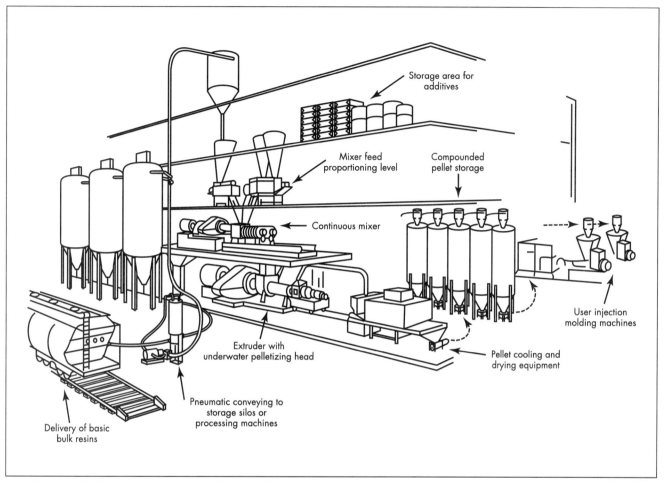

Fig. 17-3 Typical in-plant compounding system for an injection molder.

Vacuum Conveying Systems

Manual transfer of resin from containers (such as bags or gaylords) to processing units is labor intensive, sometimes unsafe, and usually expensive. Vacuum conveying systems are often used instead. Vacuum conveying equipment is relatively low-cost, clean, and flexible.

Typical vacuum conveying systems consist of a vacuum power unit, one or more vacuum chambers, a cyclone filter, resin pickup device, and assorted valves, tubing, and couplers for routing distribution of the resin. To meet the changing resin transfer needs of processors, new designs are constantly being developed.

The power unit is the heart of the vacuum conveying system, generating the negative pressure needed to transport pellets—a vacuum of approximately 10 in. (254 mm) Hg. A variety of power units are commercially available. Small- and medium-sized processors, especially custom molders, want versatile and efficient small units that can be quickly moved between containers located near or on presses. Larger processors usually require higher powered units for the transportation of large volumes of resin over long distances to or from regional or central storage containers.

In operation, a pickup lance (or tube), inserted into the bottom of the container, is used to withdraw resin particles from the shipping container (bag, drum, or gaylord) for transport to the molding machine's hopper, or to another type of container for storage and later distribution. It is important to make only a small opening in the bag, drum liner, or gaylord liner to minimize exposure of resin granules to airborne contamination and humidity. Flexible shrouds are available for covering drums and gaylords to protect against undue moisture absorption and adsorption.

The resin picked up by the lance is transported through tubing to a vacuum chamber where it is deposited for temporary storage until it is distributed to final storage or to processing equipment. The container should be tilted slightly for an even level of resin near the lance and minimize the chance of particles being left behind as it is removed. Tilting can be done manually when emptying bags or drums. Gaylords, however, require commercially available machinery for holding and tilting. A cyclone filter, located between the vacuum chamber and the power unit, collects fines and dust carried over into the vacuum manifold. For extremely dusty resins, a second cyclone filter may be employed.

The size and configuration of conveying units differs depending on the length of transport, transport rates needed, and distribution system complexity. The simplest, a single station system, incorporates a vacuum power unit, a cyclone filter, connection tubing, and a lance. Once the vacuum chamber is filled and the power unit shut down, the rotary air lock is opened and resin flows by gravity into the feed hopper mounted atop a processing unit.

Flexible tubing is frequently used on single station units, whereas rigid tubing is generally used on larger ones. In small systems, the entire unit simply sits on top of the machine's material hopper and

CHAPTER 17   PLASTIC MANUFACTURING

has a flexible tube with a lance extending into the material source (gaylord, drum, bag, etc.). This type of system also has a sensor extending into the hopper to signal when to draw material and refill the hopper.

A multiple-station sequencing system can be configured in two ways: as a single vacuum chamber with individual conveying lines to the stations, or as a single supply and vacuum unit connected to multiple vacuum chambers with tee valves. In either case, a programmable controller is needed to direct the routing of resin, and to establish fill, dump, purge, and idle times.

Continuous conveying can be used to transport resin to a large vacuum chamber from which it will be distributed. The vacuum chamber is equipped with both high- and low-level detectors to ensure an adequate supply of resin and to assist the rotary valve in its function as an air lock.

Container Dumper/Pressure Unload System

When materials are received in gaylord containers, a container dumper and pressure unload system can quickly empty the box-loads of material into a bulk storage silo. The operator loads each box into a dumping unit that transfers the material into a collection hopper; from here it is directed to a pneumatic conveying system. System throughput is based on the loading and unloading cycle time into the container dumper.

An electrically-controlled, hydraulically-powered container dumper contains a swiveling bucket which receives containers and up-ends them for gravity transfer into a collection hopper with a conical-bottom and open top. The rotary air lock feeder is fitted to the discharge of the collection hopper and moves the material into the pneumatic conveying system. The pneumatic pressure blower provides the air pressure for conveying the material from the collection hopper source.

This basic container dumper unit can be used for all throughput ranges, with various options to decrease loading and unloading times. The throughput of the pressure transfer take-away system depends on the conveying distances, and take-away rate determined by the container load or unload cycle time. This time varies according to fork truck or pallet jack loading methods, and includes travel time from the container storage location. An automated roller system can decrease the cycle time. As a stand-alone operation, five minutes is a good estimate. The *take-away rate* is calculated as follows:

$$C_h = 60 \text{ min/h} \div T_c \qquad (1)$$
$$R = C \times W$$

where:

C_h = cycles per hour
T_c = container load or unload cycle time in minutes
R = take-away rate
C = cycles
W = weight of material per container

For example, for 1,000-lb (454-kg) containers, the take-away rate would be ≥ 12,000 lb (5,443 kg)/h determined as follows:

$$C_h = 60 \text{ min/h} \div 5 \text{ min} = 12$$
$$R = 12 \times 1,000 \text{ lb } (454 \text{ kg}) = 12,000 \text{ lb } (5,443 \text{ kg})/\text{h}$$

Bulk Bag and Pressure Unload System

Bulk bags may be unloaded with a system designed especially for such containers. Fork trucks hoist materials delivered in 2,000-lb (907-kg) fabric sacks into a support frame unit. Once the bag's discharge chute is unfurled, material flows into the collection hopper and enters the pneumatic conveying system. A structural steel support frame suspends the bulk bag above the collection hopper

while the bag is unloaded. From the upper section of the support frame, a structural beam extends to accept the bulk bags from the floor position and transfers them laterally within the frame for discharge into the collection hopper. The unit is usually configured with a motorized vertical hoist and a manual or motorized lateral trolley.

As with the container dumper-fed systems, the bulk bag handling device can be used for all throughput ranges. The hoist automation options can reduce the bulk bag load or unload cycle time per unit weight handled. The pressure transfer take-away system depends on the conveying distance, and a take-away rate determined by the bulk bag load or unload cycle time. This time varies based on the hoisting methods and includes travel time from where the bulk bag containers are stored. Typically, five minutes is the minimum. Therefore, for 2,000-lb (907-kg) bulk bags, the take-away rate would be ≥ 24,000 lb (10,886 kg)/h, using Equation 1.

AUTOMATIC AND HIGH-VOLUME RESIN HANDLING SYSTEMS

This section discusses material containers, system selection criteria, bulk unloading systems, intraplant transfer systems, and system automation.

Material Containers

A bulk lot of plastic resin is usually transported by a truck which typically carries 1,250 ft³ (35 m³) of material for delivery to the customer's storage silo. Most often, the truck is equipped with a positive displacement pumping unit, which unloads the trailer into the standard plastic material silo, via the fixed fill line. In locations with less well-developed transportation systems, or when dried resin is being delivered, the user must supply a land-based pressure unit to pump the material.

Where rail facilities are near the storage silos, railcars are an effective delivery method. Specialized railcars can store up to 5,200 ft³ (147 m³) of material in four or five separate compartments. To accommodate the railcars, the customer needs to provide a land-based unloading system that extracts the material from the railcar and delivers it to the storage silo. It is best to utilize off-production times to unload this large-capacity delivery vessel.

System Selection Criteria

Choosing the proper systems includes consideration of throughput requirements, material type and usage, operator invention, and physical layout.

Throughput requirements. Material delivery system design depends on the consumption rate, which is the total usage of all the points within the plant. The total rate may involve intermediate load points, such as surge bins, before the processing lines. A general rule is to at least double the consumption rate for the material in use. This allows surge capacity in the silos to service the plant while the operation is running. Another variable is the amount of time available to unload a railcar. For example, if a 200,000 lb (90,720 kg) railcar can only be unloaded during the eight-hour night shift, a 25,000 lb (11,340 kg)/h rate is established. A railcar unloading rate also can be affected by the availability of railcars present at particular positions on the spur, or demurrage charges for railcars left on site.

Material type and usage. A key factor in the system design is the number of different materials to be unloaded, and their compatibility. If two materials are unloaded simultaneously, then two unloading systems will probably be required. If materials are not compatible, and contamination is an issue, two separate unloading manifolds will be required.

Operator intervention. The skill level of workers available to make hardware connections to the railcar, silos, and associated unloading equipment determines the amount of automation required. Typically, the flexible hose connection from the manifold to the selected railcar compartment is made manually. The silo destination must be selected through a similar hose change station (that is, connection to the manifold). Although costly, the implementation of diverter and selector valves can eliminate most manual connections.

Physical layout. The specification of a system is based on the amount of material conveyed over the distance required. Conveying distances must include factors for vertical runs and elbows, as well as horizontal travel.

In continuous or intermittent batch vacuum systems, the entire run from railcar pickup to silo deck is by vacuum. The rail siding-to-silo distance should be kept to a minimum. This is sometimes difficult to control, however, since these locations are fixed by the plant layout. Planning to keep these distances short during the plant design stage will minimize conveying problems and later equipment costs.

The conveying operation continuous vacuum and pressure system is divided into two phases: a vacuum draws the material into the cyclone receiver and air lock assembly, and pressure transfers the material from the cyclone receiver and air lock assembly to the destination. While the rail siding-to-silo distance is typically fixed, the design of this system can be based on the placement of the unloading equipment. The unloading equipment should be closer to the railcar than the silo, since, for a given pump size, greater capacities are attainable on the pressure side than the vacuum side.

Bulk Unloading Systems

There are two bulk unloading systems: bulk truck unloading and railcar unloading.

Bulk truck unloading. Most plastic material delivery trucks are equipped with a self-contained means of pressure unloading the material into the silo. The delivery operator simply makes a flexible connection from the tanker to the selected silo's fill line. Delivery is regulated by the tanker operator and ceases when the tanker is empty or halted by an overfill condition.

In some localities, bulk delivery trucks do not have self-contained unloaders and depend on a user-supplied pressure blower for unloading. A flexible connection is made from a pressure blower positioned near the bulk trailer unload pad to the tanker, and from the tanker to the selected silo. A land-based pressure blower is required for a tanker delivering dried material, since self-contained bulk unloaders can only utilize ambient air as the pneumatic conveying medium. Since ambient-air conveying would compromise the dryness of the material, a closed-loop dehumidifier should be incorporated into the land-based pressure delivery system.

Railcar unloading systems. Railcar unloading systems are available in a wide variety of configurations, from simple low-volume batch vacuum types, extracting 200 lb (91 kg) batches from the railcar, to high-volume dual blower systems continuously transferring 30,000 lb (13,608 kg)/h via vacuum and pressure. These primarily utilize dilute phase conveying technology. *Dilute phase* and *dense phase* refer to the air-to-material ratio of the material being moved, which affects the system's speed. Dilute phase systems can run at a higher speed than dense phase. The main types of railcar unloading systems are categorized as follows.

Intermittent batch vacuum system. This system is an inexpensive solution that uses a single vacuum unit and vacuum receiver(s) on each silo for low-volume railcar unloading over relatively short railcar-to-silo distances (<500 ft [<152 m]). The vacuum unit draws material from the railcar discharge fitting into a silo deck-mounted vacuum receiver. The pump draws a vacuum on the vacuum receiver that is equipped with a discharge valve (or one-way flapper valve) for a timed loading interval. Once this time has elapsed, the system's

vacuum is broken by energizing a vacuum breaker valve that induces air at the pump inlet, or the pump is simply turned off, causing the batch contents to dump into the silo. This sequence is repeated until the silo is full, as sensed by a high-level silo indicator or a chamber-mounted level switch.

Determination of which silo is to be loaded is typically made by a flexible connection of the individual vacuum chamber's vacuum line to the single pump, as well as by a selection of the railcar manifold to the selected silo's fill line. These systems are adequate for volumes in the range of 6,000-10,000 lb (2,722-4,536 kg)/h.

Continuous vacuum system. This has the same basic design as the intermittent batch vacuum system, but it utilizes a rotary air lock on the vacuum receiver in place of the discharge valve or one-way flapper dump throat, allowing the system to unload continuously rather than loading and dumping intermittently. By eliminating the dump time and the time required to re-establish conveying velocities, rates can be increased by up to 25% over intermittent batch equipment. This becomes an effective, fairly low-cost solution to achieving a conveying rate of 10,000-15,000 lb (4,536-6,804 kg)/h over relatively short railcar-to-silo distances (<500 ft [<152 m]).

Like the intermittent batch system, the continuous vacuum system has a vacuum unit that draws material from the railcar discharge fitting to a silo deck-mounted vacuum receiver. There, the rotary air lock allows for continuous reception and dumping, while providing a transition zone from vacuum to atmospheric conditions within the silo. Railcar evacuation occurs continuously until the silo is full or an overfill condition is present in the continuous vacuum receiver. These systems will handle volumes in the 10,000-15,000 lb (4,536-6,804 kg)/h range.

Single blower combination pull-push system. This system uses a single positive displacement pump to provide the vacuum power to pull the material into a cyclone/air lock assembly, and pressure power to push the material to the silo destination. This system unloads continuously, generally with higher rates over longer distances than intermittent batch or continuous vacuum systems. This is the simplest version of the continuous vacuum and pressure system, yielding rates in the 12,000-20,000 lb (5,443-9,072 kg)/h range (see Fig. 17-4).

The system consists of a positive displacement pump with a cyclone receiver connected to the vacuum inlet (through protective filtration). The cyclone receiver unit receives the material via vacuum conveyance and is equipped with a rotary air lock on its discharge. The pump's pressure outlet is connected to a conveying line adapter beneath the air lock on the cyclone receiver, providing the process air for pressure conveyance. In large systems, because the air may be heated due to compression, a process cooler may be incorporated to reduce the process air temperature, preventing material degradation. The rotary air lock serves as the transition zone between vacuum and pressure conveying, and acts as the metering device for the material entering the pressure conveying line. Material is continuously evacuated from the railcar unloader to the silo with intermediate transfer at the cyclone/air lock assembly until the silo reaches a high level or an overfill condition occurs in the cyclone section.

The cyclone section provides the air-to-material separation of material entering the unit via vacuum conveyance. The cyclonic action reduces conveying velocity to allow the heavier material to fall out of the cyclone. The lighter dust and fines are carried into the vacuum pump's protective filter. The material exiting the cyclone enters a small collection hopper mounted above the rotary air lock. The collection hopper is equipped with a level switch to energize a vacuum breaker valve upon overfill to cease material entry while maintaining pressure conveyance in a self-clearing attempt.

The rotary air lock provides a seal between the system's vacuum and pressure side, while serving to meter the material into the active

CHAPTER 17   PLASTIC MANUFACTURING

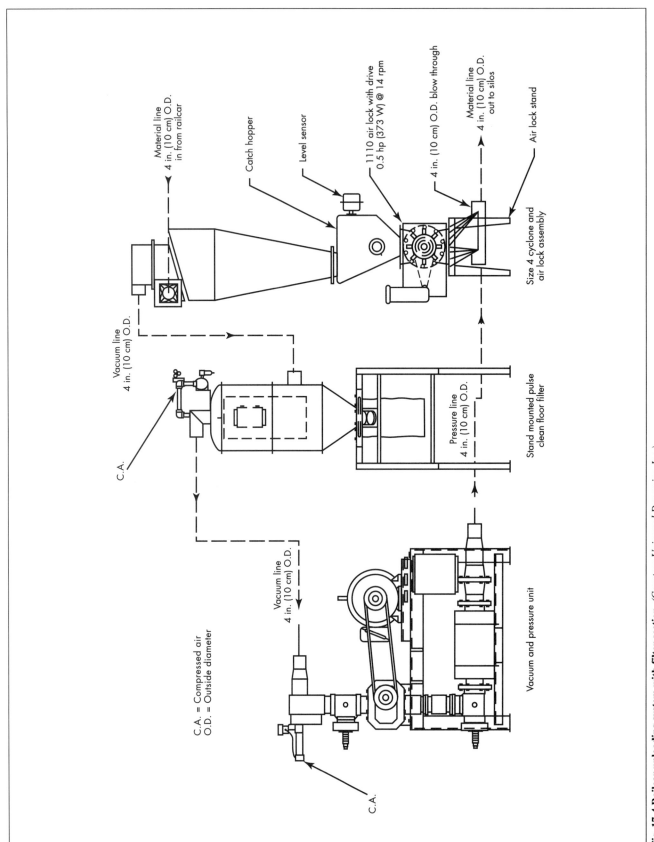

Fig. 17-4 Railcar unloading system with filter section. *(Courtesy Universal Dynamics, Inc.)*

pressure line. A shear protector should be present on the air lock to prevent material shearing. Also, a vent should be present to relieve the positively pressurized air lock rotor pockets as they return to the material entry zone, preventing a throughput-reducing material "bubbling" effect. The cyclone can be replaced with a filter section if materials are particularly fines-laden, dusty, or powdery. In this case, lighter materials are not carried out of the process, but remain in the system's pressure via filtration blow-back.

Selection of which silo is to be loaded is made by flexible connection from the pressure-side conveying line to the selected silo's fill line. Railcar manifold selection also must be made. This fill line often can be used for truck connections as well. These systems can be designed to suit almost any requirement, but typically handle volumes in the 12,000-20,000 lb (5,443-9,072 kg)/h range.

Dual blower combination pull-push system. Similar to the single blower combination pull-push system, the dual blower combination pull-push system utilizes two positive displacement pumps: one to provide the vacuum power to pull the material into a cyclone and air lock assembly, and one to provide pressure power to push the material to the silo destination. This system also unloads continuously, but with even higher rates over longer distances than the single blower versions, due to the ability to size the vacuum and pressure sides of the system independently, using separate pump units. While nearly any rate requirement can be met, systems of this type typically deliver 20,000-30,000 lb (9,072-13,608 kg)/h.

Single motor/dual blower combination pull-push system. This rarely-supplied dual motor/dual blower system uses separate vacuum and pressure blowers, but combines them in one assembly using a single motor. The features of a dual blower combination system are present, but in a small footprint package.

Dense phase systems. Used primarily for relatively low air-to-material ratios and slower speeds, dense phase systems are used for bulk unloading with highly abrasive materials that can damage conveying equipment or tubing, or with materials that become degraded by dilute phase conveying velocities. These systems are designed for all ranges of throughput requirements. Material must be transferred into a pressure vessel pneumatically or via gravity flow beneath the railcar, where valves energize to seal the inlet and outlet of the pressure vessel. Then it is pressurized by compressed air or other motive source. The discharge valve is opened to pressure-convey the material at very low velocities in a plug flow pattern to the destination. These systems can be designed to suit almost any volume requirement, but typically fall in the 15,000-20,000 lb (6,804-9,072 kg)/h range.

Physical railcar connection details. Connections and fittings are required for railcar unloading systems. The back-side air inlet filter fits the standard railcar compartment inlet to prevent large particles in the rail area from being conveyed in the material line airstream. The front-side line adapter connects to the railcar product outlet with a quick disconnect fitting for the railcar manifold, via a flexible hose. To ventilate the railcar compartment, the metal hatch filter, with a cartridge filter element, is attached to the railcar deck. This allows air to displace material as it exits and prevents railcar implosion if back-side air entry is blocked.

The railcar manifold consists of fixed piping installed on the vacuum side of the railcar unloading system, with branch adapters at anticipated railcar compartment discharge positions. Each branch is normally capped with a quick disconnect fitting. For line connection, a flexible tube length is fastened between the selected manifold branch adapter and the front-side line adapter.

Destination bins and silos. Destination bins (typically, bulk silos) must be adequately ventilated to allow free exhaust of process conveying air. For protection against mass flow conditions, silos are generally equipped with open ventilators or vent filters with a vacuum/pressure relief valve. Intermittent batch and continuous vacuum systems need less filtration because the material enters the silo by gravity, generating only minor airflow by-product displacement. Continuous vacuum/pressure systems require more filtration since positively pressurized process air must be exhausted through the tank deck.

Railcar unloading costs. Costs are largely determined by the throughput required. *Equivalent length* is the linear length adjusted for the direction of flow; for example, if the flow is vertical, one unit of length is equal to two units of equivalent length. A continuous vacuum/pressure system provides the ability to convey material at nearly any rate required (15,000-30,000 lb [6,804-13,608 kg]/h is typical) over almost any distance required (<400 ft [<122 m] on the vacuum side, 1,200 ft [366 m] on the pressure side is typical). It is sometimes cost-effective to purchase two lower throughput systems that can unload two cars simultaneously rather than one high-volume single material system. In addition to the basic equipment, it will generally cost another 10–15% of the equipment cost for hardware, and 20–30% for mechanical installation.

Intraplant Transfer Systems

Transfer systems within the plant include silo/bin discharge pressure systems and sequential intermittent batch vacuum systems.

Silo/bin discharge pressure systems. Inside the plant, material often needs to be transferred in high volumes from one operation to another, such as from a classification system to a large surge bin. This is effectively handled by a pressure blower operating with an air lock assembly on the discharge of the supply bin. The pressure blower outlet is routed to a conveying line adapter on the underside of the rotary air lock. Pressure process piping is routed from the supply bin to the destination.

The conical discharge of the source supply bin or collection hopper is fitted with a rotary air lock sized according to the conveying rate. The air lock should be fitted with a shear protector to prevent material degradation as well as a vent line, that is often routed to the air-only section of the source supply bin. The destination bin must be equipped with adequate ventilation and filtration to handle the pressure system's conveying air.

Sequential intermittent batch vacuum systems. When many destinations must be served from a single source, sequential intermittent batch vacuum systems are used. A single vacuum pump is used, with one or more vacuum receivers located at each destination. A vacuum manifold with sequencing valves distributes the single vacuum source to the many destinations.

The standard receiver for conveying plastic pellet material consists of a material hopper with a coarse screen filter to protect the conveying air outlet. Mildly dusty materials may be processed with this type of receiver, allowing the fines to exit the screen and be collected at the central pump filter. For very dusty materials and powders, the pellet screen is replaced with a cartridge or bag filtration section. The discharge of the vacuum receiver is equipped with a discharge valve or, more often, a one-way flapper device.

The vacuum pump is best placed near the station farthest away from the source. This reduces the length of the vacuum line, thereby reducing the static pressure drop when conveying to the most demanding station on the system. At the least, a protective filter is required for the pump, however, if the level of fines is high, a prefilter cyclone or actively-pulsed dust collector may be desired. The maximum rate usually attainable for this style of system in a multiple station operation is 6,000-10,000 lb (2,721-4,536 kg)/h.

CHAPTER 17 PLASTIC MANUFACTURING

System Automation

Complete design of an automated system must include controller design and line proofing.

Controller design. In an effort to reduce operator involvement, maintenance, and troubleshooting, a wide variety of alarms and control features are available:

- High vacuum signal—sent when line blockage or a clogged filter on the vacuum system is sensed.
- High pressure signal—sent when line blockage on the pressure system is sensed.
- Amperage meter—connected to pump motors to gage proper operating conditions.
- Low-vacuum signal—sent after timed interval, sensed when there is a lack of vacuum, denoting an empty railcar or bin.
- Low pressure sensor—senses pressure required to start pressure conveying and sends alarm signal if low.
- High-temperature sensor—senses pressure line temperature to operate cooler valve or initiate shut down of pressure system.
- "No-load" sensor—senses material exiting the vacuum receiver to warn of a flow problem or low supply condition.
- Low-level signal—sent when material reaches low level in a supply bin to denote a process problem, or in a destination bin to signal a load requirement.
- High-level sensor—initiates shut down and sends an alarm signal when high level is reached in the destination bin, or suspends operation when high level is reached in an intermediate collection point.

Line proofing. Since most material source-to-destination connections are made manually, a proof system is often desired to prove they are connected properly. A means of determining whether the proper material source is connected to the proper destination must be established. For example, a selector switch operated by a supervisor can indicate the proper source-to-destination route for the material. Then, when the operator connects the proper destination line to a particular source, a circuit is completed which allows conveying to proceed if the connection is correct, or issues an input to a control system if the connection is not right.

FEEDING AND BLENDING SYSTEMS

Feeding and blending systems may be volumetric or gravimetric, depending on how material is measured while used in the process. Volumetric systems come in many configurations, but the trend is to use gravimetric systems because they provide greater accuracy and better process control.

Volumetric Feeding Systems

Volumetric systems, as the name implies, feed resin by volume, and are not self-adjusting for any variations in bulk density or material head loading in the feed hopper. There are several types of volumetric feeders.

Rotary feeder. The rotary feeder consists of a star-shaped rotor enclosed in a cast housing with a material inlet at the top and a discharge port at the bottom. The rotary feeder valve is illustrated in Figure 17-5. Tolerances between the rotor and feeder body are close, ensuring proper separation of the upstream and downstream processes. These devices may be used to handle fine and free-flowing powders without flooding. A disadvantage to this type of feeder is that material may become stuck in the vane pockets.

Disk feeder. This feeder has a rotating disk mounted off-center under a hopper. The hopper bottom is sealed against the rotating disk with a groove that fills with material. This groove extends out from under the hopper and an extractor removes the material from

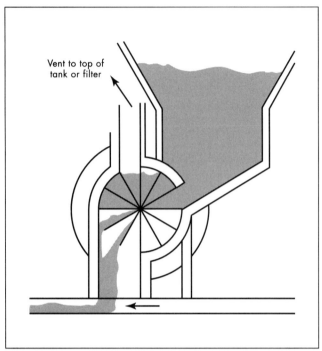

Fig. 17-5 Rotary feeder valve. *(Courtesy Chapman and Hall, "Injection Molding Handbook")*

it. Flow rates are a function of material density, speed of the disk, and geometry of the groove. Disk feeders work well with materials that are highly cohesive and have high shear factors.

Slot feeder. The slot feeder uses multiple vanes much like a venetian blind mounted horizontally. When the slots are static and overlapping, the material *bridges* above the slots. When the slots move, the bridge is broken and the material flows through the slots. This device mounts directly under a bin and works with stringy material, powders that do not flood, and other materials that are predictable in cohesive strength.

Vibratory feeders. Vibratory feeders move material that could otherwise be damaged by screw or belt feeders. A pan or tray supports the material and carries the material to be discharged. In operation, the direction of material motion is a vector at an angle to both the tray and the flow direction, causing the material particles to hop down the tray. Tray frequency and displacement, material flow characteristics, and head pressure of the material on the tray determine how well the material is conveyed. Vibratory feeders are practical when abrasive or friable material must be conveyed or when the contact point of the feeder must be easily cleaned.

Belt feeders. Belt feeders may be used as volumetric metering devices, and can be useful as extraction devices under bins and silos where high volumes of fragile material must be handled. The belt feeder shears material from the hopper on the silo by using an inlet gate attached to the feeder. This gate provides an adjustable profile of material on the conveyor belt. Probably the most critical element in the proper design of a belt volumetric feeder is the inlet from the feed bin onto the feeder belt. The opening must be properly designed to allow passage of the material at maximum flow. The feeder can then reduce flow by lowering the shear gate or reducing belt speed. Generally low in cost, belt feeders best convey materials with low moisture levels, granular materials, and, with care, some powders.

Single screw feeder. The single screw feeder is probably the most used device for feeding color and additives into injection or extrusion processes. Material is pushed by a horizontal screw from the feed hopper (under the pressure of material in the feed hopper) through a tube and into the processing machine.

Feeder controls. An *open loop control system* provides no feedback from the process for the controller to adjust output for changes in the feeding process, such as head loading or variations in bulk density. When feedback loops, such as motor speed or weigh cell outputs from the feeder or process are incorporated, a *closed loop system* results, which responds to process variables and self-adjusts to keep system performance within acceptable tolerances.

Gravimetric Feeding Systems

With more sophisticated methods of blending and control, accuracy and performance improve significantly. Gravimetric systems are usually more accurate than volumetric systems. Depending upon the material, blender design, and control system, a gravimetric system's accuracy may increase by a factor of ten when compared to its volumetric counterpart.

A gravimetric system is simply a volumetric system with one or more weigh cells. With gravimetric systems, as with closed-loop volumetric controls, more process and performance information is fed back to the control system. As more data are extracted for use by the controller, the system provides better performance through self-tuning.

Volumetric systems are unable to adjust their performance for variations in material bulk density or flow characteristics of difficult-to-handle materials such as powders. Increased accuracy and tighter process control are significant reasons for using a gravimetric system. With increasing costs for feedstock and additives, accuracy and inventory control are prime user concerns.

From the user's perspective, there are several advantages to gravimetric systems:

• Accuracy and reliability.
• Quick cleaning and material changes.
• Maintenance and diagnostics.
• Reporting functions—statistical process control (SPC), statistical quality control (SQC).
• User friendly.

More gravimetric systems use stainless steel components—from the feed hoppers to the vacuum take-off—reducing the risk of rusting and product contamination. Better welding and fabrication techniques reduce the probability of cross-contamination during changeover, because there is a reduced possibility that pellets or additives will be trapped on rough edges or ledges. Modular design and construction of the system allows access to virtually all the key components for quick cleaning, part replacement, and rearranging system throughput capabilities (such as changing the size of the auger, motor, gearbox, etc.).

Weighing system. The key component in any weighing system is the load cell, which must weigh material accurately and consistently. The system must be designed to deal with electrical noise, vibration, and perturbations in the production environment. Weighing and conveying components of gravimetric systems are sized more closely to the processing rates for Just-in-Time material delivery. The designer should size the load cell to weigh the minimum amount of material needed to maintain the maximum production rate. This significantly improves the accuracy and performance of a gravimetric system.

Control system. Current technology allows designers to use devices which permit the control system to evaluate and determine its course of action or correction, within defined parameters, to optimize performance and improve accuracy. In addition, the technol-

ogy has *recipe* capability and, once set up for various materials, the gravimetric feeders can store the data in memory. Therefore, a recipe can be recalled, allowing the user to begin processing the product much faster.

Blending Systems

Blending is the use of two or more feeders to meter different ingredients into a process according to a recipe. Auger or vibratory feeders are most often used in blending systems. There also may be a passive or active mixing device. On a volumetric blender, the feeders are positioned around the blending device, that may be a series of baffles through which the different materials fall (passive), or a mixer driven by a motor (active). Material is simultaneously metered into the mixer and the mixed blend is then fed into the process. The choice of feeders and mixers again depends upon the characteristics of the material being fed. For example, a vibratory blender or feeder will have difficulty accurately feeding hard-to-flow material.

Special considerations may be required for the feed hopper design when feeding irregular or hard-to-flow materials such as regrind. Depending upon the quality of the regrind used, a larger feed hopper throat opening may be required to minimize the possibility of material bridging.

For the volumetric blending systems, as with volumetric feeders, setup and calibration require the making of catch samples over a fixed time frame. Each sample is then weighed, and the metering rate can be calculated from the time and weight measurement. Then, if necessary, the controls are adjusted, another sample is taken, and another control adjustment is made. The process is repeated until the rate is at the desired setting. Periodically, the user should check the accuracy of the feeder or blender because, as materials change and equipment ages, calibration can drift.

Selecting a System

When selecting a feeder or blending system, the user must be specific about requirements. A feeding system selection work sheet is shown in Figure 17-6. Several factors are to be considered:

• Material characteristics such as the density and friability of powder, pellets, regrind, etc.
• Throughput.
• Accuracy.
• Installation (machine mounted, floor mounted, etc.).
• Recipes for blender applications.
• Voltages available.
• Control interfaces with any distributed control or monitoring system and/or the primary processing device (for example, an extruder or injection molding machine [IMM]).
• Control and operational requirements (reporting, data, etc.).
• Cost and budget constraints.
• Simplicity of installation, operation, and set up.
• Ease of maintenance.
• System design allows for future change or growth.

Evaluating the material characteristics is very important in selecting the proper type of feeder system to use. If the material varies in bulk density, is hygroscopic or hard-to-flow, volumetric systems may not be able to accurately feed it. Because the material may have a tendency to clump and bridge, it may not evenly flow into the delivery device (screw, belt, vibratory tray, etc.), resulting in poor performance of the feeding system. Often with hard-to-flow material, flow aid devices (agitators, rappers, etc.) may be required to get a more even flow of material to the feeder. Consistent material flow to the delivery device is critical to the performance of the feeding system.

CHAPTER 17   PLASTIC MANUFACTURING

Feeding System Selection Work Sheet

Material: _____

Friable: yes_____   no _____

Bulk density: _____lb/ft³ (kg/m³)

System voltage:_____

Process throughput: maximum_____lb (kg)/h   minimum_____lb (kg)/h

    1. Additive throughput: maximum_____lb (kg)/h   minimum_____lb (kg)/h

    2. Component throughput: maximum_____lb (kg)/h   minimum_____lb (kg)/h

    3. Other:_____

For blending systems, this is the minimal amount of information required for each material component. For single additive systems, if there are plans for the feeder to run more than one type of material, provide this information for each material to be run through the same feeder. Because of the different handling and feeding characteristics of each material, a configuration for one material may not work if the material is changed. Injection molders should also provide the cycle voltage of the injection molding machine (24V or 110V) and the screw recovery time.

Fig. 17-6 Feeding system selection work sheet. *(Courtesy Universal Dynamics, Inc.)*

The auger may not be the best choice for a delivery device with friable material that easily fractures or splinters in the handling process. Vibratory and belt feeding systems may do a better job.

Feeders do not have an infinite feed-rate turndown. As an example, a feeder metering material at a rate of 100 lb (45 kg)/h will not be able to accurately feed that same material at 1 lb (0.5 kg)/h. The feeder manufacturer should be able to tell the user what the expected ranges of throughput will be for a specific configuration. Optimum feeder performance occurs in the middle ranges of the throughput curve. When operated at the fringes of the range, accuracy and performance suffer.

No feeding equipment manufacturer can say with certainty what the accuracy of a system will be. Generally, closed-loop volumetric systems are more accurate than open loop systems, and gravimetric systems are more accurate than volumetric systems. Beyond that, accuracy depends upon the material, type of feeder, and the environment. Material variations occur, feeder components wear, and the environment will change because of these variables. Accuracy confirmation may be obtained by testing the equipment performance through catch samples and weighing the results. If accuracy is critical, vigilance and periodic calibration may be required. The ultimate test is the quality of the final product and at some point the increased cost of the incremental improvement in feeder performance is not justified by the improvement in product quality. Specifications and tolerances are developed by a company according to the standards in its industry, which vary from market to market.

MATERIAL CONDITIONING SYSTEMS

Resin moving from storage to the molding machine often requires a drying stage due to hygroscopic properties of the material. Efficient heating and drying of plastic resins can be important to the manufacture of a consistently acceptable product that meets quality requirements. The processor must pretreat plastic resins in strict adherence with the manufacturer's recommendation.

Plastic resins may be either hygroscopic or nonhygroscopic, depending on whether or not the resin will absorb or adsorb moisture. *Nonhygroscopic resins* collect moisture only on the pellet surface (*adsorption*), making it easy to remove. *Hygroscopic resins*, however, collect moisture throughout the pellet (*absorption*), making its removal more difficult. Wherever it is found, the presence of moisture presents potential problems, from cosmetic surface blemishes to serious structural defects.

Typical nonhygroscopic resins are polyethylene (PE), polypropylene (PP), polystyrene (PS), and polyvinyl chloride (PVC). Fillers such as talc, calcium carbonate, carbon black, and wood flour, when added to nonhygroscopic resins like PE or PP in sufficient quantity, can make the resin behave like hygroscopic resins.

Surface moisture on nonhygroscopic plastic pellets can be effectively removed using only heated ambient air, but removal of moisture collected within hygroscopic pellets requires dehumidified heated air. Both systems require that the resin be exposed to adequate airflow heated to the proper temperature for the time prescribed by the resin manufacturer. The equipment required for these drying systems varies considerably in terms of cost and complexity.

Hot Air Drying Systems

The airflow required for drying systems is determined by the amount of material to be processed. A standard reference is to plan for airflow of 1 ft³ (0.03 m³) per lb/h (62 L/min per kg/h) of material processed. For example, a system processing 150 lb/h would require a 150 cubic feet per minute (CFM) drying system. A system processing 150 kg/h would require a 9,300 L/min system.

The drying vessel (hopper) must be large enough to permit the resin to remain inside for the time required to complete the drying. A system operating at 150 lb/h with a resin that dries in four hours will require a hopper holding at least 600 lb (4 h × 150 lb/h = 600 lb). Similarly, one operating at 150 kg/h with a resin that dries in four hours would require a 600 kg hopper.

In processing, centrifugal fans move the air, and the heat source is usually an electric heater, though gas-fired heating systems are gaining in popularity for some applications. A hopper specifically designed for drying provides the necessary residence time to dry the material. A drying system for hygroscopic materials requires the addition of a dehumidifier to the system.

A simple hot air drying system consists of the process air fan with an inlet filter, a heating system, a control system, and a drying hopper. Controls include a basic temperature control with digital readout of set point and actual temperature, a blower heater interlock, and some sort of overtemperature protection, such as an alarm or shutdown.

Dehumidifying Drying Systems

For hygroscopic materials, a dehumidification unit is added to lower the dew point of the air. The lower the dew point, the more moisture the air can hold. A dew point of at least $-20°$ F ($-29°$ C) is required to have an effective dehumidifying drying system. Most modern systems are designed to provide dew points of $-40°$ F ($-40°$ C) or lower. The dew point of air can be reduced by several means including refrigerating the air, compressing and cooling the air, or by passing the air through a desiccant material. Refrigerating dryers are unable to reach dew points below 40° F (4° C) which is not sufficient for an effective dehumidifying drying system. Compressing and cooling the air, while effective in lowering the dew point, is both complicated and expensive. Simple and affordable desiccant dryers can be designed to lower the dew point of air well below $-40°$ F ($-40°$ C), making them capable of drying all the hygroscopic resins in use today.

A *desiccant* is a material with a natural affinity for moisture. The most commonly-used desiccant is a synthetically-produced crystalline metal alumina-silicate from which the water of hydration has been removed, permitting it to adsorb moisture. When used in a dehumidifying dryer, the desiccant eventually becomes saturated. However, it can be renewed through a process called *regeneration*, that is accomplished by heating the desiccant to drive off the collected moisture. After a cooling period, the desiccant is again able to adsorb moisture, making it ideal for use in drying systems.

The typical dehumidifying drying system consists of the process air fan, dehumidifier, an electric or gas-fired air heating system, a control system, the drying hopper, and a process air filter. The dehumidifier itself includes the desiccant regeneration system.

Single rotating bed. A single desiccant-coated honeycomb wheel rotates slowly, exposing part of the wheel to process air, part to regeneration, and part to cooling prior to returning to the process.

Multiple indexing bed. This is usually a three-bed arrangement, with one bed on process, one regenerating, while the third is being cooled prior to going on line to the process.

Twin stationary beds. One bed is on process while the second is being regenerated and then cooled prior to going on to process (see Fig. 17-7). The twin stationary bed dehumidifier is simple, with relatively few moving parts, making it easy and inexpensive to maintain. The initial investment is usually lower than the other designs.

Selecting a bed design. Systems utilizing the twin bed design are the most widely used, followed by the multiple indexing beds, and then the single rotating bed. All of these systems are designed to provide a continuous supply of dry air. Both the multiple indexing bed and single rotating bed work very effectively, although they tend to be mechanically complex, costly to maintain, and usually involve a higher initial investment.

Drying System Controls

Electro-mechanical controls or more sophisticated microprocessors provide temperature control and some form of overtemperature alarm or shutdown. The more sophisticated versions may include dew point monitoring and dew point-based regeneration, ampere monitoring diagnostics, and other specialty functions.

Special Equipment

Standard systems are often customized for processing specific materials. The drying hopper may be redesigned for a material with erratic flow tendencies. Other materials may have drying needs that require additional equipment to the standard drying system. With material requiring high drying temperatures, the hot return air from the drying hopper may result in less efficient moisture adsorption by the desiccant, reducing the overall drying efficiency. In this case, a cooling coil is inserted into the return air line to lower the temperature to a point where the adsorption efficiency of the desiccant is restored.

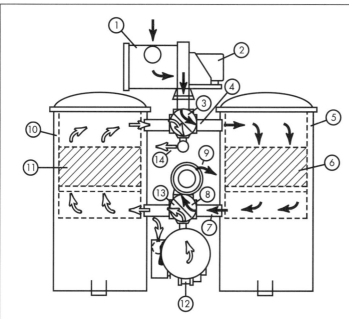

Dehumidifying and drying the air:
1. Process air enters drying system.
2. Process air blower.
3. Air passes through upper valve in upper duct of system.
4. Upper duct moves air.
5. Process tower where air will be dried.
6. Moisture adsorption takes place in desiccant bed.
7. Process air leaves by lower duct.
8. Air moves through valve.
9. Process air to be delivered to material being dried.

Desiccant bed regeneration:
10. Tower being used for desiccant regeneration.
11. Saturated desiccant bed being regenerated.
12. Regeneration system air heater and blower.
13. Heated air passes through valve in lower duct to enter tower and heat saturated bed, which then releases moisture to be carried out of system.
14. Regeneration air passes through lower valve and is vented.

Turning upper and lower valves in ducts allow dehumidifying and regenerating functions to be switched from tower to tower, where they occur simultaneously.

Fig. 17-7 Dehumidifying drying system. *(Courtesy Universal Dynamics, Inc.)*

CHAPTER 17   PLASTIC MANUFACTURING

Problems are also encountered with materials that contain additives which vaporize at standard drying temperatures, where the vapor may pass through the filter and recondense in the desiccant bed, coating the desiccant and rendering it partially or completely ineffective. In this instance, a special secondary cooling and filtering system is employed to recondense and remove the troublesome by-product from the drying loop. Nearly any pelletized plastic resin can be properly dried, although special designs increase the cost of the system.

HANDLING OF MOLDED PARTS

While the finished product can be removed in many ways from the primary production equipment, special consideration should be given to flexibility in product output, method of handling secondary operations, packaging, product identification, intermediate and final component count, and interfacing with existing production and quality control procedures. Certain primary plastic production processes require high speed: for example, part removal, cutting, counting, and performing secondary operations. Processes that are not properly designed for quick changeover can be cumbersome to set up, start up, or disassemble. Since global competitiveness dictates the need for minimum inventory and short delivery times, it is essential to design flexible, quick-change manufacturing processes and implement a continuous improvement program to achieve these goals.

The secondary and packaging operations are combined with the primary production and conversion manufacturing process as often as possible to save time and cost and improve logistics. Once the most efficient primary production and conversion process is developed, the maximum number of secondary operations are planned to run concurrently with the primary process. In the plastics industry, the cell or workstation principle is the most cost-efficient manufacturing method, producing finished products faster than with earlier methods. In the past, components manufactured at various locations were made in batches and moved to the next operation, with many product-staging stations located throughout the manufacturing process. When rearranging the manufacturing process to cell or workstation operation, it is important to recognize that most primary plastic production and conversion equipment is more complex than metalworking or similar machines.

FREE-DROP SYSTEMS FOR MOLDED PARTS HANDLING

Of all the ways to handle parts coming from an IMM, some of the simplest and least expensive allow the parts to fall free from the mold. Designing parts and molding equipment for free-fall can result in a very consistent molding cycle when compared to having an operator remove the parts after each cycle.

Description

In the simplest case, parts are allowed to fall directly into a box for bulk packing. When full, the box is removed and replaced with an empty one. Often the operator watches for the box to fill and exchanges the container.

This simple system can be made more sophisticated by adding a weighing or part counting system to determine that a container is full, and alert a human operator via a light or audible warning system to make a container change. A counting system also can be used to index a conveyor to move the full and empty boxes into their respective positions, or even interface with the molding machine to stop the molding cycle. Neither manual nor counting methods allow for parts orientation, however, so they are generally best suited for small parts with no cosmetic (appearance) requirements.

An offshoot of the box-filling approach is to have the parts fall onto a conveyor, upon which they are taken to be packed or to some other postmolding operation (for example decorating, packaging, inspection, assembly, etc.). In some cases, the conveyor is indexed to the cycle of the molding machine, rather than running continuously. This allows the parts a specified cooling period of several molding cycles, with the cooling period more precisely controlled than if the belts were continuously running.

Part Orientation

When large objects such as 5 gal (19 L) pails are molded, a system (technically a free-drop system) is often used where the parts are ejected and allowed to fall from the mold, but with a sophisticated "pail catcher" unit. The pail catcher is located under the molding area of the machine and has a bucket assembly on the end of a vertically movable arm. When the pail is ejected from the mold, the bucket catches the pail and lowers it, usually to a conveyor, for removal to a secondary operation area. Orientation of the part is imperfect, but the pails are standing. Special sensors on the catching unit are directly interfaced to the molding machine. If a pail does not fall properly, the pail catcher will not allow the machine to begin its next molding cycle, thus protecting the mold from potential damage. While not inexpensive, a pail catcher system is considerably less costly than a similarly capable, full-fledged, top-entry, side-entry, or turret robot.

Another approach to part orientation for free-fall parts is to use specially designed chutes. To accomplish orientation, however, the parts must generally have a high aspect ratio, that is, length divided by height (or vice versa) should be greater than 4:1. An example of this type of part is a medical petri dish, usually about 4 in. (102 mm) in diameter by about 0.5-in. (13-mm) high.

Because of the high aspect ratio, chutes can be designed to guide the parts so they are partially oriented as they leave the chutes. Without electrical sensors of some form, the chute cannot determine top from bottom, but it can keep the parts from becoming scrambled after falling from the molding machine. In some applications, this partial orientation is sufficient.

Another high aspect ratio application of free-fall orientation was the molding of airline snack trays, about 8-in. (203-mm) long by 4.5-in. (114-mm) wide by 0.6-in. (15-mm) deep. The parts were molded in a two-cavity mold, with the long axis of the parts vertical. When it was time to eject the parts from the mold, the mold was opened only about 3 in. (76 mm). This prevented the parts from turning around as they fell. Thus partially oriented, the parts fell into a specially designed chute, like a long, rectangular funnel, placed under the molding area of the machine (see Fig. 17-8). The bottom of the funnel was made into a long radius curve and joined a U-shaped slide. As the parts continued through the radius portion, they were rotated and then they exited into the U-shaped slide. When the parts reached the end of the slide, a curved piece of wire on one side of the slide tipped over each tray, causing it to fall face-up onto the pile of previously molded trays. After about 100 cycles, the stack of trays was manually removed and packed. This simple approach resulted in considerable savings to the molder (and the customer), compared to what a more sophisticated system might have cost to do the same job. Ultimately, the system produced about two million trays.

Other approaches to part orientation and handling include what are called guide chutes and swing chutes. These are mechanisms built into and mounted in the mold itself, acting as both parts removal and guidance mechanisms.

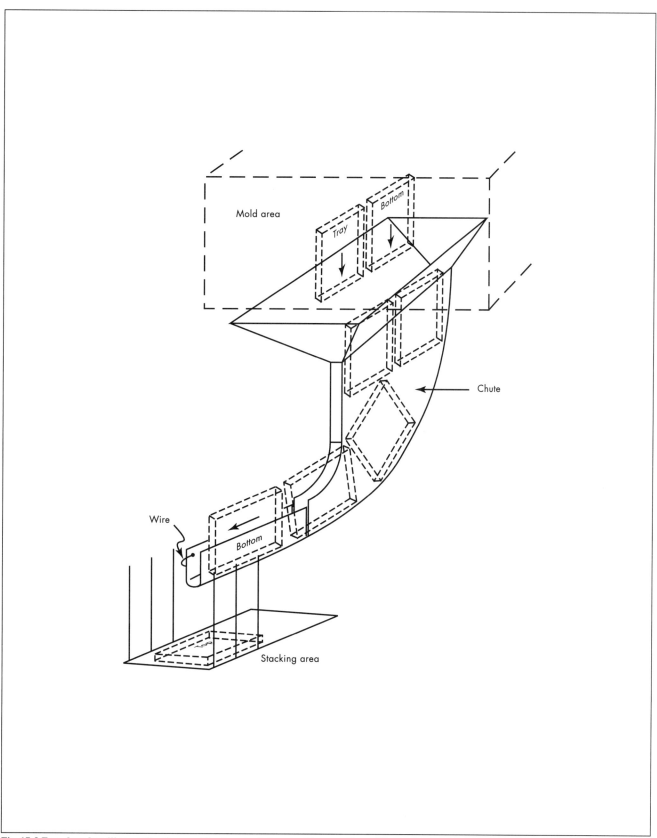

Fig. 17-8 Free-drop handling application resulting in oriented parts. *(Courtesy Neward Enterprises)*

CHAPTER 17   PLASTIC MANUFACTURING

Guide chutes are moving rails used primarily for flat objects like petri dishes. The rails move to receive the parts as they are ejected, and then guide them out the bottom of the mold into a waiting parts handling system (conveyor, parts stacker, etc.).

Swing chutes are rotating arms mounted on the mold. The arms, generally fitted with vacuum cups, rotate into the mold just as it is opening and the parts are to be ejected. As soon as the arms receive the parts, they begin to swing back to their original position while the mold closes. This allows for an extremely fast cycle, with positive part transfer and orientation. The arms can be actuated with air or cams; however, the fastest (and most expensive) versions are driven by a servomotor. Some typical applications for swing chutes are closures, petri dishes, and berry baskets.

Advantages and Limitations

To have the parts fall free (or not) requires that the part, mold, and downstream equipment are designed and built with that in mind. Often, this requires no special considerations, but the designers of the part, mold, and downstream equipment all should make conscious decisions to achieve effective free-fall handling and make sure that the advantages of lower cost and faster implementation are not offset by the limitations realized.

The disadvantages of free-fall are possible part damage (scuffing, breaking, or scratching), possible tool damage if a part hangs up in the tool when the mold closes, and a limited ability to orient the parts. Less important problems are part contamination due to dust particles in the air, and separation of parts from sprues and runners. In a properly designed system that anticipates these possibilities, they should not be of major concern.

CONVEYING SYSTEMS FOR PART HANDLING

Conveyors, along with controls for indexing, cycle count, weigh scale systems, and pick/place equipment for secondary work, can be effectively used to move molded plastic parts. Process control of conveyors and related equipment can allow quality control personnel to optimize their time on the shop floor. Start looking at any human handling of parts that does not add value to the end product. This could justify an automation program. Once management has determined the budget, and the return on investment required, investigating available equipment can begin. Motorized conveyors can be a cost-effective option.

Moving Parts to a Central Location

Moving parts to a central location for packing or secondary work is simple, and can be done with conveyors and turntables. This helps minimize the time personnel wait for product to be molded so they can do packing or secondary work. With parts being delivered at closer intervals, personnel do not wait at each machine for product. Consequently, fewer people may be needed and their time may be used more productively.

Moving Parts that Need Cooling

One area of cost reduction is the handling of parts that need cooling before secondary work can be done, or before the part is packed. When cooling time is necessary, a conveyor equipped with variable speed drive or clutch/brakes, or both, and indexing controls can be used. The finished part can be ejected onto the conveyor. A signal, used to initiate conveyor motion, is given from an output off the molding machine. After the conveyor belt has traveled a set distance to clear the drop zone for the next shot, the conveyor stops and waits for the next signal. If a robot is being used, the signal to begin motion generally comes from the robotics' programmable logic controller (PLC) and the conveyor is placed outside the press. The required part cooling time helps determine the length of conveyor needed for the application. If a long conveyor is required, the available floor space also must be determined. If there is not enough floor space, then stacked, vertical, or spiral conveyors may be considered. Again, which of these is selected depends upon the required cooling time and the available floor space.

Automated Box Filling

A second area of possible cost reduction is the filling of boxes. Some parts may need to be layer-packed with protective dunnage and some may just need to be stacked in a box. Automating either of these may require use of a robot along with a conveyor.

If the parts are to be bulk-packed, the quantity of parts in the box could be determined by weigh scales or cycle counting. In either instance, a conveyor equipped with box filling and indexing capabilities should be used.

A box filling system that requires gravity, or the motion of one box to move another within the filling zone, may require personnel to watch the equipment for jams. Part of the automating goal is to minimize personnel time around the press. While more expensive, a powered, indexed conveying system can be better at accomplishing this objective than less costly equipment.

Cycle counting generally can be used if the final number of parts required in the box is divisible by the cavitation in the mold. If you have a problem with gate freeze-off and the number of parts per cycle is not consistent, a weigh scale could be used. Gate freeze-off, however, indicates an unstable operation that affects part quality. It is better to solve problems like this before automating.

Weigh scales are available for weight-only or for count-by-weight. The most flexible purchase is one capable of both, since the production requirements may change. Most weigh-scale equipment does not do well in an environment where static electricity is present, which is almost always true in plastics manufacturing. When buying scale equipment for automation, make sure it has a successful track record in the plastics industry and around high-static areas. Static electricity can randomly reset scales and zero-out set points.

Robotics with Box-holding Conveyors

If the concern is both potential part damage and formal packing, adding a full-fledged robot may be the best choice. Robotics with a box-holding conveyor, using extremely accurate indexing abilities, can still allow for optimum automation. Some questions that need to be considered in this approach are:

- Is the box size consistent?
- How fast does a box need to be changed out of the fill zone? (The conveyor supplier will need the machine cycle time required to make parts so belt speeds can be calculated.)
- Is dunnage a requirement? If so, will the robot have enough time to insert it or will separate handling equipment be needed?
- Is it possible to close the box before an inspection takes place? (If so, the box closing equipment could be incorporated into the box handling system.)
- How many boxes per hour will be required? If many boxes are needed, does the requisite floor space for the conveyors exist, or should a full-plant conveyor system be investigated?
- Is orientation of the product on a conveyor system required for downstream secondary work? (If so, selection of the proper conveying equipment is critical to minimizing the observation time of personnel. Also consider implementation of pick and place equipment at these secondary stations.) Will the conveyor frame design contribute to easy installation of the pick and place hardware?

Other characteristics of the part will affect conveyor selection. Does the product require any special handling? Is marring of surfaces unacceptable? There are mar-preventive belts available for conveyors, but keep in mind the word "preventive." Conveyor suppliers who say their belt will not mar the product may not consider the sometimes inconsistent ejection of parts or how parts land on a belt under the drop zone. If marring is a problem, seriously consider the use of robots.

Other special requirements may be water bath conveyors for cooling of thick-walled parts. In the case of parts molded from nylon, moisture conditioning may be required to produce the dimensional change expected in end-use environments, reducing subsequent dimensional variations from varying humidity. Sometimes moisture conditioning is used to temporarily increase toughness before assembly operations.

Conveyors with Part and Runner Separators

Parts may have runners that need to be separated. Some molders use sprue pickers, while others prefer simple conveyors with separation equipment. Several different types of separation equipment are available. One of these consists of roller separators. That is, rollers located at the end of either a cleated or flat belt conveyor. As the part and runner go over the rollers, separation is accomplished by gaps between the belt and roller, or between roller and roller, as the smaller of the molded pieces (either part or runner) drops through the gap and the larger is passed on to another conveyor or separate container.

Another type of separator uses a belt with fingers projecting from its surface to grab either the part or the runner and separate them. Suppliers of part and runner separation equipment will evaluate the application, considering cycle time, preference of conveyor style, and a sample of the parts having runners. They generally ask for a minimum of three complete shots for evaluation. If a runner has a tendency to curl up, the processor should send a curled-up runner to the equipment supplier.

Other separation equipment includes auger, drum, and vibratory separators. When selecting this type of equipment for automation, precise geometric sizes and differences between the items to be separated must be sent to the equipment supplier. Two or three steps in the separation process may be required to achieve the desired results.

Improved Quality Control

Process control on a molding machine helps quality assurance and processing personnel. When given a signal from the process control equipment that a bad cycle has taken place, the underpress conveyor can reverse direction and deposit the part(s) from that bad cycle away from the good parts, as shown in Figure 17-9. Inspection personnel periodically stop and check for any bad parts. If present, they can inform those in charge of monitoring and correcting the molding process. Use of process control on a box filling system helps to prevent bad parts from getting mixed with the good.

Implementation

Each plant has its own automation requirements and different levels of automation it wants to attain. Conveyors are usually required to fully complete the automation process. They are not just driven belts, rollers, or ropes, but pieces of equipment to pass material from one stage of production to another. Whatever parts are being molded, the conveyor equipment must be reliable and capable of withstanding the traffic flow around it.

Generally, conveyor equipment can be implemented quickly. If management requires equipment to automate part handling in a short time frame, consider conveyors, and someone who can supply turnkey systems. A quality turnkey vendor, while sometimes more expensive, will generally have good support vendors who work together to resolve situations when they arise.

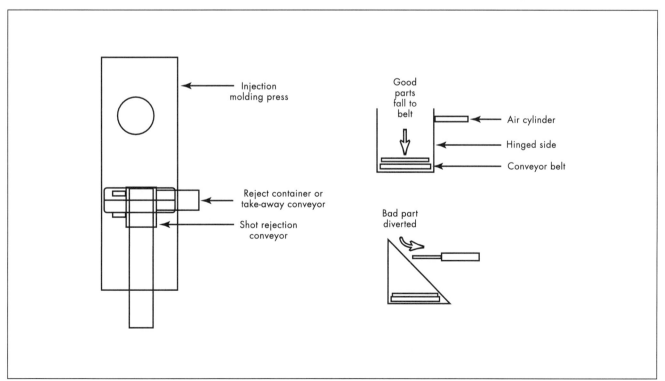

Fig. 17-9 Parts from a bad cycle are rejected by reversing the conveyor. *(Courtesy EMI Plastics Equipment)*

CHAPTER 17 PLASTIC MANUFACTURING

Case Study: Electric Track Vehicles

A large manufacturer of plastic medical devices required an integrated automated material transport system to complement their high-volume molding operation. They were using a material delivery system where totes from the molding presses were placed on pallets and delivered to the marking, assembly, and packing machines. However, they neglected to address the issues of good manufacturing practices (GMP), quality, security, and machine utilization in their operation. Thousands of full and empty totes on pallets awaited transport from process to process.

To eliminate the need for manually moving the pallets, the Manufacturing Engineering department selected an electric track vehicle (ETV) system to deliver molded parts from more than 35 injection molding presses to the marking, assembly, and packaging lines. The ETV has the ability to change elevation without the use of a lift and travel at ceiling elevation to deliver plastic components. Four loops of ETV track were interconnected to permit all of the vehicles to support any group of machines.

In this application, the ETV held a clamshell container (see Fig. 17-10) directly below the output conveyor at any of the molding presses. With the clamshell doors open, a prescribed amount of plastic components were released into the container. The clamshell doors closed and the ETV was ready to travel. The injection molding press's programmable logic controllers (PLCs) and the ETV personal computer (PC) controller performed a "handshake" communication to confirm the stock keeping unit (SKU) number, lot number, and destination. The ETV then traveled vertically, and inverted so that the clamshell container was suspended below the ETV (Fig. 17-11). Several checks en route confirmed that the uniquely identified vehicle, with the uniquely identified lot of plastic components, was destined for the scheduled marking, assembly, and packaging machine on one of the lines. The ETV positioned above the appropriate bowl feeders at the destination machine, opened the clamshell doors, and dropped the plastic parts.

After dumping their components, all ETVs were routed to an air shower area. Because of high static buildup, the plastic components tended to adhere to the sides of the container, even though it was specially designed to minimize static. To be 100% sure and to avoid mixed lots, sizes, or colors, an air shower thoroughly cleaned the interior of the container.

This application produced several benefits. Labor savings occurred when personnel were no longer needed to move pallets of totes from process to process. Machine operators can monitor their equipment 100% of the time, now that the nonvalue-added transac-

tion of moving and dumping totes has been eliminated. Eliminating the pallets of full totes throughout the plant has cut down on fork lift traffic, and improved space utilization and work flow. With a new host scheduling system directing the ETV, components are routed on a JIT basis, improving utilization of equipment. The system eliminates any human contamination and contact with the plastic components, important where cleanroom conditions are required. Quality control is improved as the smaller lots are statistically tracked within and between processes.

ROBOTIC SYSTEMS FOR PARTS ORIENTATION

Whenever in-line secondary operations from a molding system are planned, a robot that retrieves the parts from the mold and delivers them properly oriented for the next operation is usually the most effective solution. Complete robot and downstream secondary operations systems are available to accommodate a variety of molded parts.

Robots, with their uninterrupted sequence, can remove molded parts and all but eliminate the time spent transferring production from one station to another. Another important gain for robot automation is saving valuable floor space. Secondary operations can be placed close together, and directly in line with parts removal. Redundant work areas can then be dedicated to more productive operations, resulting in further increases in productivity.

It is not recommended to base secondary automatic operations upon a feed system that allows parts to fall randomly from the mold, and then re-orients them using an unscrambling system of some kind. Although systems are available for this purpose, they are never 100% efficient in the unscrambling and re-orienting function. Consequently, they reduce the effectiveness of downstream equipment. A robot that performs the secondary operation itself can be used. However, this increases the mass and complexity of the system which adversely affects cycle time. The ideal robot is simple, lightweight, and fast.

With the continued development of lightweight servodriven robots, the cycle time penalty associated with robotic part retrieval equipment in the past can now be minimized, eliminated, or even reversed to permit faster than free-fall cycle times.

The benefits of robot part retrieval can now be planned as a part of the manufacturing strategy. These benefits include:

- Reduced labor costs.
- Little or no loss of cycle time when compared to free-fall.
- No scrap due to the contamination or marring that would occur during free-fall.
- No mold open delay needed to avoid closing on trapped parts.

Fig. 17-10 Open "clamshell" container on electric track receives molded parts. *(Courtesy Translogic Corporation)*

Fig. 17-11 Inverted container travels to its destination, where it will open and release its load. *(Courtesy Translogic Corporation)*

• No mold protection stoppages occur.
• Reduced mold maintenance costs from safer operations.
• More reliably oriented delivery to the next phase in the secondary operations.

High-speed Lightweight Robot Arm for Parts Retrieval

Robots now can be built from lightweight carbon fiber construction, accelerated at 25 Gs or more, and attain linear velocities of almost 60 ft (18 m)/sec, all of which permit part retrieval in as little as 300 milliseconds.

An example of a high-speed robot arm is shown in Figure 17-12. This design has two carbon fiber arms driven by a 6-hp (4,500-W) brushless DC servomotor. These tubular arms slide on ultra-high molecular weight (UHMW) polyethylene strip bearings mounted on the surfaces of the fixed steel tubes. A pulley and cable system converts the radial motion of the motor to linear robot motion.

A 1.5-hp (1,100-W) centrifugal fan is connected to the tube system, pulling high-volume, low-pressure air through it and entering through the receiver orifices at the right side of the robot arms. With the robot in the forward position, after the mold opens, the receivers align with the cores of the mold and are shaped to correspond with geometry of the molded parts. When the mold ejection system ejects the parts, they are impelled by the high-volume airflow into the receivers. At that point, a vacuum transducer can be used to verify that all parts are present, delivering a permissive signal through the machine/robot interface, and allowing the robot to exit, the clamp to close, and the cycle to repeat.

The arm permits the robot to retrieve the parts in a definite orientation as fast or faster than they can fall free by gravity, with a single axis of linear motion. Secondary operations can now be fed parts by a separate transfer mechanism which will remove the parts from the robot during the next molding cycle.

Robotic Cells with Downstream Secondary Operations

Manufacturing engineers can specify and design completely automated cells to permit molding lines to run automatically, and build in all of the benefits mentioned earlier. Systems or cells can be designed to include discrete part operations such as:

• Parts retrieval.
• Assembly.

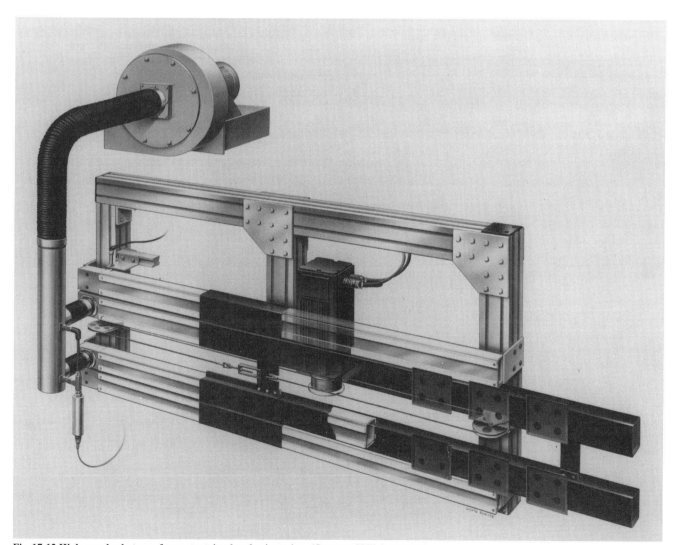

Fig. 17-12 High-speed robot arm for part retrieval and orientation. *(Courtesy CBW Automation)*

CHAPTER 17   PLASTIC MANUFACTURING

• Decoration.
• Welding.
• Inspection.
• Stacking.
• Layer packing.
• Wrapping.
• Carton filling.
• Palletizing.
• Lot identification.

Almost any other manipulation or secondary operation can be included. Single source responsibility for these systems is often chosen to provide strong vendor support during the installation and debugging of the equipment, and the training of personnel who will be responsible for running and maintaining it.

Robotic cell with part orientation and packaging. The robot shown at the right side of Figure17-13 is designed to retrieve 32 aerosol caps from a 500-ton (4.5-MN) molding system running at a cycle time of between six and seven seconds. Upon retrieval, the parts are transferred by an L-cam transfer vacuum plate to a conveyor, still in oriented condition, and fed to a marshaling zone where they are allowed to array in a pattern corresponding with the shipping carton size. There, a twin x-y axis layer packer with a vacuum pickup plate picks up the complete array of caps, shuttles them to align with the carton, and then layer packs the caps until the carton is filled. Filled cartons are conveyed onward, new empty cartons are shuttled into position, and the process repeats.

Robotic cell with assembly operation. In Figure 17-14, a system that retrieves, assembles, and stacks two-piece petri dishes is shown. In this case, the parts are molded in a 400-ton (3.6-MN) machine, in a 2×12 cavity hot-runner stack mold with bases on the clamp side and covers on the injection side of the mold.

This system is an example of where high-speed robotic retrieval was the catalyst for permitting the molder to move up in molding technology from 2×8 to 2×12 cavity molds, increasing productivity by almost 50%.

PLANNING AND IMPLEMENTING AN AUTOMATED MOLDING CELL

This section discusses the benefits of automation, the planning process, features of automation equipment, and risk assessment.

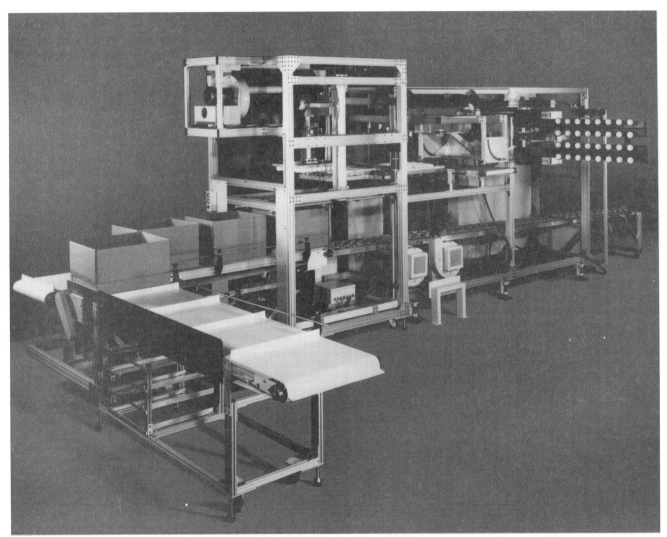

Fig. 17-13 Robotic retrieval system that transfers 32 aerosol caps oriented for packing into cartons. *(Courtesy CBW Automation)*

TOOL AND MANUFACTURING ENGINEERS HANDBOOK

CHAPTER 17   PLASTIC MANUFACTURING

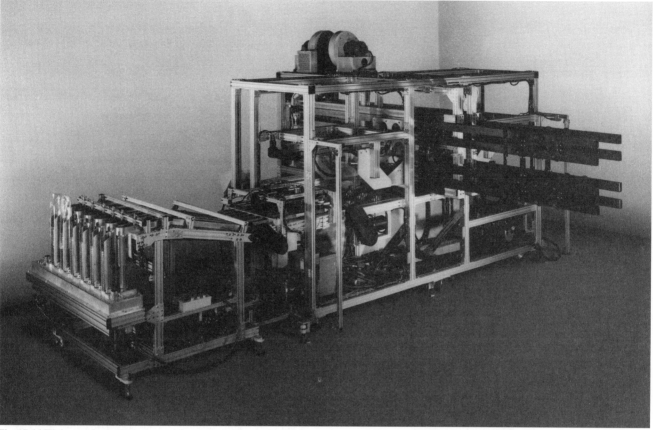

Fig. 17-14 High-speed robotic system retrieves, assembles, and stacks two-piece petri dishes. *(Courtesy CBW Automation)*

Benefits of Automation

Automation of parts handling in injection molding is usually considered for the following reasons:

- Improve part quality (less damage).
- Improve productivity (faster cycle time).
- Improve yield (less scrap).
- Reduce labor.
- Improve worker safety.
- Reduce work-in-process (WIP).

Part quality. A consistent cycle time is key to a stable and repeatable injection molding process. Semiautomatic operation with manual part removal is inherently inconsistent, whereas robotic part removal is consistent.

Allowing parts to free-fall after ejection in an automatic molding cycle can result in part damage due to scuffing, breakage, or grease contamination. Robotic part removal avoids this damage.

Productivity. A reduced overall molding cycle time can sometimes be achieved through automation. The most obvious scenario eliminates slow manual part removal in a semiautomatic operation. However, there are other automation alternatives to robotics that can further reduce cycle times.

Yield. Any manual or randomly-performed operation on a molded part is a source of output variability. Scrap is made whenever an outcome falls outside the tolerance allowed for any characteristic that is critical to a part. That characteristic may be aesthetic, dimensional, or performance-related. Automation's consistency improves product yield, if the equipment is properly chosen and set up.

Reduce labor. By automating manual operations, the direct cost of labor is reduced or eliminated.

Worker safety. Manual handling of parts can contribute to carpal tunnel syndrome, back injuries, or more serious injuries from hot melt or clamp mechanisms. Injury claims cost money and demoralize workers, further impacting overall productivity. Manual operations can be reduced or eliminated with automation.

Reduce work-in-process inventory. WIP represents an inventory of parts or material. Average inventory has a fixed annual cost, whether it is finished goods in a warehouse or WIP on the plant floor. Automating operations to eliminate WIP avoids these costs.

The Planning Process

A systematic approach (Fig. 17-15) to planning any automated molding cell project and consideration of peripheral features is critical to success.

Identify desired benefits. The list of reasons for automating given previously are desired benefits. The first step in planning automation is to decide which benefits are most likely to be achieved for the part(s) in question and rank them in order of importance. The type of part being molded will influence this step of the process. For example, a multiple cavity mold producing 16-oz (0.5-L) dairy containers at a six-second cycle will produce a different list of benefits than a single cavity mold producing automotive fascias at a 90 second cycle. Table 17-1 lists the benefits for this example in order of importance.

A benefits list should not only apply to the production of a single part, but should be applied to a group or family of parts to be run in the same molding cell. In the case of a group of parts, focus on

CHAPTER 17   PLASTIC MANUFACTURING

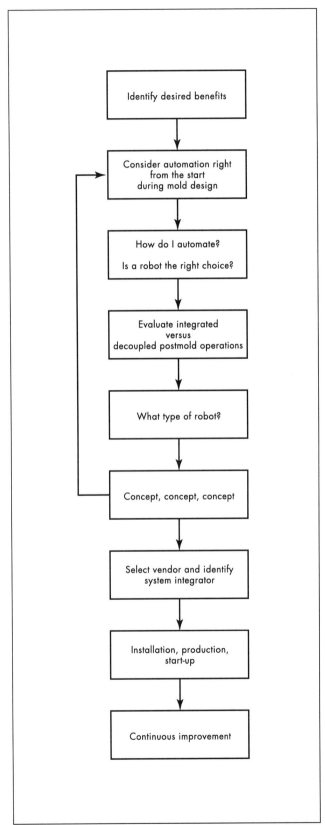

Fig. 17-15 Automation planning process. *(Courtesy Husky Injection Molding Systems, Ltd.)*

benefits common to all, or most of the group. For example, you may produce five different computer parts on the same machine, but only one requires manual degating of a cold runner. In this scenario, worker safety and reduction of labor associated with manual degating will not rank high on the list of benefits. In fact, it may not even be on the list. However, part quality will be very important and common to all five parts.

Consider automation from the start. The typical product development cycle for an injection-molded component is:

- Product idea leads to product design.
- Product design defines part design.
- Mold purchased.
- IMM located or bought.
- Long pause . . .
- Then, "Do I need automation?"

If automation is not considered from the start, the automation can be overcomplicated, or worse, impossible. Higher part production costs can erode or eliminate the planned profit margin.

Suppliers of automation equipment should be selected not simply based on price, but on their ability to take part in the product development cycle, speeding it up and arriving at the most cost-effective solution.

Once the part design is fixed, a preliminary mold design is complete, and the IMM that will be used is known, it is time to involve the automation supplier. The automation supplier must be capable of supplying the robot end-of-arm tool (EOAT), be able to plan the downstream cell together with the project manager, and understand basic mold design to speed through the next step.

When laying out the mold, consider how the part handling will be automated. Assembly of parts from a family mold, palletizing, or labeling are examples of operations that can be influenced by the mold layout. Often arbitrary mold design decisions can significantly increase the difficulty and expense of performing automated operations after part removal. The complexity, reliability, and speed of part removal from the mold can be improved if the EOAT and mold design are coordinated. As an example, it may be necessary to coordinate the ejection motion for the part with the gripper position in the EOAT. To do this, pins in the mold that are tied to the ejector motion can be used to push back on the EOAT during part transfer. This kind of intimate design coordination between the mold and automation can minimize cost and complication and improve system reliability.

Most EOATs cannot manipulate the part from a mold face that has a sticking problem somewhere. The amount of "stiction," or the force required to pull the part out of or off the core must be near zero; perhaps more importantly, it must be consistent from one shot to the next. Robots typically cannot originate or duplicate the complex motion of a human extracting a part. There are more complex requirements that apply to "unscrewing" molds, molds with side action, molds with rack drive motions, etc. These devices need to operate consistently and may require custom sequencing to navigate around resulting obstructions.

With quick runs and Just-in-Time inventories, molds often do not stay in a press very long. A range of molds which may run in a particular machine need to be reviewed for commonality for the automation investment to be spread across them. For example, many small presses under 150 tons (1.3 MN) use mold after mold with a subrunner system ejecting off the moving mold half. Each time, a sprue picker could be justified. With the "quick-change" and "teach and store" features on most sprue pickers and robots, the problem of automation changeover time is eliminated.

CHAPTER 17   PLASTIC MANUFACTURING

TABLE 17-1
Automation Benefits Depend on the Type of Part

	16 oz. (0.5 L) Dairy Container		Automotive Fascia
Productivity	A 0.5-second reduction in cycle increases output by 9%. If product can be automatically packed, labor can be reduced.	Productivity	Robotic takeout is faster than manual.
Part quality	Avoidance of scuffed or cracked parts due to free-fall ejection.	Part quality	Free-fall ejection will scratch the part.
Yield	Free-fall ejected parts can be contaminated by tie bar grease.	Yield	Avoiding free-fall or irregular cycle time will reduce scrap.

Almost all molding plants change tools several times a week, so the automation system must change over quickly too. Today, some suppliers have parallel processing controllers which let the user teach a new sequence while the present job is running. Quick change end-of-arm tooling and program storage also permit robot job change-overs in minutes.

Is a robot the right choice? Many applications may be better served by using either an alternative part take-out device, or a specialty IMM to combine process steps.

Examples of alternative part take-out devices are: a bottom pail catcher for industrial containers, or a swing chute. A *swing chute* has a set of small arms attached to a rotating shaft that is driven by a servomotor and is built into the mold. The parts are swung out off the cores while the mold is in motion and as a result, swing chutes can actually reduce molding cycle times. These devices are best suited to fast cycles in dedicated molding cells.

A multimaterial part can be produced by using a robot to place molded inserts into a mold and then overmolding, but this also can be accomplished using a specialty machine. As an example, an IMM with multiple injection units and either a rotating platen or rotating core plate can integrate these steps and do it faster with less scrap. Often, multicolored automotive lenses are produced using a rotary platen machine. Another alternative approach is using either co-injection or sequential injection into a specially designed mold.

Usually, justification analysis and selection of a robot type is based upon cycle time (mold open time and overall time), sequence required, flexibility required, payload requirement, and sizing to the molding machine. Presses over 200 tons (1.8 MN), with longer cycle times (over 15 seconds), allow the robot to do more than just take parts or runners out. Degating, parts separation, weighing, hot stamping, stacking, palletizing, box loading, tray filling, quality control staging, and ultrasonic welding are a few potential postmolding operations for the extra robot time.

To review an application, automation suppliers review sample parts, mold press specifications, plant and work cell layouts, overhead limitations, application and process information, and mold drawings. In addition, automation objectives, flexibility requirements, justification, and budget parameters can dictate the path of automation alternatives and project success. Labor reduction, added value, decreased scrap, increased machine utilization, change in cycle time, change in plant output, mold safety, operator safety, decrease in workers' physical strain, improved cycle consistency, cavity traceability, etc., are some of the variables to study in planning the project. Most plastic automation projects achieve payback within six to eight months. However, there are many examples where payback occurred with the first avoidance of a part hang up and mold damage.

Examples of applications where robots provided fast payback are:

- In a medical application that could not be touched by human hands and required cavity traceability and part collection for a postmolding assembly operation.

- High cavity, fast cycle garment hangers that were tangled during automatic operation, took extra labor to collect and box. The use of robots eliminated tangling, reduced labor, and increased quality yield, which translated into increased machine utilization. Increased machine utilization reduced the need for capital expense for additional machines.
- Large part removal that caused operator back strain and longer cycles was improved with robots.
- In an application where edge-gated parts needed degating, runner separation, runner placement into a granulator, and cooling before pack out. These nonvalue-added material handling steps were better suited for a robot.

Beyond the justification of consistent cycles, reduced tool damage, cavity traceability, reduced labor, and increased machine yield, carefully planned automation systems which provide added value in the postmolding process have helped molders secure longer contracts and increase profits. Reduced in-house engineering resources and experience often lead molders to enter relationships with full systems suppliers. Now it is common for system sales to include safety guarding, conveyors and downstream components, integration, approval of layout drawings, installation, and training.

Integrated versus decoupled postmold operations. An *integrated postmold operation* is a manufacturing step performed within the molding cell immediately after molding. A *decoupled postmold operation* is a manufacturing step that occurs somewhere else in the plant or in another plant. A decoupled process requires that some WIP inventory is handled from molding to the next step. Both approaches have advantages and disadvantages, which vary as the molded part, downstream processes, and type of business changes. For example, the issues facing a molder of automotive lenses on a Just-in-Time basis versus a seasonal molder of resin furniture will vary because of the nature of their businesses.

When deciding on integrated versus decoupled postmold operations, cost and manufacturing flexibility are the deciding, and often conflicting factors. The following is a list of considerations and how they impact cost and flexibility.

Floor space. Typically, plant space in the molding room is more costly per square foot than what would be called "warehouse" space.

Annual cost of WIP. Work-in-process inventory has an average annual cost.

Does time after molding impact quality of next operation? Depending on the part design, material, and subsequent operations, it may be beneficial or necessary to perform the next operation on the basis of one of the following time periods:

- Only after heat treating or annealing.
- Only after complete ambient cooling.
- A specific or consistent time after molding.
- Immediately after part removal.

CHAPTER 17   PLASTIC MANUFACTURING

Family of parts. A balance is required between the cost of being able to change over quickly and produce short runs, versus longer runs, more inventory, and longer changeover times.

Cycle time and labor balance. A downstream operation cannot be integrated if there is not a cycle time balance. However, downstream operations can run faster if there is no issue with starting and stopping. In this case, there may be idle labor that could be better used by decoupling.

Is visual inspection necessary? Can computer-integrated manufacturing (CIM) monitor the progress and assure quality by using statistical process control (SPC)? Is machine vision inspection a more reliable alternative?

Is the molding room air conditioned? Air conditioning may be necessary to run very cold mold temperatures without mold sweating to minimize the molding cycle. In this case, it is likely most cost-effective to minimize the size of the molding room and do downstream operations elsewhere.

What type of robot? The decisions made up to this point influence the type of robot selected as well as its required capabilities. The following are features of four different types of robots.

- Side entry robots.

  - Ideal for very short cycle times since take-out motion is minimized relative to a top entry robot.
  - Better suited to dedicated molding.
  - Low overhead height.
  - Can service wide parts that are larger than the horizontal tie-bar spacing.

- Top entry robots.

  - Use less floor space than side entry.
  - Easy to integrate with an IMM without modifying original safety gates.
  - Better suited to many postmold operations such as stacking, palletizing, or box loading.
  - Does not restrict access to mold area.

- Turret robots.

  - This is a top entry robot with a rotating base rather than a linear one.
  - Can swing to either side of the molding machine.
  - Has a large arc-shaped work envelope for doing postmold operations.
  - Ideal for large, deep draw parts.
  - Slower than top entry.

- Floor-mounted articulated arm robots.

  - Maximum flexibility with six servo axes.
  - May require higher skill level to use.
  - Uses considerable floor space.
  - Sometimes slower take-out cycle.
  - Only practical for small tonnage machines (approximately 500 tons [4.5 MN] and less).

Robots range from simple pick-and-place units to servomotor-driven, multiaxis machines, sometimes with complex arm end tooling that performs single to multiple operations in various steps. Most robots are used with primary plastic production and conversion equipment, and most often with IMMs.

Simple sprue pickers. Simple sprue pickers are generally pneumatically-driven. A vertical main stroke moves down to the centerline to grip the sprue, and after returning to the vertical up position, the arm swings out, extends, and releases the sprue, usually into a tote

or granulator. Often, the sprue picker releases the sprue into a beside-the-press granulator which then uses an unloader to return the regrind back up to the hopper. A proportioning loader may be used to control the mix of virgin material and regrind. This closed loop process decreases labor at the press and granulator, ensures sprue removal, cleaner regrind, and lowers energy consumption. Sprue pickers are being used less often, as even smaller presses are utilizing three-axis air or electric drive motions for parts transfer control and quality requirements.

During injection molding, automated auxiliary equipment can be used to remove molded parts by removing the cold-molded thermoplastic or hot-molded thermoset sprues.[1] Not only will an automated sprue picker ensure that the sprue has been removed from the mold cavity, but it may also reduce molding cycle time, thereby increasing the production rate. During molding with some molds, materials, or plastic melt processing conditions, the sprue tends to be well-packed. When the material does not sufficiently shrink, or when it exerts extra force on the wall of the metal sprue section of the mold, the plastic sprue will not easily release.

A simple sprue picker is one of the many different robots that can be used within and around the IMM. A typical sprue picker includes:

- A vertical support base plate that attaches to the top of the fixed platen of the IMM.
- A horizontal support arm located over the mold and attached to the top of the support base plate. The plate permits adjusting the picker arm location in the mold height direction when the mold opens.
- A vertical picker arm with a pneumatic cylinder (operating at about 60-80 psi [414-552 kPa] air pressure) to move the arm.
- A control system that can range from simple manual or mechanical settings to microprocessor controllers recording the motion of the device, storing it in memory, and quickly recalling the program, providing a more accurate and quicker method of setting up the sprue picker functions.

To use a simple sprue picker, one has to understand the target requirements. The basic manual or mechanical device will be sufficient to remove molded sprues if operating time is not critical, and if repeated mold changes that would require frequent resetting of the operating parameters are not required. However, many molders take advantage of microprocessor-controllable devices, where the picker's down and up motion can occur within seconds. When first starting up a mold that will use the microprocessor-controlled sprue picker, the IMM operator makes adjustments on the picker while watching it operate in its different axes of movement with time. This setup is stored in memory, and the job is run. After the mold is stored and later reinstalled in the IMM, the setup sequences are quickly recalled. In addition to setting up specific sequences, many different preprogrammed sequences are available.

In operation, after the mold opens, automatic controls for the simple sprue pickers can cause a sequence of motions where:

1. The picker's arm quickly moves down.
2. Arm moves toward sprue.
3. End of arm grips sprue.
4. Sprue is pulled out of mold.
5. Arm with sprue is quickly raised.
6. Sprue is released from the device.

Grips can be mechanical, with or without a twisting motion during gripping of the sprue, or based on a vacuum suction system. Computerized programs are available that permit the picker to swing away from the IMM prior to releasing the sprue. Sprues can be deposited in specific locations and positions, and released to the rear or to the operator's side of the molding machine.

Simple sprue picker devices are designed to increase productivity and ensure minimal waiting time at the IMM. Their construction influences their usefulness and maintenance characteristics. An engineer should look for:

- Tight tolerance in the pneumatic cylinder to eliminate side loading and permit repeatability of the device's actions.
- Oil-less seals if a "medically clean" IMM operating environment is needed.
- Sequence electrical switches with repeatability and long life.
- Safety devices to ensure the picker does not malfunction (for example, the picker arm dropping on the closed mold or remaining between the mold halves) if air pressure or electrical power is lost, etc.
- Simple, manual adjustment controls.
- Low-maintenance requirements.

The control systems available vary and meet practically any situation confronted by the molder. Available systems can:

- Change speed as the sprue is released.
- Adjust the motion program to adapt to various size molds and molding machines.
- Incorporate a mold release spray.
- Provide diagnostics to self-check their operation, alerting the operator if the sprue is not being removed, or if a sequence is not functioning properly, or that switches require adjustments or replacement.
- Reprogram the controller to accommodate sequences other than those already stored.
- Assure that adjusting the manual control of each motion and operating the computer program are user friendly.

Top entry or side entry robot configurations. These configurations are the most often used in the IMM industry. Top entry robots usually mount to the stationary platen, descend vertically into the mold area, grasp the parts, ascend vertically, traverse toward the outside of the molding machine (away from the operator), descend, and release the parts (see Fig. 17-16).

Top-entry, traversing part-removal robots are preferred wherever possible. Side entry robots require the removal of the safety gate of the mold press for operation. By design, side entry robots take up more room beside the press. However, where low ceiling heights or special thin-wall, high-speed applications are required, side entry systems are used.

Top entry robots, mounted to the stationary platen, use a main vertical arm to enter the mold area, and a "kick," "crosswise," or "strip" stroke to move forward and back to pull the parts away from the mold. When the main arm returns up with the parts or runner, the robot carriage supporting the vertical arm and strip stroke traverses along a beam that carries the parts or runner outside the safety gate.

Outside the safety gate, the robot can perform secondary operations as long as there is sufficient cycle time to do so. For example, degating parts from the runner, depositing runner(s) into a granulator, placing parts into collection devices, pad printing, hot stamping, palletizing, box filling, layer packing, etc. If the desired functions take longer to accomplish than the time available to the robot before it must get back above the mold to pull the next shot, a faster robot drive may be considered. The servodrive robot can sequence faster than a pneumatically-driven one because it controls acceleration and deceleration. Three-dimensional or coordinated motion control can allow multiple axis movement simultaneously, which may decrease cycle time.

The side entry robot can mount to the stationary platen or the floor. The robot reaches into the IMM via the side of the mold, grasps the parts, then retracts horizontally and releases the parts. In this case, the gate is typically removed or opened, then, most importantly, properly safeguarded.

Calculating strokes, hard stops, and clearances. Because the strokes of a robot are usually application dependent, it is nearly impossible for a custom molder to unerringly plan and size a robot that will handle all future applications that may run in a particular IMM. However, a formal study of 420 IMM applications by a robot manufacturer produced the following stroke calculation formulas that can be used as a guideline for successful installations such as the one shown in Figure 17-17.

For each axis, the stroke can be calculated as:

$$X = 0.5\,H + G_w \qquad (2)$$
$$Y = 0.6\,(D)$$
$$Z = 1.1\,(0.5\,V + G_h)$$

where:

X = X-axis of the robot, the traverse stroke
Y = Y-axis of the robot, the reach of forward strip, stroke position
Z = Z-axis of the robot, the vertical stroke
H = horizontal tie bar spacing
G_w = gate width
D = IMM open daylight
V = vertical tie bar spacing
G_h = gate height

The travel of a robot is typically limited by hard stops at the end of each major axis, both for safety reasons and the safeguarded area required. Many manufacturers also offer adjustable hard stops, enabling the fractional use of the total stroke available, and with the benefit that the physical barriers may be set to utilize a minimum work envelope, reducing the amount of floor space required.

The recommended clearance between the physical barrier and the outer edge of the EOAT, or any part of the robot when a part is in the EOAT, is 18 in. (46 cm) according to industry standards.[2]

Select vendor, identify system integrator, and design-in safety. Consider forming a partnership with the automation supplier so he or she can be a full participant in the whole planning process. However, if automating for the first time, it may be necessary to bring at least two vendors through the process. It is best to inform them that they are competing not only on price, but on how well they can contribute to defining the right solution.

With CAD programs, it is possible to lay out the entire cell far in advance of installation to check for interference and feasibility of operation. Often, it is best if the automation supplier performs this role, even if he or she is not the system integrator.

Depending on in-house capabilities and human resources, the molder usually identifies who will be the system integrator.

The intention of this section is to assist a person or persons in the design of an IMM robotic work cell. Research the necessary codes, guidelines, and regulations that apply to the areas and work cells involved. The Society of the Plastics Industry (SPI) requires that the system integrator be responsible for conformance.[3, 4]

Gates and proper safety guarding. Precautions may be the responsibility of either the customer or the supplier. It is critical that all safety guarding be in compliance with national standards. ANSI and OSHA guidelines generally define that the entire work envelope of the robot be guarded and not accessible to an operator during automatic operation. Many molders have used simple guarding at the conveyor drop area, that by itself is not compliant with OSHA and ANSI standards. While there is a cost and inconvenience with proper guarding, any user of automation should realize the potential

CHAPTER 17   PLASTIC MANUFACTURING

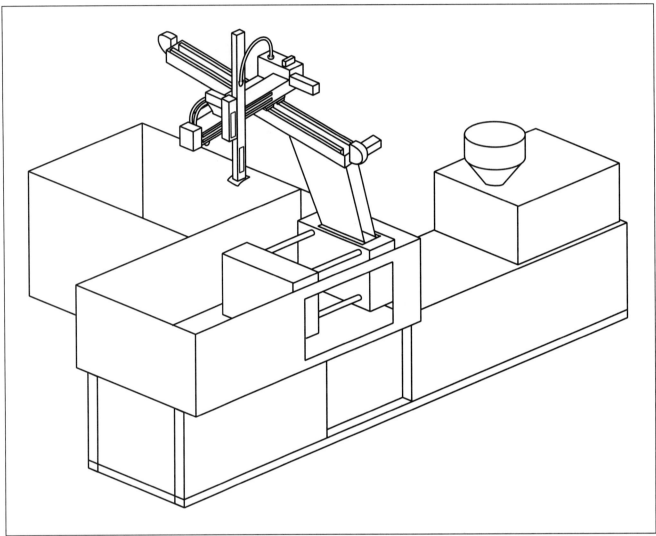

Fig. 17-16 Top entry robot. *(Courtesy Automated Assemblies Corporation)*

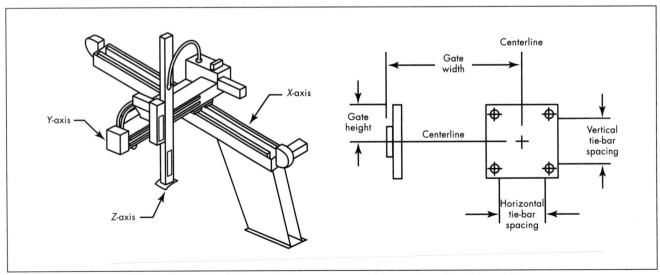

Fig. 17-17 Dimensions for calculating strokes, hard stops, and clearances. *(Courtesy Automated Assemblies Corporation)*

CHAPTER 17   PLASTIC MANUFACTURING

harm to personnel that can occur without safety equipment. High-speed servorobots can run at speeds over 160 in. (406 cm)/sec, which could fatally injure someone in the path of motion.

The rear gate or nonoperator-side gate sometimes must be altered to allow the parts to be removed from the mold and placed on either a conveyor or assembly machine. In all cases, a barrier guard that will surround the work envelope of the IMM and the robot is required (see Fig. 17-18).[5]

Given the liability issues, the automation vendor is likely to insist that the molder take this responsibility. Among other things, being the system integrator requires the molder to ensure that the robot and peripheral automation is installed correctly, that the IMM is equipped with a robot interface, and proper interlocked safety gates are installed.

Physical barrier. A physical barrier should enclose the full work envelope of the robot.[6] The barrier must allow full access to both sides of the IMM to facilitate mold change. The floor height must exceed 84 in. (213 cm).[7] If the robot discharges to the nonoperator side of the IMM, the physical barrier is straightforward to construct. It can be as simple as a room constructed of panels secured to the floor with electrically interlocked access doors.

The access doors must be capable of disabling drive power when they are opened. Some form of time delay must be introduced to assure that the robot is at rest before the access door allows entry. Additionally, to prevent someone from getting caught inside the enclosure, the door must not be able to restart the robot when it is closed. A person inside the physical barrier must have the assurance that the door cannot be closed, or the robot enabled while inside the area. An exit conveyor or some form of transfer device is required to move the parts from inside the barrier to outside where secondary operations can be performed. Figure 17-18 shows a barrier design.[8]

If the robot discharge is to the operator's side of the IMM, an added complexity must be considered: how does a technician operate the IMM? The physical barrier must allow access to the IMM

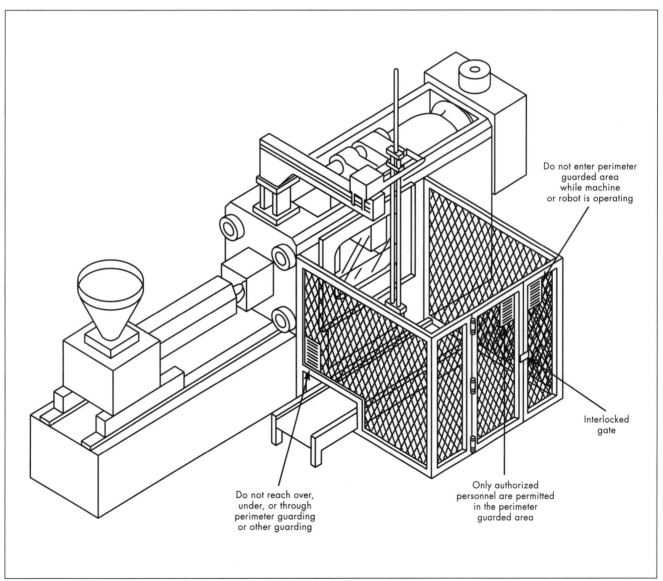

Do not enter perimeter guarded area while machine or robot is operating

Interlocked gate

Only authorized personnel are permitted in the perimeter guarded area

Do not reach over, under, or through perimeter guarding or other guarding

Fig. 17-18 Top entry robot with perimeter guarding and part drop at rear of injection molding machine. Note: The signs depicted in this illustration are intended to point out the hazards that should be addressed. *(Courtesy Society of the Plastics Industry, "ANSI/SPI B151.27-1994")*

CHAPTER 17 PLASTIC MANUFACTURING

controls and the operator's gate. Operations should not require that a person stand inside the work envelope of the robot.

If the robot's discharge must be to the operator's side of the IMM, the user must prevent the robot's moving parts and any personnel from being in the shared area at the same time. One method of doing this is to construct a tunnel area that will protect personnel. The tunnel must be an armored structure, so designed that it would withstand a full speed, full payload impact by the robot and still protect personnel.[9]

Lockout. The access gates to the physical barrier must be electrically interlocked such that, when an access door is opened, the drive power to the IMM and the robot will stop, and the equipment will come to rest. The main power must have lockout and tagout capability. This provides the person who must enter the barrier a way to lock the main power off and prevent the potential start-up of the equipment by other personnel.[10]

Loss of load. The robot's physical barrier must be capable of withstanding a force equivalent to that which would be caused by the full payload being thrown by the robot traveling at full speed. This could happen if a gripper circuit or end effector lost its holding capability. The barrier must be capable of protecting any personnel outside the area should such an event occur.[11]

Below gate blocker. Many IMMs are manufactured so that a crawl space allows access to the robot's safeguarded area. Most often this is an access below both the front and rear gate, between the floor and the bottom of the gate, large enough for a person to crawl into. Blocking this access should always be considered. A simple blocker panel that resides below the gate and is fastened to the floor will prevent access.[12]

Robot placement, maintenance, and catwalk design. The typical installation of a top entry robot consists of a structurally suitable pedestal or base bolted to the top surface of the stationary platen, using a structurally-qualified bolt pattern. The robot height varies with the tonnage of the IMM: the greater the tonnage, the higher the robot. Robots vary in weight, from 150 lb (68 kg) for a sprue picker to 10,000 lb (4,536 kg) for a large top entry robot, depending on the IMM tonnage. This presents two issues: First, the bolted connection is the only element that attaches the robot to the molding machine. It is a connection that experiences rapid cycling and reversing loads. Therefore, the bolts must be preloaded properly and analyzed for fatigue.

If a bolted connection has failed the fatigue analysis, one option would be to support the robot externally to the platen, perhaps with outboard supports on the main axes. An outboard support eliminates much of the loading about the centerline of the IMM, thereby allowing additional capacity to be allocated to the remaining two restraint axes. Other options may include increasing the bolt diameter, increasing the number of bolts, or changing the bolt spacing. Increasing the pedestal's base plate thickness can reduce localized stresses and deflections, thereby helping to ensure the load path is as evenly distributed to each bolt as possible.

Secondly, because much of a robot is usually not accessible, maintenance presents some difficulties. To provide easier access to the robot, commercially-available rolling stairs are often used. However, some areas over the IMM still may be inaccessible from a rolling stair set. An alternative solution is to use a catwalk deck and ladder or catwalk deck and stair set. The catwalk deck and ladder is a deck mechanically fastened to the robot along its main axis, with an integrated ladder or stair set. In most cases this allows good access to maintenance points, allowing routine maintenance to be safely completed. Provisions should be made to allow users to follow a three-point rule: two hands and one foot contact should be made when on the ladder. It is also worth noting that treads should have

some form of traction assist (dimples, perforation, etc.), in case the user's shoes are oily.

Installation and start-up. Many people view automation as being perfect and infallible, and, as a result, immediately expect 100% efficiency once the process is started. This, of course, is not true. A learning curve and ramp-up time for efficiency is normal. Therefore, this should be expected and planned for when making production commitments to customers.

Internal support is a must for a successful automation project. All personnel affected by the introduction of automation have to be supportive and involved. It is best to define a team responsible for the success of the cell with definite rewards linked to success. In support of this team effort, personnel need to be properly trained in advance or at the time of installation, not after the fact.

Properly trained personnel will support success, and make possible continued success and improvements. Automation equipment requires preventative maintenance for efficient performance. Trained and vested personnel working with the equipment every day are the people most likely to spot potential improvements that can reduce cycle times and increase efficiency.

Time must be allowed for all the initial variables to stabilize, at which time the mold should have all its cavities filling ("shots"), ejecting freely, and producing acceptable parts. This can take anywhere from five to 100 shots.

The first shots will typically be short shots, in which the cavities are only partially filled. A short shot probably will not be able to be grasped by the robot's EOAT. The robot cannot be used at this point. This means the process technician will manually open the gate and retrieve the partial shot, resulting in an inconsistent mold open time, introducing variation in the cycle times. This will continue until the process technician can retrieve a full part in semi-automatic mode without the use of the robot. This may continue for ten or more cycles until the robot and the IMM can be put into automode to retrieve full parts.

Features of Automation Equipment

For a more advanced level of automation than simple part removal (often termed pick and place), different features of robots and peripheral automation equipment provide varying levels of flexibility, user friendliness, capability, and reliability. Knowledge of what these features offer is essential to the planning process.

Types of robot drives. There are many top-entry or side-entry robot drive types in use today: pneumatic, electric frequency, and electric servo. Usually cost and flexibility, or application requirements, help make the decision about which drive to use. Tables 17-2 and 17-3 give the features of several robot and drive types.

There is sometimes debate over whether to select AC-variable frequency drives or servodrives. The main difference between AC-variable frequency drives and AC servocontrol drives is that the AC-variable frequency motor has zero torque, whereas the AC servomotor at zero rpm has full torque. Therefore, when a small move must be made, the servomotor can easily make it without overshooting. The AC-variable frequency motor may make the move, overshoot, reverse, overshoot, reverse, and then go into oscillation.

A second difference is that a servomotor is continually under power and always correcting its position. It rotates inside a range established by two index markers. It rotates to one, reverses, and rotates back to the other, with full torque of the motor. The AC-variable frequency motor moves to a position within an accuracy window, and then applies a brake to hold its position.

A hard stop is probably the most accurate method of positioning because it does not rely on a programmed window created by a set of marks. As small as the range may be, it introduces error. The positional accuracy of the robot largely depends on the structural integrity and the bearing design of the machine. These two components, combined with the accuracy of the gearbox and feedback device, produce the robot's positional accuracy. Robots designed using finite element analysis (FEA) often have been optimized for the lightest construction and the stiffest structure.

Interfacing requirements (IMM to robot). A robot must be electrically interfaced with an injection molding machine and requires hardware connections and software. The IMM manufacturers most often supply some form of robot interface. There are several interface standards. The most common in the USA is the SPI-AN-116; in Europe, EuroMap VS 12.0; and in Japan, JIRA 1006, 1009, 1010. These interfaces use standard communications signals that are provided through dry relay contacts. These signals include "Gate Closed," "Mold Open," "Mold Closed," and others. If the IMM manufacturer does not supply a standard interface connector, the user can usually arrange to have the IMM manufacturer install one. For liability reasons many robot suppliers will provide, but not install, the connector, and the molder is discouraged from tapping into the signals. With advances in controls and programmability of the IMM, this is no longer as simple as it was with relay-controlled IMMs.

The robot cycle. Proper interfacing makes the robot cycle part of the IMM cycle. For example, when the robot is in the mold area, the mold is prohibited from closing. If the IMM gate is opened, the robot drives are disabled. When the robot arm is down and forward, the robot control allows the IMM ejectors to move forward. It should be noted that the robot/IMM interface creates a unique circumstance: when the robot is in use, the molding machine and the robot must be in the same mode, for example, "Full Automatic" operation. When the IMM is in "Semiautomatic Mode," the robot must be in manual mode or "Not in Use" status.

Emergency stop circuit. The robot is interfaced with the IMM though an industry standard interface. These standards require the robot's emergency stop circuit, and that of any auxiliary machine interfaced with the robot controller, to share a common, hard-wired emergency stop circuit. This will result in drive power shutdown of the robot, IMM, and auxiliary machine that may cause a hazard when any one of the emergency stop switches is activated.

If a properly installed, electrically-interlocked barrier guard surrounding the robot's safeguarded area is opened, the control and drive power are disabled. In addition, auxiliary equipment in close proximity may require that its drive power be disabled if there is a possibility of danger.[13]

Ejector control. The IMM signals the robot arm to descend into the mold area upon a full "Mold Open" signal. The arm then moves forward, dwells, then signals the IMM to send the ejectors forward.

TABLE 17-2
Three Main Types of Robot Drives

Types	Features
Pneumatic	For simple, low-cost, point-to-point motion. Typically used for rotary axes. For main robot axes, this drive does not provide sufficient flexibility for advanced automation cells.
Frequency-controlled A/C induction motor	Moderate cost level. Typically used on main robot axes. Used as a lower cost and lower performance alternative to A/C servo. Provides position programming flexibility through the use of a position encoder. Stops and holds position with a mechanical brake. Therefore, long-term reliability is not as good as A/C servo.
A/C servo	Highest cost, fastest payback, lowest overall true cost. Used for both main robot axes and rotary axes. Highest acceleration and speed performance. Greatest positioning accuracy and repeatability. Highest level of reliability. For advanced automation, this is the ideal type of robot drive for the main robot axes.

TABLE 17-3
Robot Types and Features

	Sprue Pickers	Top-entry Traverse Robots			
		All Air	Air with Electric Traverse	3-axis Electric Frequency	3-axis Servo
Features	Pick sprues Simple parts pick	Point-to-point	Multiple stop on traverse	Teach X, Y, Z positions	3-axis
Limitations	Drops high Low payload	Limited stop points	Cannot stack or pelletize	No coordinated motions	None
Benefits	Low cost	Lower cost pick and place	Degate separate placement	More flexibility for downstream	Full flexibility
General market price range	$6,000-9,000	$20,000-24,000	$22,000-28,000	$40,000+	$50,000+
Typical tonnage	30-200 (0.27-1.8 MN)	50-300 (0.4-2.7 MN)	150-300 (1.3-2.7 MN)	2,001 (1.81 MN)	2,001 (1.81 MN)

CHAPTER 17 PLASTIC MANUFACTURING

At this point, the parts are grasped by the EOAT. After a dwell time or when part presence is sensed, the arm retracts and signals the ejectors to retract. The IMM then signals the robot to ascend with the parts. It is noted there are many exceptions to this sequence. Molds, for example, may not require the arm to extend or retract. A portion of this sequence may be modified to accommodate the specific condition.

"Gate Open" and "Gate Closed" signals. The gates on the IMM are electrically interlocked such that if the gate is opened, the motion of the IMM quickly stops. Most often there are two gates, referred to as the front (operator's side) and rear (nonoperator's side) gate. The front is usually the side with the IMM control console. When a robot is used, the SPI interface connects into this circuit. If the IMM gate is opened, both the robot and the IMM quickly stop, and the drives are disabled while the control power may be maintained. This signal should come from a control switch not easily defeated, as should any interlock switch in the work cell. The following is a reference excerpt on control reliability: "When required by the performance requirements of the safeguarding, the device, system, or interface shall be designed, constructed, and installed such that a single component failure within the device, interface, or system shall not prevent normal stopping action from taking place but shall prevent a successive machine cycle. This requirement does not apply to those components whose function does not affect the safe operation of the machine tool."[14]

"Mold Open" and "Mold Closed" signals. The "Mold Open" and "Mold Closed" signals from the IMM permit the robot to either enter the mold or not descend until the appropriate signal is received. (This is commonly referred to as "permissive signals.") This signal is given from the IMM controller that is hard-wired through a 24V DC isolation relay (most often) to an input on the robot controller.

Robust "Mold Open" signals and noise. Some leading IMM robot suppliers recommend that a robust mechanical limit switch be installed in series with the derived "Mold Open" signal on those IMMs that use an alternate means of sensing the "Mold Open" position. There is a possibility that the IMM "Mold Open" signal could be corrupted by electrostatic or electromagnetic noise that can be high in the molding room. Siphon feeds for materials, the injection processes, and the mold opening process all produce tens of thousands of volts in static electricity. The common use of 50-100 hp (37,000-75,000 W) motors, ultrasonic welding equipment, coupled with sometimes poor grounding practices inside a factory, can produce thousands of volts of electromagnetic noise. This can result in erratic operation and other unknown problems. "Mold Open" and "Mold Closed" signals must be robust and reliable to assure safety for the personnel and the mold.

Types of robot controls. To plan the most effective automation solution and improve upon it once it is in place, the robot controls must be flexible. Flexibility and ease of use are both important, but independent of each other. It is important to specify a controller architecture that suits the user. The primary decision is whether the sequences are performed in a lead-through teach method, or from a preprogrammed (canned) list. Both architectures have their benefits. The canned sequences are very easy to use and apply, usually with menus of options that can be turned on or off, creating the exact sequence required. However, if you need an additional motion, it may not be possible to add it in. Lead-through teaching allows you to alter the sequence and the input/output (I/O) options, the ultimate in flexibility. However, with a lead-through teach method, each sequence must be created from scratch or produced by altering a template. Any conditional branches and conditional I/O status must be set. There are many packages available that allow the molder to alter the application sequence quickly without the need to rely on an outside source. To optimize a process without stopping production, a robot control with a feature that allows small position changes made while the robot is running is extremely useful.

Teach pendants and control points. In an integrated work cell, such as a robot and IMM, there are several control points, including the following:

- Service disconnect.
- Teach pendant.
- Control pendant.
- Emergency stop switches and circuit.
- IMM control panel.
- Ancillary control interfaces.

Issues to understand about control points:

- The robot controller should have a disconnect 6.5 ft (2 m) off the floor, or lower, with lockout capability. This should be different from the disconnect used for the IMM, since troubleshooting will be performed with either the IMM, robot, or both main power connections disconnected. (A third disconnect should be provided for ancillary equipment such as assembly machines, conveyors, etc.)
- The robot control pendant is not always the same as the teach pendant. The *control pendant* is used to enable a programmed sequence with the IMM running in full automatic mode. This control pendant should be near the IMM control panel, since both must be used together to enable an automatic cycle (with only a single point of control).
- The teach pendant may or may not be part of the control pendant. It is important for the teach pendant to be placed such that, when it is in use, a full view of the EOAT and mold interaction is maintained. It is also helpful if the molded part discharge location is visible.
- In cells utilizing remote, movable pendants, the pendant must be designed so that if the pendant is dropped, a cycle could not inadvertently be started.
- The IMM control panel must be fully accessible at all times. The robot work envelope and physical barrier cannot obstruct the control of the IMM.
- The emergency stop circuit must be interconnected with all control points. For example, if a work cell contained a control pendant, a teach pendant, and an ancillary machine (such as a box loader), all three of the above emergency stop switches and the emergency stop switch on the IMM must be electrically interlocked with the physical barrier doors and gates.[15]

Teaching the robot. The robot should not exceed 10 in. (25 cm) per second when in the teach mode. The robot should be taught from outside the physical barrier where the operator is safeguarded.[16]

Attended program verification (APV) is a most emotionally-charged topic among integrators, users, advocacy groups, and original equipment manufacturers (OEMs) supplying robots. Described simply, *APV* is a tool that allows the teacher of the robot (never more than one person) to enter the safeguarded area and verify the robot's application program at program speed. It is not intended for quality control (QC) work or for production manufacture. The intense debate comes in with the question, "How will the operator be safeguarded inside the safeguard boundaries?"

Following are the APV paragraphs from two of the applicable industry guidelines. As with all guidelines, there are areas that overlap, and that conflict from one guide to the next. The best that can be done is to give a sincere review of each application and each industry guideline to arrive at a sensible and safe solution.

"Motion of the robot initiated from the pendant shall be under slow speed control as described in 4.8. An exception that may be permitted is as follows: when full programmed speed is provided for attended program verification, it shall require constant actuation of an enabling device and of the motion controls to continue robot motion."[17]

"Before entering the perimeter guarded area, the operator shall ensure that all necessary safeguards are in place and functioning, and that the slow speed of the robot, maximum 10 in. (25 cm)/sec is functional."[18]

"Generally, attended program verification should not be permitted. There are some very rare exceptions to the rule. For example, there will be cases when video cameras, mirrors, inspection points, and other remote means of verifying a process will not work, in which case APV may be required. For those very rare cases, a combination of safeguards should be installed to safeguard the operator. For example, perhaps inside the safeguarded area boundaries there would be safe spots, identified and activated with presence-sensing mats. In another approach, a safety drop bar could restrict the envelope of the robot, resulting in a robot-unreachable position for the teacher to stand in."[19]

Peripheral equipment. The work cell requires a means to move parts from the safeguarded area. A solution is to install a simple conveyor to move the parts from the robot unload position to an area where an inspector or packer can work. The conveyor thus becomes part of the work cell. In many cases, the conveyor can be electrically interfaced so that a handshake signal will allow the conveyor to be indexed forward after a part is released onto it. Many robot manufacturers supply a second machine interface for this purpose. This is usually two inputs, two outputs, and an emergency stop circuit. This type of universal handshake interface allows easy integration of a simple conveyor, a more complex assembly machine, pack out device, or some other auxiliary machine.

Specialized equipment used to perform operations such as labeling, hot stamping, degating, etc., are best sourced from specialty suppliers that focus on this type of equipment. A general machine builder cannot be expert at all things.

Peripheral device control can be centralized at the robot controller, or decentralized by interfacing to the robot controller. Centralized control provides convenience for the operator since it can be run from one point. However, this may not be the most efficient way to integrate the system because all elements cannot be fully tested until final installation with the robot. With the relatively low cost of simple programmable logic controllers (PLCs), the peripheral device control can be run independently and then interfaced via simple relay signals with the robot controller.

Each piece of equipment in a work cell should have its own controller and operator interface. A second machine interface should link the pieces. It is important that the operator interfaces be located near enough to create a single point of control.[20]

Risk Assessment

The designer, integration installer, and user should all consider performing a risk assessment of the work cell. Functionally, the work cell must be reviewed for hazards created by each task the robot or ancillary equipment performs, and each situation created when the equipment fails to perform or complete its task. Conditions for startup, preventative maintenance, QC, teaching, and repair should all be carefully reviewed. Simple items such as how to clear a jammed part, troubleshoot sticking parts, and where to change end effectors need to be thought out and planned.[21]

References

1. Rosato, D. V., and Rosato, D. V. *Injection Molding Handbook*, Second Edition. New York: Chapman and Hall, 1995.

2. American National Standards Institute (ANSI)/Robotic Industries Association (RIA) 15.06. *Industrial Robots and Robot Systems Safety Requirements*, paragraph 5.5. Ann Arbor, MI: ANSI/RIA, 1992.

3. ANSI/Society of the Plastics Industry (SPI) B151.27. *Plastics Machinery–Robots Used with Horizontal Injection Molding Machines.* Washington: ANSI/SPI, 1994.

4. The following guidelines are associated with the construction and design of an integrated robot and IMM work cell. These should be used in conjunction with Occupational Health and Safety Administration (OSHA) CFR-1910. Washington: various dates.

- ANSI/National Fire Protection Association (NFPA) 70. *National Electrical Code.* Quincy, MA: ANSI/NFPA, 1996.
- ANSI/National Electrical Manufacturers Association (NEMA) ICS 2. *Industrial Control and System Controller.* Rosslyn, VA: ANSI/NEMA, 1993.
- ANSI/NFPA 70E. *Electrical Safety Requirements for Employee's Workplaces.* Quincy, MA: ANSI/NFPA, 1995.
- ANSI/NFPA 70. *Electrical Standards for Industrial Machinery.* Quincy, MA: ANSI/NFPA, 1994.
- ANSI/American Society of Mechanical Engineers (ASME) B20.1. *Standards for Conveyors and Related Equipment.* New York: ANSI/ASME, 1993.
- ANSI/Institute of Electrical and Electronic Engineers (IEEE) 730.1. *Software Quality Assurance.* New York: ANSI/IEEE, 1989.
- ANSI/SPI B151.1. *Horizontal Injection Molding Machines, Safety Requirements.* Washington: ANSI/SPI, 1990.
- ANSI/SPI B151.27.
- ANSI/RIA 15.06.
- ANSI Z244.1. *Personnel Protection, Lockout/Tagout of Energy Sources.* New York: ANSI, 1982.
- ANSI Z535.1. *Safety Color Code.* New York: ANSI, 1991.
- ANSI/ASME B.15.1. *Mechanical Power Transmission Apparatus, Safety Standards.* New York: ANSI/ASME, 1996.
- ANSI/ASME B20.1B. *Conveyors and Related Equipment.* New York: ANSI/ASME, 1994.
- ANSI Z535.4. *Product Safety Signs.* New York: ANSI, 1991.

5. ANSI/SPI B151.27. ANSI/RIA 15.06, section 6.

6. ANSI/RIA 15.06, paragraph 6.4.1. OSHA CFR 1910.212. *General Requirements for All Machines.*

7. ANSI/Underwriters Laboratories (UL) 1740. *Standard for Industrial Robots and Robotic Equipment*, paragraph 4.1.6.5. OSHA CFR 1910.219. *Mechanical Power–Transmission Apparatus.* Washington: ANSI/UL, 1996.

8. ANSI/SPI B151.27.

9. ANSI B11.19. *Performance Criteria for the Design, Construction, Care and Operation of Safeguarding when Referenced by the Other B11 Machine Tool Safety Standards*, paragraph 4.1.1.2.4. New York: ANSI, 1990.

10. OSHA CFR-1910.147. *The Control of Hazardous Energy (Lockout/Tagout).* Washington: OSHA, 1996.

11. ANSI/UL 1740, paragraphs 58 and 60. ANSI/RIA 15.06, paragraph 5.14.

12. ANSI B11.19, paragraph 4.2.1.2.4.

13. ANSI/UL 1740, paragraph 41.2. ANSI/RIA15.06, paragraph 6.3.3.

14. ANSI B11.19, paragraph 5.5.1.

15. NFPA 79. *Electrical Standards for Industrial Machinery*, paragraph 7.9.3. ANSI/RIA 15.06, paragraph 6.3.3 and 5.13.

16. ANSI/RIA 15.06, paragraph 6.5.

17. ANSI/RIA 15.06, paragraph 4.6.5.

18. ANSI/SPI 151.27, paragraph 6.1.3.

19. ANSI/SPI 151.27, paragraph 6.1, 5.2.1. ANSI/RIA 15.06, section 6.

20. ANSI B11.19. ANSI/RIA 15.06. ANSI B11.20 (*Machine Tools–Manufacturing Systems/Cells–Safety Requirements for Construction, Care, and Use.* New York: ANSI, 1991).

21. ANSI/RIA 15.06, paragraph 6.1.1.

CHAPTER 17   PLASTIC MANUFACTURING

Bibliography

Mitchell, P. *Tool and Manufacturing Engineers Handbook*, Volume 8, *Plastic Part Manufacturing*. Dearborn, Michigan: Society of Manufacturing Engineers, 1996.

OSHA 1910 Compliance Manual for General Industry. Santa Monica, California: The Merritt Company, 1994.

Rosato, D.V., and Rosato, D. V. *Injection Molding Handbook*, Second Edition. New York: Chapman and Hall, 1995.

U. S. Department of Labor, Occupational Safety and Health Administration, OSHA Standards, Part 1910. Washington: various dates. OSHA guidelines are available on the Internet at www.osha.gov.

CHAPTER 18

ASSEMBLY

CHAPTER CONTENTS

INTRODUCTION

This chapter emphasizes the strategies and equipment needed for parts handling and presents design considerations for automated parts supply systems, part orientation equipment, oriented parts transfer and placement, assembly machines and systems, pneumatic automation devices, and flexible automation for assembly.

The functions of a complete parts handling system are:

- Singulate (separate) parts from bulk storage.
- Orient singulated parts.
- Present acceptably oriented parts at a known location (the location can be determined through measurement or mechanically through the use of tooling).
- Return or recycle unacceptably-oriented parts to bulk storage.

UNDERSTANDING THE APPLICATION

Perhaps the most common oversight in planning for automation is understanding the significance of parts handling equipment. Before parts can be automatically assembled or processed, they must be fed and oriented correctly at feed rates in excess of the downstream requirement. The efficiency of this downstream process can be directly dependent on the performance and reliability of the parts feeding equipment.

When considering a parts feeding solution, the following key issues must be evaluated:

- Is the part capable of being fed automatically?
- What type of parts handling solution best meets the needs of the application and process?
- Is the company offering the automated solution also capable of addressing the needs of the application after the sale?

Before any automated solution is considered, focused attention must be given to the part. The shape, size, weight, composition, and condition of the part must be evaluated to determine if an automated solution is achievable.

To effectively and efficiently feed and orient a part, the shape of the part must be consistent so that an orientation method can be properly designed. If the part contains flashing or debris, or is malformed or inconsistent in shape, inefficiency will result. The quality of the part handled is very important to the success of the automation equipment.

Sometimes, parts are designed with minimal thought given to how automatic feeding equipment must handle them. Most of the design attention is placed on the integrity of the part and how it will perform when assembled in the final product.

In the part design phase, it is very important to hold discussions with the application engineers from a parts feeding company to evaluate the performance expected in automatic feeding and orienting of the part. Many times, a small orientation feature can be added to the part before releasing the final part design to manufacturing. The addition of such a feature can make a big difference in the success and cost of the automation project.

Part size and weight also play a big role in the automation evaluation process. Typically, parts larger than 10 in. (254 mm) in length or greater than 8 in. (203 mm) in diameter are too large for conventional automatic feeding. For example, a 10-in. (254-mm) long bolt or plastic bottle would be considered feedable as would an 8-in. (203-mm) diameter plastic lid or bearing sleeve. Part weight also must be evaluated to make sure the proposed automation solution is capable of handling it.

After the part is qualified as feedable, attention must be focused on the type of feeder that best meets the application specifications. Part composition (metal, plastic, ceramic, etc.), part surface condition (oily, wet, dry, powder, etc.), and ergonomic and economic variables need to be reviewed. Determine the solution that best satisfies the complete list of application specifications.

In many application environments, the vibratory parts feeder offers the most versatility. Parts with complex shapes and designs have greater opportunity to be oriented into the desired position through the use of vibration. Conversely, parts with simple shapes that require high feed rates tend to fall into the centrifugal or orienting and elevating feeder category. It is important to thoroughly review the application with an experienced parts handling supplier early in the process to build the foundation for a productive automation solution.

SIZING THE EQUIPMENT

When sizing parts feeding equipment, focus should be placed on selecting a system large enough to efficiently and effectively feed and orient the parts. Parts handling equipment should be sized to require the least amount of floor space without sacrificing system productivity.

Sometimes companies in need of automation work backwards. Before discussing their need with a qualified parts handling equipment manufacturer, they develop space criteria for the overall automation system and force fit the parts feeding solution into a predetermined envelope of space. Space restrictions like this often compromise efficiency and productivity.

Size selection of equipment is best left in the hands of parts handling equipment manufacturers. Part size, feed rate, complexity of part shape, as well as part composition will directly influence the equipment size.

*The Contributors of this chapter are: Randy Baird, Parts Handling Business Unit Manager, FMC; Warren Burgess, President, Burgess and Associates; Jim Calhoun, Industrial Products Marketing Manager, FMC MHEO; Walter Hessler, Vice President of Sales and Marketing, PHD, Inc.; William Murray, Assistant Professor, University of Washington; Jim Schanstra, President, FTI International, Inc.
The Reviewer of this chapter is: William Murray, Assistant Professor, University of Washington.*

CHAPTER 18   ASSEMBLY

Many factors influence how the parts respond to vibration. If the part size is large, voids may occur as parts vibrate into single file order. If the part has a complex shape, obtaining the desired orientation may require the recirculation of parts that are in an orientation different from that desired. Part composition influences how well the part responds to high frequency, low-stroke vibration (for example, rubber parts will not feed as well as plastic parts). Considerations such as these support the need for communication with a qualified parts handling equipment manufacturer.

JUSTIFYING THE AUTOMATION PROJECT

Prior to starting any automation project, it is important to set goals and determine why the automating of a particular assembly process is necessary. The following are possible reasons, where one or all may apply.

- Increased productivity—many times the use of automation will allow an operator to perform more than one task. In other situations, the automation device can actually assist in an operation, resulting in increased productivity.
- Labor savings—automation usually performs tasks that are very repetitive, which can lead to fatigue and boredom if performed manually. Automation can free a worker to perform additional, more highly-skilled assembly functions. One type of automated parts handling system consists of a storage supply hopper, vibratory parts feeder, an in-line track, and a part placing device. This system reduces the requirement for a full time employee to hand load the machine. Assuming one shift operation, payback for this system would be less than one year. In multiple shift operations, payback can be as little as four months.
- Quality—automation can lead to increased consistency and quality. In general, automatic systems require a higher quality supply of parts than that required for hand assembly.
- Safety—some types of automation devices are ideal for use in hazardous environments. In addition, automation often results in a reduction of work-related injuries, especially chronic problems, such as carpel tunnel syndrome and back injuries.

CONSIDERATIONS FOR PARTS

Part shape and quality are key factors in determining the productivity and cost of an automated assembly system. The product designer should be aware of how part geometry affects the rate of orientation, the ease that a part may be oriented, and the reliability of the methods that must be used to orient the parts, as well as the related economic consequences.

The quality of the manufactured part plays a primary role in the productivity of an automatic operation. Costly delays may be caused when defective parts jam in tracks or mechanisms. A few common dimensional problems that may cause jamming include:

- Burrs on stampings and forgings.
- Flash on injection and plastic-molded parts.
- Incomplete parts.
- Deformed pieces.
- Lack of threads.
- Lack of holes.
- Out-of-tolerance holes.

The probability of parts being dimensionally out of tolerance must be thoroughly investigated prior to the beginning of an automated assembly project. Start by getting the dimensional tolerances for the parts. Information must be obtained about the incoming parts that are not within tolerance. These parts must be eliminated either at the point of manufacture or prior to the introduction into the automated process system.

Often, the orientation mechanisms and tooling used to detect out-of-tolerance parts are similar to those that orient the part in an automatic process. Probes, electronic imaging, and other devices are often employed. When there is evidence of an out-of-tolerance dimension, the part must be rejected.

The ingenuity and cost to conceive, design, and build a bowl feeding system that will adequately protect an assembly system from out-of-tolerance parts could be more than "tooling" a bowl, which orients the within-tolerance part into a given attitude.

Part condition is important. Lubricants and chips must be removed. If electromagnetic vibratory feeders are to be used, the parts must be cleaned and dried thoroughly. When parts are cleaned, savings can be realized by using the resonant free-piston-type vibratory drive with special "wet part" tooling in the bowls. These feeders will also handle parts that are coated with lubricants (cutting oils, etc.).

Internal part defects require special detection equipment. They seldom affect the output of the automated manufacturing system. They do, of course, affect the quality of the final product. For example, stress fractures that are not visible to the naked eye are a typical problem in the fastener industry. With the many devices on the market today, it is suggested that the speed and dependability of operation under normal factory conditions be thoroughly investigated prior to making production and quality commitments. Experience and ingenuity in the handling of this possible difficulty should be sought by the project engineer. The more experienced vendors can make estimates of the costs involved to detect internal defects. Questionable solutions should be identified and evaluated with respect to the effect they will have on the project.

AUTOMATED PARTS SUPPLY SYSTEMS

Automated parts supply systems are accessories that store bulk parts and meter them to orienting equipment, such as bowl feeders. The volume of parts stored is a function of how often the user wishes to fill the storage system (once per shift, etc.). The need for manual replenishing of parts into the parts feeder should be eliminated. The vibratory storage hopper's controls can automatically meter parts into the feeder when signaled. Typically, some type of flow switch is positioned in the parts feeder to constantly monitor the level of parts in the bowl. The supply of parts to bowl feeders should be enough for efficient operation of the bowl tooling, but not overflow the mechanical action.

When parts are not free-flowing, the type of automated supply system to be used is not always obvious. In this case, a supply of parts must be tried with different hopper or supply configurations to ensure reliability of operation. When the correct supply system is used, it will eliminate the need for constant monitoring by an operator. Often, a good automated supply system will pay for itself within three to four months.

Several types of equipment for automatically supplying parts to orienting devices are presented in Figs. 18-1 through 18-8.

BASIC HOPPER

The basic hopper is an inverted cone or pyramid with an opening at the bottom, closed off by a sliding gate (see Fig. 18-1). A vibratory bulk feeder is placed directly under the gate. The bulk feeder moves the parts from the hopper and deposits them into an orienting system after the orienting system signals that parts are required. The bulk feeder is arranged so that when it is carrying parts away from the hopper, parts will flow out of the bottom of the hopper. When the bulk feeder is shut off, back pressure builds up and parts cease to flow out of the hopper. Standard hoppers are used for parts that do not interlock or "match stick." The range of parts that can be handled by such a hopper may be extended by applying vibration to the walls of the hopper, approximately one-third of the way up the side. The vibration must be shut off simultaneously when the bulk feeder ceases to carry parts away from the mouth to prevent "packing." Standard hoppers are available in sizes up to 50 ft³ (1.4 m³).

MOVABLE-WALL HOPPERS

Movable-wall hoppers were invented to provide a free flow of parts that tend to interlock and collect in the standard hopper. These hoppers are also inverted pyramids. One of the walls is hinged at the top so that the entire wall will vibrate when driven by a free piston, pneumatic air motor (see Fig. 18-2). The intensity of vibration increases along the sides as the parts approach the gate, with the most active vibration at the hopper gate. The vibration should be activated only when parts are carried away from the mouth of the hopper to avoid the packing of parts in the gate area. These hoppers are available in sizes up to 50 ft³ (1.4 m³). Movable-wall hoppers are also available with elongated gates for use with extra large parts that tend to match stick easily, such as gutter nails and long threaded bolts (see Fig. 18-3).

HOPPER-ELEVATOR COMBINATION

An automatic supply hopper feeding into an elevating cleated belt or a magnetic belt is convenient for loading orienting devices that are located some distance above the floor (see Fig. 18-4). The ease of inspection, loading of the hopper, and the resulting dependability of the station operation will usually offset the increased price of the cleated elevating belt used to raise the parts to the vibratory bowl feeder.

BULK FEEDER SUPPLY

A bulk feeder, as shown in Figure 18-5, is sometimes more suitable for the supply of parts to an orienting process than a conventional hopper. The vibratory action of the bulk feeder spreads, settles, and distributes a supply of bulk parts that would very likely jam in the conventional or vibrating plate of the hopper. Many times, it has provided a reliable uniform supply of parts when all other methods have failed.

COIL SPRING HOPPER

The vibratory system of the coil spring hopper shown in Figure 18-6 illustrates a spring supply system. Closed-end, cylindrical-coiled springs may be untangled, singulated, and fed out for use in an automated operation. Coil and wire characteristics are important in determining the practical use of this method.

WIRE FORM HOPPERS

An arrangement such as illustrated in Figure 18-7 may sometimes be used to achieve a reasonable rate of singulated wire forms, such as drapery hooks, to a packaging or assembly process. The equipment is always completely custom built and a matter for research and development (R&D) consideration.

PORTABLE HOPPERS

The hopper illustrated in Figure 18-8 is either a basic hopper or a movable-wall hopper without the bulk feeder attached. It is used for handling batches throughout a process. When the hopper is filled at the exit of a machine operation or some other operation, the gate is fully closed. When filled, the hopper is moved to the part handling workstation for the next operation and placed upon supports that align it with a bulk feeder. The gate is then opened and the hopper operates as a conventional automated hopper. This arrangement reduces the floor space required for storing parts between machines. Also, there is less tumbling of parts since they do not need to be transferred from container to hopper prior to the next operation.

LINERS

Heavy-duty, urethane sheet liners may be bonded to the inside surfaces of the hoppers and the bulk feeders. These liners are a good investment. Not only do they provide excellent wearing surfaces, but they will reduce the noise of the parts in the hopper or bulk feeder to an acceptable level.

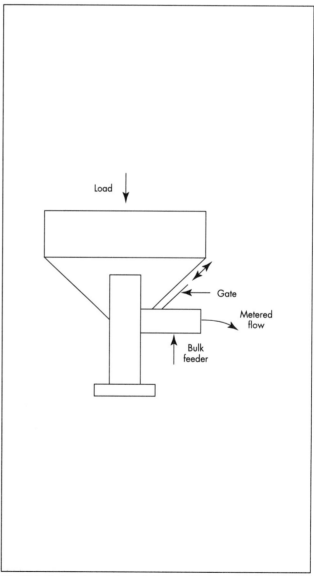

Fig. 18-1. Basic automated supply hopper. Electromagnetic and pneumatic types are used to meter free-flowing parts to orienting devices and are available in sizes up to 50 ft³ (1.4 m³).

CHAPTER 18   ASSEMBLY

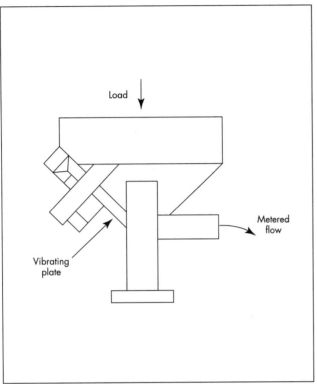

Fig. 18-2. Vibrating plate supply hopper. Electromagnetic and pneumatic types are used with parts that interlock and jam and are available in sizes up to 50 ft³ (1.4 m³).

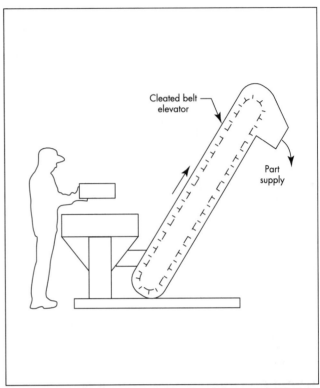

Fig. 18-4. Elevating hopper for ease of loading. It can use any of the hoppers shown in Figures 18-1, 18-2, and 18-3, with a cleated elevating belt to raise the supply of parts as required.

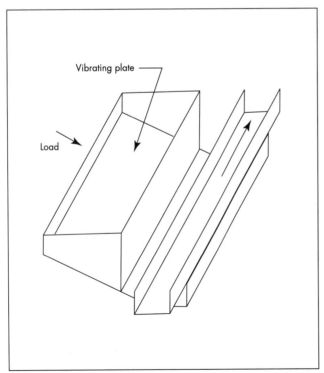

Fig. 18-3. Elongated vibrating plate hopper. Electromagnetic and pneumatic types are used for long parts that "match stick," such as gutter nails, long threaded parts, etc.

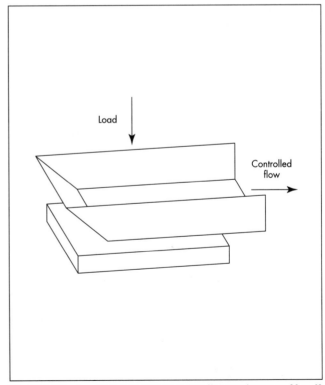

Fig. 18-5. Vibratory bulk feeder that can handle part sizes up to 30 × 60 in. (76 × 152 cm).

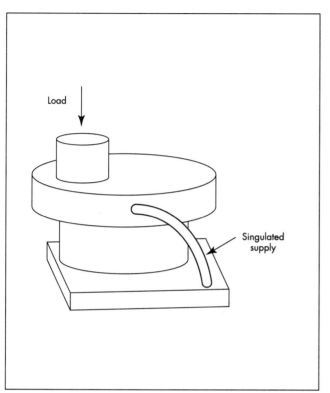

Fig. 18-6. Coil spring hopper. Untangles, singulates, and feeds out cylindrical, closed-end coil springs.

Fig. 18-8. Portable hopper. Ideal for batch control, it also saves floor space and reduces transfer tumbling of parts into and out of hoppers.

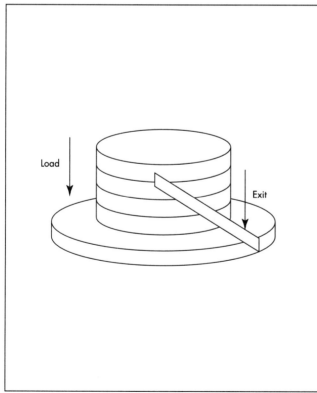

Fig. 18-7. Wire form hopper. A high-speed vibratory untangling system for four slide-type wire forms. Each application is custom-made.

PARTS ORIENTATION EQUIPMENT

When starting an automation project, consult an automation company to identify the best means of feeding and orienting the parts. Most companies will evaluate the parts and offer recommendations to enhance productivity. Sometimes this means design changes to the parts so that they can be automatically fed. A simple part design change can often assure proper orientation, maximize the efficiency, and reduce the cost of the automation system.

Given that proper parts orientation is achievable, a look at the downstream process is warranted. The oriented products must now advance to the assembly or secondary work cell. Consideration needs to be given to parts accumulation. The parts feeder output rate should be specified at rates over the machine output rate. This will keep the downstream process constantly supplied with oriented parts.

Oriented parts need to be accumulated and stored so that they are accessible to the downstream process. Several methods exist to accumulate parts: vibratory in-line feeders, gravity tracks, and conveyors. The method selected is very dependent on part configuration and system layout.

When selecting a storage track, the length of the in-line track is determined by the in-feed rate of the downstream process. The track should be long enough to store a one-minute supply of parts. For example, a 0.25-in. (6.4-mm) diameter part multiplied by a rate of 60 parts/min equals a 15-in. (381-mm) track length. As feed rates increase, the track length may accommodate less than a minute's supply of parts. However, if the track length is effectively reduced, the parts feeder output rate may need to be increased. Accumulation of oriented parts is thus an important consideration in maintaining productivity.

CHAPTER 18 ASSEMBLY

VIBRATORY BOWL FEEDERS

Vibratory bowl feeders are by far the most commonly used means for presenting parts in a desired attitude. However, vibratory bowl feeders are usually configured for a particular part. To use it for a different part requires that the bowl portions of the feeder be retooled or replaced.

As illustrated in Figures 18-9 and 18-10, the parts are loaded into the storage area, and conveyed up and around spiral or helical tracks by means of vibration. The bowl and track system is supported by a system of inclined springs arranged in a circular pattern. The springs are attached to a balance weight that acts as an inertial platform to aid in the efficiency at which the springs absorb and release energy. The spring action becomes more effective as the inertia of the balance weight increases. The balance weight reduces the vibratory energy that reaches the mounting table and resilient pads further reduce the vibration transmitted to the mounting plate.

For a simple understanding of vibratory feeding, consider a part resting on the track of Figs. 18-9 or 18-10. The track goes through several thousand vibration cycles per minute. The vibration moves the track up and forward at a relatively high rate of speed. The track then moves down and away from the part, allowing it to fall through a trajectory onto the next track location. The vibration path may be arranged in a circular fashion as in Figures 18-9 or 18-10, or in a straight path.

In bowl feeders, the parts are conveyed through various geometric devices called tooling. Only parts with the correct attitude are allowed to pass. The rest are rejected back to the supply part of the bowl. Sometimes clever geometry can be used to change the attitude of the part passing through rather than rejecting it to enhance the delivery rate. Parts with the incorrect orientation may be easily rejected back to the supply portion of the bowl for another trip up the track. This is a principal advantage of bowl feeders.

There are two types of vibratory bowl feeder drives in general use: electromagnetic bowl feeder drives and free-piston pneumatic drives. Even though they each convey parts with a vibratory action, there are distinct differences in performance.

Electromagnetically-driven Bowl Feeders

Electromagnetic drives perform well for many operations and are the most widely used of the vibratory drives. Electric power is often readily available, and it is therefore more convenient to use electromagnetic drives rather than pneumatic ones.

However, there are limitations. The electromagnetic drive is sensitive to load. It creates movement by operating very close to the resonance of a spring system, which is usually 1-2 hertz (Hz) (cycles per second) away from the natural frequency of the spring system. When relatively high-density parts are loaded into a vibratory bowl feeder, the natural frequency of the system can easily vary more than 1-2 Hz and the electromagnetic drive no longer operates satisfactorily. Thus, electromagnetic drives should be used for light to moderate loads.

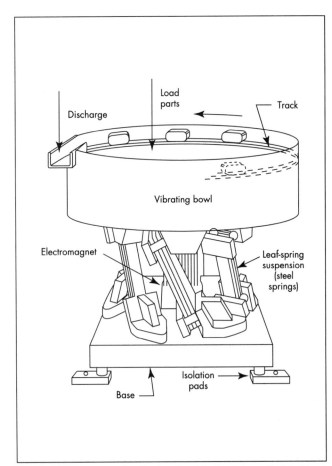

Fig. 18-9. Electromagnetic vibratory bowl feeder drive, cylindrical bowl and base.

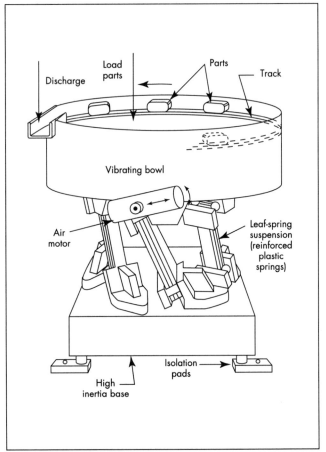

Fig. 18-10. Free-piston, pneumatic vibratory bowl feeder drive and cylindrical bowl.

All vibratory drives will age with time and the natural frequency will drop. Under light operating conditions, this aging characteristic is of little importance. Under heavier loads and higher rate outputs, the electromagnetic drives may require periodic readjusting of the power, retuning of the spring system, and regapping of the electromagnet to meet production.

This drive is powered by one or more electromagnetic magnets. The single magnet version pulls in the vertical direction along the axis of symmetry for the drive (see Fig. 18-9). When multiple magnets are used, they are arranged in a balanced manner along the periphery of the leaf spring's upper ends. The electromagnetic drives operate on alternating current (AC) at frequencies either equal to AC, or by splitting the AC current, with frequencies equal to twice the current.

In the U.S., AC is very close to 60 Hz and the common voltages available for operation are usually 120-, 220-, and 440-volt (V). The smaller drives are usually operated at the lower voltages. The larger drives may operate at the higher voltages found in industrial areas. The 220 V is often three phase and the 440 V is almost always three phase. This is mentioned because of the care necessary for connecting multiple large electromagnetic drives. Electromagnetic drives operate on a single phase current and are connected across part of the three phase supply. When several large electromagnetic drives are used, the connection of these drives must be balanced to prevent problems from overloading one phase of the three-phase transformer.

Electromagnetic drives for bowls up to 24 in. (61 cm) will usually operate on 120-V single-phase AC power. Bowls above this size often will be operated on 220 V or 440 V. However, larger electromagnetic drives operating at higher power levels are also susceptible to power "spikes" that may damage the controls.

Vibratory feeder operation. The electromagnetic parts feeder is a two-mass system. Mass one consists of the heavy base and rubber isolator feet, as well as the electromagnet. Mass two consists of the bowl mounting plate (often called the cross arm), the armature, and the bowl. The two masses are connected through four sets of leaf springs.

When the magnet receives power, vibration occurs because a pulsating magnetic field is established between the armature and the magnet. The springs permit the armature to move toward and away from the magnet, which imparts the vibration into the bowl that ultimately moves the parts. The leaf springs are mounted at an angle, causing the parts to lift off the bowl surface as they convey forward.

In countries using 60-Hz power, parts feeders normally vibrate at a frequency of either 3,600 or 7,200 vibration cycles per minute.

To get a closer estimate of feeder speed, use the following:

$$F_S = F \times A \times K \qquad (1)$$

where:

F_S = feeder speed
F = frequency (cycles or vibrations per minute)
A = amplitude (length per cycle, for example, inch per cycle)
K = constant (factor is 1.3)

for example:

F = 3,600 cycles/min
A = 0.06 in./cycle
K = 1.3

then:

3,600 cycles/min $\times$ 0.06 in./cycle $\times$ 1.3

The estimated feeder speed or part travel = 281 in./min (119 mm/sec).

Due to the effects of gravity, friction, and other factors, the maximum rate of part travel actually achievable is reduced.

The 7,200 vibrations/min parts feeder is generally used when handling parts that are difficult to orient and sensitive to vibration. In this feeder, the parts are not moved as far per cycle, but are moved twice as many times as the 3,600 vibrations/min unit. This lower stroke at a higher frequency results in better control of the part as it moves through the orientation devices.

Vibratory parts feeder tuning. Proper tuning is important not only to develop maximum spring energy level, but to keep the coil assembly cool. When a drive unit is undertuned, the spring tension is not great enough to allow the feeder mass to return to its neutral position before the next magnetic pulse takes over. Therefore, the mass remains in a state that never allows it to return to its starting or neutral position, and thus restricts the full motion each 1/120 sec. A normal 60 Hz current produces 120 magnetic cycles/sec and transmits 120 mechanical cycles/sec to the bowl. Also, when the unit is undersprung (undertuned), the magnetic energy developed by the coil assembly is not being used and is dissipated in the form of heat. The heat, if prolonged, could shorten the life of the coil or cause it to be badly burned.

Overspringing (overtuning) the drive unit would demand more energy from the coil assembly than is available. While this may not cause harm to the coil, it will result in minimizing spring energy development.

A good balance between coil assembly energy development and spring tension is very important for a smooth and efficient feed system. At this balance point, the parts will feed at maximum efficiency with minimum current requirements. The addition or removal of springs on the base drive may be necessary to obtain the balance needed. Coil clatter is a warning sound that indicates the coil gap should be checked and reset.

The driving force used to actuate the bowl feeders is accomplished by using two or three electromagnetic coils. The coils act upon and pull face plates that are constrained by leaf springs attached to the cross arms, causing and translating a torsional vibration in a vertical direction. When the drive base moves the parts at maximum efficiency with minimum current requirements, the unit is said to be tuned. The mass of the feeder bowl is the determining factor in tuning the unit. The rubber feet placed at each corner of the base drive play an important part in tuning and must be of the proper durometer (hardness) measurement.

Free-piston, Pneumatically-driven Bowl Feeder

A free piston, pneumatic drive is illustrated in Fig. 18-10. Except for the air motor and high inertia base, its appearance is the same as the electromagnetic drive of Fig. 18-9. It generates a vibratory action that moves parts up the tracks and through the "tooling" as does an electromagnetic drive. Both drives provide a means to control the movement speed by varying the vibration amplitude.

The pneumatic drive is resonant and the electromagnetic drive is not. This explains why the pneumatic free-piston drive provides many of the features not possible with the electromagnetic drive.

- Constant speed with variation in bowl load.
- Peak operating speeds do not fade with time.
- Dead spots from asymmetric "tooling" weights may be tuned out of a bowl track system.
- Higher speeds are possible.
- Higher rates in passing through precision and intricate tooling are possible.
- Can use the more efficient reinforced-plastic springs.
- Greater flexibility is possible because setup is faster and simpler. A spring change and air gap adjustment for the electro-

CHAPTER 18 ASSEMBLY

magnetic feeder requires more than one hour, but it takes less than seven seconds for an adjustment on the pneumatic feeder.

- The flexibility of using different pieces of "tooling" and different bowls is greatly expanded.
- Although the costs of operating both electromagnetic and pneumatic drives are almost nominal, the pneumatic drive costs less to operate. It operates in resonance, has a more efficient inertia system, uses more efficient springs, and self-tunes to maintain operation at the true resonance of the system.
- Maintenance is nominal.
- Drive is quieter.
- Unrelated to resonant operation, but important to those who work with hazardous materials (such as aerosols), the pneumatic drive may be considered explosion-proof.

The costs of customized drives with relatively simple tooling are very comparable up through 18-in. (457-mm) bowls. Beyond this, the pneumatic drives cost about 10% less than the electromagnetic drives. In the smaller sizes, the convenience of the available power is often the deciding factor.

Determining Bowl Size

The size of the bowl feeder drive will depend upon the size of the bowl to be carried. This, in turn, will depend upon the size of the part to be handled. In Figure 18-11, a curve is presented illustrating the variation in bowl size with part length. A track width of about 1.3 times the part width is usually satisfactory.

Three types of bowls are illustrated in Figures 18-12, 18-13, and 18-14. These bowls may be mounted directly to the drive plates of the vibratory bowl feeder drive. The spiral bowl is the easiest to use because parts flow freely up the track as it spirals out to the exit. The spiral bowls offer less storage space in the bottom than the cylindrical bowls and are readily available in cast aluminum, stainless steel, or mild steel (see Fig. 18-12).

The stability of the parts moving up the spiral bowl tracks is affected by the vibration of a bowl feeder drive, which is precisely circular, while the outer wall of the spiral bowl angles out approximately 1.5°. This causes side instability, and in some cases may eliminate the spiral as a suitable bowl for use with precision tooling.

The cylindrical bowl in Fig. 18-13, has its outer walls in line with the direction of vibration from the bowl feeder drive. The parts are more stable and tooling can be more precise. However, one track is above the other, and this leads to possible jamming of parts between tracks. Part dimensions and methods for allowing parts to enter the first track must be considered.

Bowl loading can be a critical factor for electromagnetic drives. It is even more important when using cylindrical bowls because the fluctuating load is located farther away from the axes of vibration. The outside track configuration of Fig. 18-14 provides advantages with regard to the ease of tooling and accessibility. Rejected parts fall back into the outer tray and are conveyed around and down an inwardly-sloping surface to re-enter the tooling tracks. The tracks are circular and have the stability of the cylindrical bowl. They also tend to have part jams between tracks. The cylindrical and outside track bowls are available in either mild or stainless steels.

It is recommended that the critical pieces of tooling for part orientation are reproducible from detail drawings and manufactured from tool steel. Also, they should be easily replaceable and adjustable.

Bowls may be lined with high-grade urethane sheet for wear and noise. Unless contamination is a factor, a mild steel bowl lined with urethane is a better investment than stainless steel. Urethane will outwear stainless by 50 times. Linings of inclined nylon or plastic fibers may be used to achieve speeds approaching 1,500-2,500 in./min (0.64-1.06 m/sec).

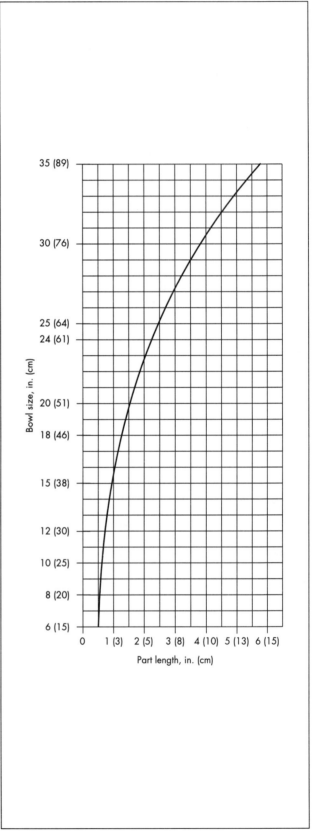

Fig. 18-11. Bowl size in relation to part length.

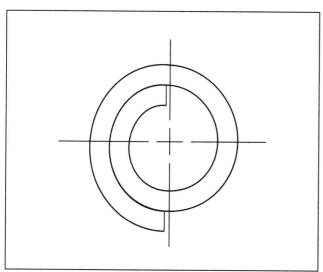

Fig. 18-12. Track layout of a spiral bowl.

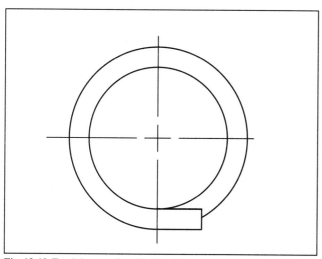

Fig. 18-13. Track layout of a cylindrical bowl.

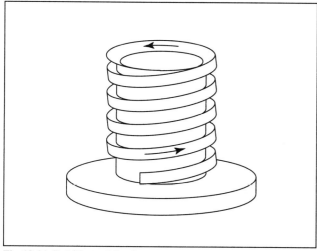

Fig. 18-14. Outside track bowl.

ORIENTING ON LINEAR VIBRATORY CONVEYORS

Long, thin, or intricate parts that do not orient and feed very well on the curved tracks of bowl feeders may often work better on the precision straight tracks of a resonant linear vibrating feeder. The feeding vector of the resonant feeder track is adjustable (both vertical and horizontal components) and controlled over the entire track from inlet to outlet. A resonant pneumatic drive with properly sized and placed inertial balance weights and adjustable spring angles will provide this necessary control.

Speeds on precision tracks where the parts are closely contained to prevent overlapping are attainable up to 500 in./min (212 mm/sec) on the horizontal and close to 1,000 in./min (423 mm/sec) when inclined downward at 6-8°. For example, linear pneumatic resonant feeders have been used successfully to orient and singulate needle bearings and force them into centerless grinders at rates in excess of 1,000 in./min (423 mm/sec).

Some typical examples of the orientation capabilities provided by this type of linear feeder are thin clock and timer bearing plates oriented with respect to hole patterns, long posts and studs oriented with respect to the neck-down area on one end, and parts that must be oriented with precision profiling.

Many types of tracks for different parts may be easily interchanged (see Fig. 18-15). Resonant feeders have been developed in up to 120-in. (3-m) lengths with variable, spring-angle track mounts using only one pneumatic motor.

Linear electromagnetic feeders are also available. For the most part, the spring angles are fixed (welded), and one electromagnet is required every 16-18 in. (406-457 mm) to provide dependable feeding. It is recommended that these feeders be used for only the simplest and short track-type of orientation tooling projects. Various attempts to improve the problems resulting from fixed spring angles by attaching the springs to massive weights have improved the general feeding somewhat. However, flexure of the track is often induced, which results in slow or dead spots when the track length exceeds 10-12 in. (254-305 mm), and it is impossible for the one feeding angle to meet all requirements. Dependable feeding then becomes more of an art than a science.

LINEAR FIBER VIBRATORY FEEDERS

Both pneumatic resonant and electromagnetic linear feeders can be used to orient and feed parts on tracks lined with inclined fibers. The part speed is approximately 2.5 times that of the part on a metal track surface.

The feeder may be arranged as shown in Fig. 18-16. The orientation feeder conveys parts up an incline considerably greater than that possible with a linear feeder conveying parts on bare metal or urethane. The parts are singulated and oriented with rejected (misoriented) parts forced to drop onto a return feeder. The return feeder moves the rejected parts back to the supply area to the orientation feeder for another trip through the tooling.

Fiber systems are fast and quiet. The efficient conveying action of the fibers compensates for possible marginal feeding performance present with the linear electromagnetic feeder drive and provides a dependable system.

The tooling possible on fiber feeders is rather large scale compared with that of the vibratory bowl feeders and is limited to items having more easily-distinguished part shapes. Fiber electromagnetic drives can be tooled at speeds up to 1,000 in./min (423 mm/sec) and the resonant pneumatic can be tooled at speeds up to 1,400 in./min (593 mm/sec). Pneumatic fiber feeders are more capable for tooling parts because they can adjust to the best driving angle of the vibratory surface. The pneumatic feeder will also carry far more weight.

CHAPTER 18   ASSEMBLY

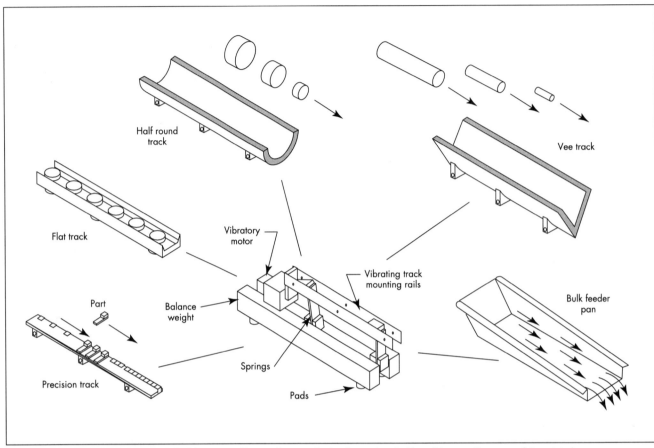

Fig. 18-15. Interchangeable tracks used with resonant linear vibratory feeder for custom tooling. *(Courtesy Burgess and Associates)*

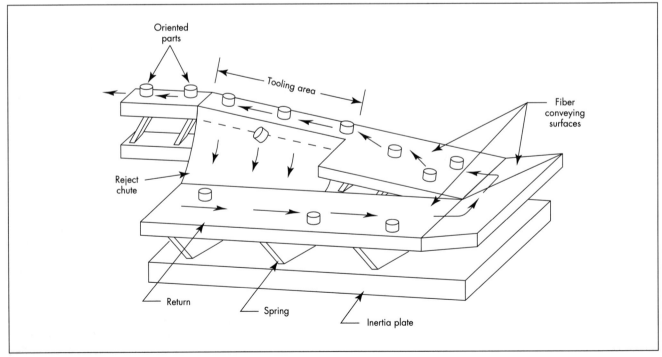

Fig. 18-16. A fiber-orienting track system.

HORIZONTAL BELT FEEDERS

Belt feeders may be used to orient and feed parts. One belt is inclined upward and conveys the part through the tooling, which separates the properly oriented parts, rejecting misoriented parts onto the second belt. The second belt returns the parts to a recirculation point. Very high speeds may be attained by using a belt orienting system. The cost of the basic equipment is usually less than that of linear vibratory equipment.

CENTRIFUGAL FEEDERS

This nonvibratory feeder is the fastest of the bowl-type feeders (see Fig. 18-17). An inclined, centrally-located disk supplies parts to an orienting rim located around the disk. Feed rates of the centrifugal feeders are much higher than those of vibratory feeders. The centrifugal feeder is adaptable to not only simple configurations, but also some complex configurations. The cost is considerably more than that of the vibratory feeder handling the same size part.

HOPPER ELEVATORS

The arrangement illustrated in Figure 18-18 is that of a cleated belt passing through a bulk storage hopper and dragging out parts for orientation. The belt then proceeds in an upward direction, inclined a few degrees from the vertical. In a preferred arrangement, the cleats on the belt are also inclined sideways. The sides of the structure contain the parts as they advance upward. Upon reaching an opening, the parts roll or slide out and pass through linear tooling much the same as in a linear vibratory feeder. The oriented parts are accepted and the misoriented parts are rejected down a chute back to the storage hopper. Singulation of parts and simple tooling may be achieved by the sizing of the cleats.

This is not a system for fragile parts. It is for parts whose size makes them impractical to handle in bowl feeders. The rates achieved with a system such as this are usually in the 40-80 parts per minute range. The cost is considerably greater than a vibratory feeder sys-

tem, because rugged units are needed. Bearings, gear boxes, and drive motors should be heavy-duty. This is a practical machine for parts such as piston rings, pistons, castings, and forgings. It also may be used successfully for oil filter cans, oil filter can covers, and other bulky stampings.

PRECISION ROLLS

Precision rolls are located at an angle, rotate to convey the parts down the slope, and may be used to sort parts based upon cross-sectional dimensions. They also may be used to orient headed parts that would cause difficulty in the normal slotted-type bowl tooling. Precision rolls do not move parts at a very high speed and speed is sacrificed for the precision attained.

DRUM FEEDERS

Drum feeders are used for feeding screws, wire studs, rivets, etc. If a drum feeder can be used, it is probably more economical than any of the other orienting devices. Parts are picked up by vanes as the drum rotates and then dropped onto tracks that accept only the part orientation desired. Parts are allowed to slide down the tracks extending out of the drum. If a misoriented part enters in the track, it is difficult to remove as it slides down the track after leaving the drum.

SENSING

Sometimes, a relatively inexpensive orienting device is used when orientation with linear feeders or bowl feeders would be quite costly. The parts are singulated and fed into the sensing device where the geometry of one end or the other is sensed. If the geometry is appropriate, the part is moved on through. If the geometry is reversed, the part is quickly rotated and then moved through.

In cases where singulation may be essentially achieved, but the part is too difficult or too intricate for conventional tooling developed within any reasonable time by a craftsman, the parts may be fed under a sensing head, which compares the part with an accept-

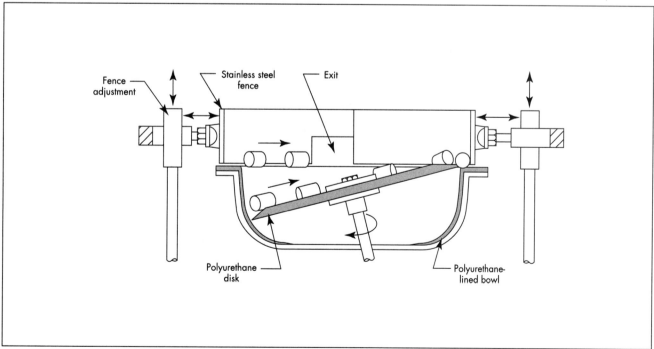

Fig. 18-17. Rotating centrifugal feeder for high-speed orientation of parts. *(Courtesy FMC Corp., Material Handling Equipment Division)*

CHAPTER 18   ASSEMBLY

able picture of the part. Parts that do not meet this test are rejected, usually with an air jet. Parts feeding systems relying on more sophisticated sensing are presented in the last section of this chapter.

PART QUALITY

The quality of a part with respect to its geometric shape and dimensions is the most important factor in the reliability of any orientation tooling developed. It must be the basis upon which the craftsman customizing a bowl tooling operation is held accountable. However, there will be parts that are out of tolerance. If the manu-

facturer can provide the craftsman with a sampling of such parts, it may be possible to provide a means for ejecting these parts before they exit from the bowl with the oriented parts. Some parts may be detected visually, such as partial heads on bolts, lack of threads on bolts, visible cracks on bolts, and incomplete shots from injection molding machines or die cast machines. There are parts that have internal defects and thus are not easily detected. The development of practical machinery to detect bolts with internal stresses that may cause fatigue failures and similar problems is an ongoing process. There have been claims to having accomplished this, but as with any new technology purchase, it should be carefully evaluated.

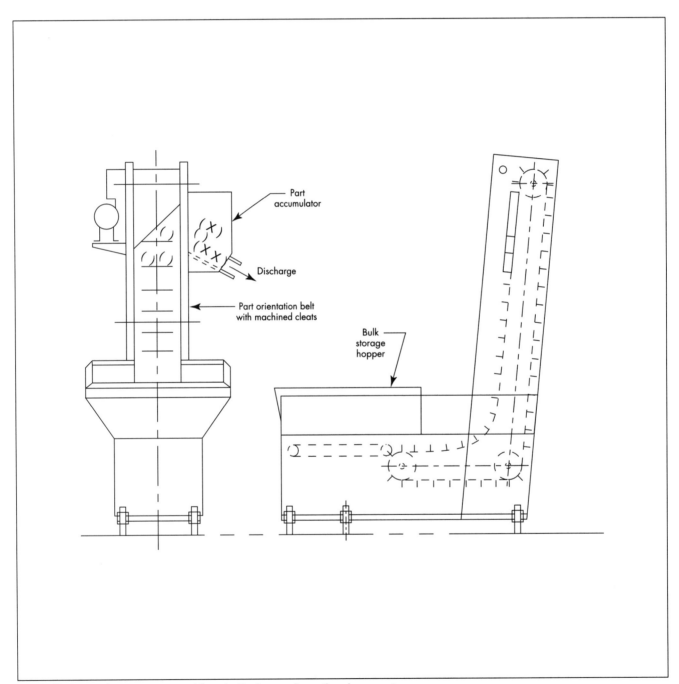

Fig. 18-18. Hopper elevator arrangement for orienting large and sometimes heavy parts.

ORIENTED PARTS TRANSFER

This section presents several approaches to moving oriented parts, including gravity tracks, linear vibratory feeders, belts with guides, tube transfer, and chain transfer.

GRAVITY TRACKS

The simplest and least expensive of all transfer or exit tracks is the gravity track shown in Fig. 18-19. Oriented parts move from the bowl feeder, enter a gravity track, and slide down into position waiting to enter a placement device or an assembly system.

LINEAR VIBRATORY FEEDERS

A linear vibratory feeder provides a positive means for taking oriented parts from the exit of a bowl feeder or other orienting device, moving them in a positive manner across spaces of up to 20 ft (6.1 m) per single feeder, and maintaining orientation all the time (see Fig. 18-15).

When precision is required to prevent overlapping of parts, and the distance to be traversed is more than 12 in. (305 mm), a resonant pneumatic vibratory feeder is recommended. Resonant pneumatic feeders with the control of the feeding vector, permit the accumulation of many thin parts with the precision necessary to prevent them from overlapping under pack pressure (see "Orienting on Linear Vibratory Conveyors" described earlier).

Electromagnetic linear vibratory feeders are also used for transfer tracks. Greater care is required to configure the track to ensure feeding without any slow or dead spots. Slow and dead spots will occur in operation after a period of time, and adjustments must be made. Using an electromagnetic drive for dependable horizontal transfer requires considerable experience.

Using linear vibratory feeders from the bowl exit to the escapement mechanism lowers the heights required for the bowl feeders as compared to those using gravity tracks. They also make it easier to observe the operation of an automated assembly machine, and remove foreign objects or deformed parts from bowls before they jam.

The resonant, pneumatic linear vibratory feeders can provide enough power to force parts rapidly into escapement jaws and even into centerless grinders, saving the cost of another escapement (see "Oriented Parts Placement" later in this chapter).

BELTS WITH GUIDES

The use of belts with guides is an inexpensive and fast way of transferring oriented parts (see Fig. 18-20). Care is required at the entrance and exit transition points.

TUBE TRANSFER

Both pressure and vacuum tubes successfully transfer oriented parts to the point of use (see Fig. 18-21). Urethane tubes extruded with internal contours are often used to maintain the orientation of cap screws, hex nuts, and many other devices as the parts are moved from the exit of a feeding system to the entrance of an escapement by vacuum or compressed air. For example, vacuum tubes move finished spark plugs up and across aisles and down to an area some distance away for inspection, packaging, etc., without damage to the precisely set gap. Finished and ground machine parts may be moved through urethane tubes and gently accumulated without damage from impinging on each other. Rates of 40-50 ft/sec (12-15 m/sec) have been achieved in the movement of parts in this manner.

CHAIN TRANSFER

A tabletop conveyor chain configuration as shown in Fig. 18-22 permits the attachment of arms and other holding devices extend-

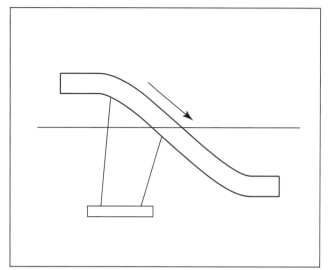

Fig. 18-19. Gravity exit track.

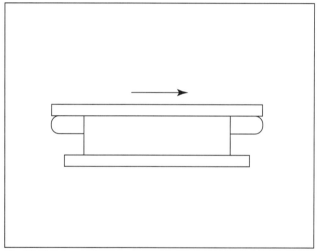

Fig. 18-20. Belt transfer.

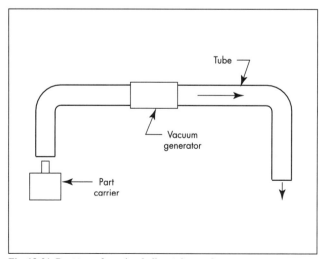

Fig. 18-21. Part transfer using hollow tubes and pressure or vacuum.

CHAPTER 18   ASSEMBLY

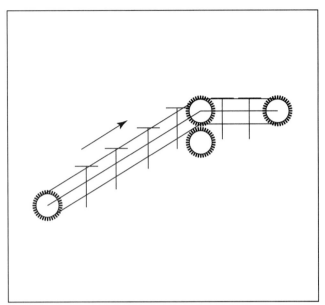

Fig. 18-22. Side-mounted chain transfer.

ing out to the sides of the chain for the support and movement of components which must not in any way touch each other.

ORIENTED PARTS PLACEMENT

There are many methods used to place parts for assembly. These methods include gravity tracks, force feeding into pockets using linear feeders, reciprocating plunger and jaw combinations, pick-and-place robots, and fastener devices.

GRAVITY TRACKS

The inclined column of parts in a gravity track will force a part out of the bottom of the track exit into the pocket of a jaw or the side of a nest at a speed suitable for many of the moderate-speed operations. A 30° track, for example, has been observed to move 1-in. (25.4-mm) diameter parts into a pocket on an index table when the table is indexing at a rate of 30 parts per minute. A shuttle cylinder may be located at the track exit to further increase the cycle rate (a factor of two is common).

If the operation with this inexpensive method is marginal for a given rate of speed, the rate may be increased by mounting the exit track on resilient mounts, and providing vibratory energy in a direction parallel to the movement of the parts on the inclined section of the track. This tends to make the track frictionless and gravity becomes more effective.

FORCE FEEDING INTO POCKETS USING LINEAR FEEDERS

Oriented parts that have been transferred on a linear vibratory feeder from an orienting device to a point of use, such as the jaws of an escapement or the pockets in an index table nest, can be forced into the jaws or the pockets using the feeding action itself (see Fig. 18-23). Data from resonant pneumatic feeder investigations indicate that a line of oriented parts waiting to be moved into a pocket will reach full track speed within four vibratory cycles. The parts then move at the speed of an unobstructed track into the pocket or jaw.

The time required to move a part into position is a key determination of whether or not an escapement is also required. The time required to move a part into position is based on the following:

- The time available to insert the part. The maximum operation rate is restricted by the insertion time.
- The time to accelerate the part to full speed.
- The time to move the part over a defined distance.

RECIPROCATING PLUNGER AND JAW COMBINATIONS

A much-used escapement system for placing oriented parts includes a jaw mechanism with an aperture through which the oriented parts are fed (see Fig. 18-24). A plunger then makes contact with the oriented part and places it in its final position. Simultaneously, the jaws are cammed aside to permit the part to move in a direction usually perpendicular to its entering path.

When these plunger-type escapements are used on synchronous systems, such as an index table, all plungers should be monitored to prevent the table from being indexed unless they are in the fully retracted position. When the plunger-type escapement is used on asynchronous systems, it is often best that each workstation operate independently and at maximum speed. As soon as the monitored part is in the jaws, and a nest is monitored to be in place to receive the part, the plunger extends and places the part. When the extend stroke is monitored as being completed, the plunger is immediately retracted. Simultaneously, the nest is released, and the jaws are presented for the receipt of another oriented part. Such an escapement will place parts as fast as parts and nests are placed in position.

The present discussion will not describe the many types of escapements used for placing single or multiple parts. If a cylinder-type plunger is used, the time to shift the valve spool, extend a cylinder, retract a cylinder, move another oriented part into place, and replace a filled nest with an empty nest, can all be determined or estimated in a fairly close manner.

Be prepared to make a critical evaluation of purchased equipment. Often, the extend and retract cycles are unduly limited by a system not sized for fast operation. If the engineer is capable of estimating what the extend and retract cycles should be, and is able to measure what they actually are, the engineer has then progressed toward improving the productivity of a system.

PICK-AND-PLACE MECHANISMS

When direct placement with a reciprocating plunger and jaw arrangement is not practical, a "pick-and-place" mechanism is often used. A cam-driven arm, on the end of which jaws are located, is positioned to pick up the oriented part, move it across a prescribed distance, and place it into position in an assembly or nest, etc. (see Fig. 18-25). These mechanisms are dedicated to one part, are more expensive, and require more space. After a part is released, the pick-and-place system moves to pick up another part and return it, holding it poised for insertion into the next assembly.

ROBOTS

Robots are the ultimate pick-and-place devices. They can be programmed to select a part, pick it up, change the orientation of the part (moving about one or more axes), and place it into a pocket or an assembly. A robot is much more expensive than any of the escapement devices discussed earlier, but with the exception of grippers or end effectors, a robot is a flexible tool that can be used for a wide range of applications. For a complete discussion of robots see sections in Chapters 13 and 17, "Industrial Robots" and "Robotic Systems for Parts Orientation," respectively.

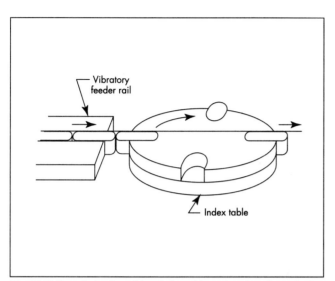

Fig. 18-23. Parts being forced into index table pockets by a linear feeder.

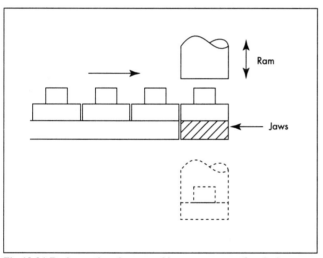

Fig. 18-24. Reciprocating plunger and jaw arrangement for placing parts.

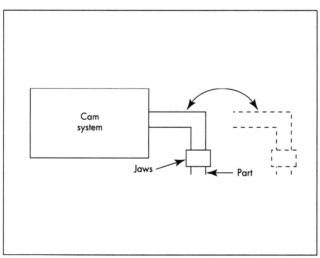

Fig. 18-25. A pick-and-place mechanism.

FASTENER DEVICES

There are many standard fastener units on the market, such as screwdrivers, nut runners, riveting machines, etc. (see Fig. 18-26). The fasteners are often oriented at a remote location and blown through urethane tubes with interior contours into the jaws of the device. The fastener device may be machine mounted, such as at a workstation, or handled manually.

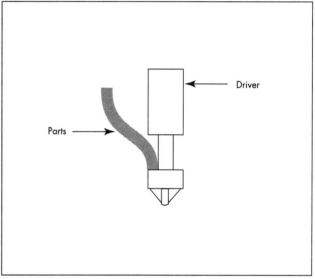

Fig. 18-26. Arrangement for driving screws.

ASSEMBLY MACHINES AND SYSTEMS

The discussion for assembly machines and systems includes the qualification process for parts and the rate comparisons for assembly systems. It also describes an operator-assisted workstation, a synchronous assembly for a rotary index table and carousel, an asynchronous linear assembly without pallets, and an asynchronous pallet loop system: both level one and two.

QUALIFICATION OF PARTS

When a defective part is introduced into an automated assembly system, and causes a jam or goes through the assembly process and results in a defective product, the cost to the manufacturer can be excessive. This is why many manufacturers are now requiring 100% inspection of all parts used in automated assembly systems. However, 100% inspection is not always a guarantee.

One defective part in a batch of 100,000 parts has been known to occur. Nevertheless, this is the trend in what is being demanded of part quality for automated assembly. The long range effect of this trend on assembly system design will be important. Synchronous systems will become more dependable and, therefore, more productive. Asynchronous systems, wherein pallets are driven at a preselected speed by belts and conveyors, will correspondingly lose their principal advantage over synchronous indexing systems.

Automated inspection systems (preferably located at the source of manufacture) will become more and more sophisticated. As shown

CHAPTER 18   ASSEMBLY

in Figure 18-27, parts are oriented, cleaned, dried, and put through the necessary testing devices as they leave the point of manufacture.

Because unqualified (off-the-shelf) parts, such as fasteners, still have defect rates of three to five parts per thousand, engineers developing an assembly system must know about the quality of the particular parts that will be used.

RATE COMPARISONS FOR ASSEMBLY SYSTEMS

A broad variety of machines and systems is available for automated assembly. A general outline of some of the system concepts is shown in Fig.18-28.

OPERATOR-ASSISTED WORKSTATION

The operator places parts into a tool, such as a press, to be assembled, welded, or have some other operation performed on them. These parts must be selected from a bulk supply, oriented, and placed into the assembly fixture. By using automated orienting devices, such as a vibratory bowl feeder, the parts may be oriented and presented to the operator automatically. The operator can then pick them up in an oriented position from a predetermined spot and place the part into the assembly fixture. On average, assisting the operator in this manner will increase the operator's output by a factor of two.

A typical installation is shown in Figure 18-29, where an operator is taking parts from the end of a linear vibratory transfer feeder and placing them into a nest. The cost of a typical bowl feeder, linear transfer feeder, automatic supply hopper, pedestal, and all controls is on the average ≤25% of the annual cost of one operator.

The part quality for an operation like this does not have to be exceptional, and quality such as that usually found in purchased parts will be adequate. The operator provides first level inspection by discarding incomplete or out-of-tolerance parts.

SYNCHRONOUS ASSEMBLY—ROTARY INDEX TABLE

The subject of how a rotary index table operates, as shown in Figure 18-30, is covered in other sources (see Bibliography). The rapid drop in productivity based on the number of assembled parts when nonqualified parts are used has been well documented for many years (see Fig. 18-31). Yet, index tables are being used every

day to assemble two parts successfully at rates of 10,000-14,000 assemblies per hour, because the necessary attention is being given to the quality of the parts fed into it. When part quality can be held to better than one defect in 100,000, high-speed assembly on an index table becomes practical.

To improve an index system up to the highest productivity possible, variable speed index tables are recommended.

A disadvantage to using index tables is that they get crowded when several workstations are located on the table. Also, access for maintenance or changeover is limited. However, these limitations must be balanced against the fact that index tables are one of the least expensive means for assembling product.

SYNCHRONOUS ASSEMBLY—CAROUSEL

At considerably greater expense, the workstations of the index table may be added to and spread out by arranging them along a belt or chain in a carousel arrangement. Often an answer as to whether or not to use a carousel or an index table can be arrived at by drafting a detailed plan view of the work area.

The carousel is not as fast as the index table. The index table has less inertia and can index at cycle rates up to two and a half times greater than that of a carousel.

LINEAR ASYNCHRONOUS ASSEMBLY

The linear vibratory feeder of the resonant type provides an inexpensive and efficient means for assembling parts when the base part may be conveyed as a platform on which the assembly is made.

In Figure 18-32, the base part is oriented and fed into the entrance of the linear feeder. The base part is then stopped at a workstation where the second part is guided into place. This is repeated throughout many parts and workstations.

Spaces can be economically provided between stations for the accumulation of subassemblies, providing the system with the basic characteristics of an asynchronous system.

These systems provide good access and high productivity. Using the resonant free-piston drive, the manufacturer always has the option of increasing the speed of the assemblies as improvements and developments are made in various workstations. This variable speed feature is part of the standard controls for the resonant feeder. Since

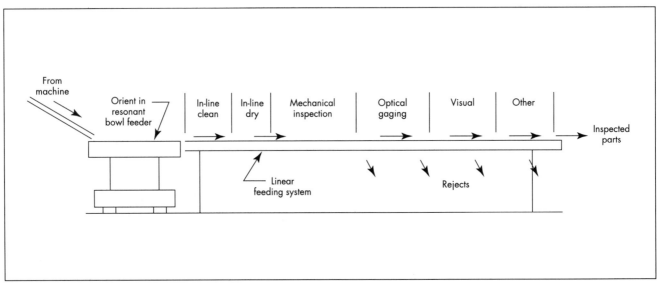

Fig. 18-27. A 100% inspection system.

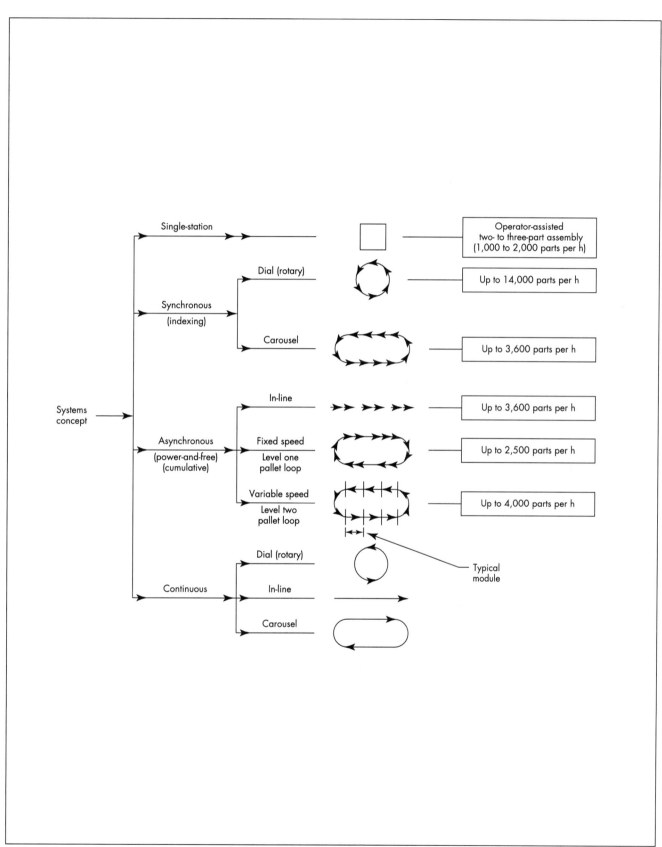

Fig. 18-28. Basic concepts for automated assembly systems.

CHAPTER 18   ASSEMBLY

there is only one moving part in the entire linear feeding system, maintenance for the feeder is negligible.

Assembly rates will depend on several factors, including the dimensions of the base part. Production rates can be estimated accurately with inexpensive trials on standard feeders. Rates are usually in the 3,000-4,000 cycles per hour range.

ASYNCHRONOUS PALLET LOOP SYSTEMS— LEVEL ONE

Level one considers systems wherein the traverse speed of the pallets is constant throughout the system. It is similar in plan to that shown in Figure 18-33 (without the variable speed modules). These systems have the basic characteristics of the asynchronous systems, wherein pallets can accumulate ahead of the workstation. They are usually belt- or chain-driven, and can be expected to achieve assembly rates up to 2,500 parts/h.

Increases in productivity during production are difficult, unlike the level two systems discussed next.

One of the primary features of level one asynchronous loop systems is that they achieve reasonably high productivity with parts not 100% qualified. As the quality of the parts increases, the justification for using the level one system becomes primarily that of price. The price is approximately 20-30% less than the synchronous indexing carousel system and greater than the rotary index table.

ASYNCHRONOUS PALLET LOOP SYSTEMS— LEVEL TWO

The level two pallet return loop-type system is the most productive asynchronous system (see Fig. 18-33). Its costs are 10% less than the fixed speed systems of level one. Yet, it provides features important to productivity not included in any other system.

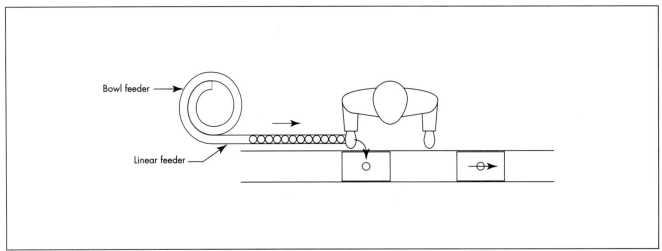

Fig. 18-29. Operator moving oriented parts from a linear vibratory transfer feeder to a nest.

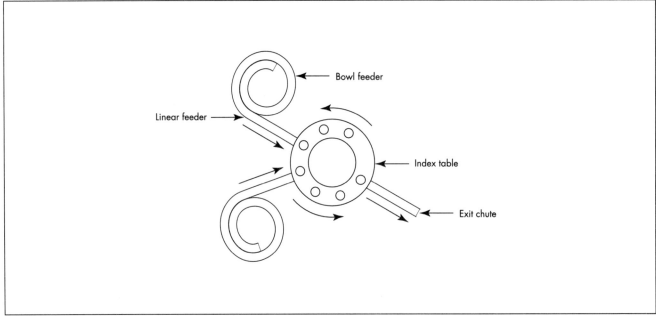

Fig. 18-30. Rotary index table.

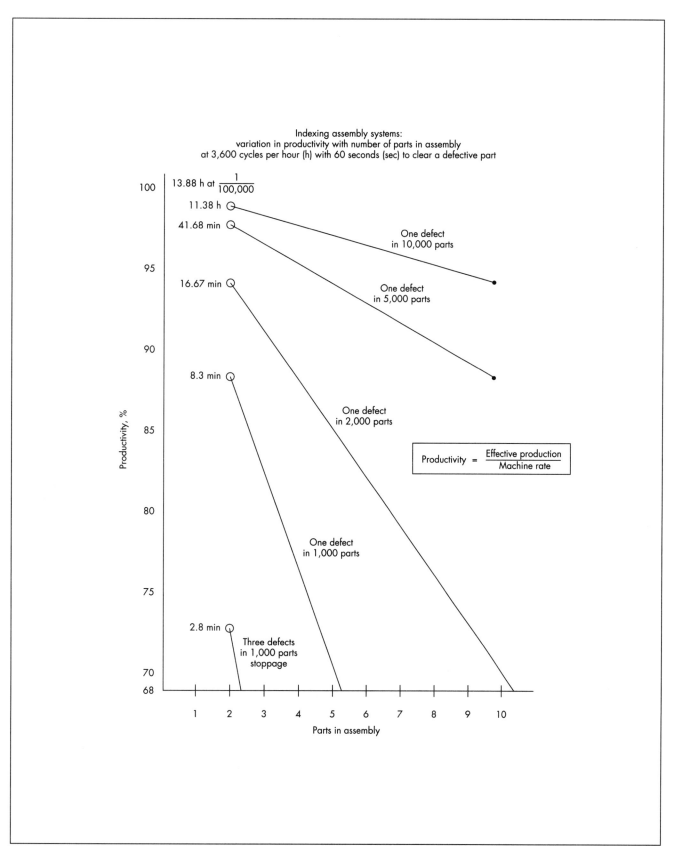

Fig. 18-31. Variation of productivity with many parts assembled on an index table for five part qualities.

CHAPTER 18   ASSEMBLY

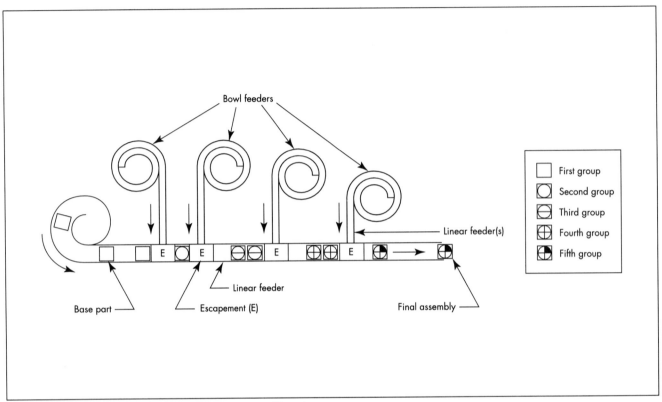

Fig. 18-32. Plan view concept of a linear asynchronous assembly system.

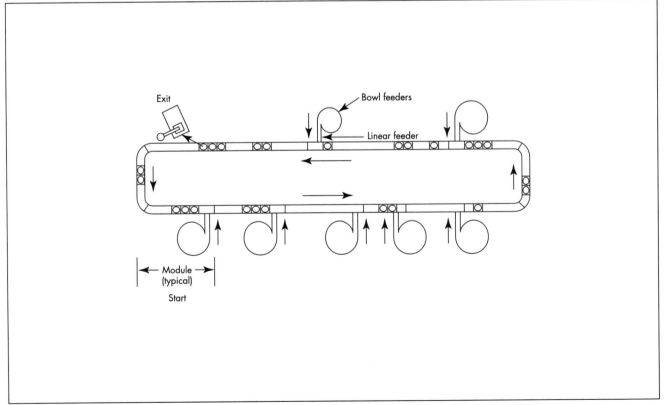

Fig. 18-33. Plan view concept of an asynchronous pallet loop system—level two with variable speed modules.

The system is made up of linear vibratory conveying tracks carrying the pallets up to and through each workstation. A separate track is provided for each workstation and is made up of inclined fibers. They are capable of moving the pallets into and out of the workstations at speeds up to two and one half times that of the belt- and chain-driven asynchronous systems. Further, the fibers move the pallets into the workstations more efficiently, without the skidding that takes place between the belts or conveyor surfaces and the pallets of the level one systems. Production rates from 150-160% higher than the level one systems are possible with level two systems. Because of the design simplicity of the track systems that move the pallets around the loop, the total cost of the level two system is comparable at about 10% below that of the level one system.

Each module consists of a track conveying the pallets into and out of a workstation. The variable speed available to each module facilitates ongoing improvement and development during production. The speeds can be varied by simply controlling a throttle valve, and improvements in the methods of assembly can be immediately incorporated in the process. The optimum speed for each workstation is easily determined. Any asynchronous loop system is more productive when each station can operate at its top speed to make up the time lost from trying to clear a malfunction.

SUMMARY

Vibratory parts handling equipment plays a significant role in improving productivity in a broad range of industries. Equipment is found throughout the automotive, pharmaceutical, consumer products, electronics, fastener, packaging, and food industries. Each environment has its specific set of application criteria.

When considering automation solutions, it is extremely important to focus on the up-front parts feeding and orientation portion of the project. Without consistent feeding of product, not even the best assembly or downstream processing equipment will produce the desired level of efficiency.

Take time to understand the current process and clearly identify the objectives that justify the need for automation. After these are clearly defined, work with a qualified parts handling manufacturer who will provide the level of expertise and support needed to accomplish the objectives. Closely evaluate the supplier's capabilities in manufacturing, mechanical and electrical engineering, as well as sales and service support before discussing the details of your application. Selecting a qualified supplier will keep all efforts focused on the automation project, instead of trying to overcome the deficiencies of an underqualified supplier.

PNEUMATIC DEVICES FOR AUTOMATION

Parts placement, positioning, and handling are fundamental to all industrial manufacturing operations, from manual to fully automated. These basic functions are seen in a wide range of applications including assembly, packaging, and machine loading. This section discusses how grippers, multimotion actuators, powered slides, cylinders, escapements, switches, and sensors can be combined to develop reliable and cost-effective devices for handling and placing parts in a wide range of applications. It also includes an overview of the various actuators and application design criteria for each.

APPLICATION CRITERIA

The first step in developing an automated pneumatic assembly function is to analyze the application and list the application crite-ria. The following is a list of items to identify prior to starting the design of the pneumatic device.

- Determine the number of axes of linear travel (x, y, z).
- Calculate the length of travel required in each axis.
- Find the amount of rotation required in each axis.
- Ascertain the weight of the part to be assembled.
- Decide what type of end effector will be used to grasp the part.
- Define the position accuracy required for assembly.
- Determine the part feeding method or presentation.
- Determine the required cycle time.
- Decide on what electrical interface will be used.

When designing a pneumatic device for assembly, it is important to start with the very last component on the unit and work backward. Using this advice, the gripper is the best place to start.

GRIPPERS

Grippers can be the most design-intensive components of an assembly device. Building a special gripper to handle a specific part becomes very expensive and time consuming. Many applications use a standard, commercially-available gripper, that when properly tooled, performs the same function as a special gripper. Standard grippers are available in a wide range of styles and sizes to cover the variety of parts being handled. Most of these units are pneumatic and provide parallel (linear) or angular (rotational) jaw motion.

Grippers are single- or double-acting, with the double-acting units having the ability of gripping internally or externally on a part. Many grippers use two jaws, or fingers, to grip a part. In some situations, three jaws are used to simplify tooling. Internal springs may be used to ensure that grip force is maintained in the event of pressure loss. These same springs can be used to add grip force to a double-acting gripper. Locking grippers are also available. These grippers contain an internal clutch mechanism that locks onto the part until the actuator forces the jaws open. Some commercially available grippers have proximity switches or sensors, which provide an electrical interface between the gripper and controls for the loading or unloading device.

The key to successful use of standard grippers is tooling the fingers or jaws to properly grasp the part. It helps to lock on specific features of a part. This ensures accurate registration and maximizes the gripper's strength. Considerations for gripper design are:

- Working media—how much pressure can or should be applied?
- Electrical feedback—are sensors used?
- Jaw motion—in what direction is the movement?
- Internal or external grip—where will the object be held?
- Object surface—smooth, textured, etc.
- Speed—will the movement be fast or slow?
- Safety factor—what are the dangers to the worker?

ROTARY ACTUATORS

Standard pneumatic rotary actuators rotate, attach, or position a part during the assembly process. They can also serve as a power source to drive an arm for rotation into and out of the work envelope. These fluid-power actuators are available in a wide range, from miniature sizes up to large units capable of producing torques in excess of 3,000 in.-lb (339 Nm).

Standard rotary actuators can be specified for any amount of rotation up to and including 720°. The rotational motion that rotary actuators provide can be very quick, or deliberate and smooth. This is accomplished through built-in speed controls and cushions for dampening shock at the end of rotation. Maximum control on pneumatic rotary actuators is achieved by using part of the unit as a hydraulic control. The actuator produces an extremely smooth rotation while using the simplicity of pneumatic power. This type of

CHAPTER 18 ASSEMBLY

rotary actuator can be essential when handling precision parts requiring delicate motion.

As with the other components discussed in this section, rotary actuators can be combined with another actuator to provide multiple-axis rotary motion. Considerations for rotary actuator design are the following:

- Dynamic torque (twisting movement and forces).
- Bearing load.
- Speed.
- Backlash.
- Number of positions.
- Mounting.
- Shock absorber.
- External stops.

MULTIMOTION ACTUATORS

Combined linear and rotary actuators can be very useful in a wide variety of pick-and-place and transfer operations. For this reason, standard pneumatic and hydraulic actuators are available that provide this combination from a single output shaft. The linear and rotary motions can be controlled separately, providing an independent reach-and-turn function. This motion is ideal for transferring and repositioning parts.

Like the rotary actuators and cylinders, a wide range of strokes and rotation can be specified, making it easy to adapt these units to various machine tools. When combined with swing-arm grippers or other tooling, the reach-and-turn action provides the perfect motion for pick-and-place and loading and unloading applications. Considerations for multimotion design are:

- Dynamic torque.
- Push-pull.
- Side loading.
- Backlash.
- Shot pins.
- External bearings.
- External shocks and stops.
- Accuracy or repeatability.
- Mounting.
- Cycle time.
- Number of positions.

POWERED SLIDES

Powered linear slides provide fixtured linear motion. They utilize hardened ground shafts and linear ball bushings to support the load. Because of this construction, they can handle longer strokes than cylinders and are used in applications where side loading occurs. These slides are generally powered by a pneumatic cylinder.

The travel on slides ranges from a fraction of an inch to several feet, with payloads of hundreds of pounds. Slides come in two basic styles, a cantilever type and a saddle type. The cantilever slide is most often used with the main body and cylinder static, and the tool plate extends and retracts. The saddle slide is generally used with the end block static and the saddle (or center block) traveling between the end blocks. Each slide type has its advantages based on mounting requirements and usage.

The fact that slides can be specified for travel and load carrying capability makes it easy to design for a wide range of applications. Slides can be used individually or combined to yield multi-axes of linear motions. Considerations for slide design are:

- Cantilever- or saddle-type design.
- Bearing capacity (what is best for side load?).

- Force required.
- Amount of deflection.
- Speed.
- Number of positions.
- Accuracy or repeatability.

CYLINDERS

Cylinders can be powered pneumatically or hydraulically for a wide range of applications. They can be simple stand-alone air cylinders for pushing, clamping, and positioning, or sophisticated multi-axis pick-and-place devices.

Variations on the basic cylinder include an air or oil tandem for smooth control, a three-position cylinder for positioning, a back-to-back cylinder for four-positions with a double-rod end, compact four-positions with a double-rod end, compact cylinders for high force in a short package, and rodless cylinders for long travel lengths. Air or hydraulic cylinders used for assembly can incorporate a nonrotating piston rod. This can be done internally using a spline and hollow rod construction or externally using an attached guide rod. Both are commercially available and have the advantage of a consistent rod position throughout their stroke range. This is critical when attaching tooling, such as grippers. The nonrotating piston rod ensures the gripper is always positioned properly to handle the part.

The following is a list of factors for consideration when designing with a cylinder.

- Force required—push and pull.
- Column strength-rod.
- Rod side load.
- Torque on nonrotating rod.
- Cycle time.
- Number of positions.
- Accuracy or repeatability.
- Mounting considerations.
- Speed.

ESCAPEMENTS, SWITCHES, AND SENSORS

Escapements utilize basic linear motion for isolating individual parts in conjunction with feeder bowls and magazine feeds. The escapement incorporates two sequenced nonrotating shafts, which are used to trap and then release one part at a time. It can be tooled to fit a wide range of part sizes and shapes. Design considerations include side load impact, load cycle time, and tooling.

Switches and sensors can be used to tie the pneumatic actuators to a controller or sequencer. They provide feedback so the controller knows where the actuator is, triggering the next event. These switches can be mounted on the actuator for maximum efficiency of space and design time. They are actuated by a magnetic band on the actuator's piston, and in some cases, by standard inductive proximity switches mounted directly on the unit.

Sensors can be incorporated with rotary actuators and grippers to provide multiple signals through the rotation or jaw movement. These are used with a set-point module, which provides four adjustable outputs throughout the movement of the actuator. Design considerations for switches and sensors include:

- What type of current will be used (AC or DC)?
- What is the sink or source?
- How many signals are required?
- Is there a cable strain relief?
- What type of controller is used?
- Does the sensor fit the rotary actuator or gripper?
- Is the rotary actuator set-point module within 180° of rotation?
- Does it have a quick disconnect?

FLEXIBLE AUTOMATION FOR ASSEMBLY

The increasing technological pace over the past decade and the push toward a single worldwide marketplace have reduced the market life of many general purpose industrial and consumer products to a relatively short period, often no more than one to two years. For manufacturing companies to remain competitive and maintain or increase market share in this new global marketplace, it is paramount that they reduce their time-to-market, which is the time it takes to get a product through the design process, in full production, and to the market in volume. Assembly is an increasingly important part of modern production for high-volume products (for which production is measured in the hundreds of thousands of units per month). Therefore, the time required to design and implement automation systems for the assembly of new or redesigned products is a crucial component of time-to-market for high-volume products. The traditional approach for high-volume assembly has been to use custom-designed, dedicated automated assembly systems that rely on hard tooling. However, the long lead time necessary to design and implement these complex assembly systems is becoming prohibitive in the face of rising pressure for improved time-to-market.

For this ecomomically important and growing class of products, short market life dictates the commercial importance of time-to-market, and high market demand imposes the necessity for automation. Together, these factors are giving rise to a growing demand for modular, flexible automation for assembly.[1, 2, 3] Here, flexible refers to a system that can handle a wide variety of parts through reconfiguration involving changes primarily in the software, with little to no changes in the hardware. With flexible assembly systems, a significant reduction in time-to-market is achievable because a considerable portion of the assembly cell hardware can be specified much earlier in the product design cycle than is possible with dedicated automation. In this regard, flexible automation for assembly is important to achieving the full benefits of concurrent engineering. Furthermore, the ability to reuse these flexible assembly modules and rapidly reconfigure them for new or redesigned products is economically attractive, since the capital equipment involved can be depreciated over multiple generations of products.

FLEXIBLE PARTS FEEDERS

Although great strides have been made in flexible automation systems for the assembly of discrete parts, the technology for parts feeding has not kept pace. Frequently, feeding parts to flexible assembly systems is the bottleneck for high-volume assembly.[4, 5, 6, 7] Feeding is the positioning and orienting of a part in a manner that allows a robot to grasp it in the flexible assembly system. Flexible parts feeders have been evolving, primarily through the addition of sensors to vibratory bowl feeders. Now, vision-based, flexible parts feeders are commercially-available products.[8, 9]

Bowl Feeders with Sensing

Sensors have been added to vibratory bowl feeders for two main reasons: the nondestructive qualification of parts and the determination of part pose. In either case, stationary instrumentation is added to sense parts as they move by on the output track of a vibratory bowl feeder or on a conveyor that has been fed by a vibratory bowl feeder. A variety of acoustic, inductive, capacitive, and microwave sensors have been used for nondestructive qualification of parts[10, 11]

and machine vision systems have been used for determination of part pose[12] or simultaneous pose determination and nondestructive qualification.[13]

These systems have some means, typically an air jet or pneumatically-activated mechanical gate, that eliminates parts that have been deemed unacceptable from the output stream. In nondestructive parts qualification systems, the failed parts are diverted to a rejection bin; whereas in the pose determination systems, parts in an incorrect pose are diverted to a chute that returns them to the bowl of the vibratory feeder. Although these systems are capable of providing a stream of qualified parts in a specific pose, they are not fully-functional flexible parts feeders. Because the parts are sensed on a moving conveyor, part location typically is not measured and the parts cannot be grasped by a robot without additional sensing or tooling to mechanically locate the parts.

Modern Flexible Parts Feeders

In the current vision-based, flexible parts feeding systems, some form of conveyor system is used to singulate the incoming bulk parts. Then, singulated parts are presented on a back-lit conveyor to a downward-looking charged coupled device (CCD) camera (see Fig. 18-34). In one type of flexible feeder, multiple parts are presented to the vision system for each image,[14, 15] whereas for another type of flexible feeder, programmable mechanical gages align singulated parts in single file as they move through the system, and a single part is presented to the vision system for each image.[16]

For either type of parts feeder, parts presented to the vision system will be on the back-lit conveyor in one of the small number of stable poses possible for that part. Based on the part geometry and the desired location of the part within the product being assembled, there are a limited number of possible points where the part can be grasped or picked—especially if a single pick point is to be accessible for multiple poses of the part. Stable poses are classified as pickable or unpickable, depending on the accessibility of a pick point. For example, if the part is upside down, no pick point is accessible and the pose is unpickable.

A major task of the vision system in a flexible parts feeder is to determine the pose of the part. Identification of part style or differentiation between part styles is not required since only one type of part is fed at a time. In one type of flexible feeder, template matching is used to discern part pose by extracting a silhouette of the part from the image and comparing that silhouette to an array of templates generated in the calibration or training procedure. A mirror positioned at 45° next to the part allows both a top view and a side view of the part to be captured in a single image. This feature adds additional information that is useful when a top view is not sufficient to distinguish part pose.[17] In the type of feeder system that allows multiple parts in the camera field of view, the image must first be processed to determine all possible candidate parts. Afterwards, a suite of vision processing tools is applied in turn to each candidate part in the image. These vision processing tools range from connectivity analysis to advanced tools for disambiguation of similar but distinct stable poses.[18]

After a presented pose is identified as pickable, the vision system must determine the position and orientation of the part. Because the part is at rest on a flat surface, orientation of the part is restricted and can be described simply by a rotation about an axis perpendicular to the back-lit conveyor. After the part location information for a pickable pose has been transmitted to the robot, the part is grasped by the robot and the desired manipulation or assembly task is carried out. In operation, any part in an unpickable pose is rejected and the next part is considered. At a point in the cycle that depends on the particular flexible parts feeder, parts in unpickable poses are in-

CHAPTER 18   ASSEMBLY

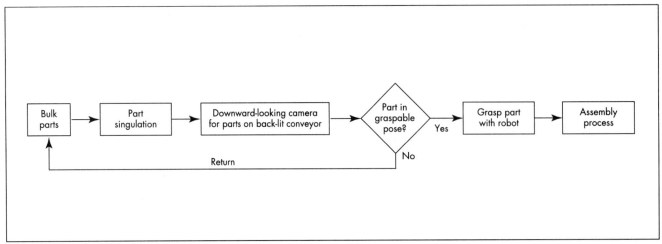

Fig. 18-34. Block diagram of a flexible assembly cell consisting of a vision-based, flexible parts feeder and a robot.

dexed off the back-lit conveyor to a separate conveyor that returns these parts to the bulk parts hopper.

Although the commercially-available flexible feeders differ significantly in the details of their approach to parts feeding, these systems perform the same basic functions:

- Isolate parts on the flat, back-lit output feeder conveyor.
- Determine part pose.
- Calculate the part location for parts that are in a graspable pose.
- Recirculate parts that are in an ungraspable pose.

Flexible feeders are designed to handle parts with a major dimension of up to 2.5 in. (64 mm). Cycle times, which depend upon the capabilities of the robot being used and on the details of the parts being fed, range from one to four seconds per part, with two-to-three seconds per part (20-30 parts per minute) being typical. While these feeders cost as much as several bowl feeders combined, the inherent flexibility easily justifies the cost in some applications. The economic evaluation of flexible automation depends heavily upon the value associated with the benefits of flexibility.

Other than the limitations on part size and cycle time mentioned earlier and the obvious limitation that parts must be durable enough to withstand multiple passes through the feeder, the major limitation of these flexible part feeders is that the part location may not be sensed before the part is grasped by the robot. This may be due to errors in the vision processing, errors in the robot and gripper, part-to-part variations, and grasping error. The total distance error between the actual pick point and the ideal pick point may be as large as ±0.08 in. (±2 mm).[19, 20] To overcome this difficulty, part-specific grippers are often required on the robot. This is so that the part is correctly registered in the gripper despite grasping errors, which can be large with respect to the overall process tolerance.

Emerging Technology

In an assembly cell incorporating a flexible feeder, knowing the location of the part relative to the robot gripper would be significantly more useful than knowing the part location on the output conveyor of the flexible feeder. Several ways of directly measuring the part-in-hand location for a part in the grasp of a robot have been reported. One method, which has been used successfully for years in component placement on circuit boards, is to use an upward-looking CCD camera to measure features of a part held by the robot. This method, however, is restricted to planar parts and only allows correction in $(x, y,$ and $\theta)$. To handle nonplanar parts or to correct for part mis-

alignment in more than three degrees of freedom, which are common with discrete mechanical parts, more complex sensing is required. Conventional solutions range from two CCD cameras for stereo vision to more sophisticated, real-time, 3D sensing systems. Recently, two novel, straightforward approaches to directly measuring the part-in-hand location of a part in the grasp of a robot have been developed.[21, 22, 23] These approaches are inexpensive because they do not require sophisticated sensors; simple because they are self-calibrating and do not require a CAD model of the part; and robust because recalibration is relatively quick and easy.

The first of these approaches uses a nest of three simple optical beam sensors, each of which responds to the presence or absence of an object along the beam line.[24, 25] The robot passes the part through this sensor nest at a constant velocity. The position of the robot is recorded when each beam is first broken by the part, and again when the beam is reconnected after the part passes. From this information, the location of the part relative to the robot gripper can be calculated in real time quickly enough for adjustment of the paths required in the subsequent assembly operation. For cylindrical parts, this system has been shown to be accurate to 0.001 in. (0.025 mm).

The second approach uses a CCD camera to observe how a grid of laser lines breaks across the part in the robot's grasp.[26] After the robot has picked up a part from the output conveyor of the flexible feeder, the part is positioned near a sensor pod where the CCD camera takes an image of the intersections of a tic-tac-toe pattern of laser lines on the part. From the information available in this image, the location of the part relative to the robot gripper can be quickly calculated for adjustment of the paths required in the assembly operation. In a tray-loading application incorporating a flexible feeder, this approach has been shown to compensate for more than 90% of the error in part-in-hand location that was present after the part was grasped from the output conveyor of the flexible feeder.

Systems using these approaches for measuring parts are not commercially available at present. However, these approaches provide significant improvements in overall accuracy, are sufficiently simple, inexpensive to produce, and easy to use, and may be available for sale in the near future.

FLEXIBLE ASSEMBLY SYSTEMS

The basis for most flexible assembly systems is a robot or robots fed by one or more flexible parts feeders. Since the need for flexibility varies widely, an entire assembly line might be put together from flexible assembly cells or a single flexible assembly cell might be added to an assembly line that is otherwise composed of dedicated assembly cells. Flexible assembly systems are designed and built by the manufacturer needing the assembly system, or by an automated systems manufacturer. In either case, product design engineers should participate in specifying the types and ranges of assembly flexibility that would be useful for the products being considered.

Another successful approach to modular, flexible automation for assembly is to use a tray-based automation system, which completely separates the process of positioning and orienting the parts from the assembly process. In such a system,[27, 28] two conveyor systems are used, one conveyor on which pallets that carry the assembled product move through the assembly system, and another conveyor system on which the component parts to be assembled are automatically moved throughout the assembly system in plastic trays. Each tray for component parts is designed to hold 20-200 parts of a single part style in an accurately-located geometric matrix of accurately-shaped cavities. Because the trays undergo precise registration in each cell of the assembly system, the accurate location of the parts in the cavities of the trays allows subsequent acquisition and assembly of the parts with an accurate, but blind (not vision-guided), pick-and-place robot. While the part tray and a portion of the robot gripper are specific to the part being manipulated, the remainder of the assembly cell is generic, and therefore a good example of modular, flexible automation for the assembly of discrete parts.

However, simply using a tray-based automation system for assembly leaves unanswered the question of how to load the parts into the trays in the first place. For this purpose, one commercially-available solution is the APOS (advanced parts orienting system).[29, 30] APOS is a vibratory device designed to induce circular vibrations of adjustable magnitude and frequency in a flat, inclined tray containing a matrix of identical cavities designed to capture a specific part. Bulk parts are dumped on the APOS tray, which is vibrated until a sufficient number of cavities are filled. Once captured, the parts are held precisely in a particular position and orientation, suitable for subsequent acquisition and assembly of the parts with a pick-and-place robot. When APOS works properly for a given part, it is robust and very economical in high-volume applications.[31] However, the range of parts that can be handled by APOS is somewhat restrictive: allowable part sizes range up to 2 × 2 in. (51 × 51 mm), part shapes must be such that they do not tangle easily, and parts with some aspect ratios are more suitable for APOS than others. Additionally, the part cavities in APOS trays must capture parts in only the proper orientation and reject all other orientations, as well as hold and maintain registration for captured parts. APOS is not completely flexible: a slight change in a part, either due to a design change or a change in the fabrication process, may necessitate the design and fabrication of new trays for that part, which can be costly in terms of lead time and tray cost.

An alternative approach to getting the parts into trays is to have the part suppliers load the parts on trays at their site as a value-added service. However, the shipment of parts in trays is expensive relative to shipment of parts in bulk; more trays may be required than if the parts were shipped in bulk; the logistics of returning empty trays to the supplier to be refilled are a complication; and the trays sustain significantly increased rates of wear and tear during shipping.

Another automated approach to getting the parts into trays is to build a flexible tray-loading cell using a flexible feeder and a robot. A flexible automated tray loader of this type was successfully developed and used as a testbed for evaluating the feasibility of part-in-hand measurements.[32] In this cell, bulk parts first are singulated and presented by a vision-based, flexible parts feeder. The robot then picks a part from the feeder output station and presents the part to a second sensor system consisting of two CCD cameras and two laser line generators, where the location of the part relative to the robot gripper is sensed. Finally, correcting for measurement errors in how the part was grasped, the robot places the part in one of the slots in the output tray. The principal feature of this flexible automation cell is two-stage sensing: initial crude, fast sensing in the flexible parts feeder to determine part location with sufficient accuracy to allow the robot to grasp the part; and final sensing of the part to allow for accurate placement of it in the output tray. Final sensing is necessary to accommodate errors introduced in grasping the part, which can be significant, especially with a generic gripper capable of handling multiple part styles.

References

1. Ross, E.M. "Flexible Parts Feeders for Robotic Assembly." *Assembly* October 1994: 24-28.
2. Wolfson, W., and Gordon, S.J. "Designing a Parts Feeding System for Maximum Flexibility." *Assembly Automation* 1997, 17(2): 116-121.
3. Yoshida, K. "High-speed Product Assembly, Present and Future." Proceedings of the 1993 Flexible Parts Feeding for Automated Handling and Assembly Workshop. Ann Arbor, MI: Robotic Industries Association, 1993: 91-108.
4. Ross, E.M. "Flexible Parts Feeders for Robotic Assembly." *Assembly* October 1994: 24-28.
5. Wolfson, W., and Gordon, S.J. "Designing a Parts Feeding System for Maximum Flexibility." *Assembly Automation* 1997, 17(2): 116-121.
6. Davis, W.F. "The Systems Approach to Parts Handling." *Proceedings of the Flexible Parts Feeding for Automated Handling and Assembly Workshop. Ann Arbor, MI: Robotic Industries Association*, 1993: 169-180.
7. Friedberg, M.E., Jakiela, M.J., and Ulrich, K.T. "A Computer-based Technical and Economic Model: Choosing Automated Assembly Parts Presentation Equipment." *Flexible Assembly Systems*. New York: American Society of Mechanical Engineers, 1990, DE-Vol. 28: 85-89.
8. Wolfson, W., and Gordon, S.J. "Designing a Parts Feeding System for Maximum Flexibility." *Assembly Automation* 1997, 17(2): 116-121.
9. Mangle, K., Richard, G., and Desrude, W. "Robots + Vision = Flexible Assembly." *Assembly* March 1997.
10. Buckley, S. "Force-field Sensing for QC." *Tooling and Production* 1989, 54(11): 57-59.
11. Glabicky-Fegan, M.A. "Elimination of Downtime in an Automated Assembly Operation by Nondestructive Qualification of Feed Parts." *Materials Evaluation* 1987, 45(11): 1,280-1,284.
12. Suzuki, T., Sakata, T., Kawana, T., and Kohno, M. "An Approach to a Flexible Part-feeding System." *Proceedings of the 1st Conference on Assembly Automation*. Kempston, Bedford, England: IFS (Publications) Ltd., 1980: 275-286.
13. Cokayne, A. "The Way of the World." *Assembly Automation* 1991, 11(4): 29-32.
14. Nesnas, I.A.D. "Computer Vision Strategies for Flexible Part Feeding." *Proceedings of the International Robotics and Vision Conference*. Dearborn, MI: Society of Manufacturing Engineers, 1997.
15. Quinn, R.D., et al. "Design of an Agile Manufacturing Workcell for Light Mechanical Applications." *Proceedings of the IEEE International Conference on Robotics and Automation*. Washington: Institute of Electrical and Electronics Engineers, Computer Society Press, 1996: 858-863.
16. Wolfson, W., and Gordon, S.J. "Designing a Parts Feeding System for Maximum Flexibility." *Assembly Automation* 1997, 17(2): 116-121.

CHAPTER 18   ASSEMBLY

17. Gordon, S.J. 1994. "Programmable Reconfigurable Parts Feeder." US Patent Number 5,314,055.

18. Nesnas, I.A.D. "Computer Vision Strategies for Flexible Part Feeding." *Proceedings of the International Robotics and Vision Conference*. Dearborn, MI: Society of Manufacturing Engineers, 1997.

19. Ibid.

20. Murray, W.R., and Pohlhammer, C.M. "A Technical Approach for Flexible Tray Loading: Proof-of-concept Experiments on Using Direct Calibration to Determine Part-in-hand Location." *Robotics and Computer Integrated Manufacturing*. New York: Pergamon, 1997.

21. Ibid.

22. Canny, J.F., and Goldberg, K.Y. "A RISC Approach to Sensing and Manipulation." *Journal of Robotic Systems* 1995, 12(6): 351-363.

23. Paulos, E., and Canny, J. "Accurate Insertion Strategies Using Simple Optical Sensors." *Proceedings of the IEEE International Conference on Robotics and Automation*. Washington: Institute of Electrical and Electronics Engineers, Computer Society Press, 1994, 2: 1,656-1,662.

24. Canny, J.F., and Goldberg, K.Y. "A RISC Approach to Sensing and Manipulation." *Journal of Robotic Systems* 1995, 12(6): 351-363.

25. Paulos, E., and Canny, J. "Accurate Insertion Strategies Using Simple Optical Sensors." *Proceedings of the IEEE International Conference on Robotics and Automation*. Washington: Institute of Electrical and Electronics Engineers, Computer Society Press, 1994, 2: 1,656-1,662.

26. Murray, W.R., and Pohlhammer, C.M. "A Technical Approach for Flexible Tray Loading: Proof-of-concept Experiments on Using Direct Calibration to Determine Part-in-hand Location." *Robotics and Computer Integrated Manufacturing*. New York: Pergamon, 1997.

27. Hitakawa, H. "Advanced Parts Orientation System has Wide Application." *Assembly Automation* 1988, 8(3): 147-150.

28. Product and sales literature. Sony Corporation, Factory Automation Division, 1994.

29. Hitakawa, H. "Advanced Parts Orientation System has Wide Application." *Assembly Automation* 1988, 8(3): 147-150.

30. Product and sales literature. Sony Corporation, Factory Automation Division, 1994.

31. Hitakawa, H. "Advanced Parts Orientation System has Wide Application." *Assembly Automation* 1988, 8(3): 147-150.

32. Murray, W.R., and Pohlhammer, C.M. "A Technical Approach for Flexible Tray Loading: Proof-of-concept Experiments on Using Direct Calibration to Determine Part-in-hand Location." *Robotics and Computer Integrated Manufacturing*. New York: Pergamon, 1997.

Bibliography

Bakerjian, R., and Mitchell, P. *Tool and Manufacturing Engineers Handbook. Continuous Improvement*, Volume 7. Dearborn, MI: Society of Manufacturing Engineers, 1993.

By, A.B., Caron, K., Crochetiere, W., Cheng, C., and Rothenberg, M. "An Adaptable Feeding Approach Based on the Modular Automated Reconfigurable Assembly System Concept." *Proceedings of the 2nd Flexible Parts Feeding for Automated Handling and Assembly Workshop*. Ann Arbor, MI: Robotic Industries Association, 1994.

Eade, R. "Automatic Assembly: The Key is Orientation." *Manufacturing Engineering* 1989, 102(3): 64-69.

Ho, Y., and El-Gizawy, A.S. "A Programmable, Multi-part Presentation System for Robot Assembly." *Proceedings of Intelligent Manufacturing Systems*. Oxford, NY: Pergamon, 1994: 519-523.

Hollingum, J. "Sweeping it Over the Carpet." *Assembly Automation* 1995, 15(3): 29-30.

Maul, G.P., and Hildebrand, J.S. "Research for Low-cost Flexible Feeding of Headed Parts Using Bi-directional Belts." *International Journal of Production Research* 1985, 23(6): 1,121-1,130.

Ross, E.M. "Flexible Parts Feeders for Vision-guided Robots." *Proceedings of the Flexible Parts Feeding for Automated Handling and Assembly Workshop*. Ann Arbor, MI: Robotic Industries Association, 1994.

Wick, C., and Veilleux, R. *Tool and Manufacturing Engineers Handbook. Quality Control and Assembly*, Volume 4. Dearborn, MI: Society of Manufacturing Engineers, 1987.

Yeong, M., Ruff, L., and DeVries, W. "A Survey of Part Presentation, Feeding and Fixturing in Automated Assembly Systems." *Proceedings of the 3rd ASME Conference on Flexible Assembly Systems*. New York: American Society of Mechanical Engineers, 1991: 83-90.

CHAPTER 19

FINISHING, PAINTING, AND COATING

CHAPTER CONTENTS

Planning and implementing an integrated finishing system requires several areas of expertise. The planner should be able to design the display (holding method) of product(s) to be painted and provide guidelines for proper cleaning, paint application, and cure of the coating. The display also should be designed ergonomically if any manual handling is required. The planner should consider the handling and conveyance method for transport through the processes and a control system that runs the moving equipment and provides production information. The process times, materials, equipment for preparation and cleaning, coating application, and curing of products must be properly selected.

This chapter provides manufacturers with guidelines to make decisions about the display of product(s), the best-fit conveyance to carry the display through the process equipment, and the design of the conveyance. The total system should properly integrate the prepaint and postpaint premanufacturing processes.

DESIGN ELEMENTS

Planning is the most important part of any project. Effectiveness in system planning requires the prospective buyer to do much more than determine a desire or need. If the expertise for analysis is internally available, the system may be planned, analyzed, and specified. After definition, the finishing system and the material handling system designs can be solicited from appropriate equipment suppliers and the systems may be put into place in the factory.[1]

To implement a system where the expertise is not entirely available, solicit help from a supplier or consultant. Beware that suppliers may be more interested in selling their products and reluctant to examine the process demands outside the specific request or limits of their product line. Although spray booth and conveyor manufacturers are very knowledgeable about a particular product, they may not have the resources to afford a team knowledgeable about finishing and material handling systems. The other choice is to purchase the services of a consultant, who is in business to extend knowledge and expertise to his or her client.

When selecting the system type, the design team should consider whether the process conveyance will service the prepaint manufacturing portion of the operation or handle the paint process as a separate operation.

Operations with fabrication cells operating with a Just-in-Time (JIT) philosophy can have the paint conveyance routed to the cells for product or part loading. However, integration of interplant departments may require upgrading the paint conveyance from a synchronous chain monorail, appropriate for a paint shop, to a flexible path, power-and-free system. The integrated system can provide accumulation buffers between the departments to insulate them from both scheduled and unscheduled downtime, staggered department shift times, differences in process rates, etc. In addition to prepaint integration, the facility designer can deliver the products or components to the postpaint processes. For example, components can be delivered to the point of use in the assembly process. As in the prepaint integration with the paint system, the postpaint processes may influence the choice of paint conveyance.

These interdepartmental influences on the paint system mean that the designers should examine the integration of painting into the total operation before designing a paint-only system.

PRODUCT AND CARRIER RELATIONSHIP

Designing a structural carrier, such as a hook or fixture to hold a product, component, or group of components for proper presentation to both operators and each of the finishing processes, is critical to the success of the system. The carrier is attached to the transport conveyance to allow easy removal, without being vulnerable to inadvertent disconnection. A group of carriers is called a package, which holds all the painted components for one product (for JIT systems). The product features, quantity of product per carrier, quality-of-finish goals, and structural integrity should be considered in the design of the carrier.

Product Features

When designing and developing paint systems, it is extremely important to understand the attributes of the product or components to be coated. The product's or component's size, mass, shape, proper state of assembly, and design as it relates to the ease or difficulty of painting should be understood. Placing someone with paint expertise on the product and process design team is advantageous to the organization.

Begin the conveyance design by suspending or supporting the units for presentation to all the individual processes of an industrial paint system. The product or parts presentation should be in the best orientation for cleaning and application of coating, whether for spray or dip processes. The designer, at times, will be faced with the need to compromise on the part attitude that is best for cleaning or application of paint, but not necessarily best for both.

Certain product features send caution messages to the finisher. Cup-shaped areas may trap pretreatment solutions when in the spray zones or dip tanks, carrying solution from one stage to another. These cupped areas waste and contaminate pretreatment solutions and rarely

The Contributors of this chapter are: William Craig, Research and Development Engineer, Rhodes International, Inc.; Robert Macomber, President, Socio Tec Integrators.
The Reviewers of this chapter are: William Craig, Research and Development Engineer, Rhodes International, Inc.; Larry Crawley, Business and Technology Director, E.I. Dupont De NeMours & Co.; Bill Meredith, Research Fellow, E.I. Dupont De NeMours & Co.; John Moore, Research Associate, E.I. Dupont De NeMours & Co.; Sherril Stoener, Manager of Engineered Systems, LPS Technology, Inc.

CHAPTER 19   FINISHING, PAINTING, AND COATING

yield a good quality coating. Further, solution is typically carried with the parts into the drying oven, causing them to fail to dry completely. In immersion painting, cup-shaped areas are intolerable. Where cupped areas cannot be avoided, parts should be oriented in a way that will prevent collection of solutions, or drainage holes should be provided.[2]

Deeply recessed areas are difficult to paint by most spray paint application methods. A classic example is the inside bottom of a wastebasket. Air, entrained in the paint spray, collects in the deep recesses and prevents the entrance of sufficient spray.[3]

Electrostatic spraying, while dramatically more efficient than conventional spray processes, makes greater demands on the designer. The *Faraday cage effect* is the phenomenon whereby charged paint particles are attracted most strongly to exterior edges and corners, and are repelled from the interiors of narrow recesses and sharp interior corners. Where exceptional exterior and edge coverage are important, the Faraday cage effect can be an asset, but not when complete overall coverage is required. Designing corners with generous radii makes the effect less severe. Parts with narrow grooves, fins, or louvers are also susceptible to the Faraday cage effect.[4]

It is usually important to present the part in a way that achieves the best paint coverage, considering paint thickness desired and class of finish required to meet both functional and aesthetic goals. These goals affect durability and customer perception. If the application criteria conflict with cleanability, then manual removal of wash solution from recesses may be necessary. Where practical, the hooks should be designed to cant or angle the part to present it appropriately for both the cleaning and paint application methods.

The goal of product orientation is to maximize product quality. Document the goals for quality at the beginning of a project so that all participants clearly understand the expectations.

Quantity of Products per Carrier

A single product per carrier is defined as a having one product to a single conveyance carrier. The determination of this density ratio depends on the limitation of being able to properly finish one product per carrier. This is usually a function of the size of the product and the capability of the finishing process to reach all areas of it. Some displays with different density ratios are illustrated in Fig. 19-1. The finishing quality level and unique finish-effect requirements can also limit the product-to-carrier ratio. A density ratio of two or more (two or more products per conveyance carrier) is primarily limited by carrier size and quality issues.[5]

One of the most important factors for ensuring the greatest cost-efficiency of the system is to strive for the highest product-to-conveyance ratio possible, while still meeting the finishing objectives. The loading and unloading of the product(s) also must be considered because this process can be affected by the conveyance system selected (for example, accumulating versus nonaccumulating conveyors).[6]

Quality-of-finish Goals

The selection of a conveyance system is influenced by the goals set for finish quality. The highest finish quality may demand a floor-mounted system to minimize the possibility of dirt contamination. Other ways to reduce product contamination from overhead conveyors include carrier design alternatives and drip or dust pans. However, the best way is to eliminate conveyor track, carrier structure, and movement above the product to be finished. Nevertheless, an overhead system regularly cleaned and properly lubricated can provide a relatively noncontaminating finishing environment.[7]

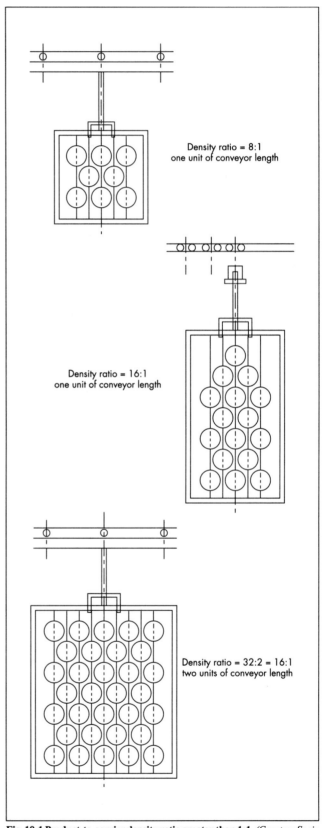

Density ratio = 8:1
one unit of conveyor length

Density ratio = 16:1
one unit of conveyor length

Density ratio = 32:2 = 16:1
two units of conveyor length

Fig. 19-1 Product-to-carrier density ratio greater than 1:1. *(Courtesy Socio Tec Integrators)*

CHAPTER 19   FINISHING, PAINTING, AND COATING

Structural Integrity of Carrier

The structural rigidity of the carrier frame and hanger should be considered. There is a natural conflict in paint systems between minimizing the carrier mass to reduce the energy required for the dry-off and cure processes, and maintaining hook integrity when they are exposed to severe manual handling and process conditions.

If carriers are periodically or frequently removed or manually-handled, they should be designed for the forces to which they will be subjected. If they will be subjected to stripping of paint buildup by burn off, high-pressure hydraulic force, or other abnormal operational conditions, the structure should be designed appropriately. The structural members should also utilize cross-sections that maximize the use of outside corners and minimize or avoid the use of inside corners. Inside corners can decrease the thoroughness of cleaning and permit product contamination between the stripping and cleaning process cycles.

Hook designs should utilize structural tube shapes with high strength-to-weight ratios for longer or high-stress members, and round bar stock for shorter or lower-stress members. Carriers should be designed to hold up under day-to-day usage over time, with little or no maintenance. However, they do not necessarily need to be designed to sustain conveyance chain pull forces without deformation. Carriers should be designed to resist deformation to:

- Provide consistent product presentation for consistent and predictable quality.
- Minimize maintenance.
- Maintain ease of loading and unloading of the product.

For large and heavy unit load carriers (such as auto-body carriers), the structure should resist tuning fork-type vibration. For cantilevered support structures, limiting the structural members' stress to 6,000 psi (41.4 mPa) under static loading forces will minimize objectionable vibration.

The structure or frame should not shadow or prevent the finishing application equipment from producing a quality finish.

CONVEYANCE EQUIPMENT

The basic conveyance equipment should be determined early in the design process. First, it should be determined whether the need is for synchronous versus asynchronous conveyance, fixed path versus variable path, and overhead versus floor-type systems. Then, describe the requirements of the transport device to serve the needs and demands of the finishing equipment and plant manufacturing operations. The material handling system services not only the finishing operation, but also integrates the finishing system into the manufacturing process. Whether this material handling system is a single entity moving through the plant or a series of material movement strategies, it can be viewed as a single manufacturing plant entity. The marriage of the material handling system with the finishing system must be successful if the finishing process is to be incorporated into the plant production system.[8]

Systems that can be applied to industrial finishing include:

- Overhead chain monorail with exposed rivetless keystone chain.
- Overhead chain monorail with the chain enclosed in the track (light-duty).
- Inverted chain monorail with rivetless keystone chain.
- Overhead power-and-free conveyor (medium- or heavy-duty keystone and light-duty enclosed track).
- Inverted power-and-free conveyor (medium- or heavy-duty keystone and light-duty enclosed track).
- Floor truck (chain-on-edge).
- Accumulating truck-type system.

- Two-strand (skid) type.
- Tow conveyor or overhead tow conveyor.
- Roller conveyor (live, gravity, and/or accumulating).
- Hand-pushed monorails.
- Bridge cranes.
- Automated guided vehicle.
- Pedestal and fixture conveyor.

Chain Monorail Systems

The overhead chain monorail (OCM) system offers one of the least expensive means of conveyance, but with low flexibility. A detailed description of this type of system is given later in this chapter and in Chapter 9 of this handbook.

An alternative to the OCM is an inverted chain monorail (ICM). It has a chain attached to four-wheel trolleys for stability. These four-wheel trolleys can be the same free trolleys utilized in inverted power-and-free systems. The flexibility is low like the overhead chain monorail, but it allows clear accessibility above the product. The cost can be lower than the OMC, depending on the percentage of the track that is floor mounted to offset the extra cost of multiple-member track rails.

Both the OCM and ICM are characterized by having a fixed path, one speed per chain, without accumulation, on fixed product spacing. These systems can be the least expensive alternatives for the conveyance portion of the total paint system. However, they can inflate the cost of the finishing equipment and possibly the total system. The total system cost and flexibility can be improved by utilizing multiple types of systems where applicable. See Chapter 10 for more on "Overhead Handling and Lifting Devices."

Power-and-free Conveyor Systems

The overhead power-and-free (OHPF) conveyor has a proven history of flexibility for moving many products through most painting processes (see Fig. 19-2). A basic concern with OHPF, as well as for other overhead conveyors, is that the track and carrier structure are above the product, with potential for dropping dirt or dust that contaminates the product's finish. A new dimension to the power-and-free system is added when it carries the products from below (inverted). The inverted power-and-free conveyor (IPF) provides a stable support for the products to be finished and can be less expensive than the OHPF (see Fig. 19-3).

Both of these systems (OHPF and IPF) can provide the flexibility of multiple paths (switching) and multiple chains, allowing the designer to change product speed and product carrier spacing, and make relatively small elevation changes.

Floor Truck

The floor-mounted truck system, using a keystone chain (rivetless conveyor chain) mounted on edge (chain-on-edge or COE), has been successfully used in many paint systems. This type of conveyor allows the system designer a choice of multiple chains, so that different product spacings can be used on each. The chain can slide, eliminating the detrimental effects of paint processes on trolley wheels. The COE can change elevations with vertical curves. However, vertical curves are not negotiated as well as with power-and-free systems. A skuck (modified COE) system has added accumulation and switching capabilities.

Floor-mounted Skid

The floor-mounted skid can flexibly handle the paint process environment. As with the modified COE, the skid system can be used with multiple paths and relatively complex transfer equipment. However, elevation usually requires the use of vertical transfers.

CHAPTER 19   FINISHING, PAINTING, AND COATING

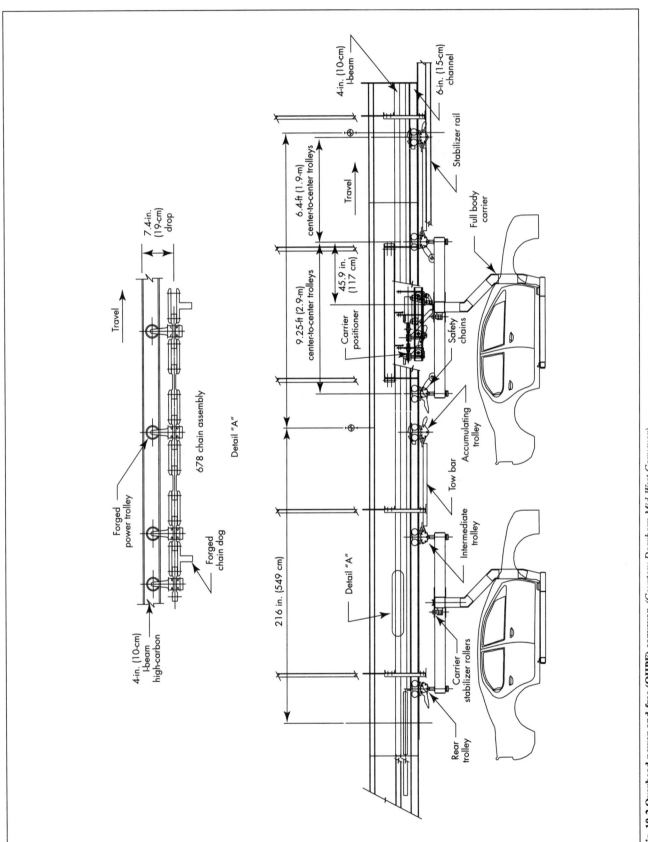

Fig. 19-2 Overhead power-and-free (OHPF) conveyor. *(Courtesy Dearborn Mid-West Conveyor)*

CHAPTER 19   FINISHING, PAINTING, AND COATING

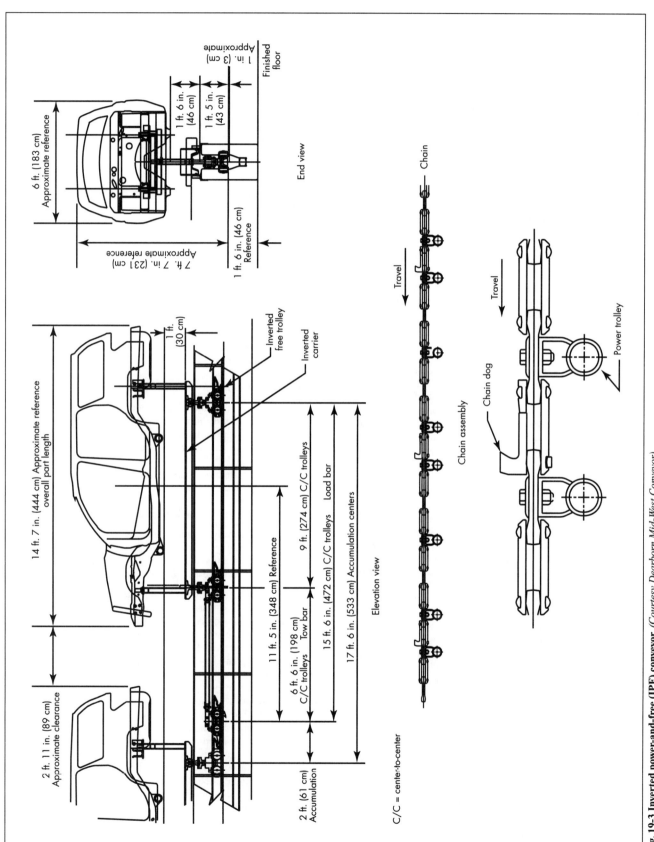

Fig. 19-3 Inverted power-and-free (IPF) conveyor. *(Courtesy Dearborn Mid-West Conveyor)*

CHAPTER 19   FINISHING, PAINTING, AND COATING

Tow Conveyors

Tow conveyors (both floor and overhead) are normally utilized for distribution centers and warehouse delivery systems. Tow or drag chain can deliver products to, from, and through various processes. Where production rates are low, or a wide variety of products require system flexibility, tow chain conveyor systems may be the best choice. The track for the chain is either embedded in the floor or suspended from above the product. The products are set on four-caster trucks designed for the product's mass and size. The floor conveyor has a drop-in pin to engage the cart to the chain. The overhead tow truck is equipped with a front-mounted mast that engages with a chain pusher attachment. Although flexible path, multiple chains, and variable speed/center chains can be added, tow conveyors have not been proven as reliable for high production processes. The floor conveyors operate with a slot in the floor, which tends to fill with dirt, debris, cleaning fluid, and shot. The production capacity of this conveyor type in a paint process should be limited to 10-30-minute cycle times.

Tow Cart Systems

Tow cart systems utilize floor-type caster trucks driven by a floor-mounted, 0.375-in. (9.5-mm) pitch high-tensile continuous chain. This system is used in furniture systems and other applications. Tow cart systems are discussed more at the end of this chapter.

Roller Conveyors

Live roller, belt/roller, slider belt, and roller flight conveyors have occasionally been used for special paint applications. The painting processes, as well as the conveyor, drive the use of a fixture to properly hold or display the product or components, and separate (bumper) the product. Roller conveyors are not well suited to paint processes, but they can integrate with other systems, such as bridge cranes or monorails, in either a synchronous or batch operation.

Hand-pushed Monorail and Bridge Cranes

For low production systems with 2,000-lb (907-kg) maximum weights, a pair or more of hand-pushed, four-wheel trolleys can suspend the load and be easily pushed between processes. Standard track and trolley can be furnished with 4-6-in. (10-15-cm) S-beam sizes. This equipment also can be equipped with switches for variable path systems and utilizes side pusher chains for powered process zones or elevation changes. When coupled with bridge cranes for large area coverage, hand-pushed monorails are very economical and work well with batch-type production processes.

Guided Vehicle (Automated and Manual)

Utilizing guided vehicles in paint systems should be restricted to special or extremely difficult-to-handle unit loads. If the load is extremely large and the paint process is accomplished with the part stationary, this method of conveyance can be considered. The guided vehicle is best suited for cycle times of 15-60 minutes or more.

Some features of guided vehicles, such as automatic pickup, unload, charging, and routing, along with easy manual intervention, can make them viable for some applications. However, guided vehicles should not be subjected to deleterious paint process environments.

Pedestal and Fixture Conveyors

Chain(s) and track mounted from below, which hold a carrier or fixture for presenting a product for processing, can take many forms. Inverted keystone chain conveyors supporting a rotating pedestal fixture have been used to paint automotive wheels for many years.

There are many conveyor cross-section designs that can be assembled into appropriate configurations specific to a system's requirements. Conveyor components include:

- Keystone chain.
- Roller and engineering chain.
- Enclosed-track and chain.
- A variety of track and rails.

They can be designed to accommodate some of the following system paths:

- Over-and-under.
- Vertical curves.
- Flat.
- Horizontal turn.
- Carousel loops.

A quick reference guide to conveyance system types and their attributes is provided in Table 19-1.

FINISHING EQUIPMENT CONSIDERATIONS

There are several finishing equipment variables that can influence the choice of conveyance system:

- Dip tank versus spray product preparation process.
- Bottom-entry versus horizontal-entry ovens.
- Electrodeposition versus spray primer surfacing equipment.
- Cure temperature.
- Clear coat.
- Continuous line versus modular (stop station).

The dip type of product preparation, and electrodeposition dip primer equipment will limit the portion of the system that can be serviced by an overhead conveyance. Spray processes can be serviced by either overhead or floor-mounted conveyor equipment. Bottom entry (gravity seal) and the number of elevation changes may require a system that can utilize simple vertical curves rather than more complex vertical transfers (conveyor elevators) to enter and exit the ovens.

Several other factors that impact selection involve:

- Length of conveyor track devoted to the process, versus delivery and storage.
- Ratio of production rate to the length of the carrier.
- Field installation restrictions, such as welding limitations.

If the system has a long track length devoted to delivery and storage, consideration is warranted for multiple spacing systems. This allows accumulation or long carrier spacing intervals along extended delivery portions of the system (the multiple chain and speed attribute of the power-and-free conveyor).

Determining the capacity of a system to handle the desired throughput for multiple path- (switching-) type systems should be based on good conveyor practice. System speed limitations, carrier dynamics, reliability, control issues, and noise should be taken into consideration. For a fixed path conveyor, the production rate is set by the maximum application process speed.

Other process-driven conditions that can individually, or in combination, affect system type determination are: modular processing stations with high-speed indexing to allow maximum in-station time (possibly automatic), delivery lengths and buffers between processing areas, and continuous-paced (low-speed) areas for manual operations. Depending on such needs, it can be decided if a single conveyance type is flexible enough to handle all of these criteria, or whether multiple system types can accommodate the variable conditions. A single conveyance type that serves the demands of the

TABLE 19-1
Attributes of Conveyors for Painting Operations

System Type	Fixed Path	Single Chain	Nonaccumulating	Multiple Path	Multiple Chain/Speed	Accumulating	Vertical Transfers	Vertical Curves	Suitable for Paint	Relative Cost	Production
Overhead chain monorail	•	•	•					•	Yes	1.0	High
Inverted chain monorail	•	•	•					•	Yes	1.25	High
Overhead power-and-free				•	•	•		•	Yes	4.0	High
Inverted power-and-free				•	•	•		•	Yes	3.5	High
Chain-on-edge slider	•		•		•			•	Yes	3.0	High
Accumulating truck				•	•	•		•	No	3.5	High
Two strand				•	•	•	•		No	2.5	High
Tow conveyor		•	•	•	•				No	2.0	Moderate
Roller conveyor				•	•	•	•		No	3.5	Moderate
Hand-pushed monorail				•		•	•		Yes	0.7	Low
Bridge crane				•			•		Yes	1.25	Low
Automated guided vehicle				•	•	•	—	—		6.0	Moderate
Pedestal fixture	•	•	•		•					2.0	High

Increased flexibility →

(Courtesy Socio Tec Integrators)

CHAPTER 19   FINISHING, PAINTING, AND COATING

process areas (indexed or continuous) and other areas (such as delivery, prepaint or postpaint functions, and storage) may require some compromises.

Another option is to use simpler conveyors through the continuous (slow speed) areas and then transfer the hooks with products to an appropriate accumulation and delivery-type system. Product transfer decisions also may be driven by other process demands. For example, using an overhead type of conveyor for a dip process and an inverted for a top coat process.

Conveyor selection issues, other than function, that also need to be addressed are the cost, ergonomics, space, maintenance needs, and level of technology.

Finishing Environment Effects on Conveyors

Paint finishing system environments can be especially harmful to conveyor components such as chain, trolley wheel bearings, load bar and carrier pivot connections, and track rails. These components may be subjected to adverse conditions, from the degreasing and etching chemicals of the product surface preparation equipment, to the high temperatures of the dry-off or cure ovens, to the harsh in-line hook and carrier paint stripping processes.

Product Surface Preparation Equipment

The product surface preparation equipment normally falls into one of three application equipment categories:

- Level conveyance through a spray-type, multiple-stage washing and etching process.
- Dip-type system that utilizes a vertical curve track for product immersion into processing liquid tanks and possible spray application between immersion stages.
- Abrasive blasting or manual abrasive preparation.

Either the dip or the spray process can cause serious track deterioration for carbon steel track applications. The etching chemical stage can cause a normal track to fail structurally in several years. As an alternative and a better choice, stainless steel track members can be considered, but should be evaluated in terms of cost and trolley wheel loading.

Product preparation processes also can have detrimental effects on the conveyor trolley wheel components. This problem is much more difficult to control because of contributing variables including: wheel bearing type, type of bearing seals (if any), lubricant, lubricant application, and preventive maintenance.

Paint Application Equipment

Paint application can, depending upon the selected methods, add variables such as overspray (paint buildup) to both the moving and stationary conveyor components. The floor-mounted systems can accumulate enough paint buildup on the track and shrouds for it to be a considerable source of contamination.

The paint application equipment affects the chain and trolleys. Spray booths may require some type of mechanical shroud, labyrinth seals, "c" hooks, air knife, or air pressure differential to minimize buildup on chain and trolleys, especially with liquid clear coatings. The moving conveyor equipment subjected to overspray requires periodic cleaning, with a frequency determined by chain arrangements, shroud effectiveness, type of spray equipment, and air movement in the booth. Other types of application processes such as electrocoating, powder coating, autodeposition, etc., can also harm conveyor components.

Paint Curing Equipment

Dry-off and cure ovens can affect the conveyor trolley wheels that pass through them. The oven temperature and the temperature

that the wheels attain (based on the time and location of the trolleys in the oven) determine the severity of the effect and the selection of trolley wheel type.

The three basic process environments—preparation, application, and cure—can each provide a troublesome effect on the conveyor components, but the real problem is a result of the combination of all three. There is no standard system component design package for paint systems. The criteria for conveyor design must be established, considering all the factors of the process environment, plus any factors for prepaint and postpaint processes that the conveyor will serve. In general, all the trolley wheels that are subjected to cure oven temperatures of 200-400° F (93-204° C) will use full complement bearings without ball retainers.

Other design decisions for these wheels that can only be answered on a system-by-system basis include:

- Bearing seals versus no seals.
- Bearing plugs versus no plugs.
- Standard full complement versus less one ball.
- Lubricant type. No silicone in paint shops or ovens of any type.
- Lubricant application methods and frequency.
- Wheel loading and duration of heavy loads.
- Maintenance procedures.

These variable combinations present a challenge for the conveyor system designer and require a thorough integrated system analysis.

SYSTEM LAYOUTS

Developing a final layout that best fits the application is difficult. The designer, however, should develop two or three rough concept layouts that should be as diverse as practical and utilize a common set of process and facility criteria.

Process Specifications

The first step in the creation of an integrated system design is to develop a specification appropriate to the industry and product paint criteria. The specification should define the level or degree of preparation for paint (wash and clean), application material (paint type), color schemes, corrosion protection (thickness and number of coats), and cure requirements. Other specifications may include dry-off and cool-down between processes.

The specification should attempt to quantify the basic process goals for both the aesthetic and protective requirements desired in the market, as well as provide the information needed to develop the system criteria.

Although many other elements must be planned for a complete paint system, the conveyance usually integrates all the paint processes and the total facility. The conveyance method integrates the processes (paint, as well as prepaint and postpaint functions) into a total system. The design team should utilize the conveyance method as the means of controlling the process for the day-to-day facility production requirements.

Quantify Process and Facility Criteria

The second and most important step in successfully developing rough concepts is to quantify the process and facility criteria. The information needed will include:

- Type of paint material (for example, powder, liquid, thermal cure, ambient cure).
- Number of booths (based on the number of colors, number of coats, etc.).
- Size of paint hooks and packages required.
- Size of product to be painted.
- Rate of paint hooks and packages per hour.

CHAPTER 19   FINISHING, PAINTING, AND COATING

With this information, the design team will be able to:

- Determine spacing of hooks and packages.
- Calculate the speed of the conveyance system for each process as a function of hook spacing and the rate of hooks to be painted.

It is desirable to minimize hook spacing for ovens and dryers while allowing appropriate spacing for the paint application equipment to perform to the level of quality desired. The designer should consider and utilize the following functional drivers:

- Determine minimum hook spacings required for the horizontal turn radius and vertical curve angle desired. The spacings should meet the test of good conveyor practice and not allow products to touch (part-to-part or part-to-hook).
- Quantify all process times required to achieve the desired level of quality. Such as:

  - Washer times for each anticipated pretreatment stage (three- five- or seven-zone).
  - Proper time to drain the product within and between washing stations, and at the end of the washer to avoid carryover of contaminants to the next stage.
  - Time required to completely dry off the product.
  - The time required to cool the parts to the desired temperature for the paint application process.
  - The time or number of hook spaces required for each color-specific or multipass booth.
  - The time needed to flash off (or evaporate) the solvent at a rate that will allow the proper flow of paint.

- The total oven time required to completely cure the product after it is painted.

An oven will be required unless the paint material being considered is a nonforced or ambient air-dried coating. For high-solid liquids and powder, it is extremely important to first determine the time required to bring the substrate (product) up to the desired temperature and have the second "zone" hold that desired temperature for the time required to completely cure the coating material. The designer should not forget the mass of the hooks and moving portion of the conveyance when making the thermal calculations for bringing the product up to the peak metal temperature (PMT). The nonmoving conveyance mass should be considered in calculating the time required to preheat the oven prior to starting production.

Other information needed includes:

- The time required to cool the products before manual handling at the unload.
- The mass of the parts on the conveyor.
- Is the conveyor empty, partially full, or full? The answer will affect the operating temperature in the oven.
- The requirements for removing all product from the washer and into the dry-off process at the end of a shift, or any other paint process functions (to eliminate rust buildup).
- The functions or processes appropriate for both the prepaint and postpaint process steps. Such as:

  - The proper display and amount of time for ergonomically loading the system.
  - The time and line length required to unload the product(s) for pack out, transfer to a different conveyance, or delivery to the next point of use.
  - The banks required for intradepartmental differences in production rate, start and stop of shift times, unscheduled downtime buffers, or scheduled downtimes.

Rough Concept Layouts

After developing the criteria list, the team should develop two or three different rough concept layouts. It is important that the team not consider these layouts as final or be too focused on detail.

First, design one layout for maximizing the equipment and minimizing labor costs. The second alternative should attempt to reduce the amount of equipment needed.

The difference between the two alternatives cannot be defined without knowledge of the criteria described earlier. The designers may want to design the first alternative with a power-and-free conveyor as the system integrator, and the second with a single-path chain monorail. These layouts may also use overhead-supported or inverted conveyor options.

The design team should also understand that a monorail system can do anything that a power-and-free can do. However, depending on the functions required, there is a point where the power-and-free conveyor becomes less complex and perhaps less expensive. What the design team should consider is that a monorail has one (mono) track path (rail) with one chain and one-chain spacing (unless multiple chain monorails are utilized in the system design).

With the power-and-free system, the free carrier can traverse any or all of the path routings. It can also utilize chains in specific zones with process-specific speeds and product and carrier spacings. The free carrier also can switch or use flexible paths to enter or exit different chains.

When the two layouts are defined, the team may elect to develop a third alternative utilizing the best attributes of the first two.

PLANNING FOR AN INTEGRATED PAINT SYSTEM

After the design team has developed two or three rough concept layout alternatives, it is time to evaluate them to determine the best fit for the facility, product, total system, and budget.

The design team determines whether the lowest cost fits the return-on-investment (ROI) requirement, or the highest cost best fits the goals. What is important is the ability of the organization to make a profit to ensure its long-term survival and growth. A favorable return-on-investment for a revised or new paint facility is of paramount importance. Compliance issues are also increasingly urgent, as a function of local, national, and international policies.

Assuming the team has selected the basic process equipment and developed the overall two or three rough layout concepts, it can get more specific about guidelines for the final design of the conveyances to be used as the integration mechanism. The remainder of the chapter specifies the guidelines for designing the most commonly utilized paint conveyance system (overhead chain monorail).

CHAIN MONORAIL SYSTEM

The overhead chain monorail is a very flexible, economical, and reliable conveyor. In addition, if components are selected properly, the system will easily handle the damaging effects of the various paint process characteristics—high temperature, pretreatment chemicals, abrasive blasting, and paint—in combination. The key is to select the proper components and combine them into a conveyance system that can, if desired, be the integrator for the whole facility.

Conveyor System Design

In designing a conveyor system, size and carrying capacity must first be determined. Carrying capacity is a function of the total unit

CHAPTER 19   FINISHING, PAINTING, AND COATING

load of the carriers plus the anticipated products (live load) being conveyed. Table 19-2 can be utilized to select the conveyor nominal trolley wheel size and its associated track rail size. These load capacities are approximate and will vary depending on the equipment manufacturer, vertical curve angle (if any), metallurgy of the track, and a plethora of individual system conditions, such as harshness of service environment.

The load bar referred to in the right-hand column of Table 19-2 is a linking device that distributes the load between two individual, two-wheel trolleys with minimum centers between them. Load bars can be used for heavy loads where the chain tension is too low to warrant increasing the system size. The cost of load bars is far less than going up to the next system size. Load bars are only used on the trolleys to carry an occasional heavy load.

The design team should be very involved with system sizing and component selection, especially when reviewing competitive bids from several conveyor contractors. In a competitive bid process, the team should have the tools to make informed decisions.

For the severe conditions of a paint system, the designers should be conservative and assemble a system that will be relatively maintenance-free and minimize unscheduled downtime. The designers should consider reducing the rating of the maximum chain tension from the manufacturer's normal system recommendations to:

- Enclosed-track chain with 0.25-in. (6-mm) pin–500 lb (227 kg).
- 348 (X-75-13) keystone chain tension–derate to 800-1,000 lb (363-454 kg).
- 458 (X-100-16) keystone chain tension–derate to 1,500-1,800 lb (680-817 kg).
- 678 (X-150-22) keystone chain tension–derate to 4,000-4,500 lb (1,814-2,041 kg).

The reduced tensions will allow for comfortable recovery from problems caused by day-to-day operational variables, such as lubricator interruptions and occasional or intermittent heavy loading conditions. The design for reduced chain tension coupled with high-drive capacities will also minimize the possibility of speed surge. Speed surge, or inconsistent speed of the product or components through the paint application booths, can reduce finish quality, producing uneven, light, or heavy coatings. Avoiding speed surge should be a prime factor in the design of the monorail conveyor. Other factors which contribute to speed surge include too many obstructions, such as turns and curves relative to the length of the conveyor or length per drive, and simultaneous or concurrent horizontal or vertical flexing of the chain through turns and curves for individual roller turn rollers or multiple turns. Inadequate supports and bracing allowing the rail to deflect vertically or horizontally, can also contribute to surge.

The recommended total number of *obstructions* (turns, plus compound vertical curves) for paint conveyors is:

- Enclosed chain, 0.25-in. (6-mm) pin, 30 obstructions.

- 348 (X-75-13) chain, 3-in. (76-mm) pitch with 0.375-in. (9.5-mm) pin, 40 obstructions.
- 458 (X-100-16) chain, 4-in. (102-mm) pitch with 0.625-in. (15.9-mm) pin, 60 obstructions.
- 678 (X-150-22) chain, 6-in. (152-mm) pitch with 0.875-in. (22-mm) pin, 60 obstructions.

The number of obstructions for systems using keystone chains (348, 458, 678) can be increased if the design team uses single-bearing traction wheel turns rather than multiple-bearing roller turns. For paint systems sensitive to surge, practical wheel turns should be utilized for all horizontal turns with angles of 90° or greater. The cost of an installed 180° traction wheel turn is approximately equal to a 180° roller turn. The extra cost of traction and other wheels for the 90° and between 90° and 180° is a good investment.

The friction (compound factor) for all angle roller, bearing traction wheel turns ranges between 1-2%, as a function of the diameter of the wheel. The corresponding friction for a 90° roller turn ranges from 3-4%, and 180° roller turns have 6-7% friction. Traction wheels can produce profound benefits in systems of 1,500 ft (457 m) or longer. Their use influences the number of drives required, minimizes or eliminates surge, minimizes tensions, reduces unscheduled downtime, and may reduce the total cost of the system, considering both initial investment and operational cost.

From an investment and operational point of view, the number of drives should be minimized. However, the good practice of minimizing both the maximum tension of the chain and the required pull force of the drives should not be compromised. If the conveyor system can be appropriately designed to use one drive instead of two, while maintaining minimum recommended tensions, the system's complexity will be reduced considerably. In this case, the drive will not require balancing controls. If the system must have multiple drives, the reduced friction of traction wheels can reduce the number of drives required, which will minimize system complexity. Remember that a smaller radius may be used for traction wheel turns where product clearance will allow.

Another overall recommendation in the area of system design pertains to the other obstruction type, vertical curves. The use of vertical curves should be minimized, but not to the point of sacrificing the processes or efficient plant space utilization. Repetitive curves or a series of curves in close proximity should be carefully located. If the repetitive curves are dimensionally located to each other so that the trolleys or chain pitch result in "bumps," or chain flex occurs simultaneously, surge may result. The designer should avoid this situation keeping in mind that the chain pitch will vary between nominal and actual, and that normal pin/center-link wear will occur during the life of the system. A commonly experienced problem is the use of improper vertical curve track radii for keystone chains. The keystone chains will bind and not be able to flex if they are exposed to improper radii. This will result in surge as well as repeti-

TABLE 19-2
Selection Guide for Conveyor Trolley Wheel and Track Rail

Nominal Trolley Wheel Size in. (mm)	Single Trolley lb (kg)*	Two Trolley with Load Bar (Four Wheel) lb (kg)*
Enclosed-track 2 (51)	100 (45)	200 (91)
3 (76)	200 (91)	400 (181)
4 (102)	400 (181)	800 (363)
6 (152)	1,200 (544)	2,400 (1,089)

*Approximate Unit Load Capacity

(Courtesy Socio Tec Integrators)

CHAPTER 19   FINISHING, PAINTING, AND COATING

tive stresses in the chain links, resulting in premature fatigue failure of the chain. Paint systems should utilize a 10-ft (3-m) radius (minimum) to a 12-ft (3.7-m) radius for 348 and 458 keystone chains, a 16-20-ft (4.9-6.1-m) radius for a 678 chain, and a 3-ft (0.9-m) radius or greater for enclosed-track systems. These radii for the vertical curves of keystone chains are based on 24-in. (61-cm) trolley centers. Longer trolley centers may require larger radii. For tight layout areas, smaller radii can be utilized. Consult with equipment suppliers for special conditions.

Chain Pull Basics

To select the system size, first determine the tensions that the chain will be subjected to. For each proposed layout, this will require approximating the number of drives needed or inputting the data for obstructions and loads into a computerized program. A personal computer (PC) or the services of a systems or engineering house may be the best way to run the calculations. The computer-based chain pull program will allow the team to easily run different scenarios of drive and take-up locations, resulting in better-informed decisions and is more practical than hand calculation.

There is an important difference between chain tension and chain pull. A conveyor is a continuous loop, endless strand, or closed loop, which means that changes in one area will affect the total system and will require recalculating everything. A conveyor requires a drive to pull the chain (or hold it back, in some systems or conditions). The drive has an engagement lug called the *drive pusher dog* or cat dog (because it is attached to a caterpillar-type drive chain). At the drive's pusher dog engagement point, force required to pull the conveyor will be applied. The chain passing away from the drive will

have a magnitude of tension (out) and the chain approaching the drive will have a different magnitude of tension (in). The drive pull is the difference between the "in" tension and the "out" tension. For example, in many systems, the chain's maximum tension point may be at the apex of two or more vertical curves. The drive (if not located at this point) will see little increase in pull from either direction (other than frictional forces) and the chain could have the highest tensions at the apex, not at the drive.

Trolley Wheel Friction

To understand the chain pull process, the designer must understand trolley wheels.

The wheel shown in Fig. 19-4 is a full complement ball bearing without a ball retainer (cage) to hold the balls to a uniform spacing. For paint systems with caustic atmospheres and high temperatures, a ball cage will not hold up, so a cageless or full complement ball bearing must be used. The wheel shown utilizes a triple labyrinth outer seal made up of outer, intermediate, and inner segments.

The total wheel friction is a function of three factors: rolling friction, bearing friction, and seal friction.

- *Rolling friction* is the retarding factor for a wheel's outer tread rolling on a surface. (The factor for a hardened tread riding on a medium carbon, hot-rolled track is about 0.2.)
- *Bearing friction* is the retarding force to the wheel moving along the track. This results from friction between the diameter of the bearing balls and the outer tread diameter of the wheel. In an equation, it is usually expressed as: d = bearing diameter, and D = wheel diameter.

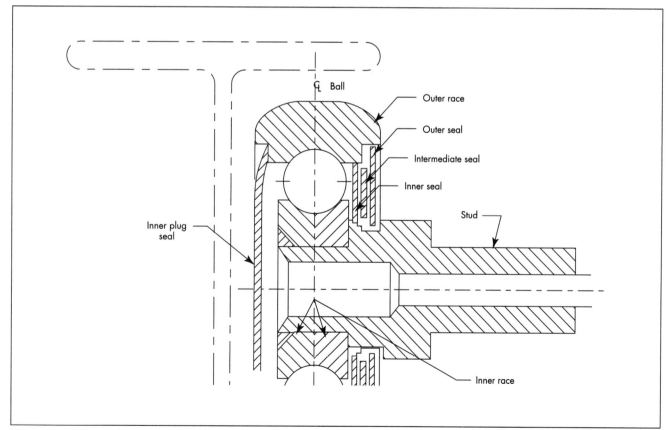

Fig. 19-4 The trolley wheel. (*Courtesy Socio Tec Integrators*)

CHAPTER 19   FINISHING, PAINTING, AND COATING

• *Seal friction* is the drag imposed by the seal (if any is utilized) on the system.

The largest contributor to the total wheel friction is $d \div D$, or the bearing diameter divided by the basic size of the wheel tread. The typical total friction for various trolley wheels under normal paint shop conditions is:

• Enclosed-track—0.025 (2.5%).
• 3 in. (76 mm)—0.024 (2.4%).
• 4 in. (102 mm)—0.02 (2%).
• 6 in. (152 mm)—0.015 (1.5%).

These factors will vary considerably depending on lubrication, condition of seals, and caged versus full complement (without a cage) bearing. The full-complement bearing has greater friction than a caged bearing, but is required for a paint system.

Obstruction Friction Factors for Horizontal Turns

Also important to understanding chain pull is knowing how compound factors are calculated, which gives insight as to how the turn-to-turn, point chain pull calculations are developed for the total system pull calculations.

A compound factor for a horizontal turn chain conveyor component (obstruction) is derived by using a point-to-point calculation. The derivation only considers the frictions developed through an obstruction due to chain tensions. Trolley loading shall be considered separately.

The following derivation is an approximation and not as accurate or reflective of actual values. This calculation neglects the following:

• The eccentricities between the pull force (centerline of chain) and friction surfaces.
• Chain flexing between center link and chain pins. (Traction wheel turns do not impart such flexing other than at the entrance and exit of a turn.)

The derivation is treated here as generic to show the point-to-point method of calculation.

A horizontal roller turn is assumed to have rollers, radius, with rollers on centers, initial tension of one roller, and roller friction.

Using Figure 19-5, calculate the force (F) on the individual rollers in a turn.

$$F = \text{SIN}\, \frac{a}{2} = \frac{(1 \div 2)F}{t} = \text{SIN} = \frac{a}{2} = \frac{F}{2t} \qquad (1)$$

$$f = 2\, \text{SIN}\, \frac{a}{2}\, (t) \qquad (2)$$

Substituting $\text{SIN}\, \dfrac{a}{2}$ for $\dfrac{x}{2r}$ (opposite divided by the hypotenuse)

$$F = 2 \left(\frac{x}{2r} \right)(t) \qquad (3)$$

$$F = \frac{x}{r}\, (t)$$

where:

F = force on the roller
t = initial tension of one roller

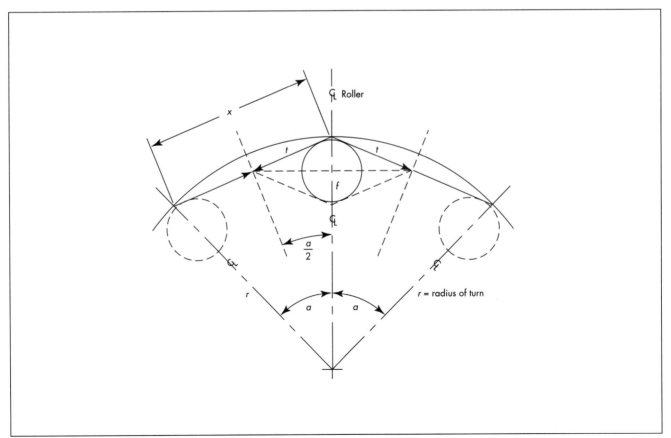

Fig. 19-5 Individual rollers in a turn. *(Courtesy Socio Tec Integrators)*

CHAPTER 19   FINISHING, PAINTING, AND COATING

f = roller coefficient of friction
x = roller center
r = radius

Using Figure 19-6, we derive the compound factor formula for a complete turn.

The pull at roller point 1 can be written:

$$\text{Point 1} = P + P\left(\frac{x}{r}\right)f = P\left(1 + \frac{x}{r}f\right) \qquad (4)$$

where:
P = roller pull
x = roller center
f = roller friction
r = radius

Let $\left(1 + \frac{x}{r}f\right) = C$ $\qquad (5)$

Then point $1 = PC$

$$\text{Point 2} = P\left(1 + \frac{x}{r}f\right) + P\left(1 + \frac{x}{r}f\right)\left(\frac{x}{r}f\right) \qquad (6)$$

$$= P\left(1 + \frac{x}{r}f\right)\left(1 + \frac{x}{r}f\right)$$

$$= PC^2$$

Then point n pull $= PC^n$

where:
x = roller center
f = roller friction
C = compound factor
P = roller pull
n = number of rollers

For example, take a 12 ft radius, 45° roller turn with 18 (n) rollers on 6 in. (x) centers, each roller having a 2% rolling friction (f).

$$C = 1 + \left(\frac{x}{r} \times f\right) \qquad (7)$$

$$C = 1 + \left(\frac{0.5 \text{ ft}}{12 \text{ ft}} \times 0.02\right) = 1.000833$$

$$C^n = 1.000833^{18} = 1.0151$$

The actual compound factor used for this turn is 1.0151.

The difference between this calculated compound factor and the actual tested value is due to the previously mentioned inaccuracies including eccentricities and chain flexing.

Short Method for Computing Chain Pull

The total amount of chain pull on a system is equal to the sum of three functional areas:

- Level of pull load increased from all friction obstructions.
- Vertical curve lift loads.
- Take-up tension compounded through the total closed loop.

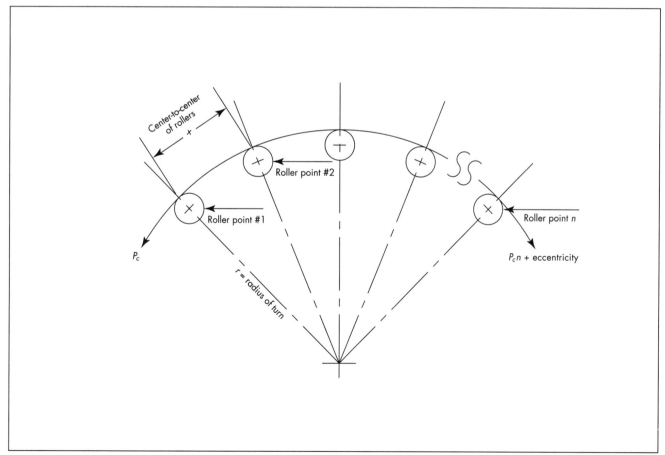

Fig. 19-6 A complete roller turn. *(Courtesy Socio Tec Integrators)*

CHAPTER 19 FINISHING, PAINTING, AND COATING

1. Determine level of pull load. The chain pull, because of loading, is equal to the product of the overall compound factor (O_A) and the total moving load.

$$C_p = O_A \times \Sigma M_L \qquad (8)$$

where:

C_p = chain pull (under level load conditions)
O_A = overall compound factor
ΣM_L = total moving load

To compute the overall compound factor:

$$O_A = \frac{[(1 + \bar{f})^{\Sigma y} - 1](1 + \bar{f})}{(1 + \bar{f}) - 1} \left(\frac{z}{\Sigma y} \right) \qquad (9)$$

where:

$\bar{f}$ = average friction factor for all turns and curves
Σy = total quantity of turns and curves
z = trolley friction (%)

For 4-in. (10-cm) wheels, trolley friction is 1.5% (2.0% for severe conditions) and for 6-in. (15-cm) wheels, it is 1.02% (1.6% for severe conditions).

2. Determine the average friction factor by considering each individual turn.

$$\Sigma f = t \times f \qquad (10)$$

where:

t = number of individual turns
f = friction factor

For example:
10 individual turns $\times$ 0.014 (friction factor) for ten 36 ft (11 m) traction wheels
10 turns $\times$ 0.04 (friction factor) for ten 36 ft (11 m) 90° radius roller turns
10 turns $\times$ 0.033 (friction factor) for ten vertical curves

$$\bar{f} = \frac{\Sigma f}{\Sigma c} \qquad (11)$$

where:

$\bar{f}$ = average friction
Σf = total friction factors
Σc = total curves

$$\frac{\Sigma f}{\Sigma c} = \frac{0.14 + 0.4 + 0.33}{30}$$

$$= \frac{0.87}{30}$$

$$= 0.029 \text{ factor or } 2.9\% \text{ friction for 30 obstructions}$$

The overall compound factor can now be found using Eq. 9:

$$\frac{(1.029^{30} - 1) \times 1.029}{1.029 - 1} \times \frac{1.5}{30} = 2.4086$$

3. Compute moving load. To compute the total moving load, take the sum of the weight of the following system components:

$$\Sigma M_L = W_{CH} + W_t + W_c + W_p \qquad (12)$$

where:

ΣM_L = total moving load
W_{CH} = weight of the chain

W_t = weight of the trolleys (plus any miscellaneous accessories mounted to chain or trolleys)
W_c = empty weight of all carriers on the system
W_p = total weight of the products being conveyed

4. Calculate pull for level load. Multiply overall compound factor by total moving load.
Step 1 (chain pull Eq. 9) $\times$ Step 2 (moving load Eq. 12) = weight for level load
5. Determine the amount of chain pull caused by vertical curves. The chain pull, due to each vertical curve, is equal to:

$$C_p = E_{vc} \times (1 + \bar{f}^{\Sigma o}) = \text{weight per vertical curve} \quad (13)$$

where:

C_p = chain pull
E_{vc} = equivalent load on vertical curve
$\bar{f}$ = average friction factor for all turns and curves
Σo = quantity of obstructions from that curve to the drive (in the direction of travel)

Declines will decrease the amount of chain pull, while inclines will increase chain pull. Each vertical curve should be calculated and then the sum computed. The equivalent load on vertical curves is equal to the chain pull to propel the weight up the incline (or decline).

To calculate the equivalent load for a 30° vertical curve use SIN 30° $\times$ the total quantity of loads on that angle or 0.5 $\times$ total moving weight. To be more precise, the load can be separated at the lesser angles in the arcs of the vertical curves and utilize SIN 15°.

6. Find the amount of pull due to the take-up tension. The chain pull, due to the take-up, is equal to:

$$P = T_T \times [(1 + \bar{f})^{\Sigma y} - 1] \qquad (14)$$

where:

P = pull
T_T = take-up tension
$\bar{f}$ = average friction
Σy = total quantity of curves and turns

The minimum tension in a closed loop should be about 100 lb (45 kg) for enclosed conveyor chains and about 200 lb (91 kg) for keystone conveyors. From an operational standpoint, the minimum tension is required to keep the chain from disassembling itself. These chains are rivetless and minimum tensions must be maintained. The designer should carefully locate the take-up unit to minimize the collapsing force on it from preceding downhill vertical loads. The best general location for the drive and take-up units is to place the drive high and the take-up low, in close proximity to each other. A high pull-through condition on the take-up units will cause excessive pull and tension in the conveyor. The main concern is the tension on the take-up that will be needed for Step 6.

7. Total chain pull. Again, the total amount of chain pull (C_p) is equal to the sum of three functional area calculations. The total lever pull takes into consideration all friction for the conveyor (assuming no vertical curve lift loads), the added pull for the vertical curves, and the compounding of the pull induced by the tension of the take-up unit.

Conveyor Component Selection

This section provides the team with enough basic information to make informed decisions for sizing, selection, and system design. It

CHAPTER 19   FINISHING, PAINTING, AND COATING

gives more detail on chain and trolleys, track, drives, take-ups (tensioners), horizontal turns, vertical curves, support steel, and power-and fill components.

Enclosed and keystone chain. Some companies try to save on initial investment costs by purchasing used or refurbished chain and trolleys. While this may be practical for ambient delivery systems and short single-drive paint systems, some care should be exercised with multiple-drive systems. Pin wear will reduce the ultimate strength of the chain, and can cause surge or severe speed fluctuations due to variances in chain pitch.

All keystone chain components should be from the same manufacturer, drop-forged from steel (for example, SAE 1046), and heat-treated as follows:

- Pins—320 to 415 Brinell (hardness reference standard).
- Center links—320 to 400 Brinell.
- Side links—310 to 390 Brinell.

The pin's center link bearing surface also should be machined to an appropriate and consistent dimension. The ultimate strength of the chain should be a minimum of 20 times the maximum system tension (that is, 458 chain with 1,800 lb [817 kg] tension $\times$ 20 = 36,000 lb [16,330 kg] ultimate strength). Most 458 chain manufacturers produce a 48,000 lb (21,773 kg) ultimate strength chain.

Enclosed-track chain and wheels are provided by many manufacturers, with much variation in quality and capability. In some cases, manufacturers may offer more than one class of component. Most manufacturers of this class of chain utilize stamped links with forged pins. Wheels are manufactured with large differences in capacity and service capability. For paint systems, it is usually recommended that the team research the highest quality wheels with proven use in paint systems. Normally, machined tires and inner races should be utilized instead of stamped components. In paint systems, light-duty wheels should not be used.

Lubrication of chain and trolleys. When the team has selected the most appropriate components, the proper day-to-day operation of the system will depend on having an appropriate lubricant delivered, at an appropriate rate and interval, to the required friction points. The two points requiring lubrication are the bearing surface between each chain pin and its mating center link surface, and the ball bearing of the trolley wheels. There are common lubricants for both of these critical areas, which can be delivered by standard lubrication devices. Most of the lubricants for paint systems used today are molybdenum-di-sulfide dispersed in a low-flash solvent. Do not use any silicone-based lubricants.

For example, a system that operates eight hours per day, will require one to two applications per shift. If the lubricator does not function for two to three shifts, the conveyor will probably malfunction. The best practice for new paint operations may be to call on the services of a lubrication house with paint system experience to provide total service.

Trolley brackets and wheels. Trolley brackets are usually forged from C1035 steel and should be heat-treated to a hardness of Rockwell 25 on the "C" scale. Each bracket is mounted with one wheel, and two brackets are attached together to make a trolley assembly. Each power trolley bracket should have an integral-forged, wheel-mount swage boss. The swage boss should be machined to an appropriate dimension and properly swaged to a wheel, ensuring that the wheel's inner race will not rotate on the swage boss during normal use. The ball bearings should be allowed to move, and the inner race bore should not be allowed to move steel on steel against the swage boss. This problem is especially likely to occur on trolleys with a poor swage (wheel-to-bracket) in high temperature systems. The two brackets of the trolley should be attached with two

high-grade locking bolts and nuts (such as Grade 5 bolts with torque prevailing deformed thread nuts) appropriately torqued to the hardware manufacturer's specifications.

The trolley wheel of choice should be a high-quality, full complement ball bearing. The semi-open type, with triple labyrinth outer seals and no inner caps, is often selected. Conveyor trolley bearings are loosely toleranced to allow for the conditions to which they are subjected. However, the bearing components should be manufactured from high-quality materials, and heat-treated and finished to a precision bearing quality level.

Conveyor track. The enclosed-track rail should be made from a roll-formable, high-strength, low alloy (HSLA) type of steel. The carbon content should be as high as possible, while still being formable, and formulated with a high level of wear-hardening additives. Roll-formed rail components may need heat treating on high wheel-load bearing surface areas for vertical curves and horizontal turns. Horizontal turns can have the greatest wear problem, since the chain has single horizontal wheels on 8-in. (20-cm) centers, as compared to two vertical trolley wheels for vertical curves. Remember that high wear means contamination of the painted product is much more likely to occur. As discussed earlier, to reduce wear, the team should minimize the tension in the system.

The rail for keystone chain systems is made from hot-rolled, standard-sized "S" beams, S3 at 5.7 lb/ft (8.5 kg/m), S4 at 7.7 lb/ft (11.4 kg/m), and S6 at 12.5 lb/ft (18.6 kg/m). The metallurgy for the rails should be high carbon, and will vary by manufacturer from American Society for Testing and Materials (ASTM) C1035 to C1055. C1045 is recommended as a minimum for all straight track, and C1055 for all horizontal turns and vertical curves. The rail should also conform dimensionally to the American Institute of Steel Construction (AISC) standards. It is important that the web of the "I" cross-section of the rail be centered and perpendicular to the top and bottom flanges. If the distance from the web of the left or right flange is too great, the trolley brackets will rub the flange tip, causing contamination and chain pull problems.

A system will have hundreds of rail splices, and they can contribute to surge. The splices, or field joining, of the rails should be saw cut and controlled to produce as smooth a junction as possible for the trolleys and rail ends.

Conveyor drives. The recommended drive type for overhead chain monorails and power-and-free conveyors:

- Uses a floating frame, caterpillar drive to engage the conveyor chain instead of a sprocket turn drive.
- Has caterpillar drive locations virtually any place along the conveyor's length.
- Requires sprocket drives located at conveyor turns.
- Caterpillar drives require less horsepower, because the diameter of the caterpillar drive sprocket is smaller than the conveyor turn diameter of a sprocket drive.
- Has a floating frame overload electromechanical cutout protection feature instead of a fixed-frame drive, which has no reliable electromechanical overload protection. (This drive cutout will detect overloads due to hang-ups and process equipment such as washers, booths, and ovens and shut down the conveyor with minimal damage to the processing equipment.)
- In the industry today, the "best" drive is one with a rotary floating reducer and frame, and a caterpillar drive.

The drive units, as well as the take-up (tensioner) devices, should be provided with maintenance platforms when the drive components are not easily accessible from the floor. These drives and take-up devices are critical to the operation and should be easily accessible

CHAPTER 19   FINISHING, PAINTING, AND COATING

by maintenance personnel. They should allow easy, ergonomic repair and regular preventive maintenance.

Take-up units. Take-up units maintain a minimum tension in the closed-loop conveyor, preventing the chain from going slack, coming apart, and opening the closed loop.

Four important aspects of take-up (tensioners) are the expansion joints, length of travel, actuation methods, and actuation forces.

- Expansion joints should be structurally capable of handling the wheel loading for the monorail. (Formed sheet metal expansion joints are appropriate for short and light trolley loads only.)
- The expansion joint travel length should accommodate the expansion of the conveyor chain length from its daily heating up and cooling caused by the ovens and dryers. (For 1,000 ft [305 m] or more paint systems, a 2-2.5 ft [0.6-0.8 m] travel take-up unit is the minimum recommended choice.)
- Actuation of the take-up units is best served by an air cylinder, which can accommodate constant force over a long travel length, but can be easily varied in force by changing the amount of pressure applied.
- The maximum force of the take-up actuator can be controlled by sizing the cylinder to be appropriate without being excessive.

Horizontal turns for enclosed-track conveyors. Enclosed-track conveyor turns are most often made from formed cross-section rail rolled to a smooth radius, training the chain which has integral rollers. The turn is made from straight track rolled to a radius, with no other components or fabrication needed. As discussed earlier, it is recommended that the inside surface that has contact with the chain's tension reaction wheels be heat-treated. This is necessary because the metallurgy of the rail is compromised when roll-formed.

An enclosed-track horizontal turn may sometimes be manufactured with a single-bearing traction wheel having a rim for guiding the chain through the turn, with no rotation of the chain rollers. These traction wheel turns can be helpful in problem areas, but should not normally be part of the design.

Horizontal turns for keystone chain. Keystone chains cannot negotiate any horizontal change in direction unless they are guided by some form of antifriction bearings to interface with the chain and guide it through the arc of the turn. The guidance can be accomplished by a single-bearing, traction wheel turn, or a multiple roller or roller turn.

There are advantages and disadvantages to traction wheels versus multiple-roller turns. Where roller turns are utilized, they should be equipped with excellent quality components, such as:

- Frames capable of withstanding the conveyor tensions.
- Roller turn rollers of high quality (only to be utilized in ambient temperatures of 50-150° F (10-66° C).
- Roller bearing rollers for higher tension systems.

Roller-turn rollers should utilize 0.5-in. (1.3-cm) diameter mounting bolt/shafts for 348 chains as a minimum, at least 0.63-in. (1.6-cm) diameter shafts for 458 and 678 chains, and possibly 0.75-in. (1.9-cm) diameter shafts for high-tension 678 chains. Rollers should be constructed with double-row ball bearings for 348 and 458 chains, and double-row tapered roller bearings for high-tension 678 chains.

All rollers should be initially packed for life with an appropriate grease lubricant, and equipped with grease fittings.

The outer tire or chain contact surface should be hardened, but less than the chain link hardness.

Traction wheel turns should utilize double-row, tapered roller bearings for ambient temperature areas, and a graphite bushing for high-temperature applications. The diameter of the wheel shaft should be 1.9 in. (4.8 cm) for 348, and 2.9 in. (7.4 cm) for 458 and 678 applications.

Vertical curves. Recommended radii for vertical curves for each conveyor size appear earlier in this chapter. Radius of bend for vertical curves is a very important factor in achieving a good system. Vertical curves are not complicated since they are merely straight rail formed into an arc with no other fabrication or components.

When selecting the vertical curve's angle of incline and decline, the designer should check product clearances. The horizontal closure will reduce the product-to-product clearance while carriers are hanging vertically on an inclined rail.

Support steel. The support structure required to suspend an overhead chain monorail is a necessary part of the project. The first decision is whether to hang the conveyor from the overhead building structure, or to support the conveyor from floor-supported columns specifically installed for the conveyor. The team should have a basic understanding of the usable live load capacity of the bottom chord of the roof trusses, joists, or beams. If the roof structure has sufficient capacity to support the total conveyor load, then it will probably be best and least expensive to support from above. If the building does not have the capacity, it is generally best to support all the low-elevation track from a network of floor-supported columns, as long as the columns do not cause too many obstructions. For high track, it is usually best to reinforce the building to support the additional live load. To make informed decisions, the team usually has an architectural firm help develop cost estimates for alternative methods of supporting the system.

For new buildings, the team should estimate live load requirements for conveyors to enable the building design group to produce a plan that will allow the total system to be supported from overhead. The team should look at two alternative building costs for conveyor and equipment loadings supported from a roof structure or the floor.

For paint systems, the ovens and dryers often support the conveyors traveling through this equipment. Paint booths usually will not be capable of supporting the conveyor. Pretreatment washers can be designed either to support or not support the conveyor.

Power-and-free components. Power-and-free conveyors evolved from the overhead chain monorail conveyor, and utilize the same basic components in their construction. A power-and-free conveyor is a powered overhead chain monorail conveyor placed above a free rail system with separate "free" trolleys for carrying the live load. This free trolley system can be disengaged, engaged, diverted, or converged to different paths from the powered monorail system. Thus, power-and-free, monorail power with a separate free trolley can be engaged with many different monorail chains, speeds, and engagement pusher centers.

Power-and-free components can withstand the damaging conditions of the paint process as well as the monorail. This makes it possible for power-and-free conveyors to be the primary conveyance system for the automotive industry, in both overhead and inverted arrangements. Power-and-free systems offer the flexibility, durability, high rate of production, and stability required by many high-end paint systems. Flexibility usually means higher costs. The apparent cost of the power-and-free system will be two to three times that of a comparable capacity chain monorail. The system has tremendous flexibility, however, compared to any other paint conveyance system, and can possibly reduce the total cost of the paint system by lowering the cost of labor and process equipment such as ovens, washers, and dryers. The power-and-free can allow multiple carrier spacing for close packing of the product in the ovens, while allowing the necessary longer centers in the spray booths. This will reduce the required length of the ovens, compared to systems using overhead chain monorails.

The system design team may use a consultant, engineering house, or conveyor contractor experienced in power-and-free conveyors and

CHAPTER 19   FINISHING, PAINTING, AND COATING

paint processes to evaluate whether power-and-free is the best choice for the application.

TOW CHAIN CONVEYOR SYSTEM

The tow line chain conveyor system is one of the most versatile, economical, and reliable conveying systems in use today for finishing systems, especially in the furniture industry. It is very effective for case goods—three-dimensional products like assembled furniture, such as desks, chairs, etc.—in manufacturing plants with a wide range of product sizes and low or flexible production rates. Standard tow chain conveyor options include: flexible paths, variable speed drives, multiple conveyor drives, automatic chain-to-chain transfer stations, delay stations, close pack conveyance, and flexible cart centers.

Some newer tow conveyor lines provide as much or more flexibility as power-and-free conveyors or overhead conveyors, but for less capital investment. These tow systems are simpler to install and operate than the overhead conveyors.

Figure 19-7 is an example of a case goods finishing system with five different coating finishes, requiring five different application and drying operations, on a three-dimensional product. The product is carried on standard carts 36 × 33 in. (91 × 84 cm) in size. Each cart has a special pallet top designed to handle the largest size product for that system. The tabletop is often more than double the length of the cart, and is built to rotate around its center. Some carts are equipped with racks that can be used to finish flat products, such as shelves. The number of special racks used is determined by the production schedule and product mix. The products are conveyed through four different ovens to dry the coatings on one chain conveyor with multiple drives.

The products are towed through the work areas for stain and wash coat, oil stain, hand wipe, sealer coat, first top coat, second top coat, and on-line sanding. After each coating is applied, the product is conveyed through four ovens, designed to meet the curing time and drying temperature specifications defined by the coating supplier. Ovens may use electric, natural gas, propane, or steam energy. Some recirculate air with one large blower or multiple recirculating fans, or use infrared heat with little or no air circulation.

In addition to the ovens, the finishing system shown in Figure 19-7 is designed for air drying, open solvent flash off, or evaporation of solvent, with an enclosed solvent flash tunnel and ambient air cooling operations. Cooling tunnels with refrigerated air are available when there is not enough space for ambient-air cooling.

The cart tops are designed to allow the products to be rotated 360° while the sanding and spraying operations are performed. The typical finishing system has several 90° automatic rotators. The turntable top allows the operator to rotate the product for faster and better spray coating and sanding. The primary advantage in rotating the tops is in the drying operations. When the ware is turned 90° it can be bunched together in what is typically referred to as a *close pack*. The ware centers then change from 16 ft (4.9 m) to approximately 3 ft (0.9 m) centers in the oven and flash areas. As shown in the layout, the carts and conveyor path are designed so the product can be towed with the ware in line and at 90° to the direction of travel. The system can be designed so that a cart can be delayed at each station if additional time is required. In the example shown, the carts are automatically respaced to 16 ft (4.9 m) after each oven.

The finishing system shown utilizes one tow line conveyor with two drives that are synchronized electronically. Other systems may use multiple conveyors with single drives. In those cases, carts are transferred from one line to another automatically, as needed to meet production requirements.

Planning the Conveyor System

Much of the planning for a tow chain conveyor is similar to that previously discussed. Chain monorail and tow chain conveyor systems have chains, tracks, horizontal turns, lubrication, vertical curves, take-ups, drive controls, and attachments (racks or carriers). The components may vary in design, but serve the same function in the conveying operation, and require similar design considerations when preparing the layout and sizing the components.

These two systems differ because the monorail conveyor carries the product on trolleys pulled around overhead rails, while the tow chain conveyor system carries the product on top of carts pulled across the factory floor.

Sizing for production requirements. The first step in selecting the conveyor system size is to determine the carrying capacity. The carrying capacity includes:

- The size and weight of the cart with turntable top.
- The size and weight of the ware rack, if required.
- The product weight (live load).

All of these affect the drive size and allowable chain pull.

Since the tow line conveyor is always resting on the concrete factory floor, the weight of the conveyor racks and ware are not as critical as in monorail applications where the building steel and roof trusses provide support.

The key to designing a tow conveyor system, in addition to the weight and size of the carts and ware, is knowing the maximum production requirements, in terms of carts per eight-hour shift. Information needed to determine this includes:

- Distance between cart centers, for both open and closed spacing.
- Location and number of delay stations.
- Number of carts at rest at each delay station.
- Number of loaded and empty carts in the system.
- Number of automatic turning stations.
- The amount of time in the ovens, and the number of carts in close pack at each location.
- Number of conveyor lines required.
- Information about building size, including location of walls, building columns, construction and condition of factory floor, and location and clearances of roof trusses.

Knowing the capacity of the building steel is not as critical as when monorail conveyors are installed. With tow chain conveyors, the carts are generally equipped with four 5-in. (13-cm) diameter casters rated for carrying 750 lb (340 kg) each on a concrete floor. The factory floor is normally capable of carrying several times the cart and product weight. A tow cart normally will weigh 200-400 lb (91-181 kg) depending on the weight of the product to be conveyed. This allows live loads of up to 1,000 lb (454 kg) per cart to be carried with a sizable safety factor. Some special applications, such as transporting marine engines through a finishing system, may require special designs.

Chain pull basics. As in the monorail system, the second step in selecting the system size is to determine the tension to which the chain is subjected. Defining the tension for a proposed layout requires approximating the number of drives and compiling layout data for obstructions and loads. Chain pull calculation for a tow line conveyor is simpler than for monorail conveyors because tow conveyors are generally all in the same plane, with the occasional exception of elevation changes when lowering the track for aisles. Only a short distance up or down, this change is relatively insignificant compared to the elevation changes of overhead conveyors. Special tow line conveyors for operating on more than one floor are also available, but are outside the scope of this chapter. These and other special

CHAPTER 19   FINISHING, PAINTING, AND COATING

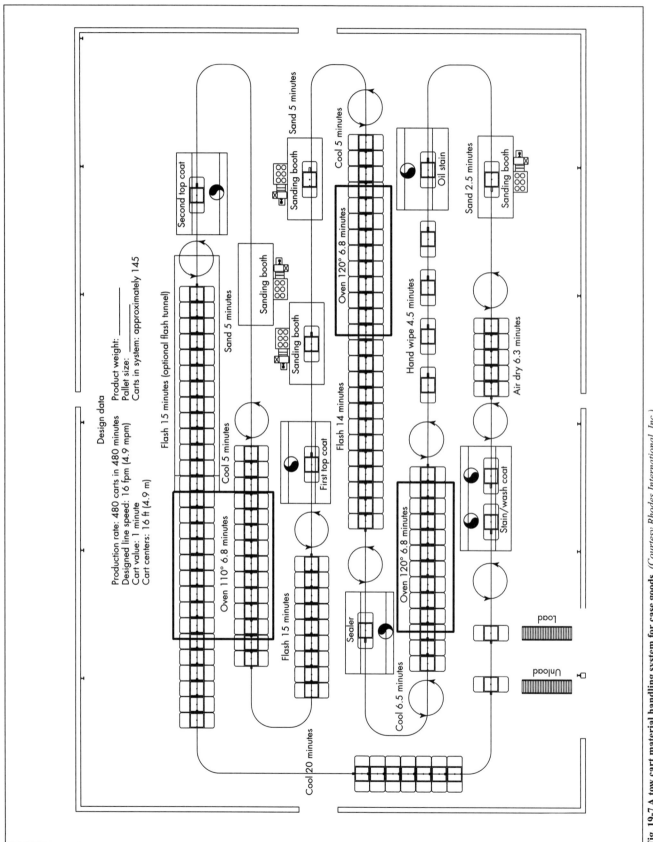

Fig. 19-7 A tow cart material handling system for case goods. *(Courtesy Rhodes International, Inc.)*

CHAPTER 19   FINISHING, PAINTING, AND COATING

requests should be referred to the conveyor manufacturer for help with options and special design considerations.

The conveyor towing capacity depends on the design strength of the tow chain, the chain weight, the number of 90° turns, the number of carts, the weight of the cart with necessary turntables and racks, changes in elevation, the live load weight of ware, and the number of drives.

Conveyor Components

The basic components of a tow chain conveyor system have their own design requirements. This includes tow chain, tow chain track, horizontal turns, the tow chain conveyor drive, cart design, cart turning devices, delay stations, the cart transfer system, and a control panel for the conveyor system.

Tow chain. Carts are pulled around the finishing room by a cart pin that engages with the conveyor chain links. The conveyor chain is a special 0.38-in. (9.7-mm) pitch, precision-calibrated, high tensile strength chain. It is pulled around the tow track by one or more variable-speed drives installed in drive pits below the factory floor. The chain is made into a continuous loop by special connecting links installed when the chain is threaded through the conveyor track and drives. An illustration of the conveyor chain is shown in Fig. 19-8.

Tow chain track. The tow chain conveyor track is available in two styles, open and closed. The tow chain conveyor track is usually installed on top of a concrete floor, but also can be embedded in the concrete so that the top of the track is flush with the factory floor. A combination of the two types of installation is used when the track

is lowered at aisle crossings so that hand carts, trucks, and fork lifts can easily cross the track. Installation cost is proportional to the amount of floor cuts necessary to install the track flush with the floor. (See Figures 19-9a, b, and c for tow chain and track options.)

The tow chain conveyor track comes in the open high-side style shown in Figures 19-9a and b and closed style shown in Fig. 19-9c. The on-floor high-side track is used most often. Some conveyors used in finishing operations are subject to paint overspray and dirt. The on-floor tow chain track's high sides prevent most dirt from getting into the chain area. In paint booths, the track and chain are shielded from paint overspray by the turntable deck mounted over the cart. Special shielding over the track shrouds it, preventing most paint and dirt from falling into it.

Carts are pulled around the finishing room with a floating pin connected to the cart that can engage with any of the horizontal conveyor chain links (see Fig. 19-8). In straight sections of track, the chain orientation is maintained by a slot the width of the chain link (see Fig. 19-9a, b, and c). Standard 90° horizontal turns guide the chain at each change of direction in the finishing room. The 0.38-in. (9.7-mm) pitch conveyor chain is pulled around the tow track by one or more variable speed drives installed in drive pits below the factory floor. A standard tow conveyor package may include: multiple conveyor chains, automatic chain-to-chain transfer stations, delay stations, close pack conveyances, and flexible cart centers.

Horizontal turns. Most systems require four or more horizontal turns. These turns reduce the frictional forces on the conveyor chain, reducing chain pull and drive horsepower. A typical horizontal turn is shown in Fig. 19-10. The turns are a combination of specially-

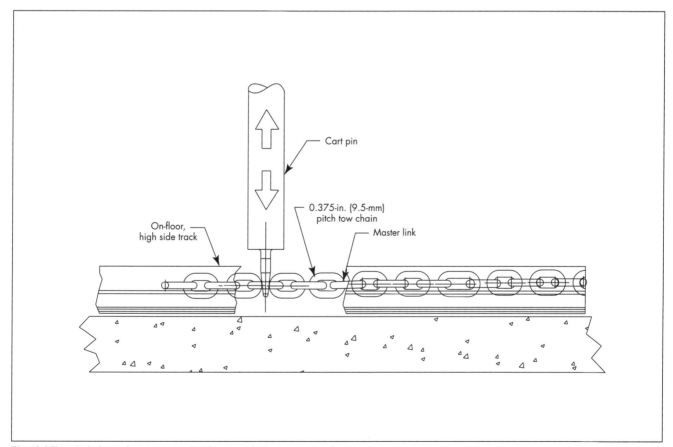

Fig. 19-8 Tow chain in on-floor open track. *(Courtesy Rhodes International, Inc.)*

CHAPTER 19   FINISHING, PAINTING, AND COATING

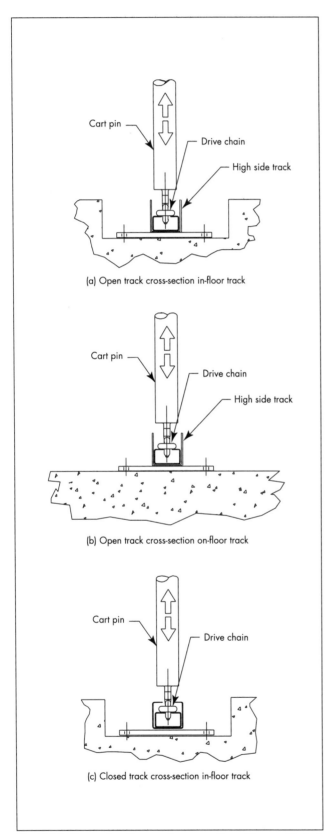

(a) Open track cross-section in-floor track

(b) Open track cross-section on-floor track

(c) Closed track cross-section in-floor track

Fig. 19-9 In-floor and on-floor track cross-sections. *(Courtesy Rhodes International, Inc.)*

machined steel idler rolls and a low-coefficient-of-friction, high-density, machined plastic track. Standard turns are 90° with a radius of 4.5 ft (1.4 m). See Figure 19-7 for an illustration of the 90° horizontal turn used in tow conveyor systems.

Tow chain conveyor drive. The tow chain conveyor drive is mounted in a pit below the factory floor. The drive differs from a monorail drive in that the chain is pulled by a 0.38-in. (9.7-mm) pitch sprocket, not a pusher dog as in the monorail. Typical chain conveyor speeds range from 5-20 fpm (1.5-6 mpm) with horsepower in the 2-5-hp (1,492-3,730-W) conversion range. The speed and horsepower are limited by the maximum allowable load for the chain, the number of drives in service, and the length of the ovens and spray booths necessary to keep pace with faster speeds. See Figure 19-11 for a schematic drawing of a typical drive design.

Cart design. Tow carts are pulled around the finishing system on predetermined centers in even increments of the links of the tow chain. The cart is designed with a flat tabletop that rotates. The top is usually as wide as the cart, but can be much longer. The length is limited by the conveyor path and the spacing between the carts, in open spacing. A standard cart size might be approximately 3 ft² (0.3 m²). The top might be 3 × 6 ft (0.9 × 1.8 m) or more. Important features of the cart are shown in Figures 19-12 and 19-13 and described as follows:

- Turntable—this allows parts to be rotated in the spray booth to simplify spraying operations. It also allows carts usually spaced on 16-ft (4.9-m) centers to be rotated and passed through the oven in a close pack. This results in using shorter conveyors through the oven, and longer drying times at the specified conveyor speeds (see Fig. 19-12).
- Tow pin—this is the means of moving the carts. The tow pin is located in a tube centered over the conveyor chain and it drops into the moving chain that pulls the carts through the system. The tow pin can be disengaged from the moving chain by pushing down the stop bar (see Fig. 19-13).
- Stop bar—each cart has a stop bar located across the leading edge of the cart. The stop bar lifts the tow pin whenever it is tripped by a delay station or interference to the travel of the cart (see Fig. 19-12), thus stopping the leading cart. The trailing cart continues to travel with the tow chain. When the stop bar makes contact with the lead cart, the stop bar lifts the tow pin out of the tow chain, which no longer powers the cart.
- Pull tab—a pull tab is a bar mounted on the cart, off-center from the conveyor track. This bar is used to pull carts across the drive stations. Limit switches are located around the system so that when the pull tab passes, it trips the switch.
- Beaver tail—the tail on each cart is on the side opposite the stop bar. It extends beyond the cart frame and trips the stop bar on the trailing cart whenever the carts are in the close pack mode. Slip-on extensions to the beaver tail are also available to increase the closed pack spacing. This also allows larger parts to be handled than the normal cart design (see Fig. 19-13).
- Casters—each cart has two sets of casters. Four 5-in. (13-cm) diameter casters carry the cart around the track on the factory floor. This set of casters consists of two rigid casters and two swivel casters (see Fig. 19-13). In addition to the floor casters, the standard cart has a series of inverted casters that support the turntable. The turntable has a center shaft that rotates inside a second tube attached to the tow cart, keeping the turntable centered on the cart.

Carts can be equipped with special racks to hold small parts, or may be as simple as a flat top that a desk, table, chair, or bookcase might sit on while the cart passes through the finishing operations.

CHAPTER 19   FINISHING, PAINTING, AND COATING

The cart design is generally standard from job to job, with only the details of the top changing to meet the special requirements of the product to be conveyed.

Cart turning devices. One of the features of the tow chain conveyor is the flexibility of the system. Being able to rotate the part for spray painting and sanding is an example. There are two ways of rotating the part or cart tabletop. One device uses a paddle wheel attached to the turntable, located under the tow cart, to rotate the ware. In the case of the paddle wheel turner, a curved steel guide is positioned in the conveyor path, between the path of the casters. When the paddle wheel engages the curved guide, it causes the paddle wheel to rotate as the cart is pulled past the guide. The bottom turner guides are located everywhere the product needs to be rotated. See Figures 19-14a and b for illustrations showing the paddle wheel turner and how the restricted movement of the turner paddle gradually rotates the cart top as it passes the station.

The second popular way to rotate the cart tops is with a small pneumatic tire mounted at the same height as the turntable. This device is located outside the cart path, but with the wheel overhanging the path. When the wheel comes into contact with the tabletop, the interference created by the wheel causes the top to rotate as the cart passes the turning station. See Figures 9-14c and d for a plan view of this tool for turning the ware.

Delay station. Delay stations are placed ahead of operations that may require special steps or operating times that may vary slightly from cart to cart. The station consists of a means to stop a cart by engaging the stop bar on the cart. When the stop bar is actuated, it causes the tow pin to be lifted out of the tow chain, allowing the conveyor chain to continue to run, passing freely under the carts.

Automatic systems have limit switches that provide inputs to a programmable logic controller (PLC). The PLC can keep track of the carts, has storage memory of the inputs and outputs received, can print reports, and controls the system operation. The PLC respaces the carts at the proper cart centers by timing when they are to be released, besides performing other functions.

Automatic systems are also available without PLCs. Limit switches, counters, and timers are used to perform some of the logic functions handled by a PLC. Unlike the PLC-controlled system, this type does not have any memory or print out capabilities. In this scheme, each station works independently of the others. The station inputs start and stop counters and timers that capture or release carts, keeping the system synchronized. This mode of control can work quite well without the additional complexity of the computer, but some systems may require the extra features available from a computerized system.

Cart transfer system. Some finishing systems may have more than one conveyor system, making it necessary to transfer carts from one line to another for different operations. The transfer shown in Figure 19-15 shows three tow chains spaced only a few inches apart, a delay station set up at the transfer station, and two transfer arms

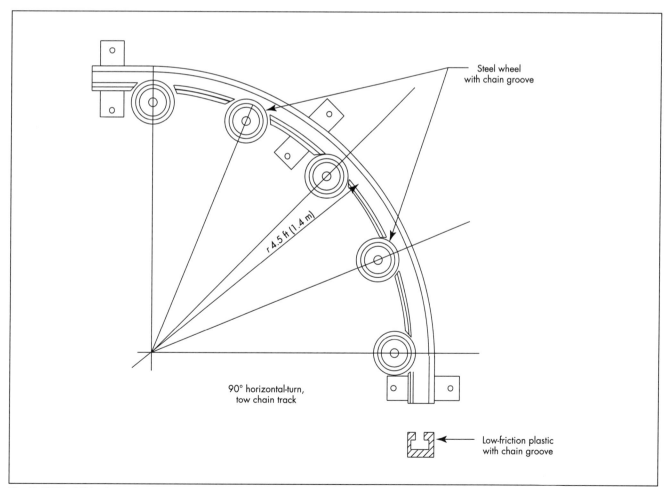

Steel wheel with chain groove

r 4.5 ft (1.4 m)

90° horizontal-turn, tow chain track

Low-friction plastic with chain groove

Fig. 19-10 The 90° horizontal-turn tow chain track. *(Courtesy Rhodes International, Inc.)*

CHAPTER 19   FINISHING, PAINTING, AND COATING

located on either side of the tow track. The whole device is mounted in a pit, so that the air cylinders and linkage mechanisms are below the floor, except for pusher bars. The sequence of operation is:

1. A cart is sensed and a signal is given to the transfer device for the specific transfer desired.
2. The stop bar on the cart is engaged by a delay station, lifting the cart tow pin out of the conveyor chain.
3. The pusher bar engages the cart pull tab and moves the pin tube over the selected conveyor path.
4. The delay station releases the stop bar and the pin falls into the tow chain at the spacing determined by the sensing devices.

Conveyor control panel. A simple control panel should include the following basic features:

- Main disconnect for drive motors and controls.
- Control transformer, push buttons, signal lights, relays, etc.

- Start-up warning horn.
- Low air-pressure alarm.
- Variable speed drive controls.
- Balance circuit for multiple-drive systems.
- Enclosure meeting the requirements of the standards issued by the National Electrical Manufactures Association (NEMA)[9] and Underwriters Laboratories, Inc. (UL) for Type 12 enclosures.[10]
- Digital speed indicator.

Other control panels for the tow conveyor may involve the use of a PLC. Panels with PLCs get data inputs from remote sensors that detect and count carts in the system, along with other information, such as operating time, downtime, cause of downtime, and other data. PLC units can be tailor-made to produce reports and perform other functions not practical in the basic system. This type of unit requires programming skills to maintain operations and change operating parameters.

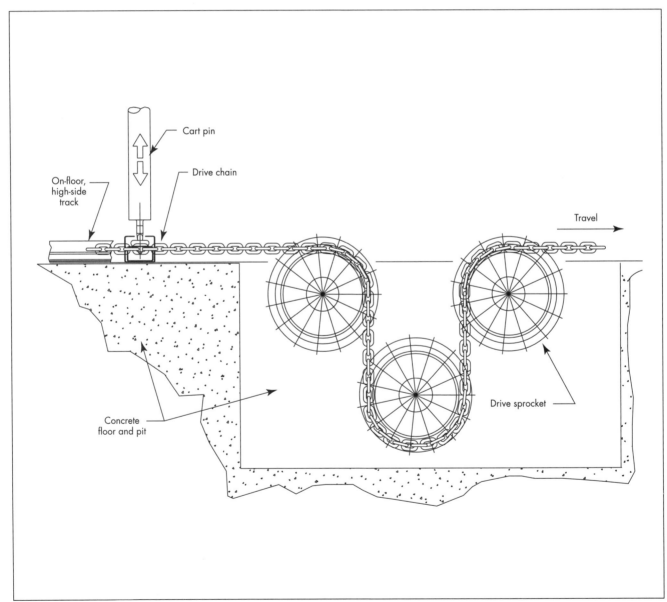

Fig. 19-11 On-floor track and drive units. *(Courtesy Rhodes International, Inc.)*

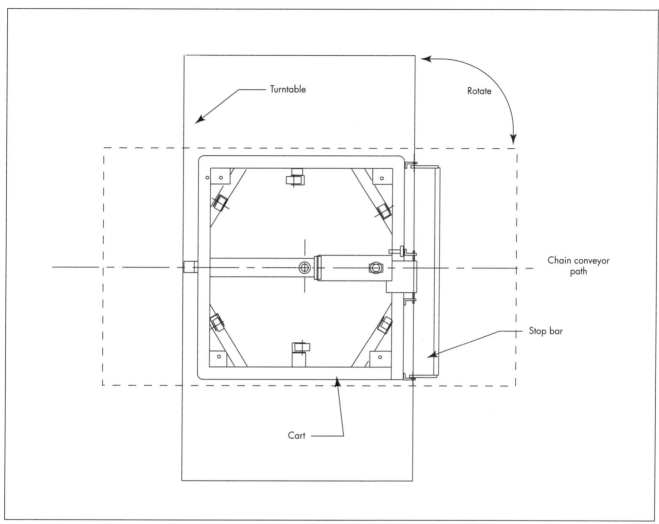

Fig. 19-12 The tow cart—top view. *(Courtesy Rhodes International, Inc.)*

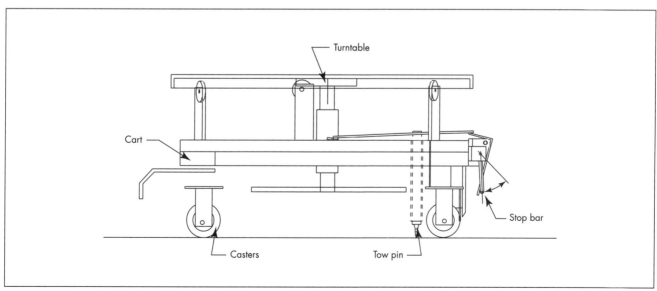

Fig. 19-13 The tow cart—side view. *(Courtesy Rhodes International, Inc.)*

CHAPTER 19   FINISHING, PAINTING, AND COATING

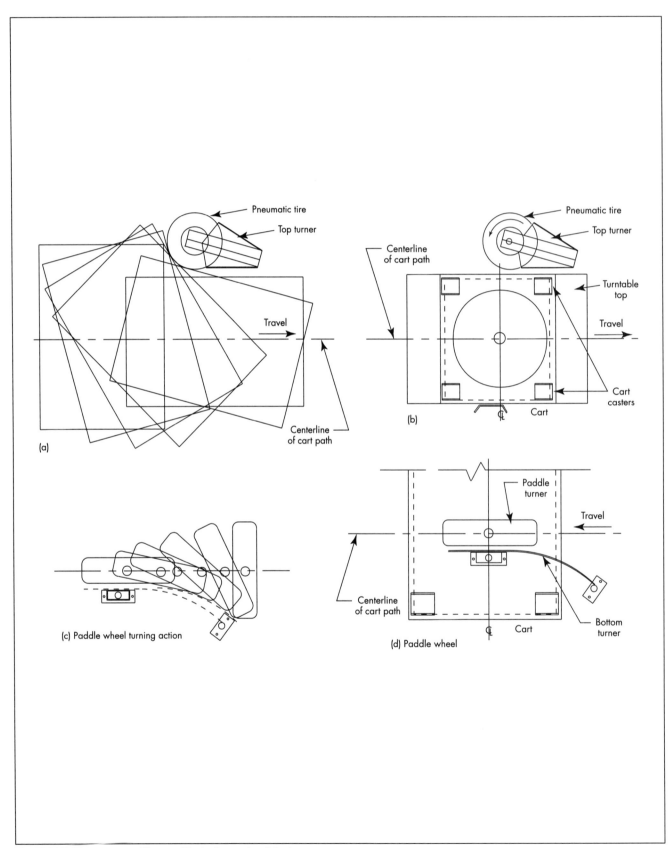

Fig. 19-14 Tabletop turners. *(Courtesy Rhodes International, Inc.)*

CHAPTER 19   FINISHING, PAINTING, AND COATING

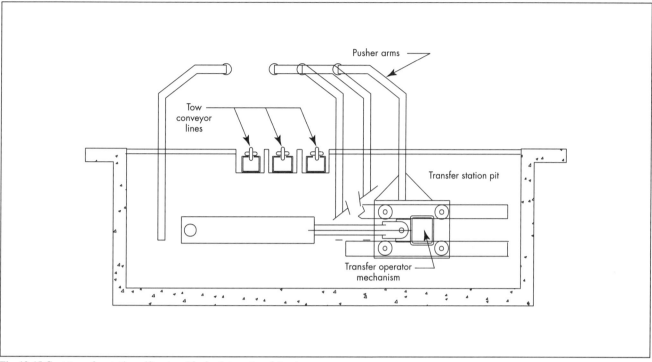

Fig. 19-15 Cart transfer station. *(Courtesy Rhodes International, Inc.)*

SUMMARY

The objective of a total finishing system should be to integrate the most appropriate process with the proper conveyance of the part through that process. This requires planning to ensure that the products to be painted are efficiently accessed by all the necessary preparation and finishing equipment, evaluating the practical alternatives, assuring environmental compliance, incorporating future product demands, and correctly blending the finishing system into other functions of manufacturing.

The best conveyor system design will result from considering the functional aspects of various conveyor types and layout alternatives. The design should integrate the finishing and material handling equipment that fits the facility's needs. An objective means of comparing the advantages and disadvantages of each alternative will reveal the most appropriate solution.

An engineered planning methodology results in providing a conveyor system of the proper type, with a layout that fits with the total manufacturing facility, and utilizes components that will withstand the rigors of the paint operation and provide a contamination-free and maintainable environment.

References

1. Milner, J. "Value of Full Service Engineering for Industrial Finishing and Material Handling System Integration." SME Technical Paper MS870638. Dearborn, MI: Society of Manufacturing Engineers, 1987.
2. Stauffer, J., ed. *Finishing Systems Design and Implementation: A Guide for Product Parameters, Coatings, Process, and Equipment.* Dearborn, MI: Society of Manufacturing Engineers, 1993.
3. Ibid.
4. Ibid.
5. Macomber, R. "Integration of Appropriate Conveyor Systems into Paint Finishing Systems." SME Technical Paper FC:90-563. Dearborn, MI: Society of Manufacuring Engineers, 1993.
6. Ibid.
7. Ibid.
8. Stauffer, J., ed. *Finishing Systems Design and Implementation: A Guide for Product Parameters, Coatings, Process, and Equipment.* Dearborn, MI: Society of Manufacturing Engineers, 1993.
9. National Electrical Manufacturers Association (NEMA). Rosslyn, VA.
10. Underwriters Laboratories, Inc. (UL). Northbrook, IL.

CHAPTER 20

MOVING AND HANDLING SCRAP AND WASTE

CHAPTER CONTENTS

INTRODUCTION

This chapter discusses various types of metal scrap, a basic conveyor selection chart, a brief description of available scrap handling conveyors, and overviews of several metal scrap handling systems. Following these guidelines will help minimize the risk associated with the expense of automating scrap material handling. While this chapter has a bias toward metal scrap, many of the principles apply to other materials as well.

Almost every production process generates scrap as a by-product. Scrap collection and handling procedures can be time-consuming tasks, resulting in no value added to a product. Unfortunately, this is often accepted as an unavoidable expense of the manufacturing process and overlooked as a potential source of cost savings.

One method for scrap handling by small companies that perform machining operations is to collect materials at each machine. A low-cost method is to use empty drums salvaged from metalworking fluid purchases. However, employee safety is a major concern with this practice. A safe means to remove tangled bushy turnings with a rake, shovel, hoe, or hook may be required to remove small broken chips from machine cutting fluid sumps (not to be confused with machine lubricant sumps).

When the container is full, it is moved with a material handling device to a central collection area. Small, company-owned containers are dumped into larger containers owned by a scrap dealer. Often, scrap must be transferred from one container to the other by means of an additional piece of material handling equipment.

Scrap dealer containers may be located outside the main plant building in an open-sided, roofed storage building (EPA regulations require a covered storage area to prevent the leaching of cutting fluids into the ground water because of rain). Savings on plant floor space and ease of pickup and replacement by the scrap dealer make this a logical choice. However, this further complicates the transfer of scrap materials by adding more travel distance and secondary handling problems.

This practice is sufficient for job shop operations with low scrap rates and may not require investment in dedicated scrap handling capital equipment. However, protective clothing may be needed to avoid exposing operators to the risk of cuts and lacerations from sharp metal edges. This risk is further compounded by the possibility of infection caused by cutting oils or synthetic lubricants. Lifting injuries can also result from moving and dumping materials, unless proper equipment is supplied and safe practices are followed.

Larger manufacturing operations with higher scrap volumes employ a combination of dedicated material handling equipment and manual methods for scrap collection. Scrap can be accumulated in self-dumping hoppers and transferred to central collection areas with fork lift trucks.

Manual handling systems offer flexibility of machine placement and plant layout. As the company's manufacturing requirements change, equipment can be relocated without additional cost to move, modify, or replace dedicated material handling equipment.

A disadvantage for the manual handling method is the labor expense incurred to collect and transfer the scrap. Using fork lift trucks adds the additional cost of truck purchases and annual maintenance expenses. In larger manufacturing operations, integrating automated conveyor equipment with production equipment can be a cost-effective solution for many scrap material handling problems.

Metal scrap handling conveyors must be selected according to the type and size of scrap material, as well as the presence of any metalworking fluids. When automating metal scrap handling applications, it is important to manage the process efficiently without disrupting manufacturing production.

Failure to study the type of scrap to be moved is a frequent cause of application failure. Scrap is normally not a homogenous material with reliable characteristics. The worst possible combinations of metalworking fluid flow or lack of it, fine or coarse materials, and large or small foreign matter must be considered before final equipment selections are made.

TYPES OF METAL SCRAP

The most common categories of metal scrap are:

- Bushy steel scrap (machine shop turnings and borings).
- Broken steel chips (shoveling chips).
- Bushy aluminum chips.
- Broken aluminum chips.
- Bushy brass and bronze scrap.
- Fine brass and bronze scrap.
- Cast iron scrap.
- Stamping scrap.
- Die cast scrap.

Bushy Steel Scrap (Machine Shop Turnings and Borings)

Steel scrap from turning and boring operations will include some fine particles, but mostly consists of spirals of various lengths and cross-sections. Bushy chips can be either tight or loose. Tight chips are long, compressed strings of material, of varying weight, making them denser and easier to handle. The loose variety consists of strings that gather in big lightweight bundles. A typical machine depart-

The Contributor of this chapter is: Dave Steffens, Manager, Applications Engineering, Prab, Inc.
The Reviewer of this chapter is: David Alkire Smith, President, Smith & Associates.

CHAPTER 20   MOVING AND HANDLING SCRAP AND WASTE

ment will generate spirals ranging from very fine hair-like pieces to heavy brittle helixes. Unless this material is conveyed away from the machine during operation, it will develop into troublesome large wads or bundles in the waste containers. Cutting fluids usually make up much of the weight of this material—up to 30%. Bulk density ranges from 5-20 lb/ft³ (80-320 kg/m³). Turning and boring tooling with the proper chip breaker geometry can reduce the problem of bushy chips.

Broken Steel Chips (Shoveling Chips)

Bushy steel chips that have been passed through a continuous crusher will usually be classified as shoveling grade chips with a particle size no larger than 2-3 in. (5.1-7.6 cm) in the major dimension. Broken chips are the most common variety of metal scrap, often referred to as "6s and 9s" because of their general shape. Milling machines, broaches, or lathes fitted with chip breakers can also generate this type of scrap. Due to the irregular nature and relatively large surface area of each chip, a great deal of coolant or lubricant can be present. Bulk density ranges from 60-100 lb/ft³ (961-1,602 kg/m³).

Bushy Aluminum Chips

Created in the same manner as bushy steel chips, this material is very light and fluffy with an extreme tendency to tangle. The density can range from 2-10 lb/ft³ (32-160 kg/m³).

Broken Aluminum Chips

Generated in the same way as "steel shoveling grade chips," this material is not any higher in density than bushy chips. These corn-flake-type particles are extremely difficult to move by gravity.

Bushy Brass and Bronze Scrap

Produced by the same methods as bushy steel and aluminum, bushy brass and bronze scrap is generally more brittle and more easily reduced to fine particles by crushing. Material densities range from 5-20 lb/ft³ (80-320 kg/m³).

Fine Brass and Bronze Scrap

Many brass and bronze machining operations generate fine particles and dust. This material is usually free-flowing, granular, and can be very sticky, especially after removing fluids from the scrap. Bulk density can range from 50-100 lb/ft³ (801-1,602 kg/m³).

Cast Iron Scrap

Machining operations on castings generate particles of various sizes, ranging from about 0.125 in. (3.18 mm) to fine dust. A considerable amount of coolant, generally water soluble, can be carried with cast iron scrap. Bulk density ranges from 60-100 lb/ft³ (961-1,602 kg/m³).

Stamping Scrap

Particle size can range from very small discs generated by perforating operations to fairly large, heavy-gage, irregularly-shaped pieces that result from the trimming of automotive parts. Electrical motor lamination scrap is a particularly difficult material to convey due to its thin gage and tiny particle size. Lubricant content ranges from very small amounts on stamping operations to very large amounts used in deep draw forming. Bulk densities ranging from 50-150 lb/ft³ (801-2,403 kg/m³) are common.

Shredding stamping scrap is rarely a consideration in manufacturing operations, but it is popular in scrap yards. Large hydraulic shredders and rolling ring crushers are utilized. Extreme-duty appli-cations use 12 in. (30 cm) pitch steel belt conveyors or specially built equipment for applications such as shredding car body components.

Die Cast Scrap

This material consists of biscuits, runners, gates, sprues, and risers trimmed from die castings. It also can include reject castings. A small amount of die lubricant will usually adhere to the material, although not enough to severely limit remelt operations. Particle size may range from small chunks to long awkward pieces of irregular shape. Due to sharp edges, thin projections, and irregular shapes, die casting scrap has a tendency to catch on conveyors and tangle.

CONVEYOR UTILIZATION

A goal in every manufacturing operation is to maximize productivity. Successful implementation of scrap material handling equipment can save money in many ways.

- Labor is used to manufacture product instead of handling scrap.
- Indirect labor expenses associated with material handling activities can be reduced or eliminated.
- Productivity gains from maximizing equipment uptime.

For example, in stamping applications, when scrap handling equipment is added, presses run continuously instead of stopping to change containers or clean out scrap. Scrap handling devices also help prevent tooling damage by taking scrap away from dies. Die cast cycle times are increased by implementing continuous scrap-to-remelt systems. Metalcutting machine tools incorporate small conveyors to continuously remove chips and turnings, allowing operators to perform machine loading and unloading or quality control procedures instead of stopping the equipment to shovel chips.

With conveyors, other savings come from reducing the costs of purchasing fork lift trucks, scrap containers, and the maintenance and upkeep expenses of this equipment. Savings in heating or air conditioning expenses are also realized from eliminating the need to move scrap to outdoor containers. In-floor conveyor systems also save valuable floor space.

Safety is important whenever conveyors are used. OSHA-compliant guarding of drive components should be standard in equipment from every manufacturer, but the purchaser must verify the compliance of any equipment installed. Push button emergency stop devices are recommended for in-floor systems. They are interlocked to the main control panel and can shut the system equipment off in an emergency. For many large in-floor systems, because the conveyor components cannot be seen from where the electrical control panel is usually located, locking-style, nonfused disconnect switches should be located at each drive motor location. Both devices offer additional employee protection.

In stamping operations, conveyors improve safety by eliminating the need for operators to reach into bolster areas to remove scrap. In die cast shops, workers can be distanced from high-temperature furnaces and molten metals. Conveyors can eliminate lacerations from handling sharp metal and injuries resulting from slipping on oily floors. They can also minimize employee exposure to lubricants, reducing health problems and medical claims. Housekeeping may sound trivial, but it directly relates to labor savings and safety. The need can be eliminated for oil-absorbing materials, mop and bucket brigades, and removing scrap from under moving equipment.

The impact of environmental regulations in the manufacturing sector must not be overlooked. Conveyor systems can be used with other processing equipment such as chip wringing, thermal drying, or washing systems to recover cutting fluids and lubricants. They also can be designed to segregate alloys, which can increase the value of the scrap.

TYPES OF METAL SCRAP HANDLING CONVEYORS

This section discusses:

- Standard drive configuration conveyors.
- Eccentric-driven oscillating conveyors.
- Rotary-driven screw conveyors.
- Hydraulic fluid-driven conveyors.
- Hydraulic and sluice fluid-motion conveyors.

Table 20-1 illustrates various types of ferrous and nonferrous metal scrap and the metal scrap handling equipment available. It indicates the suitability of a particular conveyor to specific materials and conditions.

STANDARD DRIVE CONFIGURATION CONVEYORS

The most popular conveyor design utilizes a head shaft and tailshaft arrangement. Included in this family are hinged steel belt, metal mesh belt, pivoting hinged belt, drag, magnetic, troughing belt, and bucket elevator designs.

The standard drive configuration has an electric motor and worm gear box combination at the discharge end of the conveyor. The drive components pull the loaded belt or chain rather than push. Conveyor head shaft components are located at the drive end of the conveyor. Tailshaft components are located at the opposite end or loading area.

Both head shaft and tailshaft assemblies are positioned in a horizontal plane. They are usually parallel to the ground and always in the same plane with respect to each other.

Gang drives can sometimes be used to run multiple conveyor belts from a single drive. This design is popular for small conveyors located under stamping dies.

Tubular drag conveyors utilize a variation of the head shaft and tailshaft concept. Like their standard configuration counterparts, they have an electric motor and worm gear box combination for drive components that pull the chain.

Unlike other conveyor designs, tubular drag conveyors use drive shaft components (the drive assembly), sprocket turns or specially formed bend assemblies (when changes of direction are required), and idler boxes (tail end devices). Shafting components do not need to be either parallel to the ground or in the same plane with respect to each other.

As a rule of thumb for all of these conveyor designs, the drive will be located at the highest point in the conveyor. Straight horizontal run applications allow the drive placement to be at either end.

Hinged Steel Belt Conveyors

Hinged steel belt conveyors are made up of individual die-formed segments connected with through pins. Sometimes referred to as *piano hinge conveyors,* they are inexpensive and rugged. The conveyors are classified by belt pitch. Belt pitch is the distance between the through pins or hinge loops of the belting. Conveyors can be supplied with 1, 1.5, 2.5, 4, 6, 9, or 12-in. (25, 38, 64, 104, 152, 229, or 305-mm) pitch belting. A variety of metric-pitch belting is also available. Note: metric conversions made in this chapter will have to be matched to the closest standard metric pitch (if available).

The individual hinge styles also vary. "Dimpled" belting should be specified for stamping scrap steel belt applications. Dimpling creates an upset pattern on the hinge surface. This helps to prevent the oily scrap from sticking to the hinge. Perforated hinges increase

coolant drainage through the belt, and are often used on conveyors for scrap from turning or milling machine centers.

Light- and medium-duty steel belt conveyors are of the 1-4-in. (25-100-mm) pitch series. Typical scrap rates for 1-in. and 1.5-in. (25- and 38-mm) pitch steel belt conveyors are less than 500 lb (227 kg)/h. For 2.5-in. (6-cm) pitch conveyors, 1,000-4,000 lb (454-1,814 kg)/h can be handled. For 4-in. (100-mm) pitch conveyors, 4,000-9,000 lb (1,814-4,082 kg)/h is common.

Heavy-duty conveyors are the 6 and 9-in. (152 and 229-mm) pitch series. For scrap rates between 10,000-20,000 lb (4,536-9,072 kg)/h, 6-in. (152-mm) pitch conveyors are used. For applications over 20,000 lb (9,072 kg)/h, 9- or 12-in. (229- or 305-mm) pitch conveyors are required (Fig. 20-1). These numbers should serve as a general guideline only. Other factors such as the angle of incline, overall length, width, and scrap loading conditions also need to be considered.

Hinged steel belt conveyors are more versatile than any other type of metal scrap conveyor. They can be used for any type of metal scrap, from bushy to fine material, wet or dry, in any volume, and in a wide variety of conveyor paths. They are capable of combining horizontal and elevating movements.

However, there are a few disadvantages to this type of system. The hinge belt conveyor has many moving parts and a tendency to jam up and self-destruct unless it is carefully designed for the application. It serves best as an elevating conveyor for wet or dry materials that do not contain a large percentage of fines.

Metal Mesh Belt Conveyors

Metal mesh belting is not recommended for handling chips from turnings or stamping scrap, but it is sometimes utilized in die cast operations for air-quench cooling of castings. Air quench conveyors typically run slowly, 4-6 ft (1.2-1.8 m)/min, and incorporate fans to accelerate casting cooling rates. The metal mesh belt is inexpensive and promotes air circulation around the casting, although it is not as strong as other types of belting. With air quenching, no waste water stream is generated. Water quenching leaves trace amounts of residual heavy metal particles in the water, and therefore the waste water must be handled according to federal, state, and local regulations. The air quenching process is much slower than water quenching, and is generally used for smaller parts.

Pivoting Hinge Steel Belt Conveyors

Materials that are 0.03-in. (0.8-mm) thick or less, such as those found in motor- or transformer-lamination stamping scrap, present particular problems. The thin scrap catches in the openings of hinged steel belting. Pivoting hinge steel belt conveyors incorporate a unique design to solve this problem. The exposed hinge gap is eliminated and the belt pivots forward as it travels past the conveyor head shaft to assist in the discharge. The carry surface has an upset or textured pattern (see Fig. 20-2).

Pivoting hinge steel belt conveyors were designed specifically for light-duty motor-lamination scrap handling applications. The unique action of the pivoting hinge without an exposed hinge gap reduces housekeeping by virtually eliminating scrap carryover problems. However, these conveyors are not suited for heavy-gage stamping scrap or die cast materials. Other limitations are similar to those of steel belt conveyors.

Drag Conveyors

This type of conveyor includes: top and bottom running drag conveyors, side chain conveyors, and tubular drag conveyors.

Top- and bottom-running drag conveyors. A drag conveyor consists of a rectangular trough, varying from 12-48-in. (305-1,219-mm) wide, fitted with wear bars and support angles to accommodate parallel strands of chain in the upper and lower corners of the trough.

CHAPTER 20   MOVING AND HANDLING SCRAP AND WASTE

TABLE 20-1
Conveyor Selection Chart

Scrap	Coolant Volume	Straight Line Primarily Horizontal				Combination Straight and Incline				Multi-directional Path			Vertical Path	
		Oscillating	Screw	Reciprocating	Trough belt	Hinge belt	Drag	Single chain drag	Magnetic	Tubular drag	Pneumatic	Hydraulic and sluice	Dumper and lifter	Bucket elevator
Die casting	—	•												
Bushy steel	Low			•		•		•					•	
	High			•		•		•					•	
Broken steel 3 in. (76.2 mm) maximum	Low	•	•	•	•	•	•	•	•	•	•	•	•	•
	High			•		•	•	•	•	•		•	•	
Bushy aluminum	Low			•		•		•					•	
	High			•		•		•					•	
Broken aluminum	Low	•	•	•	•	•	•	•		•	•	•	•	•
	High			•		•	•	•		•		•	•	
Bushy brass	Low			•		•		•					•	
	High			•		•		•					•	
Fine brass	Low	•	•	•	•		•	•		•	•	•	•	•
	High			•			•	•		•		•	•	
Cast iron	Low	•	•	•	•	•	•	•	•	•		•	•	•
	High			•		•		•	•	•		•	•	
Stampings	Dry	•			•	•		•	•				•	
	Sticky	•				•		•	•				•	

CHAPTER 20   MOVING AND HANDLING SCRAP AND WASTE

Drag plates, or flights, are flexibly attached to the chains 12-24 in. (305-610 mm) apart, depending on the application. Cast or forged "H" chains can be used instead of the flighted chain design. Power is transmitted through a head shaft fitted with suitable sprockets and driven at a very low speed. Chain speeds of 3-10 ft (0.9-3.0 m)/min are typical (see Fig. 20-3). Multiple discharge points are simple to provide on drag conveyors since the carry run is on the bottom side and discharge gates are easily incorporated into the design.

Side chain drag conveyors. Side chain conveyors transport curly turnings, tangled bundles, large or small stamping scrap, motor lamination scrap, die cast scrap, or any combination of these materials. The side chains are contained in a liquid-tight housing. The conveyors operate with materials that are wet, dry, or flooded with coolants. Side chain flights are hinged to ride over jams, skimming part of the material away. Successive flights reduce the jams and gradually eliminate the problem. These conveyors are used for short or long runs and inclines to 45° (see Fig. 20-4).

The side chain conveyor's ability to handle varied materials, combined with its liquid-tight construction, makes it a very versatile conveyor. Any material carried back on the return flight is contained inside the trough, eliminating housekeeping problems.

Although side chain conveyors are higher in initial purchase price, low maintenance requirements and improved housekeeping offset the difference and result in savings over the life of the equipment. However, the side chain conveyor is limited in carry width sizes and capacity when compared to steel belt conveyors, and in general, side chain drag conveyors require more motor horsepower than comparable equipment.

Tubular drag conveyors. Tubular drag conveyors are designed with a single strand, universal-jointed chain attached to flights inside a round or square casing. The universal joints in the chain permit changes in direction along both horizontal and vertical planes. Material can be moved in either direction because the chain is conveyed in a loop (see Fig. 20-5).

Providing that the material is reasonably dense, a high capacity conveyor can be installed in a relatively small and easily accessible trench. Narrow floor plates can be used to cover the trench, giving convenient access to the conveyor at any point on its length.

Tubular drag conveyors are best suited for fine or broken chips. Chips from a broaching operation are ideal. Multiple discharge points are made possible by incorporating mechanical or pneumatic gates.

This conveyor is not suited for solids such as stamping scrap, die cast scrap, castings, reject parts, or curly and stringy turnings.

Advantages and disadvantages of drag conveyors. Drag conveyors offer several benefits. They are well suited to handle finely divided materials with or without coolant flow. They are also capable of conveying on an incline, usually less than 45°. Because material is carried on the bottom run of chain, and the return portion of the chain runs back over the top of the carrying area, any material clinging to the chain or flights is automatically recirculated and given another chance to discharge. Thus, the drag conveyor compares with other single path conveyors because carryover problems are minimized. Maintenance is easy since all components are visible when the cover plate is removed.

However, there are a few limitations to this system's use. Except when side-chain drag conveyors are used, bushy turnings, stamping scrap, die cast scrap, and large solids should be avoided. Bushy turnings can wrap around the flights and cause jamming. Stamping scrap and solids can jam between the conveyor spreader bars or the upper strand of the flighted chain.

Magnetic Conveyors

Magnetic conveyors are designed with a stainless steel top surface fixed to a sealed frame. There are no external moving parts except for the head shaft and sprocket. The magnet moves inside the frame below the stainless steel carrying surface, attracts the particles of scrap metal, and moves them toward the discharge area.

The sealed magnetic conveyor is a popular choice due to its low maintenance requirements. All moving components are contained inside the frame and typically run in an oil bath. The volume of oil depends on the width and length of the conveyor (1-5 gal [4-19 L] volumes are typical). Some manufacturers' magnetic designs use internal track and sprocket components fabricated from ultra-high molecular weight (UHMW) polyethylene. The low coefficient of friction of this material eliminates the need for internal lubrication.

In general, magnetic conveyors handle small-, light-, and medium-gage ferrous scrap, 10-gage (3.5-mm) thick and 8 × 8 in. (203 × 203 mm) or less in size (see Fig. 20-6). They are particularly suitable for applications involving very small particles, or those submerged in coolant tanks. The action of the conveyor has a filtering effect on the coolant. Sheet metal scrap may contain very fine pieces having sharp corners, which would tend to hang up in the moving

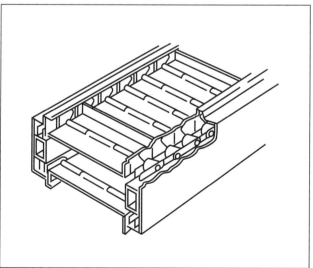

Fig. 20-1 Steel belt or hinge belt conveyor. *(Courtesy Prab Conveyor)*

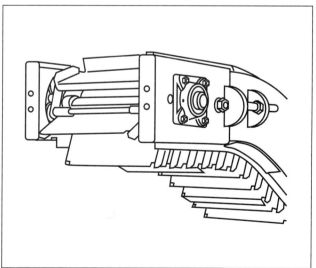

Fig. 20-2 Pivoting-hinge steel belt conveyor. *(Courtesy Prab Conveyor)*

CHAPTER 20   MOVING AND HANDLING SCRAP AND WASTE

parts and cracks of hinge belt conveyors. Although more costly than a hinge belt conveyor, the magnetic conveyor may be less expensive in the long run when such fine particles predominate.

Despite these advantages, there are several limitations to the magnetic conveyor. Internal magnetic assemblies are typically spaced every 12 in. (305 mm). Scrap larger than 10 in. (254 mm) in length can disrupt the magnetic fields between two adjacent magnetic assemblies, reducing their carrying capacity. Spacing the internal magnet assemblies at interval distances greater than 12 in. (305 mm) also reduces the carrying capacity of the unit. Magnet assembly speeds can be increased to offset this reduction, but may cause a decrease in the life expectancy of the conveyor. Also, magnetic conveyors are not suited for dump loading or bushy turnings. Large heavy scrap can damage the thin stainless steel carry surface and should be avoided.

Troughing Belt Conveyors

Troughing belt conveyors can transport most kinds of metal scrap successfully for heavy-duty, high-speed applications. Belting materials are pulled across a series of angled rollers that form a troughing action. Belts can be made from various materials, including polyvinyl chloride (PVC), nitrile rubber, polyurethane, nylon, and other synthetic materials (see Fig. 20-7).

Troughing belt conveyors are suitable for long run and gradual elevations not exceeding a 20° angle. They typically run at higher speeds and can carry higher volumes of materials than other conveyor types. However, their normal applications are outside a manufacturing plant, because this type of conveyor has a tendency to spill material, and a certain amount of carryover has to be expected due to sharp particles sticking to the relatively soft belt surface. They are not suitable for the impact of heavy objects or large bundles of tangled turnings. They are also limited to material temperatures under 300° F (149° C). In general, while most rubber belting is limited to 150° F (66° C), special belting materials are available to reach 400° F (204° C).

Bucket Elevators

Heavy-duty, chain-type bucket elevators are an excellent choice when vertical movement of material is a requirement. A single or double strand of high-strength chain is fitted with closely-spaced, hardened steel buckets. Conveyed material is received in the boot section, and the buckets dig the material out of the boot section, then elevate and discharge it with a centrifugal action (Fig. 20-8).

High chain speeds allowed with this type of equipment result in greater capacity for the cost involved. Bucket elevators can elevate materials at a 90° angle of incline, though the optimum angle of incline is approximately 75°. The carrying capacity decreases as the angle of incline approaches 90°. Straight style configurations are most often utilized. Multiple bend sections also can be fabricated according to the application requirements.

Bucket elevator conveyors are widely used to handle grains, cereals, and other food items. Light-duty agricultural bucket elevators should not be used in metal scrap handling applications. As with many different conveyor designs for manufacturing, heavy-duty construction is required.

Fig. 20-4 Side chain drag conveyor. *(Courtesy Prab Conveyor)*

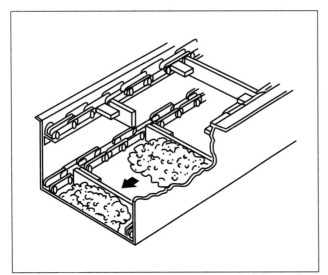

Fig. 20-3 Bottom-running drag conveyor. *(Courtesy Prab Conveyor)*

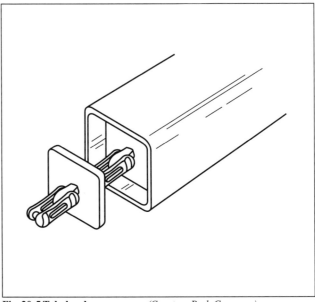

Fig. 20-5 Tubular drag conveyor. *(Courtesy Prab Conveyor)*

CHAPTER 20   MOVING AND HANDLING SCRAP AND WASTE

Materials moved must be free-flowing, so bucket elevators are best suited for broken chips. Tangled scrap, such as turnings, should not be handled. Wet materials also can be a problem. Material that tends to pack can jam in the boot section. Utilizing a vibratory feeder mechanism helps control the feed flow rate of the material, and reduces jamming.

ECCENTRIC-DRIVEN OSCILLATING CONVEYORS

Oscillating conveyors use electric motors with an eccentric drive or offset counterweight devices to induce the motion in the carry surface of the conveyor. The carry surface moves in an elliptical motion, imparting energy into the material and propelling it forward.

"Flat stroke" oscillators use pneumatic or hydraulic cylinders to move the carry surface. The forward stroke is slower than the reverse stroke. The fast reverse stroke pulls the carry surface out from under the material. An analogy of this action is pulling a tablecloth out from under a set of dishes on a table.

With an oscillating conveyor, a horizontal trough of any desired shape is reciprocated with a frequency ranging from 400-600 cycles per minute. Material moves at a speed of approximately 15 ft (4.6 m)/min. Material flow rates can be controlled by using a variable speed pulley or counterweight mechanism (see Fig. 20-9).

Oscillating conveyors are often used for in-floor collection, and are a cost-effective method for traveling horizontal distances. They offer a low maintenance alternative to traditional steel belt conveyors. Pit depth and width dimensions can be kept to a minimum, resulting in savings over other conveyor designs that would require additional space for maintenance or servicing.

The biggest advantage of the oscillating conveyor, when compared to traditional steel belt conveyors, is the elimination of housekeeping

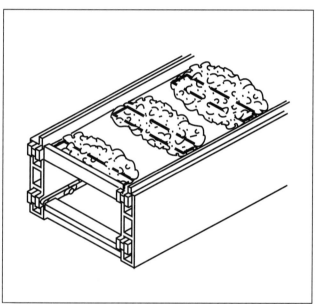

Fig. 20-6 Magnetic conveyor. *(Courtesy Prab Conveyor)*

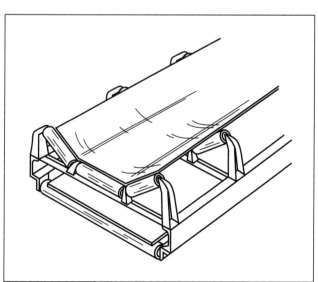

Fig. 20-7 Troughing belt conveyor. *(Courtesy Prab Conveyor)*

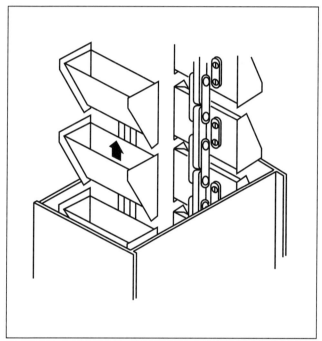

Fig. 20-8 Bucket elevator conveyor. *(Courtesy Prab Conveyor)*

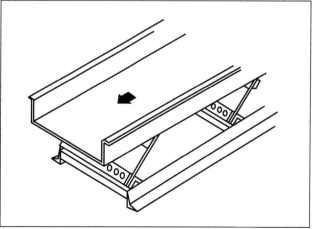

Fig. 20-9 Oscillating conveyor. *(Courtesy Prab Conveyor)*

CHAPTER 20   MOVING AND HANDLING SCRAP AND WASTE

problems caused by material carryover. A steel belt conveyor allows small pieces of oily scrap to stick to its surface and drop to the floor when it returns. Material also tends to get caught in hinge joint openings. These problems do not occur with oscillating conveyors.

This type of conveyor is very low in first cost and has very low maintenance cost due to the small number of moving parts. It is widely utilized in the die casting industry for in-floor transfer of trim scrap back to remelt furnaces. A variation of the oscillating conveyor is also used as a furnace feed device. Other applications include in-floor stamping scrap collection systems.

Oscillating conveyors must be solidly anchored to the floor. Otherwise, material flow is reduced and progressive destruction of the conveyor and its mountings will occur. Only horizontal or downward sloping material movement should be planned with oscillating conveyors.

Unlike steel belt conveyors that carry material on the moving belting surface, oscillating conveyors impart energy to the scrap. The eccentric throw, or offset distance, forces the scrap forward into the air on the carrying surface. Sticky fluids may impede material movement, since the flow is not as positive when compared to other types of conveyors. The oscillating conveyor is also limited by material size and rate.

Coil spring-assisted units are required for high material rates or heavy impact loading. Light- and medium-duty oscillating conveyor designs use glass filament composite flippers (flat springs). Heavy-duty designs use coil springs or steel leaf springs to allow greater trough loading, and resistance to impact damage. The stiffness of the spring serves to support and align the trough. When empty, most of the power required to oscillate the trough is stored and released in the spring. As loading is increased, the positive eccentric-type drive will maintain a constant amplitude in the trough.

Pneumatically-driven flat stroke oscillators are a variation of the larger motor-driven, eccentric units. This design offers a low-profile method of removing scrap from underneath stamping dies. Some advantages when compared to pneumatically-driven devices are location flexibility, low-profile design, and ease of installation. The principal disadvantage is that they are more expensive to operate than electric motor-driven counterparts.

ROTARY-DRIVEN SCREW CONVEYORS

Screw conveyor designs use rotary motion to move materials. Electrically- or hydraulically-powered motors run the gear boxes to produce the required torque for rotating the helicoid.

Screw conveyors consist of a rotating helicoid inside a formed trough. They are heavy-duty, operate at relatively low speeds, and have proven to be very effective in the straight-line conveying of crushed or flowable metal scrap.

Drive components can be located at either end of the conveyor. Conveyor helicoid flight pitch angles can be varied to facilitate feed rates. Multiple helicoids can be driven from one common drive. However, while moderate upward slopes can be negotiated, average angles of incline are less than 35°. Steeper angles require higher helicoid speeds or special flighting.

Troughs come in many sizes, shapes, and thicknesses. Troughs that are made with abrasion-resistant steels can increase wear resistance and equipment longevity (see Fig. 20-10). The screw conveyor is particularly well-suited for multiple discharge or continuous distribution. Materials travel in one direction with no carryover problems. Troughs (typically formed in 10 ft [3 m] sections) can be welded together liquid-tight.

Screw conveyors are not suited for solids such as die cast scrap, stamping scrap, reject parts, or castings. Materials conveyed should be free-flowing. *Free-flowing* refers to how easily the scrap will become entangled with other pieces. Ball bearings or grains of dry

sand are examples of free-flowing materials. Die cast and stamping scrap materials are very susceptible to entanglement. Some bushy materials will wrap around the helicoid shaft, reducing its ability to move material.

HYDRAULIC FLUID-DRIVEN CONVEYORS

Reciprocating ram conveyors and dumper and lifter designs use electric motors that drive pump assemblies containing hydraulic fluids to produce motion. Motion and length are determined by design of the hydraulic cylinder components. Drive cylinders are almost always located at the rear end of reciprocating ram conveyors. For dumper and lifter devices, they are located at the lowest elevation point, where they push the load to the dump point and then retract to their original point of origin.

Reciprocating Conveyors

Reciprocating conveyors haul large volumes of bushy turnings, small chips, and coolant. Barbs and wedges on a hydraulically-driven push rod or ram, contained inside a formed trough, move the material forward. Barbs on the side of the liquid-tight trough prevent the material from moving backward as the rod is retracted. A hydraulic cylinder strokes the ram forward and reverse in 5 ft (1.5 m) increments. Hydraulic equipment is preferred over pneumatic, because it provides a smooth, powerful motion. Typical installations are below floor line. Trough sections can be cast in-floor, supported from the pit floor, or hung from the edge of pit steels (see Fig. 20-11).

Some advantages of reciprocating conveyors are that they are low in initial, maintenance, and operating costs. Trough sections can be welded liquid-tight. Lengths of 300-400 ft (91-122 m) are not uncommon. Conveyors can be installed horizontally or pitched to facilitate coolant drainage.

Despite these advantages, there are a few limitations. Reciprocating conveyors are not suited for solids such as die cast scrap, reject parts, or castings. Installations are in straight line runs. Changes in conveyor direction must be accomplished by additional conveyors.

Dumpers and Lifters

Dumpers and lifters can elevate tote bins of metal scrap for dumping into shredders, crushers, or chip wringing equipment (Fig. 20-12). In general, dumpers rotate around a fixed point. Changes in

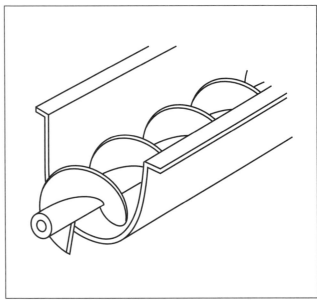

Fig. 20-10 Screw conveyor. *(Courtesy Prab Conveyor)*

CHAPTER 20   MOVING AND HANDLING SCRAP AND WASTE

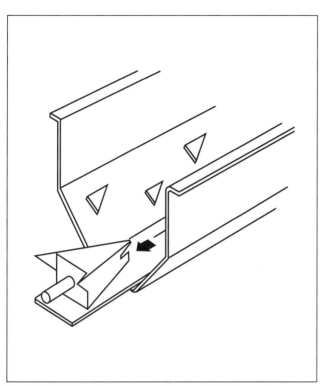

Fig. 20-11 Reciprocating conveyor. *(Courtesy Prab Conveyor)*

elevation are a result of the rotation angle. Lifters are designed for vertical movement and rotation to facilitate dumping. Incline angle elevation movement is also an option. Dumpers are low cost, require minimum floor space, and are generally used to handle batch processing of materials. Lifters can elevate 4,000-lb (1,814-kg) loads to dump heights of 25 ft (8m).

Standardization of tote bin size and type is crucial for the unit to operate effectively. Safety enclosures or guards should be utilized, and dumpers and lifters should be firmly anchored in place.

PNEUMATIC CONVEYORS

Pneumatic conveyors use the principles of velocity and air pressure to move materials inside piping. Fans or pumps provide the air source. Rotary air lock devices introduce the materials into the airstream. Air dissipation devices such as cyclones are located at the discharge end of the piping to slow the air down, allowing the material to disperse downward while the air is directed upward (typical directional changes).

Crushed steel, crushed aluminum, brass, cast iron, etc., can be conveyed successfully in high-velocity pneumatic conveyors. Pressure conveyors for dense or dilute materials can move fairly large volumes of chips over long distances. Vacuum design systems are also available (Fig. 20-13).

Pneumatic conveyors are very cost-effective on long runs at large capacities. It can handle high volumes of material both horizontally and vertically. Pneumatic or mechanical gates can be used to create multiple discharge points. An application example would be crushed and dried chips conveyed from chip processing coolant recovery equipment to storage silos. Specially-reinforced elbows are a must due to the abrasive action of the material.

This type of conveyor should not be used for curly or stringy turnings and large solids. Noise from equipment can be an issue. External sources for inlet air should be used to prevent heat or air conditioning loss.

HYDRAULIC AND SLUICE FLUID-MOTION CONVEYORS

Hydraulic and sluice conveyors move "rivers" of fluids in a contained trough. The high velocity of the fluids physically moves the material in the coolant stream.

Hydraulic and sluice conveyors move crushed scrap along sluicing trenches (if ample coolant is available) and the trenches are carefully planned to avoid hang-up points. Pumps and velocity nozzles

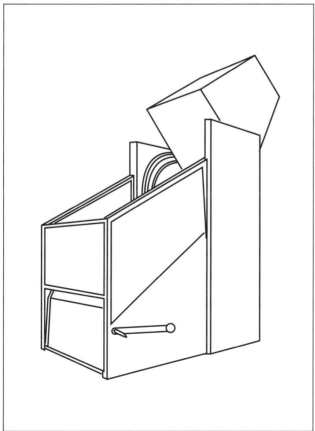

Fig. 20-12 Dumper and lifter conveyor. *(Courtesy Prab Conveyor)*

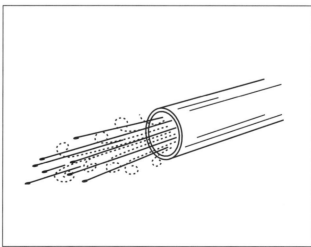

Fig. 20-13 Pneumatic conveyor. *(Courtesy Prab Conveyor)*

CHAPTER 20   MOVING AND HANDLING SCRAP AND WASTE

arc arranged at strategic points along the trench to move materials (Fig. 20-14). This type of conveyor is almost exclusively limited to water-soluble coolant flowing at a rate of 500-3,500 gal (1,893-13,248 L)/min. Petroleum-based lubricants have higher viscosities and do not produce the required flow rates to move materials.

Velocity nozzles are positioned in areas where changes in direction occur. Corners should have large, rather than sharp, radius bends. Large volumes and high coolant velocities are required to move material in the trough.

This type of conveyor is very simple and virtually maintenance-free. Sluice trenches are capable of multiple direction changes. However, hydraulic and sluice conveyors are only feasible with large amounts of coolant, and high energy output is required to keep the material moving. Coolant misting problems also must be addressed.

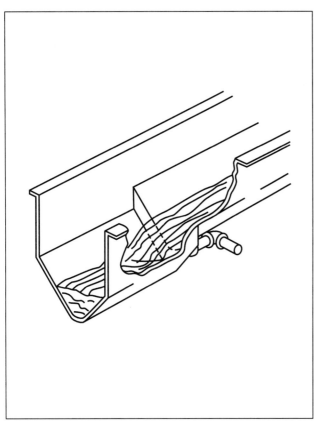

Fig. 20-14 Hydraulic and sluice conveyor. *(Courtesy Prab Conveyor)*

CHUTING AND DISTRIBUTION SYSTEMS

The proper selection of metal scrap handling conveyor equipment is an important process. Equally significant is designing scrap chuting or distribution systems to fill scrap dealer container(s). For applications where containers are located outside the building, the type and number of containers the scrap dealer utilizes must be addressed. For single container applications, simple fixed chuting will direct scrap into the box.

There are two limitations to this method, however. First, the scrap is not well distributed over the length of the container. This results in using a smaller container or sending an individual outside to shovel the scrap in the container to redistribute it. Second, when the box becomes full, the remaining scrap collection system will be shut down while waiting for the scrap dealer to replace the container.

A better option is to discharge the scrap into two containers with left and right or pivoting discharge chuting. An automated level-sensing option is worth the additional expense. This eliminates the need for someone to monitor the level in the containers. A simple gyro and pilot light combination located on a system's electrical control panel can alert workers when the desired scrap level is reached in each container.

The most often-used level sensors are the drop wire and ultrasonic designs. Drop wire designs use a low (usually 24 V DC) current between two drop wires. When the metal scrap fills the container to the desired level, the conductive material makes a circuit. Ultrasonic level sensors detect scrap levels by measuring the reflection of an ultrasonic pulse emitted from the device. The time taken for this echo to return to the sensor is directly proportional to the distance because sound has a constant velocity. Both designs can light a pilot light to indicate a box-full condition, or reposition a chute to a new location to continue filling the container.

For high volumes of scrap, a shuttle scrap distribution system is used to automatically fill two containers. It uses 6- or 9-in. (152 or 229-mm) pitch steel belt conveyors to transport and elevate the scrap. Container sizes usually range from 30-40 ft (9-12 m) long. Smaller containers can be filled by less expensive pivoting chutes, but fill quickly. Figure 20-15 shows a shuttle conveyor system, and the layout of a shuttle conveyor application is illustrated in Figure 20-16.

Small scrap costs less to handle, fills containers more evenly, maximizes the weight in the container, and requires fewer hauls by the scrap dealer. Adding scrap choppers to presses, or incorporating features into die designs to minimize scrap size is important. Chop large skeletal blanks into several smaller pieces.

For very high-volume systems, baling may be necessary. Railroad cars may be used in place of traditional gondolas or smaller "roll-off" style scrap containers. This high level of scrap production is common in large automotive stamping facilities, where scrap rates as high as 80,000 lb (36,288 kg)/h are not unusual.

Road load restrictions will limit the weight of scrap in the container. Roadway weight limits vary depending on location and season. Truck gross weights of 80,000 lb (36,288 kg) or approximately 50,000 lb (22,680 kg) of scrap can be used as a guideline. Container size and pickup frequency should be discussed well in advance with the scrap dealer.

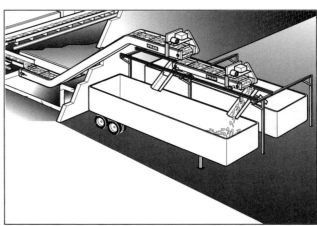

Fig. 20-15 Shuttle conveyor system. *(Courtesy Prab Conveyor)*

CHAPTER 20   MOVING AND HANDLING SCRAP AND WASTE

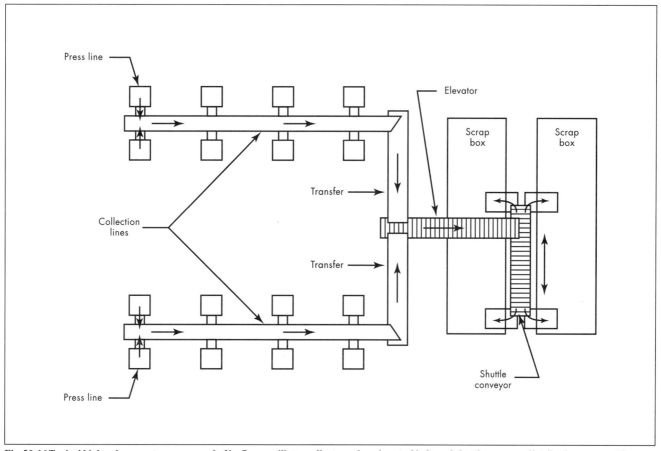

Fig. 20-16 Typical high-volume system composed of in-floor oscillator collectors, elevating steel belt, and shuttle conveyor distribution system. (*Courtesy Prab Conveyor*)

ELECTRICAL CONTROLS

An electrical control panel for an in-floor system is essential. Because in-floor equipment is out of sight of machine operators, locking nonfused disconnect switches on each drive motor is a good safety feature. Monitoring the equipment electronically ensures that it is operating properly at all times. Incorporating conveyor component rotation sensing and automatic level sensing devices augments the system.

Make sure to include "bin present" sensors to ensure that scrap containers are properly in place and ready to receive scrap. Photo eye sensors, ultrasonic sensors, or proximity sensors can be used. Failure to use such a device may result in a large pile of scrap on the ground outside the building.

APPLICATION EXAMPLES

Examples of moving and handling scrap and waste include:

• Single-unit machined chips and turnings collection.
• In-floor systems for machined chips and turnings.
• Above-floor stamping scrap collection.
• In-floor stamping systems.
• Die cast scrap handling systems.

SINGLE-UNIT MACHINED CHIPS AND TURNINGS COLLECTION

An example of a single-unit conveyor application is a steel belt conveyor in a CNC lathe. Most original equipment manufacturers offer either 1, 1.5, or 2.5-in. (25, 38, or 64-mm) pitch steel belt conveyors as optional equipment for scrap removal.

The conveyor consists of a lower horizontal section designed to collect chips and turnings. Sheet metal skirting directs the scrap into the conveyor. Drainage holes and a bottom cover direct coolants back into the machine sump.

The scrap travels up an inclined section that incorporates skirting and a top cover to contain the scrap. Angles of incline range from 45-60°. Compression-style top covers prevent the turnings from "balling up." An upper horizontal section allows the scrap to travel away from the machine tool and discharge into a scrap container.

Electrical controls are required for the operator to turn the unit on and off. A preferred method is to interface the conveyor controls with the machine tool controls. This ensures that the conveyor is running while the lathe is operating.

IN-FLOOR SYSTEMS FOR MACHINED CHIPS AND TURNINGS

High-volume manufacturing operations require efficient scrap removal and cutting fluid recovery. Reciprocating ram conveyors are one effective method. Production screw machine facilities are frequent users of this type of scrap transfer conveyor (see Fig. 20-17).

CHAPTER 20   MOVING AND HANDLING SCRAP AND WASTE

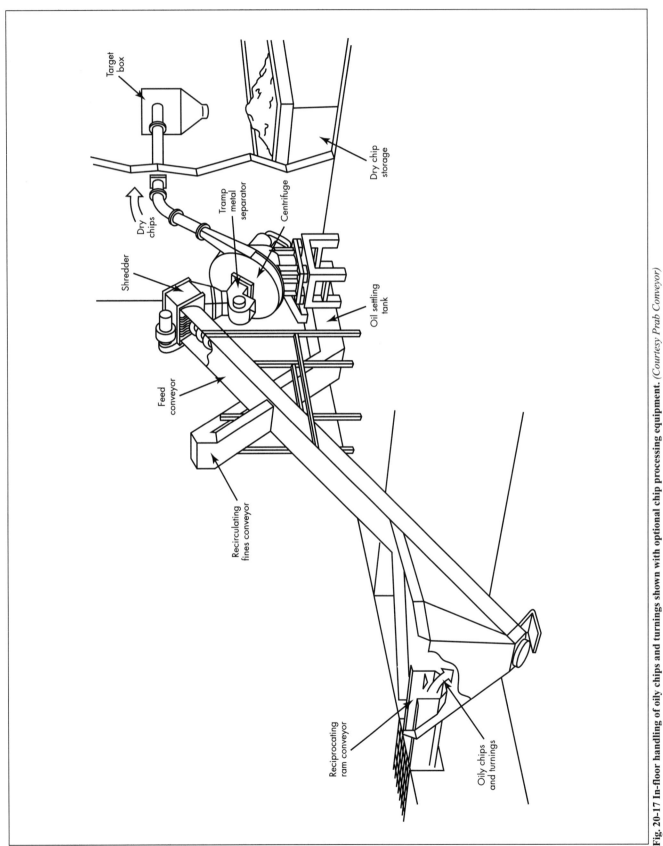

Fig. 20-17 In-floor handling of oily chips and turnings shown with optional chip processing equipment. *(Courtesy Prab Conveyor)*

CHAPTER 20   MOVING AND HANDLING SCRAP AND WASTE

In these applications, a steel belt or screw conveyor removes scrap from each machine. These conveyors discharge chips and turnings into a reciprocating ram conveyor located below floor line. Cutting fluids are drained through the scrap conveyor and redirected back to the machine sump. This method often leaves only residual lubricants on scrap metal chips and turnings.

Other system strategies are to flood chips and turnings out of machines with generous amounts of lubricants, and discharge both lubricant and scrap into the in-floor conveyor system. Either method places heavy demands on the conveyor system to handle combinations of scrap and lubricants.

Reciprocating ram conveyors can handle high volumes of scrap. A general guideline for broken steel or cast iron chips is a rate of 12,000 lb (5,443 kg)/h. They are particularly efficient for handling the troublesome combination of broken chips, turnings, and bushy chips. For bushy steel chips and turnings, throughput rates are typically 7,000 lb (3,175 kg)/h. The average length for a single reciprocating ram conveyor will range from 50-400 ft (15-122 m).

Casting the troughs in the concrete floor is the most popular method of installation. Other methods are hanging the troughs from pit steels or mounting them on legs supported from the pit flooring. Changes in direction are accomplished with additional conveyors. Low- to medium-volume coolant flows (up to 500 gal [1,893 L]/min) are easily handled by trough sections welded liquid-tight during installation.

After the scrap and lubricants from machinery have been collected and transferred to a central destination, they need to be elevated out of the floor. Steel belt, side chain, drag, or screw conveyors are used for this task. Scrap may then be discharged directly into containers. While this choice is comparatively inexpensive, cutting fluids and lubricants adhere to the chips and turnings and are transferred to scrap containers, resulting in the cost of replenishing lost coolants or lubricants. Approximately 1 gal (3.8 L) of water-soluble coolant is lost for every 2 ft³ (0.06 m³) of scrap material handled.

Another issue is environmental concerns. Special procedures must be implemented to prevent soil contamination both on- and off-site. An additional problem is the diminished value of the scrap when it is contaminated with excess lubricants.

Cutting fluids can be recovered by specially-designed part separation equipment that removes tramp metal. Shredders or crushers can then reduce tangled turnings into a shovel grade of chip to facilitate the fluid separation process. The scrap material is then spun in a centrifuge or compressed into a "puck." Better known as chip processing equipment, these systems incorporate many types of conveyors to transfer materials. The resulting processed chips contain less than 2% residual moisture (by weight).

Throughput capacities for chip processing systems depend on volume. For example, system equipment that can process 2,000 lb (907 kg)/h of steel chips might process only 1,200 lb (544 kg)/h of aluminum scrap. Another rule of thumb is that chip processing equipment in continuous operation will recover 15-25 gal (57-95 L)/h of water-soluble coolant.

High-volume machining operations often require fluid management strategies in addition to chip processing equipment. Filtration equipment is used to remove fine particles from the coolant before pumping it back to the machine tools. The level of coolant purity is dictated by the manufacturing process.

Usually, a steel belt and drag conveyor combination is located in a double tank. Coolant streams containing chips and turnings are directed into the steel belt conveyor side of the tank. The larger chips and turnings are elevated out of the floor. The fines are flushed through the steel belt and flow over a weir into the drag conveyor portion of the tank, where they are allowed to gravity-settle to the bottom of the tank. A drag conveyor operating at low speed removes the settled fines and elevates them out of the floor. Coolant is then pumped from the tank into a filtration unit. Various methods, such as filter bed media systems, are employed to further purify the coolant stream. Treated coolants are then pumped back to the machinery for reuse.

Other examples of systems for processing scrap from machining operations may be found in Chapter 15.

ABOVE-FLOOR STAMPING SCRAP COLLECTION

For scrap removal from the bolster area, sheet metal chuting is the least expensive option and deserves careful attention. The angle of repose on the chuting should be 35° or greater to ensure that the scrap will not stick to the chuting.

When chuting is not an option, small low-profile conveyors can be used to transfer the scrap out from under the die. Low-profile units typically use rubber belt designs to carry the scrap. Some use a combination of rubber belting and magnetic assemblies for this purpose. An air cylinder reciprocating a small formed trough is another way to move the scrap.

After the scrap is removed from the die set area, it is usually collected in a conveyor that elevates the scrap and discharges it into a container. Steel belt (piano hinge style), pivoting hinge steel belt, or magnetic conveyors can be used.

A typical press installation may incorporate a combination of chuting and larger elevating conveyors. A minimum of 12-18 in. (305-457 mm) clearance between the top of the container and the bottom of the elevating conveyor will allow the fork lift operator to remove and replace the container without damaging the conveyor.

Although this combination of equipment works well, a fork lift operator is still required to remove the scrap from the press area and transfer it to a second container located outside. In-floor collection systems minimize the need for fork lift operators and provide the largest payback opportunity.

IN-FLOOR STAMPING SYSTEMS

Light- and medium-duty in-floor stamping scrap collection conveyor systems can consist of either 2.5-in. (63-mm) or 4-in. 102-mm) pitch steel belt conveyors. Rubber belting conveyors should be avoided since they are easily cut by the razor sharp edges of metal scrap, resulting in downtime on the equipment and additional maintenance expense to replace the belting. Oscillating conveyors are also used for in-floor collection.

For some applications, a single steel belt, pivoting hinge steel belt, magnetic, or side chain conveyor can collect scrap in lower horizontal sections, elevate it out of the pit, and discharge it into a container. With oscillating conveyors, an additional elevating conveyor is required at the end of the system to transport the scrap out.

Depending on the number of machines producing scrap, a combination of several types of conveyors may form a scrap transfer system. Figure 20-18 shows an in-floor collection system with a swivel chute and Figure 20-19 shows the layout of a swivel chute conveyor.

DIE CAST SCRAP HANDLING SYSTEMS

Die cast material handling applications place many demands on conveying equipment. The first challenge is to cool hot castings immediately after removal from the tooling. At this point, the parts and scrap (sprues, gates, and risers) are still attached. Die cast cooling conveyors utilize water quench tank systems for this process. Hot castings are dropped into tanks or pits filled with water. A conveyor transfers the castings out of the tank to a trim operation. Water quench

CHAPTER 20   MOVING AND HANDLING SCRAP AND WASTE

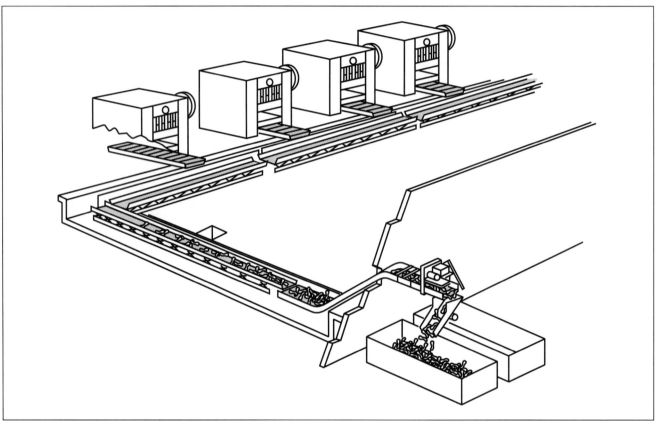

Fig. 20-18 In-floor collection system with swivel chute. *(Courtesy Prab Conveyor)*

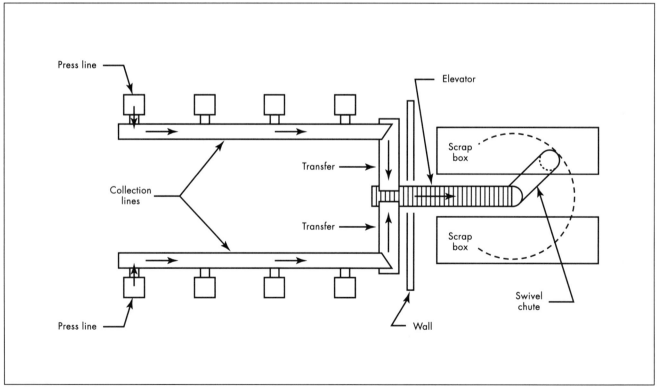

Fig. 20-19 Plan view layout: magnetic feeders, in-floor oscillating collectors, elevating steel belts, and swivel chute. *(Courtesy Prab Conveyor)*

CHAPTER 20   MOVING AND HANDLING SCRAP AND WASTE

systems cool the castings quickly, allowing operators to place them into trim presses. As discussed in the section on metal mesh belting, air quenching is sometimes used for smaller parts, or to avoid the need for waste water handling and disposal.

Unlike stamping or machining scrap, aluminum and zinc alloy die-cast trim scrap is transferred back to remelt furnaces and reused in the production process. Trim scrap typically accounts for 30% of the total shot weight. The efficient collection, return, and remelting of the alloys result in significant cost savings.

Most layouts incorporate oscillating conveyors located in shallow trenches to collect scrap as it is ejected from the trim operation.

The scrap is elevated out of the floor with steel belt conveyors and discharged into a furnace-feed oscillator. A furnace-feed oscillator utilizes high-temperature stainless steel chuting to direct the scrap into the furnace through a scrap charging port. This equipment combination meter-feeds scrap into the remelt furnace.

Meter-feeding versus dump loading is the preferred method of scrap remelt. Meter-feeding scrap at a continuous rate helps to maintain both molten metal bath levels and temperature in the furnace. This helps ensure a continuous flow of alloy to the launder system and prevents the furnace refractory lining from being damaged (see Fig. 20-20).

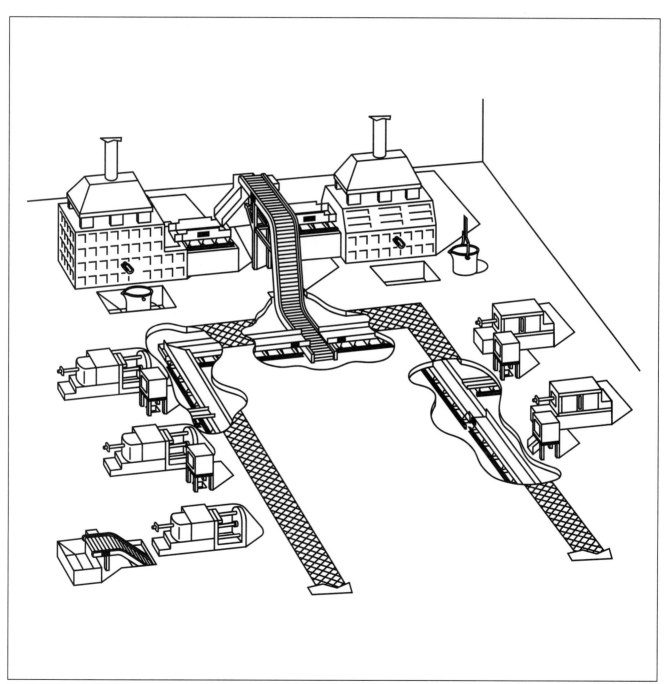

Fig. 20-20 Scrap-to-remelt system. *(Courtesy Prab Conveyor)*

CHAPTER 20 MOVING AND HANDLING SCRAP AND WASTE

Safety is always important, yet die casting furnace temperatures (1,200-1,500° F [649-816° C]), and molten metals pose risk. Conveyor systems consistently and efficiently handle the remelt scrap, eliminating the need for operators to work near furnace equipment.

PREPURCHASE STRATEGIES

When choosing conveying equipment, the first step for the project should be to establish a written set of goals. Items to consider are:

- An effective solution to the specific conveying need.
- The greatest economy without sacrificing reliable operation.
- Low operating cost and minimum maintenance.
- Flexibility to meet future needs.

The goals form an overview of the strategies and required efficiencies for scrap material management. By defining the scope of the project, material handling vendors will be able to provide appropriate equipment recommendations and pricing information.

ECONOMIC JUSTIFICATION

All capital expenditures need to be scrutinized for economic justification. Each of the original goals should be reviewed, and a case generated for purchasing the equipment. The focus should be on the utilization of metal scrap handling conveyor equipment as a cost-saving solution. A typical payback period for the return on investment (ROI) should be two or three years.

Economic justification can be based on any of the following project goals:

- Increases in productivity from reducing machine cycle times or increasing part production.
- Reduced maintenance labor expenses from improved housekeeping.
- Reduction of material handling labor by adding in-floor scrap transfer systems.
- Savings from reducing or eliminating fork lift truck traffic.
- Increased value of scrap by separating and cleaning it, yielding a higher price per pound.
- Reduced costs from filling scrap dealer containers more efficiently, eliminating the need for shoveling material to level the load.
- Reduced lost-time injuries from cuts and lacerations or lifting accidents.
- Other innovative opportunities for cost savings.

COLLECT APPLICATION INFORMATION

First, basic application information must be collected. For stamping applications, scrap size, press rates (strokes per minute), pieces per stroke, die lubrication utilized, space restrictions, electrical requirements, and scrap container size information are good starting points. For die cast applications, scrap size, shots per hour rates, trim press layouts, electrical requirements, furnace types, and location information are important considerations. For machined chips and turnings, alloy composition, scrap volume, amount of tramp metal bar ends, reject castings or parts to be rejected, types and volumes (gal [L]/min) of lubricants or coolants used, central cool-

ant collection and recovery systems, filtration requirements, number of machines, and scrap container locations should be reviewed before defining the project goals.

Other processes will have their own parameters and requirements to consider. It is important to obtain accurate information. Undersizing the equipment will usually result in premature failure. This leads to an increase in maintenance costs or additional capital expenditures to repair or replace the equipment. Oversizing will add needless expense to the purchase price, making the project more difficult to justify.

Equipment installation requirements must be reviewed. Both mechanical and electrical costs must be taken into consideration. Modifications to existing equipment or plant structural components may be required. Electrical power requirements, local building and electrical codes, and building structural elements must be checked before proceeding with the project.

In-floor systems require pits or trenches. Pits need to be either cast in the concrete (new construction) or cut into the concrete. Accurate estimates for this task, including concrete and soil disposal fees should be obtained. Oil-impregnated concrete in older factories may require special landfill disposal permits.

Because cutting concrete floors in a plant can produce large amounts of dust, precautions to contain the airborne dust may need to be considered. Concrete dust can potentially contaminate coolant sumps, damage machinery or parts, and can be a respiratory irritant. In addition, special hearing protection may be required for workers in adjacent areas during cutting operations.

Floor plate covering, which can withstand deflection loads caused by fork lift trucks or other machinery traffic, must be planned for all conveyor pits. It is best to consult with a registered professional engineer to determine load requirements and floor plate design criteria.

Standard over-the-road truckloads are limited to 40 ft (12 m) lengths. Individual conveyor segments are typically limited to 20 ft (6 m) lengths. Standard sheet steel varies from 3-20 ft (0.9-6 m) in length. Sheet lengths of 10-12 ft (3-3.7 m) are easier to handle during forming and conveyor fabrication. Long sections of conveyor equipment can be difficult to move inside a manufacturing facility with existing equipment already in place. New plant construction allows easier component movement and installation, without risking machine damage or personal injury.

The final step before purchasing equipment is to confirm equipment delivery lead times. Equipment deliveries can take from 8 to 16 weeks, or longer, depending on the scope of the project. The vendor delivery schedule should coincide with any other equipment or building construction details. It may be necessary to organize multiple vendor tasks for various portions of the project.

Bibliography

Mason, Frederick. "Chip Processing Gets New Life." *Manufacturing Engineering* 114(3). Dearborn, MI: Society of Manufacturing Engineers, 1995.

Smith, David A. *Die Design Handbook*. Dearborn, MI: Society of Manufacturing Engineers, 1990.

Smith, David A. *Fundamentals of Pressworking*. Dearborn, MI: Society of Manufacturing Engineers, 1994.

Smith, David A. *Quick Die Change*. Dearborn, MI: Society of Manufacturing Engineers, 1991.

Quick Die Change Video. Dearborn, MI: Society of Manufacturing Engineers, 1992.

APPENDIX A

INDUSTRY ASSOCIATIONS AND STANDARDS

Please note: any omissions are not intentional and information is subject to change.

BELGIUM

EAN—European Article Numbering International, Central Secretariat, Rue Royale 145, 1000 Brussels, Belgium, Phone: (32) 2 227 1020, Fax: (32) 2 227 1021, E-mail: info@ean.be, Website: http://www.ean.org, http://www.aliis.be/ean

CZECH REPUBLIC

ODETTE—Organization for Data Exchange by Tele-transmission in Europe, General Correspondence, AIA, Opletalova, 29, 11000 Praha, Czechoslovakia, Phone: (42) 2 266 788, Fax: (42) 2 261 501, Website: http://www.telexis.it/odette/e_skel.htm

ENGLAND

Health and Safety Executive Guidance on Regulations Manual Handling Operations 1992, (see HSE)

HSE—Health and Safety Executive, Information Manager, Broad Lane, Sheffield, England S3 7HQ, Phone: 0114-289-2920, Website: http://www.open.gov.uk/hse/hsehome.htm

FRANCE

ODETTE—Organization for Data Exchange by Tele-transmission in Europe, GALIA, 96, Avenue du general Le clerc, 92514 Boulogne Billancourt Cedex, France, Phone: (33) 1 482 59 395, Fax: (33) 1 460 59 200, Website: http://www.telexis.it/odette/e_skel.htm

GERMANY

ODETTE—Organization for Data Exchange by Tele-transmission in Europe, General Correspondence, ODETTE, Verband der Automobilindustrie e.V. (VDA), Westendstrasse 61, D-60079 Frankfurt am Main, Germany, Phone: (49) 69 97507 283, Fax: (49) 69 97507 300, Website: http://www.telexis.it/odette/e_skel.htm

ITALY

ODETTE—Organization for Data Exchange by Tele-transmission in Europe, ODETTE Italia, Telexis, Corso Marconi, 10, 10125 Torino, Italy, Phone: (39) 11 686 2603, Fax: (39) 11 686 2478, Website: http://www.telexis.it/odette/e_skel.htm

NETHERLANDS

ODETTE—Organization for Data Exchange by Tele-transmission in Europe, ODETTE Nederland, MEENTWAL 1, 3432 GL Niewegein, The Netherlands, Phone: (31) 30 603 3369, Fax: (31) 30 604 5516, Website: http://www.telexis.it/odette/e_skel.htm

POLAND

ODETTE—Organization for Data Exchange by Tele-transmission in Europe, FSO, ul. Jagiellonska 88, 00-992 Warszawa, Poland, Phone: (48) 22 11 6523, Fax: (48) 22 11 8813, Website: http://www.telexis.it/odette/e_skel.htm

SPAIN

ODETTE—Organization for Data Exchange by Tele-transmission in Europe, ODETTE ESPANA, ANFAC, Fray Bernardino Sahagun, 24, 28036 Madrid, Spain, Phone: (34) 1 345 1001, Fax: (34) 1 359 4488, Website: http://www.telexis.it/odette/e_skel.htm

SWEDEN

ODETTE—Organization for Data Exchange by Tele-transmission in Europe, EDI Center, ODETTE, Box 5510, S-114 85 Stockholm, Sweden, Phone: (46) 8 782 0949, Fax: (46) 8 782 0864, Website: http://www.telexis.it/odette/e_skel.htm

SWITZERLAND

ISO—International Organization for Standardization, Central Secretariat, 1 rue de Varembé, Case Postale 56, CH-1211, Geneva 20, Switzerland, Phone: (41) 22 749 01 11, Fax: (41) 22 733 34 30, E-mail: central@iso.ch, Website: http://www.iso.ch

UNITED KINGDOM

Institute of Materials Management, Cranfield Institute of Technology, Cranfield, Bedford, United Kingdom, MK43 OAL.

ODETTE—Organization for Data Exchange by Tele-transmission in Europe, ODETTE United Kingdom, SMMT, Forbes House, Halkin Street, London SW1X 7DS, United Kingdom, Phone: (44)171 235 7000, Fax: (44) 171 235 7112, Website: http://www.telexis.it/odette/e_skel.htm

Pallet Racking Safety: A User's Guide, (see Institute of Materials Management)

The Contributors of this appendix are: Frank Gue, Consultant, Industrial Education Services; *William T. Guiher,* Vice President, Material Handling, Inflection Point, Inc. *John Healy,* Excecutive Director, National Wooden Pallet and Container Association; *Robert C. Keeton, CMfgT,* Manufacturing Engineer, Borg-Warner Automotive; *David Luton,* President, David Luton & Associates, Inc.; *Robert K. Rothfuss,* Vice President, Sales and Marketing, Buckhorn, Inc.; *Marilyn S. Sherry,* Program Manager, Automotive Industry Action Group; *Dr. Paul S. Singh,* Associate Professor and Director of The Consortium of Distribution Packaging Research, School of Packaging, Michigan State University; *David Studebaker,* President, Studebaker Technology, Inc.; *Dr. Mark White,* Associate Professor and Director of The William H. Sardo Jr. Pallet & Container Research Laboratory, Virginia Polytechnic Institute and State University.

The Reviewers of this appendix are: Michael J. Bleau, Sales Manager, Mechanical Presses, Schuler, Inc.; *Dale P. Brautigam, PE,* Vice President, Manufacturing and Engineering, LubeCon Systems, Inc.; *William D. Craig, PE,* Senior Research and Development Engineer, Rhodes International, Inc.; *Ann E. Dunkin, PE,* PCA Materials Engineering Manager, Hewlett-Packard Company; *Robert J. Lawless,* President, Creative Storage Systems, Inc.; *John E. Layden,* President, Pritsker Corp.; *Marc Maszara,* Director of Corporate Development, Knight Industries; *David C. Preusse,* General Sales Manager, Wittmann Robot and Automation Systems; *Randall Schaefer,* Director of Systems Integration, Spartan Motors; *Bruce A. Steffens,* Account Executive, Arlington Rack and Packaging Co.; *W. Allen Sullivan, CPA,* Chief Financial Officer, Spirax Sarco, Inc.

APPENDIX A INDUSTRY ASSOCIATIONS AND STANDARDS

UNITED STATES

AAMA—American Automobile Manufacturers Association, 1401 H St. NW, Suite 900, Washington, DC 20005, Phone: (202) 326-5500, Fax: (202) 326-5567, Website: http://www.aama.com

AAMA Regional Offices:

Great Lakes: IL, IN, KY, MI, OH

7430 Second Ave., Suite 300, Detroit, MI 48202, Phone: (313) 872-4311

North Central: IA, MN, MT, ND, SD, WI (see Great Lakes)

Northeastern: CT, MA, ME, NY, RI, VT

One Center Plaza, Suite 210, Boston, MA 02108, Phone: (617) 227-1011

Mid-Atlantic: DC, DE, MD, NJ, PA, VA, WV

8604 Lime Kiln Court, Gaithersburg, MD 20879, Phone: (301) 216-0883

Pacific Coast: AK, CA, HI, NV, OR, WA

925 L St., Suite 260 Park Executive Bldg., Sacramento, CA 95814, Phone: (916) 444-3767

Rocky Mountain: AZ, CO, IA, NE, NM, UT, WY (see South Central)

South Central: AR, KS, LA, MO, OK, TX

225 E. 16th Ave., Suite 1070, Denver, CO 80203, Phone: (303) 832-1492

Southeastern: AL, FL, GA, MS, NC, SC, TN

325 John Knox Rd., Bldg. 400, Suite 403, Tallahassee, FL 32303, Phone: (904) 422-0668

ACGH—American Conference of Governmental Industrial Hygienists, 1330 Kemper Meadow Dr., Cincinnati, OH 45240, Phone: (513) 742-2020, Fax: (513) 742-3355, Website: http://www.acgih.org.welcome.htm

AEM—Automated Electrified Monorail Product Section of the Material Handling Institute, (see MHI)

AGVS—Automated Guided Vehicle Systems, (see MHI)

AHAM—Association of Home Appliance Manufacturers, 20 N. Wacker Dr., Suite 1231, Chicago, IL 60606, Phone: (312) 984-5800, Fax: (312) 984-5823, Website: http://www.aham.org

AIAG—Automotive Industry Action Group, 26200 Lahser Rd., Suite 200, Southfield, MI 48034, Phone: (810) 358-3570, Fax: (810) 358-3253, Website: http://www.aiag.org

AIM—Automatic Identification Manufacturers Association of the U.S.A., 634 Alpha Dr., Pittsburgh, PA 15238, Phone: (412) 963-8588, Fax: (412) 963-8753, Website: http://www.aimusa.org

AME—Association for Manufacturing Excellence, 380 West Palatene Rd., Wheeling, IL 60090-5863, Phone: (847) 520-3282, Fax: (847) 520-0163, Website: http://www.trainingforum.com/ASN/AME/index.html

AMM—Association of Mezzanine Manufacturers, 8720 Red Oak Blvd., Charlotte, NC 28217, Phone: (704) 522-7826, Fax: (704) 522-7826, Website: http://www.mhi.org

AMT—Association for Manufacturing Technology, 7901 Westpark Dr., McLean, VA 22102-4206, Phone: (703) 893-2900, Fax: (703) 893-1151, Website: http://www.mfgtech.org

ANSI—American National Standards Institute, 11 West 42nd St., New York, NY 10036, Phone: (212) 642-4900, Fax: (212) 398-0023, Website: http://www.ansi.org

APICS—The Educational Society for Resource Management (American Production and Inventory Control Society), 500 West Annandale Rd., Falls Church, VA 22046, Phone: (703) 237-8344, Fax: (703) 237-4316, Website: http://www.apics.org

APMHC—Association of Professional Material Handling Consultants, 8720 Red Oak Blvd., Suite 224, Charlotte, NC 28217, Phone: (704) 558-4749, Fax: (704) 558-4753, Website: http://www.mhi.org

ASME—American Society of Mechanical Engineers, 22 Law Dr., P.O. Box 2900, Fairfield, NJ 07007-2900, Phone (U.S. and Canada): (800) 843-2763, Phone (Mexico): 95-800-843-2763, Phone (outside North America): (201) 882-1167, Fax: (201) 882-1717, Website: http://www.asme.org

ASME B20.1b-1995, (see ASME)

AS/RS—Automated Storage/Retrieval Systems, (see MHI)

AS/RS & AGVS Users Association, P.O. Box 723008, Atlanta, GA 31139, Phone: (770) 435-3713, Fax: (770) 319-0473, Website: http://www.teleport.com/~dunkin

Association for Facilities Engineering, 8180 Corporate Park Dr., Suite 305, Cincinnati, OH 45242, Phone: (513) 489-2473, Fax: (513) 247-7422, Website: http://www.afe.org

Auxiliary Equipment Product Section of the Material Handling Institute, (see MHI)

CASA/SME—Computer and Automated Systems Association of the Society of Manufacturing Engineers, (see SME)

CEMA—Conveyor Equipment Manufacturers Association, 9384-D Forestwood Lane, Manassas, VA 20110, Phone: (703) 330-7079, Fax: (703) 330-7984, Website: http://www.cemanet.org

CLM—Council of Logistics Management, 2803 Butterfield Rd., Suite 380, Oak Brook, IL 60521-1156, Voice: (630) 574-0985, Fax: (630) 574-0989, Website: http://www.clm1.org

CMAA—Crane Manufacturers Association of America, (see MHI)

Conveyor Product Section of the Material Handling Institute, (see MHI)

Department of Labor (see Occupational Safety and Health Administration)

E.A.S.E.—Ergonomic Assist Systems and Equipment Council, (see MHI)

EIA—Electronic Industries Association, 2500 Wilson Blvd., Arlington, VA 22201, Phone: (703) 907-7500, Fax: (703) 907-7501, Website: http://www.eia.org

FMA—Fabricators and Manufacturers Association International, Inc., 833 Featherstone Rd., Rockford, IL 61107, Phone: (815) 399-8700, Fax: (815) 399-7279

HFES—Human Factors and Ergonomics Society, P.O. Box 1369, Santa Monica, CA 90406-1369, Phone: (310) 394-1811, Fax: (310) 394-2410, Website: http://hfes.org

HIBCC—Health Industry Business Communications Council, 5110 N. 40th St., Suite 250, Phoenix, AZ 85018, Phone: (602) 381-1091, Fax: (602) 381-1093, Website: http://www.hibcc.org

HMI—Hoist Manufacturing Institute, (see MHI)

ICM—Institute of Caster Manufacturers, 11 S. LaSalle St., Suite 1400, Chicago, IL 60603, Phone: (312) 201-0101, Fax: (312) 201-0214

IEA—International Ergonomics Association, Center for Industrial Ergonomics, Academic Building Room 437, University of Louisville, Louisville, KY 40292, Phone: (502) 852-7173, Fax: (502) 852-7397, Website: http://www.spd.louisville.edu/~ergonomics/international_ergonomics_association.html

IIE—Institute of Industrial Engineers, 25 Technology Park/Atlanta, Norcross, GA 30092, Phone: (770) 449-0461, Fax: (770) 263-8532, Website: http://www.iienet.org

IMCS/MHI—Industrial Metal Containers Section of the Material Handling Institute, (see MHI)

Industrial Ventilation Manual, (see American Conference of Governmental Industrial Hygienists)

Institute of Packaging Professionals, 481 Carlisle Dr., Herndon, VA 22070, Phone: (703) 318-8970, Fax: (703) 814-4960, Website: www.packinfo-world.org

ISC—Integrated Systems and Controls Council, (see MHI)

APPENDIX A   INDUSTRY ASSOCIATIONS AND STANDARDS

ITA—Industrial Truck Association, 1750 K St. NW, Suite 460, Washington, DC 20006, Phone: (202) 296-9880, Fax: (202) 296-9884

LDEM—Loading Dock Equipment Manufacturers, (see MHI)

LMPS—Lift Manufacturers Product Section, (see MHI)

MHEDA—Material Handling Equipment Distributors Association, 201 Route 45, Vernon Hills, IL 60061, Phone: (708) 680-3500, Fax: (708) 362-6989, Website: http://www.industry.net/c/origindex/mheda

MHI—Material Handling Institute, 8720 Red Oak Blvd., Suite 201, Charlotte, NC 28217, Phone: (704) 522-8644, Fax: (704) 522-7826, Website: http://www.mhi.org

MHIA—Material Handling Industry of America, (see MHI)

MHMS—Material Handling and Management Society, 8720 Red Oak Blvd., Suite 224, Charlotte, NC 28217-3990, Phone: (704) 525-4667, Fax: (704) 558-4770, Website: http://www.industry.net/c/orgunpro/mhi/mhms

MMA—Monorail Manufacturers Association, (see MHI)

NEC—National Electrical Code, (see NFPA)

NFPA—National Fire Protection Association, 1 Batterymarch Park, Quincy, MA 02269-9101, Phone: (617) 770-3000, Fax: (617) 770-0700, Website: http://www.nfpa.org

NSF—National Science Foundation, 4201 Wilson Blvd., Arlington, VA 22230, Phone: (703) 306-1234, TDD: (703) 306-0090, Website: http://www.nsf.gov

NWPCA—National Wooden Pallet and Container Association, 1800 N. Kent St., Suite 911, Arlington, VA 22209, Phone: (703) 527-7667, Fax: (703) 527-7717, Website: http://www.pallet-mall.com/litco/nwpca.htm. For a complete listing of specifications and standards for wood pallets, refer to the NWPCA Uniform Voluntary Standard.

OCM—Overhead Components Manufacturers Product Section of the Material Handling Institute, (see MHI)

Order Selection, Staging, and Storage Council, (see MHI)

OSHA—Occupational Safety and Health Administration, (Labor Department), 200 Constitution Ave. N.W., #S2315, Washington, D.C. 20210, Phone: (202) 219-8151, Fax: (202) 219-6064, Website: http//www.osha.gov

PMA—Precision Metalforming Association, 27027 Chardon Rd., Richmond Heights, OH 44143, Phone: (216) 585-8800, Fax: (216) 585-3126, Website: http://www.industry.net/c/orgindex/pma

PMMI—Packaging Machinery Manufacturers Institute, 4350 N. Fairfax Dr., Suite 600, Arlington, VA 22203, Phone: (703) 243-8555, Fax: (703) 243-8556, Website: packexpo.com

Revised NIOSH Lifting Equation (see U.S. Department of Health and Human Services)

RIA—Robotic Industries Association, 900 Victors Way, Box 3724, Ann Arbor, MI 48106, Phone: (313) 994-6088, Fax: (313) 994-3338, Website: www.robotics.org

RI/SME—Robotics International of the Society of Manufacturing Engineers, (see SME)

RMI—Rack Manufacturers Institute, (see MHI)

RPCPA—Reusable Plastic Container and Pallet Association, (see MHI)

SMA—Shelving Manufacturers Association, (see MHI)

SME—Society of Manufacturing Engineers, One SME Drive, P.O. Box 930, Dearborn, MI 48121, Phone: (313) 271-1500, Fax: (313) 271-2861, Website: http://www.sme.org

UCC—Uniform Code Council, Inc., 8163 Old Yankee St., Suite J, Dayton, OH 45458-1839, Phone: (937) 435-3870, Fax: (937) 435-7317, Website: http://www.uc-council.org

U.S. Department of Health and Human Services, Centers for Disease Control and Prevention, National Institute for Occupational Safety and Health (NIOSH), 1600 Clifton Rd. NE, Atlanta, GA 30333, Phone: (404) 639-3311, Website: http://www.cdc.gov/niosh/homepage.html

Alternate Contact

NIOSH, Division of Biomedical and Behavioral Science, 4676 Columbia Parkway, Cincinnati, OH 45226, Phone: (513) 533-8465, Website: http://www.cdc.gov/niosh/homepage.html

NIOSH—National Institute for Occupational Safety and Health, 1600 Clifton Rd. NE, Atlanta, GA 30333, Phone: (404) 639-3311, Website: http://www.cdc.gov/niosh/homepage.html

WERC—Warehousing Education and Research Council, 1100 Jorie Blvd., Suite 170, Oak Brook, IL 60523-2243, Phone: (630) 990-0001, Fax: (630) 990-0256, Website: http://www.werc.org

WMS—Warehouse Management Systems, (see MHI)